W9-APU-901

DETERMINATE STRUCTURES

STATICS, STRENGTH, ANALYSIS, DESIGN

DETERMINATE STRUCTURES

STATICS, STRENGTH, ANALYSIS, DESIGN

Samuel E. French, Ph.D., P.E.

Delmar Publishers

I(T)P™ An International Thomson Publishing Company

Albany • Bonn • Boston • Cincinnati • Detroit • London • Madrid •
Melbourne • Mexico City • New York • Pacific Grove • Paris •
San Francisco • Singapore • Tokyo • Toronto • Washington

NOTICE TO THE READER

Publisher does not warrant or guarantee any of the products described herein or perform any independent analysis in connection with any of the product information contained herein. Publisher does not assume, and expressly disclaims, any obligation to obtain and include information other than that provided to it by the manufacturer.

The reader is expressly warned to consider and adopt all safety precautions that might be indicated by the activities herein and to avoid all potential hazards. By following the instructions contained herein, the reader willingly assumes all risks in connection with such instructions.

The publisher makes no representation or warranties of any kind, including but not limited to, the warranties of fitness for particular purpose or merchantability, nor are any such representations implied with respect to the material set forth herein, and the publisher takes no responsibility with respect to such material. The publisher shall not be liable for any special, consequential, or exemplary damages resulting, in whole or part, from the readers' use of, or reliance upon, this material.

Delmar Staff
Acquisitions Editor: Paul Shepardson
Developmental Editor: Jeanne Mesick
Project Editor: Thomas Smith
Production Coordinator: Karen Smith
Art/Design Coordinator: Michael Prinzo

Printed in the United States of America

For more information, contact:

Delmar Publishers
3 Columbia Circle, Box 15015
Albany, New York 12212-5015

International Thomson Publishing Europe
Berkshire House 168-173
High Holborn
London WC1V 7AA
England

Thomas Nelson Australia
102 Dodds Street
South Melbourne, 3205
Victoria, Australia

Nelson Canada
1120 Birchmont Road
Scarborough, Ontario
Canada M1K 5G4

International Thomson Editores
Campos Eliseos 385, Piso 7
Col Polanco
11560 Mexico D F Mexico

International Thomson Publishing GmbH
Königswinterer Strasse 418
53227 Bonn
Germany

International Thomson Publishing Asia
221 Henderson Road
#05-10 Henderson Building
Singapore 0315

International Thomson Publishing—Japan
Hirakawacho Kyowa Building, 3F
2-2-1 Hirakawacho
Chiyoda-ku, Tokyo 102
Japan

2 3 4 5 6 7 8 9 10 XXX 01 00 99 98 97 96

Library of Congress Cataloging-in-Publication Data

French, Samuel E., 1930–
Determinate structures : statics, strength, analysis, design / Samuel E. French.
p. cm.
Includes index.
ISBN 0-8273-6000-2
1. Structural engineering. I. Title.
TA633.F74 1996
624.1'7—dc20 95-25175
CIP

CONTENTS

PREFACE

This book is about structures and the way that structures sustain the loads imposed on them. The study is broken into six parts:

PART I STATIC SYSTEMS OF FORCES
a detailed general study of static forces and the computation of the forces and force systems that act on a structural member.

PART II STRENGTH OF MATERIALS
a detailed general study of the stresses and deformations that occur within a structural material when it is subjected to external forces and loads.

PART III STRUCTURAL ANALYSIS
a detailed general study of the ways in which a determinate building system as a whole will resist and sustain the gravity loads and the lateral loads that will be imposed upon it during its service life.

PART IV ENGINEERING OF CONCRETE AND MASONRY STRUCTURES
a specialized study of the engineering involved in using concrete or masonry in structures braced against sidesway, with detailed applications in the design of slabs, beams, columns, foundations and the lateral bracing system.

PART V ENGINEERING OF STEEL STRUCTURES
a specialized study of the engineering involved in using structural steel shapes in building frames braced against sidesway, to include roofing and flooring systems, columns and the lateral bracing system.

PART VI ENGINEERING OF TIMBER STRUCTURES
a specialized study of engineered timber structures with applications in general building systems braced against sidesway, with particular concentration on post and beam systems and the lateral bracing system.

The material covered in this presentation has been highly channelled and focused. Intense effort has been made to remove clutter while retaining a broad basic approach to such a multifaceted subject. The textbook is specifically directed toward civil engineering structures; there is no pretense that it will cover all topics in all disciplines of engineering.

effort has been made to remove clutter while retaining a broad basic approach to such a multifaceted subject. The textbook is specifically directed toward civil engineering structures; there is no pretense that it will cover all topics in all disciplines of engineering.

There should be no misconception, however, that the coverage is superficial. It is true that only the essential topics are covered, but those topics are recognized as being indeed essential and they are covered in rigorous detail. It is intended that a graduate who has completed a course of study using this textbook will be quite comfortable beginning a career involving the design or construction of routine structures in today's industry, to include structural systems of concrete, masonry, steel and timber.

The basic design tables required to support such an extensive study are included in a special supplementary Technical Manual.

The textbook is intended for use in any accredited four-year curriculum in engineering or technology or in an accredited two-year curriculum in technology. In a two-year curriculum, the material would likely be presented in the second and third semesters as two consecutive courses of five semester credit hours each. In a four-year curriculum, the material would likely be presented in four consecutive courses of three semester credit hours each, probably beginning in the second semester and extending through the fifth semester. The textbook has been specifically prepared such that it may be adapted to either sequence of study.

The end product of the studies in this textbook is the analysis and design of statically determinate structural systems, that is, systems in which all of the forces in the system can be determined from simple statics. The use of deformation conditions in such systems is not needed, hence calculus is not needed. Typical examples of statically determinate structural systems include diaphragm-and-shearwall systems, braced post-and-beam systems, braced steel or concrete frames and all of the common types of trussed systems.

Such statically determinate structural systems constitute probably 85% of all construction in today's industry. There is a reason, of course, for such dominance: Statically determinate systems offer real advantages in cost, ease of fabrication and ease of construction. They are, however, limited in height. Problems with uplift under the braced panels or shearwalls become too severe to permit heights greater than about five or six stories. Even with this limitation, statically determinate structures form the overwhelming majority of all structures being built today in practically every city and town in the world.

Those who extend their training into the more complex structural systems such as high-rise continuous frames will undergo considerably more training in mathematics than is required for this study of low-rise determinate systems. Deformation conditions will be required in such studies, hence integral calculus will be absolutely essential for any such advanced studies. Also, further training in matrix methods and numerical methods will be necessary for advanced computerized applications.

It has been noted that calculus is not essential for the study of determinate structural systems. Nonetheless, a student who has a background in calculus will be much better equipped to understand several of the topics in strength of materials that are presented in this text. If at all possible, acquiring a basic background in calculus is recommended for all students in the engineering sciences.

Ideally, this text would present a continuous cohesive development of structures from one part to the next, with no need for repetition of material. In reality, however, it is recognized that some users of the book will use only the first parts of the book, some will use only the last parts, and some will use only the middle parts. As a consequence, some duplication of the subject matter is included throughout the text in an effort to make certain parts of the book more understandable when used alone.

In the same vein, there are some instructors who will insist that a particular topic be included in the text, while other instructors would omit that topic from their courses even if it were to be included. In the interest of flexibility, several of these topics of peripheral interest have been collected in Chapters 12 and 15. Individual instructors may pick topics from those chapters as their personal experience dictates (and as class time permits).

Further, effort has been made to isolate some topics in order that they may be deleted where appropriate. A typical example is Chapter 5, which presents systems of forces in three dimensions. If three dimensional systems are not needed in a particular curriculum, the chapter may be dropped with no loss in continuity.

Similarly, the chapters on structural design give concrete first, followed by steel and then timber. The author prefers this sequence in order that connections of steel and timber members to their concrete footings and bearing walls can be undertaken without interruption. Other instructors may choose to present steel and timber before undertaking concrete. Those instructors may simply take the materials in any sequence they prefer; the chapters on the various materials are written to be taken in any order desired.

The language of structures is mathematics; those who would understand structures must first understand the language. It is expected therefore that a student beginning the study of statically determinate structures presented in this textbook will have a solid background in plane geometry, college-level algebra and college-level trigonometry. Persons having low academic records in these subjects would be well advised to raise their competence in them before beginning a study as rigorously mathematical as structures.

In the preparation of the chapters on the design of concrete, masonry, steel and timber, it was presumed that the student will have taken the usual introductory course in engineering materials and materials testing. Consequently, the basic physical composition of these materials is not repeated in the chapters on design. The chapters begin with engineering properties of the materials, that is, with allowable stresses and deformations.

The author is again pleased to acknowledge the contributions of his wife, Sherry, to the preparation of this textbook. As with the author's earlier textbooks, she has typed and edited the manuscript of this textbook with truly professional skill; the author takes this opportunity to acknowledge her contribution and to express his appreciation for her patience and forebearance.

Samuel E. French, Ph.D., P.E.
Martin, Tennessee, 1995

Also available from Delmar Publishers:

Reinforced Concrete Technology
Samuel French, Ph.D., P.E.
Order #0-8273-5495-9

Understanding Soil Mechanics
Jack Roberts, Ph.D.
Order #0-8273-6869-0

Construction Surveying: Layout and Dimension Control
Jack Roberts, Ph.D.
Order #0-8273-5723-0

Practical Surveying for Technicians
Robert Landon
Order #0-8273-3941-0

Fundamentals of Construction Estimating
David Pratt
Order #0-8273-6135-1

Estimating with Timberline Precision
Mark Reich, Judd Youell
Order #0-8273-6002-9

Estimating for Residential & Commercial Construction
Bert Benedict, Gordon Anderson
Order #0-8273-5498-3

Construction Project Management: Planning and Scheduling
Henry Naylor, PE
Order #0-8273-5733-8

Managing Construction: The Contractual Viewpoint
Keith Collier
Order #0-8273-5700-1

Structural Steel Design
ASD Method, Order #0-8273-5705-2
LRFD Method, Order #0-8273-6221-8

PART 1

STATICS

CHAPTER

1

PRINCIPLES OF STATICS

1.1 Introduction to Mechanics

The term "mechanics" has a very specific meaning in engineering. Mechanics is the word that is used to define the study of the forces and force systems that act on a structural member. The study applies equally as well to the gears in a truck transmission as to the girders in a skyscraper. Once the size of the forces that act on a member have been determined, a member of proper size and shape to sustain those forces can then be selected.

Within the study of mechanics, there are several very natural subdivisions. Machine parts, for example, are subject to motions, accelerations and vibrations; the study of the forces that act on such moving elements has been separated into a branch of mechanics called *dynamics*. The study of dynamics is usually associated with mechanical engineering rather than structural engineering but dynamic loads (such as wind and earthquake) can also occur on buildings.

Another of the natural subdivisions that occur in the study of mechanics deals with members that are *not* subject to dynamic motions or accelerations. These members, such as the beams and columns in a building, spend their entire service life bearing their loads in a motionless state. Such motionless conditions are called static conditions, and the branch of mechanics that deals with the forces on these motionless members is called *statics*. Chapters 1 through 7 of this textbook are devoted to the study of statics, that is, the study of motionless structural members subject to static loads.

It is noted, however, that conventional studies in statics deal with forces that are applied to the outside of a member. There are obviously other forces and force systems that must be acting inside the material itself as the member resists and sustains these externally applied loads. The study of the forces and deformations that occur internally in a structural material is commonly called *strength of materials*. Perhaps a more accurate name for such a study is *mechanics of materials*, a name that is in fact preferred by many who deal with this subject. Chapters 8 through 12 of this textbook are devoted to the study of strength (or mechanics) of materials, that is, the study of the ways in which a material resists and sustains loads.

For the sake of simplicity, the study of statics and strength of materials is usually concentrated on single members. Structures are not built of single members, however, but rather are built of hundreds or even thousands of members. The loading of one member in such a structure will necessarily create reactions which propagate to other members throughout the structure.

Finding the distribution of forces throughout a structure can sometimes be extremely complex, depending on the type of structure. The determination of these forces throughout a system is called structural analysis; chapters 13, 14 and 15 of this textbook present an introduction to the analysis of simple, routine structures.

Once the loads that are acting on each member in a structure are known, it then becomes possible to select the members that will sustain those loads. The first choice to be made in selecting such a member, however, is to select the material from which the member is to be built. In today's construction industry, the four most common materials from which to build such structural members are concrete, masonry, timber or steel.

Each of these four major construction materials, concrete, masonry, timber and steel, has its own characteristics in the ways it will carry load. Both concrete and masonry, for example, are heavy, weak and brittle, that is, they will carry comparatively large loads as compression members but very little load as tension members. In comparison, steel is incredibly strong, both in tension and compression, so strong, in fact, that extremely thin members are commonly used in steel members which invites serious problems with wrinkling or buckling. And, unlike any of the other three materials, timber has "grain," which produces weak layers of material alternating between layers of stronger material; such variations produce particular behavior problems in timber which must be considered whenever a timber member is selected to carry transverse loads.

The selection of members to carry the calculated loads must therefore consider the ways in which the particular material will respond to the applied loads. All four of these materials are presented in later chapters: members built of reinforced concrete are presented in chapters 16 through 22, masonry is presented in chapter 23, steel is presented in chapters 24 through 28 and timber is presented in chapters 29 through 33.

The study of structures thus reduces very naturally to general studies in statics, strength of materials and structural analysis, followed by specific studies in concrete, masonry, steel and timber. Such a natural sequence of study is adopted here but it is emphasized that none of the individual studies just listed should be viewed as an entity; each study depends heavily on the work that has preceded it and each study shapes the work that will follow it. The study of structures should not be viewed as a series of short stories; it should be viewed as a series of closely intertwined chapters in one long continuing story.

But all such ambitious undertakings must begin with a single first step. That first step in structural engineering is the study of statics, and the study of statics begins with a general look at standard practices.

1.2 Notations, Symbols and Practices

Any real quantity has magnitude, that is, it has size. A line, for example, has length; a line is 3 feet long or 12.61 meters long or 5.46 inches long. A force, however, has not only magnitude, but it also has direction. When working with a force, both the magnitude and the direction of the force must be considered.

Consider the force in the wire of Figure 1-1a, for example. The force acting on the hook may be shown as indicated in Figure 1-1b as a force F acting downward along the axis of the wire. Similarly, the force supporting the weight may be shown as a force P acting upward along the axis of the wire. Both of these forces represent the tension in the wire and both indicate the magnitude and the direction of the forces exerted by the wire at its two ends.

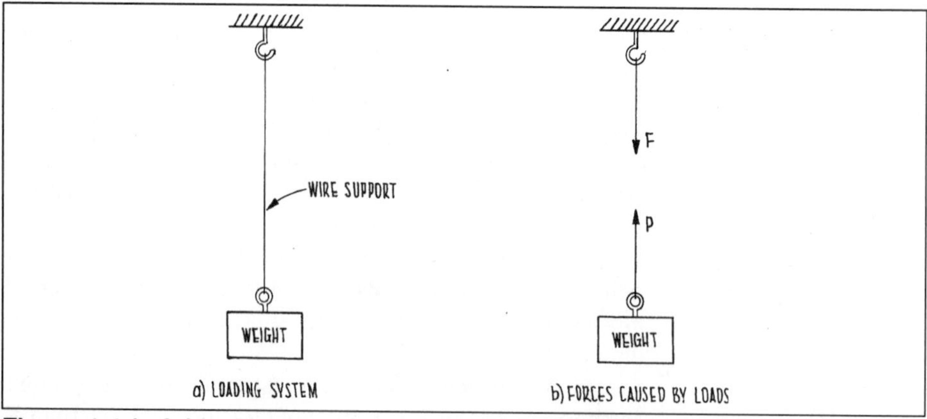

Figure 1-1 (a & b) Magnitude and direction of a force.

In the force system of Figure 1-1, the centerline of the wire defines the direction, or *line of action*, of the forces F and P. Also, the forces F and P have magnitude; it should be apparent that the magnitude of the force in the wire must be equal to but opposite in direction to the force P. Further, both forces have a different point of application, that is, the force F is applied to the hook and the force P is applied to the weight, as indicated in Figure 1-1b.

Each of the two forces shown in Figure 1-1b thus has three elements which completely define the force. Each force has 1) magnitude, 2) direction, and 3) point of application. Any force can be defined completely by these three elements.

The graphic symbols used in presenting Figure 1-1 are typical of the symbols used throughout the study of mechanics when one is sketching the physical conditions of a system. The hook placed in an unyielding support is self explanatory, as is the unidentified hanging weight W suspended by wire from the hook. In most cases, such symbols will need no further explanation or definition.

In some cases, however, some further explanation is in order. Consider, for example, the support conditions shown in Table 1-1. The symbols presented in Table 1-1 are typical of those used to sketch support conditions in mechanics.

Table 1-1 Support symbols.

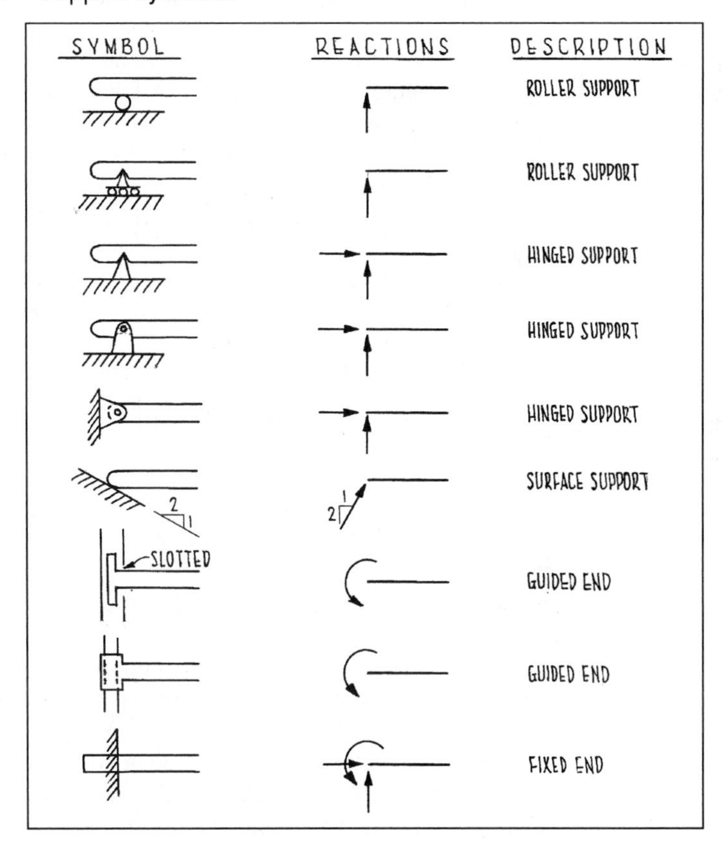

One feature of the supports in Table 1-1 warrants emphasis. Note that all of the indicated hinged or roller supports will resist uplift forces. While the sketch itself may or may not suggest such a capability, such a capability is always assumed to exist.

Note also that roller supports will not resist motion in the direction in which they roll. They are assumed to be absolutely without friction in that direction. The only resisting force offered by the support to such rollers is a force perpendicular to the supporting surface.

As a further example of support reactions, consider the cylinder of weight W on the flat surface of Figure 1-2a. The single resisting force exerted by the supporting surface is normal to the contact surface at the point of contact. Without friction, there can be no other force generated by the cylinder on the flat surface.

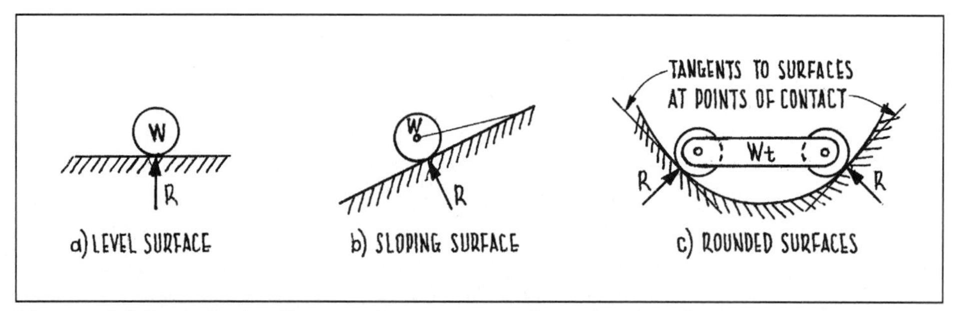

Figure 1-2 (a, b & c) Contact forces exerted on circular shapes.

Now consider the cylinder of Figure 1-2b, in which the supporting surface has been tilted. The wire support prevents the cylinder from rolling, but the resisting force exerted by the supporting surface remains normal to the surface at the point of contact. Without friction, there can still be no other force generated by the cylinder on this flat surface.

Similarly, the rounded surface of Figure 1-2c exerts its resisting forces normal to the tangents at the points of contact. In Figure 1-2c it is assumed, of course, that the system is at rest.

The term *prismatic* is often used in mechanics to describe bars, beams, columns and other elements that are long and slender and which have a constant cross section. In sketches, prismatic members are represented only by their centerlines, such as the frame shown in Figure 1-3. Dimensions in these simplified sketches are also shown to the centerline. Any errors incurred by such practices are considered to be negligible.

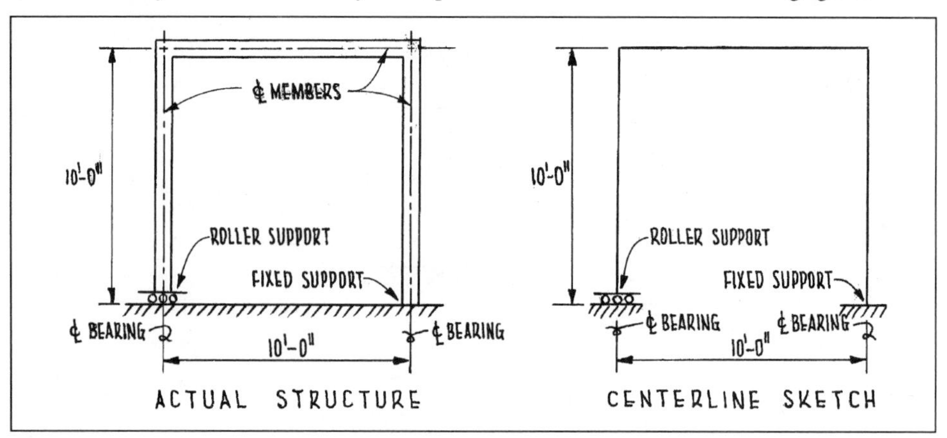

Figure 1-3 Centerline sketch of frame.

In statics, all bodies are considered to be *rigid bodies*. In fact, statics is often called *rigid body mechanics*. In rigid bodies, any deformations due to loads are considered to be so small compared to the centerline dimensions that such deformations can be ignored. For example, a column exactly 18 feet long will actually compress slightly under its axial load, but its length is nonetheless taken as exactly 18 feet in all calculations. All such slight variations in dimensions due to bending, twisting, compression, tension or temperature effects are ignored in rigid body mechanics.

There are at present two systems of measurement in use in American engineering. The older system, the Imperial (British) system, utilizes the familiar feet and inches for measurement of length, pounds for measurement of force and seconds for measurement of time. The more recent system, the *Systeme Internationale* (SI), utilizes meters for measurement of length, Newtons for measurement of force and seconds for measurement of time.

It is assumed here that anyone who has completed the ordinary high school requirements for physics will be somewhat familiar with the SI system. For those who need a review, an outside review of the system is strongly recommended.

For those only vaguely familiar with the SI system, it is pointed out that the SI system is *not* the same as the metric system. The SI system uses the Newton as its unit of force while the metric system uses the kilogram. The difference is of paramount importance in the study of mechanics, which is, as noted earlier, the study of forces.

It is strongly recommended that those not familiar with SI units take time at this point to study the SI system in detail. The remainder of this text is written assuming that the reader is familiar with the SI system.

The symbols (other than abbreviations) used to denote units in this textbook follow those used in civil engineering practice. A list of the more common symbols follows.

Imperial (British) Units		SI Units	
Foot	ft.	Length (meters)	1.06m
Degrees	°	Degrees	°
Minutes	'	Minutes	'
Seconds	"	Seconds	"
Inch	in.	Length (mm)	1060
Pound	lb.	Newton	N
Pound·ft	lb·ft	Newton·meter	N·m
1000 pounds = 1 kip	k	1000 Newtons	kN
Kip-feet	k·ft	KiloNewton-meters	kN·m
Feet and inches	6'-5"		
Minutes and seconds	6' 5"	Minutes and seconds	6' 5"

When working either in the metric system or the SI system in engineering drawings, it is common practice to give all dimensions in millimeters. When this practice is followed, there is then no abbreviation needed to identify the units, such as *mm* or *cm* or *m*. This practice also obviates all problems in trying to find the decimal in sun faded blueprints or in inconsistent switching back and forth between millimeters, centimeters and meters. Further, a dimensional accuracy of 1 mm is automatically possible (even though dimensioning closer than 10 mm is rarely seen). The practice of giving metric dimensions in millimeters is followed in this textbook.

1.3 Transmissibility

A force may be applied anywhere along its line of action. Such a statement may seem to be in conflict with the earlier description of a force, but it is readily shown to be true. Consider, for example, the wagon of Figure 1-4. As indicated in Figure 1-4a, a force of 50 lbs is required to hold the wagon in position on the incline.

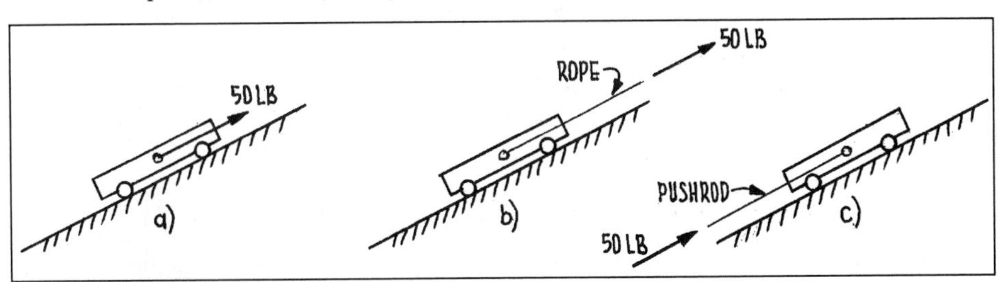

Figure 1-4 Transmissibility of a force.

If one imagines a weightless, dimensionless rope attached to the wagon at the same point of application shown in Figure 1-4b, the actual 50 lb load could actually be located at any point along the rope and the wagon would be completely unaffected by the change. Or, if one imagines a weightless, dimensionless pushrod positioned at the same point of application as shown in Figure 1-4c, the actual 50 lb load could then be located at any point along the pushrod and the wagon would again be completely unaffected by the change.

To reiterate, the principle of transmissibility states that a force may be located anywhere along its line of action, provided that the force retains its magnitude, its direction and its point of application to the rigid body.

1.4 The Force Vector

In mathematics, a directed line segment is called a *vector*. A force, therefore, is a type of vector. A vector, however, need not have a point of application; a vector can be moved around as needed to expedite calculations so long as its magnitude and direction are unchanged. In future calculations, forces sometimes will also be treated as vectors, where such manipulation or movement does not change the problem or cause confusion. In such cases, the forces will be called "force vectors"; however redundant, the term will serve to emphasize that a force is being treated as a vector.

Two forces that act along the same line of action are said to be *collinear*; two such collinear forces are shown in Figure 1-5. The magnitudes of two collinear forces may be summed algebraically to find the resulting overall force; the direction of the sum is that of the numerically larger force. This sum of the two collinear forces may then be used instead of the two original collinear forces in all further rigid body calculations.

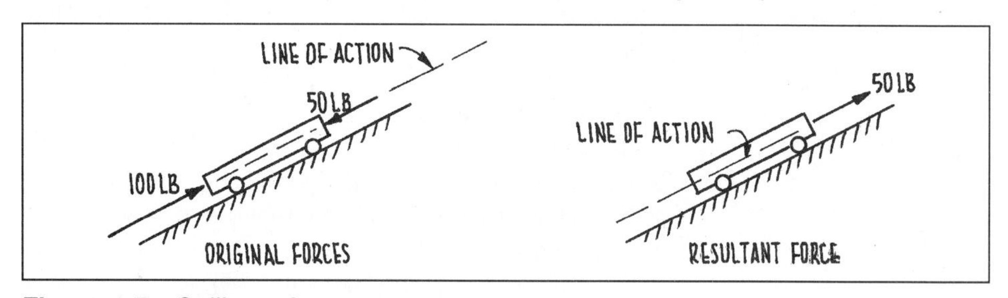

Figure 1-5 Collinear forces.

The magnitude of a force is always positive; a force of negative magnitude cannot exist in nature. If a force bears a negative sign in mechanics, its direction is negative, not its magnitude.

1.5 The Parallelogram Law

When there are two or more noncollinear forces acting at a single point of application, the forces may be summed to find the *resultant* of their combined effects. Consider, for example, the two forces acting on the rigid body of Figure 1-6. These two forces may be added together to obtain a single resultant force that will produce the same end result as the two individual forces.

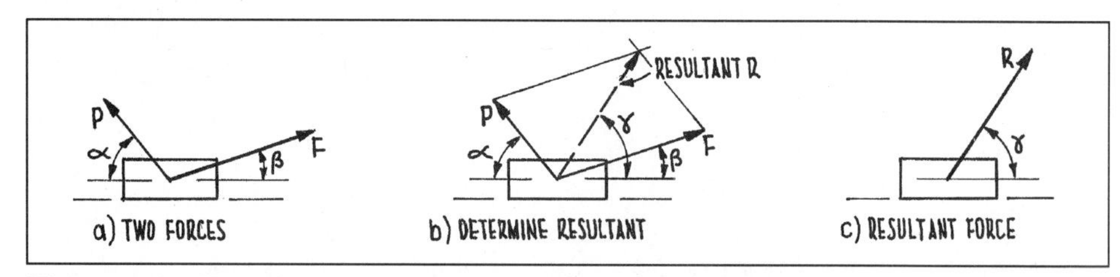

Figure 1-6 Resultant of two forces.

The resultant of the two forces shown in Figure 1-6a is found by completing the parallelogram as shown in Figure 1-6b. The resultant force R will pass through the same point of application as shown, and will have a direction at an angle γ above the horizontal. The single resultant force R shown in Figure 1-6c will in fact produce the same net result as the two forces F and P shown in Figure 1-6a.

This principle of a *parallelogram of forces*, such as that shown in Figure 1-6b, was first used in the sixteenth century by Stevinus. The principle was formally proved and adopted by Newton in the seventeenth century. It forms the basis of the addition and subtraction of forces in today's science of mechanics.

Before proceeding into some example calculations using the parallelogram of forces, the geometry of a parallelogram warrants examination. A typical parallelogram is shown in Figure 1-7a, with all angles and sides identified. Some features of the parallelogram can be deduced from the propositions of plane geometry.

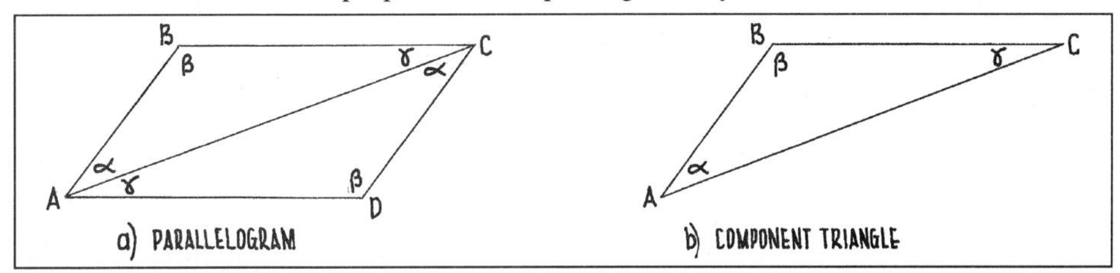

Figure 1-7 (a & b) Geometry of a parallelogram.

It is noted that triangles $\Delta\overline{ABC}$ and $\Delta\overline{CDA}$ are congruent triangles, hence angle $\angle\overline{ABC} = \angle\overline{CDA}$; this angle is labeled β. Since opposite sides of the parallelogram are equal and parallel, the angles $\angle\overline{ACB}$ and $\angle\overline{CAD}$ are seen to be transverse angles and are therefore equal. Similarly, the angles $\angle\overline{CAB}$ and $\angle\overline{ACD}$ are also transverse angles and are therefore equal.

Given the two sides $\overline{AB}$ and $\overline{AD}$ (the usual case in a parallelogram of forces), and having found the angle β, the length a^2 of the line $\overline{AC}$ is readily calculated from the law of cosines. The parallelogram is seen to be composed of two similar triangles, one of which is shown in Figure 1-7b. The law of cosines is applied to find the length of side b:

$$b^2 = a^2 + c^2 - 2ac\cos\beta \tag{1-1}$$

The angles α and γ shown in Figure 1-7b can now be found readily by the law of sines:

$$\frac{a}{\sin\alpha} = \frac{b}{\sin\beta} \text{ and } \frac{c}{\sin\gamma} = \frac{b}{\sin\beta} \qquad \text{(1-2a, b)}$$

Equations (1-2) are solved directly for the angles α and γ.

Alternatively, once the side b has been found, the interior angles α and γ could be found by reapplying the law of cosines, but the calculations are generally simpler using the law of sines.

Another property of the parallelogram that is frequently useful is the sum of its interior angles. The sum of the interior angles of any n-sided figure is given as (n-2)(180). For any four-sided figure, therefore, the sum of the four interior angles is 360°, or, the sum of two triangles as shown in Figure 1-7.

Some examples will illustrate the use of the parallelogram of forces in finding the resultant of two forces. It should be observed in these examples that the two forces being summed will have a common point (usually the point of application) and that their resultant will also have that same common point.

Example 1-1

Parallelogram of forces.
Addition of two forces.

Given: Two forces as shown.

To Find: Magnitude and direction of the resultant force

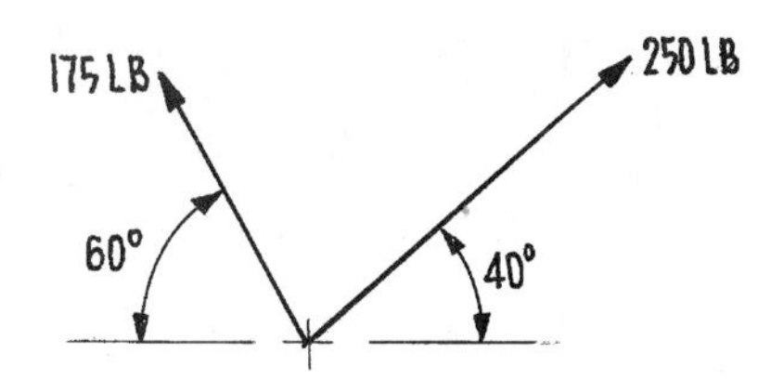

Solution: The parallelogram of forces is completed as shown in the following sketch.

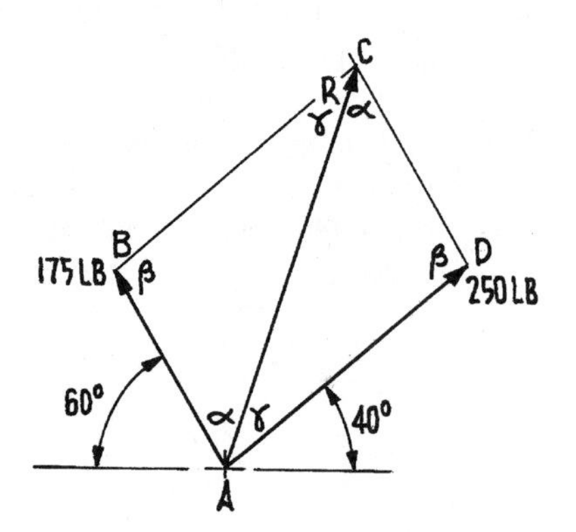

The sketch of the parallelogram is drawn roughly to scale, using the magnitude of the forces to indicate their length.

The angle $\angle\overline{BAD}$ is readily calculated, recognizing that the sum of the four angles at A must be 180°:

$$\angle\overline{BAD} = \alpha + \gamma = 180^0 - 60^0 - 40^0 = 80^0$$

The angle β is now calculated, using the fact that the sum of the four angles of a parallelogram is 360°:

$$360^0 = 2(\alpha + \gamma) + 2\beta = 2(80) + 2\beta$$

$$\beta = 100^0$$

The magnitude of R is calculated from the law of cosines, where BC = AD:

$$R^2 = \overline{AB}^2 + \overline{BC}^2 - 2(\overline{AB})(\overline{BC})\cos\beta$$

$$R^2 = 175^2 + 250^2 - 2(175)(250)\cos 100$$

$$R = 329\ lb$$

The direction of R is found by finding the angle γ from the law of sines:

$$\frac{\overline{CD}}{\sin\gamma} = \frac{\overline{AC}}{\sin\beta}, \quad \frac{175}{\sin\gamma} = \frac{329}{\sin 100}$$

$$\gamma = 31.58°$$

The final result is shown in the following sketch.

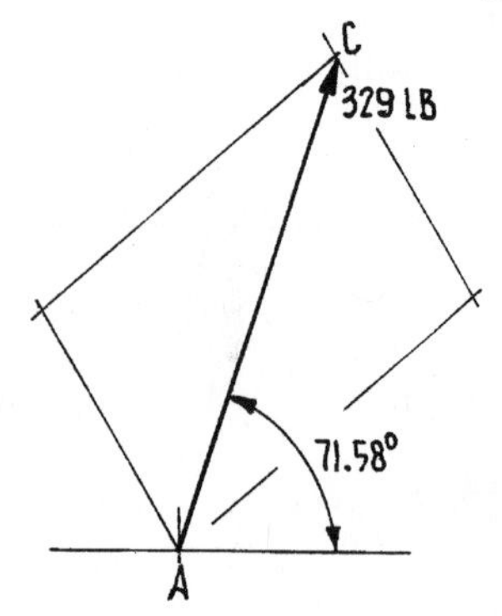

Example 1-2

Parallelogram of forces.
Addition of two forces.

Given: Two forces as shown.

To Find: Magnitude and direction of the resultant force.

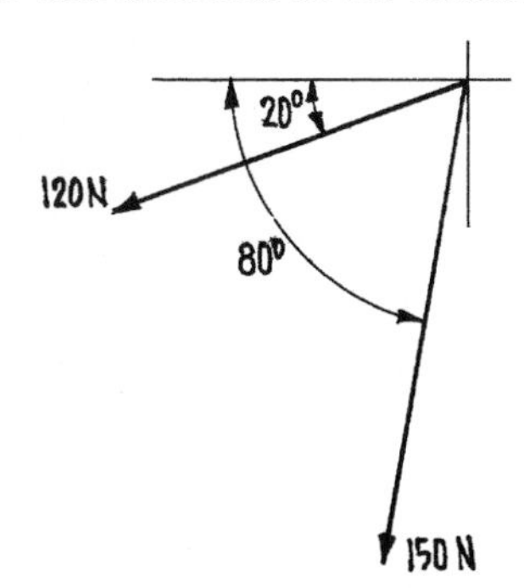

Solution: The parallelogram of forces is completed as shown in the following sketch.

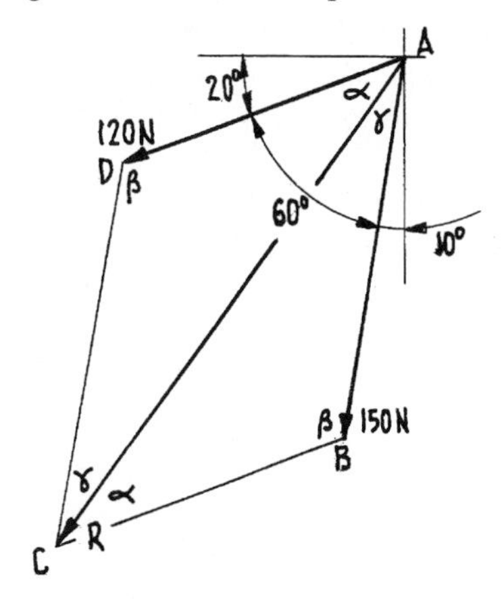

The angle β is computed as before, where the sum of the interior angles is 360°:

$$360^0 = 2(\alpha + \gamma) + 2\beta = 2(60) + 2\beta$$
$$\beta = 120^0$$

The magnitude of the resultant R is found from the law of cosines:

$$R^2 = \overline{AB}^2 + \overline{BC}^2 - 2(\overline{AB})(\overline{BC})\cos\beta$$
$$R^2 = 120^2 + 150^2 - 2(120)(150)\cos 120^0$$
$$R = 234N$$

The angle α is found using the law of sines:

$$\frac{R}{\sin\beta} = \frac{\overline{AB}}{\sin\alpha}; \quad \frac{234}{\sin 120} = \frac{150}{\sin\alpha}$$
$$\alpha = 33.72^0$$

The final result is shown in the following sketch.

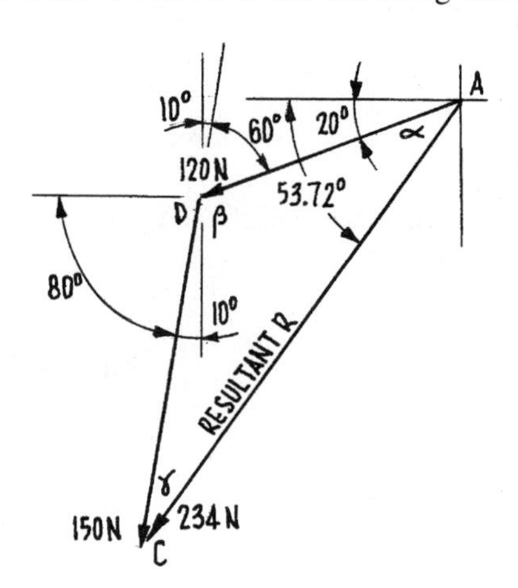

A variation of the parallelogram law makes use of the property of a parallelogram that the opposite sides of a parallelogram are equal in length and parallel in direction. As it is applied, the variation simply places the two force vectors tail-to-head. The sum of the two force vectors then extends from the tail of the first to the head of the last. An example will illustrate the procedure.

Example 1-3

Sum of two forces.

Given: Two forces of Example 1-2.

To Find: Magnitude and direction of the resultant force.

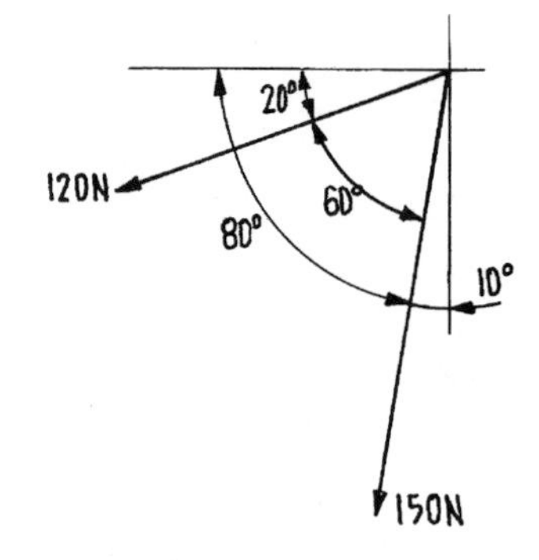

Solution: The force vectors are placed tail-to-head as shown. It does not matter which is placed first.

The resultant R extends from the tail of the first force vector to the head of the last, as shown. It should be immediately apparent that the foregoing sketch is simply half the parallelogram of forces that was used to solve Example 1-2. The numerical solution is of course identical to that of Example 1-2. The angle β is found by summing all angles around the point D:

$$360^0 = 80^0 + \beta + 60^0 + 10^0 + 90^0$$
$$\beta = 120^0$$

The magnitude of the resultant R is found from the law of cosines:

$$R^2 = 120^2 + 150^2 + 150^2 - 2(120)(150)\cos 120^0$$
$$R = 234\text{N}$$

The angle α is found from the law of sines:

$$\frac{R}{\sin\beta} = \frac{\overline{AB}}{\sin\alpha}; \quad \frac{234}{\sin 120} = \frac{150}{\sin\alpha}$$

$$\alpha = 33.72^0$$

The end result is seen to be identical to the final sketch for Example 1-2. Any number of forces may be summed using the parallelogram law. One simply sums any two of the forces to obtain their resultant, then sums a third force to this resultant, a fourth force that resultant and so on. An example will illustrate the procedure for summing four such forces.

Example 1-4

Sum of several forces using the parallelogram law.

Given: Four forces as indicated.

To Find: Magnitude and direction of the resultant force.

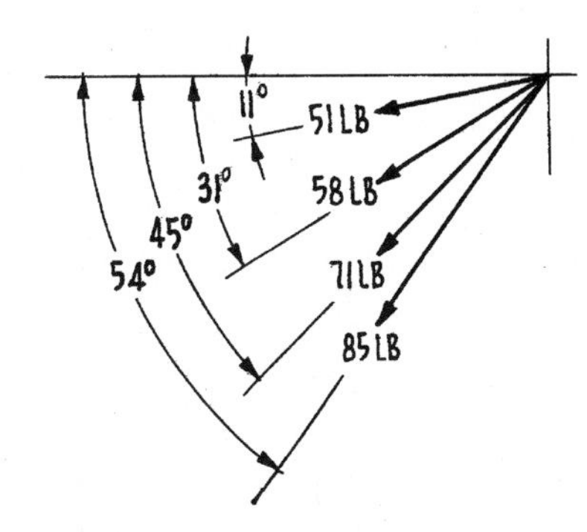

Solution: The top two forces are arbitrarily selected for a starting point. The internal angles are determined and placed on the sketch as shown.

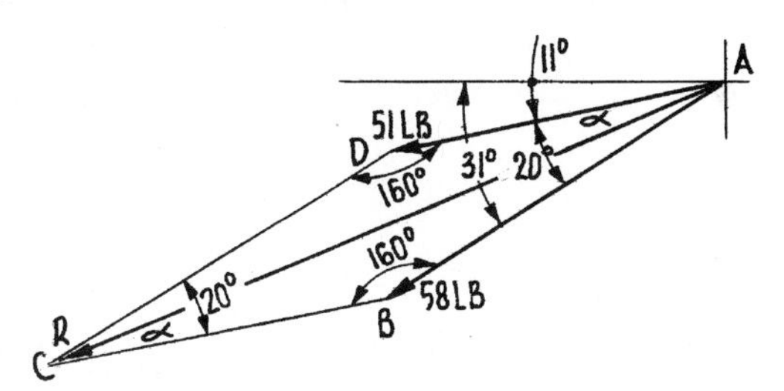

The resultant R is calculated from the law of cosines:

$$R^2 = \overline{AB}^2 + \overline{BC}^2 - 2(\overline{AB})(\overline{BC})\cos\beta$$

$$R^2 = 51^2 + 58^2 - 2(51)(58)\cos 160^0$$

$$R = 107\ lb$$

The angle α is found from the law of sines:

$$\frac{R}{\sin\beta} = \frac{\overline{AB}}{\sin\alpha}; \quad \frac{107}{\sin 160} = \frac{58}{\sin\alpha}$$

$$\alpha = 10.65°$$

The resultant has a magnitude of 107 lb at an angle 21.68° from the horizontal. This resultant is now summed with the third force. The internal angles are determined and placed on the sketch as shown.

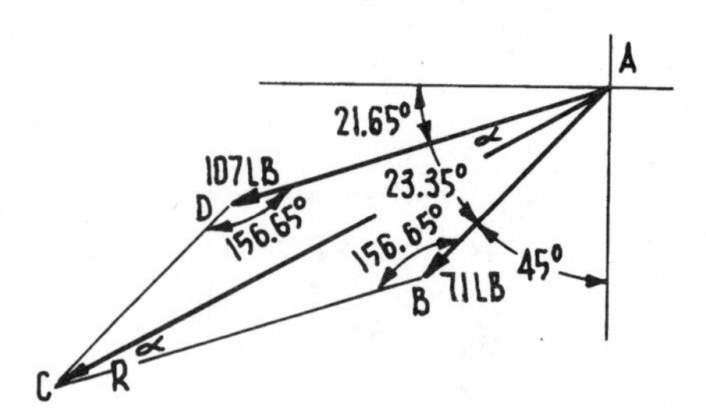

The resultant R is again calculated from the law of cosines:

$$R^2 = \overline{AB}^2 + \overline{BC}^2 - 2(\overline{AB})(\overline{BC})\cos\beta$$

$$R^2 = 71^2 + 107^2 - 2(71)(107)\cos 156.65°$$

$$R = 175\ lb$$

The angle α is again found from the law of sines:

$$\frac{R}{\sin\beta} = \frac{\overline{AB}}{\sin\alpha};\ \frac{175}{\sin 156.65} = \frac{71}{\sin\alpha}$$

$$\alpha = 9.26°$$

The resultant has a magnitude of 175 lb at an angle of 30.91° from the horizontal. This resultant is now summed with the last force. The internal angles are determined and placed on the sketch as shown.

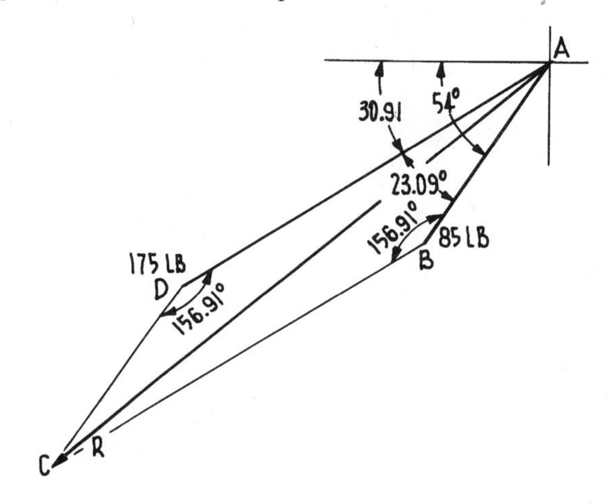

The resultant is again calculated from the law of cosines:

$$R^2 = \overline{AB}^2 + \overline{BC}^2 - 2(\overline{AB})(\overline{BC})\cos\beta$$

$$R^2 = 85^2 + 175^2 - 2(85)(174)\cos 156.91°$$

$$R = 255\ lb$$

The angle α is again found from the law of sines:

$$\frac{R}{\sin\beta} = \frac{\overline{AB}}{\sin\alpha};\ \frac{255}{\sin 156.91} = \frac{85}{\sin\alpha}$$

$$\alpha = 7.50°$$

The resultant of the four forces has the magnitude and direction shown in the adjacent sketch. This single force will produce the same total load in the same direction as the original four forces.

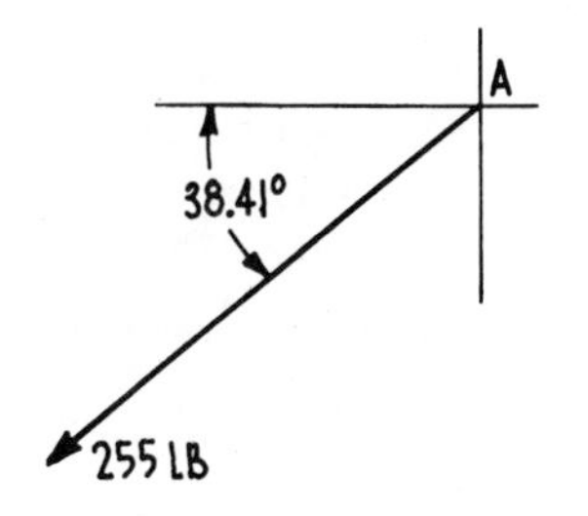

It is also possible to sum the four forces of Example 1-4 using the head-to-tail type of vector solution. Shown graphically, the rearrangement of the force vectors is presented in Figure 1-8. Such a reduction of a complex system of forces to its simplest resultant is called *composition of forces.*

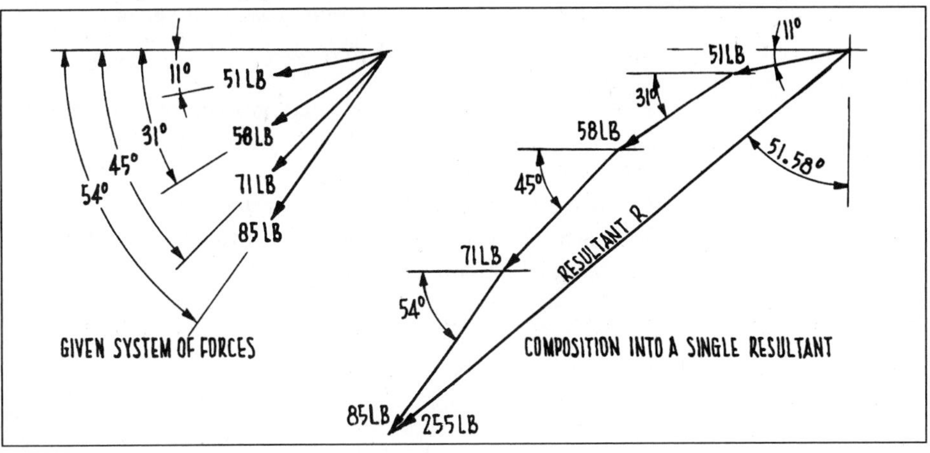

Figure 1-8 Sum of four force vectors.

In years past, the solution of problems such as that of Example 1-4 was oftentimes made graphically. The system would be drawn very accurately to rather large scale and the resultant would then be scaled from the sketch. The hand calculator has long since replaced such graphical solutions, but graphical solutions are still useful as a means to get a fast visual check of results.

The subtraction of one force from another is sometimes useful in engineering calculations. To subtract one force from another in mechanics, simply reverse its direction and use it in its reversed direction. The force obtained from such a subtraction is still called the resultant.

Review Questions

1. Define engineering mechanics.
2. What is the difference between dynamics and statics?
3. What are some of the dynamic loads that can occur on buildings?
4. How is strength of materials different from statics?
5. What is the difference between strength of materials and mechanics of materials?
6. What is structural analysis?
7. Compare briefly the properties of steel as a construction material to the properties of concrete as a construction material.
8. How is wood different from all other common construction materials?
9. Name the three elements required to completely define a force.
10. When a cylinder is in contact without friction against a flat surface, what direction will the resistance force take?
11. When a cylinder is in contact without friction against a curved surface of a larger radius, what direction will the resisting force take?

12. What does the term “prismatic” mean when applied to structural members?
13. What is meant by the term “rigid body mechanics”?
14. Define the Newton force.
15. In the SI system, what is a kilogram?
16. A small imported car has a mass of 1000 kg. In the SI system, how much does it weigh?
17. A small imported car has a weight of 1 ton. In the Imperial system, what is its mass?
18. State your body weight in the SI system.
19. State the principle of transmissibility of a force.
20. What conditions must be maintained when using the principle of transmissibility?
21. What is meant by the term “line of action”?
22. Define collinear, as it applies to forces.
23. What is the resultant of two forces that are equal, opposite and collinear?
24. What makes a force a special case of a vector?
25. How are two forces added?
26. How are to forces subtracted?
27. What is the name of the force obtained by adding or subtracting two forces?
28. How many degrees are there in the sum of the interior angles of a hexagon? An octagon? A rhombus?
29. What is the relationship between the opposite interior angles of a parallelogram?
30. Using a sketch of a triangle to define your terms, state the law of cosines mathematically.
31. Using a sketch of a triangle to define your terms, state the law of sines mathematically.

CHAPTER

2

CONCURRENT FORCES IN A PLANE

Basic concepts and operations concerning forces were introduced in the previous chapter. Those concepts and operations are extended in this chapter to include some basic applications to physical problems.

Systems of forces often fall into recognizable groupings. One such grouping consists of forces that have a common point of intersection. Such systems are the primary subject of this chapter.

2.1 Concurrency of Forces

Systems of forces that have a common point of intersection are said to be *concurrent* forces. One such system of forces is shown in Figure 2-1. The point of intersection of the lines of action is called the *point of concurrency*. In a plane, two parallel forces would have no point of concurrency and would therefore be described as *nonconcurrent* forces. Alternatively, the lines of action of two nonparallel forces in a plane must intersect somewhere in the plane; two nonparallel forces in a plane will therefore always be concurrent.

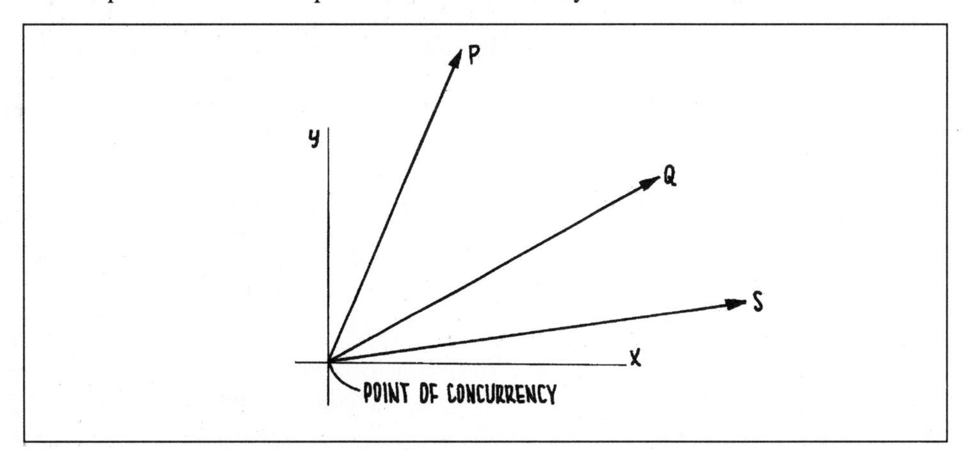

Figure 2-1 Typical concurrent forces.

In three dimensions, however, it is possible that two forces may be neither concurrent nor parallel. To demonstrate the point, one may simply hold up two or more pencils to represent the lines of actions of some forces. It is readily possible to position the pencils in three dimensions such that their lines of action are not parallel nor do they ever intersect; such force systems are neither concurrent nor parallel. The study of these general three dimensional force systems is deferred to a later chapter.

The parallelogram law was introduced earlier as a means to reduce a system of concurrent forces in a plane into a single resultant. Though the term *concurrent* was not applied to the system of forces at that time, the forces were, in fact, concurrent. It is recalled that reducing a system of concurrent forces into a single equivalent resultant, as in Example 1-4, is called *composition of forces.*

The parallelogram law may also be applied in reverse, that is, the parallelogram law may be used to replace a single force by two concurrent components. The two component forces thus derived will produce the same net result that the original force would produce. By repeated application of the parallelogram law, each of the component forces so derived could be replaced in turn by two other concurrent component forces, and so on. Such a replacement of a single force by two or more concurrent components is called the *resolution of a force.*

An example will illustrate the resolution of a force into two concurrent components.

Example 2-1

Resolution of a force into concurrent components

Given: Desired magnitude and direction of a force.

To Find: Concurrent forces at the indicated angles that will produce the desired force.

15°
DESIRED FORCE
600 LB IN THIS
DIRECTION
30°
LINES OF ACTION OF
ALTERNATIVE FORCES

Solution: Complete the parallelogram of forces and determine the interior angles in the parallelogram.

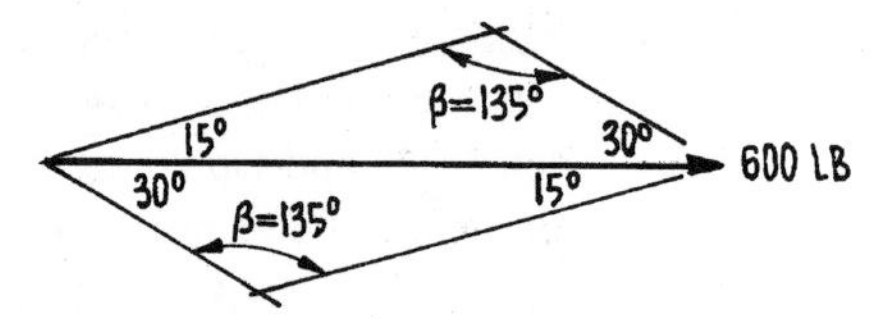

The force F is found by the law of sines:

$$\frac{600}{\sin 135} = \frac{F}{\sin 30^0}$$

$$F = 424\,lb$$

The force P is similarly found by the law of sines:

$$\frac{600}{\sin 135} = \frac{P}{\sin 15^0}$$

$$P = 220\,lb$$

The alternative force system is shown in the following sketch. These two forces will produce a 600 lb resultant force along the required line of action.

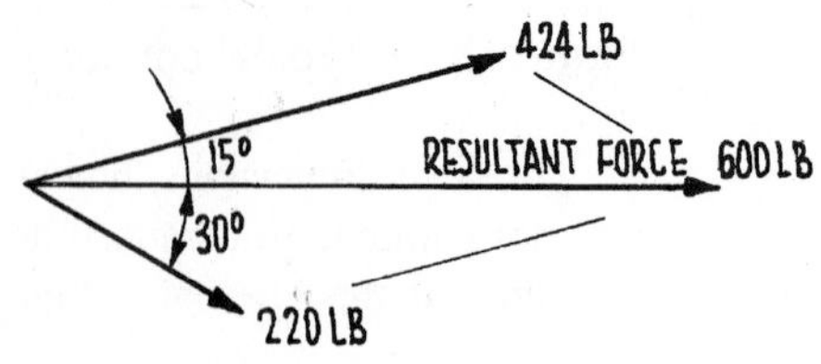

It is not often of interest in engineering work to resolve a force into its concurrent components at some unusual angle, though it is readily possible as shown in the foregoing example. It is far more useful in engineering to resolve a force into its concurrent x and y components in rectangular coordinates. Such a procedure is developed next.

2.2 Rectangular Components of a Force

It is common practice in engineering to refer forces to a rectangular coordinate system. The algebraic signs of the coordinate system are usually taken from the point of application of the force. Such a force and the Cartesian coordinate system are shown in Figure 2-2. Force F_x is positive if it is directed to the right and force F_y is positive if it is directed upward.

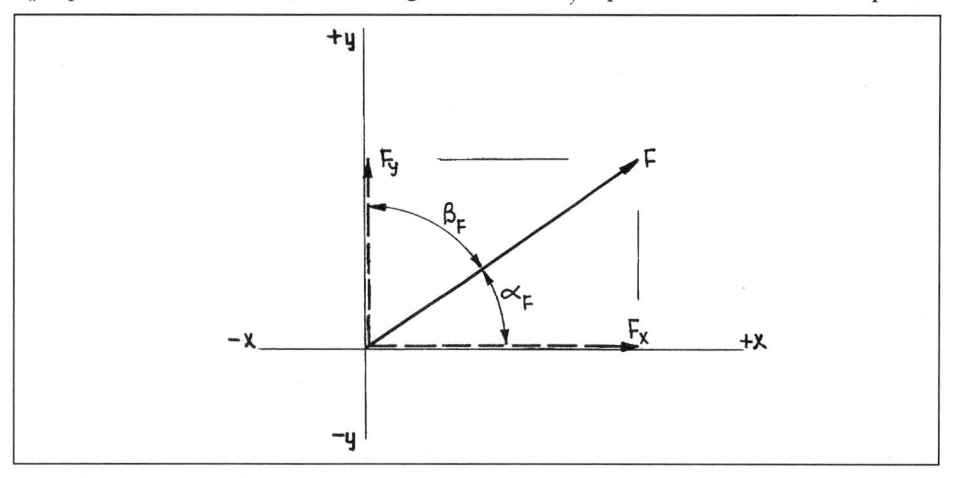

Figure 2-2 Forces in rectangular coordinates.

In Figure 2-2, the horizontal component or x-component of the force F is shown as force F_x, with α_F being the angle between the force F and the X axis at the tail of the force. Similarly, the y-component of the force F is shown as force F_y with β_F being the angle between the force F and the y axis at the tail of the force. The x and y components of the force F are readily computed:

$$F_x = F\cos\alpha_F \qquad (2\text{-}1a)$$
$$F_y = F\cos\beta_F \qquad (2\text{-}1b)$$

The quantities $\cos\alpha_F$ and $\cos\beta_F$ are called the *direction cosines* of the force F. The *direction angle* α_F is measured from the x axis to the line of action of the force and the *direction angle* β_F is measured from the y axis to the line of action of the force. (In a later chapter, the third dimension will be added, in which the direction angle γ will be used as the angle measured from the z axis to the line of action of the force.)

From the geometry of Figure 2-2, it is noted that the direction angles α_F and β_F are complementary. As a consequence:

$$\sin\alpha_F = \cos\beta_F \text{ and } \sin\beta_F = \cos\alpha_F \qquad (2\text{-}2)$$

This property of the direction angles will be useful in later derivations.

For most calculations in engineering mechanics, all forces will be resolved into their rectangular components. Calculations will be performed using these components rather than the original forces. The practice greatly reduces the mathematical complexity that can sometimes occur. Some examples will illustrate the resolution of forces into their rectangular components.

Example 2-2

Resolution of forces into rectangular components.

Given: Forces as shown.

To Find: Rectangular components of the two forces.

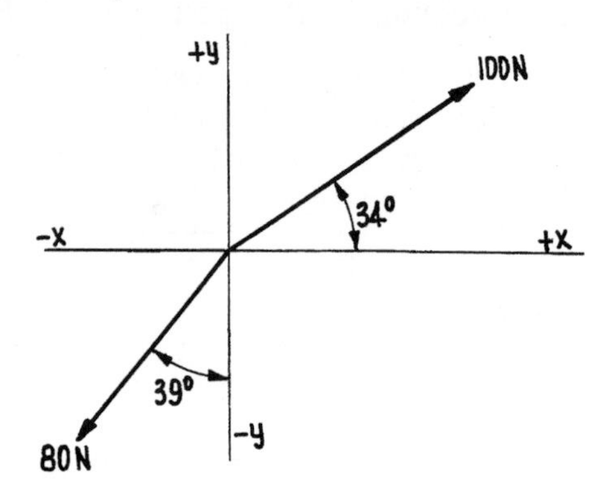

Solution: As a first step, it is necessary to find the direction angles α and β to the coordinate axes. These angles are found readily and entered on the sketch as shown.

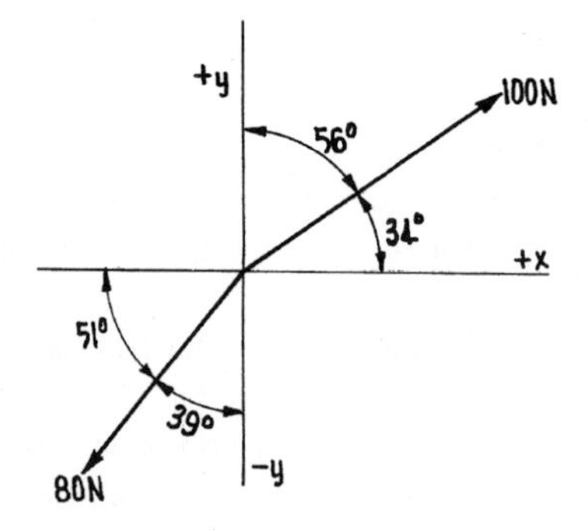

The x and y components of forces are found from the direction cosines. For the 100N force, denoted F:

$$F_x = 100 \cos 34 = 100(0.829) = 82.9\text{N} \quad \text{(to the right)}$$
$$F_y = 100 \cos 56 = 100(0.559) = 55.9\text{N} \quad \text{(upward)}$$

For the 80N force, denoted P:

$$P_x = 80 \cos 51 = 80(0.629) = 50.3\text{N} \quad \text{(to the left)}$$
$$P_y = 80 \cos 39 = 80(0.777) = 62.2\text{N} \quad \text{(downward)}$$

The x and y components of the two forces are shown in the following sketch.

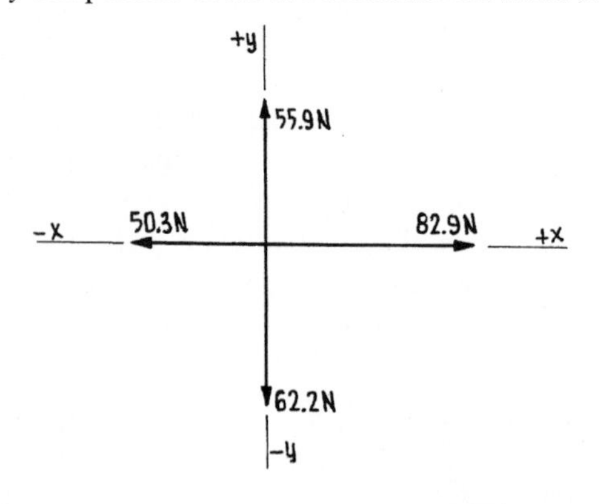

From the solution of Example 2-2, it is immediately apparent that the resulting component forces are *collinear,* that is, they have the same line of action; they could therefore be added algebraically to find their resultants. In this case, however, finding the resultants of the two forces was not a part of the required solution and will not be done here.

It is noted at this point that in a more rigorous treatment of mechanics than this, the direction angles α and β would always be measured from the positive x axis and the positive y axis to the action line of the force, with angles measured counterclockwise being positive. For such a case, the direction angles of Example 2-2 would be those shown in Figure 2-3.

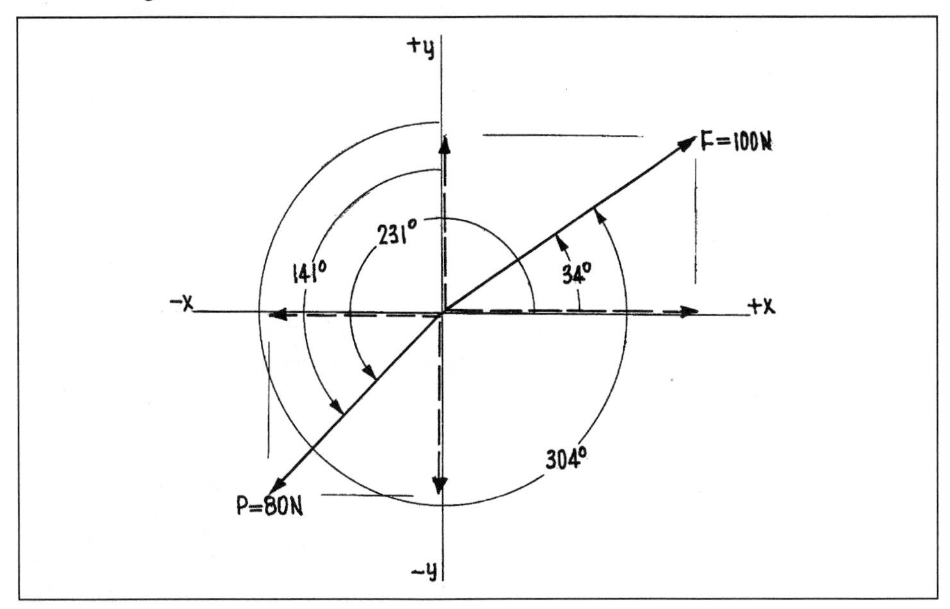

Figure 2-3 Exact direction angles.

It is again emphasized that the magnitude of a force is always positive. A negative sign for a component in a rigorous analysis indicates only that its direction is negative, that is, the force is directed downward or to the left.

The calculation of the x and y components of the two forces would then be, for the 100N force:

$$F_x = 100 \cos(+\,34) = +82.9\text{N}$$
$$F_y = 100 \cos(+304) = +55.9\text{N}$$

and, for the components of the 80N force:

$$P_x = 80 \cos(+231) = -50.3\text{N}$$
$$P_y = 80 \cos(+141) = -62.2\text{N}$$

The advantage of such a rigorous treatment is, of course, that the calculation automatically gives the direction sign of the various forces, a valuable feature should one be writing a computer program. In less rigorous treatments of mechanics such as that presented in this textbook, the direction angles α and β are simply taken to the nearest x and y axes, with positive signs, and the directions of the resulting components are then set visually, as was done in Example 2-2.

2.3 Resultant of Several Forces

The sum of several forces to find their resultant is readily accomplished by using the rectangular components of the forces just developed. Some examples will illustrate the procedure.

Example 2-3

Resultant of several forces.

Given: Three forces as shown.

To Find: Magnitude and direction of the resultant.

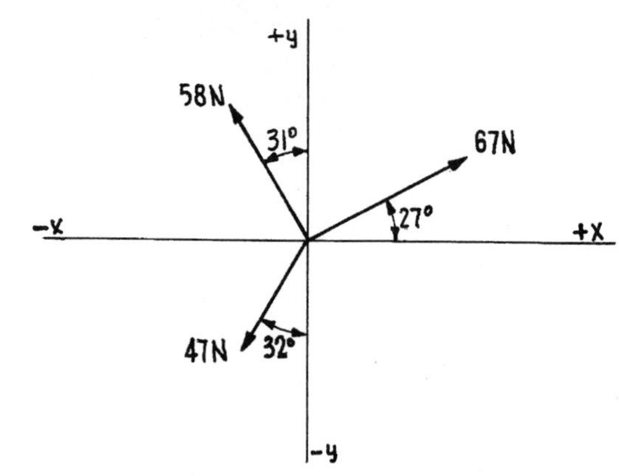

Solution: The remaining direction angles are determined and entered on the sketch, along with the x and y components of each force.

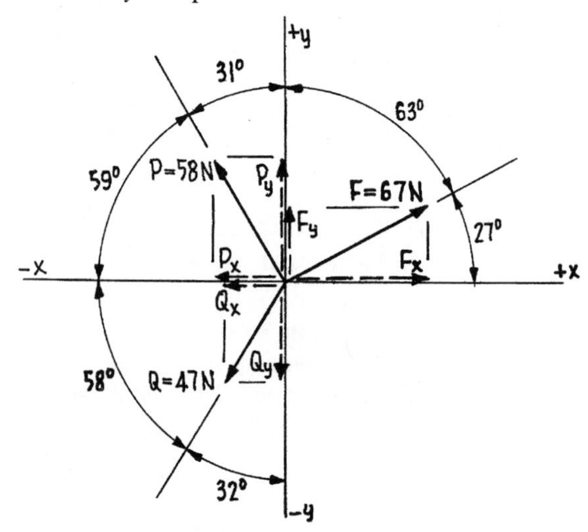

The x and y components are calculated by using the direction cosines. For the force F:

$$F_x = F \cos \alpha_F = 67 \cos 27 = 59.7\text{N}$$
$$F_y = F \cos\beta_F = 67 \cos 63 = 30.4\text{N}$$

For the force P:

$$P_x = P \cos\alpha_P = 58 \cos 59 = 29.9\text{N}$$
$$P_y = P \cos\beta_P = 58 \cos 31 = 49.7\text{N}$$

For the force Q:

$$Q_x = Q \cos\alpha_Q = 47 \cos 58 = 24.9\text{N}$$
$$Q_y = Q \cos\beta_Q = 47 \cos 32 = 39.9\text{N}$$

The component of the resultant force in the x direction, R_x, is the sum of the x components:

$$R_x = +F_x + P_x + Q_x = 59.7 - 29.9 - 24.9 = +4.9N$$

The component of the resultant force in the y direction, R_y, is the sum of the y components:

$$R_y = +F_y + P_y + Q_y = 30.4 + 49.7 - 39.9 = +40.2N$$

The two components R_x and R_y and their resultant R are shown in the following sketch.

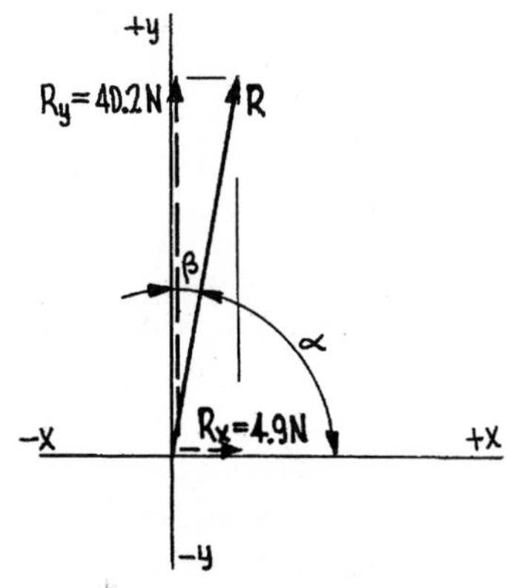

The resultant R is calculated using the Pythagorean theorem:

$$R = \sqrt{R_x^{\,2} + R_y^{\,2}} = \sqrt{4.9^2 + 40.2^2} = 40.5N$$

The direction angles are found from the direction cosines:

$$\cos\alpha_R = \frac{R_x}{R} = \frac{4.9}{40.5} = 0.1210, \quad \alpha_R = 83.05°$$

$$\cos\beta_R = \frac{R_y}{R} = \frac{40.2}{40.5} = 0.9927, \quad \beta_R = 6.95°$$

The final result is shown in the adjacent sketch.

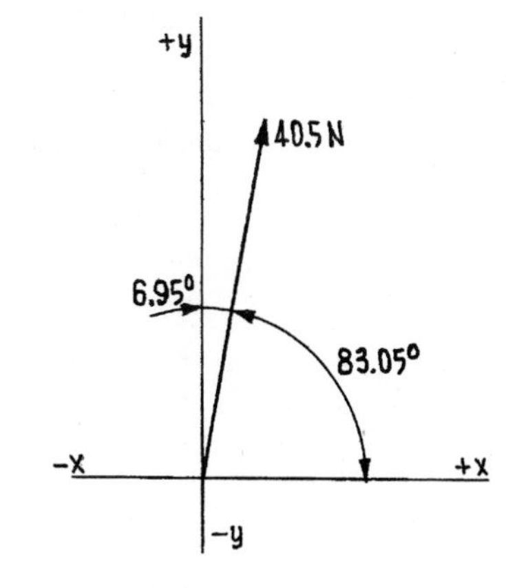

Concurrent forces may be directed either toward the point of concurrency or away from the point of concurrency. Consider, for example, the forces F and P of Figure 2-4a. Under the given conditions, F is directed away from the point of concurrency and the force P is directed toward the point of concurrency.

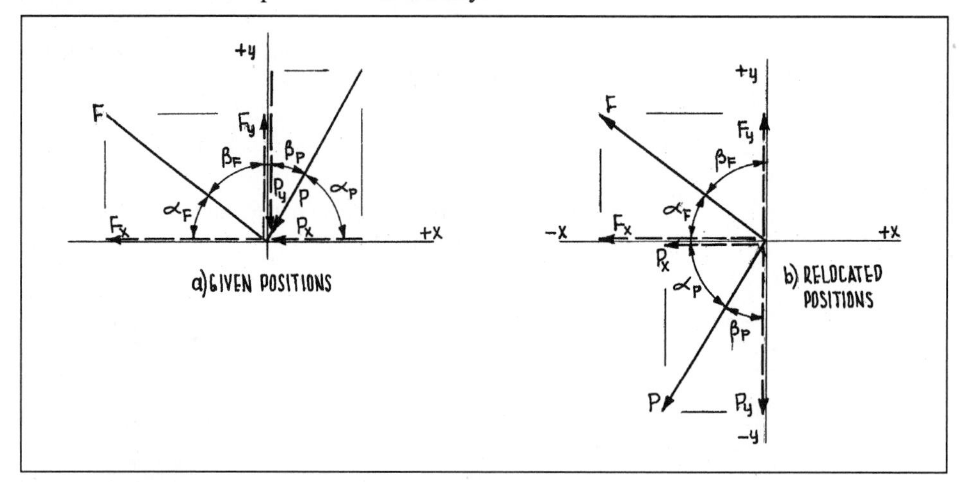

Figure 2-4 Relocation of forces.

Utilizing the principle of transmissibility, one could relocate the force along its line of action into the position shown in Figure 2-4b. In that position, both of the forces would then be directed away from the point of concurrency, and in that configuration, the direction and magnitude of the components P_x and P_y would remain unchanged, so the final resultant would remain unchanged. Whether it is better to show all forces simply as they originally occur or to relocate them into a consistent pattern is a matter of personal preference. In this textbook, forces are usually given the position in which they originally occur.

An example will illustrate the point that results are identical.

Example 2-4

Resultant of several forces.

Given: Three forces of Example 2-3 with force P relocated along its line of action into the fourth quadrant.

To Find: Magnitude and direction of the resultant.

Solution: The force P is relocated as indicated on the following sketch. Direction angles are also determined and entered on the sketch as shown.

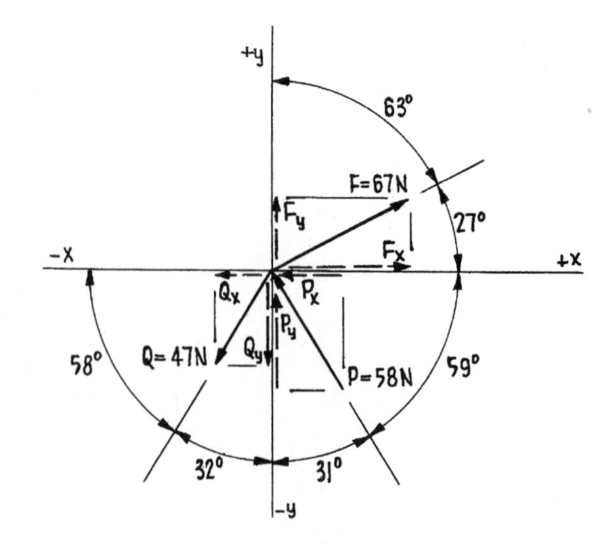

The force components are calculated as usual:

$$F_x = F \cos \alpha_F = 67 \cos 27 = 59.7\text{N}$$
$$F_y = F \cos \beta_F = 67 \cos 63 = 30.4\text{N}$$
$$P_x = P \cos \alpha_P = 58 \cos 59 = 29.9\text{N}$$
$$P_y = P \cos \beta_P = 58 \cos 31 = 49.7\text{N}$$
$$Q_x = Q \cos \alpha_Q = 47 \cos 58 = 24.9\text{N}$$
$$Q_y = Q \cos \beta_Q = 47 \cos 32 = 39.9\text{N}$$

At this point, it is noted that these numerical results are identical to those of Example 2-3. The resultant force will therefore be the same as that of Example 2-3. It is thus demonstrated that relocating a force according to the principle of transmissibility has no effect on the force system.

Example 2-5

Resultant of several forces.

Given: Three lines are tied to a boat and forces are exerted on each line as shown.

To Find: Direction in which the boat will begin to move.

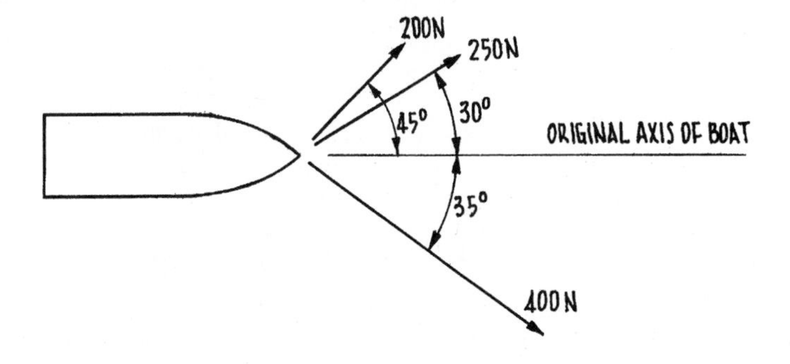

Solution: It is assumed that the boat will begin to move in the direction of the resultant force. The direction of the resultant will therefore be found. The forces are shown on the following sketch with direction angles as shown.

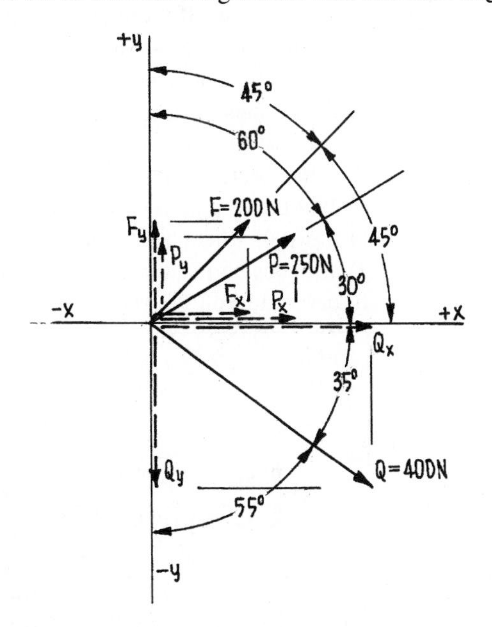

Rectangular components of forces are found as usual:

$$F_x = F\cos\alpha_F = 200\cos 45 = 141N$$
$$F_y = F\cos\beta_F = 200\cos 45 = 141N$$

$$P_x = P\cos\alpha_P = 250\cos 30 = 217N$$
$$P_y = P\cos\beta_P = 250\cos 60 = 125N$$

$$Q_x = Q\cos\alpha_Q = 400\cos 35 = 327N$$
$$Q_y = Q\cos\beta_Q = 400\cos 55 = 229N$$

Component forces are summed to find the components R_x and R_y of the resultant R:

$$R_x = +F_x + P_x + Q_x = 141 + 2\,17 + 327 = 685N$$

$$R_y = +F_y + P_y + Q_y = 141+125 - 229 = 37N$$

The direction of the resultant force is shown in the adjacent sketch.

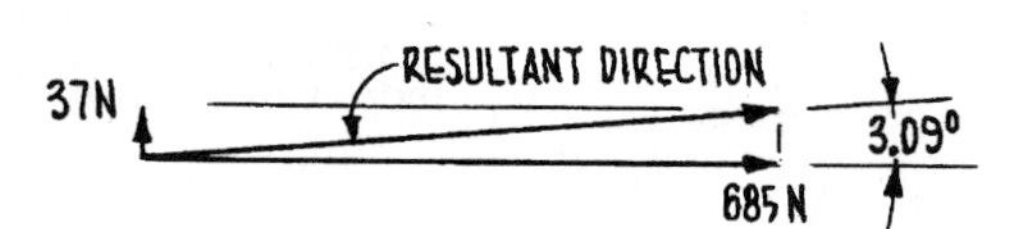

It is concluded that the boat will begin to move at an angle 3.09° to the left of its original axis.

2.4 Equilibrium of Force Systems in a Plane

The concept of *equilibrium* forms the basis of calculations throughout all of statics. A particle is said to be in equilibrium if there is no *unbalanced* force in any direction that could create motions. A particle in equilibrium can be imagined as being suspended motionless in the plane, with all forces in any one direction exactly opposed by equal forces in the opposite direction.

It has been shown that any number of concurrent forces can be composed into a single resultant. If there exists another force that is equal, opposite and collinear to that resultant, then the two forces are seen to be in equilibrium; there will be no imbalances to cause motion. It is noted also that by the definition of collinear forces, the lines of action of these two forces will coincide.

Consider, for example, the ring of Figure 2-5. The system of forces acting on the ring has been composed into a single resultant as shown. For the ring to successfully sustain the resultant of these acting forces, there must exist an opposing system of forces in the wall whose resultant is equal, opposite and collinear to that of the acting forces. That opposing resultant force is also shown in Figure 2-5; it is called the *reaction* to the forces acting on the ring.

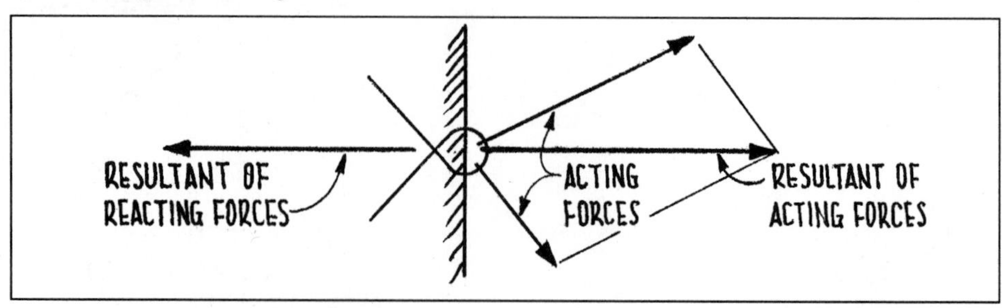

Figure 2-5 Action and reaction.

The foregoing principle that *action equals reaction* is used throughout statics for calculating the reactions under a system of forces. In such calculations, the resultant of the forces acting on a support is determined; the reaction at the support is then known to be equal, opposite and collinear to that resultant. An example will illustrate.

Example 2-6

Calculation of a reaction.

Given: System of forces acting at a point as shown.

To Find: Reaction in the supporting wall.

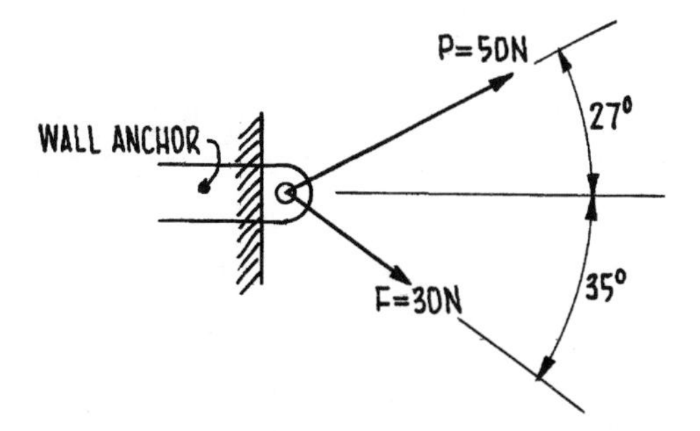

Solution: The resultant of the forces acting at the hole in the wall anchor (the padeye) will be found. The reaction in the supporting wall will be equal, opposite and collinear to that resultant. The rectangular components and direction angles are shown in the following working sketch.

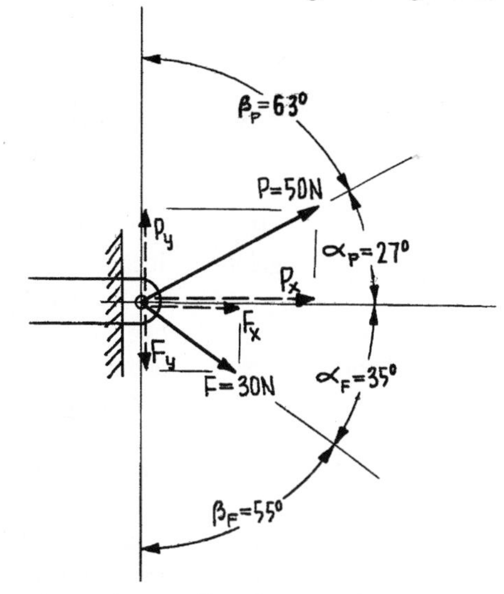

The rectangular components are found as usual:

$$F_x = F\cos\alpha_F = 30\cos 35 = 24.6\text{N}$$
$$F_y = F\cos\beta_F = 30\cos 55 = 17.2\text{N}$$

$$P_x = P\cos\alpha_P = 50\cos 27 = 44.6\text{N}$$
$$P_y = P\cos\beta_P = 50\cos 63 = 22.7\text{N}$$

The components R_x and R_y and the resultant R are calculated from the foregoing results:

$$R_x = F_x + P_x = 24.6 + 44.6 = 69.2N$$
$$R_y = F_y + P_y = 17.2 + 2\,2.7 = 5.5N$$

$$R = \sqrt{R_x^2 + R_y^2} = \sqrt{69.2^2 + 5.5^2} = 69.4N$$

The resultant of the applied forces is shown in the following sketch along with its equal, opposite and collinear reaction.

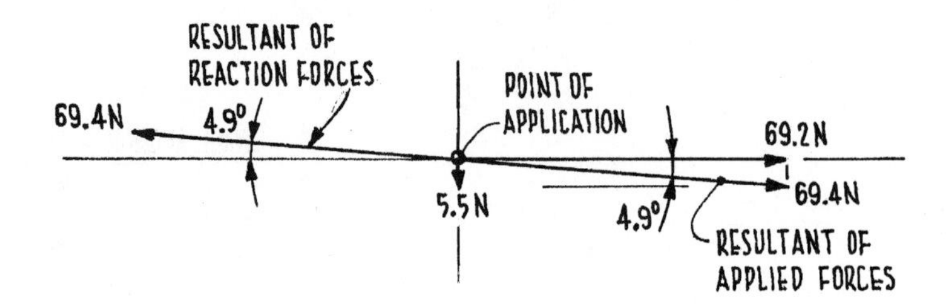

In Example 2-6, two forces caused a single reaction. A variation of this case can also occur, where a single force causes two reactions. Such a case is considered in the next example.

Example 2-7

Calculation of reactions.

Given: 60 lb cylinder supported as shown in the sketch.

To Find: Reactions at the supporting surfaces.

Solution: It is assumed that the resultant weight of the cylinder has its line of action through the center of the cylinder.

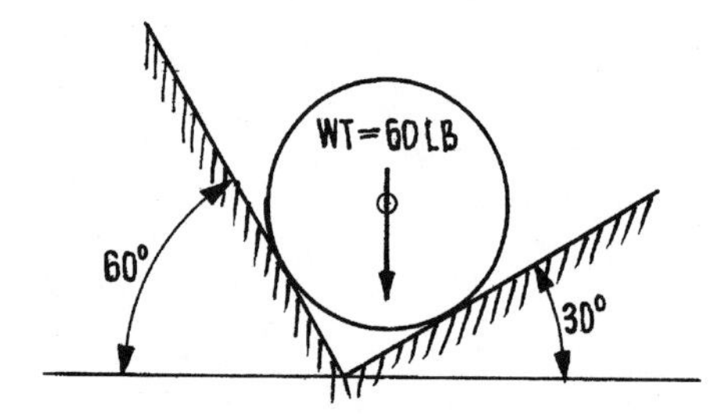

The two reaction forces will have their lines of action normal to the supporting surfaces at the point of contact, as shown in the following sketch. Their lines of action are also seen to pass through the center of the cylinder. Wt = 60 lb.

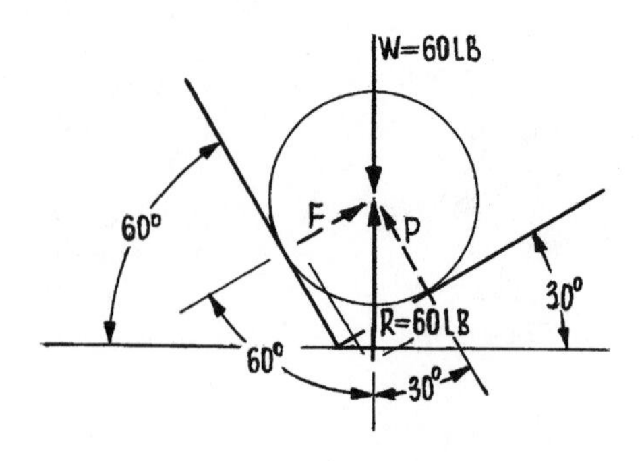

Upon examination of the sketch, it is immediately apparent that the resultant R will be equal, opposite and collinear to the weight W, and that the forces F and P are simply the component forces of the resultant R.

The reaction forces F and P are readily calculated from the geometry of the figure:

$$F = R \cos 60 = 60 \cos 60 = 30 \text{ lb as shown}$$
$$P = R \cos 30 = 60 \cos 30 = 52 \text{ lb as shown}$$

2.5 Moment of a Force about an Axis

To this point, the discussions about statics have been limited to discussions of forces. The concept of a force is readily visualized; certainly everyone has had direct experience with lifting weights, towing a boat or pushing a car, or with some other type of force system. Similarly, composing several forces into one force or resolving one force into several forces is readily visualized, due largely to our general experience with such force systems.

There is another type of loading that can occur on a structural member, however, that is not a force nor does it produce a resultant force. That loading is called a *moment*; a moment tends to produce rotation about an *axis of rotation*, or a *moment center*. While occurring generally less frequently than forces, moments are still quite common in our daily lives, if only we pause briefly to identify them.

A screwdriver, for example, produces a moment on a screw as indicated in Figure 2-6. It is emphasized that there is no resultant force anywhere on the screw; there is just the twist, or moment, being exerted by the screwdriver. There is no resultant force with its familiar line of action and its point of application.

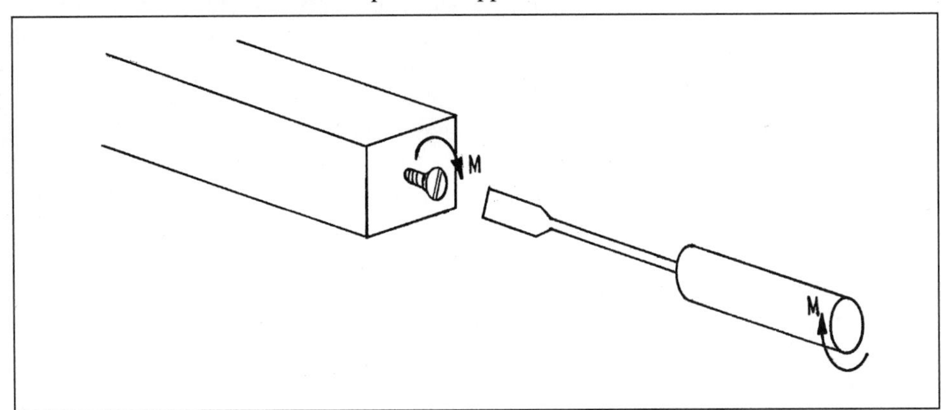

Figure 2-6 Moment exerted by a screwdriver.

It is noted also that in the rotational effects shown in Figure 2-6, the moment, if large enough, will cause rotation of the screw about its longitudinal axis (moment center). Such a moment is oftentimes called a *torque*. It is torque that rotates the driveshaft that turns the propeller of a ship; it is also torque that powers the axles that turn the drivewheels of an automobile. Torque is, in fact, one of the more familiar forms of moment in our daily experience.

Moment, or a load that tends to cause rotation about an axis, is a very general type of load that can occur in many places in a structure. Moment is defined in mechanics as a force acting over a distance; its units are force times distance. Moment is calculated about a moment center such as the point A shown in Figure 2-7. It does not take much imagination, however, to see that the "point" in Figure 2-7 could also be identified as an axis of rotation that lies perpendicular to the plane of the paper.

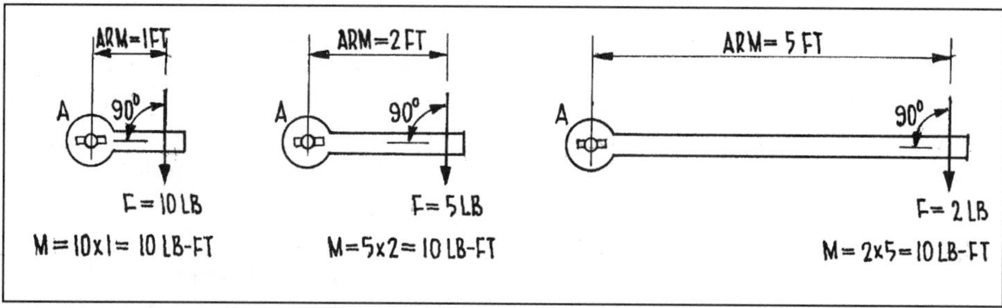

Figure 2-7 Equivalent moments about a point.

It is noted that in each of the three cases shown in Figure 2-7, the same moment is developed about the moment center at point A. Thus, a large force acting over a short distance can produce the same moment as a small force acting over a longer distance. The distance used to calculate moment is a straight line that passes through the axis of rotation and lies perpendicular to the line of action of the force; that distance is called the *moment arm* of the force.

It is also observed from Figure 2-7 that in all cases, the line of action of the force, taken in conjunction with the point A, will define a plane. A moment, therefore, always lies in a plane and it tends to produce rotation about an axis perpendicular to that plane. This concept of a moment will be used repeatedly, both here and throughout later chapters in this textbook.

As noted, the units of a moment are force times distance. In the Imperial system the units may be lb•in, lb•ft, kip•in or kip•ft. In SI, the units may be N•mm, N•m, kN•mm or kN•m. Note that periods are not used to denote these abbreviations.

As with forces, the magnitude of a moment must always be positive. A negative sign simply denotes that its direction occurs in the negative sense. As a general rule, directions are usually chosen such that a positive moment will produce clockwise rotations and a negative moment will produce counterclockwise rotations. In mechanics, the use of positive and negative signs is sometimes avoided through the use of direction indicators: ↓ or ↑.

There are several ways of calculating the moment of a force; all of them will of course yield the same numerical result. If the geometry is such that the force and the arm are conveniently aligned in their proper orientation, the method used in Figure 2-7 is obviously simple and direct and would be used. In the more general case of finding the moment of a force F about a point A, as shown in Figure 2-8, there will necessarily be some intermediate calculations.

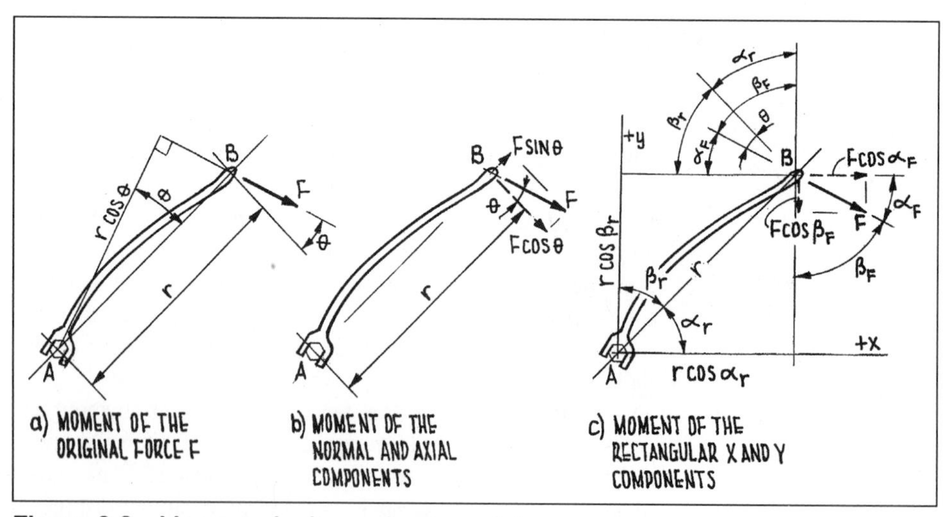

Figure 2-8 Moment of a force about a point.

In the solution given in Figure 2-8a, the location of the moment arm $\overline{AC}$ has been determined such that the arm passes through the point A and lies perpendicular to the line of action of the original force F. The moment of the force F about point A is then:

$$M = Fr\cos\theta \tag{2-3}$$

Alternatively, in the solution given in Figure 2-8b, the original force F has been resolved into two components, one whose line of action is perpendicular to the line $\overline{AB}$ and one whose line of action coincides with line $\overline{AB}$. The sum of the moments produced by these two components will be the total moment about the point A. As indicated, the component $F\sin\theta$ passes through A and it therefore has no moment arm about the point A; its moment about A is thus zero. The other component, $F\cos\theta$, has an arm of distance r; its moment about A is given by:

$$M = Fr\cos\theta \tag{2-4}$$

This result is, as expected, identical to the result found in the first solution.

In general, the third approach, as shown in Figure 2-8c, is the most widely applicable and the most frequently used of the general solutions. In that approach, both the force F and the arm $\overline{AB}$ are resolved into their rectangular x and y components. Note that the direction angles from arm $\overline{AB}$ are referenced to the point of rotation, point A. The total moment is then the sum of the moments produced by each force times its moment arm to A, with due attention paid to direction, of course. The moment is given by:

$$M = (F\cos\alpha_F)(r\cos\beta_r) + (F\cos\beta_F)(r\cos\alpha_r) \tag{2-5}$$

Numerically, this result will be identical to that of the two earlier solutions, but in its present form it does not appear to be the same. The rather intricate proof of this identity follows.

From the geometry of Figure 2-8c, it is observed that:

$$\beta_r = \alpha_F + \theta \text{ and } \alpha_r = \beta_F - \theta \tag{2-6a,b}$$

The trigonometric identities for the sum and difference of angles are applied, yielding the following equations for $\cos\beta_r$ and $\cos\alpha_r$:

$$\cos\beta_r = \cos\alpha_F\cos\theta - \sin\alpha_F\sin\theta \tag{2-7a}$$

$$\cos\alpha_r = \cos\beta_F\cos\theta + \sin\beta_F\sin\theta \tag{2-7b}$$

These quantities are substituted for $\cos\beta_r$ and $\cos\alpha_r$ in Eq.(2-5). The result is given by:

$$M = Fr[\cos\alpha_F(\cos\alpha_F\cos\theta - \sin\alpha_F\sin\theta) + \cos\beta_F(\cos\beta_F\cos\theta + \sin\beta_F\sin\theta)] \tag{2-8}$$

For complementary angles such as α_F and β_F [see Eq.(2-2)]:

$$\sin\alpha_F = \cos\beta_F \text{ and } \cos\alpha_F = \sin\beta_F \tag{2-9a,b}$$

These quantities are substituted into Eq.(2-8) to find:

$$M = Fr[(\cos^2\alpha_F + \sin^2\alpha_F)\cos\theta + (\sin\alpha_F\sin\beta_F - \sin\beta_F\sin\alpha_F)\sin\theta \tag{2-10}$$

It is noted that the first term of Eq.(2-10) becomes 1 and the second term becomes zero. The final result is then:

$$M = Fr \cos\theta \qquad (2\text{-}11)$$

Again, as expected, the same result is obtained using this approach as was obtained using either of the two earlier approaches.

The proof just given that *the moment of a force about a point is equal to the moment of its components about that point* was first given by Varignon in 1687. The statement of this general principle of mechanics is called Varignon's theorem; it will be used repeatedly in future discussions.

Some examples will demonstrate the procedures for finding the moment of a force about a point (or about an axis of rotation).

Example 2-8

Moment of a force about a point (or axis).

Given: Wrench and bolt with dimensions as shown.

To Find: Moment exerted by the wrench on the bolt.

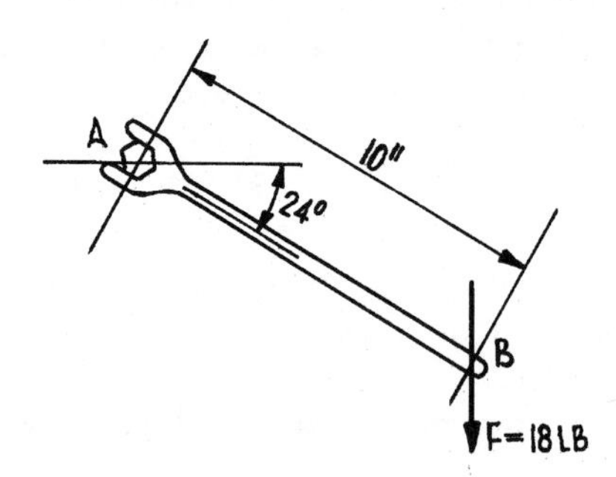

Solution No. 1: The arm to the line of action of the force is determined as indicated.

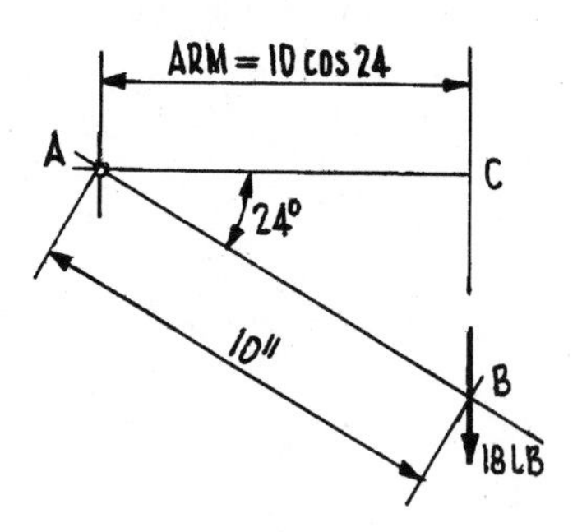

The moment is the force times its arm $\overline{AC}$:

$$M = 18(10 \cos 24) = 164 \text{ lb·in}$$

Solution No. 2: The force F is resolved into two components, F_{AB} and F_N. Component F_N is normal to the line $\overline{AB}$ and component F_{AB} lies along the line. The line $\overline{AB}$ then becomes the moment arm for the component F_N.

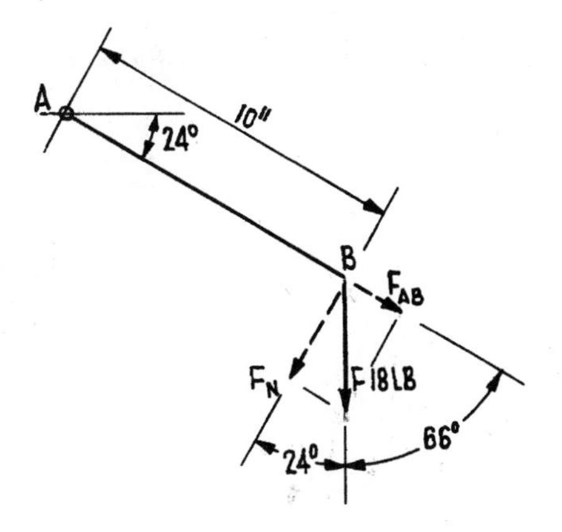

The components of the force F are given by:

$$F_{AB} = F \cos 66 = 18 \cos 66 = 7.3 \text{ lb·in}$$
$$F_N = F \cos 24 = 18 \cos 24 = 16.4 \text{ lb·in}$$

By Varignon's theorem:

$$M = F_{AB}(0)+F_N(\overline{AB}) = 0 + 16.44(10)$$
$$M = 164 \text{ lb·in}$$

Example 2-9

Moment of a force about a point (or axis).

Given: Free-form streetlight as shown.

To Find: Moment M_B at the base.

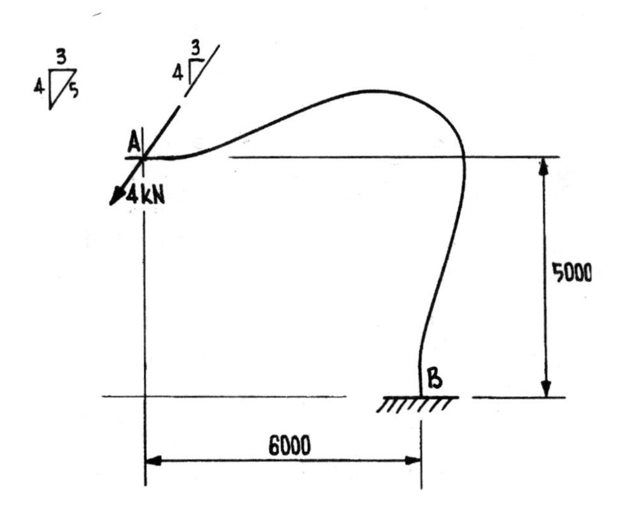

Solution: The 4kN force is resolved into its x and y components as shown.

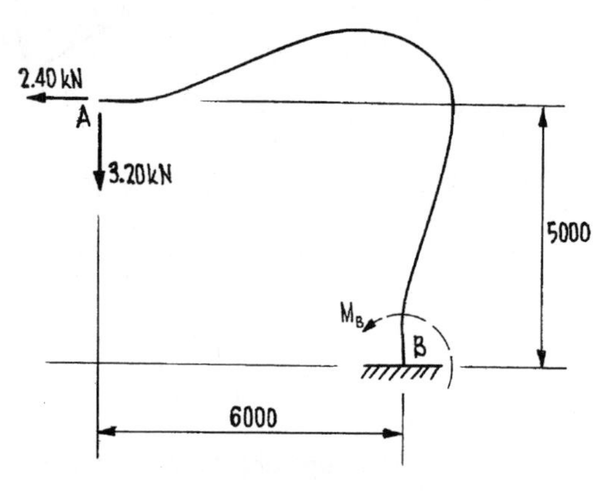

By Varignon's theorem:

M_B = 2.40(5.0)+ 3.20(6.0) = 31.2 kN·m acting in the direction shown.

Example 2-10

Moment of two concurrent forces about a point (or axis).

Given: Concurrent forces acting as shown.

To Find: Moment M_A about the base at point A.

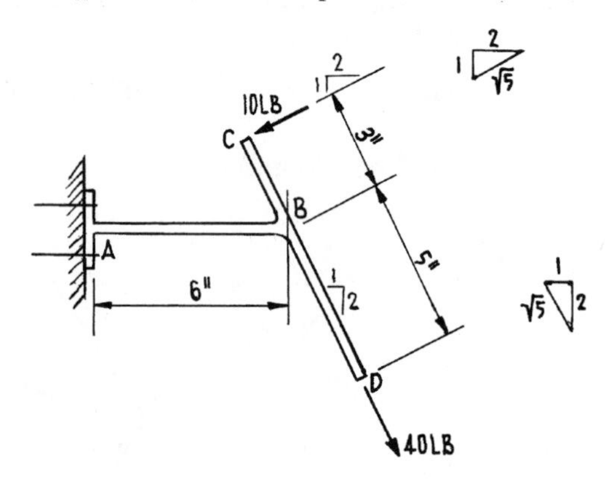

Solution: All forces and dimensions are resolved into their rectangular coordinates.

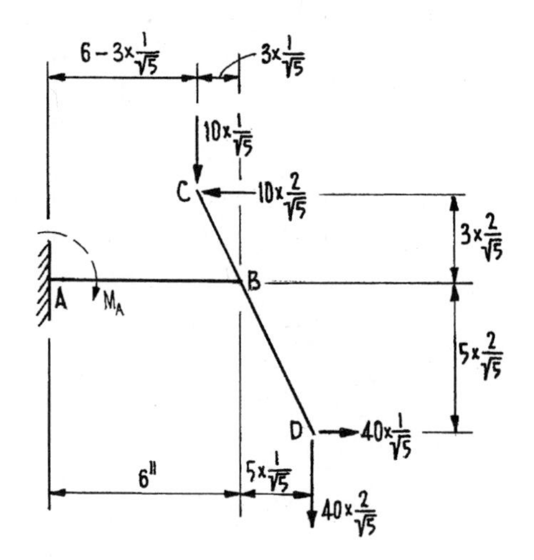

By Varignon's theorem, moments are summed about the point A.

$$M_A = \left[10\left(\frac{1}{\sqrt{5}}\right)6 - 3\left(\frac{1}{\sqrt{5}}\right)\right] - \left[10\left(\frac{2}{\sqrt{5}}\right)3\left(\frac{2}{\sqrt{5}}\right)\right]$$

$$+\left[40\left(\frac{2}{\sqrt{5}}\right)6 + 5\left(\frac{1}{\sqrt{5}}\right)\right] - \left[40\left(\frac{1}{\sqrt{5}}\right)5\left(\frac{2}{\sqrt{5}}\right)\right]$$

$$= 24.0 - 20.83 + 294.66 - 80.0$$

$$= 211.5 \text{ lb} \cdot \text{in. acting in the direction shown.}$$

2.6 Equilibrium of Free Bodies

If a rigid body is in equilibrium, every particle of mass in the rigid body is in equilibrium. Further, each of the separate members or elements in the rigid body is also in equilibrium. Consequently, all the the forces and force systems that act on each particle or member are also in equilibrium.

While the foregoing logic may seem childishly obvious, it forms the basis of all solutions for the forces and moments that act on and in a structural system. The procedure for such solutions follows:

1. Given the problem of finding a specified force or moment that is acting at a particular point in a structural system, one "removes" an element of the system (a ring, a beam, a column, etc.) which sustains that specified force or moment. A centerline sketch of the element is made.
2. *All* the external forces and moments that act directly on that element are entered on the sketch, but *only* those those external forces and moments that act directly on that element are entered on the sketch.
3. The laws of equilibrium are applied mathematically, resulting in one or more equilibrium equations that involve the specified force or moment.
4. The solution of these mathematical equations will yield the magnitude and direction of the specified force or moment.

Two new topics emerge in the foregoing procedure. The first new topic is that of producing an accurate sketch of some element or component of the structure, along with its exact and complete loading. This sketch is called the *free body diagram* of that element or component. It is indeed difficult to overstate the importance of the free body diagram in solving problems in engineering mechanics.

Further described, a *free body* is an element that has been "removed" from the structure but it has had all forces and moments that had been acting on it exactly restored. This free body with its applied forces therefore hangs statically in the plane, completely unaffected by the fact that it has been removed and is now a separate body. Logically, if the indicated forces held the body in equilibrium when it was in the overall structure, then they will also hold the body in equilibrium when it is removed from the structure.

The second of the two new topics mentioned earlier are the *laws of equilibrium* referenced in Step 3 of the procedure. Stated simply, the laws of equilibrium require that the free body remain static, which is accomplished by the following requirements:

1. There can be no translation of the free body horizontally.
2. There can be no translation of the free body vertically.
3. There can be no rotations of the free body about any axis.

As noted earlier, if the element is to remain in position without motion, then there can be no imbalance in any of the forces or moments that are acting on the body. Stated mathematically, the laws of equilibrium regarding these forces and moments are then:

$$\Sigma F_x = 0 \quad \Sigma F_y = 0 \quad \Sigma M_o = 0 \qquad \text{(2-12a,b,c)}$$

where the point 0 is any point in the plane.

It is noted that there are only three equations of equilibrium for force systems in a plane. There cannot, therefore, be more than three unknowns if an equilibrium solution is to be found. If more than three unknowns should occur, there must be additional equations derived from conditions other than statics, such as deformation relationships. Such problems are termed *statically indeterminate* problems; they are treated in advanced courses in structural analysis.

With these two new concepts just introduced, that is, the concept of the free body and the concept of the mathematical laws of equilibrium, the equilibrium solution for forces in a planar force system can now be undertaken. Some examples will illustrate the procedures.

Example 2-11

Equilibrium solution for static forces.

Given: Force system as shown.

To Find: Forces in the two wires *AC* and *BC*.

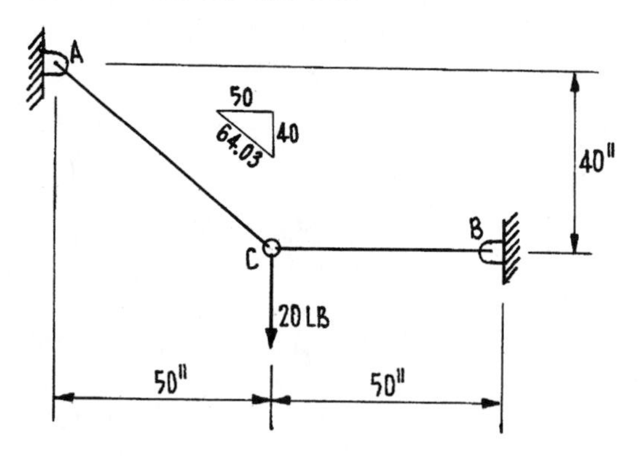

Solution: Examination of the sketch reveals that both of the unknown forces act on the ring at *C*; the ring at *C* will therefore be removed as a free body. The action lines of the unknown forces will obviously follow the axes of the wires but it is not known at this point whether the forces will be directed toward the ring or away from the ring.

For the sake of the free body, it is assumed that both of the unknown forces will be directed away from the ring. If the assumption proves to be incorrect, the solution will yield a negative sign for the force, indicating that its direction was assumed backwards.

The free body diagram of the ring can now be drawn, with the 20 lb load shown in its correct direction.

The laws of equilibrium can now be applied mathematically. Since forces will be summed vertically and horizontally, all forces will have to be resolved into their vertical and horizontal components. The force F_{CB} and the 20 lb load are already in their correct x and y components, leaving only force F_{CA} to be so resolved. The final free body diagram with all forces resolved into their x and y components is now completed as shown.

Force are summed vertically first, with the upward direction assumed to be positive:

$$\Sigma F_y = 0 + F_{CA}\frac{40}{64.03} - 20 = 0$$

$$F_{CA} = 32.02 \text{ lb}$$

Forces are next summed horizontally, with the positive direction assumed to be to the right:

$$\Sigma F_x = 0 - F_{CA}\frac{50}{64.03} + F_{CB} = 0$$

$$F_{CB} = (32.02)\frac{50}{64.03} = 25 \text{ lb}$$

In both of the foregoing solutions, the positive signs indicated that the direction assumed for the force happened to be correct.

To complete the solution, moments could be summed about point C or any other point in the system, but it is readily apparent that the three forces are concurrent and that they cannot produce any tendency toward rotations. In this case, the third equation of equilibrium does not yield anything of interest, except, of course, that all moments are zero.

The solution of Example 2-11 demonstrates one of the common practices for establishing signs in engineering mechanics. In most such free body solutions, the line of action of the unknown forces will be known but their direction will have to be assumed. It is customary in such cases to assume that the unknown force in an axially loaded member (a wire, a strut, a brace, etc.) will be in tension. A negative answer will then indicate that the force is actually in compression.

A second point demonstrated in Example 2-11 is that known forces (such as the 20 lb load) are always shown in their correct direction. Their sign will then be correct in all subsequent mathematics equations.

A third point demonstrated in Example 2-11 is that the third equation of equilibrium, $\Sigma M_o = 0$, drops out in all cases where the free body is reduced to a particle. Such a solution is therefore limited to the two force equations, $\Sigma F_x = 0$ and $\Sigma F_y = 0$, which in turn automatically limits the number of unknowns to two. Such solutions of a particle in which the equation of moment equilibrium drops out are termed *force equilibrium solutions*; no more than two unknowns may be found in such solutions.

Another example will demonstrate the application of a force equilibrium solution to a more general case.

Example 2-12

Equilibrium solution for static forces.

Given: Force system as shown.

To Find: Force in each of the two members.

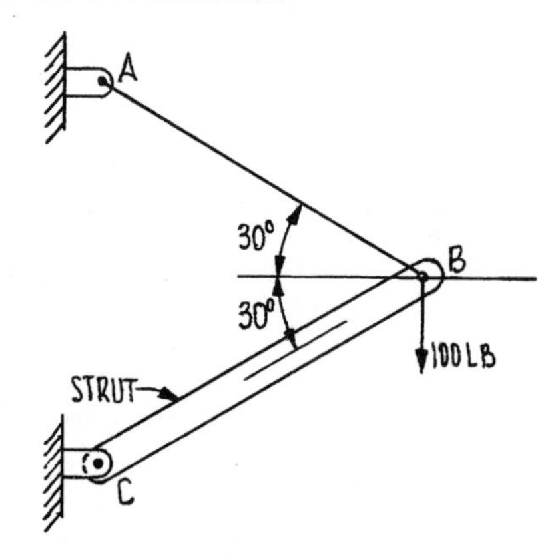

Solution: Examination of the geometry indicates that both of the unknown forces pass through the ring at *B*. Since there are only two unknown forces acting on the ring at *B*, a force equilibrium solution is possible.

The free body of the ring at *B* is now drawn, showing all unknown forces in tension, that is, "pulling" away from the ring.

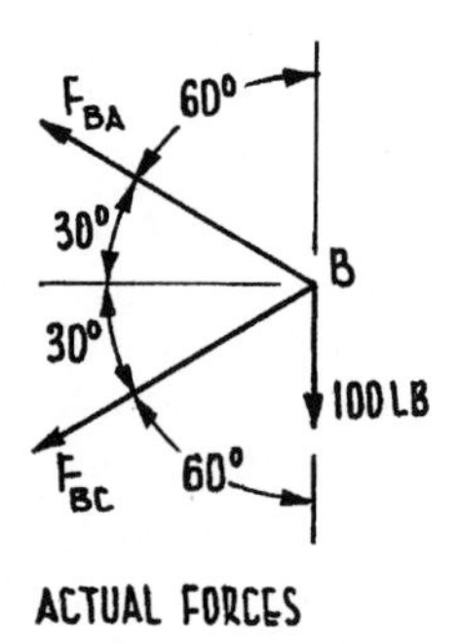

The forces on the free body are resolved into their *x* and *y* components as shown on the following sketch.

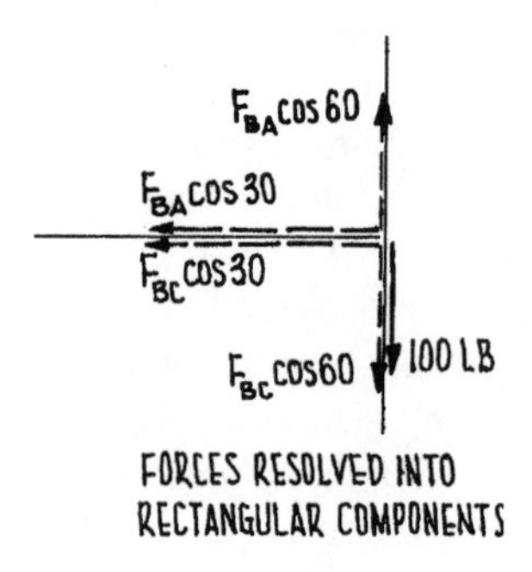

Forces are summed in the vertical direction, with the positive direction upward:

$$\Sigma F_y = 0, F_{BA} \cos 60 - F_{BC} \cos 60 - 100 = 0$$

$$F_{BA} - F_{BC} = 200$$

Forces are summed in the horizontal direction, with the positive direction to the right:

$$\Sigma F_x = -F_{BA}\cos 30 - F_{BC}\cos 30 = 0$$
$$F_{BA} + F_{BC} = 0$$

The two equations in two unknowns are solved simultaneously to find:

$$F_{BA} = 100 \text{ lb (tension)}$$
$$F_{BC} = -100 \text{ lb (compression)}$$

The positive sign for F_{BA} indicates that it is in tension as assumed. The negative sign for F_{BC} indicates that its sign was incorrectly chosen; it is actually in compression.

Another example will demonstrate the application of force equilibrium solutions into successive solutions, where the results of a previous solution are used in succeeding calculations.

Example 2-13

Equilibrium solution for static forces.

Given: Force system as shown.

To Find: Force P in the direction shown that will produce the given configuration.

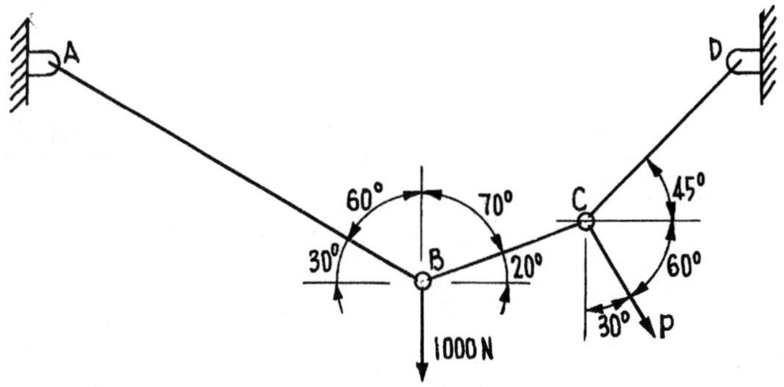

Solution: Examination of the geometry reveals that there are two unknown forces acting on the particle (or ring) at point B and that there are three unknown forces acting on the particle (or ring) at point C. A solution is therefore immediately possible only for the two forces on the ring at B. Once the forces in the wires $\overline{BA}$ and $\overline{BC}$ are known from this solution, however, there will then remain only two unknown forces acting on the ring at C, the force in the wire $\overline{CD}$ and the applied force P; the force P can therefore be determined from a second solution.

The first solution is made for the forces acting on the ring at B. The free body follows, with the forces F_{BC} and F_{BA} already resolved into their x and y components. Both unknown forces are assumed to be in tension.

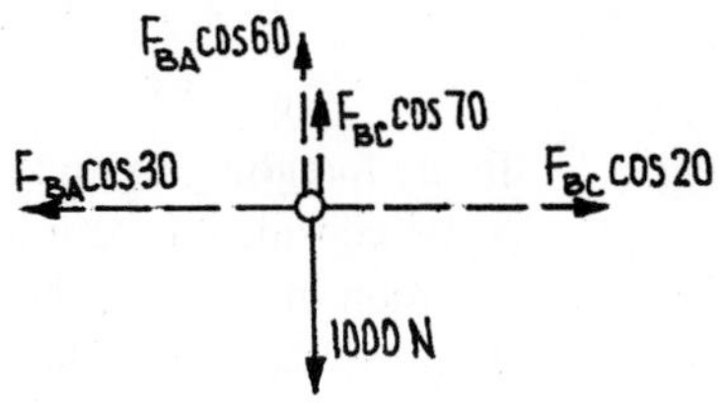

Forces are summed vertically, with upward being positive:

$$\Sigma F_y = 0;\ F_{BA}\cos 60 + F_{BC}\cos 70 - 1000 = 0$$

Forces are summed horizontally, with positive signs to the right:

$$\Sigma F_x = 0;\ -F_{BA}\cos 30 + F_{BC}\cos 20 = 0$$

The two equations in two unknowns are now solved simultaneously. The second equation yields:

$$F_{BA} = 1.085\ F_{BC}$$

This result is substituted into the first equation:

$$(1.085F_{BC})\cos 60 + F_{BC}\cos 70 = 1000$$
$$F_{BC} = 1131\ \text{N (tension)}$$
$$\text{and } F_{BA} = 122\ \text{N (tension)}$$

The positive signs indicate that the assumed directions are correct.

The solution for the forces acting on the ring at *C* can now be performed using the result just obtained for F_{CB}. Again, note that wires in tension will always "pull" on the rings at both ends of the wire. The free body of the ring at *C* is now drawn, with the forces F_{CB}, F_{CD} and *P* already resolved into their *x* and *y* components:

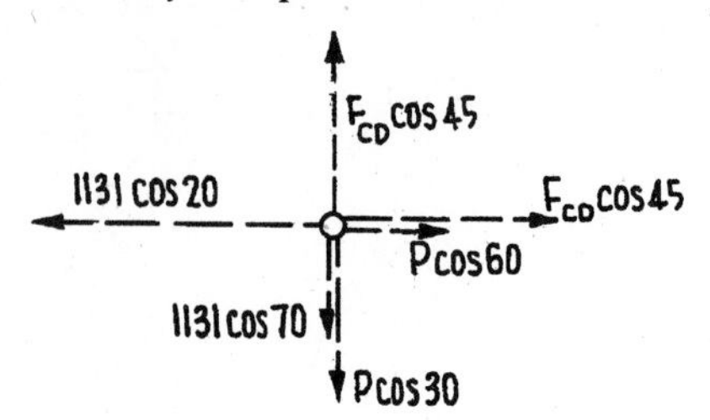

Forces are summed vertically:

$$\Sigma F_y = 0;\ -1131\cos 70 - P\cos 30 + F_{CD}\cos 45 = 0$$
$$F_{CD} = 547 + 1.225P$$

Forces are summed horizontally:

$$\Sigma F_x = 0;\ -1131\cos 20 + P\cos 60 + F_{CD}\cos 45 = 0$$
$$F_{CD} = 1503 - 0.707P$$

The simultaneous solution of these two equations yields the forces *P* and F_{CD}:

$$P = 495\ \text{N (in direction shown)}$$
$$F_{CD} = 1153\ \text{N (tension)}$$

In the foregoing examples, the free body happened to be a ring, or a point small enough to be considered a particle. It was noted that in such solutions, the third mathematical equation of equilibrium, $\Sigma M_o = 0$, drops out, leaving only the two equations for forces, $\Sigma F_x = 0$, $\Sigma F_y = 0$. The resulting solution was called a force equilibrium solution.

There are other free bodies, however, in which the third equation of equilibrium does not drop out. In such solutions, there will be three unknowns and all three mathematical equations of equilibrium will be required to solve for them. Some examples will illustrate the procedure.

Example 2-14

Equilibrium solution for static forces.

Given: Rigid beam, loaded as shown.

To Find: Reaction forces at the two supports.

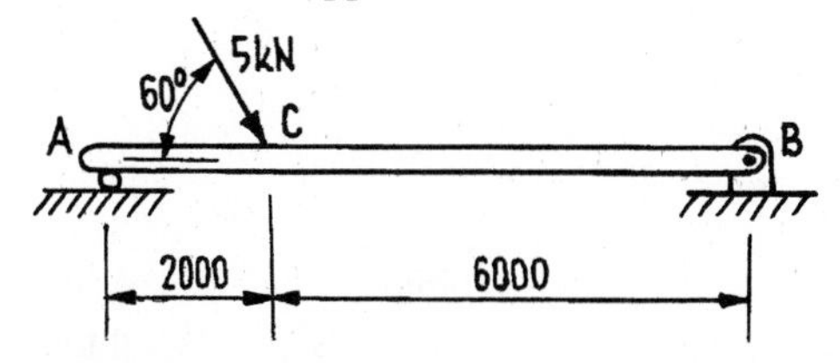

Solution: The free body diagram of the beam is drawn for the centerline of the beam. At the supports, all forces that can exist, but only the forces that can exist, are entered in their positive sense on the free body diagram. The 5 kN load is resolved into its x and y components; these are shown on the free body diagram in their correct direction.

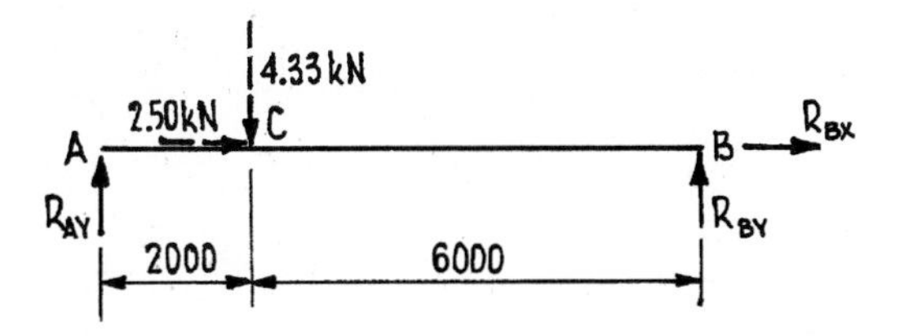

The mathematical laws of equilibrium can now be applied. It is noted that there are three unknown forces acting on this free body, R_{Ay}, R_{By} and R_{Bx}. There are three equations of equilibrium, $\Sigma F_x = 0$, $\Sigma F_x = 0$ and $\Sigma M_o = 0$, all of which can be applied. An equilibrium solution is therefore possible.

Moments are summed about the point B. The point B is deliberately chosen in order to eliminate two of the three unknowns from the resulting equation (R_{Bx} and R_{By} will have no moment arm and will drop out). Clockwise moments are given a positive sign.

$$\Sigma M_B = 0;\ R_{Ay}\,(8000) - 4.33(6000) + 2.50(0) + R_B(0) = 0$$

$$R_{Ay} = 3.25 \text{ kN upward}$$

Forces are now summed vertically. Positive sense is taken upward. The solution just obtained for R_{Ay} is used in the equation:

$$\Sigma F_Y = 0;\ +3.25 - 4.33 + R_{BY} = 0$$

$$R_{BY} = 1.08\text{kN upward}$$

$$\Sigma F_x = 0;\ +2.50 + R_{Bx} = 0$$

$$R_{Bx} = -2.50 \text{ kN (direction incorrect)}$$

$$R_{Bx} = 2.50 \text{ kN to the left}$$

Example 2-15

Equilibrium solution for static forces.

Given: Rigid beam, loaded by its own weight of 120 lb, supported as shown.

To Find: Reactions at the supports.

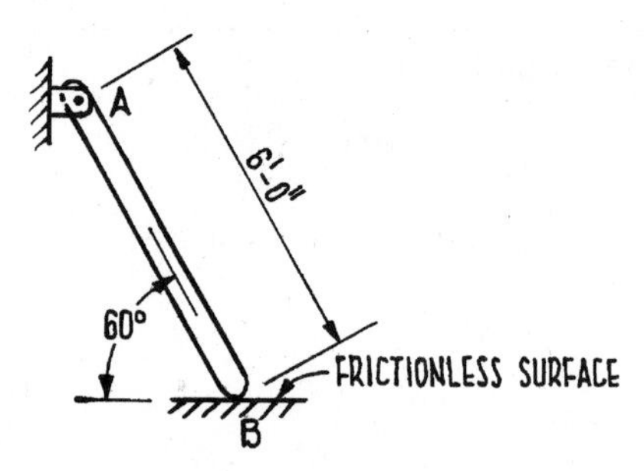

Solution: The free body diagram is drawn for the centerline of the beam. At the supports, all the forces that can exist but only the forces that can exist are entered in their positive sense on the free body diagram. The weight of the prismatic beam is assumed to act through its center of mass, at its midpoint. For simplicity in calculations, dimensions are shown in decimal form (though they could also have been shown in inches).

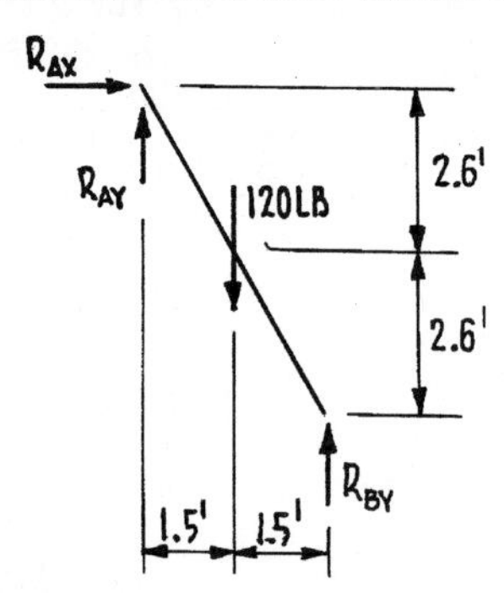

The mathematical laws of equilibrium can now be applied. It is again noted that there are three unknowns, $R_{Ax,}$ R_{Ay} and R_{By} and that there are three equations of statics, $\Sigma F_x = 0$, $\Sigma F_y = 0$ and $\Sigma M_o = 0$, all of which can be applied. An equilibrium solution is therefore possible.

Moments are summed about the point *A*. As before, a point is chosen that will eliminate as many of the unknown forces from the equation as possible. In this case, two of the unknowns, R_{Ax} and R_{Bx}, pass through *A*; they will therefore have no moment arm about *A* and will drop out of the equation. Clockwise moments are assumed to be positive:

$$\Sigma M_A = 0; + 120(1.5) - R_{By}(3.0) = 0$$
$$R_{By} = 60 \text{ lb. Upward}$$

Forces are now summed vertically. Positive sense is taken upward. The solution just obtained for R_{By} is used wherever needed in all subsequent calculations:

$$\Sigma Fy = 0; + R_{Ay} - 120 + 60 = 0$$
$$R_{Ay} = 60 \text{ lb. Upward}$$

Forces are now summed horizontally. Positive sense is taken to the right:

$$\Sigma F_x = 0; + R_{Ay} = 0$$

Example 2-16

Equilibrium solution for static forces.

Given: Structural frame, loaded as shown.

To Find: Reaction forces at the two supports.

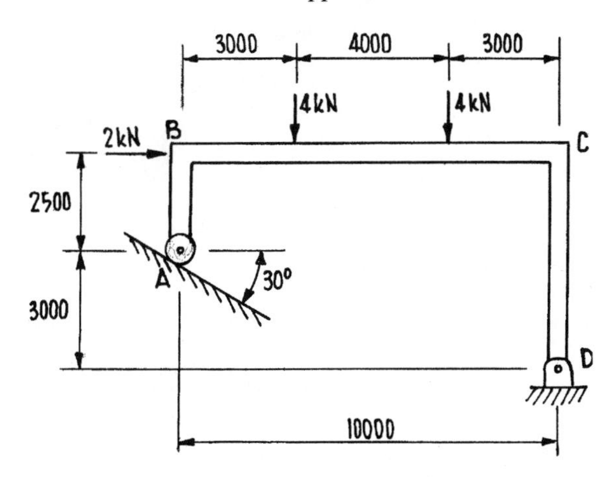

Solution: The free body diagram is drawn for the centerline of the frame. At the supports, all the forces that can exist, but only the forces that can exist, are entered in their positive sense on the free body diagram. All loads are shown in their correct directions. The reaction at *A* is shown first along its correct line of action, then resolved into its *x* and *y* components as indicated. As always, known forces are shown in their correct direction, and unknown forces are given an assumed direction.

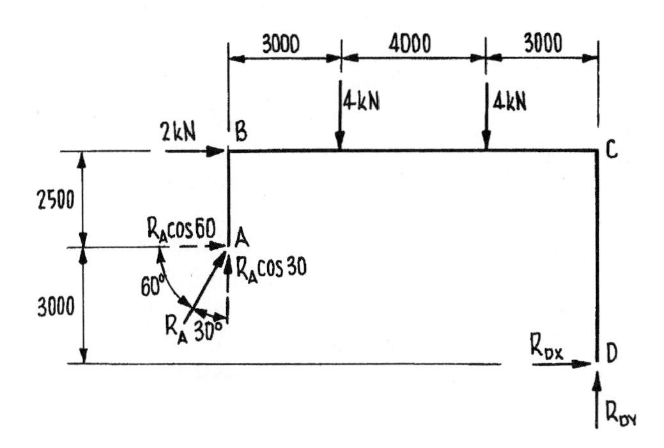

The mathematical laws of equilibrium can now be applied. It is noted that there are three unknowns and three equations of equilibrium; an equilibrium solution is therefore possible.

Moments are summed about the point *D*. As always, the point for summing moments is deliberately chosen to eliminate as many unknowns as possible, thereby simplifying the numerical work. Clockwise moments are assumed positive:

$$\Sigma M_o = 0;\ R_A \cos 60(3000) + R_A \cos 30(10000)$$
$$+2(5500) - 4(7000) - 4(3000) = 0$$

$R_A = 2.85$ kN (in direction shown)

Forces are now summed vertically. Positive sense is assumed upward. The solution for R_A is used wherever needed in subsequent calculations:

$$\Sigma F_y = 0;\ 2.85 \cos 30 - 4 - 4 + R_{Dy} = 0$$
$$R_{Dy} = 5.53\text{kN (as shown)}$$

Forces are now summed horizontally. Positive sense is assumed to be to the right:

$$\Sigma F_x = 0;\ 2.85 \cos 60 + 2 + R_{Dx} = 0$$
$$R_{Dx} = -3.43\text{ kN (direction incorrect)}$$
$$R_{Dx} = 3.43\text{ kN (to the left)}$$

Review Questions

1. What are concurrent forces?
2. How does one find the point of concurrency of two forces?
3. How can two forces be neither concurrent nor parallel?
4. What is meant by *composition* of a force system?
5. What is meant by *resolution* of a force?
6. What is a direction angle?
7. At which end of the force vector are direction angles taken?
8. What are the positive directions usually chosen for forces in a rectangular coordinate system?
9. What is a direction cosine?
10. Can a force have a negative magnitude?
11. What does it mean when calculations show a negative force?
12. What are the conditions for equilibrium of a particle in a plane?
13. Define the *reaction* of a system of concurrent forces.
14. What is moment?
15. What is torque?
16. How does one calculate the moment due to a force?
17. What is a moment arm?
18. How is the axis of rotation related to the plane of the moment?
19. Can a moment have a negative magnitude?
20. What does it mean when calculations show a negative moment?
21. What is the positive direction usually chosen when one is calculating moments in a rectangular coordinate system?
22. State Varignon's theorem.
23. What is a free body?
24. Give the procedure for drawing a free body diagram.
25. State the mathematical laws of equilibrium in a plane.
26. In a general equilibrium solution, how many unknown forces can occur on a free body?
27. In a force equilibrium solution, how many unknown forces can occur on a free body?
28. In the free body of an attachment ring, does the compressive force in a strut point away from the ring or toward the ring?
29. In an axially loaded member, is compressive force regarded as positive or negative?
30. In showing the forces exerted by the supports on the free body of a member, which of the reaction forces are shown?

CHAPTER

3

PARALLEL FORCES IN A PLANE

It was noted in the previous chapter that systems of forces often fall into recognizable groupings. One such grouping was that of concurrent force systems, or systems of forces that intersect in a common point. Concurrent force systems were presented in that chapter.

Another such recognizable grouping is that of systems of parallel forces. Parallel force systems are presented in this chapter.

A related subject introduced in this chapter is that of couples and moments. Couples and moments may be regarded as a special case of parallel forces; they are treated as such in the following discussions.

3.1 Systems of Parallel Forces

The characteristics of parallel force systems are somewhat different from those of concurrent forces. While most of the concepts developed for concurrent forces remain valid for parallel forces, a few of those concepts take on special properties. This chapter is devoted to the examination of those special properties.

Parallel forces are quite common in structural loading. All gravity loads, for example, are composed of systems of parallel forces, each force directed toward the center of the earth. While these gravity forces may technically be classed as radial forces, the size of a construction project is so small compared to the size of the earth that any deviation from vertical may be safely ignored.

An example of a parallel force system is shown in the bridge truss of Figure 3-1. All the loads acting downward on the truss are gravity loads produced either by the dead load of the structure or the live load of the vehicles. Such a parallel load system is typical of gravity loads.

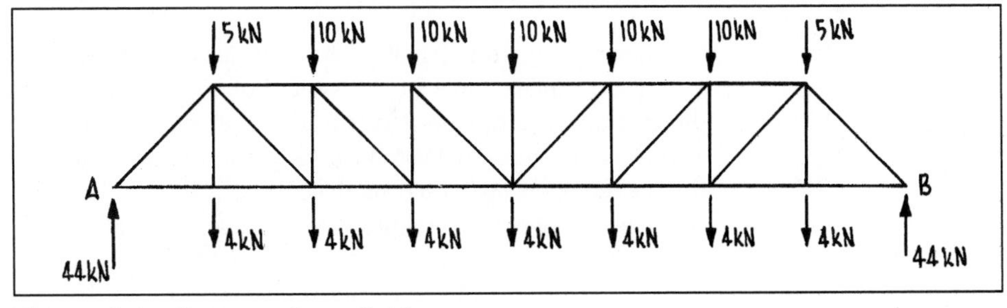

Figure 3-1 System of parallel forces.

3.2 Resultant of a System of Parallel Forces

In dealing with a system of parallel forces, the first items to be resolved are generally to find the magnitude, direction and line of action of the resultant.

Consider the three parallel forces *F*, *P* and *Q* in Figure 3-2. These forces have no point of concurrency and may not therefore be summed using the parallelogram law. As always, however, it is known that their resultant *R* must produce the same force in both the *x* and *y* directions as all of its original components combined.

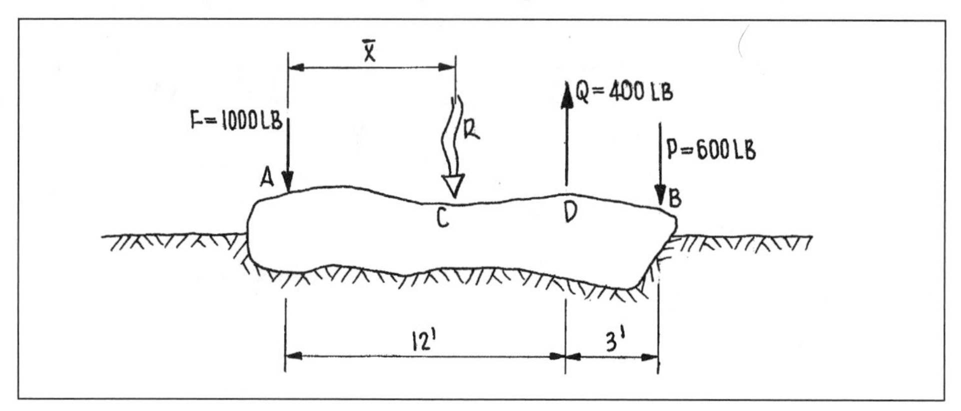

Figure 3-2 Resultant of two parallel forces.

Since there is no horizontal force exerted by any of the three original components, it is immediately apparent that the resultant cannot have a horizontal component either. From this fact, it is concluded that the line of action of the resultant must be parallel to the lines of action of the three original and parallel components.

Further, since the resultant *R* must produce the same total force vertically as all of its original components combined, the magnitude of the resultant must simply be the algebraic sum of the magnitudes of the components:

$$R = F + P - Q = 1000 + 600 - 400$$
$$R = 1200 \text{ lbs downward}$$

The direction of the resultant is in the direction of the algebraically larger forces.

The location of the line of action of the resultant can be found by Varignon's theorem: the resultant force *R* must produce the same amount of moment about any point in the plane that the original components would produce. For the force system shown in Figure 3-2, the point *A* is chosen as a convenient point for summing moments. Clockwise moments are assumed to be positive:

$$\text{Moment of Resultant} = \text{Moment of Components}$$

$$R(\bar{x}) = F(O) - Q(12) + P(15)$$
$$1200(\bar{x}) = 0 - 400(12) + 600(15)$$
$$\bar{x} = +3.5 \text{ ft}$$

The positive sign for $\bar{x}$ indicates that it does lie to the right of *A*, as assumed.

The resultant force of the system of Figure 3-2 is therefore a force of 1200 lbs, directed downward, with its vertical line of action located 3.5 ft to the right of point *A*. This resultant force will produce the same reactions under the rigid body as the three original components would produce.

The following generalities can be deduced about the resultant of a system of parallel forces:

1. The line of action of the resultant force will be parallel to the lines of action of its component forces.
2. The magnitude of the resultant force will be the algebraic sum of the magnitudes of its component forces.
3. The direction of the resultant force will be in the direction of the algebraically larger component forces.
4. The line of action of the resultant force will be located such that the moment of the resultant force about any point in the plane will be equal to the sum of the moments of the components about that point.

It is customary when sketching resultant forces to show the algebraic dimensions to their lines of action with a bar over it, such as $\bar{x}$, $\bar{y}$, $\bar{z}$, etc. It is also customary when sketching a system of forces to show the resultant force in some distinctive form in order that it can be readily identified. The double-line arrow used in Figure 3-2 is one such distinctive form; zig-zag lines or wavy lines are also frequently used.

Some examples will illustrate the procedure for finding the resultant of a system of parallel forces.

Example 3-1

Resultant of parallel forces.

Given: Locomotive wheel loads as shown.

To Find: Magnitude, direction and position of the resultant.

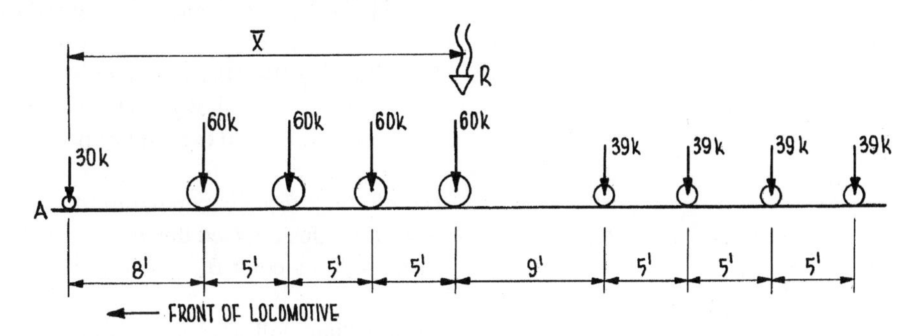

Solution: The magnitude of the resultant is found as the algebraic sum of its parallel components:

$$R = \Sigma F = 30 + 4(60) + 4(39)$$
$$= 426 \text{ kips downward}$$

The location of the line of action of the resultant is found by summing moments about some convenient point (axis of rotation) such as the point *A*.

Moment of Resultant = Moment of Components

$$426\bar{x} = 60(8) + 60(13) + 60(18) + 60(23) + 39(32)$$
$$+ 39(37) + 39(42) + 39(47)$$
$$\bar{x} = 23.2 \text{ to the right of point } A.$$

The resultant force is parallel to the component forces, having a magnitude of 426 kips directed downward, with its line of action falling 23.2 ft to the rear of the leading wheel (point *A*).

Example 3-2

Resultant of parallel forces.

Given: System of loads on a truss as shown.

To Find: Magnitude, direction and position of the resultant.

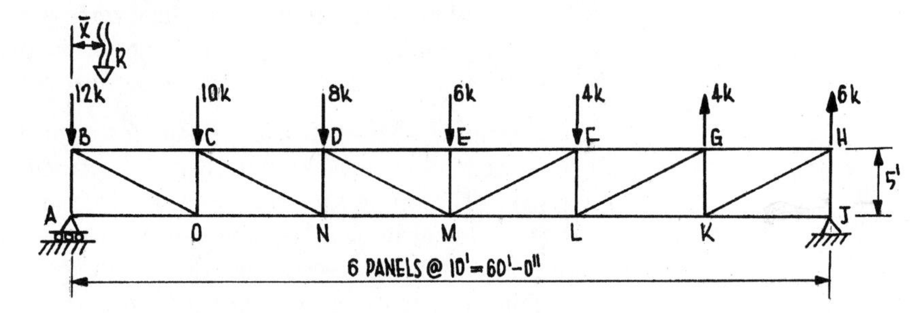

Solution: The magnitude of the resultant is found as the algebraic sum of the parallel components:

$$R = 12 + 10 + 8 + 6 + 4 - 4 - 6 = 30 \text{ kips downward}$$

The location of the line of action of the resultant is found by summing moments about some convenient point such as point *B*.

Moment of Resultant = Moment of Components

$$30\bar{x} = 12(0) + 10(10) + 8(20) + 6(30) + 4(40) - 4(50) - 6(60)$$

$$\bar{x} = 1.33 \text{ ft. to the right of point } B.$$

The resultant force is parallel to the component forces, having a magnitude of 30 kips directed downward, with its line of action located 1.33 ft. to the right of point *B*.

This resultant will produce the same external reactions as the actual system of parallel components.

Example 3-3

Resultant of parallel forces.

Given: System of wind loads on a roof truss as shown.

To Find: Magnitude, direction and position of the resultant.

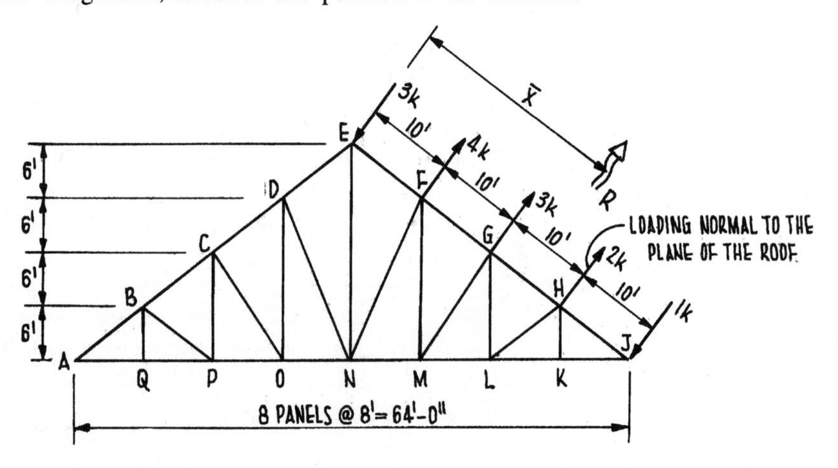

Solution: The direction of the resultant force will lie parallel to the component forces, as indicated in the sketch.

The magnitude of the resultant force is found as the algebraic sum of all parallel components. The summation is made in the direction of the components:

$$R = -3 + 4 + 3 + 2 - 1 = +5^{k} \text{ (directed outward as shown).}$$

The location of the line of action of the resultant is found by summing moments about some convenient point, such as point *E*. Clockwise moments are assumed positive:

Moment of Resultant = Moment of Components

$$-5\bar{x} = +3(0) - 4(10) - 3(20) - 2(30) + 1(40)$$
$$\bar{x} = 24.0 \text{ ft to the right of point } E.$$

The resultant force is parallel to the component forces, having a magnitude of 5 kips directed outward (a suction force) with its line of action located 24.0 feet along the slope to the right of point *E*.

3.3 Equilibrium of Free Bodies

The mathematical laws of equilibrium apply as readily to parallel forces as they apply to concurrent forces. For forces in a plane, the laws as stated earlier are repeated here for immediate reference:

$$\Sigma F_x = 0, \Sigma F_y = 0 \text{ and } \Sigma M_0 = 0 \qquad (2\text{-}12a,b,c)$$

The rules for the sketching of free bodies remains unchanged when one is dealing with parallel forces. There are, however, some different types of systems that require some introduction. Systems involving ropes and pulleys are one of those systems.

The pulley and rope system shown in Figure 3-3 is a typical system of parallel forces. In such systems it is customary to assume that there is no friction at the pulley, neither due to stiffness of the rope nor in the bearings of the pulley wheel.

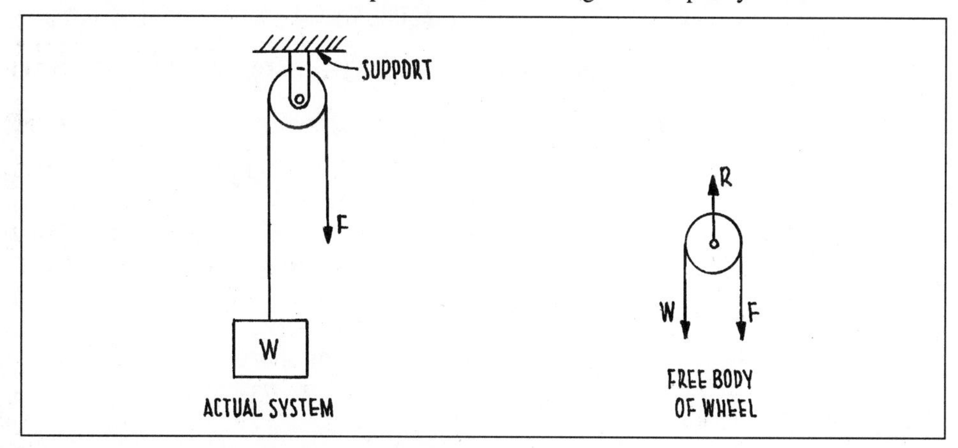

Figure 3-3 Typical pulley arrangement.

In rope and pulley systems without friction, the tensile force in any one rope is assumed to be constant. The pulley changes the direction of the rope; it does not change the force in it. With no further calculations, it is seen that the force *F* in the free body of Figure

3-3 is necessarily equal to the force W on the other side of the pulley wheel. The sum of vertical forces on the free body then provides the magnitude of the reaction R :

$$R - W - F = 0$$
$$R = 2W \uparrow$$

The magnitude of the resultant R at the attachment is thus twice the magnitude of the weight being lifted; the difference, of course, is that it must also support the additional force F being exerted by the person doing the lifting.

Further, it is observed that the force being exerted to lift the weight is downward, with the input force F being exactly equal to that of the output force W. The ratio of the output force W to the input force F is recalled from elementary physics to be the *mechanical advantage* of the system. For this arrangement of rope and pulley, the mechanical advantage is 1.

Some examples will illustrate the procedures for finding equilibrium solutions of parallel forces in pulley systems.

Example 3-4

Equilibrium solution of parallel forces.

Given: Cable and pulley arrangement as shown.

To Find: Force F required to produce equilibrium.

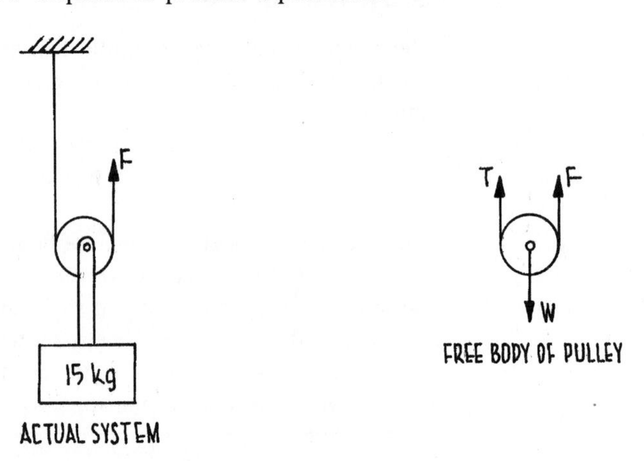

Solution: First, it is noted that 15 k_g is not a force; it is a mass. It must be converted to force:

$$W = 15(9.81\ N/k_g) = 147.2\ N.\ downward$$

The tension in the cable is assumed to be constant, hence $T = F$. Forces acting on the free body of the pulley are summed vertically to find:

$$T + F - W = 0$$
$$2F = W = 147.2$$
$$F = 73.6\ N.\ upward$$

A line tension of 73.6 N will produce equilibrium.

As a matter of interest, the ratio of output force (lifting force) to input force is 2:1 for this case. A weight of 147.2N is being lifted by a force of only 73.6N. The mechanical advantage of this arrangement is therefore 2. The advantage in force is, however, is offset by a disadvantage in travel distance; for each meter that the force moves upward along its line of action, the weight moves upward only $^1/_2$ meter.

Another observation is drawn concerning the simplicity of the system and of its solution. There are no horizontal forces involved in the solution, nor are there any moments; pulley systems are therefore seen to be just another type of problem in force equilibrium. Since there is only one equation of equilibrium left, however, the solution can have only one unknown force. Invariably, the free body is selected such that the unknown force in the free body is the tension in the cable, such as the free body of Example 3-4.

Some further examples will illustrate the procedures as well as the choice of the free bodies.

Example 3-5

Equilibrium solution of parallel forces.

Given: Cable and pulley arrangement as shown.

To Find: Force F required to produce equilibrium.

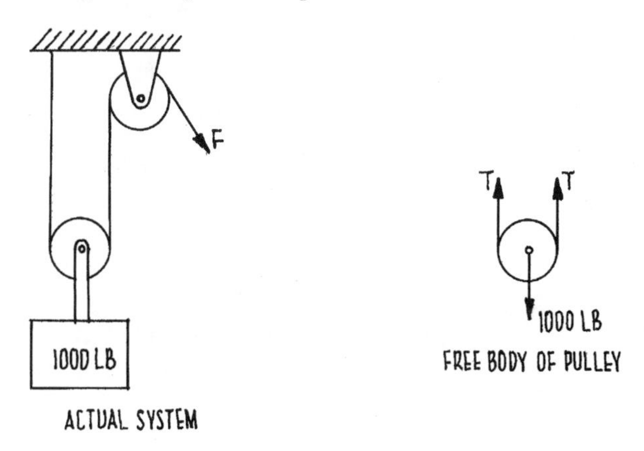

Solution: The tension in the cable is assumed to be constant as indicated in the free body. Forces acting on the free body are summed vertically to find:

$$2T - 1000 = 0$$
$$T = 500 \text{ lb upward}$$

A line tension of 500 lb. will produce equilibrium.

Again, it may be observed that the ratio of output force to input force in this system is 2. This system is no improvement over the system of Example 3-4 except that the input force is in a different direction. The second pulley in this arrangement does not improve mechanical advantage; it serves only to change the direction of the input force.

Example 3-6

Equilibrium solution of parallel forces.

Given: Cable and pulley arrangement as shown.

To Find: Force F required to produce equilibrium.

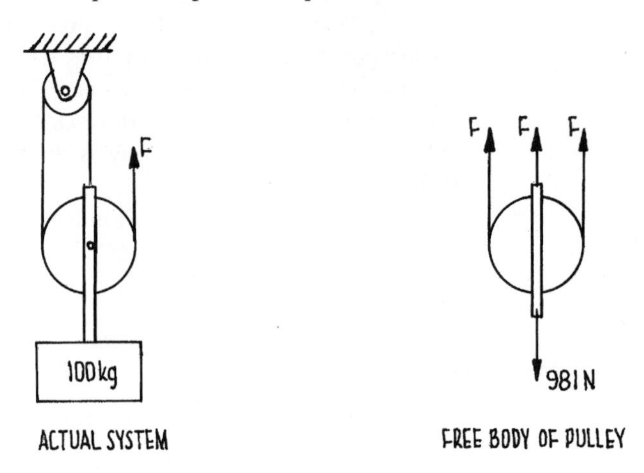

Solution: The 100 k_g mass is first converted to 981N force.

The tension in the cable is assumed to be constant as indicated in the free body. Forces acting on the free body are summed vertically to find:

$$3F - 981 = 0$$
$$F = 327 \text{ N. upward}$$

A line tension of 327 N. will produce equilibrium.

It is observed that for this arrangement of two pulleys, the ratio of output force (lifting force) to input force is 981:327 or 3:1. The mechanical advantage is therefore 3.

Example 3-7

Equilibrium solution of parallel forces.

Given: Cable and pulley arrangement as shown.

To Find: Force F to produce equilibrium.

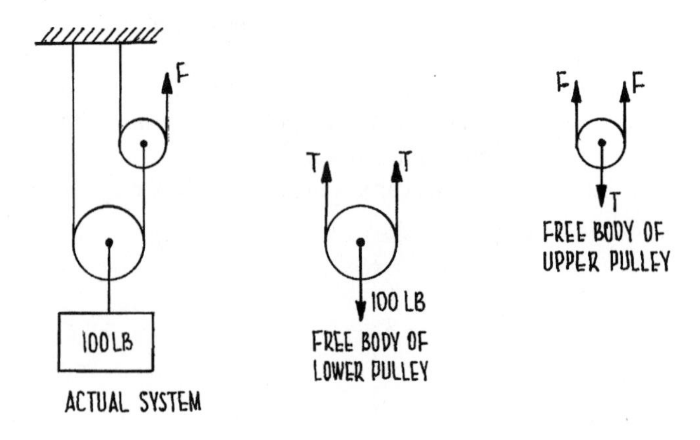

Solution: It is noted that in the given arrangement there are two separate cables. The forces in the two cables are not known to be equal. Two separate solutions involving two free bodies will therefore be necessary.

The free body of the lower pulley has only one unknown, the tension T. The free body of the upper pulley has two unknowns, the tensions T and the force F. The lower free body is therefore considered first. The vertical forces are summed to find:

$$2T - 100 = 0$$
$$T = 50 \text{ lb in tension}$$

The upper free body is considered next. The vertical forces are summed to find:

$$2F - T = 0, \text{ where } T = 50 \text{ lbs}$$
$$2F - 50 = 0$$
$$F = 25 \text{ lb in tension}$$

A force of 25 lbs. will produce equilibrium.

It is observed that for this arrangement of two pulleys, the ratio of output force to input force is 100:25 or 4:1. The mechanical advantage of this two pulley system is therefore 4.

3.4 Centroids of Geometric Plane Areas

Imagine a plane figure of some shape such as that shown in Figure 3-4. Imagine further that the figure is a very thin plate having a small amount of weight and that it is to be balanced on the point of a needle. That point in the figure on which the figure will balance perfectly is called the *centroid* or the *center of gravity* of the area.

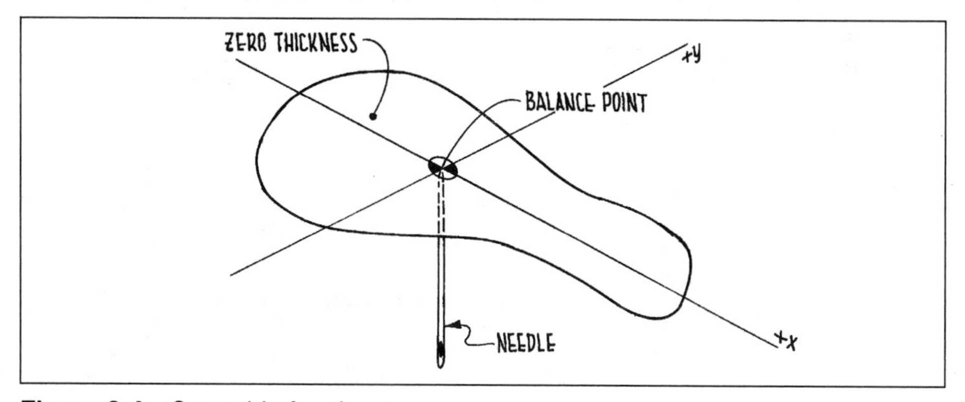

Figure 3-4 Centroid of a plane area.

The centroid of a plane area is not an academic curiosity. The centroid of a cross section is shown later to be a key feature in locating the axis of bending for beams in flexure and for columns in buckling. The position of the centroid is necessary to locate the resultant of distributed loads on a building floor or a roof. Its inclusion at this point affords a very practical application of parallel forces to a very real problem in engineering mechanics.

It is emphasized that in actual fact, a geometric plane figure has no thickness, no mass and therefore no weight. Giving it an imaginary weight and thereby a center of gravity is simply a convenient means to visualize things physically. The concept will be seen to be quite useful in later discussions.

There is a corresponding balance point in three-dimensional masses, about which the object would balance if one could only provide a support there. Such a point is usually accessible only by imagination, however, since it will probably lie somewhere deep within the mass of the body. This inaccessible balance point lies at the center of all gravity forces and is called the center of gravity of the object. As with plane figures, the resultant weight of a three-dimensional body passes through this center of gravity, or balance point, of the body.

For the more familiar plane areas, the location of the centroid is readily visualized. The centroid of a circle, for example, is intuitively recognized to be at the center of the circle. For a square or a rectangle or a parallelogram the centroid is similarly seen to be at the intersection of the diagonals, as shown in Figure 3-5.

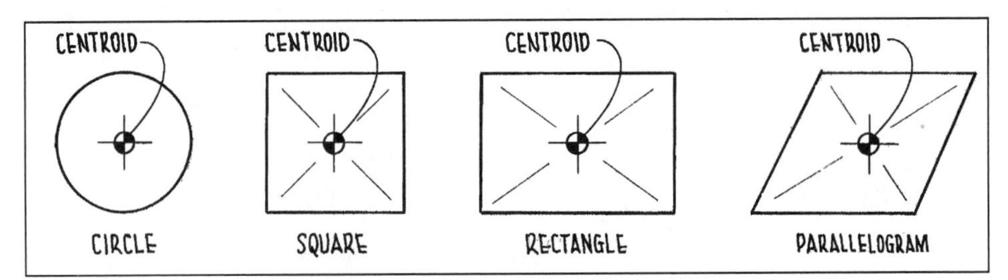

Figure 3-5 Centroids of common shapes.

For irregular plane figures, the location of the centroid is not so easily visualized and it must therefore be computed. In such cases, the figure may be assigned some small thickness t and a corresponding weight g per unit volume; the plane figure will then have a resultant force such as that shown in Figure 3-6. At equilibrium, this resultant of the gravity forces will be equal, opposite and collinear with the reaction at the balance point. It is concluded that the centroid of any plane figure may be found by treating it as if it had weight and then locating the line of action of the resultant of all gravity loads; this line of action will intersect the plane of the figure at the centroid.

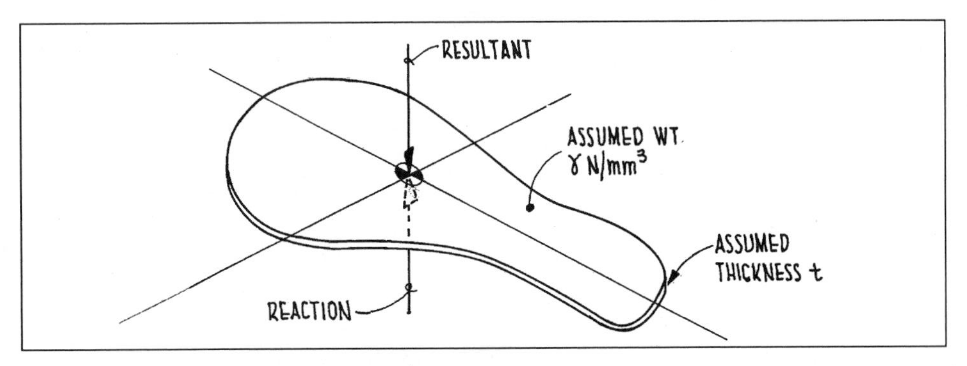

Figure 3-6 Balance point of a plane mass.

An example will illustrate the procedure for finding the centroid of a plane area.

Example 3-8

Centroid of a plane area.

Given: Plane area having the configuration shown.

To Find: Location of the centroid.

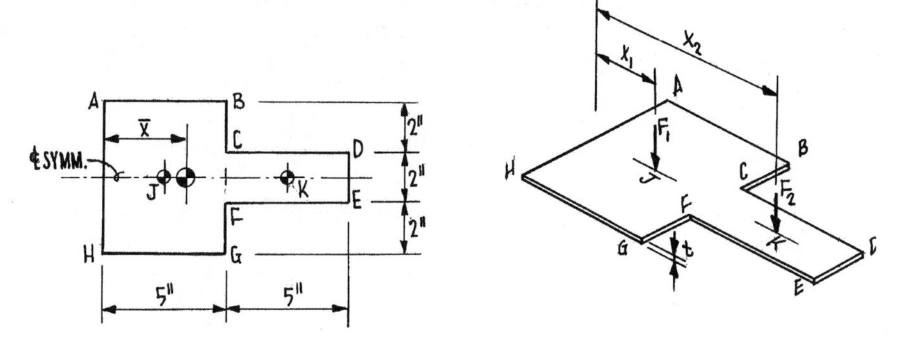

Solution: It is recognized that the area has an axis of symmetry; the centroid must lie somewhere along that axis of symmetry.

The figure is assumed to have a finite thickness t in. and a weight γ lbs/in^3. The rectangular area $\overline{ABGH}$ will then have a weight (force F_1) of γt (5)(6) lbs located at its centroid, point J.

Similarly, the rectangular area $\overline{CDEF}$ will have a weight (force F_2) of γt (5)(2) lbs located at its centroid, point K.

The total resultant force R is the sum of these two components:

$$R = \gamma t(5)(6) + \gamma t\ (5)(2) = 40\gamma t$$

The location of the resultant is found by summing moments about some point (or axis) in the figure. For convenience, the line AH is chosen:

Moment of Resultant = Moment of Components

$$R\bar{x} = F_1\,(2.5\text{ in.}) + F_2\,(7.5\text{ in.})$$
$$(40\gamma t)\bar{x} = (30\gamma t)(2.5) + (10\gamma t)(7.5)$$
$$\bar{x} = \frac{150}{40} = 3.75\text{ in. (to the right of } AH\text{)}$$

The centroid of this area therefore lies on the axis of symmetry at a distance 3.75 in. from the left edge.

Some conclusions and generalities may be drawn from the procedure used in Example 3-8. First, since *all* areas must be multiplied by the factor γ t (weight per unit area), the factor will always cancel out when moments are equated. The factor can therefore be omitted for plane areas. (An alternative viewpoint is that one simply allows the thickness to diminish to zero *after* the centroid has been found.)

A second conclusion can be drawn from the fact that the resultant force R is found by summing the component forces. Alternatively, R may be found simply as the factor γt times the total area:

$$R = F_1 + F_2 + F_3 + \ldots\ldots F_n$$
$$= \gamma tA_1 + \gamma t A_2 + \gamma t A_3 + \ldots\ldots \gamma tA_n$$
$$= \gamma t \sum_{L=1}^{n} A \qquad (3\text{-}1)$$

Similarly, the sum of moments about some point (or axis) gives some further generalities:

$$R\bar{x} = F_1\bar{x}_1 + F_2\bar{x}_2 + F_3\bar{x}_3 + \ldots F_n\bar{x}_n$$
$$\gamma t\bar{x} = \gamma tA_1\bar{x}_1 + \gamma tA_2\bar{x}_2 \tag{3-2}$$

where $\bar{x}_i$ is the distance from the axis of rotation to the centroid of each incremental area. Equation (3-2) can be solved for $\bar{x}$ and put into generalized form as:

$$\bar{x} = \frac{\sum_{i=1}^{n} A_i\bar{x}_i}{\sum_{i=1}^{n} A_i}, \quad \text{or} \quad \bar{x} = \frac{\Sigma A\bar{x}}{\Sigma A} \tag{3-3}$$

It is the generalized form of the solution given by Eq.(3-3) that will be used in all subsequent solutions.

Some examples will illustrate the procedures for some areas having one axis of symmetry.

Example 3-9

Centroid of a plane area.

Given: Plane area having the configuration shown.

To Find: Location of the centroid.

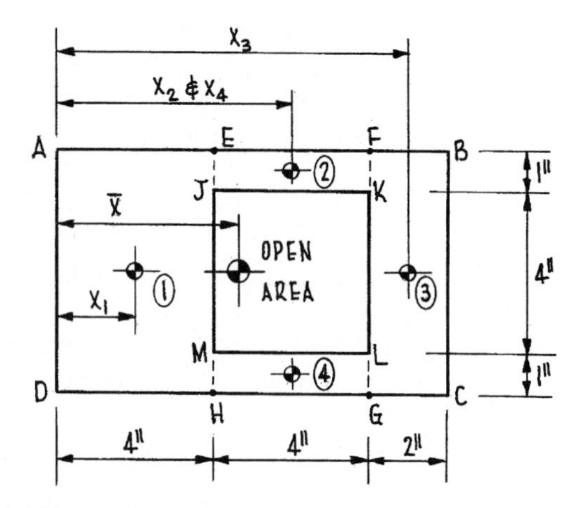

Solution: The solution will be made in the form:

$$\bar{x} = \frac{\Sigma A\bar{x}}{\Sigma A}$$

The area is broken into four segments as shown. Moments will be summed about axis *AD* :

$A_1 = 4 \times 6 = 24$ in.^{2}	$x_1 = 2$ in.
$A_2 = 1 \times 4 = 4$ in.^{2}	$x_2 = 6$ in.
$A_3 = 6 \times 2 = 12$ in.^{2}	$x_3 = 9$ in.
$A_4 = 1 \times 4 = 4$ in.^{2}	$x_4 = 6$ in.

$$\bar{x} = \frac{(24)(2) + (4)(6) + (12)(9) + (4)(6)}{24 + 4 + 12 + 4} = \frac{204}{44}$$

= 4.636 in. (to the right of line *AD*).

The centroid of this area lies on the axis of symmetry at a distance 4.636 in. to the right of the line $\overline{AD}$.

It is noted that the centroid of the area given in Example 3-9 lies in the open. If one actually wanted to balance the area on a point, it would be necessary to build some imaginary extension out to this point. At this juncture, it is important only to recognize that the centroid may actually lie in an open area; it need not fall within the body.

It is also recognized that the calculation of a centroid involves scalar quantities, such as area and moment; such quantities may be added and subtracted as desired. An example will demonstrate such a technique.

Example 3-10

Centroid of a plane area.

Given: Plane area of Example 3-9.

To Find: Location of the centroid.

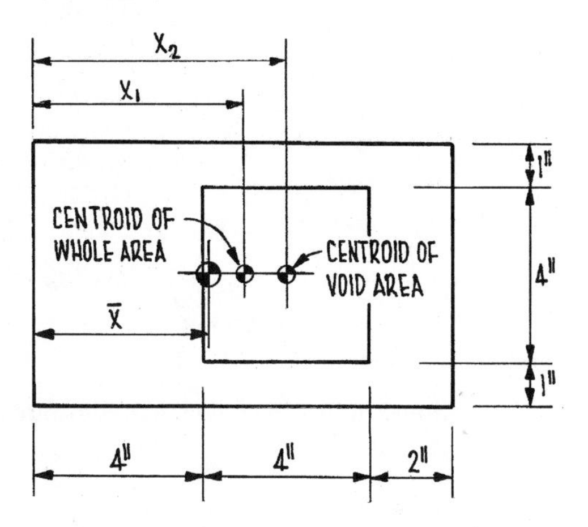

Solution: In this solution the centroid will be found by summing the moment of the entire area as if it were solid and then deducting the moment due to the voided area:

$$\bar{x} = \frac{\Sigma Ay}{\Sigma A}$$

$A_1 = A_{WHOLE} = (10)(6) = 60\text{ in.}^2\; x_1 = 5\text{ in.}$
$A_2 = A_{VOID} = (4)(4) = 16\text{ in.}^2\; x_2 = 6\text{ in.}$

$$\bar{x} = \frac{(60)(5) - (16)(6)}{60 - 16} = \frac{204}{44}$$

$\bar{x} = 4.636$ in. (to the right of line *AD*)

This result is, of course, the same as that obtained for Example 3-9.

The foregoing solutions suggest that the centroid of any regular plane area may be found simply by adding and subtracting appropriate component shapes and their moments. Such a conclusion is indeed correct. It becomes necessary in such a procedure, however, to use several basic shapes as components; in turn, it becomes necessary to know the location of the centroid of these basic shapes.

The areas and centroids of several familiar shapes are shown in Table 3-1. Others are shown in Table A-1 of the Technical Manual. With these basic shapes, one may add and subtract moments and areas to find the centroid of a wide variety of built-up (or *combined*) areas. These regular combined shapes are those that are used throughout engineering to build the beams and columns and other members used in engineered structures.

Table 3-1 Centroids of Basic Plane Areas.

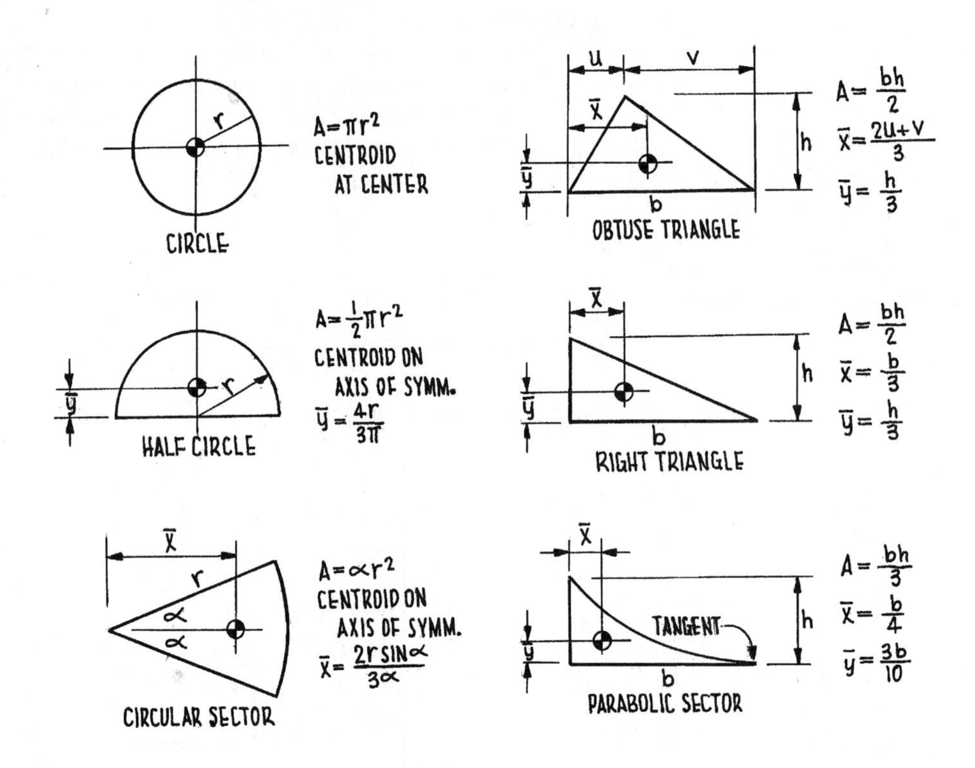

Some further examples will illustrate the calculations for finding the centroids of geometric areas.

Example 3-11

Centroid of a plane area.

Given: Plane area with configuration as shown.

To Find: Location of the centroid.

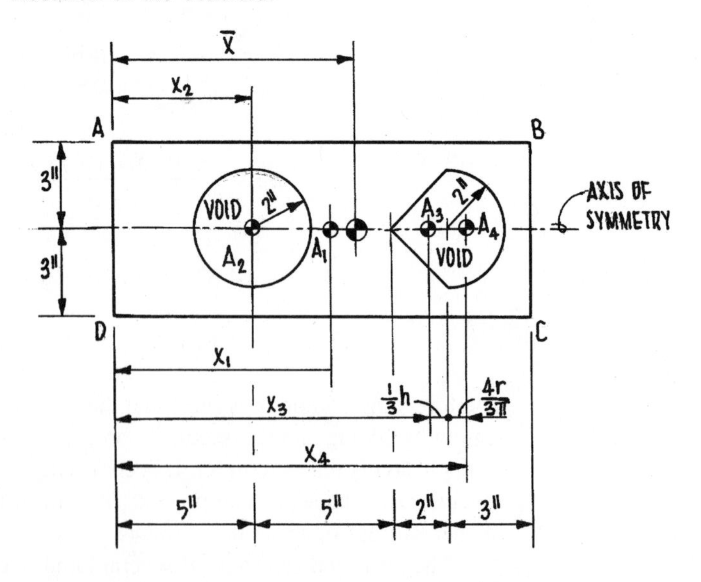

Solution: It is noted that there is an axis of symmetry; the centroid will lie somewhere along the axis of symmetry at a distance $\bar{x}$ from the line $\overline{AD}$.

The solution will be found using the general form of the equation, summing moments about line $\overline{AD}$:

$$\bar{x} = \frac{\Sigma A\bar{x}}{\Sigma A}$$

Area A_1 = Rectangle ABCD = (6)(15) = 90 in.^{2}
Area A_2 = Circle (void) = $(\pi)(2^2)$ = 12.57 in.^{2}
Area A_3 = Triangle (void) = $(^1/_2)(4)(2)$ = 4 in.^{2}
Area A_4 = Semicircle (void) = $(^1/_2)(\pi)(2^2)$ = 6.28 in.^{2}

$\bar{x}_1 = 7.5$ in.

$\bar{x}_2 = 5.0$ in.

$\bar{x}_3 = 12 - (^1/_3)(2) = 11.33$ in.

$\bar{x}_4 = 12 + [(4)(2)]/3\pi$

$$\bar{x} = \frac{(90)(7.5) - (12.57)(5.0) - (11.33)(4) - (6.28)(12.85)}{90 - 12.57 - 4 - 6.28}$$

= 7.2393 in.
(to the right of line $\overline{AD}$)

The centroid of this area lies on the axis of symmetry of the figure at a distance 7.24 in. to the right of the line $\overline{AD}$.

Up to this point in the discussions, all the areas considered have had an axis of symmetry. It is not necessary, however, that an area be symmetrical; the approach works equally well for doubly asymmetrical shapes. The distances from the reference axes to the centroid are denoted $\bar{x}$ and $\bar{y}$, and are given by:

$$\bar{x} = \frac{\Sigma A\bar{x}}{\Sigma A} \quad ; \quad \bar{y} = \frac{\Sigma A\bar{y}}{\Sigma A} \tag{3-2}$$

Some examples will illustrate the procedure for unsymmetrical areas.

Example 3-12

Centroid of a plane area.

Given: Plane area with configuration as shown.

To Find: Location of the centroid.

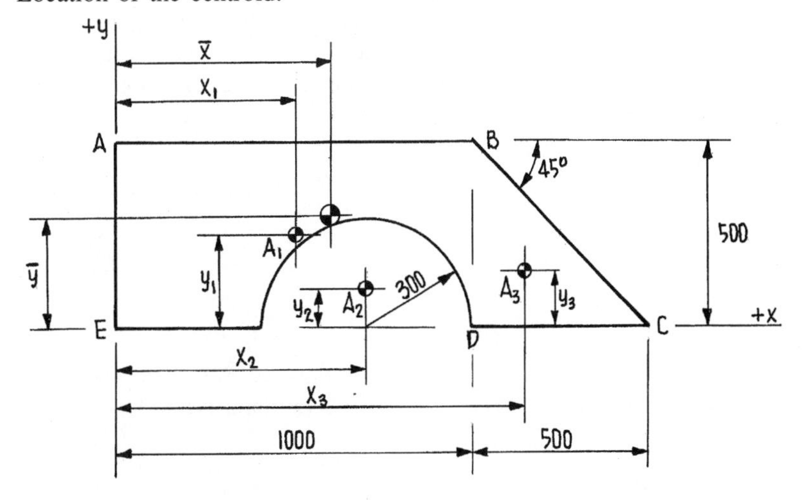

Solution: The centroid will be found using the solid area $\overline{ABDE}$ as A_1, the solid area $\overline{BCD}$ as A_2 and the void semicircle area as A_3. Reference axes are shown on the sketch. The general form of the solution is:

$$\bar{x} = \frac{\Sigma A\bar{x}}{\Sigma A} \quad ; \quad \bar{y} = \frac{\Sigma A\bar{y}}{\Sigma A}$$

$$\text{Area } A_1 = (500)(1000) = 500{,}000\text{mm}^2$$
$$\text{Area } A_2 = (1/2)(\pi)(300^2) = 141{,}000\text{mm}^2$$
$$\text{Area } A_3 = (1/2)(500)(500) = 125{,}000\text{mm}^2$$

$$\bar{x}_1 = 500\text{mm}$$
$$\bar{x}_2 = 100 - 300 = 700\text{mm}$$
$$\bar{x}_3 = 1000 + (1/3)(500) = 1167\text{mm}$$

$$\bar{y}_1 = 250\text{mm}$$
$$\bar{y}_2 = (4)(300/3\pi) = 127\text{mm}$$
$$\bar{y}_3 = (1/3)(500) = 167\text{mm}$$

$$\bar{x} = \frac{\Sigma A\bar{x}}{\Sigma A} = \frac{(500{,}000)(500) - (141{,}000)(700) + (125{,}000)(1167)}{500{,}000 - 141{,}000 + 125{,}000}$$

$= 614$mm (to the right of the origin)

$$\bar{y} = \frac{\Sigma A\bar{y}}{\Sigma A} = \frac{(500{,}000)(250) - (141{,}000)(127) + (125{,}000)(167)}{500{,}000 - 141{,}000 + 125{,}000}$$

$= 264$mm (upward from the origin)

The centroid of this area lies 614mm to the right of the point *E* and 264mm above point *E*; the area will balance on this point.

3.5 Centroids of Combination Steel Sections

It is common practice in the design of steel members to build up a member out of smaller standard sections. The centroid of these *combination sections* is an important point in the analysis of the member as a beam or as a column. Finding the centroid of these combination steel sections follows the same procedures as those just developed for geometric shapes.

A steel *section* is the term applied to the cross-sectional configuration of a steel member. There are several hundred standard steel sections commonly rolled by American steel mills, a few of which are shown in Figure 3-7.

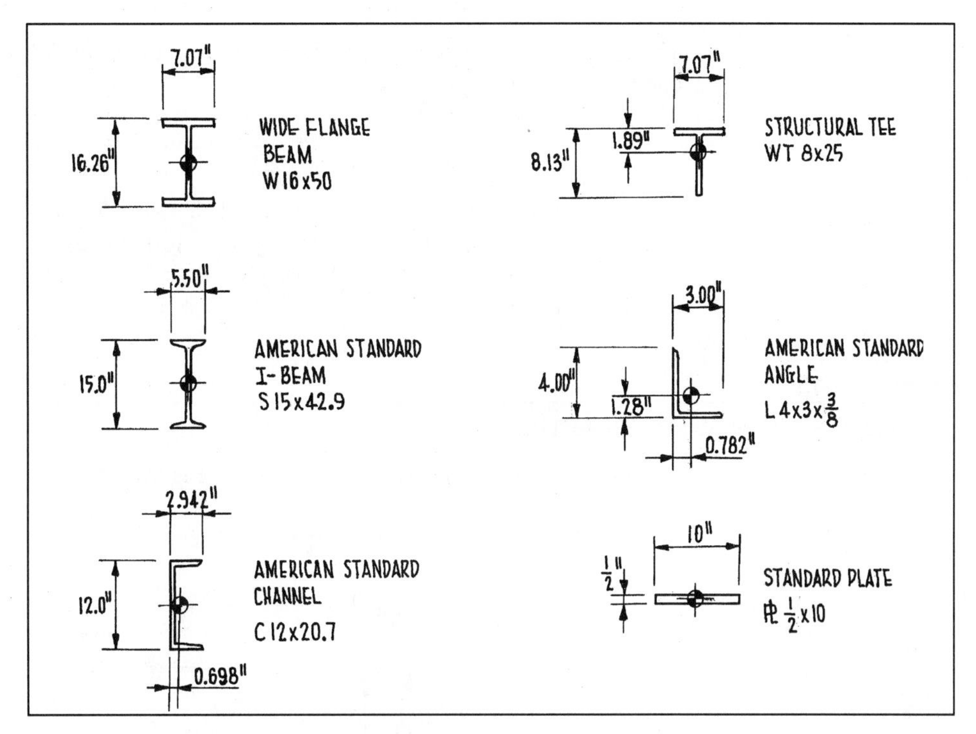

Figure 3-7 Standard steel sections.

A table of some of the commonly rolled steel sections used in American practice is included in design tables S-1 through S-9 in the Technical Manual. The tables are extracted from the *Manual of Steel Construction* of the American Institute of Steel Construction, ninth edition. This manual, called the *Steel Handbook*, gives the dimensions and properties of all the standard steel sections normally available in the U.S. The dimensions shown on the left side of the table give the cross sectional area, the overall depth of the member, the thickness of the web, the thickness and width of the flange and the location of the centroid (for asymmetrical sections). It is these properties that will be used in subsequent calculations to find the centroids of built-up members.

Consider, for example, the built-up section shown in Figure 3-8. A steel cover plate $^1/_2$ in. by 10 in. has been added to a wide flange shape, W16x50, to increase its load-carrying capacity. The combined shape is called a combination section. In this particular case, the combination section retains its symmetry about its vertical axis.

The designation W16x50 for the wide flange section means that the section has a nominal depth of 16 inches and weighs 50 lbs per foot of length. Its exact depth, not the nominal depth, must be used in all calculations; the exact depth is found in design table S-1b of the Technical Manual.

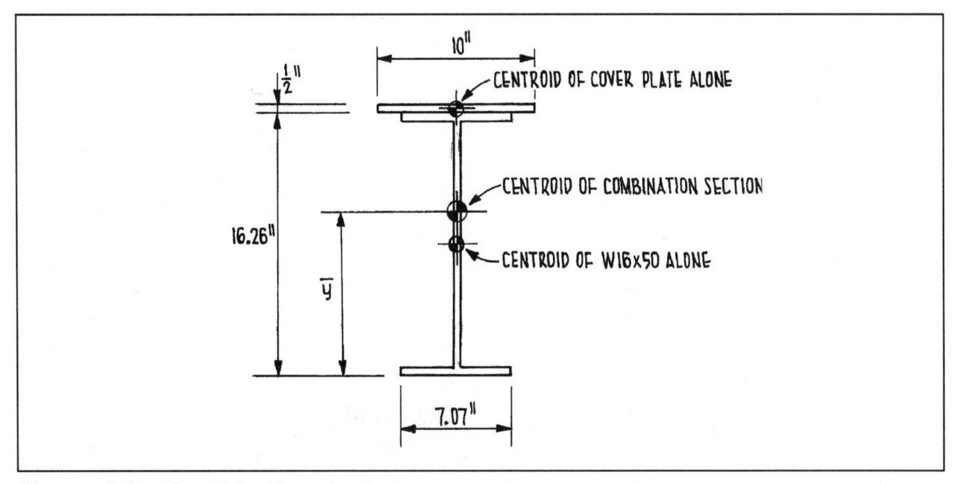

Figure 3-8 Combination section.

The centroid of the combination steel section is found in the same way the centroid of combined geometric areas was found:

$$\bar{x} = \frac{\Sigma A\bar{x}}{\Sigma A} \quad ; \quad \bar{y} = \frac{\Sigma A\bar{y}}{\Sigma A} \tag{3-2}$$

In this case, the areas A_1 and A_2 are those of the wide flange sections and the steel plate, and the distances $\bar{y}_1$ and $\bar{y}_2$ are the distances to their respective centroids.

Some examples will illustrate the procedure for finding the centroid of some combination steel sections.

Example 3-13

Centroid of a combination steel section.

Given: Combination steel section of Figure 3-8.

To Find: Centroid of the combination section.

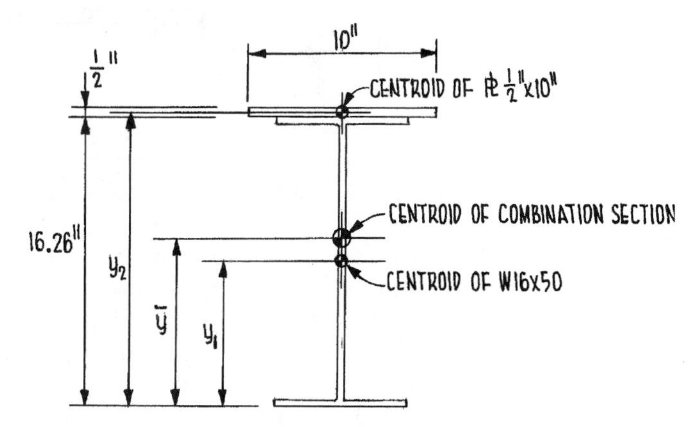

Solution: The dimensions of the W16x50 are found from the design table S-1b for wide flange sections. The relevant dimensions have been entered on the sketch.

It is noted that the combination section is symmetrical about its vertical axis. The centroid will therefore fall somewhere along that axis.

Moments are summed about the base of the W16x50. The W16x50 is taken as A_1, the ($^1/_2$)(10) area of the plate is taken as the second area A_2:

$$\bar{y} = \frac{\Sigma Ay}{\Sigma A}$$

$$A_1 = 14.7 \text{ in.}^2$$
$$A_2 = (^1/_2)(10) = 51 \text{ in.}^2$$

$$\bar{y}_1 = 8.13 \text{ in.}$$
$$\bar{y}_2 = 16.26 + 0.25 = 16.51 \text{ in.}$$

$$\bar{y} = \frac{(14.7)(8.13) + (5)(16.51)}{14.7 + 5} = \frac{202.1}{19.7}$$

$\bar{y}$ = 10.26 in. above the base of the W16x50.

The centroid of the combination section lies on the vertical axis of symmetry, 10.26 in. above the base of the W16x50.

Steel channel sections are also in common use. Channels are designated in the same way as wide flange sections; a channel *C*12 x 20.7, for example, is 12 inches deep and weighs 20.7 lbs/ft.

Steel angles are designated similarly. A steel angle designated *L*6 x 4 x 1/4 has one leg 6 inches long, the other 4 inches long, and a thickness of 1/4 inch for both legs. (The weight of an angle is not given in the general designation; it must be found in the tables.)

Example 3-14

Centroid of a combination steel section.

Given: Combination steel section as shown.

To Find: Centroid of the combination section.

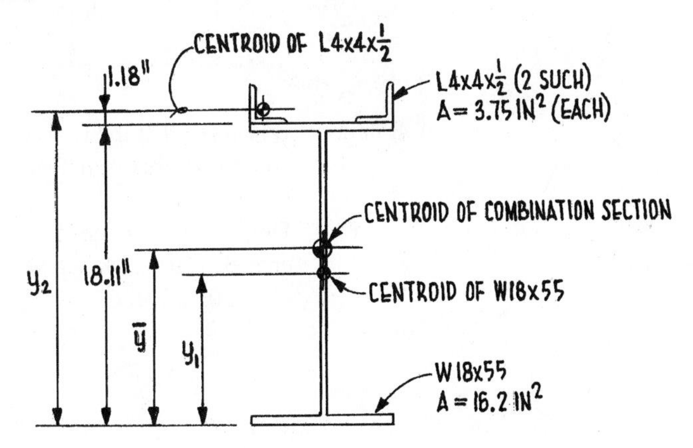

Solution: The dimensions for the given sections are found from the tables and entered on the sketch. Moments are summed about the base of the W18x55 section. The W18x55 is taken as A_1 and the area of the two channels are taken as A_2:

$$\bar{y} = \frac{\Sigma A\bar{y}}{\Sigma A}$$

$A_1 = 16.2 \text{ in.}^2$
$A_2 = (2)(3.75) = 7.50 \text{ in.}^2$

$\bar{y}_1 = 9.055$ in.
$\bar{y}_2 = 18.11 + 1.18 = 19.29$ in.

$$\bar{y} = \frac{(16.2)(9.055) + (7.50)(19.29)}{16.2 + (7.50)}$$

$\bar{y} = 12.29$ in. above the base of the W18x55.

The centroid of the combination section lies on the vertical axis of symmetry 12.29 in. above the base of the W18x55.

Example 3-15

Centroid of a combination steel section.

Given: Combination steel section as shown.

To Find: Centroid of the combination section.

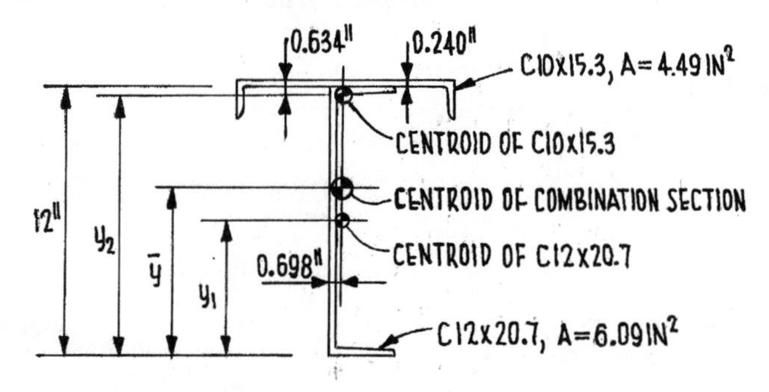

Solution: It is noted that the two centroids are aligned vertically. The centroid of the combined area will therefore lie along this common centroidal axis.

Dimensions for the given sections have been found from the tables and entered on the sketch. Moments will be summed about the base of the *C*12x20.7. The *C*12x20.7 is taken as A_1 and the *C*10x15.3 is taken as A_2:

$$\bar{y} = \frac{\Sigma A\bar{y}}{\Sigma A}$$

$A_1 = 6.09 \text{ in.}^2$
$A_2 = 4.49 \text{ in.}^2$

$\bar{y}_1 = 6.0 \text{ in.}$
$\bar{y}_2 = 12 + 0.24 - 0.634 = 11.61 \text{ in.}$

$$\bar{y} = \frac{(6.09)(6.0) + (4.49)(11.61)}{6.09 + 4.49}$$

= 8.38 in. above the base of the *C*12x20.7.

The centroid lies along the common vertical centroidal axis at a distance 8.38 in. above the base of the *C*12x20.7.

3.6 Couples and Moments

A *couple* consists of a set of two parallel forces that are equal in magnitude but opposite in direction, with their lines of action separated by a distance *d*. Such a set of forces is shown in Figure 3-9.

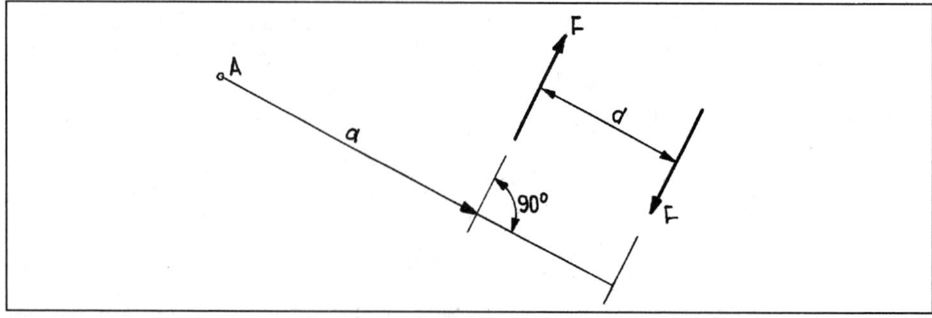

Figure 3-9 Parallel forces forming a couple.

The moment of the couple of Figure 3-9 about any point in the plane, such as point A, will always produce the same result:

$$M = -Fa + F(a + d)$$
$$M = Fd \qquad (3\text{-}3)$$

The moment of a couple is thus seen to be independent of any center of rotation; a couple may therefore be applied anywhere in its plane with equal results.

A couple cannot be composed into a single resultant force. The algebraic sum of forces would simply yield a magnitude of zero for the resultant. The resultant of a couple can only be the moment of the couple, given as Fd ; the moment of a couple is calculated simply as the moment of one force taken about some point in the line of action of the other force.

An example of moments and couples can be seen in the screwdriver of Figure 3-10.

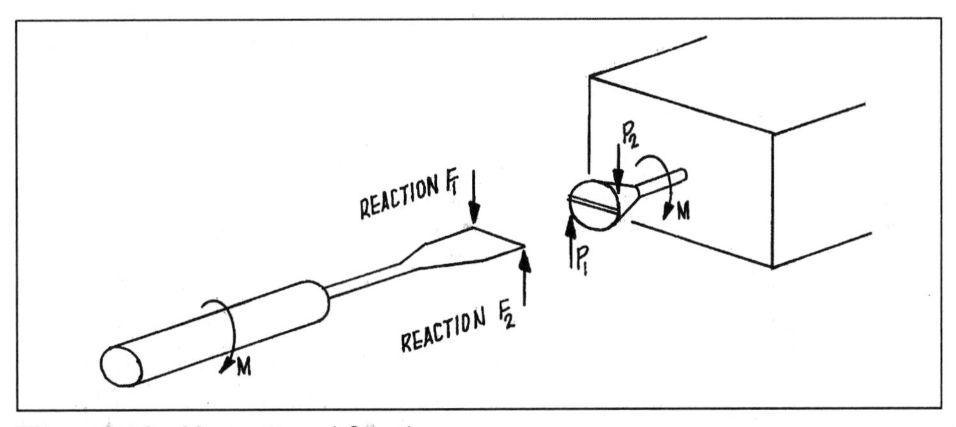

Figure 3-10 Moments and Couples.

The moment in the screwdriver shaft is pure moment, or torque, about the axis of the screwdriver; there are no resultant forces. At the point where the screwdriver contacts the screw, however, the moment is transformed into two forces, P_1 and P_2, one at each end of the slot as shown. The two forces P_1 and P_2 form a couple having a moment equal to that of the applied moment M. Further along the screw, the effect of the couple is transformed back into a pure moment, or torque, about the axis of the screw.

This easy transition shown in Figure 3-10 in going from a moment to a couple and back again is sharply in evidence throughout the study of mechanics. Very often, a moment or a couple may appear as loading on a member, and may then be transformed into the other at a reaction. Some examples will illustrate the point.

Example 3-16

Couples and moments as loads and reactions.

Given: Member loaded by forces and couples as shown.

To Find: Reactions at the support.

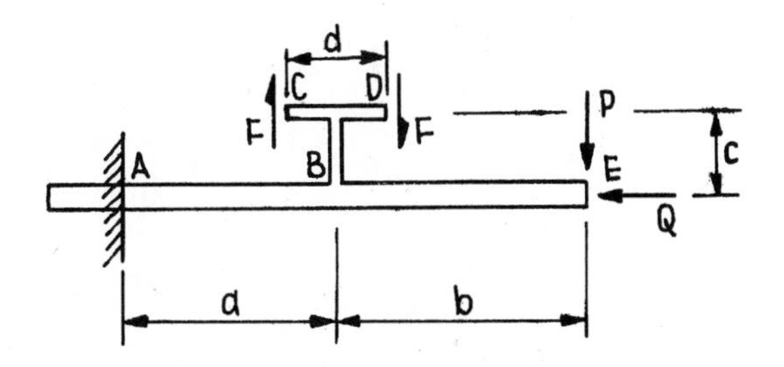

Solution: The free body diagram is drawn for the centerline of the member. All the reactions that can occur at the support at A are shown on the free body. It is noted that a support system that is resistant to rotations has not been encountered before.

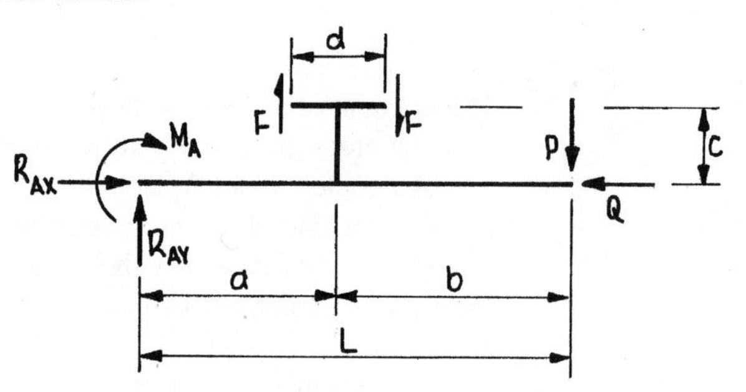

On the free body diagram, it is noted that the built-in support at an unyielding wall can resist forces both vertically and horizontally and that it can resist rotations, that is, it could develop moment such as M_A. The unknown reactions R_{AX}, R_{Ay} and M_A are shown in their positive sense.

The mathematical laws of equilibrium can now be applied. It is observed that there are three unknowns on the free body and that there are three equations of equilibrium in a plane. An equilibrium solution is therefore possible.

Moments are summed about point A. The point A is deliberately chosen in order to eliminate two of the unknowns from the resulting equation (R_{AX} and R_{Ay} will have no arm and will drop out):

$$\Sigma M_A = 0;\ M_A + R_{AX}(0) + R_{Ay}(0) - F(a - {}^{d}/_{2})$$
$$+ F(a + {}^{d}/_{2}) + PL + Q(0) = 0$$
$$M_A = -Fd - PL \text{ (direction shown for } M_A \text{ is backwards)}$$

Forces are now summed vertically; positive sense is upward:

$$\Sigma F_y = 0;\ R_{Ay} + F - F - P = 0$$
$$R_{Ay} = P \text{ (direction shown is correct)}$$

Forces are now summed horizontally; positive sense is to the right:

$$\Sigma_x = 0;\ R_{Ax} - Q = 0$$
$$R_{Ax} = Q \text{ (direction shown is correct)}$$

The final result is given in the following sketch, with all forces and reactions shown in their correct directions.

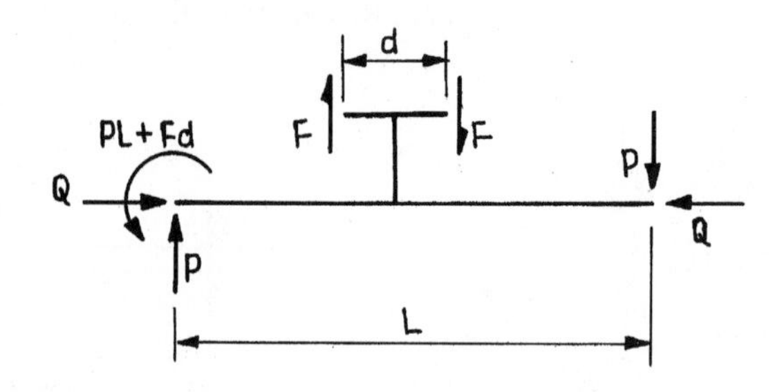

It is noted that the load P at the free end of the member produces a vertical reaction P at the support; these two forces form a couple having a moment PL.

It is noted further that the reaction moment at the support is composed of two couples, PL and Fd. The sense of the reaction moment is noted to be in opposition to the sense of the applied couples.

Example 3-17

Couples and moments as loads and reactions.

Given: Member loaded and supported as shown.

To Find: Reactions at A and B.

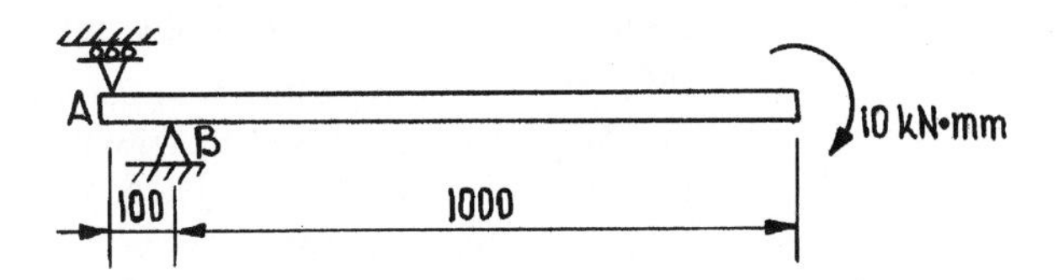

Solution: The free body is drawn for the centerline of the member. All the reactions that can occur at A and B are shown, but only the reactions that can occur at A and B are shown. Reactions are shown in what is assumed to be their correct directions.

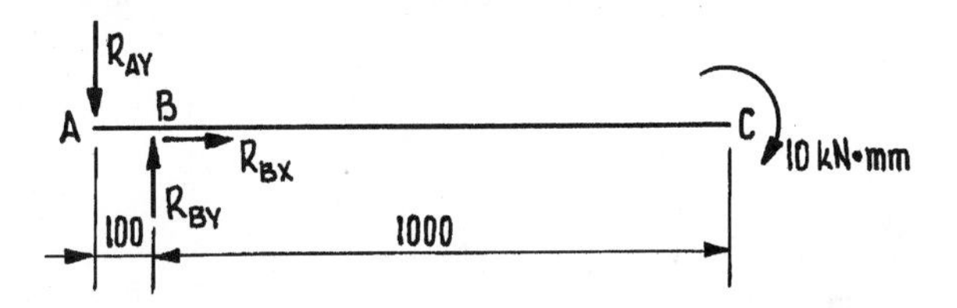

The mathematical laws of equilibrium can now be applied. It is observed that there are three unknown reactions and three equations of equilibrium. An equilibrium solution is therefore possible.

Moments are summed about point B ; both R_{Bx} and R_{By} will be eliminated from the resulting equation. Clockwise moments are considered to be positive:

$$\Sigma M_B = 0;\ -R_{Ay}\ (100) + 10$$
$$R_{Ay} = 0.10\ \text{kN}\cdot\text{mm} = 100\ \text{N}\cdot\text{mm downward}$$

Forces are summed vertically; upward forces are positive:

$$\Sigma F_y = 0;\ -100 + R_{By} = 0$$
$$R_{By} = 100\text{N upward}$$

Forces are summed horizontally; forces directed to the right are positive:

$$\Sigma F_x = 0;\ R_{Bx} = 0$$

The final reactions are shown in the following sketch.

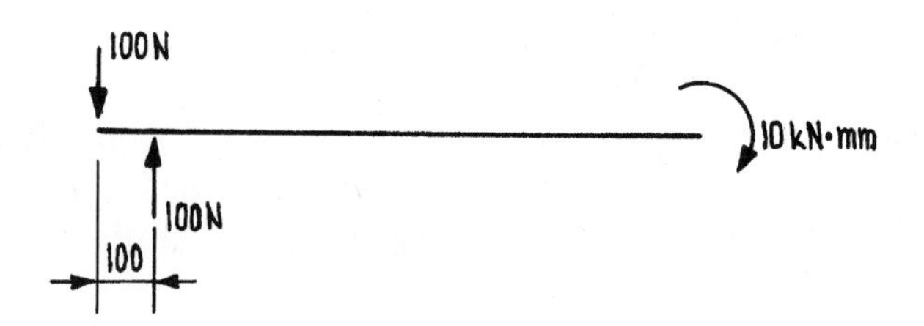

It is noted that the applied moment of 10 kN·mm is exactly opposed by a couple whose moment is 100·100 = 10 kN·mm.

3.7 Resolution and Composition of Forces and Couples

Any force may be resolved into a force and a couple. There is no significant point of theory involved in such a resolution; it is simply a useful tool when one is handling forces and moments.

Consider the force F in Figure 3-11a having its line of action passing through point A. The force may be translated to point B as shown in Figure 3-11b by adding and subtracting an equal force F at point B. The force F then appears at B as shown in Figure 3-11c, along with the new couple Fd. The force at A has been resolved into a force and a couple at B.

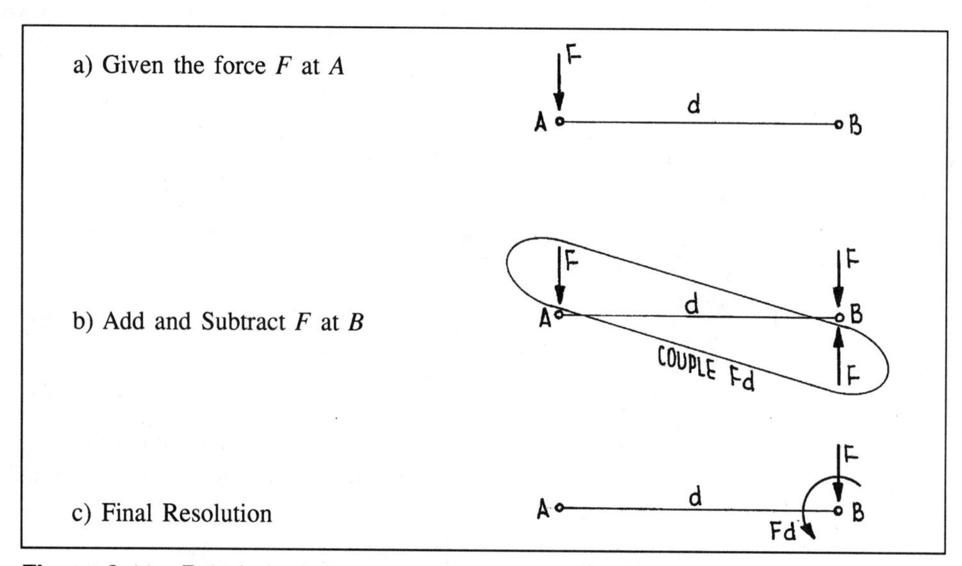

Figure 3-11 Resolution of a force into a force and couple.

The direction of the final couple Fd is found by observation; it is the direction produced by the force F at A in combination with its opposite force at B. The remaining force at B will always be the one having the magnitude and direction of the original force at A.

It is emphasized that the force and couple at B are the components of the force at A, and may be used in lieu of using the force at A; the force and couple at B will produce the same effects on a rigid body as the single force F at A would produce.

Conversely, any force and couple may be composed into a single force. The technique is opposite to that shown in Figure 3-11. The procedure is shown for reference in Figure 3-12.

a) Given a force F and A moment M at A. Transform the moment into a couple having an arm d.

F
A
M=Fd

b) Locate the point B at the distance d from A. Place the forces of the couple at A and B, such that the original force at A is opposed.

F
F
A
d
B
F
COUPLE Fd

c) Final resolution.

F
A
d
B

Figure 3-12 Resolution of force and moment into a single force.

Note that the distance d is not arbitrarily set; the translation distance is fixed by the ratio $M/F = d$.

Some numerical examples will illustrate the technique of transforming a force into a force and a couple and the converse technique of composing a force and a couple into a force.

Example 3-18

Resolution of a force into a force and a couple.

Given: Force of three kips at point A.

To Find: Component force and couple at point B that will produce the same effects as force F at point A.

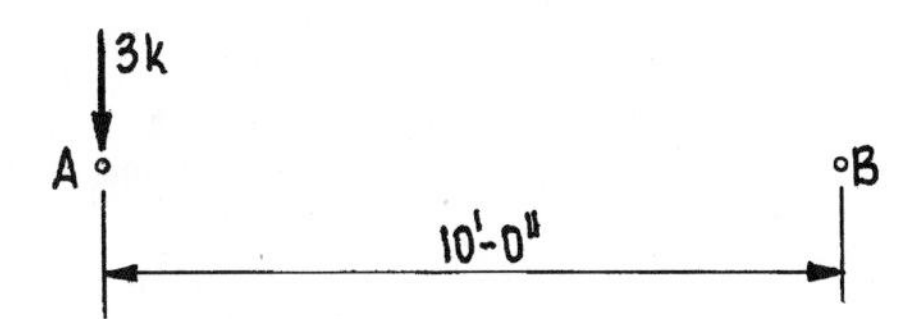

Solution: A force of three kips is added and subtracted at point B as shown in the following sketch.

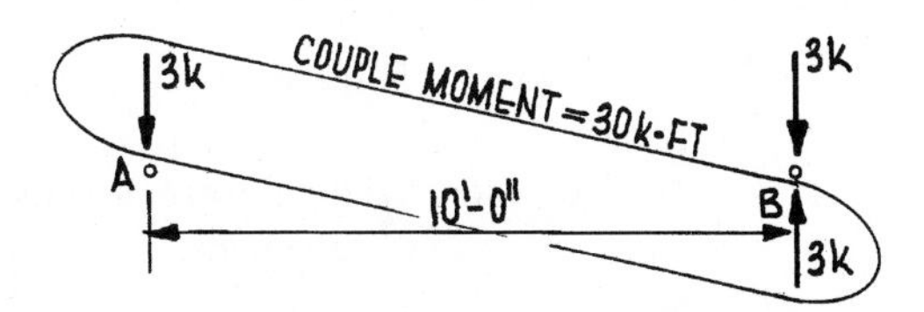

The original force at A in combination with its opposite force at B form a couple whose moment is 3x10 = kip·ft. The final result is then the force of 3 kips at B plus a couple having a moment of 30 kip·ft.

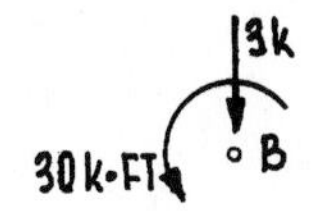

The force and couple at B are the components of the original force at A and will produce the same effects on a rigid body as the single force A would produce.

It is noted that the remaining force at B is the one having the same magnitude and direction as the original force at A.

Example 3-19

Resolution of a force into a force and a couple.

Given: Force of 100 kN at point A.

To Find: Component force and couple at point B that will product the same effects as the 100 kN force at point A.

Solution: A force of 100 kN is added and subtracted at point B as shown in the following sketch.

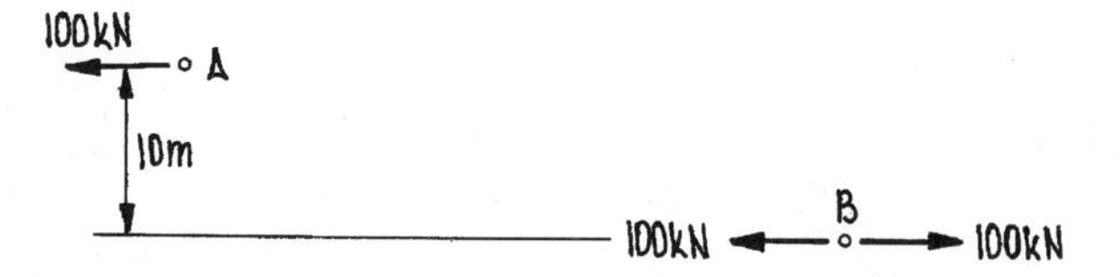

The original force at A in combination with its opposite force at B forms a couple having a moment $100 \cdot 10 = 1000$ kN·m. The final result at B is then the original force of 100 kN plus a couple having a moment of 1000 kN·m.

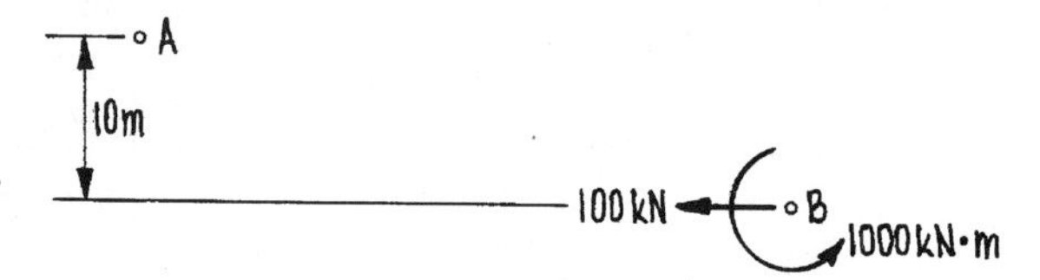

Example 3-20

Composition of a force and a couple into a single force.

Given: Force of 25 lb and a moment of 100 lb·ft at point A.

To Find: A single force at some point B such that the effects of the single force on a rigid body will be the same as the original force at A.

Solution: Transform the moment into a couple having two equal and opposite forces of 25 lb at a distance d apart:

$$d = M/F = 100/25 = 4 \text{ ft.}$$

Locate the point B at a distance 4 ft. from the point A. Place the forces of the couple at A and B such that the original force at A is opposed.

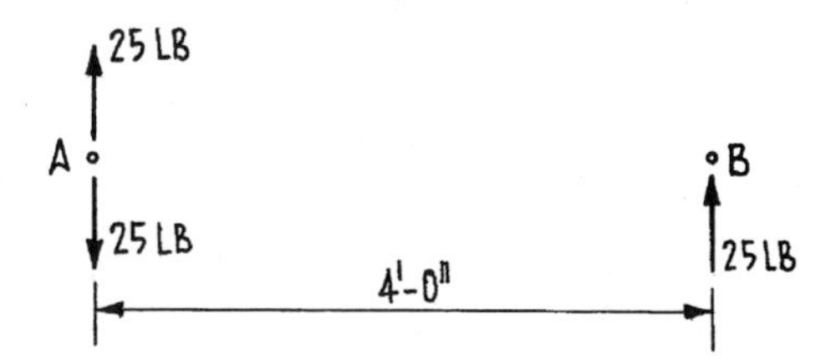

The final composition is the force remaining at the point B.

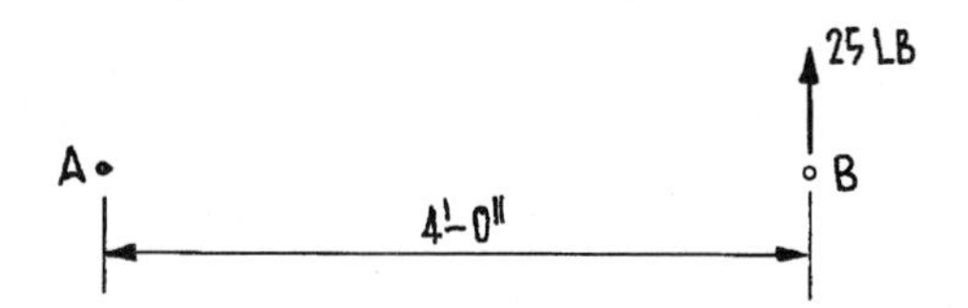

It is noted that the single force at B has the same magnitude and direction as the original force at A.

Review Questions

1. Give three examples of gravity loads on structures that will produce a system of parallel forces.
2. In finding the resultant of a system of parallel forces, how is the direction of the resultant determined?
3. In finding the resultant of a system of parallel forces, how is the magnitude of the resultant found?
4. In finding the resultant of a system of parallel forces, how is the location of its line of action found?
5. How many laws of equilibrium will generally apply to rope-and-pulley arrangements in mechanics?
6. In a rope and pulley arrangement, what simplifying assumptions must be made if the tension in any one rope is to be a constant?
7. Define mechanical advantage as it applies to rope-and-pulley systems.
8. As a system of pulleys is varied to increase output force, what happens to output travel?
9. Define the centroid of a plane area.
10. How is it that the solution for the resultant of parallel forces can be used to find centroids of an area, when there are no forces involved?
11. What does it mean when the centroid of an area does not fall within the body of the area but in some open part of the area?
12. Where does one find the sizes and shapes of the common steel sections used in American construction practice?
13. A steel section is identified as w16x40. Without referring to the steel tables, describe the section.
14. What is meant by *combination sections* in steel?
15. Define a couple.
16. How is the magnitude of a couple determined?
17. What is the difference between a moment and a couple?
18. What is the similarity between a moment and a couple?
19. Give the step-by-step procedure for resolving a force into a force and a couple.
20. Give the step-by-step procedure for composing a force and a couple into a single force.

CHAPTER

4

GENERAL SYSTEMS OF FORCES IN A PLANE

To this point, the discussions have introduced three separate types of force systems:

1. Concurrent force systems.
2. Parallel force systems.
3. Moments and couples.

On an actual structure, these forces will likely occur in combination with each other rather than as separate systems. This chapter is devoted to extending the study of statics to include various combinations of these force systems acting as loads on a structure.

The first part of this study will remain in the more familiar two dimensional or planar systems. Then, after some familiarity has been developed, the study will be extended in the next chapter into three dimensional systems. It will be seen that solutions in three dimensional systems are much like those in two dimensions; there are simply more directions and more unknowns.

4.1 General Force Systems in a Plane

In working with general force systems, one often locates centroids and centers of gravity by intuitive means. Examples of such intuitively located positions are shown in Figure 4-1, where the dead load, or weights, of various members are shown as resultant forces. The lines of action of these resultant forces have been shown to act through the centers of gravity of the members (or of segments of members).

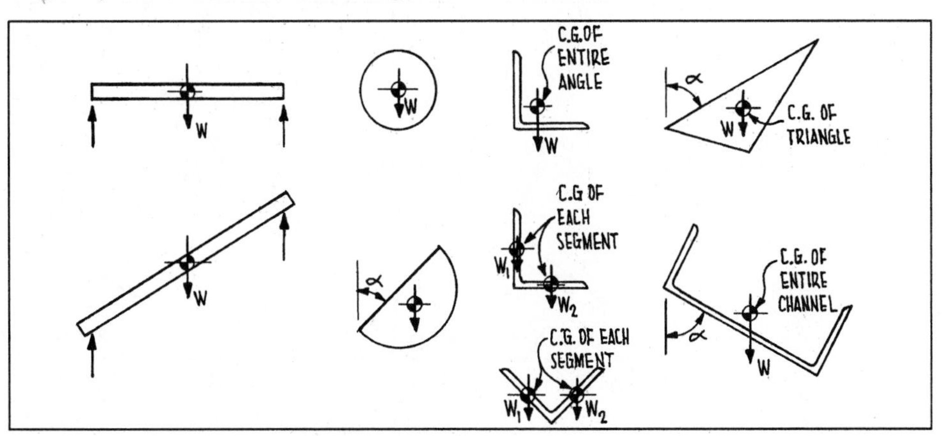

Figure 4-1 Location of resultant weights.

It must be remembered that the weight of a body is not actually concentrated at a point as indicated in Figure 4-1, but is distributed throughout the body. For calculations in rigid body mechanics, however, it has been shown that all such parallel gravity loads can be composed into a single resultant force as indicated in Figure 4-1. The line of action of this single resultant was also shown earlier to act through the center of gravity of the body (or of the segment).

As a point of review, it was found in earlier discussions that a system of concurrent forces in a plane can be composed into a single resultant force in that plane. It was similarly found that a system of parallel forces in a plane can be composed into a single resultant in that plane. And finally, it was found that a system of moments or couples in a plane can be summed algebraically to find a single resultant moment or couple in that plane. If these resultants of concurrent forces, parallel forces and moments were all to occur together, these resultants could of course be further composed into a single resultant force or a single resultant couple representing the entire system.

It is noted that the final resultant of any general system of loads will be a force or it will be a couple. It cannot be a combination of the two, since it has been observed that a force and a couple can be composed into a single force at another location. Further, it has also been shown that a single resultant force cannot be composed into a couple, nor can a couple be resolved into a single resultant force; the final resultant must therefore be either a force or a couple.

In solutions involving general systems of forces, there are several innovations in common use. One of the more frequently used innovations is that of using the mathematical laws of equilibrium in an alternative form.

Classical Form:	$\Sigma F_x = 0 \quad \Sigma F_y = 0 \quad \Sigma M_0 = 0$	(2-1a,b,c)
Alternative Form No. 1:	$\Sigma \mathrm{F}_u = 0 \quad \Sigma \mathrm{M}_A = 0 \quad \Sigma \mathrm{M}_B = 0$	(4-1)
Alternative Form No. 2:	$\Sigma M_A = 0 \quad \Sigma M_B = 0 \quad \Sigma M_C = 0$	(4-2)

In applying Alternative No. 1, moments are summed about two points in the system, points A and B, then forces are summed in a direction u parallel to line $\overline{AB}$. The total number of equilibrium equations in this solution remains three; no more than three unknowns may occur in any equilibrium solution in a plane.

In using Alternative No. 2, moments are summed about any three points in the system, A, B and C, where A, B and C are not in a straight line; points A, B and C must form a discrete triangle. The total number of equilibrium equations in this solution remains three; no more than three unknowns may occur in any equilibrium solution in a plane.

The proof of the validity of the two alternative sets of equilibrium solutions is quite straightforward. Consider the rigid bodies in Figure 4-2, subject to a general system of forces as shown. Points A, B and C are points selected at random anywhere in the plane.

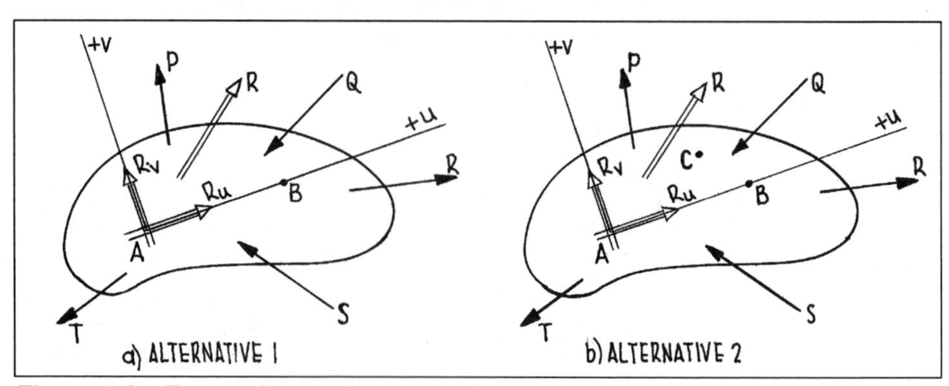

Figure 4-2 Free bodies under general force systems.

In Figure 4-2a, if ΣM_A is known to be zero, then it is known as a consequence that there is no imbalance of moments to cause rotations of the free body. It is possible, however, that there could still be unbalanced forces in the system if the resultant R passes through the point A; the component R_v would cause translation in the v direction and the component R_u would cause translation in the u direction. If, however, the sum of moments about B is also known to be zero, then it is known as a consequence that the component R_v cannot exist, leaving only one possible source of imbalance, R_u. But if the sum of forces in the u direction is also known to be zero, then as a consequence the component R_u must be zero. If, then, these three conditions are known to be true, that is,

$$\Sigma M_A = 0, \Sigma M_B = 0, \Sigma M_C = 0,$$

then the body is in equilibrium, where the u direction is parallel to the line containing points A and B.

For Alternative No. 1, the same logic holds for summing moments about A and B. For the third equation, however, rather than summing forces in the u direction as in Alternative No. 2, one may sum moments about some point C as shown in Figure 4-2b; if the sum of moments about C are known to be zero, then it is known as a consequence that the component R_u must also be zero. So, if these three conditions are known to be true, that is, $\Sigma M_A = 0$, $\Sigma M_B = 0$, $\Sigma M_C = 0$, then the body is in equilibrium, where the points A, B and C cannot lie in a straight line.

The alternative mathematical laws of equilibrium given by Eqs.(4-1) and (4-2) will be found quite useful in subsequent solutions of planar force systems.

4.2 Resultant of a General Force System in a Plane

In handling general force systems, it is sometimes desirable to know the resultant of the force system, along with its line of action. The procedure for finding the resultant of a general system will generally fall into the following pattern:

1. Resolve all forces into their rectangular x and y components.
2. Show all moments and couples as couples, with their forces shown either in the x direction or in the y direction at some arbitrarily fixed location.
3. Find the resultant R_Y of all parallel vertical (or y) forces as if these were the only forces in the system; locate the line of action of R_Y.
4. Find the resultanr R_x of all parallel horizontal (or x) forces as if these were the only forces in the system; locate the line of action of R_x.
5. Find the intersection of R_x and R_Y; the line of action of the resultant R will pass through this point.
6. Find the magnitude of the resultant R (by the Pythagorean theorem) and find its direction angles.
7. Sketch the resultant in its correct direction along its correct line of action.

Some examples will illustrate the procedure.

Example 4-1

Resultant of a general force system.

Given: General force system as shown.

To Find: Magnitude, direction and location of the resultant of the seven applied forces.

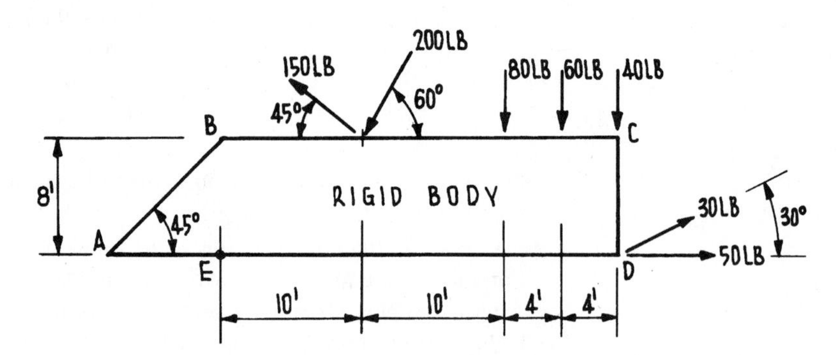

Solution: All forces are resolved into their x and y components as shown on the following sketch.

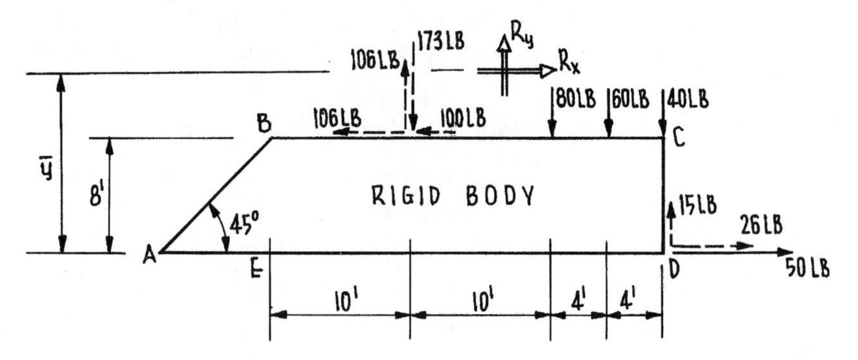

The magnitude of the resultant of all the parallel vertical forces is found by the usual methods for parallel forces:

$$R_Y = \Sigma F_Y = +106 - 173 - 80 - 60 - 40 + 15$$
$$= -232 \text{ lbs (directed downward)}$$

The location of the line of action of R_Y is found as usual, in this case by summing moments about E. R_Y is taken in its correct direction and $\bar{x}$ is assumed positive, that is, to the right of E:

Moment of Resultant = Moment of Components

$$232\bar{x} = -106(10) + (173)(10) + (80)(20) + (60)(24)$$
$$+(40)(28) - (15)(28) - (26)(8) - (50)(8)$$
$$\bar{x} = 16.4 \text{ ft (to the right of } E)$$

The magnitude of the resultant of all the parallel horizontal forces is found as usual:

$$R_x = \Sigma F_x = -106 - 100 + 26 + 50$$
$$= -130 \text{ lb (directed to the left)}$$

The location of the line of action is again found by summing moments about E. R_y is taken in its correct direction and $\bar{y}$ is assumed positive, that is, above point E:

Moment of Resultant = Moment of Components

$$-130\bar{y} = -106(8) - (100)(8) + (26)(0) + (50)(0)$$
$$\bar{y} = 12.7 \text{ ft (upward from } E\text{)}$$

The magnitude of the resultant R is found by the Pythagorean theorem:

$$R = \sqrt{R_x^2 + R_y^2} = \sqrt{130^2 + 232^2}$$
$$= 266 \text{ lb (directed down and left)}$$

Direction angles are found from the direction cosines:

$$\cos\alpha_R = R_R / R = 130/266 \quad \alpha_R = 60.7°$$
$$\cos\beta_R = R_y / R = 232/266 \quad \beta_R = 29.3°$$

The resultant is shown in the following sketch.

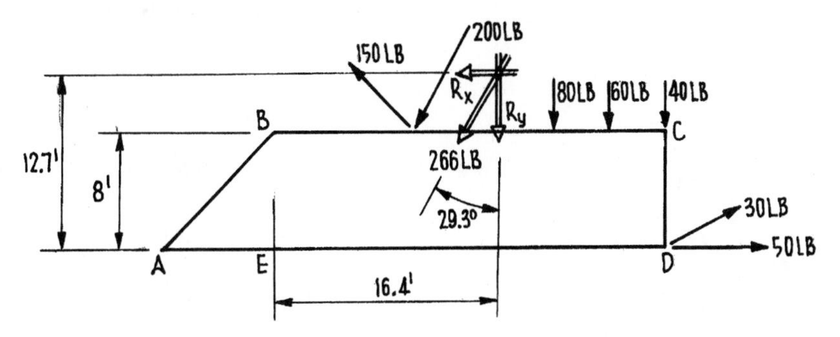

This 266 lb resultant will produce the same external reactions on the rigid body as the original seven applied forces would produce.

Example 4-2

Resultant of a general force system.

Given: General force system as shown.

To Find: Magnitude, direction and location of the resultant.

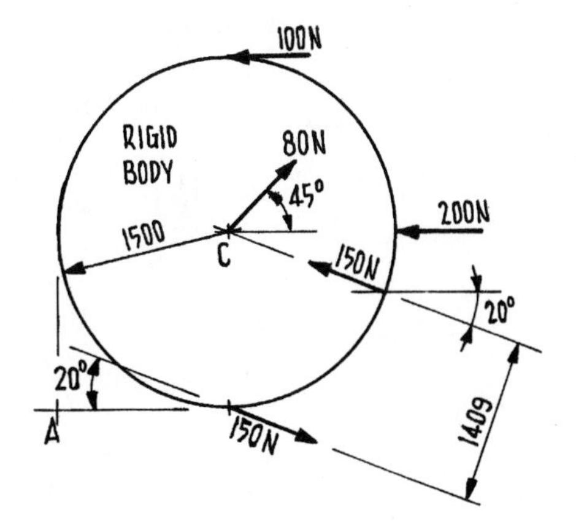

Solution: All forces are resolved into their x and y components as shown in the following sketch. Note that the couple requires no particular consideration; the two 150 N forces are simply resolved into their x and y components like any other force.

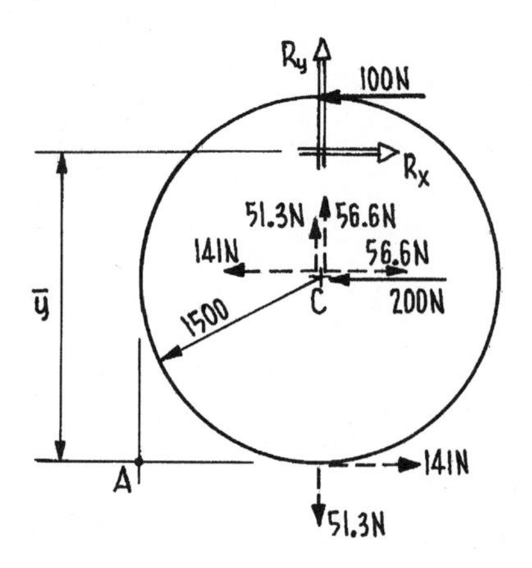

The magnitude of the resultant of all the parallel vertical forces is found by the usual methods for parallel forces:

$$R_y = \Sigma F_Y = +51.3 + 56.6 - 51.3$$
$$= 56.6 \text{ N (directed upward)}$$

The location of the line of action of R_Y is found as usual, in this case summing moments about point A. R_y is taken in its correct direction and $\bar{x}$ is assumed to be positive, that is, to the right of point A:

Moment of Resultant = Moment of Components

$$-56.6\bar{x} = -(51.3)(1500) - (56.6)(1500) + (51.3)(1500)$$
$$\bar{x} = 1500 \text{ mm (to the right of } A\text{)}$$

The magnitude of the resultant of all the parallel horizontal forces is found in the same way:

$$R_x = \Sigma F_x = -141 - 100 + 56.6 - 200 + 141$$
$$= -243.4 \text{ N (directed to the left)}$$

The location of the line of action of R_x is again found by summing moments about point A. R_x is taken in its correct direction and $\bar{y}$ is assumed to be positive, that is, above point A:

Moment of Resultant = Moment of Components

$$-243.4\bar{y} = -(100)(3000) - (141)(1500) + (56.6)(1500)$$
$$-(200)(1500) + (141)(0)$$

$$\bar{y} = 2985 \text{ mm (above point } A\text{)}$$

The magnitude of the resultant is found by the Pythagorean theorem:

$$R = \sqrt{R_x^2 + R_y^2} = \sqrt{56.6^2 + 243.4^2}$$
$$= 249.89 \text{ N (directed upward to the left)}$$

Direction angles are found from the direction cosines:

$$\cos\alpha_R = R_x / R = 243.4 / 249.89; \qquad \alpha = 13.09°$$
$$\cos\beta_R = R_y / R = 56.6 / 249.89; \qquad \beta = 76.91°$$

The resultant is shown in the following sketch.

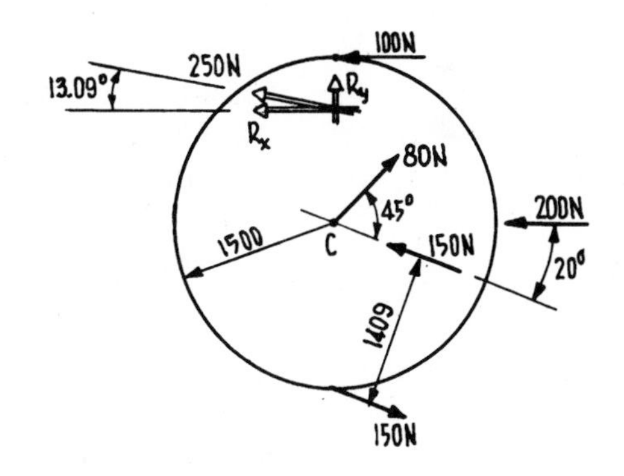

Example 4-3

Resultant of a general force system.

Given: General force system as shown.

To Find: Magnitude, direction and location of the resultant.

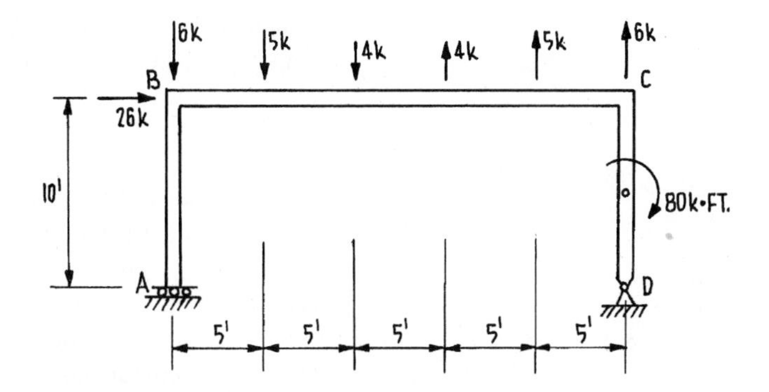

Solution: All forces are noted to be in their x and y components as given. The remaining load to be determined is the moment of 80 kip·ft.

The moment will be transferred into a couple; an arm of 10 feet is arbitrarily chosen. The couple could be placed anywhere in the plane; the couple is arbitrarily placed in the leg *CD*. The sketch of the rigid body follows.

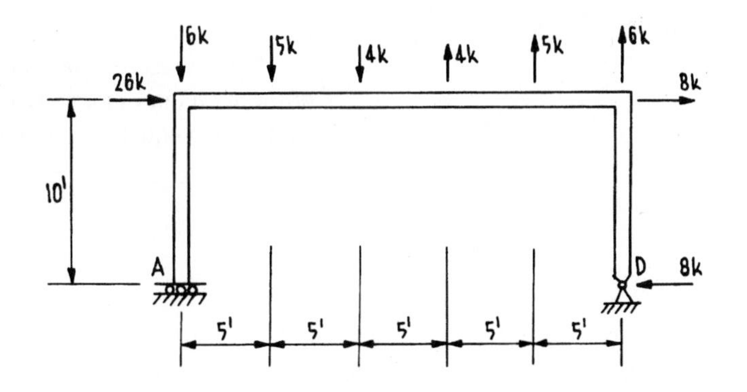

The magnitude of the resultant of all the parallel vertical forces is found by the usual method:

$$R_y = \Sigma F_y = -6 - 5 - 4 + 4 + 5 + 6 = 0$$

It is seen that there is no resultant vertical force in this system of forces. It is concluded that the resultant of vertical forces must therefore be a moment or a couple. The moment of the vertical components is found as usual by Varignon's theorem. Moments are summed about point A:

Moment of Resultant = Moment of Components

$$\begin{aligned} M \text{ due to vertical forces} &= (6)(0) + (5)(5) + (4)(10) \\ &\quad - (4)(15) - (5)(20) - (6)(25) \\ &= 65 - 310 \\ &= -245 \text{ kip·ft (counter clockwise)} \end{aligned}$$

The magnitude of the resultant of all the parallel horizontal forces is found by the usual means:

$$\begin{aligned} R_x = \Sigma F_x &= +26 + 8 - 8 \\ &= 26 \text{ k (directed to the right)} \end{aligned}$$

The location of the line of action of R_x is again found by summing moments about point A. R_x is taken in its correct direction and $\bar{y}$ is assumed to be positive, that is, above point A:

Moment of Resultant = Moment of Components

$$\begin{aligned} +26\bar{y} &= (8)(10) - (8)(0) \\ \bar{y} &= 3.1 \text{ ft (above point } A) \end{aligned}$$

The two components of the resultant are thus seen to be a horizontal force of 26 kips to the right and a counterclockwise moment of 245 kip·ft. These two components are shown on the following sketch.

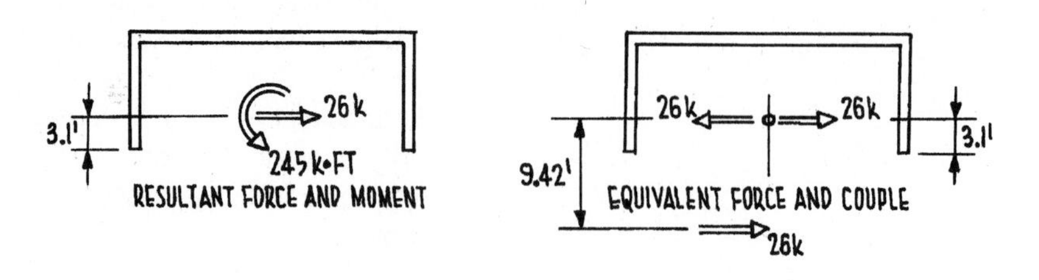

The force of 26 kips and the moment of 245 kip·ft are shown in the sketch of the force and moment. The moment is now transformed into a couple having two equal and opposite forces of 26 kip, separated by a distance of 9.42 ft. The couple is placed as shown in the equivalent force and couple. The final result is shown in the following sketch.

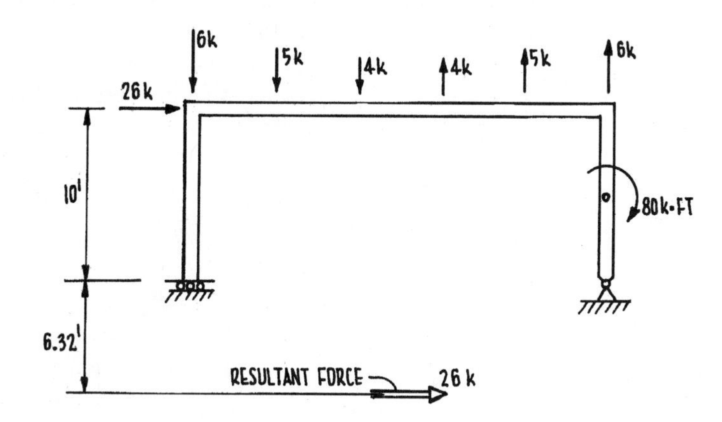

One may wonder why the moment of 80 kip·ft in Example 4-3 was transformed into a couple acting on leg *CD* of the frame, since the end result of the calculation is still the same 80 kip·ft. It is simply a trick to avoid the mistake of using the moment twice. The moment may be included in calculations for finding either the vertical component of the horizontal component, but not both. Transforming it into a couple and fixing it to the rigid body eliminates the possibility of mistakenly using it twice.

4.3 Reactions to a General Force System in a Plane

By far the most common type of problem in statics is that of finding the reactions at the supports of a structure. In such solutions there can be as many as three unknowns, to be found using the three mathematical laws of equilibrium. The procedures for using the three mathematical laws of equilibrium were developed earlier, but earlier applications were limited to simple load systems. The solution can now be extended to include more general systems of load.

Some examples will illustrate the extended procedures.

Example 4-4

Reactions to a general force system in a plane.

Given: Bar and stay as shown; bar weighs 100 lbs.

To Find: Reactions at *A* and *B*.

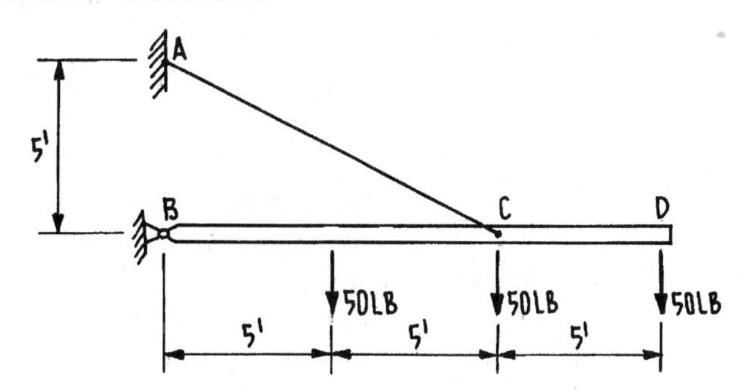

Solution: The bar *AD* is removed as a free body. Its resultant weight of 100 lb is shown acting through the center of gravity of the bar at its midpoint. All reactions are shown in their positive sense. The force in the stay is shown in tension along its correct line of action.

For the sake of subsequent calculations, all forces are resolved into their *x* and *y* components; these components are entered on the sketch.

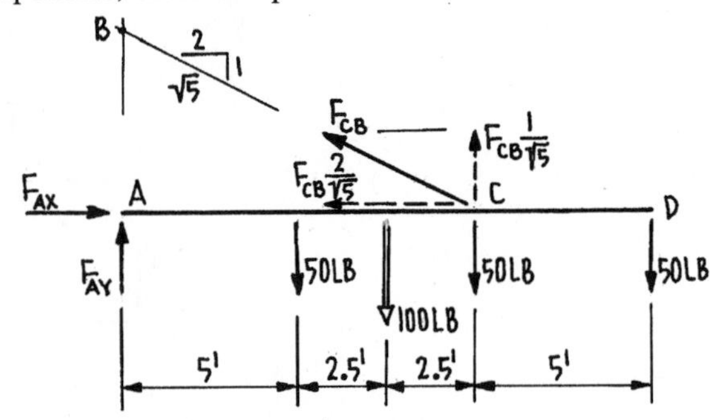

The mathematical laws of equilibrium can now be applied. It is noted that there are three unknown reactions acting on the free body, F_{AX}, F_{Ay} and F_{CB}, and that there are three equations of equilibrium, $\Sigma F_x = 0, \Sigma Fy = 0$, and $\Sigma M_o = 0$. An equilibrium solution is therefore possible.

Moments are summed about point *A*. The point *A* is deliberately chosen in order to eliminate the two unknowns at that point. Clockwise moments are considered positive:

$$\Sigma M_A = 0; \quad F_{AX}(0) + F_{Ay}(0) + (50)(5) + (100)(7.5) + (50)(10)$$

$$+ F_{CB}\left(\tfrac{2}{\sqrt{5}} x0\right) - F_{CB}\left(\tfrac{1}{\sqrt{5}} x10\right) + (50)(15) = 0$$

$$F_{CB}\left(10x\tfrac{1}{\sqrt{5}}\right) = 2250$$

$$F_{CB} = 503 \text{ lb}$$

Forces are now summed vertically. The solution just found for F_{CB} will be used in the equation:

$$\Sigma F_y = 0; \quad F_{Ay} - 50 - 100 + 503(\tfrac{1}{\sqrt{5}}) - 50 - 50 = 0$$

$$F_{Ay} = 25 \text{ lb}$$

Forces are now summed horizontally:

$$\Sigma F_x = 0; \qquad F_{AX} - 503(\tfrac{2}{\sqrt{5}}) = 0$$

$$F_{AX} = 450 \text{ lb}$$

As an alternative method of solution, the three reactions could have been found by summing moments about three points, as given by Eqs.(4-2).

In this alternative solution, moments are first summed about point *A* to find the reaction at *C*. This solution is identical to that used earlier:

$$\Sigma M_A = 0 \quad F_{CB} = 503 \text{ lbs (tension)}$$

Moments are now summed about point C. Selecting point C as a moment center eliminates the other two unknowns, F_{CB} and F_{AX}, leaving only one unknown, F_{Ay}, in the solution. Clockwise rotations are assumed positive:

$$\Sigma M_C = 0$$
$$F_{AX}(0) + F_{AY}(10) - (50)(5) - (100)(2.5) + (50)(5) = 0$$
$$F_{AY} = 25 \text{ lbs}$$

Moments are now summed about point B. Selecting point B as a moment center eliminates the other two unknowns, F_{AX} and F_{CB}, leaving only one unknown, F_{AX} in the solution:

$$\Sigma M_E = 0 - F_{AX}(5) + (50)(5) + (100)(7.5) + (50)(10) + (50)(15) = 0$$

$$F_{AX} = 450 \text{ lbs}$$

In the alternative method of solution just used with Example 4-4, the three moment centers were deliberately chosen such that each solution would include only one unknown. Such a technique is quite common in engineering mechanics. While it may require a slight amount of skill to be able to select such points, the advantages in reduced volume of calculations (and errors) make it a very worthwhile skill to develop.

Example 4-5

Reactions to a general force system in a plane.

Given: Angled beam as shown, uniform cross-section. Total weight of beam is 1500 N.

To Find: Reactions at A and B.

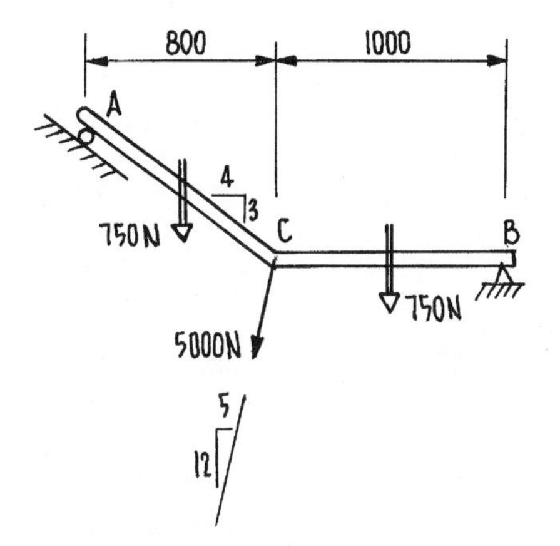

Solution: The beam AB is removed as a free body. It is noted that each segment of the beam is 1 m long; the weight of each segment is therefore 750 N and is shown as such on the free body. *All* the forces that the reactions can develop, but *only* the forces that the reactions can develop are shown on the free body. All forces and reactions are shown in their correct directions (when known) and are then resolved into their *x* and *y* components.

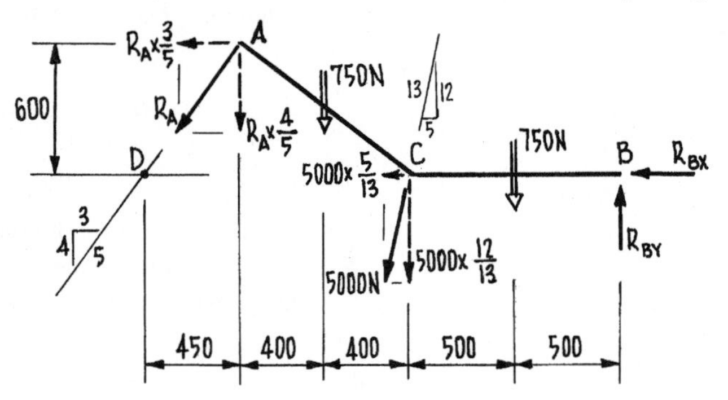

The mathematical laws of equilibrium can now be applied. There are only three unknowns; an equilibrium solution is therefore possible.

Moments are summed about point *B*; point *B* is deliberately chosen in order to eliminate the two unknowns F_{BX} and F_{By} from the equilibrium equation:

$$\Sigma M_B = 0;\ -R_A(3/5)(600) - R_A(4/5)(1800) - (5000)(5/13)(0) - (5000)(12/13)(1000) - (750)(1400) - (750)(500) = 0$$

$$R_A = -3356 \text{ N}$$

Forces are now summed vertically, using the value just found for R_A in the equation:

$$\Sigma F_Y = 0;\ -3356(4/5) - 750 - 5000(12/13) - 750 + R_{BY}$$
$$R_{BY} = 3431 \text{ N}$$

Forces are now summed horizontally:

$$\Sigma F_z = 0;\ -(-3356)(3/5) - 5000(5/13) + R_{BX} = 0$$
$$R_{BX} = 91 \text{ N}$$

As in the previous example, this example could be solved by using one of the alternative forms of the equilibrium equations, given by Eq.(4-1) or (4-2).

In the alternative solution, moments are first summed about point *B* to find the reaction at *A*. This solution is identical to that given earlier:

$$\Sigma M_B = 0;\ R_A = 3356 \text{ N (upward to the right)}$$

The sketch is now examined to find another moment center that will eliminate two of the unknowns. The point of intersection of R_{BX} and R_A, point *D*, is such a moment center. Moments are summed about point *D*:

$$\Sigma M_D = 0;\ (750)(850) + (5000)(^5/_{13})(0) + (5000)(^{12}/_{13})(1250) + (750)(1750) - R_{BY}(2250) = 0$$
$$R_{BY} = 3431 \text{ N}$$

The free body is now examined to find a third moment center that will eliminate all but the remaining unknown, R_{BX}. The intersection of R_A and R_{By} would be the required point, but it is so far out of the sketch that finding it is not considered to be worth the trouble. For this case, summing forces in the direction of the line $\overline{DB}$ [Eqs.(4-1)] will give the solution for R_{BX}:

$$\Sigma F_X = 0;\ -(-3356)(^3/_5) - (5000)(^5/_{13}) - R_{BX} = 0$$
$$R_{BX} = 91 \text{ N}$$

It should be noted from the two previous examples that the use of the alternative forms of the equilibrium equations given by Eqs.(4-1) and (4-2) are both useful and adaptable. A certain skill is sometimes required, however, in finding a suitable moment center. As a general rule, one may select the unknown that is to be found; the other two unknowns may then be eliminated by finding their point of intersection and taking moments about it. In some cases, as in Example 4-5, the "simplification" becomes more trouble than it is worth and one simply reverts to one of the other alternatives.

Example 4-6

Reactions to a general force system in a plane.

Given: Frame under general system of loads. Total weight of frame is 3600 lbs.

To Find: Reactions at *A* and *B*.

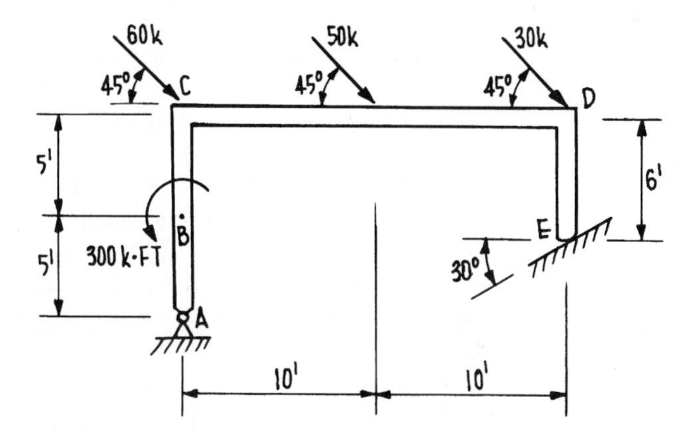

Solution: The frame is removed as a free body. It is noted that the frame has a total length of 36 feet and weighs 3600 lbs, or 100 lbs/ft of length. The weight of each segment is as shown on the free body. All forces acting on the frame are resolved into their *x* and *y* components. All reactions that *can* develop but *only* the reactions that can develop are shown on the free body in their correct directions (when known), then resolved into their x and y components.

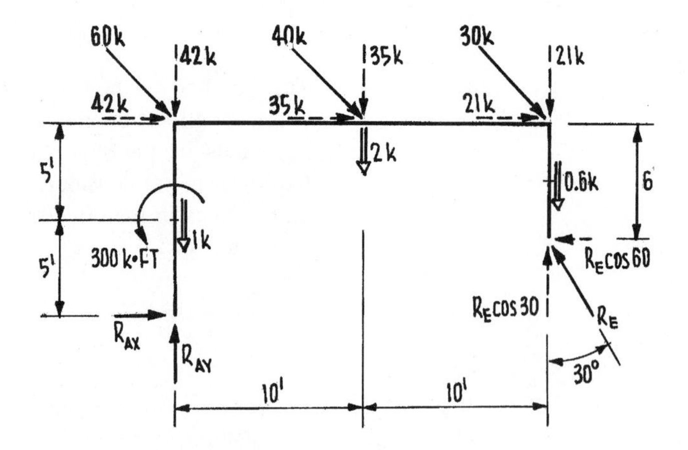

The mathematical laws of equilibrium can now be applied. It is noted that there are three unknowns and three equations of equilibrium; an equilibrium solution is therefore possible.

Moments are summed about point A to eliminate the two unknowns there from the resulting equilibrium equation:

$$\Sigma M_A = 0; - 300 + (42)(10) + (42)(0) + (1)(0) + (35)(10) + (35)(10) + (2)(10) + (21)(10) + (21)(20) + (0.6)(20) - R_E\cos30(20) - R_E\cos(60)(4) = 0$$

$$R_E = 76.7 \text{ kips}$$

Forces are now summed vertically:

$$\Sigma F_y = 0; \quad R_{Ay} - 1 - 42 - 35 - 2 - 21 - 0.6 + 76.7\cos30 = 0$$
$$R_{Ay} = - 35.2 \text{ kips (down)}$$

Forces are now summed horizontally:

$$\Sigma F_x = 0; \quad R_{Ax} + 42 + 35 + 21 - 76.7\cos60 = 0$$
$$R_{Ax} = - 59.6 \text{ kips (to the left)}$$

It should be noted in the solution of Example 4-6 that the 300 kip·ft moment appears only in the moment equation. It has no resultant force and therefore does not appear in the force equations. Note also that its point of application has no effect on the final solution for reactions, again verifying that a moment may act anywhere in the plane insofar as rigid body reactions are concerned.

Example 4-7

Reactions in a general force system in a plane.

Given: System of cylinders as shown, subject to their own dead weights.

To Find: Reactions at A, B and C.

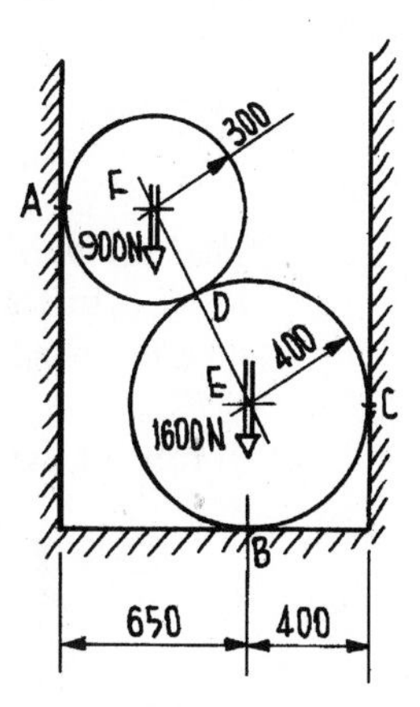

Solution: The free bodies of the two cylinders are drawn separately. All forces are shown in their correct direction, then resolved into their x and y components.

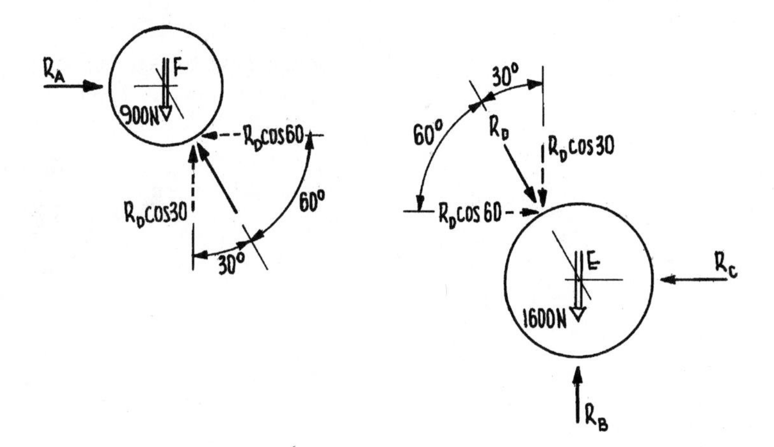

Note that the force at D "pushes" on both cylinders and must therefore be shown in both free bodies as a compressive, or pushing, force.

Note also that the sum of moments on these circular free bodies yields nothing of interest. The solution of these forces becomes one of force equilibrium, using only the two equations of force equilibrium, $\Sigma F_x = 0$ and $\Sigma F_y = 0$. As a consequence, no more than two unknowns can be accommodated on any one free body.

Examination of the two free bodies reveal that there are two unknowns on the upper cylinder but three unknowns on the lower cylinder. The reactions on the upper cylinder can therefore be found first, then these results used to find the reactions on the lower cylinder.

Forces are summed vertically on the upper cylinder:

$$\Sigma F_y = 0; \quad -900 + R_D\cos 30 = 0$$
$$R_D = 1039N$$

Forces are summed horizontally on the upper cylinder:

$$\Sigma F_x = 0; \quad R_A - 1039\cos 60 = 0$$
$$R_A = 520N$$

The results of these solutions reduces the number of unknowns in the lower cylinder to two. The remaining two reactions on this free body can now be found.

Forces are summed vertically on the lower cylinder:

$$\Sigma F_y = 0; \quad -1039\cos 30 - 1600 + R_B = 0$$
$$R_B = 2500N$$

Forces are summed horizontally on the lower cylinder:

$$\Sigma F_x = 0; \quad +1039\cos 60 - R_C = 0$$
$$R_C = 520N$$

It might have been recognized early in this solution that the two cylinders could have been removed as a single free body. Such a free body is shown in the following sketch:

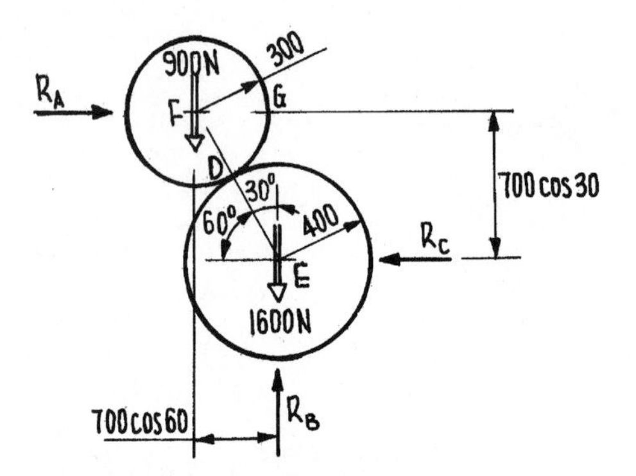

In this case, the sum of moments can now be used productively, allowing the solution for three unknowns.

Moments are summed about point E in order to eliminate the two unknowns R_B and R_C:

$$\Sigma M_E = 0; \quad R_A(700)\cos 30 - (900)(700)\cos 60 = 0$$
$$R_A = 520N$$

Moments are summed about point G in order to eliminate the two unknowns R_A and R_B:

$$\Sigma M_G = 0; \quad -(900)(700)\cos 60 + R_C(700)\cos 30 = 0$$
$$R_C = 520N$$

In order to find the reaction R_B by summing moments, it would be necessary to find the point of intersection of R_A and R_C and sum moments about that point. Since R_A and R_C never intersect, this method of solution cannot be used. The sum of forces parallel to line $\overline{GE}$ will work, however, and will be used to find reaction R_B:

$$\Sigma Fy = 0; \quad -900 - 1600 + R_B = 0$$
$$R_B = 2500N$$

The two sets of solutions are of course identical. The advantage of the second solution is that it obviates any need to find the contact force at D, thereby simplifying calculations somewhat.

Example 4-8

Reactions in a general force system in a plane.

Given: System of members and loads as shown. Dead weight of member *AB* is 60 lb and of member *CD* is 100 lb.

To Find: Reactions at *A*, *C* and *D*.

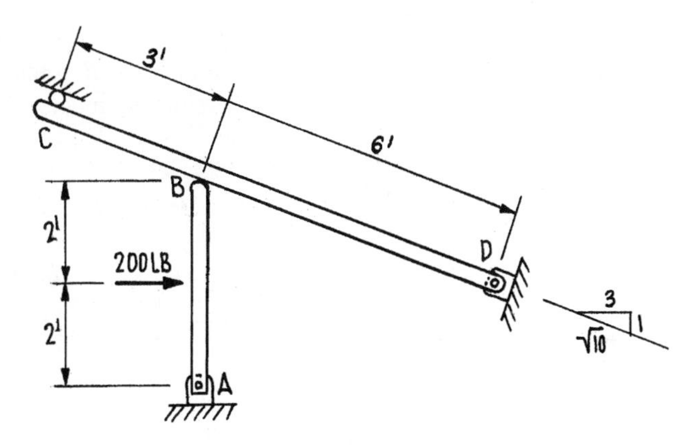

Solution: The two members are removed as free bodies. As usual, weights are shown acting through the centers of gravity.

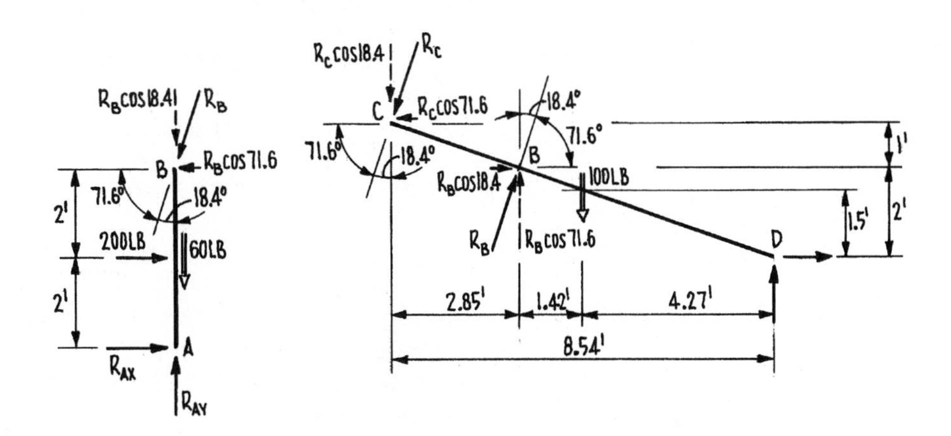

Examination of the two free bodies reveals that the free body of $\overline{AB}$ has only three unknowns while the free body of $\overline{CD}$ has four unknowns. Reactions on member $\overline{AB}$ will therefore be found first, then these results used to find the reactions on member $\overline{CD}$.

Moments are summed about point A, eliminating R_{Ax} and R_{Ay} from the resulting equation:

$$\Sigma M_A = 0; \quad (200)(2) + (60)(0) + R_B(\cos 18.4)(0) - R_B(\cos 71.6)(4) = 0$$
$$R_B = 317 \text{ lb}$$

Forces are summed vertically, using the solution for RB just found:

$$\Sigma F_y = 0; \quad R_{Ay} - (317)(\cos 18.4) - 60$$
$$R_{Ay} = 361 \text{ lb}$$

Forces are summed horizontally on member AB:

$$\Sigma F_x = 0; \quad R_{Ax} + 200 - (317)(\cos 71.6) = 0$$
$$R_{Ax} = -100 \text{ lb (to the left)}$$

The solution for RB found in this solution reduces the number of unknowns acting on member $\overline{CD}$ to three. An equilibrium solution is now possible.

Moments are summed about point D:

$$\Sigma M_D = 0; \quad -R_C(\cos 18.4)(8.54) - R_C(\cos 71.6)(3) + (317)(\cos 71.6)(2) + (317)(\cos 18.4)(5.69) - (100)(4.27) = 0$$

$$R_C = 142 \text{ lb}$$

Forces are summed vertically, using the value of R_C just found:

$$\Sigma F_y = 0; \quad -(142)(\cos 18.4) + (317)(\cos 18.4) - 100 + R_{Dy} = 0$$

$$R_{Dy} = -66 \text{ lb (downward)}$$

Forces are summed horizontally, using the values already found:

$$\Sigma F_x = 0; \quad -(142)(\cos 71.6) + (317)(\cos 71.6) + R_{Dx} = 0$$

$$R_{Dx} = -55 \text{ lb (to the left)}$$

One may wonder whether both of these members could be removed as a single free body, similar to the solution of Example 4-7. In this case, such a free body would include all five unknowns on a single free body; an equilibrium solution would not therefore be possible using this approach. Verification is left to the reader.

In the solution to Example 4-8, it should be noted that no attempt was made to use the slope lengths of member $\overline{CD}$, even though it may look simpler. With rare exceptions in the solution of problems in mechanics, it is much preferred to use a highly ordered solution, using x and y components for both forces and distances. The use of slope distances is not recommended, especially not for beginning students in mechanics.

Example 4-9

Reactions in a general force system in a plane.

Given: System of members and loads as shown.

To Find: Reactions at *A* and tension in the cable.

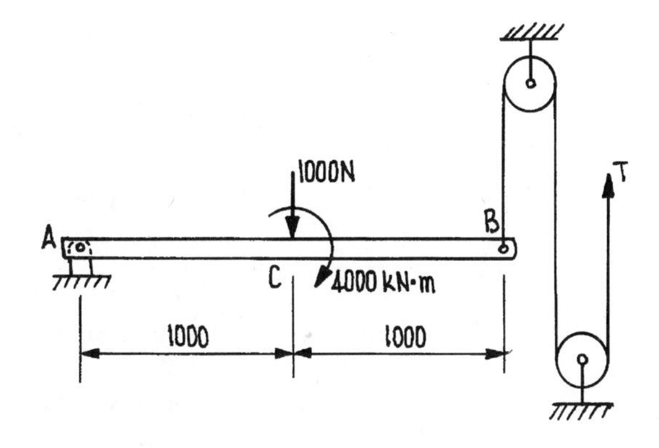

Solution: It is noted immediately that the tension in the cable will be equal to the reaction at *B*. In this arrangement of pulleys, there is no mechanical advantage; the pulleys serve only to change direction of the cable.

Member $\overline{AB}$ is removed as a free body. The moment of 4000 N·m is shown as N·mm for consistency of units.

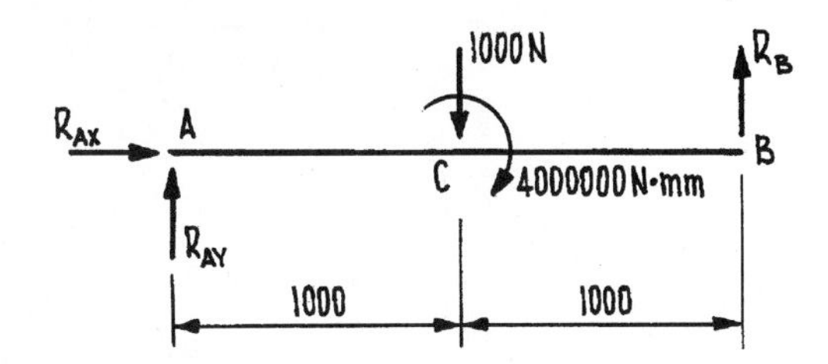

Moments are summed about *A*:

$$\Sigma M_A = 0; \quad (1000)(1000) + (4{,}000{,}000) - R_B(2000) = 0$$

$$R_B = 2500 \text{ N}$$

Moments are summed about *B*:

$$\Sigma M_B = 0; \quad (R_{Ax})(0) + (R_{Ay})(2000) - (1000)(1000) + (4{,}000{,}000) = 0$$

$$R_{Ay} = -1500 \text{ N (down)}$$

Forces are summed parallel to $\overline{AB}$:

$$\Sigma F_x = 0; \quad R_{Ax} = 0$$

Example 4-10

Reactions in a general force system in a plane.

Given: System of members as shown.

To Find: Reactions at *A*, *B* and *C*.

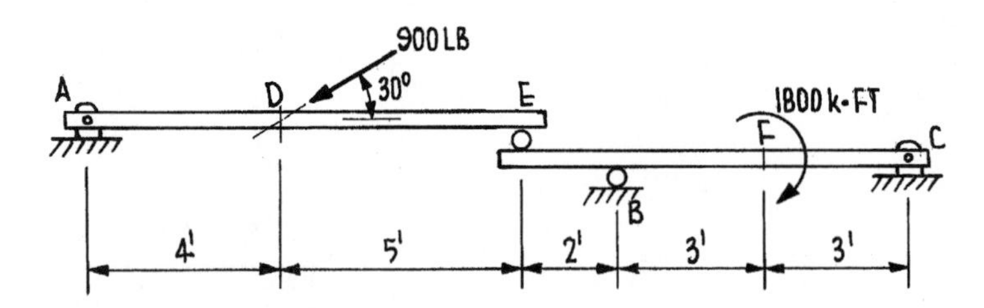

Solution: It is noted that there are a total of five reactions at *A*, *B* and *C*. An equilibrium solution of the overall system is therefore not possible. The system may, however, be susceptible to a piece-by-piece solution.

The free bodies of the two members are shown separately in the following sketch.

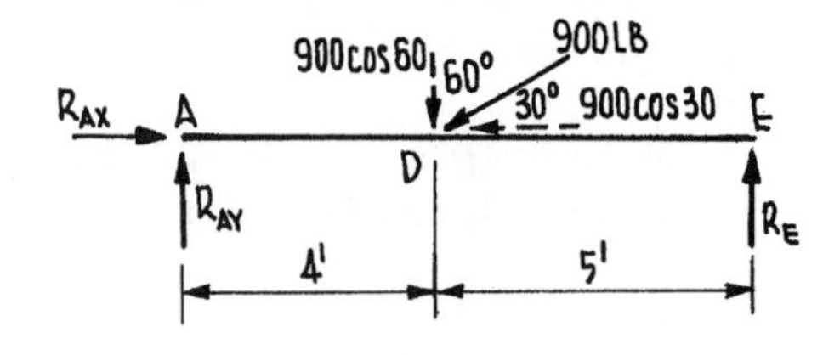

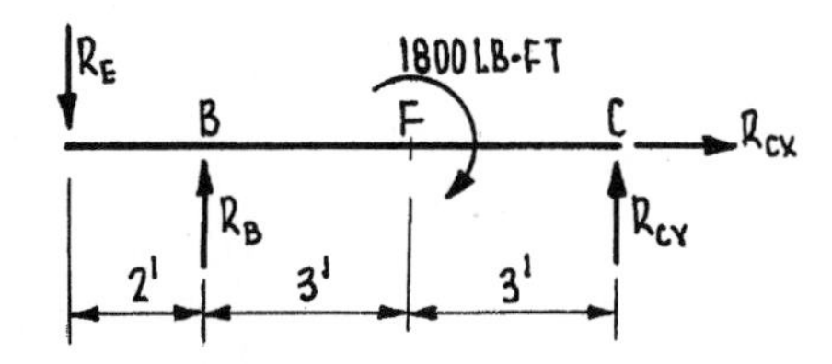

Again, note that the reaction at *E* "pushes" upward on member *AE* and downward on member *EC*. The forces are therefore shown in their correct directions on the free bodies.

It is observed that there are three unknown forces on the free body of member *AE* and that there are four unknowns on the free body of member *EC*. Reactions on member *AE* will therefore be found first, then they will be used to find the reactions on member *EC*.

Moments are summed about point *A*:

$$\Sigma M_A = 0; \quad (900)(\cos 60)(4) + (900)(\cos 30)(0) - R_E(9) = 0$$

$$R_E = 200 \text{ lb}$$

Moments are summed about point *E*:

$$\Sigma M_E = 0; \quad (R_{Ay})(9) + (R_{Ax})(0) - (900)(\cos 60)(5) + (900)(\cos 30)(0) = 0$$

$$R_{Ay} = 250 \text{ lb}$$

Forces are summed parallel to *AE*:

$$\Sigma F_x = 0; \quad (R_{Ax}) - (900)(\cos 30) = 0$$

$$R_{Ax} = 779 \text{ lb}$$

The value of R_E thus found reduces the number of unknowns on the free body of *EL* to three. An equilibrium solution is now possible for that free body.

Moments are summed about point *C*:

$$\Sigma M_C = 0; \quad -(200)(8) + (R_B)(6) + 1800 = 0$$

$$R_B = -33 \text{ lb (downward)}$$

Moments are summed about point *B*:

$$\Sigma M_B = 0; \quad -(200)(2) + (1800) - (R_{Cy})(6) + (R_{Cx})(0) = 0$$

$$R_{Cy} = 33 \text{ lb}$$

Forces are summed parallel to *BC*:

$$\Sigma F_x = 0; \quad R_{Cx} = 0$$

It should be observed from the results of Example 4-10 that some systems having several members may have an equilibrium solution. Each such system must be taken apart and carefully examined, however, before coming to a conclusion whether it does or does not have an equilibrium solution. This point is expanded further in Chapter 15.

4.4 Friction Forces

When two bodies are in contact, there will be a resistance if one tries to slide one body across the other. That resistance is called friction. Such a case is shown in the block of Figure 4-3 as it is being dragged across the supporting surface it rests on.

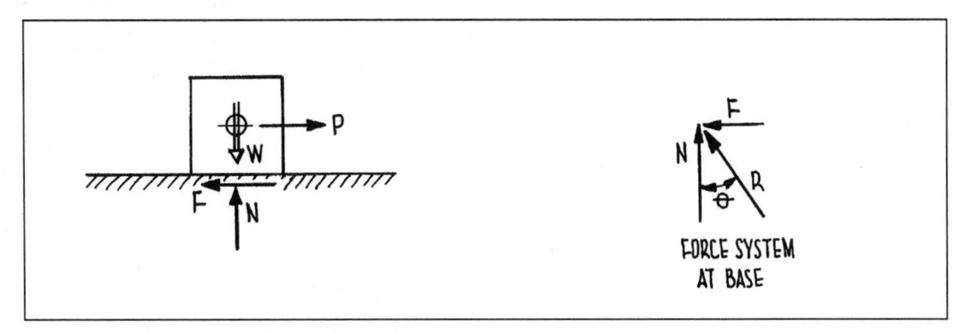

Figure 4-3 Friction forces.

If the force P in Figure 4-3 is small, there will be no motion. As the force P increases, the frictional resistance to motion will eventually be overcome and the block will start to move. The largest value that the friction force F can ever develop is the force that occurs *just as motion impends.*

The force in Figure 4-3 is normal to the contact surface. The relationship between the normal force N and the friction force F is shown in the sketch of the force system. The angle θ is called the *friction angle*, where:

$$F = N \tan \theta \tag{4-3}$$

The friction angle θ is rarely used. Rather, the value of $\tan \theta$ that occurs just as motion impends is denoted μ_s; it is called the *static coefficient of friction*:

$$F = \mu_s N \tag{4-4}$$

Note that frictional resistance depends only on contact forces, not on pressures. Consider, for example the three cases shown in Figure 4-4, where the same block is shown in three different attitudes. In one case the larger area is in contact with the surface, in the next case the smaller area is in contact, and in the third case the block has tilted up onto one edge.

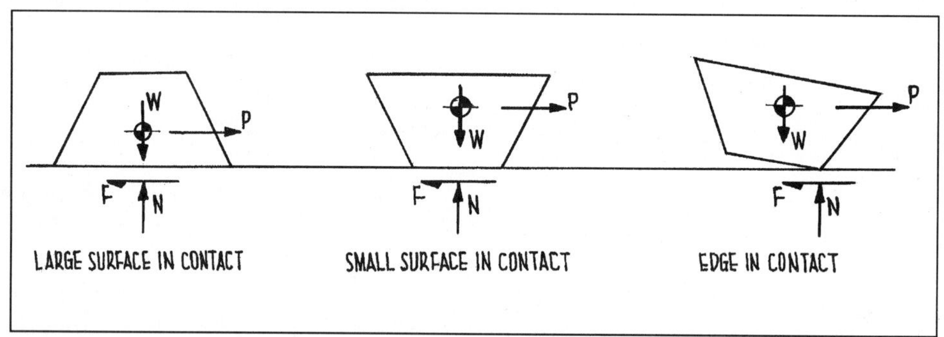

Figure 4-4 Contact areas in friction.

In all three cases shown in Figure 4-4, the friction force F that occurs *just as motion impends* will be the same. The coefficient of friction μ_s is a coefficient based only on contact forces, not on contact areas.

The value of the coefficient of friction varies widely, depending on the types of materials that are coming in contact with each other. Even then, the relative roughness of the two contact surfaces can seriously affect the coefficient of friction. Some average values for the coefficient of friction are given in Table 4-1 for some of the more common materials.

Table 4-1 Average values for the coefficient of friction.

Materials in contact	Static Friction μ_s	Kinetic Friction μ_k
Leather against wood	0.5	0.4
Wood against wood	0.5	0.4
Stone against wood	0.4	0.3
Metal against wood	0.5	0.4
Stone against stone	0.6	0.5
Leather against metal	0.4	0.3
Metal against metal	0.2	0.15
Masonry against soil	0.5	0.4
Rubber against metal	0.5	0.4
Rubber against concrete	0.7	0.5

It should be noted that two types of friction are included in Table 4-1. Static friction is the resisting force that exists before motion begins. Kinetic friction is the resisting force that occurs when motion is underway. The kinetic coefficient of friction μ_k is slightly smaller than the static coefficient of friction μ_s, indicating that is takes more force to start a body in motion than it does to maintain that motion.

Consider the block shown in Figure 4-5 being pulled across a contact surface. For all small values of the force P, the resisting friction force F will simply be equal to P; the system will be in equilibrium without any motion occurring. As the force P continues to increase, the resisting force F will also increase until it eventually exceeds its maximum value of $\mu_s N$, at which point motion will occur. At that instant, the force P can decrease until the friction force is at its maximum kinetic value, $\mu_k N$, and the velocity of motion will then remain constant as long as the force is maintained.

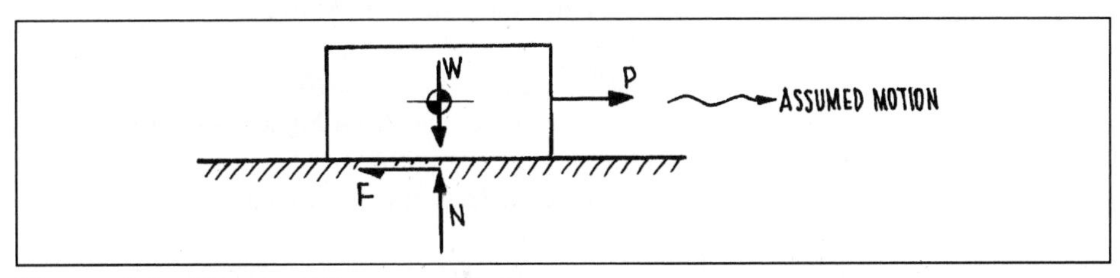

Figure 4-5 Frictional force equilibrium.

In a force system such as that of Figure 4-5, the direction of motion has been assumed to occur in the direction of the acting force P. *The direction of the friction force F always occurs in opposition to the direction of motion.* It is this feature that must be observed in solving for friction forces:

1) Show the free body with its applied forces.
2) Assume a direction of motion.
3) Show friction forces opposing the assumed motion.
4) Solve by applying the laws of equilibrium.

Some examples will illustrate the procedure.

Example 4-11

Frictional resistance to motion.

Given: Carton on an inclined surface. The end at B is to be raised until motion impends. $\mu_s = 0.35$.

To Find: Angle α when motion impends.

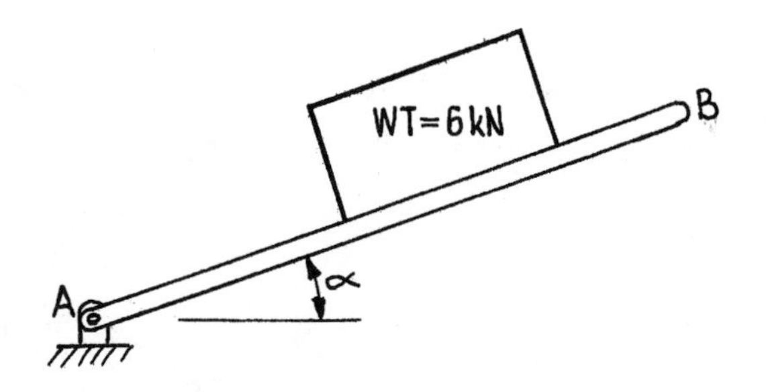

Solution: A free body of the carton is shown in the following sketch. The direction of motion is assumed to be downward to the left. The friction force F is shown opposing the motion. The normal force N is shown normal to the contact surface. The gravity force is shown vertical.

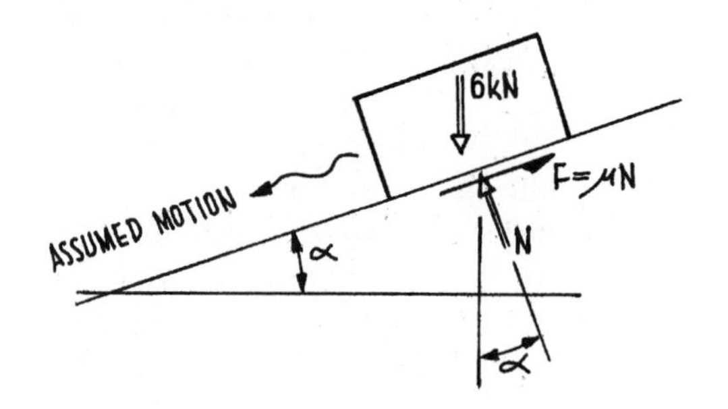

Forces are summed vertically:

$$\Sigma F_y = 0; \quad -6 + N\cos\alpha + F\sin\alpha = 0$$
$$-6 + N\cos\alpha + 0.35N\sin\alpha = 0$$

Forces are summed horizontally:

$$\Sigma F_x = 0; \quad -N\sin\alpha + F\cos\alpha = 0$$
$$-N\sin\alpha + 0.35\,N\cos\alpha = 0$$
$$0.35\cos\alpha = \sin\alpha$$
$$0.35 = \tan\alpha$$
$$\alpha = 19.29°$$

It is observed that the first statics equation ($\Sigma F_y = 0$) yielded nothing of interest. It could be used now, however, to find N if desired.

Note that the weight of the carton did not enter the solution for α. *All* objects on the surface having a coefficient of friction of 0.35 will start to slide when α = 19.29°, regardless what their weights are.

Example 4-12

Frictional resistance to motion.

Given: Carton on an inclined surface as shown. μ_s = 0.30.

To Find: 1) Force P required to prevent motion downward.
2) Force P required to cause motion upward.

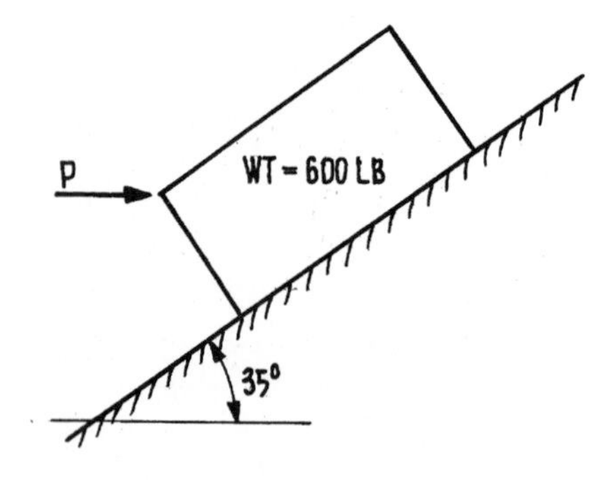

Solution: A free body of the carton is shown in the following sketch. The direction of impending motion is assumed to be down. The friction force F is shown opposing the impending motion. The normal force N is shown normal to the contact surface. The gravity force is shown vertical.

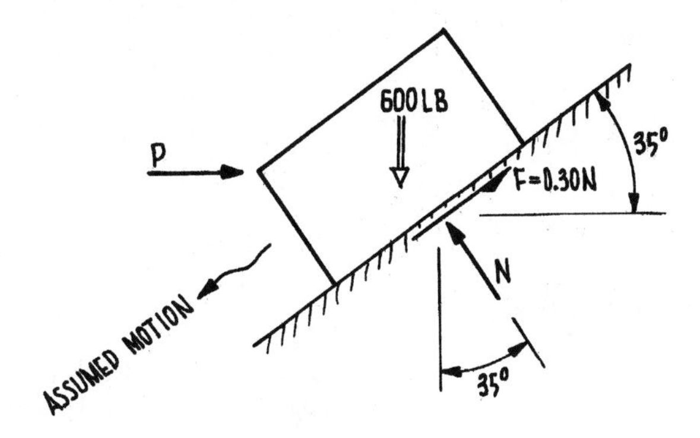

Forces are summed vertically:

$$\Sigma F_y = 0; \quad -600 + N\cos 35 + F\sin 35 = 0$$
$$-600 + N\cos 35 + 0.30\, N\sin 35 = 0$$
$$N = 605.31 \text{ lb}$$

Forces are summed horizontally:

$$\Sigma F_x = 0; \quad P - N\sin 35 + F\cos 35 = 0$$
$$P - N\sin 35 + 0.30\, N\cos 35 = 0$$

A force of P of 198.44 lb will prevent motion downward.

A second free body of the carton is shown in the following sketch for the second part of the problem. In this case the direction of impending motion is assumed upward. The friction force F is shown opposing the impending motion.

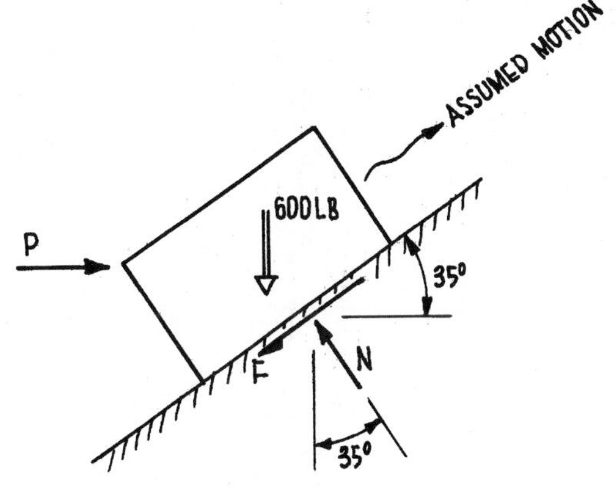

Forces are summed vertically:

$$\Sigma F_y = 0; \quad -600 + N\cos 35 - F\sin 35 = 0$$
$$-600 + N\cos 35 - 0.30\, N\sin 35 = 0$$
$$N = 927.24 \text{ lb}$$

Forces are summed horizontally:

$$\Sigma F_x = 0; \quad P - N\sin 35 - F\cos 35 = 0$$
$$P - N\sin 35 - 0.30\, N\cos 35 = 0$$
$$P = 759.71 \text{ lb}$$

A force P of 759.71 lb will cause motion to impend upward.

One may wonder at the size of a force P of 759.71 lb being required to cause motion of a 600 lb carton. It is observed, however, that the force P is pushing the carton into the contact surface, adding to the force N, which in turn increases the friction force. The force P would be applied more efficiently if it were applied parallel to the contact surface.

Example 4-13

Frictional resistance to motion.

Given: Arrangement of blocks as shown. Between the two blocks $\mu_s = 0.20$. At the lower surface, $\mu = 0.30$.

To Find: Force P required to cause motion of the lower block.

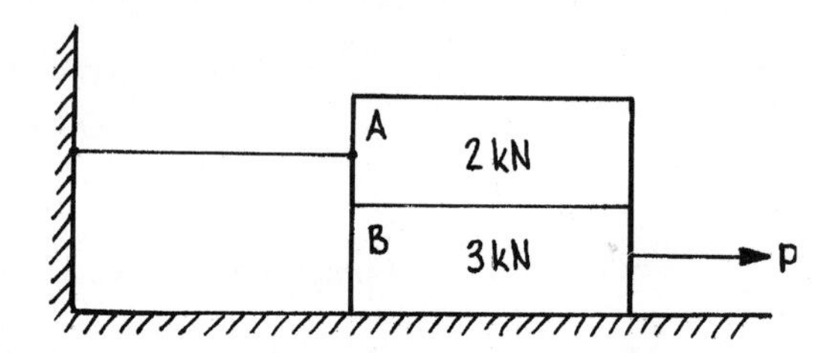

Solution: A free body of the lower block is shown in the following sketch. The direction of impending motion is assumed to be in the direction of P. Both friction forces are shown opposing the motion. The normal force from block A is the weight of the block, 2 kN. The normal force at the lower surface is the total weight of the two blocks, 5 kN.

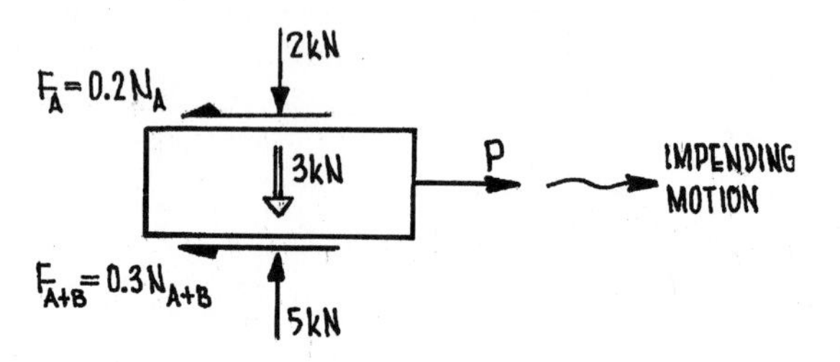

Forces are summed horizontally:

$$\Sigma F_x = 0; \quad -F_A + P - F_{A+B} = 0$$
$$-0.2(2) + P - 0.3(5) = 0$$
$$P = 1.9 \text{ kN}$$

A force P of 1.9 kN would cause motion to impend.

Example 4-14

Frictional resistance to motion.

Given: Block and weight arrangement as shown. $\mu_s = 0.40$, $\mu_k = 0.30$.

To Find: 1) Weight required to cause motion.
2) Weight required to maintain motion once it has started.

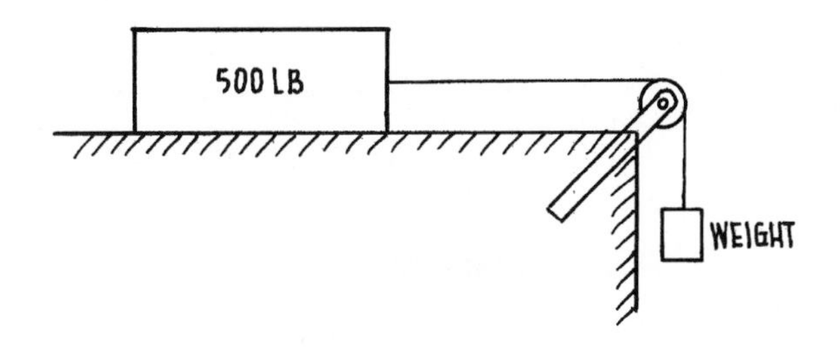

Solution: The force in the cable is assumed to be constant.

A free body of the block is shown in the following sketch. It is assumed that motion impends in the direction of *P*.

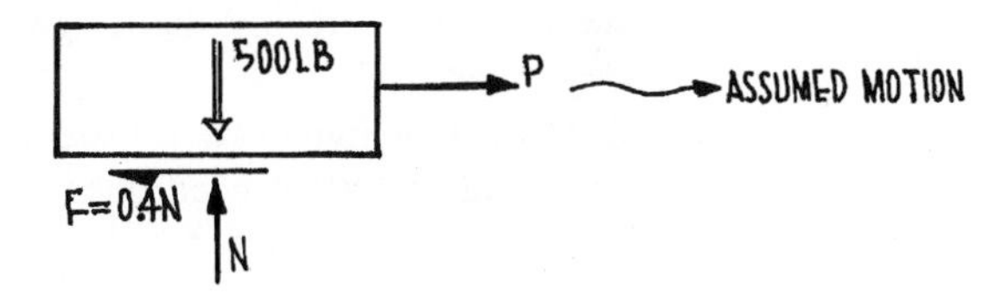

Forces are summed vertically:

$$\Sigma F_y = 0; \quad -500 + N = 0$$
$$N = 500 \text{ lb}$$

Forces are summed horizontally:

$$\Sigma F_x = 0 \quad -0.4N + P = 0$$
$$-0.4(500) + P = 0$$
$$P = 200 \text{ lb}$$

A weight of 200 lb will cause motion to impend.

A second free body is shown in the following sketch. In this case it is assumed that the body is in motion at a constant velocity. The direction of motion is assumed to be in the direction of the force *P*.

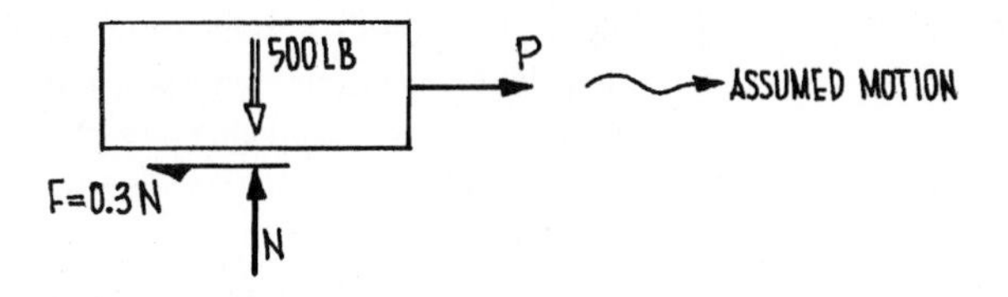

Forces are summed vertically:

$$\Sigma F_y = 0; \quad -500 + N = 0$$
$$N = 500 \text{ lb}$$

Forces are summed horizontally:

$$\Sigma F_x = 0; \quad -0.3N + P = 0$$
$$-0.3(500) + P = 0$$
$$P = 150 \text{ lb}$$

A weight of 150 lb will maintain motion once it has started.

Review Questions

1. Give an example of a concurrent force system that one might come across in daily activities.
2. Give an example of a parallel force system that one might come across in daily activities.
3. Given an example of a system of moments and couples that one might come across in daily activities.
4. How is it possible to use the weight of a rigid body as a single load through its centroid, when in reality, the weight of the body is a system of parallel forces acting on each particle?
5. Regardless how numerous a system of forces may be, the system may be composed into a resultant. What form does the resultant take?
6. When using the classical form of the mathematical laws of equilibrium, how many force equations are there?
7. When using the alternative form of the mathematical laws of equilibrium that utilizes two moment equations rather than one, in what direction are forces summed?
8. When it is desired to sum moments to eliminate two of the three unknowns in a free body, how is the moment center best chosen?
9. What is the relationship between the resultant of a force system and the reactions of that force system?
10. List the steps used to find the resultant of a force system, including its magnitude, direction and the position of its line of action.
11. Given the x and y components of the resultant of a force system, what are two ways to find the magnitude and direction (angle or rise-run) of the resultant?
12. In finding the resultant of a force system, it is advisable to show all moments as equivalent couples. Why?
13. What is the maximum number of unknowns that can be found in an equilibrium solution?
14. Why is it so essential to show all reactions on a free body in their correct directions (when known) before resolving them into their x and y components?
15. Does a compression force in a strut push or pull on its end supports?
16. In finding reactions on a free body due to applied moments or couples, what is the effect of the point of application (moment center) of the applied moment or couple?
17. In free body solutions, why is it preferable always to use x and y components rather than angled forces and distances?
18. Sketch a cable-and-pulley system having two pulley wheels that produces a mechanical advantage of 4.
19. Sketch a cable-and-pulley system having two pulley wheels that produces no mechanical advantage at all. (Mechanical advantage is 1.)
20. Sketch a free body of Example 4-8 that includes both members in the single free body, showing that the total number of unknowns on the free body is 5.

CHAPTER

5

GENERAL SYSTEMS OF FORCES IN SPACE

Most of the problems in mechanics that relate to building construction can be reduced to two-dimensional systems, that is, forces and moments in a plane. There are cases, however, when the third dimension must be considered. Such three dimensional cases are the topic of this chapter.

5.1 Three Dimensional Systems

All of the principles, laws, procedures and terminology presented in earlier chapters will extend into three dimensions with little change. The major difference, of course, is that the Cartesian coordinate system having *x* and *y* directions now becomes a Cartesian coordinate system having *x*, *y* and *z* directions. Such a coordinate system is shown in Figure 5-1, where the direction *z* is normal to the plane of the paper.

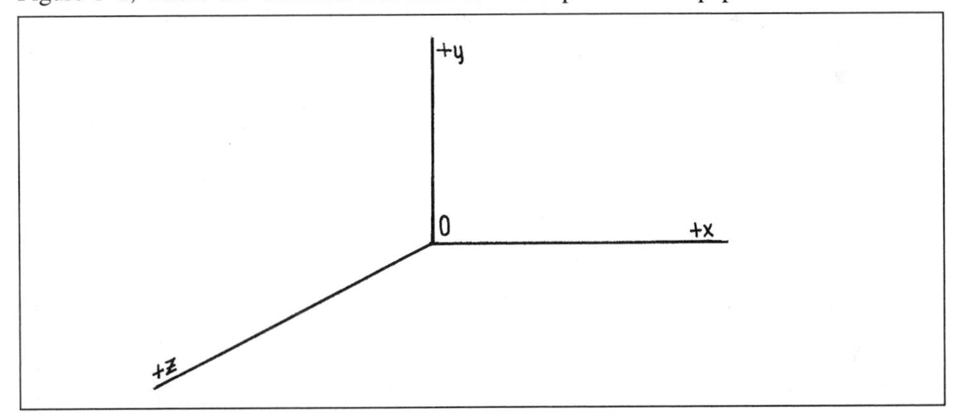

Figure 5-1 Cartesian coordinates in three dimensions.

It should be noted immediately that the *xy* plane remains the vertical plane, exactly as it was used in previous chapters. All the sketches used earlier would simply appear unchanged on that *xy* plane. An axis of rotation for moments would still be an axis perpendicular to the plane of the paper, but that direction can now be called the zz direction.

The use of the *xy* plane as the vertical plane is at variance with the practice in classical mathematics; in classical mathematics, the *xz* plane (rather than the *xy* plane) is taken as the vertical plane. Over the years, those who work in engineering mechanics on a daily basis have found that it is more natural to leave the *xy* plane as the vertical plane. The third dimension, given by the xx axis, can then be added for three dimensional problems without disturbing the two dimensional visualization.

5.2 Components of Forces and Moments in Space

A force may be shown in three dimensions much as it is shown in two dimensions; there is simply one more component. The three components of a force are shown in Figure 5-2, along with the direction angles α, β, and γ. Note that the direction angles are now in three dimensional space, as the angles between the force F and its three components; they do not lie in one of the coordinate planes xy, xz or yz.

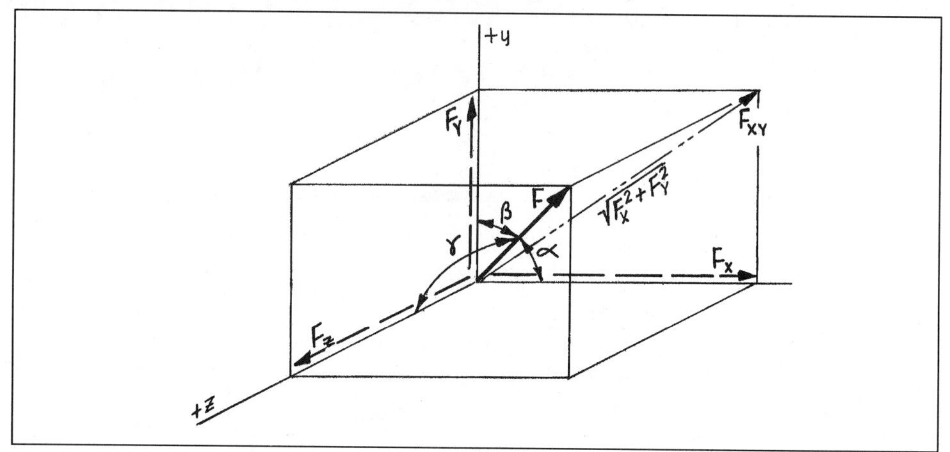

Figure 5-2 Components of a force in space.

The resultant of components F_x and F_y is shown in phantom on Figure 5-2 as force component F_{xy}, found in the usual way by using the Pythagorean theorem in a plane. This component, when added to the F_z component (again using the Pythagorean theorem) becomes the force F:

$$F^2 = F_{xy}^{\ 2} + F_z^{\ 2}$$

$$F^2 = F_x^{\ 2} + F_y^{\ 2} + F_z^{\ 2}$$

$$F = \sqrt{F_x^2 + F_y^2 + F_z^2} \tag{5-1}$$

The form of Eq. (5-1) will be referenced in later discussions as the Pythagorean theorem in space.

The three direction cosines for the force F may be found in the usual way:

$$\cos \alpha_F = F_x/F$$
$$\cos \beta_F = F_y/F \tag{5-2a,b,c}$$
$$\cos \gamma_F = F_z/F$$

Equations (5-2) may be solved for F_x, F_y and F_z. When these values are substituted into the Pythagorean theorem in space, Eq.(5-1), the result is a very basic relationship between the three direction cosines:

$$1 = \cos^2\alpha_F + \cos^2\beta_F + \cos^2\gamma_F \tag{5-3}$$

Equation (5-3) will also be a useful relationship in later discussions.

On occasion, it can become necessary to find the angle between two concurrent forces or two intersecting lines in space. Such a case is shown in Figure 5-3. The angle θ

is the angle between the two intersection lines OA and OB. Stated another way, the two concurrent forces OA and OB define a plane and the angle θ lies in that plane.

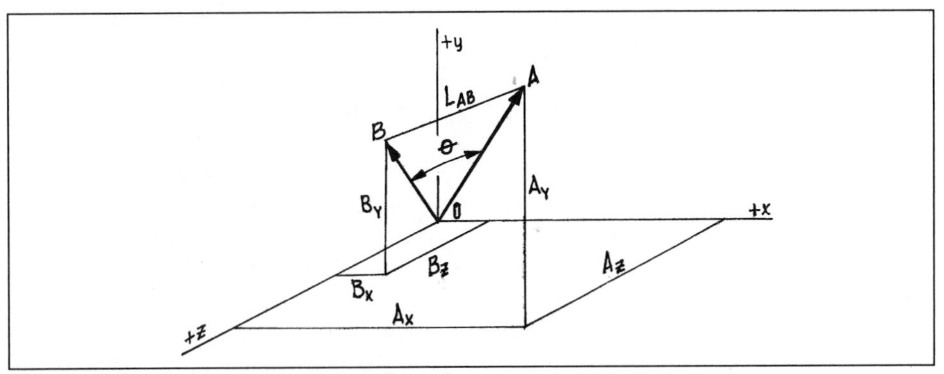

Figure 5-3 Angle between two lines in space.

The law of cosines will apply in the plane OAB formed by the two lines, where L_{OA}, L_{OB} and L_{AB} are the lengths of the lines:

$$L_{AB}{}^2 = L_{OA}{}^2 + L_{OB}{}^2 - 2L_{OA}L_{OB}\cos\theta \tag{5-4}$$

The length L_{OA}, L_{OB} and L_{AB} are found by the Pythagorean theorem in space:

$$\begin{aligned} L_{OA}{}^2 &= A_x^2 + A_y^2 + A_z^2 \\ L_{OB}{}^2 &= B_x^2 + B_y^2 + B_z^2 \\ L_{AB}{}^2 &= (A_x - B_x)^2 + (A_y - B_y)^2 + (A_z - B_z)^2 \end{aligned} \tag{5-5a,b,c}$$

Equations (5-5) are substituted into Eq.(5-4) to find:

$$L_{OA}L_{OB}\cos\theta = A_xB_x + A_yB_y + A_zB_z \tag{5-6}$$

Eq.(5-6) is now divided by $L_{OA}\,L_{OB}$, noting that the direction cosines are given by the result, hence:

$$\cos\theta = \cos\alpha_{OA}\cos\alpha_{OB} + \cos\beta_{OA}\cos\beta_{OB} + \cos\gamma_{OA}\cos\gamma_{OB} \tag{5-7}$$

Eq.(5-7) will be referenced in later discussions as the *law of cosines in space*.

Note that A_x, A_y and A_z must be given their proper algebraic signs when calculating $\cos\alpha_{OA}$, $\cos\beta_{OA}$ and $\cos\gamma_{OA}$. Similarly, B_x, B_y and B_z must be given their proper algebraic signs when calculating $\cos\alpha_{OB}$, $\cos\beta_{OB}$ and $\cos\gamma_{OB}$.

Defining or identifying a force in space is considerably more bulky in three dimensions than it was in two dimensions. Consider, for example, the force of 1000 N shown in Figure 5-4. In the sketch, the force is defined completely, to include its direction angles as well as its x, y and z components.

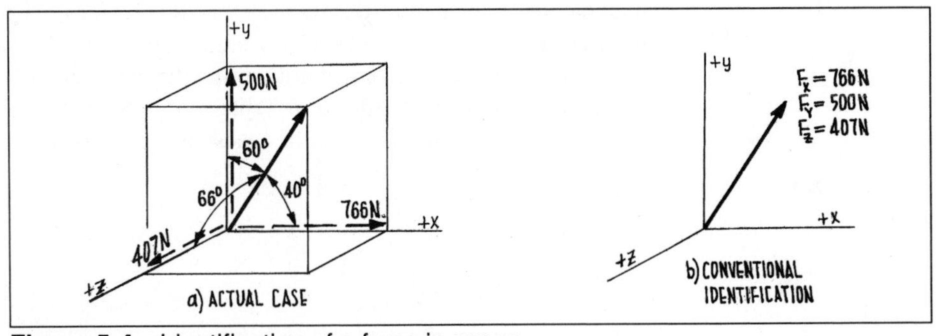

Figure 5-4 Identification of a force in space.

In two dimensions, it was common practice to define a force by stating its magnitude and one of its direction angles, usually the angle α to the x axis. If this practice is followed in three dimensions, it becomes necessary to give all three direction angles. The 1000 N force of Figure 5-4 would then be defined in three dimensions as:

$$F = 1000\text{ N.},\ \alpha_F = 40^\circ,\ \beta_F = 60^\circ,\ \gamma_F = 66^\circ$$

Far more common, a force in three dimensions may also be defined as shown in Figure 5-4b simply by stating its three components:

$$F_x = 766\text{ N.},\ F_y = 500\text{ N.},\ F_z = 407\text{ N.}$$

It is this method of identifying a force, by stating its components, that will be used predominantly in succeeding discussions. In this method, the component forces which will be needed for computations are always immediately available.

The concept of equilibrium of a free body applies equally as well in three dimensions as it does in two dimensions. Sketching of a free body remains the same, as does the identification of reactions that will act on the free body. The only change is that more forces and moments enter the problem from that third direction; these forces and moments must be considered in the equilibrium conditions.

A body in space is free to move in six directions: it may translate in any one of the x, y or z directions or it may rotate about any one of the x-x, y-y or z-z axes. If the body is to be in equilibrium, there can be no motion in any of these six directions. Stated verbally, the conditions of static equilibrium for a free body in three dimensions are therefore:

1. There can be no translation of the free body in the x-x direction.
2. There can be no translation of the free body in the y-y direction.
3. There can be no translation of the free body in the z-z direction.
4. There can be no rotations of the free body about any axis in the x-x direction.
5. There can be no rotations of the free body about any axis in the y-y direction.
6. There can be no rotations of the free body about any axis in the z-z direction.

It is immediately apparent that the three conditions of equilibrium in two dimensions have jumped to six conditions when the third dimension was added. The problem thus becomes significantly more complex.

The mathematical laws of equilibrium follow the six conditions (the *six degrees of freedom*) just stated:

$$\Sigma F_x = 0 \quad \Sigma F_y = 0 \quad \Sigma F_z = 0$$
$$\Sigma M_{xx} = 0 \quad \Sigma M_{yy} = 0 \quad \Sigma M_{zz} = 0 \qquad \text{(5-8a thru f)}$$

With these six equations, there can be as many as six unknowns in a three dimensional equilibrium solution. If there are more than six unknowns, then an equilibrium solution is not possible. (If more than six unknowns should occur, there must be additional equations developed from conditions other than statics, such as deformation relationships; as noted earlier, such problems are termed *statically indeterminate* problems.)

Within the six equations of equilibrium in three dimensions, there are four special cases. These cases are tabulated in Table 5-1. It is well to become familiar with these special cases; they can save a lot of headscratching when the mathematics of a solution just won't seem to work out.

Table 5-1 Special cases of equilibrium in space.

	Typical System	Condition of Triviality*	Remaining Nontrivial Equations
1) Forces concurrent at a point.		Sum of moments about any axis yields trivial solution.	$\Sigma F_x = 0$ $\Sigma F_y = 0$ $\Sigma F_z = 0$
2) Parallel system of forces in one direction only.	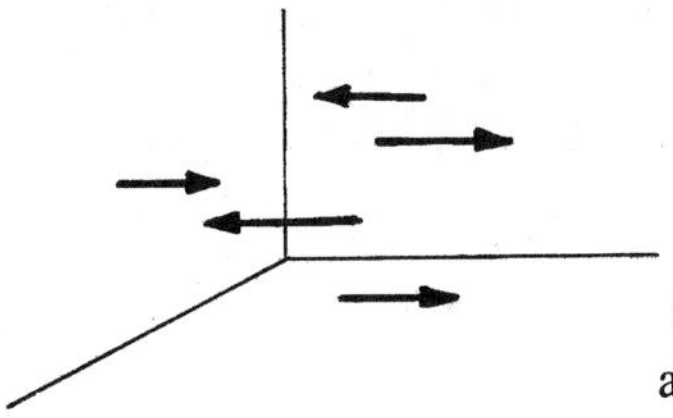	Sum of forces in other two directions yields trivial solution. Sum of moments about any parallel axis (*xx*) yields trivial solution.	$\Sigma F_x = 0$ $\Sigma M_{yy} = 0$ $\Sigma M_{zz} = 0$
3) Forces concurrent along a line.	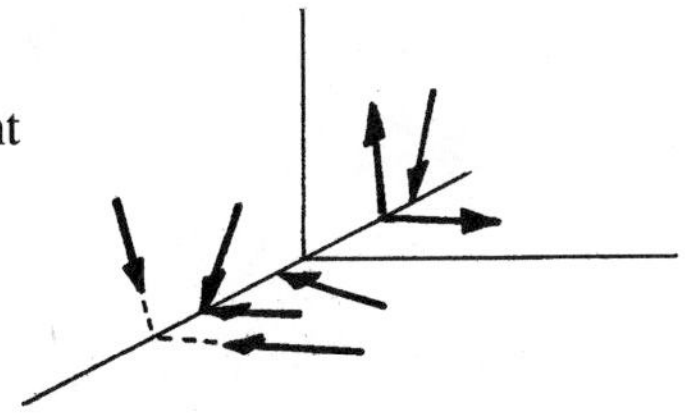	Sum of moments about any axis parallel to the axis of concurrency (*zz*) yields trivial solution.	$\Sigma F_x = 0$ $\Sigma M_{xx} = 0$ $\Sigma F_y = 0$ $\Sigma M_{yy} = 0$ $\Sigma F_z = 0$
4) General system of forces in 3 dimensions.	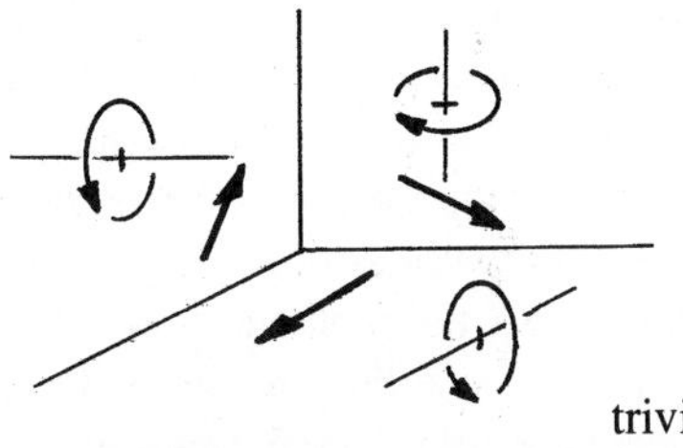	All six equations of equilibrium must be satisfied; no trivial solutions.	$\Sigma F_x = 0$ $\Sigma M_{xx} = 0$ $\Sigma F_y = 0$ $\Sigma M_{yy} = 0$ $\Sigma F_z = 0$ $\Sigma M_{zz} = 0$

*A trivial solution is one which ends up as an identity or as 0 = 0.

Case 1 in Table 5-1 was encountered earlier in two dimensional solutions. In that case, the solution became a *force equilibrium* solution having only two equations, $\Sigma F_x = 0$ and $\Sigma F_y = 0$.

Case 2 has already been encountered in the solutions for the centroid of a plane figure. One can readily visualize that the sum of all nonparallel forces is trivial and that the sum of moments about any axis parallel to the forces is trivial.

Case 3 is not possible in two dimensions but occurs frequently in three dimensions. The sum of moments about any axis parallel to the axis of concurrency will yield a trivial solution.

Case 4 is the general case, for which all six equations of equilibrium are valid and which must be satisfied.

On the subject of sketches of three dimensional systems, the sketches of free bodies in three dimensions, along with their forces and moments in six directions, can often be difficult to draw. Of particular difficulty is the sketching of moments such that their direction and axis of rotation is readily visualized. In two dimensional free bodies, the sketching of moments was not a problem; in three dimensions it requires a special notation.

It has been found that the straight-line axis of rotation of a moment can be used to define a moment rather than trying to use some curved arrow depicting the moment itself. Further, all the laws of equilibrium, the direction cosines and algebraic sums previously developed can be applied to this axis of rotation the same as they apply to the actual moment. It remains only to find some means to denote the direction of rotation when one uses this simplified bookkeeping method for handling moments.

Consider the axis of rotation *OA* shown in Figure 5-5. The moment *M* causes rotation about this axis. The double arrowhead denotes that this line is the axis of rotation for a moment; it is not a force. The double arrowhead serves also to denote the direction of rotation.

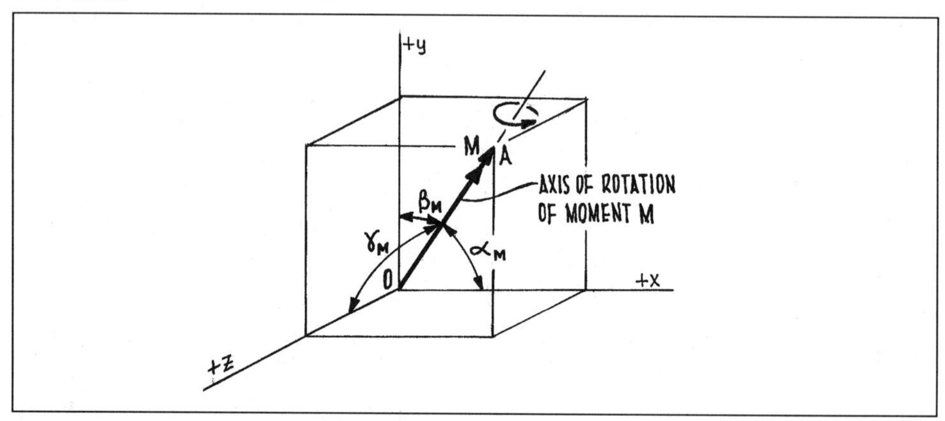

Figure 5-5 Moment vector in space.

The direction of rotation of the moment shown in Figure 5-5 is readily visualized by using the *right hand rule*. Imagine wrapping the fingers of one's right hand about the axis of rotation *OA*, with the thumb extended and pointing in the direction of the double arrowhead. The curled fingers of the right hand will then point in the direction of rotation.

It was seen earlier that a force may be assumed to act anywhere along its line of action. In direct analogy, a moment may be assumed to act anywhere along its axis of rotation. A moment's reflection will affirm that if one considers the axis of rotation to be a weightless line, the position of the moment along that line will have no effect on reactions.

A moment in space can of course have components in all three directions, that is, a single moment such as that of Figure 5-5 can cause some amount of rotation about an *x-x* axis, some amount of rotation about a *y-y* axis and some amount of rotation about a *z-z* axis. Such components of a moment are shown in Figure 5-6, along with their axes of rotation.

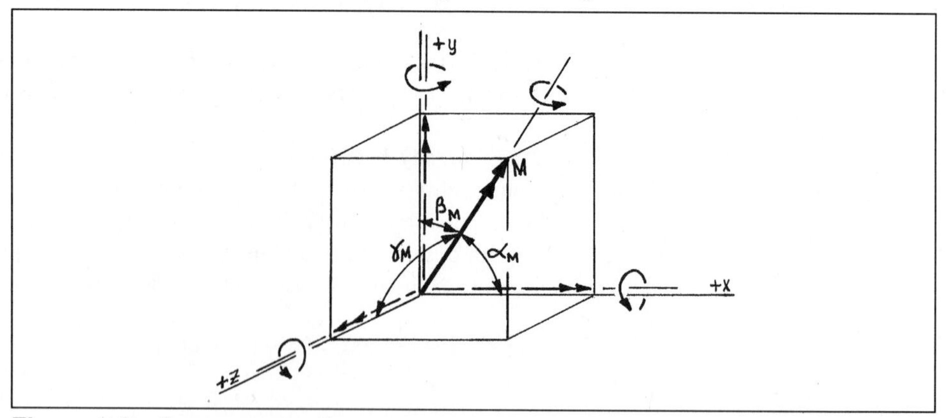

Figure 5-6 Components of a moment.

Now imagine the axis of rotation of the moment M in Figure 5-6 to be redirected along the xx axis, such that rotations will occur entirely about the x-x axis, that is, $\alpha_M = 0$, $\beta_M = 90°$ and $\gamma_M = 90°$. For this orientation of M, the direction cosines to the axis of rotation reveals that:

$$M_{xx} = M\cos\alpha_M = M$$
$$M_{yy} = M\cos\beta_M = 0 \qquad (5\text{-}9a,b,c)$$
$$M_{zz} = M\cos\gamma_M = 0$$

The result thus demonstrates that the direction cosines taken to the axis of rotation will indeed produce the correct direction for the components.

Identification of a moment in space can thus be given quite similarly to that of a force, by stating its three components. The 559 k·ft. moment of Figure 5-7, for example, has components about three axes as shown. The magnitudes of those three components about the x, y and z axes completely define the moment, as shown in Figure 5-7b.

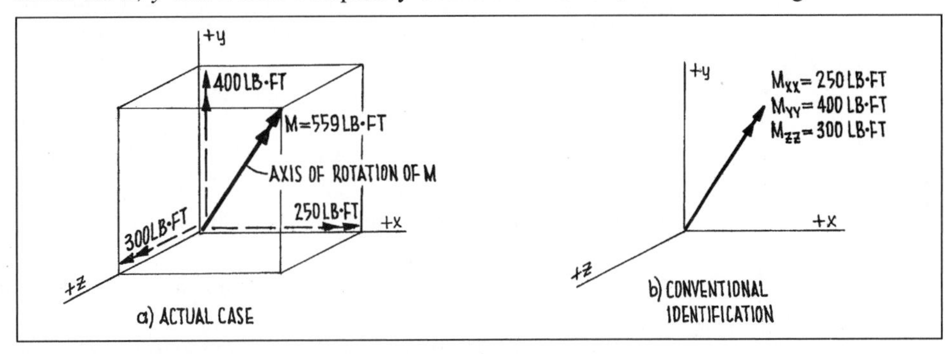

Figure 5-7 Identification of a moment in space.

The moment of Figure 5-7 can therefore be identified completely as:

$$M_{xx} = 250 \text{ lb·ft}, \; M_{yy} = 400 \text{ lb·ft}, \; M_{zz} = 300 \text{ lb·ft}$$

From these values, the magnitude of 559 lb·ft for the moment can be found, if needed, by the Pythagorean theorem in space. Further, its direction cosines and direction angles can be found, if needed, by definition:

$$\cos\alpha_M = 250/559 = 0.447; \; \alpha_M = 63.4°$$
$$\cos\beta_M = 400/559 = 0.716; \; \beta_M = 44.3°$$
$$\cos\gamma_M = 300/559 = 0.537; \; \gamma_M = 57.5°$$

The moment has thus been completely defined simply by giving the three components of its line of action. This method of defining a moment in space will be used throughout succeeding discussions.

With regard to algebraic signs for moments, recall from earlier discussions that a moment cannot have a negative magnitude. A negative sign indicates only that the algebraic direction of the moment is in its negative sense. It is a useful feature of the Pythagorean theorem that negative components, when squared, will always produce a positive resultant.

The x, y and z components of a moment, however, can have algebraically positive or negative directions. Their algebraic sign again follows the right-hand rule: the fingers of the right hand are wrapped around the x, y and z axis of rotation with the extended thumb pointing in the positive x, y or z direction; the curled fingers then point in the direction of positive rotation.

A moment in three dimensions can also be produced by a force acting about an axis. Consider, for example, the force F and its point of application A relative to the axis of rotation BB' as shown in Figure 5-8. The axis BB' is taken in this example to be parallel to the z-z coordinate axis.

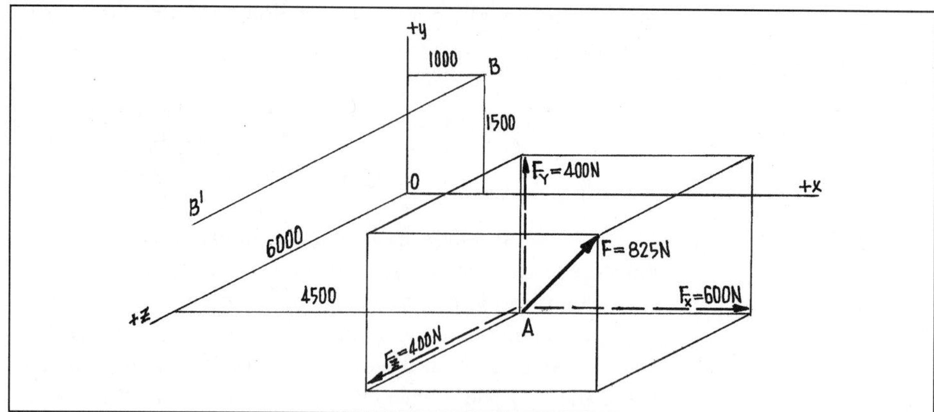

Figure 5-8 Moment of a force about an axis in space.

The moment of the component F_x about the axis BB' is:

$$M_1 = 600(1500) = +90{,}000 \text{ N}\cdot\text{mm}$$

The moment of the component F_y about the axis BB' is:

$$M_2 = 400(4500 - 1000) = +1{,}400{,}000 \text{ N}\cdot\text{mm}$$

The moment of the component F_z about the axis BB' is zero, since the force is parallel to the axis:

$$M_3 = 0$$

The moment of the force F about any axis of rotation is, by Varignon's theorem, the sum of the moments of the components about that axis:

$$M_{BB} = +90{,}000 + 1{,}400{,}000 + 0 = 2{,}300{,}000 \text{ N}\cdot\text{mm}$$

(Direction will be given by the right-hand rule.)

On occasion, one may wish to know the component of a moment along some axis of rotation other than the usual x, y and z axes. Such a case is shown in Figure 5-9. In that figure, a moment occurs along axis OA, and it is desired to know the component of that moment, M_{OB}, along some other axis of rotation, such as axis OB.

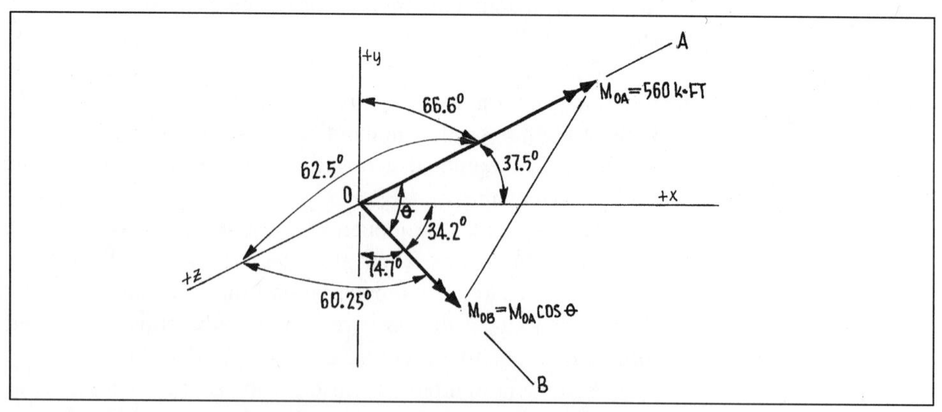

Figure 5-9 Projection of moment onto another axis of rotation.

It is observed that the axes of rotation *OA* and *OB* form a plane, and that the angle between these axes of rotation in that plane is the angle θ, as shown in the sketch. This angle θ is seen to be the direction angle between the axis *OA* and the axis *OB*. The cosine of this angle is the direction cosine between *OA* and *OB*; the moment M_{OB} is then given by:

$$M_{OB} = M_{OA} \cos\theta$$

The angle θ is found from the law of cosines in space, as given by Eq. (5-7):

$$\begin{aligned}\cos\theta &= \cos\alpha_{OA}\cos\alpha_{OB} + \cos\beta_{OA}\cos\beta_{OB} + \cos\gamma_{OA}\cos\gamma_{OB} \\ &= \cos 37.5 \cos 34.2 + \cos 66.6 \cos 105.3 + \cos 62.5 \cos 60.25 \\ \theta &= 32.05^\circ\end{aligned}$$

The component of M_{OA} that occurs along the axis *OB* is then:

$$M_{OB} = M_{OA} \cos\theta = 560(0.7804) = 437 \text{ k·ft.}$$

It should be noted that the other component of M_{OA} will lie along an axis of rotation perpendicular to *OB*; this axis also lies in the same plane as the axes *OA* and *OB*.

Up to this point, all of the foregoing discussions in this chapter have had to do with bookkeeping chores. Now that such matters have been addressed, problems in three dimensional mechanics can be undertaken.

5.3 Resultant of a General Force System in Space

As in two dimensions, a system of forces and moments in three dimensions will have a resultant. That resultant may be a force or it may be a moment. Finding a resultant in three dimensions follows the same procedures as in two dimensions.

A system of concurrent forces is shown in Figure 5-10, defined by their components in three directions.

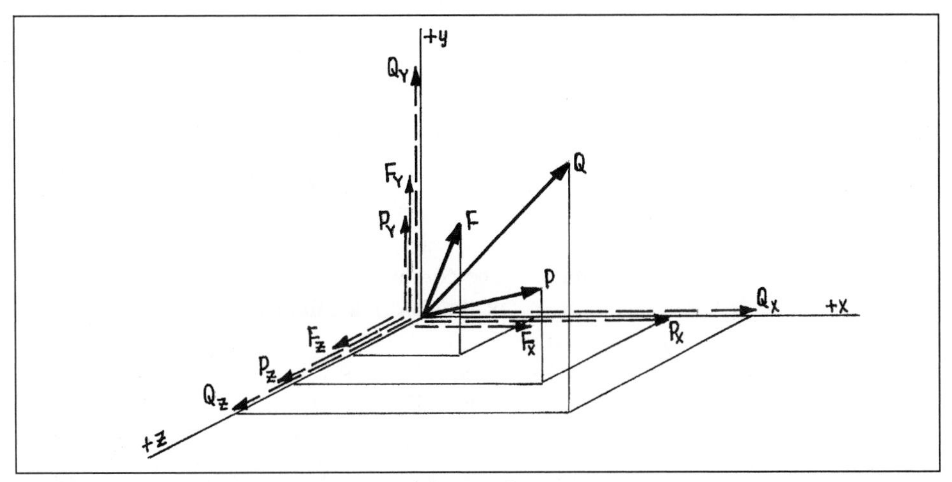

Figure 5-10 System of concurrent forces in space.

The resultant of this concurrent system of forces is found quite simply by adding the *x*, *y* and *z* components of these forces algebraically:

$$\begin{aligned}R_x &= F_x + P_x + Q_x \\ R_y &= F_y + P_y + Q_y \\ R_z &= F_z + P_z + Q_z\end{aligned} \qquad (5\text{-}10)$$

The magnitude of the resultant *R* can be found, if needed, by application of the Pythagorean theorem in space:

$$R = \sqrt{R_x^2 + R_y^2 + R_z^2} \tag{5-11}$$

The direction cosines and direction angles of the resultant may be found, if needed, by the definition of direction cosines:

$$\begin{aligned} \cos\alpha_R &= R_x/R \\ \cos\beta_R &= R_y/R \\ \cos\gamma_R &= R_z/R \end{aligned} \tag{5-12}$$

An example will illustrate the procedures for finding the resultant of concurrent force systems in space.

Example 5-1

Resultant of concurrent force systems in space.

Given: System of four concurrent forces in space.

To Find: Magnitude, direction and line of action of the resultant force.

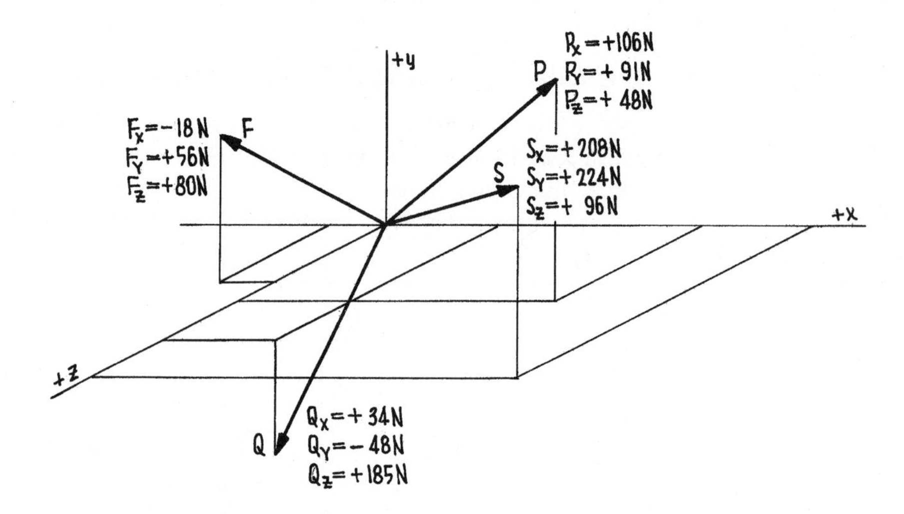

Solution: The components of the resultant are found by summing the components of the forces algebraically:

$$\begin{aligned} R_x &= F_x + P_x + Q_x + S_x = -18 + 106 + 208 + 34 = 330\text{N} \\ R_y &= F_y + P_y + Q_y + S_y = +56 + 91 - 48 + 224 = 323\text{N} \\ R_z &= F_z + P_z + Q_z + S_z = +80 + 48 + 185 + 96 = 409\text{N} \end{aligned}$$

The magnitude of the resultant is found from the Pythagorean theorem in space:

$$R = \sqrt{R_x^2 + R_y^2 + R_z^2} = \sqrt{330^2 + 323^2 + 409^2}$$
$$= 617 \text{ N.}$$

The direction cosines and direction angles are found by their definitions:

$$\cos\alpha_R = R_x/R = 330/617 = 0.535; \quad \alpha_R = 57.7^\circ$$
$$\cos\beta_R = R_y/R = 323/617 = 0.524; \quad \beta_R = 58.4^\circ$$
$$\cos\gamma_R = R_z/R = 409/617 = 0.663; \quad \gamma_R = 48..5^\circ$$

Since all three components of the resultant are positive, the resultant force lies in the near octant as shown.

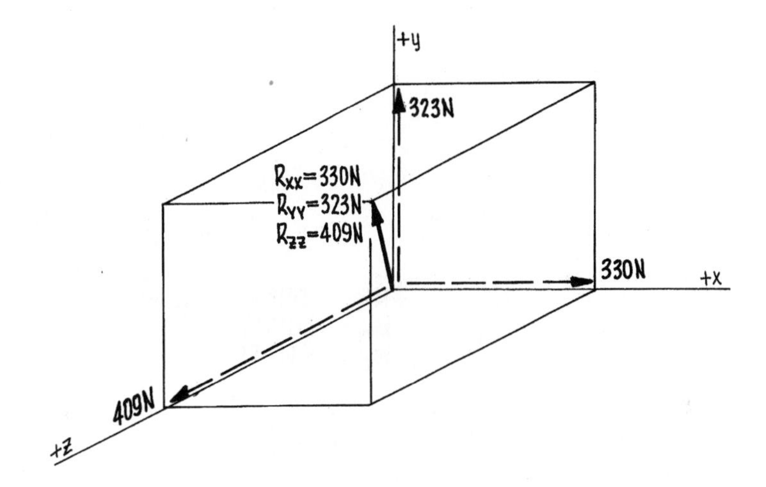

Moments having concurrent axes of rotation can be combined into their resultants in much the same way that forces are combined. An example will illustrate the procedure.

Example 5-2

Resultant of moment systems in space.

Given: Three moments as shown, having concurrent axes of rotation.

To Find: Resultant of the moment system.

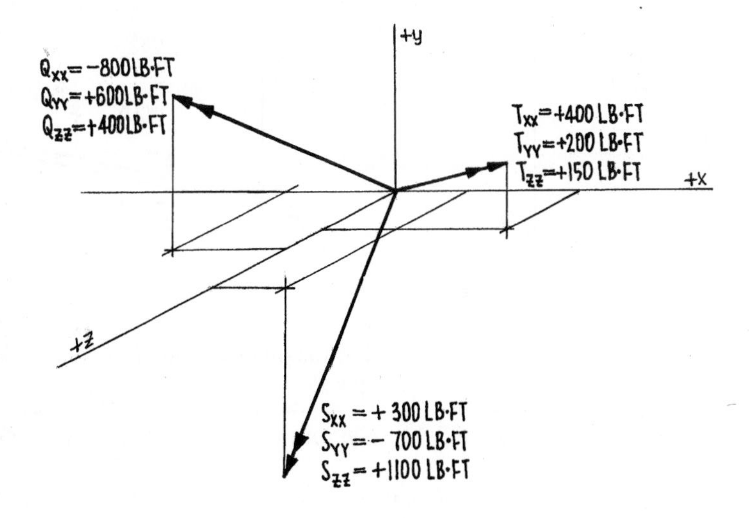

Solution: The components of the resultant axis of rotation are found by summing the component moments algebraically:

$$M_{xx} = Q_{xx} + S_{xx} + T_{xx} = -800 + 300 + 400 = -100 \text{ lb·ft}$$
$$M_{yy} = Q_{yy} + S_{yy} + T_{yy} = +600 - 700 + 200 = +100 \text{ lb·ft}$$
$$M_{zz} = Q_{zz} + S_{zz} + T_{zz} = +400 + 1100 + 150 = +1650 \text{ lb·ft}$$

The resultant moment is shown in the following sketch.

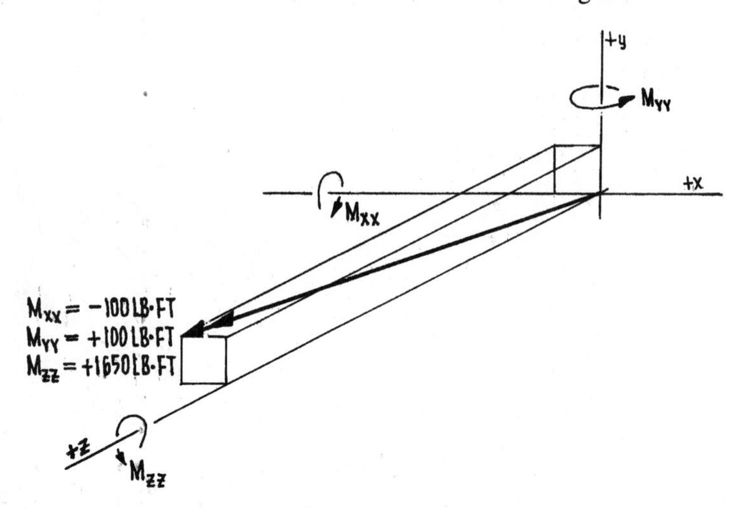

Systems of parallel forces in space will also have a resultant. In fact, a moment's reflection will affirm that finding the location of a centroid of a plane area (discussed in Chapter 3) was actually a problem in parallel forces in three dimensions rather than two dimensions.

All problems of finding the resultant of a system of parallel forces in space will eventually simplify into a form quite similar to that of finding a centroid. Consider, for example, the system of parallel forces shown in Figure 5-11. The forces have a continuously varying level for their point of application to the body.

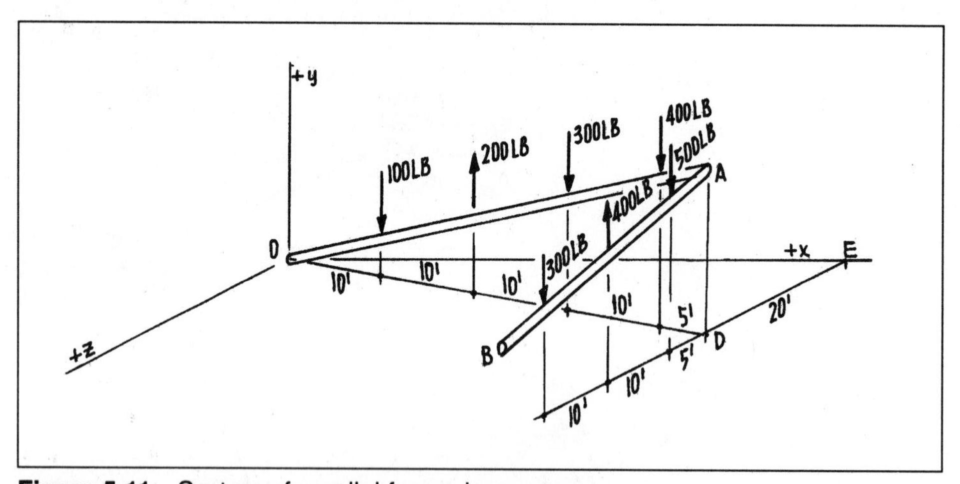

Figure 5-11 System of parallel forces in space.

Recalling that a force may be assumed to act anywhere along its line of action, one may show the system of parallel forces given in Figure 5-11 in the alternate form shown in Figure 5-12. The resultant of this system of parallel forces and the location of its line of action are found readily by Varignon's theorem; the problem is thus seen to be identical to a problem in finding the location of a centroid.

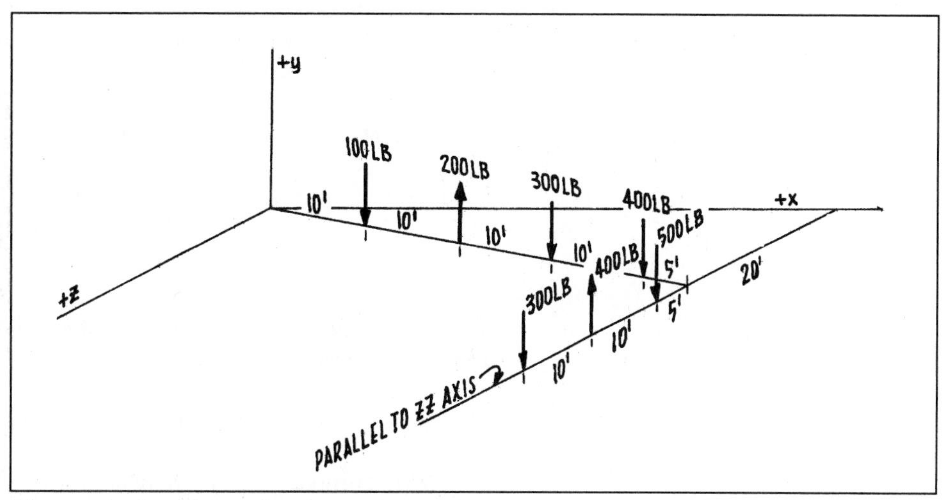

Figure 5-12 Alternative form of parallel forces.

Example 5-3

Resultant of Parallel Forces in Space.

Given: System of forces shown in Figure 5-10.

To Find: Magnitude, location and line of action of the resultant of the system of forces.

Solution: The magnitude of the resultant is the algebraic sum of the parallel forces. Positive direction is assumed upward:

$$\Sigma F_y = 0;$$
$$R = -100 + 200 - 300 - 400 - 500 + 400 - 300$$
$$R = -1000 \text{ lb}$$

The line of action of the resultant is parallel to the lines of action of the component forces. The location of the line of action will be found as usual from Varignon's theorem. The moment arms from the *x-x* and *y-y* coordinate axes are computed and shown in the following sketch:

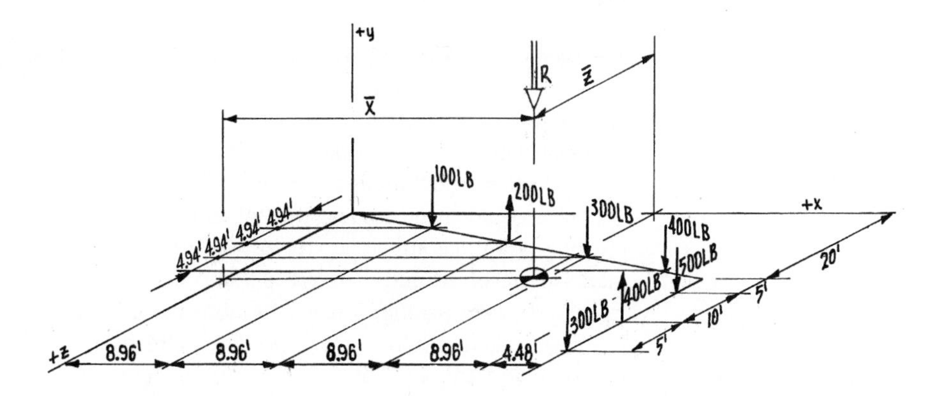

Moments are summed about the *z-z* axis to find $\bar{x}$. Clockwise moments are assumed positive:

Moment of Resultant = Moment of Components

$$1000\bar{x} = 100(8.96) - 200(17.92) + 300(26.87) + 400(35.83) + 500(40.31) - 400(40.31) + 300(40.31)$$
$$\bar{x} = 35.83 \text{ ft from } x \text{ axis}$$

Moments are summed about the *x-x* axis to find *z*. Clockwise moments are assumed positive.

Moment of Resultant = Moment of Components

$$1000\bar{z} = 100(4.44) - 200(8.89) + 300(13.33) + 40(17.78) + 500(25) - 400(35) + 300(45)$$
$$\bar{z} = 21.78 \text{ ft from } x \text{ axis}$$

The procedure for finding the magnitude and direction of a system of parallel forces is thus seen to be identical to that for finding a centroid. A system of parallel moments, rather than forces, is somewhat different, however.

The resultant of a system of parallel moments warrants a few moments' reflection. The system of four parallel moments shown in Figure 5-13 is a typical case, where the point of application of the axes of rotation is continuously varying.

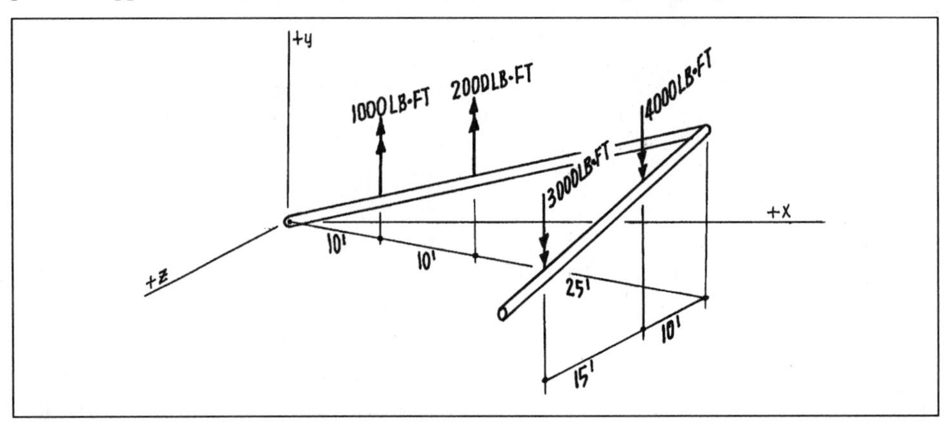

Figure 5-13 Parallel moments in space.

The moments of Figure 5-13 are seen to produce rotations only about an axis parallel to the *y-y* axis. They produce no rotations about the *x-x* axis or the *z-z* axis. Their resultant is therefore a moment M_{yy}, which is the algebraic sum of the four components. The resultant moment, like all moments, may act anywhere on the plane of the body; there are no further calculations to be made.

One could spend a great deal of time and effort in exploring these and other theoretical possibilities involving forces and moments in space. Once these forces and moments are resolved into their *x-x*, *y-y* and *z-z* components, however, they become simply three systems of parallel forces and moments in space. The solution of problems involving such systems follows the procedures already established; the solutions may indeed become more tedious, but there are no new concepts in them.

5.4 Supports for Three Dimensional Bodies

A few of the more common supports were introduced in Table 1-1 for two dimensional systems. Those symbols are now expanded to include three dimensional systems. The more common of the three dimensional suports are shown in Table 5-2.

Table 5-2 Three dimensional supports.

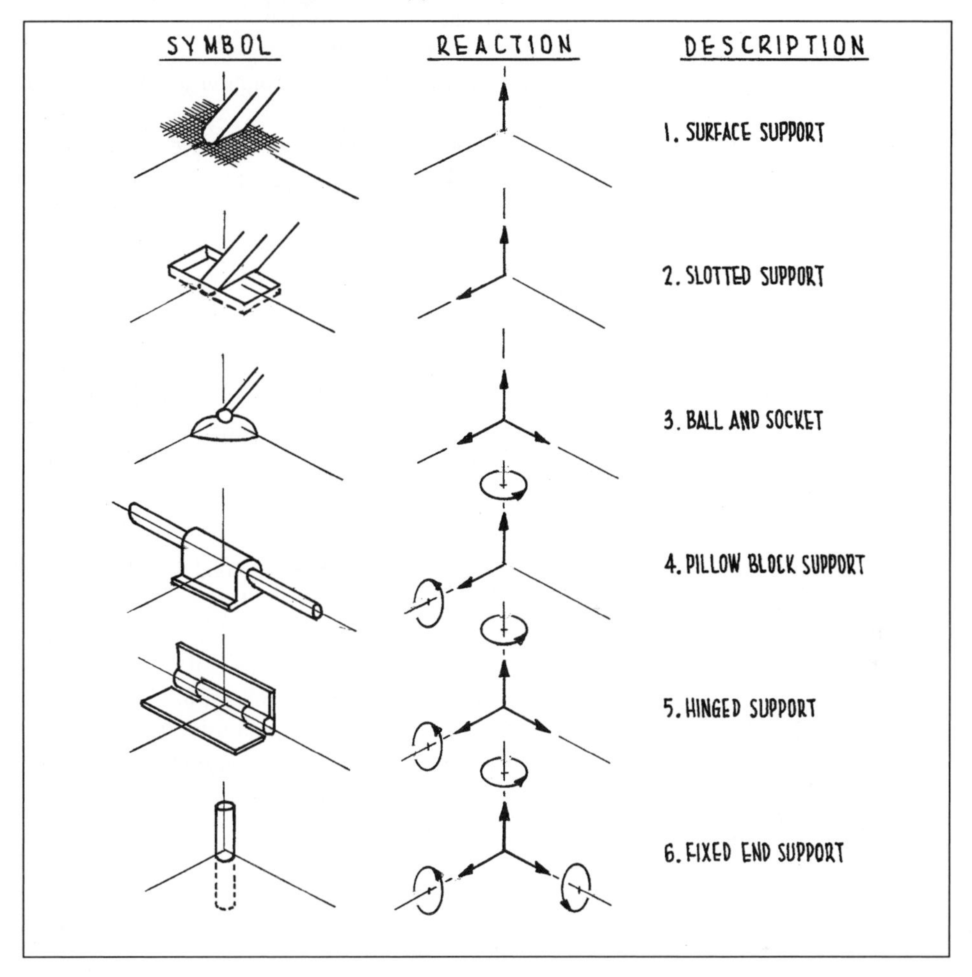

A careful examination of the symbols and their related force systems is warranted. Such supports are not accidental; they are chosen as an integral part of the design. They serve to provide a particular kind of support in one direction while providing freedom of motion in another direction.

Consider, for example, the support system represented by the smooth surface of support No. 1 of Table 5-1. Such a support system might commonly be assumed to exist under the legs of a table or chair, where friction forces are small enough to be ignored. In an actual support, smooth metal caps or "sliders" may help to enhance the assumption of zero lateral force.

Where it is essential to reduce force in one direction to an absolute minimum, the guided roller of support No. 2 might be considered. This type of support was used extensively in years past for the support at the ends of beams in highway and railroad bridges. Such supports have a long history of success under a wide variety of applications.

A ball and socket joint, such as that shown as support No. 3, is very often used at the base of a guyed tower. Such joints are specially fabricated and can sometimes be quite large. They are used in many such applications where the base of the structure cannot sustain moment in any direction, whether accidental or predictable.

The pillow block shown in Table 5-2 is also quite common. It allows a shaft to rotate freely while providing vertical and lateral support. A shoulder may be added to the shaft, in which case the pillow block will also prevent the shaft from sliding through the bearing along its longitudinal axis; the pillow block by itself does not prevent such longitudinal motion. One may also hear pillow blocks called *journal bearings*, or *thrust bearings* if longitudinal motion is prevented.

The fixed support shown in Table 5-2 is exactly that; the member is completely restrained in all six degrees of freedom. Such supports are frequently assumed to exist, but are difficult to achieve in practice.

Similarly, a hinge that permits rotation about one axis while providing complete restraint in all other directions is frequently specified but rarely attained. One should not be hesitant to use such support systems, however, just because they may not achieve 100% effectiveness. In most cases, the errors induced by friction, unwanted rotations, thermal loadings and deflections of supports can be safely ignored; in extreme cases, special corrective measures may be necessary in the design to guarantee the desired support condition.

5.5 Reactions at Supports under General Loads

As in two dimensions, the reactions on a free body in three dimensions are found by drawing the free body, then applying the mathematical laws of equilibrium. The solution of the resulting equations will yield the magnitude and direction of the reactions. (It is again noted that the line of action of a reaction is determined by the type of support and is already known.)

Some examples will illustrate the procedures for finding the reactions on a free body in three dimensions.

Example 5-4

Reactions in three dimensional systems.

Given: Bar supported by cables as shown. Dead weight of bar is 150 lbs/ft.

To Find: Forces in the three cables.

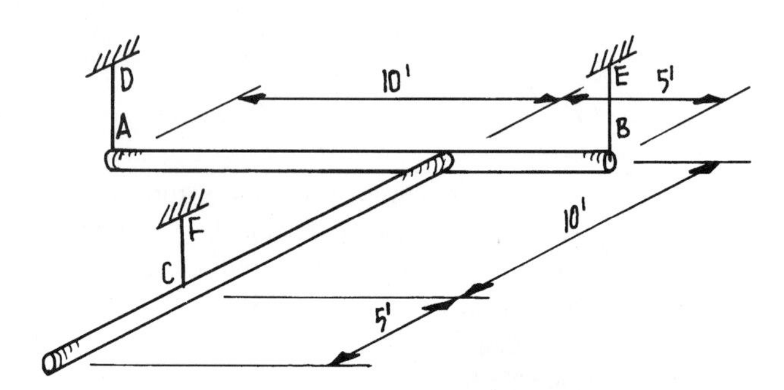

Solution: Bar *ABC* is removed as a free body. All reactions that can occur but only the reactions that can occur are shown on the free body. All cables are assumed to be in tension, "pulling" on the bar. Dead load of each of the two segments is shown acting through the centers of gravity.

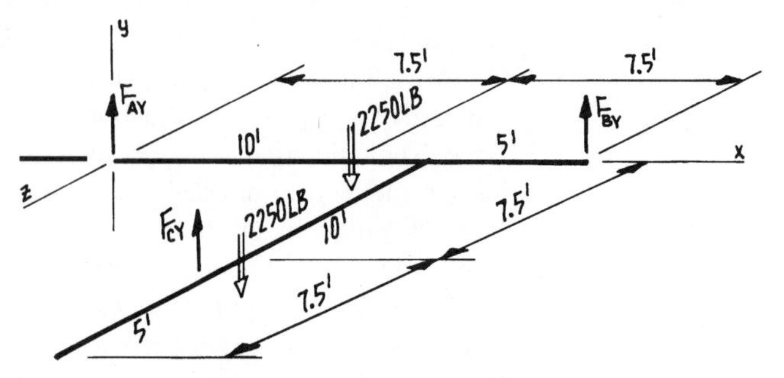

It is noted that there are three unknown reactions in this system of parallel forces. For such parallel force systems, there are three equations of equilibrium available. An equilibrium solution is therefore possible.

Moments are summed about the *x-x* axis, thereby eliminating the unknowns F_{Ay} and F_{By} from the resulting equation. The right hand rule is used for algebraic signs of moments:

$$\Sigma M_{xx} = 0;\ F_{Ay}(0) + 2250(7.5) + F_{By}(0) - 2250(0) - F_{cy}(10) = 0$$
$$F_{Cy} = 1687.5 \text{ lb upward}$$

Moments are now summed about the *z-z* axis. The value of F_{Cy} just found will enter this equation:

$$\Sigma M_{zz} = 0;\ F_{Ay}(0) - 2250(7.5) + F_{By}(15) - 2250(10) + 1687.5(10) = 0$$
$$F_{By} = 1500 \text{ lb upward}$$

Moments are now summed about an axis through the point *B* parallel to the *z-z* coordinate axis:

$$\Sigma M_{zz} = 0;\ F_{By}(0) - F_{Ay}(15) + 2250(7.5) + 2250(5) - 1687.5(5) = 0$$
$$F_{Ay} = 1312.5 \text{ lb upward}$$

It is observed that there are three unused conditions of equilibrium in Example 5-4. These extra conditions, called *redundant* conditions, will not yield any independent equations. It was noted earlier that the sum of forces in the *x-x* and *z-z* directions, for example, will yield only the trivial result 0 = 0, since there are no forces in either of these directions. The sum of vertical forces similarly yields:

$$\Sigma F_y = 0;\ 1312.5 - 2250 + 1687.5 - 2250 + 1500 = 0$$
$$0 = 0$$

This result, though a trivial result, affords a very valuable check on the accuracy of the arithmetic and algebra. Had there been an error in the solutions, the sum of forces would not have been zero, revealing that an error exists. Making such a check wherever possible is strongly recommended.

Example 5-5

Reactions in three dimensional systems.

Given: Welder's table loaded by a couple as shown. The table weighs 800 lbs.

To Find: Reactions at the four legs.

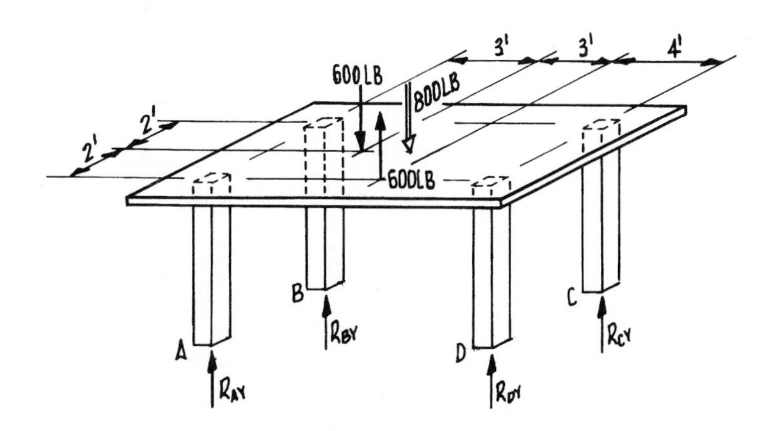

Solution: The entire table is taken as a free body. There can be no forces in the x or z direction or the table would slide laterally.

It is noted that there are four unknown reactions in this system of parallel forces, for which there are only three equations of equilibrium available. An equilibrium solution is therefore not possible; the problem is statically indeterminate.

A solution to this problem would require additional information or simplifying assumptions that are not stated in the given conditions.

Example 5-6

Reactions in three dimensional systems.

Given: Support system as shown. Dead weight of bar is 250 N.

To Find: Tension in cables AB and AD.

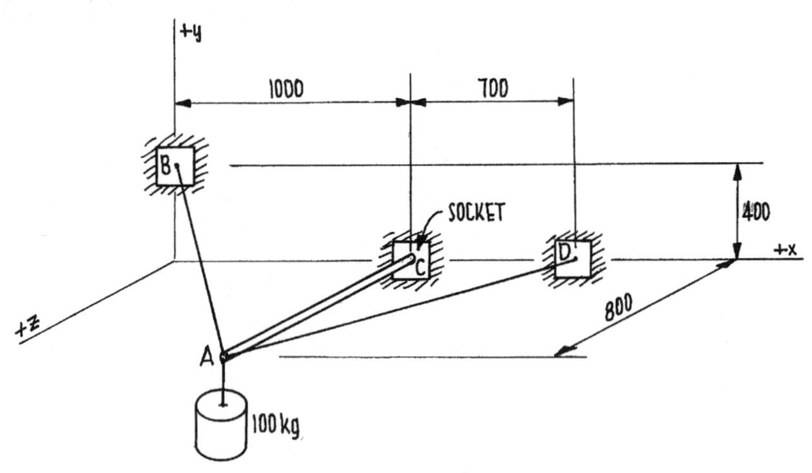

Solution: The bar AC is removed as a free body. The force exerted by the 10 kg mass is converted to 981 Newtons. The unknown reactions at C are shown in their positive sense. It is noted the line of action of the forces F_{AB} and F_{AD} will coincide with the cables AB and AD; the direction cosines of the cables will therefore be the same as the direction cosines of the forces. For cable AB, the length L_{AB} is found by the Pythagorean theorem in space:

$$L_{AB} = \sqrt{1000^2 + 400^2 + 800^2} = 1341.64$$

The direction cosines are then:

$$\cos\alpha_{AB} = 1000/1341.64 = 0.74536$$
$$\cos\beta_{AB} = 400/1341.64 = 0.29814$$
$$\cos\gamma_{AB} = 800/1341.64 = 0.59628$$

Similarly for cable AD:

$$L_{AD} = \sqrt{700^2 + 0^2 + 800^2} = 1063.01$$

$$\cos\alpha_{AD} = 700/1063.01 = 0.66850$$
$$\cos\beta_{AD} = 0/1063.01 = 0$$
$$\cos\gamma_{AD} = 800/1063.01 = 0.75258$$

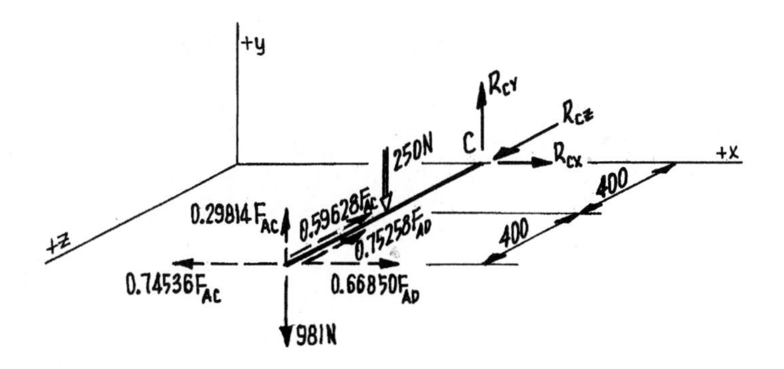

It is observed that there are five unknowns in this system of forces. It is noted further that this system of forces is concurrent to a line *AC*, for which case there are five equations of equilibrium available. An equilibrium solution is therefore possible.

Moments are summed about an *x-x* axis through *C*. Forces in the *x-x* direction are parallel to this axis and therefore produce no moment about it. Similarly, the forces in the *z-z* direction intersect this axis and their arm is zero; they produce no moment about the *x-x* axis. Only the forces in the *y-y* direction produce moment about an *x-x* axis at *C*:

$$\Sigma M_{xx} = 0;\ 0.29814\ F_{AC}(800) - 981(800) - 250(400) = 0$$
$$F_{AC} = 3709.67 \text{ N}$$

Moments are summed similarly about a *y-y* axis through *C*. Positive moment follows the right-hand rule:

$$\Sigma M_{yy} = 0;\ -0.74536(3709.67) + 0.66850\ F_{AD} = 0$$
$$F_{AD} = 4136.18 \text{ N}$$

The solution of Example 5-6 demonstrates a very common occurrence in three dimensional mechanics. In many such problems, the statics is really quite simple; it is the geometry that makes things difficult. This particularly annoying property of three dimensional mechanics will be encountered repeatedly in subsequent examples.

Example 5-7

Reactions in three dimensional systems.

Given: Support system as shown; only the bearing at *A* can take longitudinal thrust.

To Find: Reactions at *C* and *D* and tension in the cable *AG*.

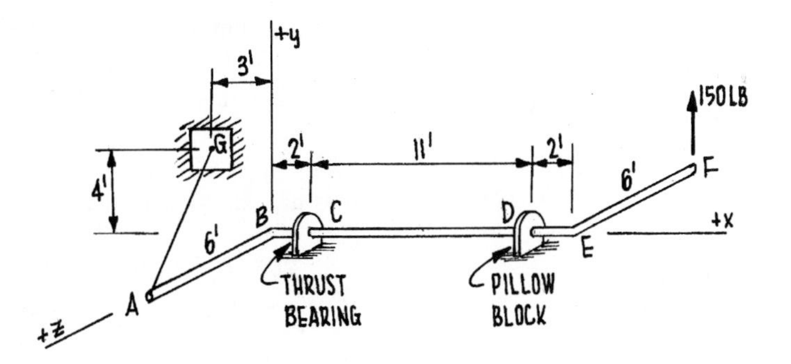

Solution: The bar *ABEF* is removed as a free body. At the supports, all of the forces that can occur, but only the forces that can occur are shown on the free body. Unknown forces are shown in their positive sense. The line of action of the unknown force at *A* (assumed in tension) lies along the cable *AG*; the direction cosines for the force F_{AG} are therefore the same as those for the cable. For the cable *AG*:

$$L_{AG} = \sqrt{3^2 + 4^2 + 6^2} = 7.81 \text{ ft}$$

$$\cos\alpha_{AG} = 3/7.81 = 0.38411$$
$$\cos\beta_{AG} = 4/7.81 = 0.51215$$
$$\cos\gamma_{AG} = 6/7.81 = 0.76822$$

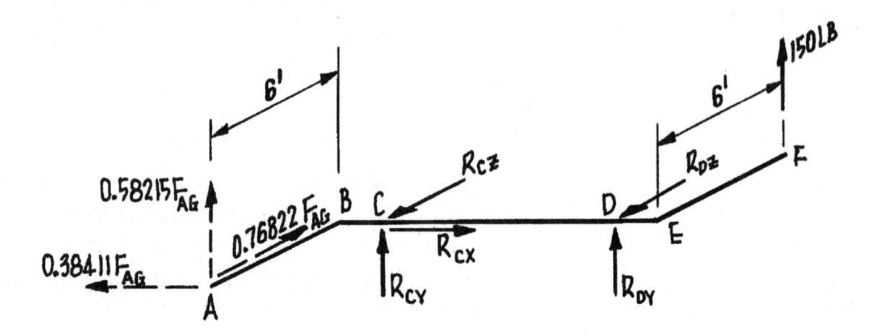

It is noted that this is a general system of forces in three dimensions; there are six unknowns and there are six equations of equilibrium available. An equilibrium solution is therefore possible:

$$\Sigma M_{xx} = 0; \ -0.51215\ F_{AG}(6) + 150(6) = 0$$
$$F_{AG} = 293 \text{ lb}$$

Moments are summed about a *z-z* axis through *C*, positive directions by right-hand rule:

$$\Sigma M_{czz} = 0; \ -0.51215(293)(2) + R_{Dy}(11) + 150(13) = 0$$
$$R_{Dy} = +150 \text{ lb}$$

Moments are summed about a *y-y* axis through *C*, positive directions by right-hand rule:

$$\Sigma M_{cyy} = 0; \ -0.38411(293)(6) - 0.76822(293)(2) - R_{Dz}(11) = 0$$
$$R_{Dz} = -102 \text{ lb (to the rear)}$$

Forces are summed in the *x* direction:

$$\Sigma F_x = 0; \ -0.38411(293) + R_{Cx} = 0$$
$$R_{Cx} = +113 \text{ lb}$$

Forces are summed in the *y* direction:

$$\Sigma F_y = 0; \ 0.51215(293) + R_{Cy} + 150 - 150 = 0$$
$$R_{Cy} = 150 \text{ lb. (down)}$$

Forces are summed in the z direction:

$$\Sigma F_z = 0;\ -0.76822(293) + R_{Cz} + 102 = 0$$
$$R_{Cz} = +123 \text{ lb}$$

The final results are shown in the following sketch:

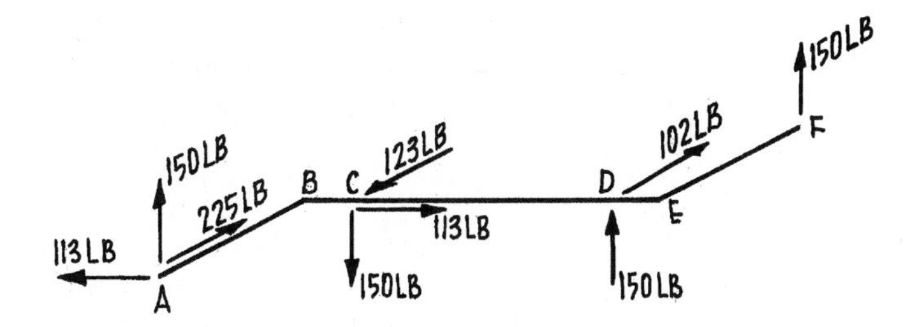

Example 5-8

Reactions in three dimensional systems.

Given: Triangular panel supported as shown. Panel is a right triangle weighing 400 N.

To Find: Reactions at A, B and C.

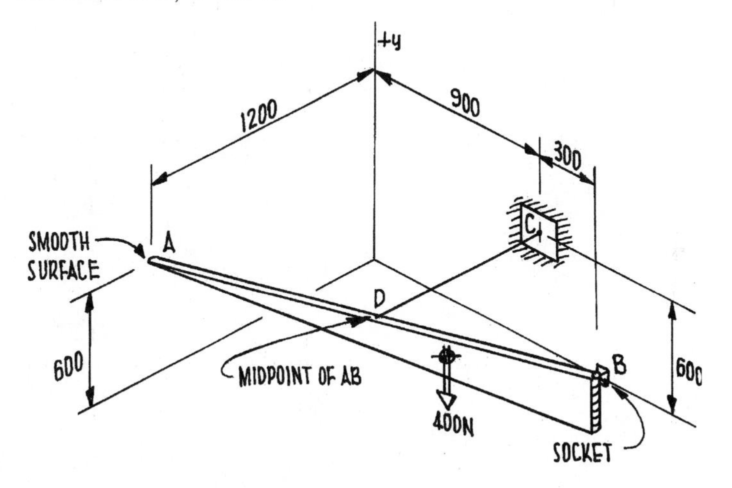

Solution: The panel is removed as a free body. At the supports, all of the forces that can occur but only the forces that can occur are shown on the free body. Unknown forces are shown in their positive sense. The line of action of the unknown force at D (assumed in tension) lies along the cable DC; the direction cosines for the force F_{DC} are therefore the same as those for the cable DC.

The length of the cable is found from the Pythagorean theorem in space. For the cable:

$$\Delta_x = 900 - 600;\ \Delta_y = {}^1\!/_2(600);\ \Delta_z = {}^1\!/_2(200);$$

$$L_{DC} = \sqrt{300^2 + 300^2 + 600^2} = 735$$

The direction cosines are:

$$\cos\alpha_{DC} = 300/735 = 0.40825$$
$$\cos\beta_{DC} = 300/735 = 0.40825$$
$$\cos\gamma_{DC} = 600/735 = 0.81650$$

It is observed that this is a system of forces concurrent to line *AB*; there are therefore only five equations of equilibrium available. Since there are only five unknowns, however, this system of forces may be solved by equilibrium.

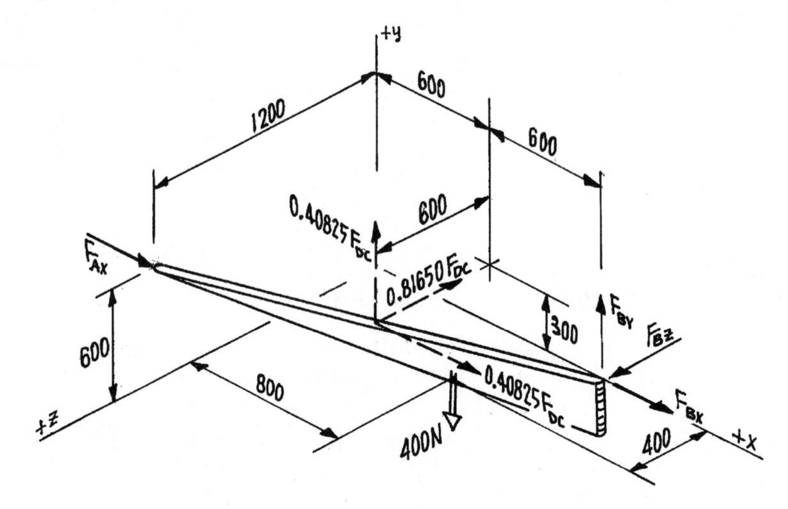

Moments are summed about an *x-x* axis through *B*:

$$\Sigma M_{Bxx} = 0;\ 400(400) - 0.40825\ F_{DC}(600) - 0.81650\ F_{DC}(300) = 0$$
$$F_{DC} = 327 \quad N = F_{CD}$$

Moments are summed about a *y-y* axis through *B*:

$$\Sigma M_{Byy} = 0;\ F_{Ax}(1200) + 0.40825(327)(600) - 0.81650(327)(600) = 0$$
$$F_{Ax} = 67\ N$$

Forces are summed in the *x* direction:

$$\Sigma F_x = 0;\ 167 + 0.040825(327) + F_{Bx} = 0$$
$$F_{Bx} = -200\ N \text{ (to the left)}$$

Forces are summed in the *y* direction:

$$\Sigma F_y = 0;\ 0.40825(327) - 400 + F_{By} = 0$$
$$F_{By} = 267\ N$$

Forces are summed in the *z* direction:

$$\Sigma F_z = 0;\ -0.81650(327) + F_{Bz} = 0$$
$$F_{Bz} = 267\ N$$

Example 5-9

Reactions in three dimensional systems.

Given: Hinged canopy guyed by a single cable. Only the hinge at *A* can take longitudinal thrust. Weight of the canopy is 1000 lbs.

To Find: Reactions at *A* and *B*.

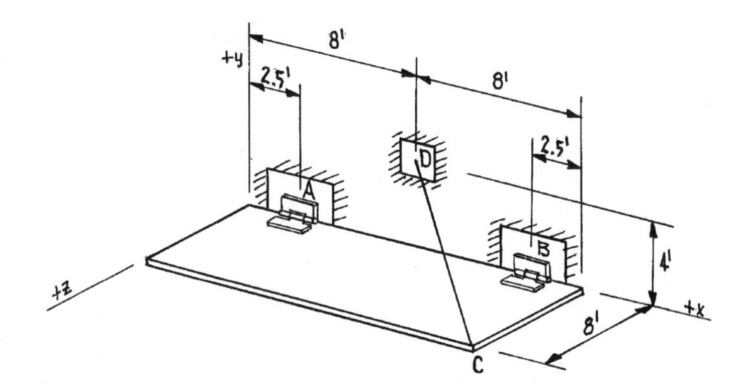

Solution: The canopy is removed as a free body. Unknown reactions are shown in their positive sense. The line of action of the force at *C* is known; it will coincide with the cable *CD*. Direction cosines for the cable *CD* are found by the usual means.

The length of the cable, L_{CD}, is found by the Pythagorean theorem in space:

$$L_{CD} = \sqrt{8^2 + 4^2 + 8^2} = 12 \text{ ft}$$

The direction cosines are:

$$\cos\alpha_{CD} = {}^{8}/_{12} = 0.66667$$
$$\cos\beta_{CD} = {}^{4}/_{12} = 0.33333$$
$$\cos\gamma_{CD} = {}^{8}/_{12} = 0.66667$$

These are also the direction cosines of the force in the cable *CD*:

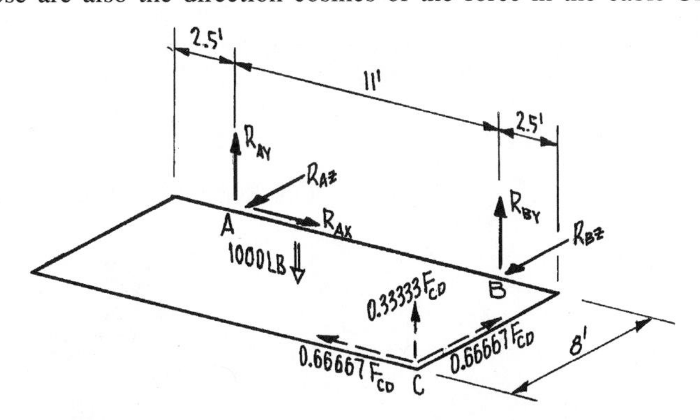

It is observed that this is a general system of forces in three dimensions; there are 6 unknown forces in the system and six equations of equilibrium available. An equilibrium solution is therefore possible.

Moments are summed about the *x-x* axis to eliminate all unknowns except F_{CD}:

$$\Sigma M_{xx} = 0;\ 1000(4) - 0.33333F_{CD}(8) = 0$$
$$F_{CD} = 1500 \text{ lbs}$$

Moments are summed about a *z-z* axis through *A*:

$$\Sigma M_{Azz} = 0; - 1000(5.5) + 0.33333(1500)(13.5) + R_{By}(11) = 0$$
$$R_{By} = -114 \text{ lbs (down)}$$

Moments are summed about a *y-y* axis through *A*:

$$\Sigma M_{Ayy} = 0; - 0.66667(1500)(8) + 0.66667(1500)(16) - R_{Bz}(13.5) = 0$$
$$R_{Bz} = 593 \text{ lbs}$$

Forces are summed in the *x* direction:

$$\Sigma F_x = 0; R_{Ax} - 0.66667(1500) = 0$$
$$R_{Ax} = 1000 \text{ lbs}$$

Forces are summed in the *y* direction:

$$\Sigma F_y = 0; R_{Ay} - 1000 + 0.33333(1500) - 114 = 0$$
$$R_{Ay} = +614 \text{ lbs}$$

Forces are summed in the *z* direction:

$$\Sigma F_z = 0; R_{Az} - 0.66667(1500) + 593 = 0$$
$$R_{Az} = 407 \text{ lbs}$$

Final reactions are shown in the following sketch.

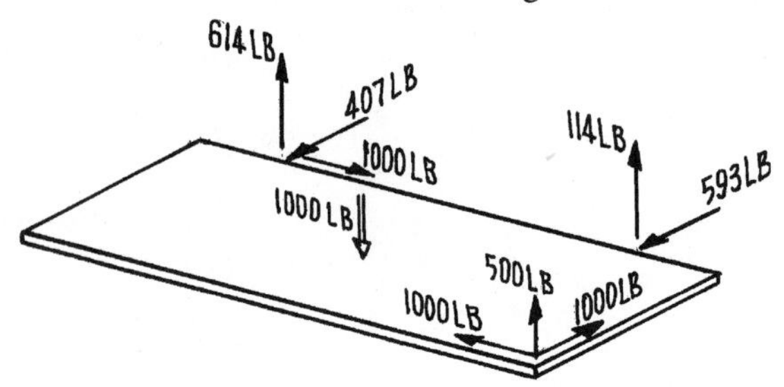

Example 5-10

Reactions in three dimensional systems.

Given: Jib crane loaded as shown.

To Find: Reactions at fixed base.

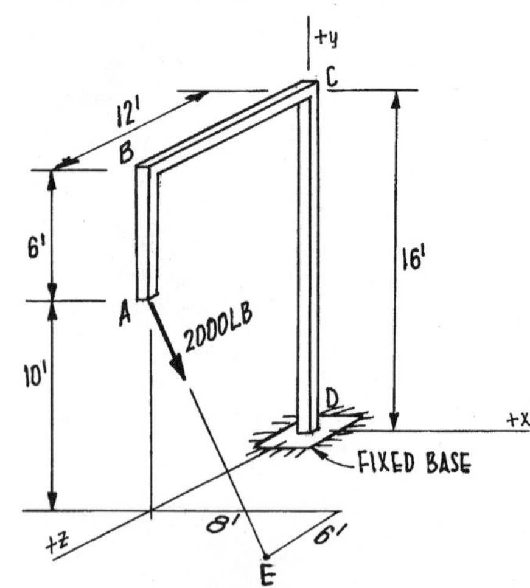

Solution: The frame is removed as a free body. Unknown forces and moments are shown in their positive sense. The 2000 lb. load is resolved into its *x*, *y* and *z* components. The direction cosines for the 2000 lb. force are found by finding the direction cosines for line *AE*.

The length L_{AE} of line *AE* is found by the Pythagorean theorem, using Δ_x, Δ_y and Δ_z:

$$L_{AE} = \sqrt{8^2 + 10^2 + 6^2} = 14.14 \text{ ft}$$

The direction cosines are:

$$\cos\alpha_{AE} = {}^{8}/_{14.14} = 0.56569$$
$$\cos\beta_{AE} = {}^{10}/_{14.14} = 0.70711$$
$$\cos\gamma_{AE} = {}^{6}/_{14.14} = 0.42426$$

The component forces are:

$$F_x = 2000(0.56569) = 1131 \text{ lbs}$$
$$F_y = 2000(0.70711) = 1414 \text{ lbs}$$
$$F_z = 2000(0.42426) = 849 \text{ lbs}$$

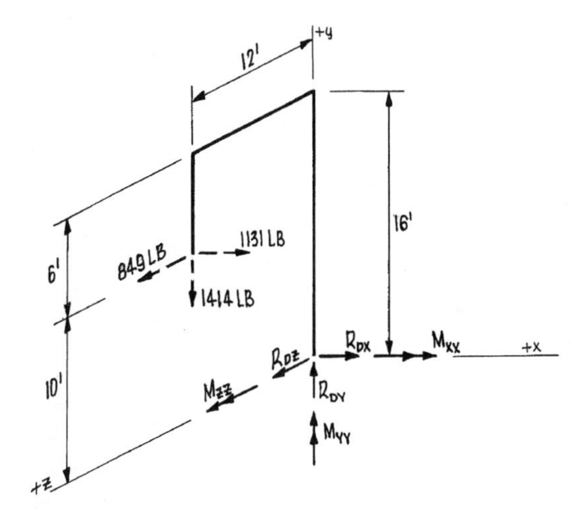

It is observed that this is a general system of forces in three dimensions. With six unknown reactions and six equations of equilibrium available, an equilibrium solution is possible.

Moments are summed about an *x-x* axis through *D*:

$$\Sigma M_{Dxx} = 0;\ 849(10) + 1414(12) + M_{Dxx} = 0$$
$$M_{Dxx} = 24460 \text{ lb·ft (opposite direction)}$$

Moments are summed about a *y-y* axis through *D*:

$$\Sigma M_{Dyy} = 0;\ 1131(12) + M_{Dyy} = 0$$
$$M_{Dyy} = 13570 \text{ lb·ft (opposite direction)}$$

Moments are summed about a *z-z* axis through *D*:

$$\Sigma M_{Dzz} = 0;\ -1131(10) + M_{Dzz} = 0$$
$$M_{Dzz} = 11310 \text{ lb·ft}$$

Forces are summed in the x direction:

$$\Sigma F_x = 0;\ 1131 + R_{Dx} = 0$$
$$R_{Dx} = 1131 \text{ lbs (to the left)}$$

Forces are summed in the y direction:

$$\Sigma F_y = 0;\ -1414 + R_{Dy} = 0$$
$$R_{Dy} = 1414 \text{ lbs}$$

Forces are summed in the z direction:

$$\Sigma F_z = 0;\ 849 + R_{Dz} = 0$$
$$R_{Dz} = -\ 849 \text{ lbs (to the rear)}$$

Example 5-11

Reactions in three dimensional systems.

Given: Triangular panel suspended as shown. Weight of panel is 2 kN. The surface *AB* is level.

To Find: Reactions at *A*, *B* and *C*.

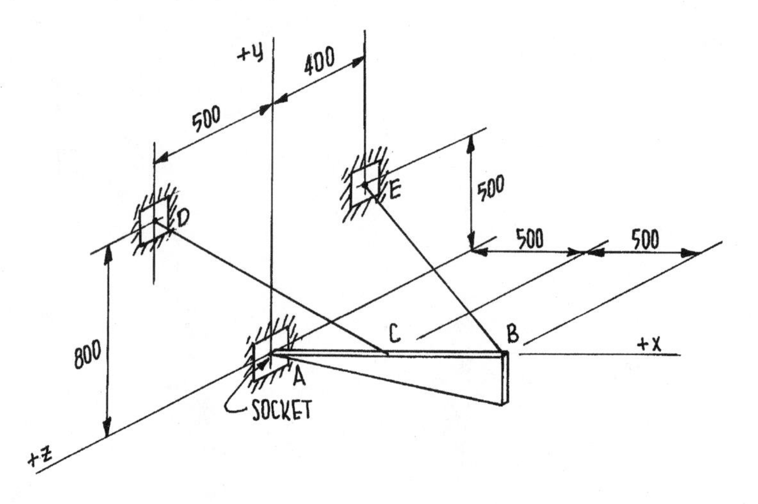

Solution: The triangular panel is removed as a free body. The forces in the two supporting cables are shown on the free body as their x, y and z components. The direction cosines for these forces are found in the usual way, by finding the direction cosines for the cables:

For cable *CD*, $\Delta_x = 500$, $\Delta_y = 800$, $\Delta_z = 500$;

$$L_{CD} = \sqrt{500^2 + 800^2 + 500^2} = 1068 \text{ mm}$$

$$\cos\alpha_{CD} = {}^{500}/_{1068} = 0.46829$$
$$\cos\beta_{CD} = {}^{800}/_{1068} = 0.74927$$
$$\cos\gamma_{CD} = {}^{500}/_{1068} = 0.46829$$

For cable *BE*, $\Delta_x = 1000$, $\Delta_y = 500$, $\Delta_z = -400$;

$$L_{BE} = \sqrt{1000^2 + 500^2 + 400^2} = 1187 \text{ mm}$$

$$\cos\alpha_{BE} = {}^{1000}/_{1187} = 0.84215$$
$$\cos\beta_{BE} = {}^{500}/_{1187} = 0.42108$$
$$\cos\gamma_{BE} = {}^{500}/_{1187} = 0.33686$$

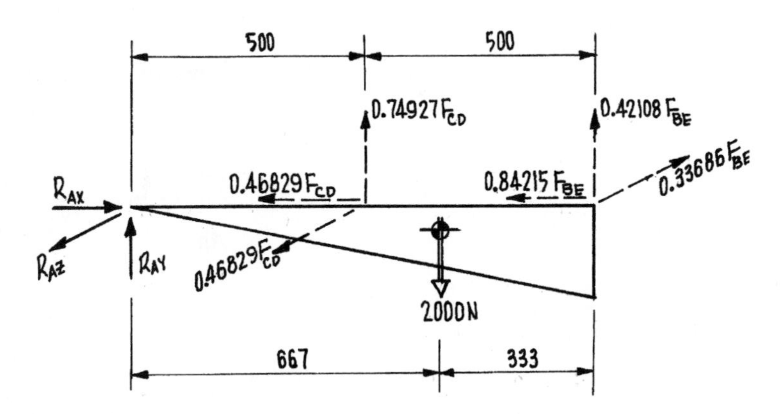

It is noted that this is a system of forces concurrent on the line *AB*; there are only five equations of equilibrium available. Since there are only five unknowns, an equilibrium solution is possible.

Moments are summed about a *y-y* axis through *A*:

$$\Sigma M_{Ayy} = 0;\ -0.46829F_{CD}(500) + 0.33686\ F_{BE}(1000) = 0$$
$$337\ F_{BE} - 234\ F_{CD} = 0$$

Moments are summed about a *z-z* axis through *A*:

$$\Sigma M_{Azz} = 0;\ + 0.74927F_{CD}(500) + 0.42108F_{BE}(1000)$$
$$- 2000(667) = 0$$
$$374F_{CD} + 421F_{BE} = 1{,}333{,}000$$

The foregoing two equations are in two unknowns; they may be solved simultaneously.

From the first equation:

$$F_{BE} = 0.694F_{CD}$$

From the second equation:

$$374F_{CD} + 421(0.694F_{CD}) = 1{,}333{,}000$$
$$F_{CD} = 2000 \text{ N}$$
$$F_{BE} = 1388 \text{ N}$$

Forces are summed in the *x* direction:

$$\Sigma F_x = 0;\ R_{Ax} - 0.46829(2000) - 0.84215(1388) = 0$$
$$R_{Ax} = 2105 \text{ N}$$

Forces are summed in the y direction:

$$\Sigma F_y = 0;\ R_{Ay} - 0.74927(2000) + 0.42108(1388) - 2000 = 0$$
$$R_{Ay} = -83\ \text{N}$$

Forces are summed in the z direction:

$$\Sigma F_z = 0;\ R_{Az} - 0.46829(2000) - 0.33686(1388) = 0$$
$$R_{Az} = -469\ \text{N (to the rear)}$$

The final results are shown on the following sketch.

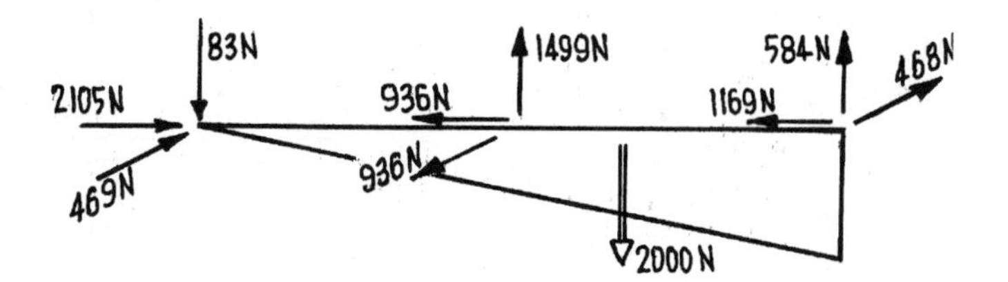

Review Questions

1. Of the three planes that exist in a three dimensional Cartesian coordinate system (the *xy* plane, the *xz* plane and the *yz* plane) which plane is the horizontal plane in classical mathematics?
2. Of the three planes referenced in Question 1, which plane is used as the horizontal plane in engineering work? Why do engineers reorient the coordinate system?
3. How is a force usually identified, or defined, in two dimensional work?
4. How is a force usually identified, or defined, in three dimensional work?
5. To what lines are direction angles measured in three dimensional notation?
6. When the line of action of a force does not intersect the coordinate *x-x* axis, how is its direction angle *a* determined?
7. Write the law of cosines in space for the angle *q* between two intersecting lines.
8. Write the Pythagorean theorem in space for the length of a line segment *OA*, where the line segment has a projection on the *xy* plane of Δ_x, on the *xz* plane of Δ_z and on the *yz* plane of Δ_y.
9. Write the relationship between the direction cosines for a line segment in space.
10. Write the mathematical laws of equilibrium for three dimensional systems.
11. How are reactions determined for a body that has more than the permitted number of unknown forces?
12. How is a moment shown when one is sketching three dimensional systems on a two dimensional sheet of paper? How is the direction of rotation established?
13. How is the algebraically positive direction of rotation determined for moments in three dimensions?
14. In three dimensions, where is the point of application of a force along its line of action?
15. In three dimensions, where is the point of application of a moment along its axis of rotation?
16. How is a moment identified, or defined, in three dimensional work?
17. What is a negative force?
18. State Varignon's theorem as it applies to three dimensional systems.
19. For a system of concurrent forces in space, how is the magnitude of the resultant determined?
20. For a system of concurrent forces in space, how are the direction cosines of the resultant determined?

21. For a system of concurrent forces in space, how many unknowns are permitted in an equilibrium solution for reactions on a free body?
22. For a three dimensional system of forces concurrent on a line, how many unknowns are permitted in an equilibrium solution for reactions on a free body?
23. For a system of parallel forces in space, how is the magnitude of the resultant determined?
24. For a system of parallel forces in space, how is the direction of the resultant determined?
25. For a system of parallel forces in space, how is the position of the line of action of the resultant determined?
26. For a system of parallel forces in space, how many unknowns are permitted in an equilibrium solution for reactions on a free body?
27. What is meant by a *redundant* equation of equilibrium?
28. What is meant by a *trivial* equation of equilibrium?
29. When the line of action of a force F is fixed by the geometry of the system, how are the direction cosines found?
30. When the line of action of a force F is fixed by the geometry of the system, why can't the force simply be shown as F_x, F_y and F_z on the free body rather than $F\cos\alpha_F$, $F\cos\beta_F$ and $F\cos\gamma_F$?

CHAPTER

6

Simple Trusses

6.1 Properties and Configurations of Trusses

A truss is a type of structure that derives its strength through the triangulation of its members. A typical truss is shown in Figure 6-1. It should be observed that the function of the truss of Figure 6-1 is to serve as a beam; the beam in this case is built as a truss.

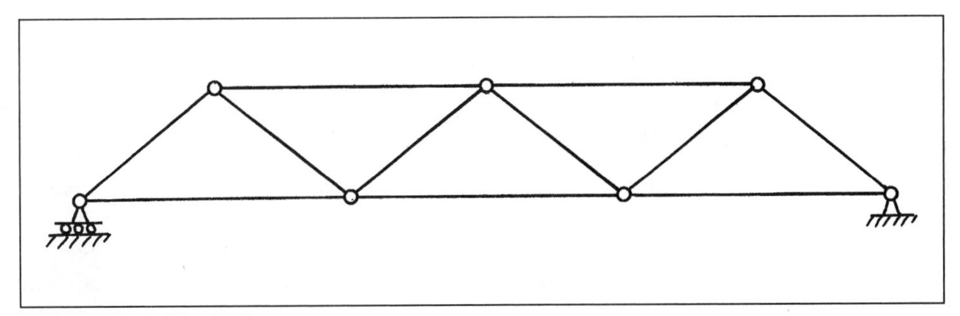

Figure 6-1 Typical truss.

Trusses are widely used throughout the construction industry and have been used in all types of applications for centuries. One of the more appealing characteristics of a truss is that long spans can be achieved using only short pieces of materials. In addition, every member in a truss can be designed to work at its maximum allowable load, creating a highly efficient structure with little or no wasted material.

There are many configurations for trusses that have been given names to identify them. Several such trusses are shown in Figure 6-2. The Warren, Pratt and Howe trusses are used very commonly for bridges, while the Fink, Parker and Bowstring trusses are used more commonly for roofs.

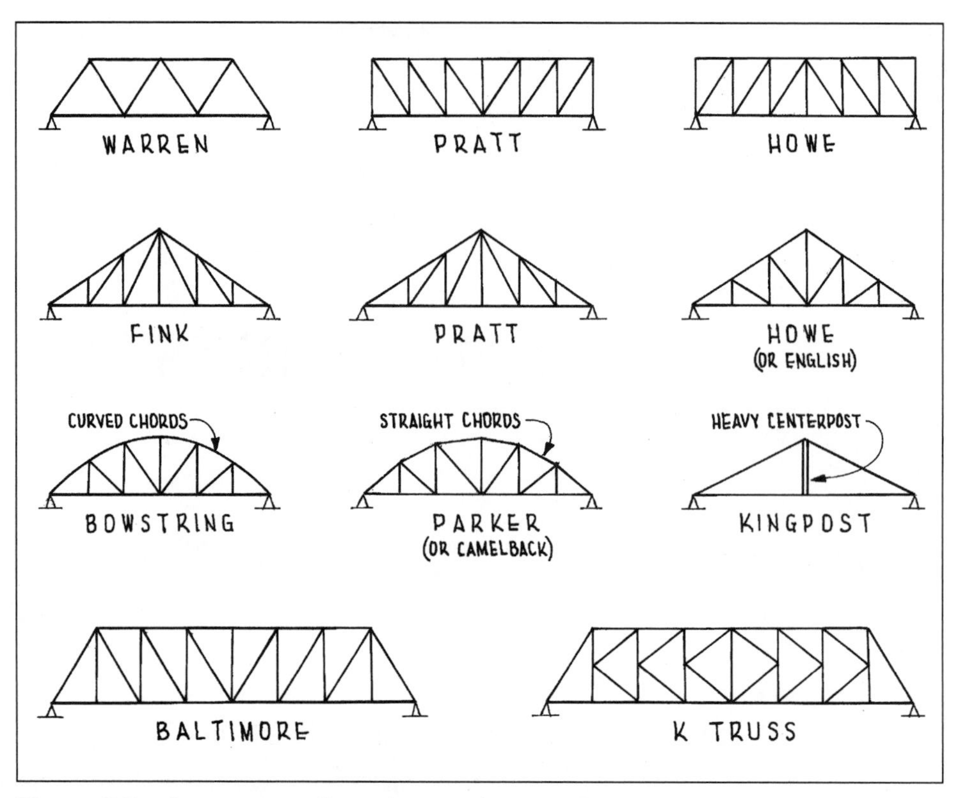

Figure 6-2 Common configurations and names for trusses.

In all cases, it should be noted that in Figure 6-2, every member of a truss is part of a triangle. It has been said that a triangle is the only completely stable configuration for a structure in two dimensions (or a tetrahedron in three dimensions). The trusses shown in Figure 6-2 take full advantage of that property of stability.

6.2 Characteristics of Trusses

The individual members that make up a truss are invariably long, slender members. In a steel truss, for example, the members are commonly built of two angles such as those shown in Figure 6-3 and tabulated in Table 5-7 in the Technical Manual. The use of two angles permits the member to receive and transmit loads symmetrically where they are attached to the gusset plates. "Stitch" bolts or rivets with spacing collars are usually placed along the length of the *double angle struts* to maintain the distance between the two angles.

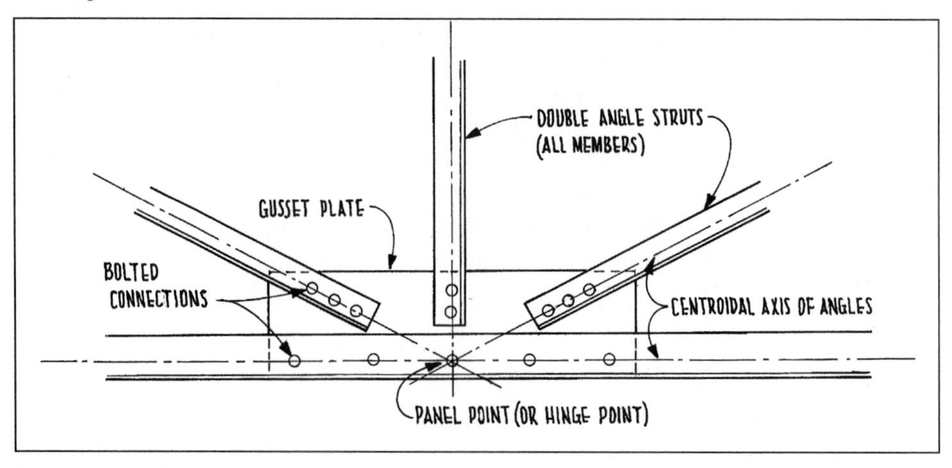

Figure 6-3 Double angle strut.

The point where two or more truss members intersect is called a *panel point*. All members coming into a panel point are assumed to come into a hinge at that point, though it is obvious in Figure 6-3 that no such hinge exists. The members are so long and slender, however, that very little error is incurred in making this assumption. This point is discussed more fully in later chapters dealing with steel and timber truss designs.

A truss is said to be *properly formed* if it can be formed by beginning with a base triangle such as those shown in Figure 6-4, then adding two members and their included hinge until the final configuration is obtained. The hinge points in Figure 6-4 are shown as open circles.

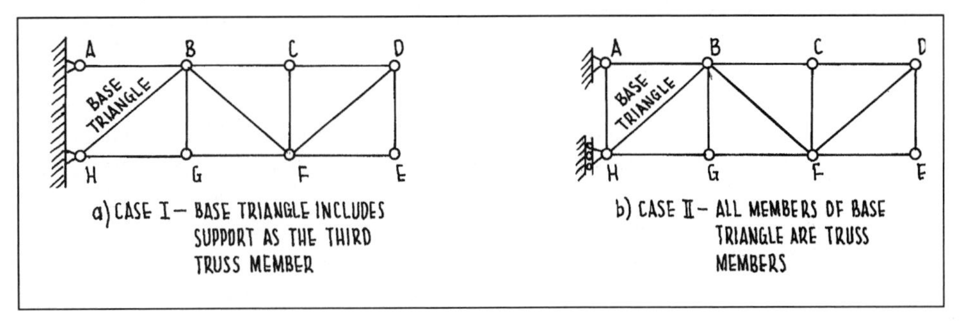

Figure 6-4 Properly formed trusses.

The trusses of Figure 6-4, for example, are formed by beginning with the base triangle *ABH*, then adding members *HG* and *GB* with their hinge at *G*, then adding *BF* and *FG* with their hinge at *F*, then adding *BC* and *CF* with their hinge at *C*, and so on until the entire truss is formed. Such a truss is statically determinate and it will be a stable truss under load.

In all schematic diagrams of trusses in this text, a hinged truss point is shown as an open circle such as those of Figure 6-4. If two members are shown crossing each other without such a hinge point, they are assumed to pass each other freely at that point.

As an example of a truss that is not properly formed, consider the truss of Figure 6-5. Beginning with the base triangle *ABN*, the truss can be properly formed to the right only as far as panel *DELM*, then it can no longer be properly formed. Or, beginning with base triangle *IHJ*, the truss can be properly formed to the left only as far as panel *EFLK*, then it can no longer be properly formed.

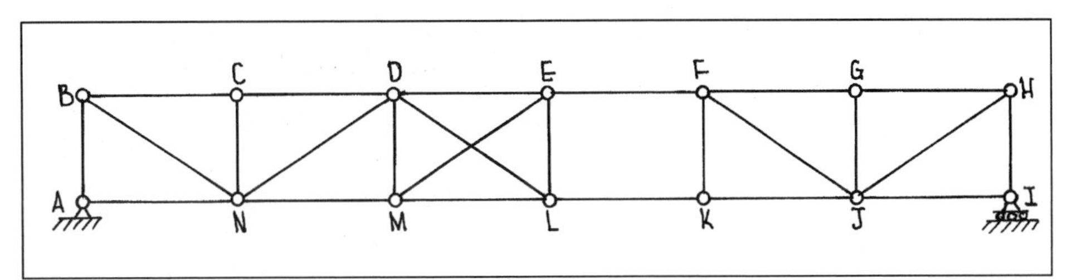

Figure 6-5 Improperly formed truss.

Examination of the truss of Figure 6-5 indicates that the panel *DELM* has an extra member, while the panel *EFLK* lacks one member. So, while the total number of members may be correct, and the total number of hinges may be correct, the truss is not properly formed. (As one means to correct the configuration of this particular truss, the extra member *ME* could simply be moved to position *LF*.)

6.3 Loads on Truss Members

A truss member may only be loaded axially. Any transverse loading on one of these long slender members would create bending in the member, which would severely limit its capacity to take axial force. For maximum efficiency, a truss member may be loaded only in tension or in compression, as shown in Figure 6-6.

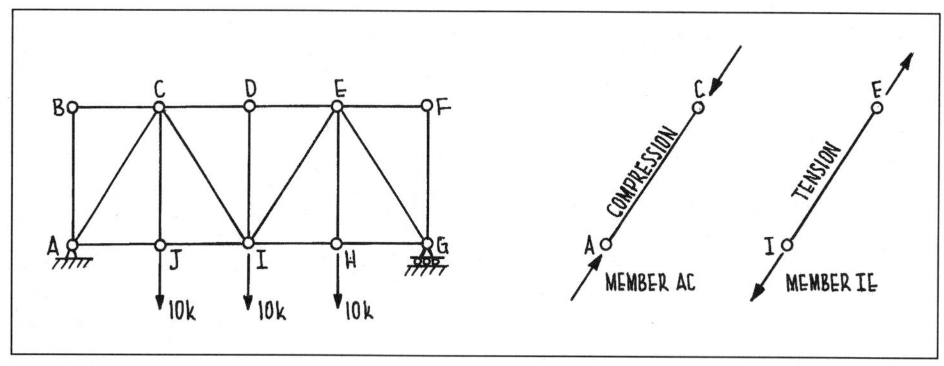

Figure 6-6 Loads on truss members.

In Figure 6-6, members *AC* and *IE* have been removed as free bodies and shown separately. Note that the only load that can come to these members is at a hinge point. Consequently, the only load that can exist is direct tension or compression. As noted in earlier chapters, compressive forces "push" toward a hinge, and tension forces "pull" away from a hinge.

Since the members in a truss may only be loaded axially, all external loads on a truss can be introduced only at hinge points. Such control over the loading of a truss is shown in Figure 6-7, where beams are used to transmit the loads from the bridge deck to the panel points of the truss.

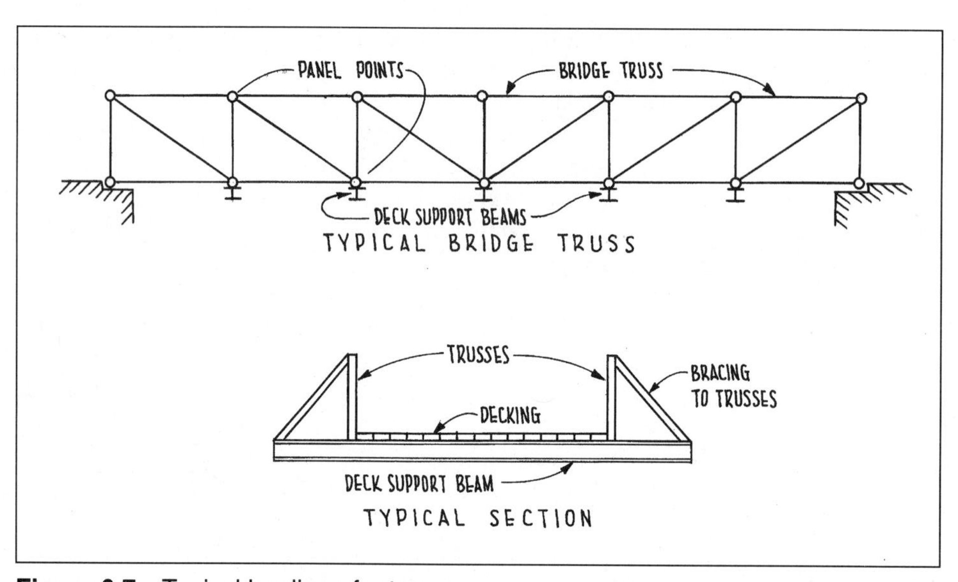

Figure 6-7 Typical loading of a truss.

Under certain circumstances some loads (such as a concrete deck) may be placed along the length of a truss member, violating the rule that loads may only be introduced at panel points. In such cases, the truss member must be designed to sustain both the axial loads and the bending loads. Such practices introduce inefficiency into the truss design, but such designs are sometimes the least costly alternative.

6.4 External Reactions on Trusses

External reactions on trusses are determined in much the same way as they are determined for beams. At times, however, their locations can produce some confusing configurations. Some examples will illustrate the solution for some typical truss reactions.

Example 6-1

Solution for truss reactions.

Given: Truss with loads and reactions as shown.

To Find: Magnitude and direction of the reactions.

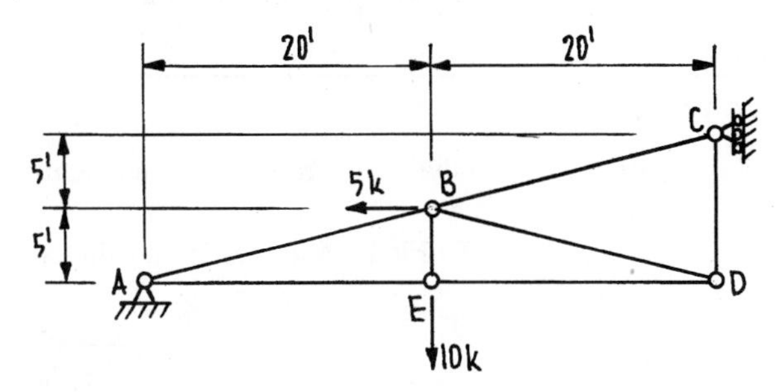

Solution: The entire truss is taken as a free body with all forces and reactions shown.

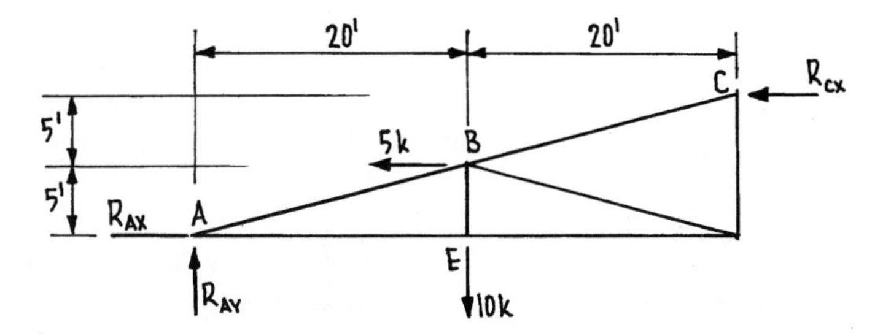

It is noted that there are three unknown reactions in this planar system; an equilibrium solution is therefore possible.

Moments are summed about point A, eliminating all unknowns except R_{CX}:

$$\Sigma M_A = 0;\ -5(5) + 10(20) - R_{CX}(10) = 0$$
$$R_{CX} = 17.5 \text{ kips in direction shown}$$

Forces are now summed vertically, eliminating all unknowns except R_{AY}:

$$\Sigma F_Y = 0;\ +R_{AY} - 10 = 0$$
$$R_{AY} = 10 \text{ kips in direction shown}$$

Moments are now summed about point C:

$$\Sigma M_C = 0;\ R_{AY}(40) - R_{AX}(10) + 5(5) - 10(20) = 0$$
$$R_{AX} = 22.5 \text{ kips in direction shown}$$

As a check, forces are summed horizontally:

$$\Sigma F_X = 0;\ +R_{AX} - 5 - R_{CX} = 0$$
$$22.5 - 5 - 17.5 = 0$$
$$0 = 0 \text{ (OK)}$$

It should be noted that the configuration of the truss never entered the solution to Example 6-1. Only the locations and directions of the forces were used. The rigid body could have been trussed or solid; insofar as external reactions are oncerned, it would have made no difference.

Example 6-2

Reactions on a truss.

Given: Truss with loads and reactions as shown.

To Find: Magnitude and direction of the reactions.

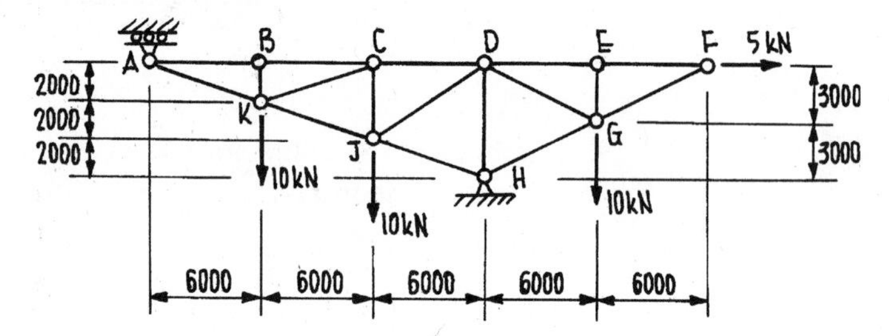

Solution: The entire truss is taken as a free body, with all loads and reactions shown.

Moments are summed about H to find R_{AY}:

$$\Sigma M_H = 0;\ R_{AY}(18) - 10(12) - 10(6) + 10(6) + 5(6) = 0$$

$$R_{AY} = 5 \text{ kN in direction shown}$$

Forces are summed horizontally:

$$\Sigma F_X = 0;\ +5 - R_{HX} = 0$$

$$R_{HX} = 5 \text{ kN in direction shown}$$

Forces are summed vertically:

$$\Sigma F_Y = 0;\ R_{AY} - 10 - 10 + R_{HY} - 10 = 0$$

$$R_{HY} = 25 \text{ kN in direction shown}$$

Example 6-3

Reactions on a truss.

Given: Truss with loads and reactions as shown.

To Find: Magnitude and direction of reactions.

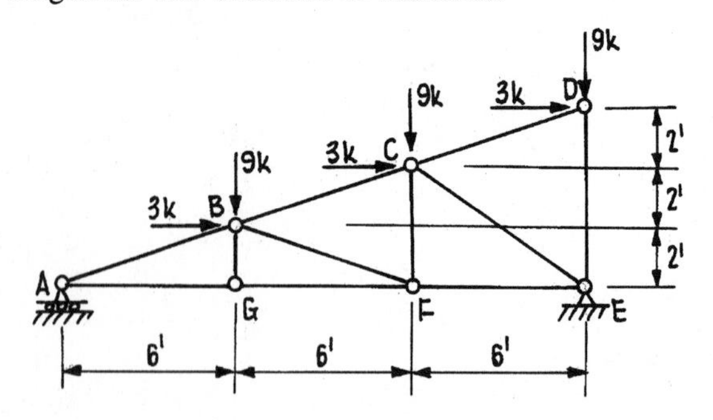

Solution: The entire truss is taken as a free body with all forces and unknown reactions shown.

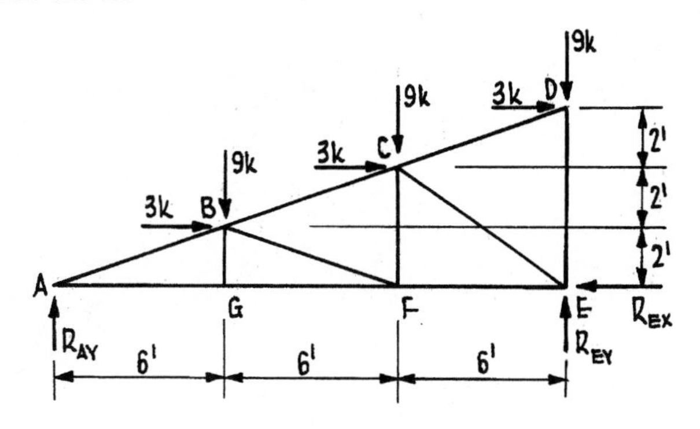

Moments are summed about point A to find R_{EY}:

$$\Sigma M_A = 0;\ 9(6) + 3(2) + 9(12) + 3(4) + 9(18) + 3(6) - R_{EY}(18)$$
$$R_{EY} = 20 \text{ kips in direction shown}$$

Forces are summed horizontally to find R_{EX}:

$$\Sigma F_X = 0;\ 3 + 3 + 3 - R_{EX} = 0$$
$$R_{EX} = 9 \text{ kips in direction shown}$$

Moments are summed about E to find R_{AY}:

$$\Sigma M_E = 0;\ R_{AY}(18) + 3(2) - 9(12) + 3(4) - 9(6) + 3(6) = 0$$
$$R_{AY} = 7 \text{ kips in direction shown}$$

As a check, sum forces vertically:

$$\Sigma F_Y = 0;\ R_{AY} - 9 - 9 - 9 + R_{EY} = 0$$
$$7 - 9 - 9 - 9 + 20 = 0$$
$$0 = 0 \text{ (OK)}$$

Example 6-4

Reactions on a truss.

Given: Water tower with loads and reactions as shown.

To Find: Magnitude and direction of reactions.

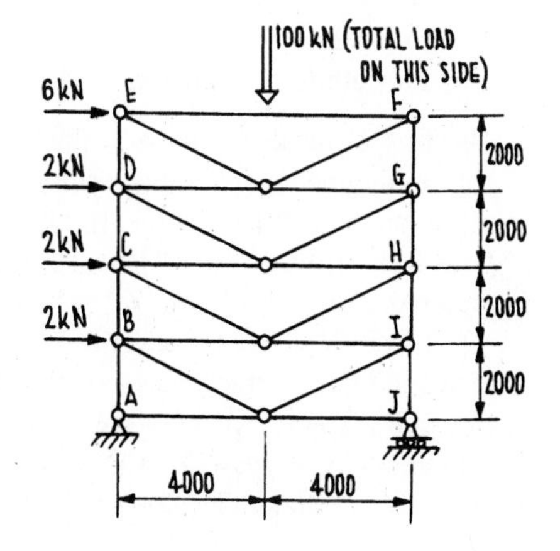

Solution: The entire truss is taken as a free body with all loads and unknown reactions shown.

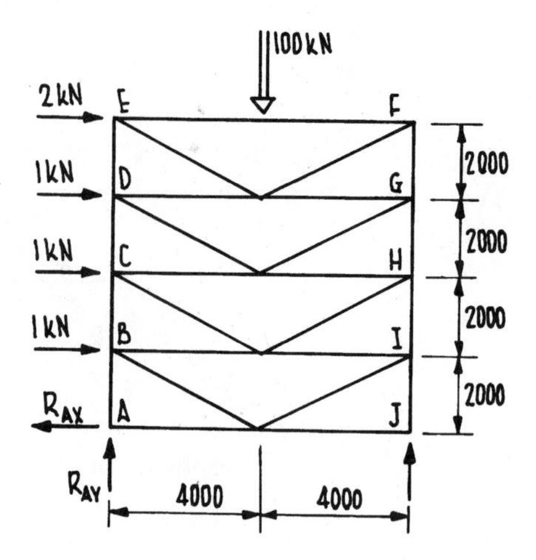

Moments are summed about point A to find R_{JY}:

$$\Sigma M_A = 0;\ 2(8) + 1(6) + 1(4) + 1(2) + 100(4) - R_{JY}(8) = 0$$
$$R_{JY} = 53.5 \text{ kN in direction shown}$$

Moments are summed about point J to find R_{AY}:

$$\Sigma M_J = 0;\ R_{AY}(8) + 1(2) + 1(4) + 1(6) + 2(8) - 100(4) = 0$$
$$R_{AY} = 46.5 \text{ kN in direction shown}$$

Sum forces horizontally to find R_{AX}:

$$\Sigma F_X = 0;\ 2 + 1 + 1 + 1 - R_{AX} = 0$$
$$R_{AX} = 5 \text{ kN in direction shown}$$

As a check, sum forces vertically:

$$\Sigma F_Y = 0;\ -100 + R_{AY} + R_{JY} = 0$$
$$-100 + 46.5 + 53.5 = 0$$
$$0 = 0 \text{ (OK)}$$

6.5 Member Forces by Method of Joints

Forces in individual truss members are found readily by simple statics. There are two approaches in common use for finding these forces:

1) Method of joints.
2) Method of sections.

The first of these approaches, the method of joints, is presented in this section.

In the method of joints, each hinge is removed as a free body. Any unknown forces acting on the hinge are found by summing forces vertically and horizontally. The solution progresses from joint to joint, utilizing the member forces from earlier solutions as required.

Since there is no resultant moment at a joint, the equation of moment equilibrium yields nothing of interest, leaving only the two equations of force equilibrium ($\Sigma F_X = 0$, $\Sigma F_Y = 0$). There can therefore be no more than two unknown forces at each joint if a solution is to be possible. Since the solution involves only force equilibrium, the method of joints is often called the method of force equilibrium.

Since no more than two unknowns may occur at any joint, it becomes necessary to plan the sequence in which the solution will be performed such that no more than two unknown forces will occur. Member forces used in earlier solutions must necessarily be used in following solutions, which means that numerical errors made in one solution will be propagated into all subsequent calculations. Extreme care must be exercised to avoid numerical errors and the resulting time-consuming tracking to correct such errors.

An example will illustrate the method of joints, or the method of force equilibrium, in finding the forces in truss members.

Example 6-5

Truss analysis by method of joints.

Given: Truss configuration and loads as shown. Reactions at *A* and *E* are given.

To Find: Force in each member.

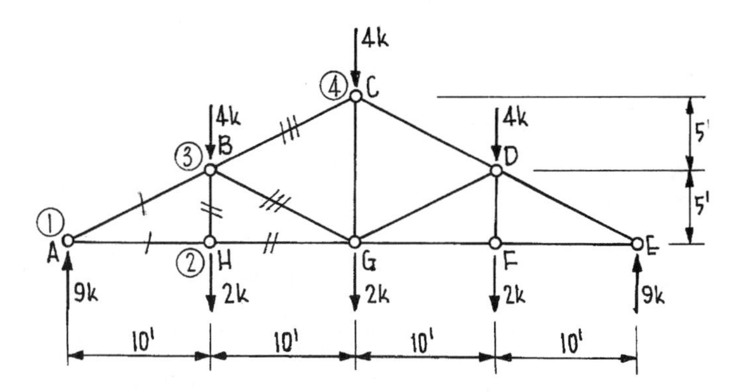

Solution: A separate summary sketch of the truss is prepared and kept aside; in this example, this summary sketch is shown at the end of the example. When a force is determined, its value is entered immediately on the summary sketch.

The sequence of joints to be used in the solution is established:

1) Begin at joint *A*. There are two members and therefore two unknown forces on the joint at *A*; joint *A* can therefore be solved. A single tally mark is placed on members *AB* and *AH* since they can be solved. The number 1 is encircled at this joint.

2) Proceed to joint *B*. With the force in member *AB* known from the solution of joint *A*, there are still three unknown member forces at joint *B*. Joint *B* cannot yet be solved.

3) Proceed to joint *H*. With the force in member *AH* known from the solution of joint *A*, there are only two unknown member forces remaining; joint *H* can now be solved. A double tally mark is placed on members *HB* and *HG* to indicate that they are solved second. The number 2 is encircled at joint *H*.

4) Proceed to joint *B*. With the force in members *AB* and *HB* now known, there remains only two unknowns; joint *B* can now be solved. A triple tally mark is placed on members *BG* and *BC* to indicate that they are solved third. The number 3 is encircled at joint *B*.

5) The symmetry of the truss is noted. Loads in symmetrical members will of course be equal, leaving only the force in member *CG* as an unknown. Joint *C* will be solved to find the force in member *CG*; a tally mark is placed on member *CG* to indicate that it is the fourth solution. The number 4 is encircled at this joint.

6) The joint *G* remains the only joint that has not been solved. All forces coming into joint *G* have already been computed, however. Joint *G* therefore becomes the "checking" joint for all earlier calculations; if joint *G* is not in equilibrium, there is an error somewhere in the earlier solutions. Joint *G* is checked for equilibrium.

The solution can now begin, with joint *A* taken first. The joint at *A* is removed as a free body with all forces shown on the joint. Known forces are shown in their correct directions; unknown forces are shown in tension.

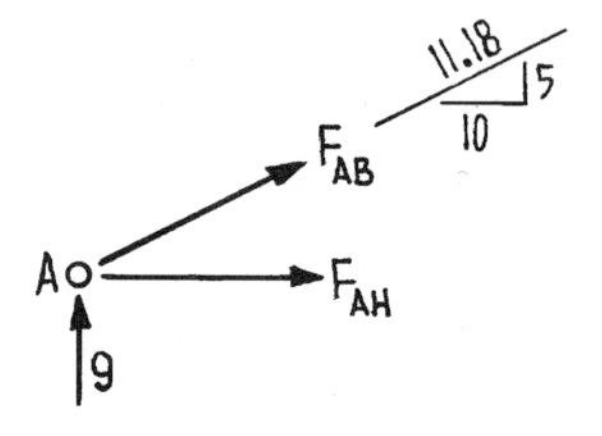

$$\Sigma F_V = 0;\ +9 + F_{AB}(^5/_{11.18}) = 0$$
$$F_{AB} = -20.12 \text{ kips (compression)}$$

$$\Sigma F_H = 0;\ F_{AH} + F_{AB}(^{10}/_{11.18}) = 0$$
$$F_{AH} = +18.0 \text{ kips (tension)}$$

These values are entered immediately on the summary sketch (shown at the end of the solution).

Joint *H* is solved next. F_{AH} is entered in its correct direction, pulling on the joint. All unknown forces are shown in tension.

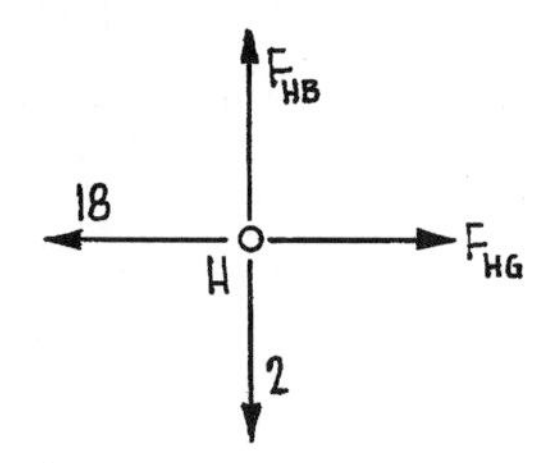

$$\Sigma F_V = 0;\ -2 + F_{HB} = 0$$
$$F_{HB} = 2 \text{ kips (tension)}$$

$$\Sigma F_H = 0;\ -18 + F_{HG} = 0$$
$$F_{HG} = 18 \text{ kips (tension)}$$

These values are entered immediately on the summary sketch (shown at the end of the solution).

Joint B is solved next. Forces AB and HB are entered in their correct directions. F_{AB} is in compression, pushing on the joint, and F_{HB} is in tension, pulling on the joint. The unknown forces are shown in tension.

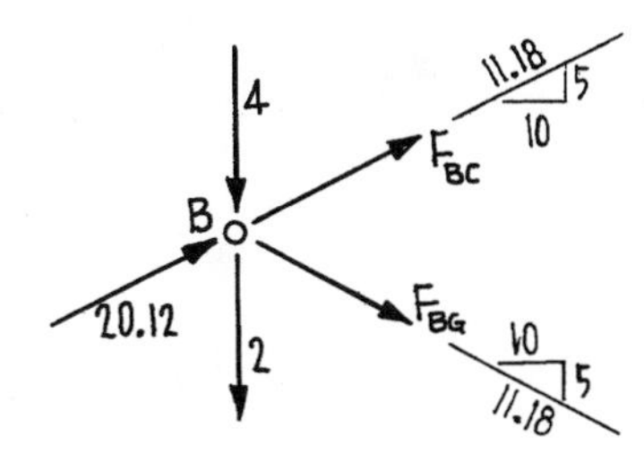

$$\Sigma F_V = 0;\ 20.12(^5/_{11.18}) - 4 - 2 + F_{BC}(^5/_{11.18}) - F_{BG}(^5/_{11.18}) = 0$$

$$\Sigma F_H = 0;\ 20.12(^{10}/_{11.18}) + F_{BC}(^{10}/_{11.18}) + F_{BG}(^{10}/_{11.18}) = 0$$

Solve simultaneously to find:

$$F_{BC} = -13.42 \text{ kips (compression)}$$
$$F_{BG} = -6.72 \text{ kips (compression)}$$

These values are entered immediately on the summary sketch (shown at the end of the solution).

Joint C is solved next. Forces BC and DC are equal, and both are in compression. Force CG is shown in tension.

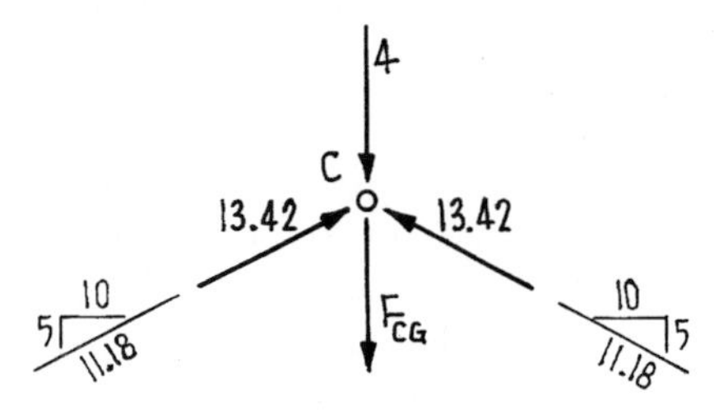

$$\Sigma F_V = 0;\ 13.42(^5/_{11.18}) - 4 - F_{CG} + 13.42(^5/_{11.18}) = 0$$
$$F_{CG} = 8.00 \text{ (tension)}$$

This value is entered immediately on the summary sketch (shown at the end of the solution).

Joint G is now checked to see that it is in equilibrium. All forces at joint G are now known and are shown on the free body in their correct directions.

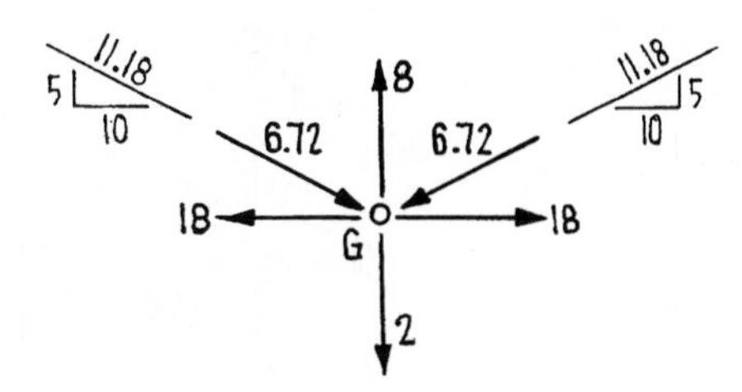

$$\Sigma F_V = 0;\ -6.72(^5/_{11.18}) + 8 - 6.72(^5/_{11.18}) - 2 = 0$$
$$0 = 0 \text{ (OK)}$$

The check shows that there are no numerical errors. The final solution is shown in the following sketch.

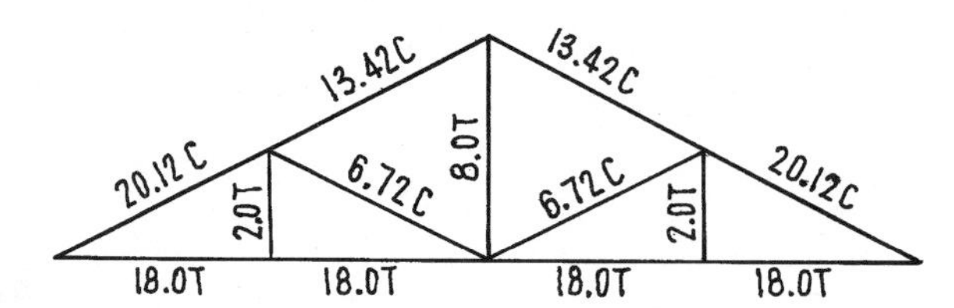

Joint H in Example 6-5 is a special type of joint. Refer to the solution of joint H in the example. All external loads coming into the joint are seen to be transmitted unchanged to joint B. Joint H is identified as a *transfer joint* and member HB is identified as a *transfer member*. In future solutions, such members will be identified and their forces solved by simple inspection.

The major points in the procedure of Example 6-5 are summarized:

- Plan a sequence of joints to be solved such that no more than two unknowns occur in any solution.
- Remove the joints in the planned sequence, showing each joint as a free body. Known forces are shown in their correct sense. Unknown forces are shown in tension. (Transfer joints may be solved visually without a free body.)
- Solve for the unknown forces on the free body by summing forces vertically and horizontally.
- When a force has been determined, its value is entered immediately on a summary sketch of the truss, without algebraic sign, followed by C or T to indicate compression or tension.
- When all forces have been determined, there will be one last joint which has not been used in a solution but for which all forces have been determined elsewhere. Check to see that this joint is in equilibrium. If it is not, there is a numerical error in the calculations.

The emphasis on good "housekeeping" practices in Example 6-5 is essential. The greatest disadvantage in using the method of joints is that of making numerical errors. The use of good housekeeping practices will help to reduce the chance of making such errors.

A second example in the method of joints will further illustrate the procedure.

Example 6-6

Truss analysis by method of joints.

Given: Truss configuration and loads as shown. Reactions at supports are shown.

To Find: Force in each member.

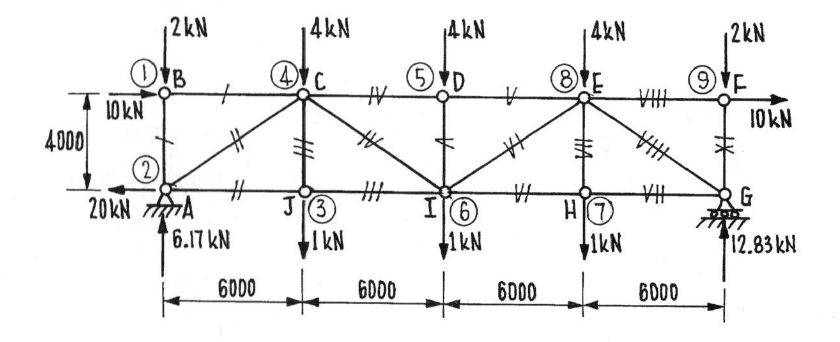

Solution: A summary sketch is prepared and set aside. It will be included at the end of the solution.

It is noted that there are several transfer joints. Joints *B*, *J*, *D*, *H* and *F* are all transfer joints. Free bodies will not be required to solve these joints.

The sequence of joints to be solved is now established. Joint *B* has only two unknowns; it will be solved first. A single tally mark is placed on the two unknown member forces *BA* and *BC*, and an encircled 1 is placed at the joint.

Joint *A* is solved second. A double tally mark is placed on the two unknown member forces *AJ* and *AC* and an encircled 2 is placed at the joint.

Joint *J* is solved next. A triple tally mark is placed on the two unknown member forces *JI* and *JC* and an encircled 3 is placed at the joint.

The sequence is extended through the remainder of the joints in the same way, leaving only joint *G* unsolved. Joint *G* will be used as the checking joint.

The solution is now performed in the sequence just determined.

Joint *B* is first. It is identified as a transfer joint. Forces in members *BC* and *BA* are solved by inspection and their values entered on the summary sketch:

F_{BC} = 10 kN (compression); F_{BA} = 2 kN (compression)

Joint *A* is second. A free body is drawn, with known forces shown in their correct directions and unknown forces shown in tension.

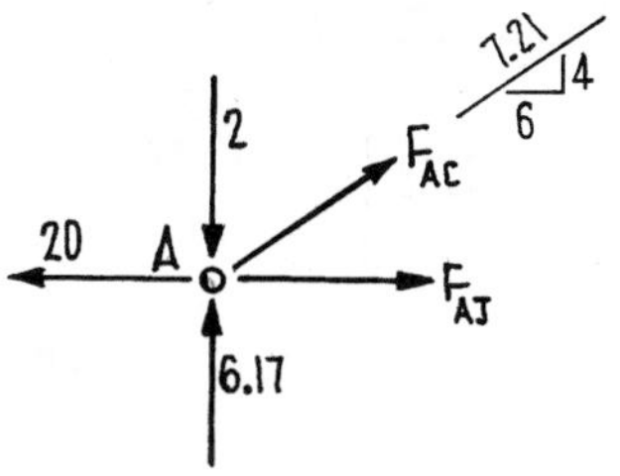

$\Sigma F_Y = 0$

$-2 + 6.17 + F_{AC}(4/7.21) = 0$

$F_{AC} = -7.52$ kN (compression)

$\Sigma F_X = 0$

$-20 + F_{AC}(6/7.21) + F_{AJ} = 0$

$F_{AJ} = 26.26$ kN (tension)

These values are entered on the summary sketch:

Joint *J* is third. It is identified as a transfer joint. Forces in members *JI* and *JC* are solved by inspection and their values entered on the summary sketch:

F_{JI} = 26.26 kN (tension); F_{JC} = 1 kN (tension)

Joint *C* is next. A free body is drawn, with known forces shown in their correct directions and unknown forces shown in tension.

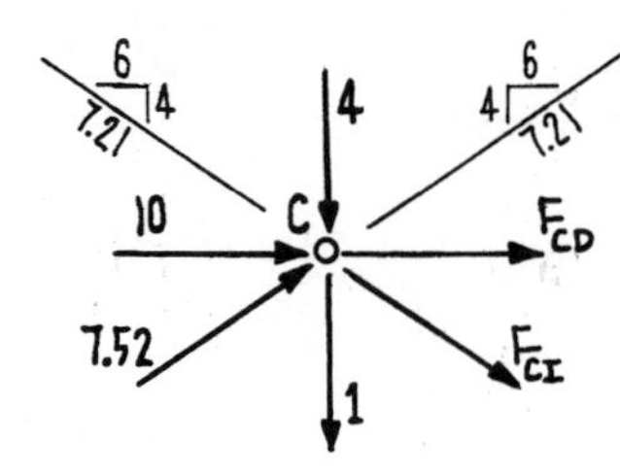

$\Sigma F_Y = 0$

$7.52(^4/_{7.21}) - 4 - 1 - F_{CI}(^4/_{7.21}) = 0$

$F_{CI} = -1.50$ kN (compression)

$\Sigma F_X = 0$

$10 + 7.52(^6/_{7.21}) + F_{CD} + F_{CI}(^6/_{7.21}) = 0$

$F_{CD} = -15.02$ kN (compression)

These values are entered on the summary sketch.

Joint *D* is next. It is identified as a transfer joint. Forces in members *DE* and *DI* are solved by inspection and their values entered on the summary sketch:

$F_{DE} = 15.57$ kN (compression); $F_{DI} = 4$ kN (compression)

The solution proceeds through all joints in the sequence. At the conclusion of the sequence, the summary sketch contains the following values:

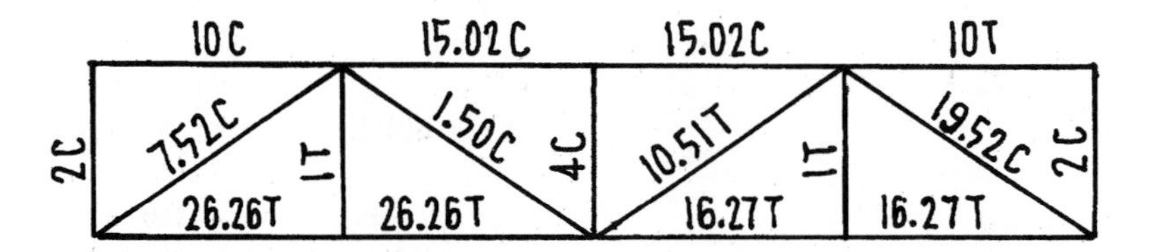

Joint *G* becomes the checking joint. All forces at joint *G* have been found from other solutions.

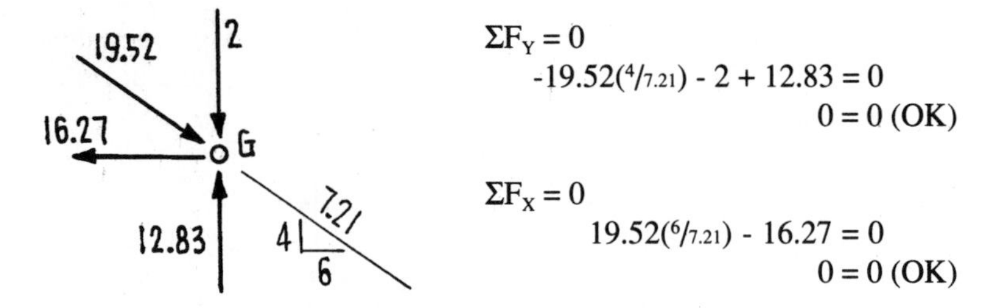

$\Sigma F_Y = 0$

$-19.52(^4/_{7.21}) - 2 + 12.83 = 0$

$0 = 0$ (OK)

$\Sigma F_X = 0$

$19.52(^6/_{7.21}) - 16.27 = 0$

$0 = 0$ (OK)

Joint *G* is in equilibrium, indicating that the numerical calculations are correct.

There is a type of truss called a K-truss that can sometimes cause a problem when one is trying to establish the sequence of joints. An example will illustrate a means to handle such trusses.

Example 6-7

Truss analysis by method of joints.

Given: K-truss configuration and loads as shown.

To Find: Sequence of joints to be used in the solution.

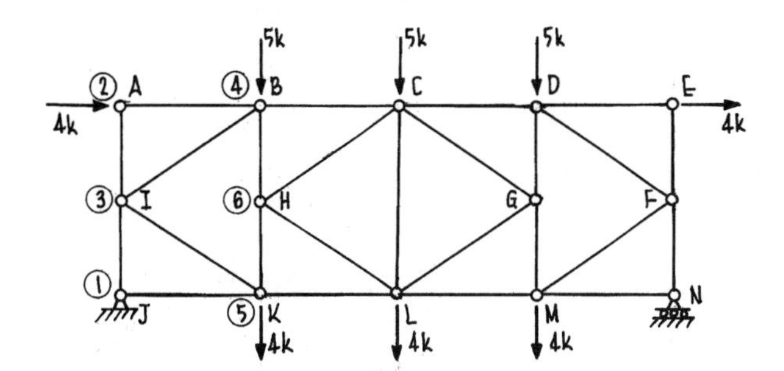

Solution: The selection of joints to be used in the sequence progresses, as usual, up to joint 6, as shown. Thereafter, both joint *C* and joint *L* have three unknowns and cannot be solved next.

Proceed to joint *N* and come backwards through joints *N*, *E*, *F*, *D*, *M* and *G*. Joint *C* can now be solved.

Joint *L* then becomes the checking joint.

Before leaving the method of joints, it is again noted that its biggest single disadvantage is in the potential for propagating numerical errors into succeeding joint solutions. Correcting such errors can indeed be a frustrating and time-consuming exercise. It is an ever-present hazard in any manual solution for member forces in a truss.

A strong advantage of the method of joints, however, lies in its mechanical simplicity and repetitiveness. For that reason, the procedure is ideally suited to computerized solutions. And, since the computer cannot make numerical errors, the biggest single disadvantage of the method of joints disappears.

Almost certainly, a computerized solution for member forces in a truss will utilize the method of joints. Such computerized solutions are readily available in the industry but are not recommended for use by students. Only when the student understands the method of solution should the student be permitted to use such software.

6.6 Member Forces by Method of Sections

It was noted in earlier discussions that there are two approaches in common use for truss analysis:

1) Method of joints.
2) Method of sections.

The second of these approaches, the method of sections is presented here.

In the method of sections, a section is taken of the truss, exposing the member force that is to be determined. A free body is then drawn for the part of the truss lying to one side of that section, with all unknown forces shown. Moments are then summed about some point in the plane such that all unknowns are eliminated except the one member force that is to be determined; in some cases, forces may be summed (rather than moments) to achieve the same result. Successive sections are cut, and the method is applied until every member force has been found.

In the method of sections, no member force found in an earlier solution is used in succeeding solutions. The primary disadvantage noted earlier in the method of joints, that of propagation of error, has therefore been eliminated. The method of sections has a disadvantage of its own, however, in that some degree of skill is required in choosing where to take the sections.

The method of sections is best illustrated by an example. Discussions following the example will then summarize the method.

Example 6-8

Truss analysis by method of sections.

Given: Truss configuration and loads as shown. Reactions at supports are shown.

To Find: Force in each member.

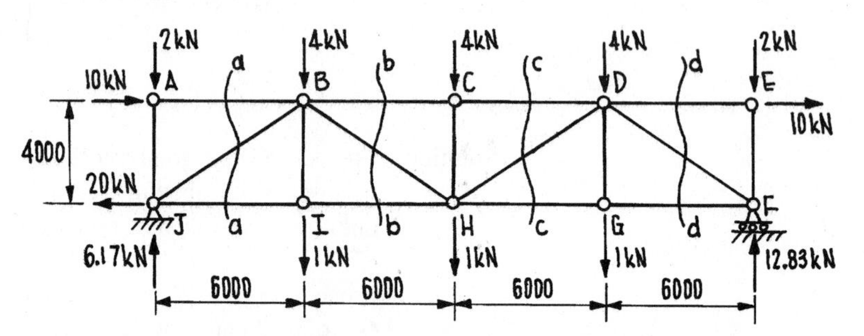

Solution: As with the method of joints, the results of the analysis will be entered on a summary sketch. The summary sketch for this example is kept aside and is shown at the end of the example.

Section *a-a* is taken in the first panel. The free body to the left of that section is shown in the following sketch.

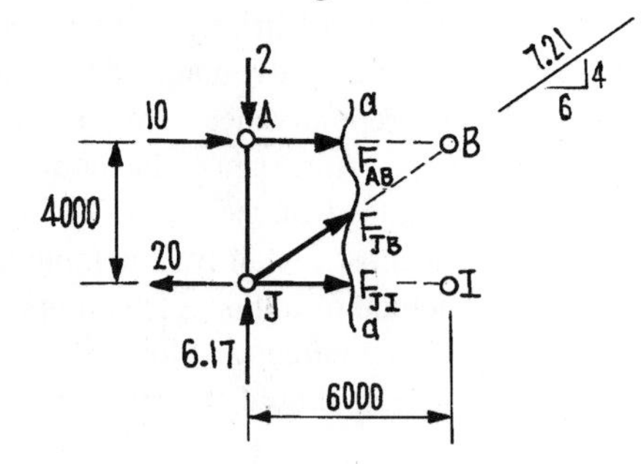

The unknown member forces F_{AB}, F_{JB} and F_{JI} have been exposed by the cut section. They are shown on the free body in tension.

Moments are taken about joint J. Forces F_{JI} and F_{JB} pass through joint J and are thus eliminated from the equation, leaving only the force F_{AB}:

$$\Sigma M_J = 0;\ 10(4) + F_{AB}(4) = 0$$

$$F_{AB} = -10 \text{ kN (compression)}$$

Moments are now summed about joint B, eliminating forces F_{AB} and F_{JB}, leaving only the force F_{JI}:

$$\Sigma M_B = 0;\ -2(6) + 20(4) + 6.17(6) - F_{JI}(4) = 0$$

$$F_{JI} = 26.26 \text{ kN (tension)}$$

Forces are now summed vertically, eliminating the two horizontal forces F_{AB} and F_{JI}, leaving only the force F_{JB}:

$$\Sigma F_Y = 0;\ 6.17 - 2 + F_{JB}(^4/_{7.21}) = 0$$
$$F_{JB} = -7.52 \text{ kN (compression)}$$

These forces are entered immediately on the summary sketch.

The next section is section *b-b* in the second panel. The free body to the left of section *b-b* is shown in the following sketch.

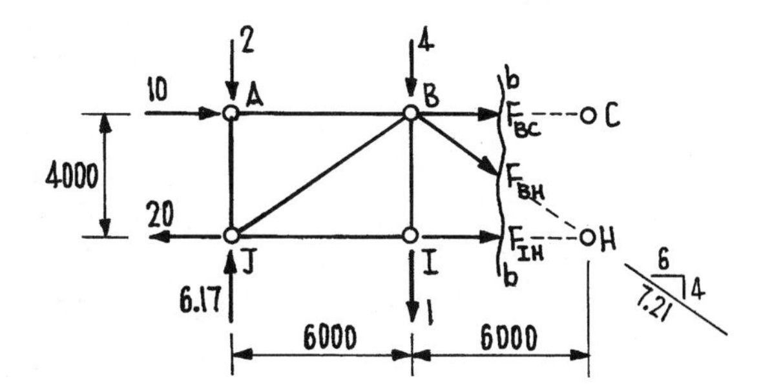

Summing moments about joint *B* eliminates F_{BC} and F_{BH}, leaving only the force F_{IH}:

$$\Sigma M_B = 0;\ -2(6) + 20(4) + 6.17(6) - F_{IH}(4) = 0$$
$$F_{IH} = 26.26 \text{ kN (tension)}$$

Summing moments about joint *H* eliminates F_{BH} and F_{IH}, leaving only the force F_{BC}:

$$\Sigma M_H = 0;\ 10(4) - 2(12) - 4(6) + F_{BC}(4)$$
$$+ 6.17(12) - 1(6) = 0$$
$$F_{BC} = -15.01 \text{ kN (compression)}$$

Summing forces vertically eliminates the two horizontal forces F_{BC} and F_{IH}, leaving only F_{BH}:

$$\Sigma F_Y = 0;\ -2 - 4 + 6.17 - 1 - F_{BH}(^4/_{7.21}) = 0$$
$$F_{BY} = -1.50 \text{ kN (compression)}$$

These values are entered immediately on the summary sketch.

The next section is taken as section *c-c*. The free body to the left of section *c-c* is shown in the following sketch.

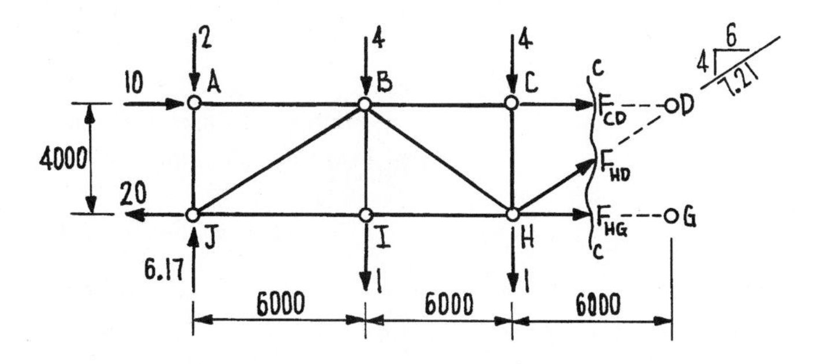

Moments are summed about joint H, eliminating forces F_{HG} and F_{HD}, leaving only the force F_{CD}:

$$\Sigma M_H = 0; -2(12) + 10(4) - 4(6) + F_{CD}(4) + 6.17(12) - 1(6) = 0$$
$$F_{CD} = -15.01 \text{ kN (compression)}$$

Moments are summed about joint D, eliminating forces F_{CD} and F_{HD}, leaving only force F_{HG}:

$$\Sigma M_D = 0; -2(18) - 4(12) - 4(6) - F_{HG}(4) - 1(6) - 1(12) + 6.17(18) + 20(4) = 0$$
$$F_{HG} = 16.27 \text{ kN (tension)}$$

Forces are summed vertically, eliminating the two horizontal forces F_{CD} and F_{HG}, leaving only F_{HD}:

$$\Sigma F_Y = 0; -2 - 4 - 4 + 6.17 - 1 - 1 + F_{HD}(4/7.21) = 0$$
$$F_{HD} = 10.51 \text{ kN (tension)}$$

These values are entered immediately on the summary sketch.

The next section is taken as section d-d. The free bodies to the left of the section are becoming too cumbersome, so the free body for this case will be shown to the right of the section.

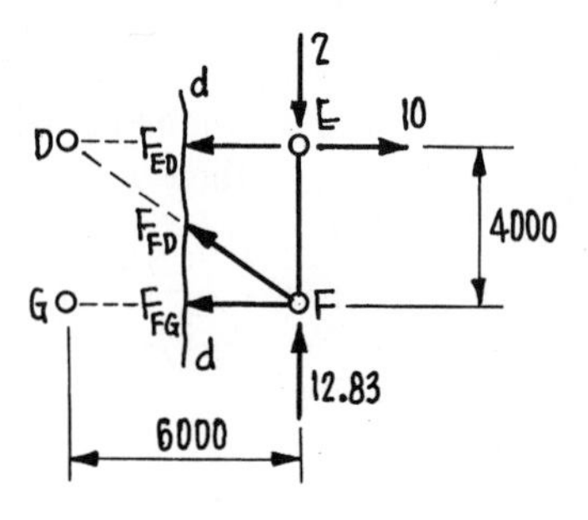

Moments are summed about joint F, eliminating F_{FD} and F_{FG}, leaving only F_{ED}:

$$\Sigma M_F = 0; -F_{ED}(4) + 10(4) = 0$$
$$F_{ED} = 10 \text{ kN (tension)}$$

Moments are summed about joint D, eliminating F_{ED} and F_{FD}, leaving only F_{FG}:

$$\Sigma M_D = 0; 2(6) - 12.83(6) + F_{FG}(4) = 0$$
$$F_{FG} = 16.25 \text{ kN (tension)}$$

Forces are summed vertically, eliminating the two horizontal forces F_{ED} and F_{FG}, leaving only F_{FD}:

$$\Sigma F_Y = 0; -2 + 12.83 + F_{FD}(4/7.21) = 0$$
$$F_{FD} = -19.52 \text{ kN (compression)}$$

These values are entered immediately on the summary sketch.

The remaining member forces are seen to be those in the vertical members. All of these members are transfer members and may be solved by inspection:

F_{AJ} = 2 kN (compression)
F_{CH} = 4 kN (compression)
F_{EF} = 2 kN (compression)

F_{IB} = 1 kN (tension)
F_{GD} = 1 kN (tension)

These values are entered directly on the summary sketch.

The final results are shown on the following summary sketch. They are of course identical to those of Example 6-6, which is the same truss.

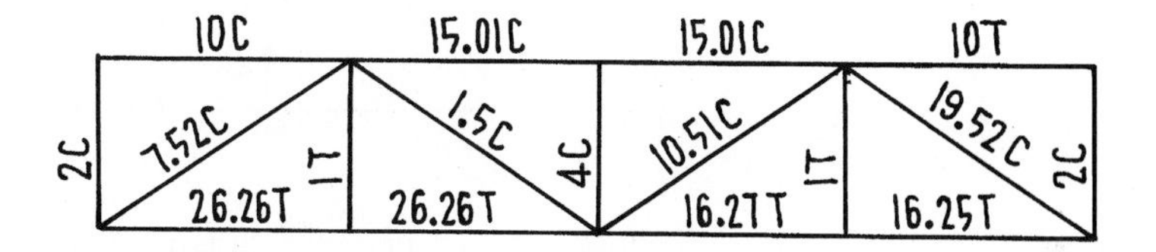

The major points in the procedure of Example 6-8 are summarized:

- Select a section that cuts the members such that the desired member forces will be exposed.
- In selecting a section, try to expose no more than three forces since there are only three equations of equilibrium.
- Identify some point to take moments about (if one exists) such that only the desired member force will appear in the equation when moments are summed. Such a point will occur at the point of intersection of the two forces that are to be eliminated.
- Repeat (where possible) to find other member forces.
- Two forces that are parallel have no point of intersection and therefore cannot be eliminated by summing moments. In such cases, forces can be summed perpendicular to these forces, thereby eliminating these forces from the resulting equation.
- When a force has been determined, its value is entered on a summary sketch of the truss, without algebraic sign, followed by C or T to indicate compression or tension.

A second example in the method of sections will illustrate the method when there are no parallel members. It will be seen in this example that it is not always possible to eliminate all unknowns except one. In such cases, a solution by method of joints may sometimes be necessary to find a particular force.

Example 6-9

Truss analysis by method of sections.

Given: Truss configuration and loads as shown. Reactions are shown on the sketch.

To Find: Forces in the truss members.

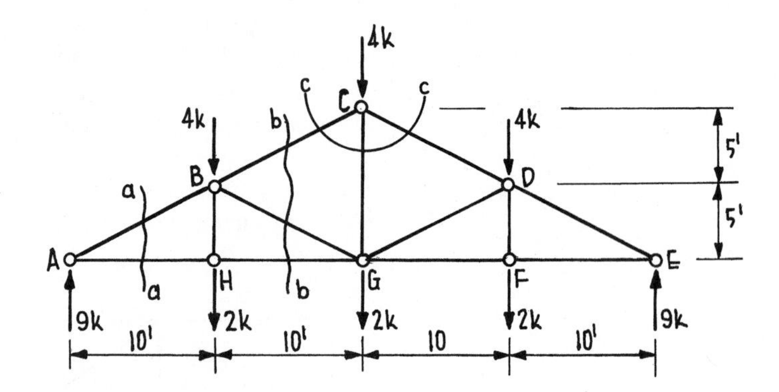

Solution: A summary sketch is prepared aside. It will be entered at the end of the example.

The symmetry of the truss and loads is recognized.

Joint H is identified as a transfer joint. The force in member HB is found by inspection and entered on the summary sketch:

$$F_{HB} = 2 \text{ kips (tension)}$$

Section a-a is taken first. The free body to the left of section a-a is shown in the following sketch.

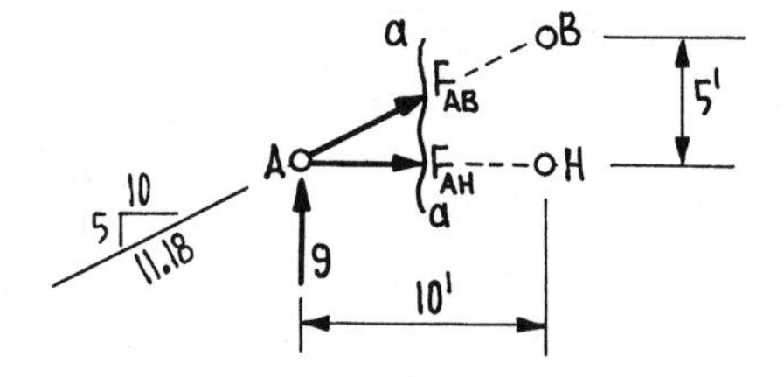

Summing moments about B eliminates F_{AB}:

$$\Sigma M_B = 0; \ 9(10) - F_{AH}(5) = 0$$
$$F_{AH} = 18 \text{ kips (tension)}$$

Summing forces vertically eliminates F_{AH}:

$$\Sigma F_Y = 0; \ 9 + F_{AB}(5/11.18) = 0$$
$$F_{AB} = -20.12 \text{ kips (compression)}$$

These forces are entered immediately on the summary sketch.

Section *b-b* is taken next. The free body to the left of section *b-b* is shown in the following sketch.

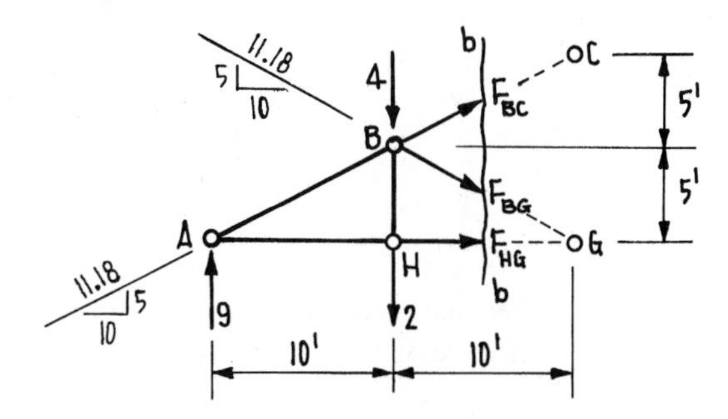

Summing moments about *B* eliminates F_{BC} and F_{BG}:

$$\Sigma M_A = 0; 4(10) + 2(10) + F_{BG}(^{10}/_{11.18})5 + F_{BG}(^{5}/_{11.18})10 = 0$$
$$F_{HG} = 18 \text{ kips (tension)}$$

Summing moments about a eliminates F_{BC} and F_{HG}. The moment of the remaining force F_{BG} about joint *A* is found by summing the moments of its vertical and horizontal components about *A*:

$$\Sigma M_A = 0; 4(10) + 2(10) + F_{BG}(^{10}/_{11.18})5 + F_{BG}(^{5}/_{11.18})10 = 0$$
$$F_{BG} = - 6.71 \text{ kips (compression)}$$

Summing moments about *G* eliminates F_{BG} and F_{HG}. The moment of the remaining force F_{BC} about joint *G* is found by summing the moments of its vertical and horizontal components about *G*:

$$\Sigma M_G = 0; 9(20) - 4(10) - 2(10) + F_{BC}(^{10}/_{11.18})5$$
$$+ F_{BC}(^{5}/_{11.18})10 = 0$$
$$F_{BC} = -13.42 \text{ kips (compression)}$$

The force in the remaining member CG cannot be found by eliminating all unknowns except F_{CG}. The solution for F_{CG} will be performed by the method of joints.

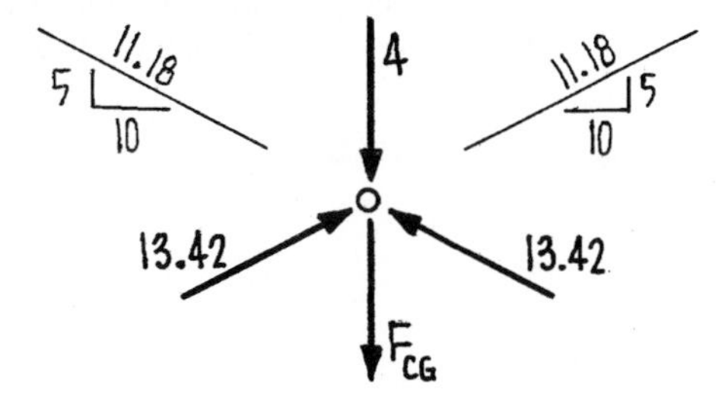

$$\Sigma F_Y = 0; - 4 + 13.42(^{5}/_{11.18}) + 13.42(^{5}/_{11.18}) - F_{CG} = 0$$
$$F_{CG} = 8.00 \text{ kips (tension)}$$

The results of the analysis are shown on the following summary sketch. These results are of course identical to those of Example 6-5 for the same truss.

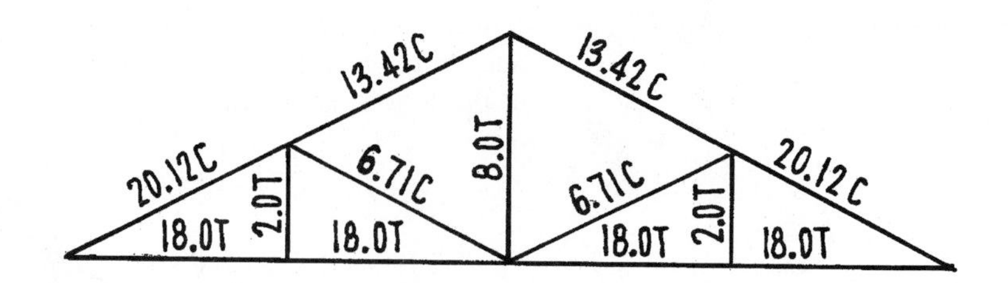

In the foregoing examples, separate free bodies were drawn for each section. As one becomes more familiar with the method, such separate sketches will probably not be necessary. One simply selects the position where the section is to be taken, then covers up the unwanted portion of the sketch with a piece of scratch paper; the visible portion will then be the free body. Summing of forces and moments then proceeds as usual, recognizing that the unknown forces are always assumed to be in tension, that is, directed away from the joint where they are attached.

Review Questions

1. What kind of loads occur in truss members?
2. Why is a truss so efficient in its utilization of materials?
3. What is the difference between a Parker truss and a Bowstring truss?
4. What is a panel point in a truss?
5. Define a properly formed truss.
6. What end conditions are assumed for the ends of truss members?
7. What is the difference in computing reactions for a truss and in computing reactions for a solid beam or frame?
8. Name the two methods in common use for computing member forces in a truss.
9. What is another name for the method of force equilibrium?
10. In the method of force equilibrium, what is the maximum number of unknowns that can be found at a single panel point?
11. What makes the method of force equilibrium a potentially time-consuming type of solution?
12. What is the primary advantage of the method of sections over the method of joints?
13. What disadvantage is introduced in the method of sections that did not ocur in the method of joints?
14. How is it that numerical errors can propagate into succeeding calculations in the method of joints but not in the method of sections?
15. Which of the two methods would most likely be used to program a computer solution?

CHAPTER

7

LOADS AND REACTIONS ON STRUCTURES

7.1 Definitions and Concepts

All of the external forces that act on a structure are called loads. Such forces may be imposed by gravity, wind, earthquake, water pressure, earth pressure, temperature changes, or any number of other causes. Regardless of the source, most of the loads occur in only a few recognizable types. The most common of those types are described in the following figures.

Figure 7-1 Concentrated load such as a wheel load, a safe, or heavy file, given in lbs or N.

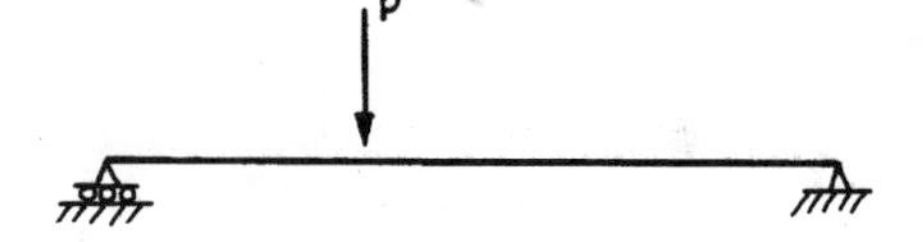

Figure 7-2 Uniformly distributed load such as floor loads or roof loads, given in lbs/ft or N/m.

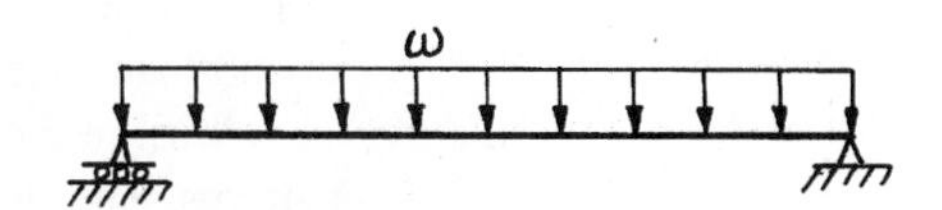

Figure 7-3 Uniformly varying loads, such as fluid pressure from standing water or wet concrete. Given in lbs/ft or N/m at the maximum point.

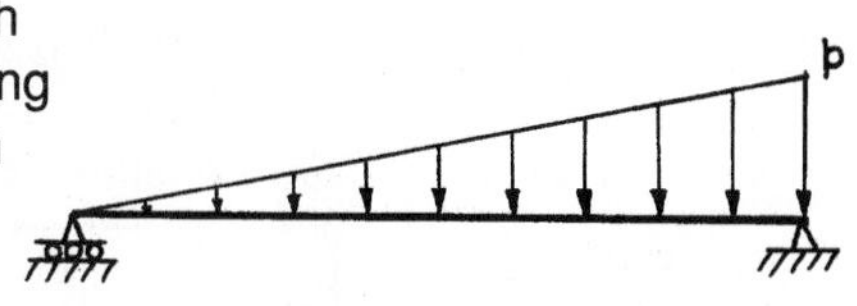

Figure 7-4 Applied moment, such as a moment produced by framing one member into another, given in lbs · ft or N · m.

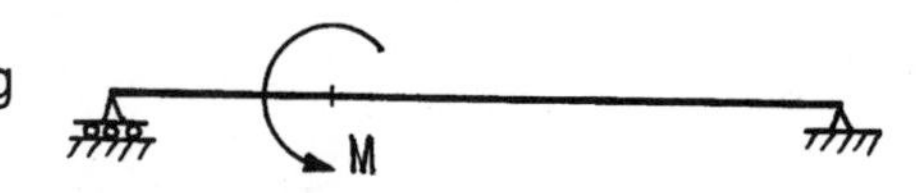

7.2 Loads and Load Systems

Loads do not always occur singly. Often, they occur in combinations, and often, the combinations will occur in patterns. Such patterns of loads may be symmetrical or antisymmetrical as shown in Figure 7-5.

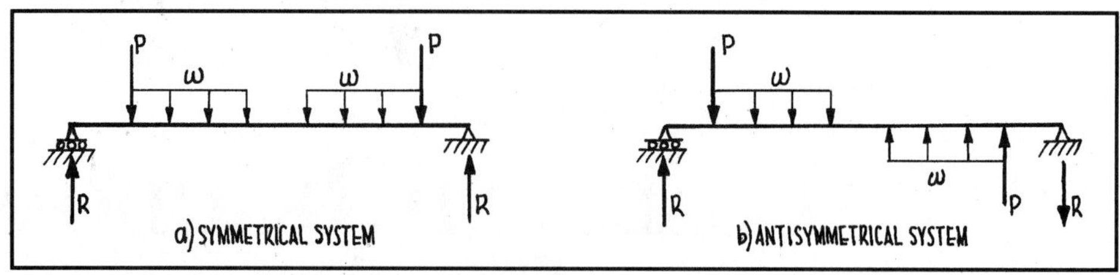

Figure 7-5 Patterns of load on a beam.

Where loads occur in recognizable patterns, such as those of Figure 7-5, the reactions can often be found intuitively. The reactions for the symmetrical load system of Figure 7-5a, for example, will also be symmetrical, that is, they will be equal and they will both be upward as shown. Similarly, the reactions for the antisymmetrical load system of Figure 7-5b will also be antisymmetrical, that is, they will be equal, but opposite in direction as shown.

The resultant force exerted by the uniformly distributed load of Figure 7-2 is that of a system of parallel forces. As shown in Figure 7-6, the magnitude of the resultant of a distributed load is the load per foot, w, multiplied by the number of feet, b. The location of the resultant is, as always, at the centroid of the load diagram.

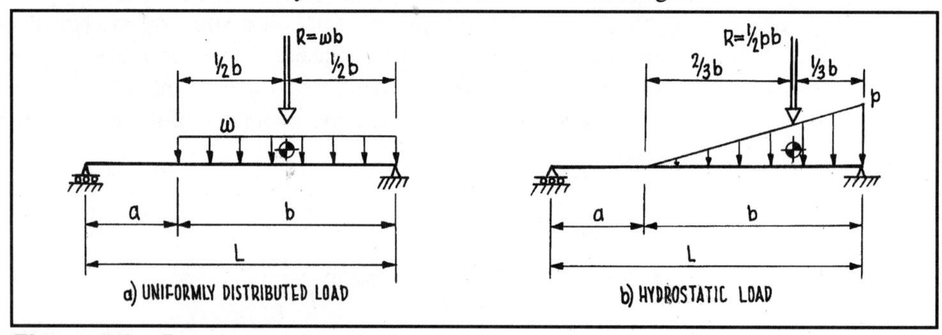

Figure 7-6 Resultants of load.

Similarly for the hydrostatic load of Figure 7-3, the resultant force is the area of the triangular load diagram, $^1/_2pb$. The location of the resultant is, as always, at the centroid of the load diagram as shown.

Most of the loads that occur on structures will occur in one of these relatively simple patterns. The reactions produced by these loads, in various combinations, is the subject of the following sections.

7.3 Reactions on Cantilever Beams

A cantilever beam is one that projects outward from its support, having an unsupported "free" end. A typical example of a cantilever beam is shown in Figure 7-7. Cantilevers are sometimes called overhanging beams.

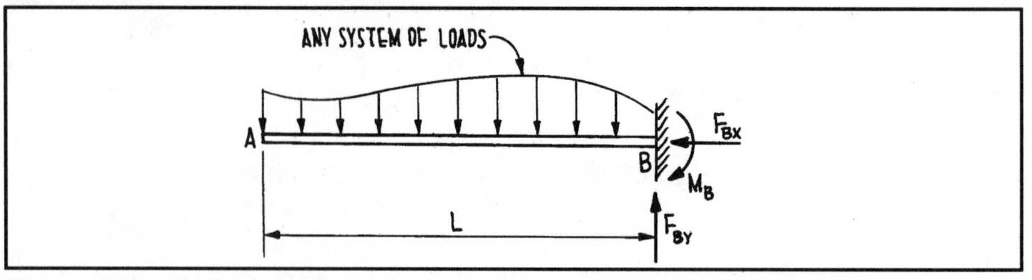

Figure 7-7 Typical cantilever beam.

Reactions on a cantilever beam are all located at the fixed end as shown in Figure 7-7. The fixed support can develop both horizontal and vertical reactions as well as a resisting moment. For cantilevers, all three reactions are seen to occur at a single point.

Some examples will illustrate the calculation of reactions on a cantilever.

Example 7-1

Reactions on a cantilever.

Given: Cantilever beam loaded as shown.

To Find: Reactions at the support.

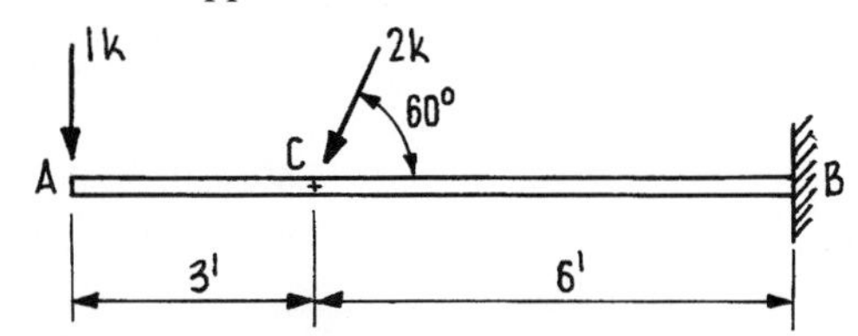

Solution: The beam *AB* is removed as a free body. All loads are resolved into their *x* and *y* components. Reactions at *B* are shown in their positive sense.

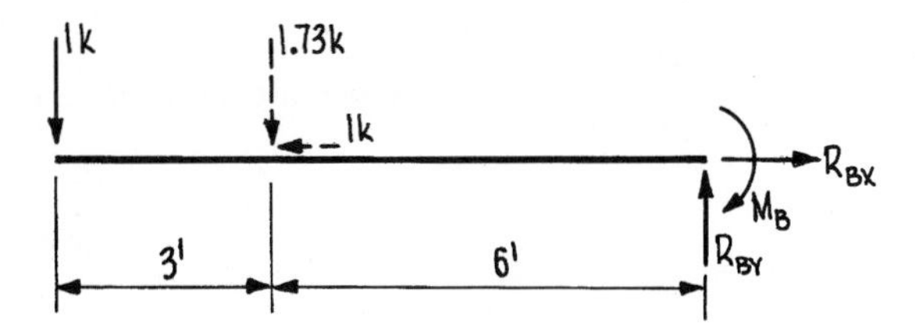

The mathematical laws of equilibrium are now applied. Summing moments about point *B* eliminates two of the three unknown reactions:

$$\Sigma M_B = 0; \quad -1(9) - 1.73(6) - 1(0) + M_B = 0$$
$$M_B = 19.4 \text{ kip·ft}$$

Forces are now summed vertically:

$$\Sigma F_Y = 0; \quad -1 - 1.73 + R_{BY} = 0$$
$$R_{BY} = 2.73 \text{ kips}$$

Forces are now summed horizontally:

$$\Sigma F_X = 0; \quad -1 + R_{BX} = 0$$
$$R_{BX} = 1 \text{ kip}$$

Example 7-2

Reactions on a cantilever.

Given: Cantilever beam load as shown.

To Find: Reactions at the support.

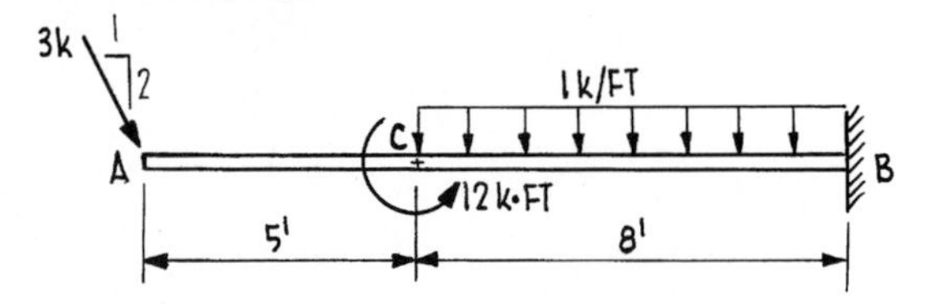

Solutions: The beam AB is removed as a free body. All loads are resolved into their x and y components. The resultant of the distributed load is entered and its line of action is located. Reactions at B are shown in their positive sense.

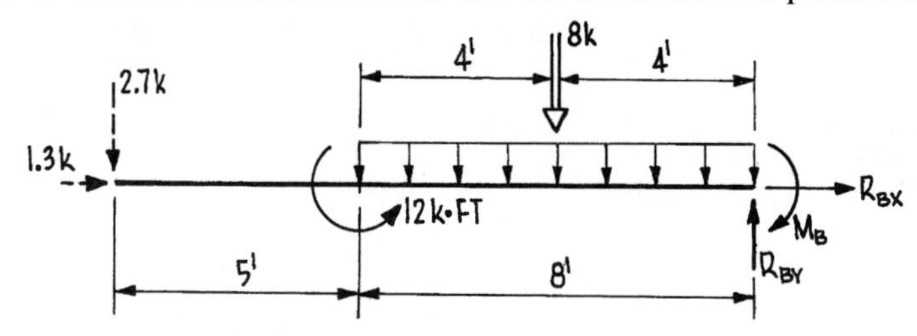

The mathematical laws of equilibrium are now applied. Moments are summed about B to eliminate R_{BX} and R_{BY} from the resulting equations:

$$\Sigma M_B = 0; \quad -2.7(13) - 12 - 8(4) + M_B = 0$$
$$M_B = 79.1 \text{ kip·ft}$$

Forces are summed vertically:

$$\Sigma F_Y = 0; \quad -2.7 - 8 + R_{BY} = 0$$
$$R_{BY} = 10.7 \text{ kips}$$

Forces are summed horizontally:

$$\Sigma F_X = 0; \quad +1.3 + R_{BX} = 0$$
$$R_{BX} = -1.3 \text{ kips (to the left)}$$

Example 7-3

Reactions on a cantilever.

Given: Cantilever beam as shown.

To Find: Reactions at the support.

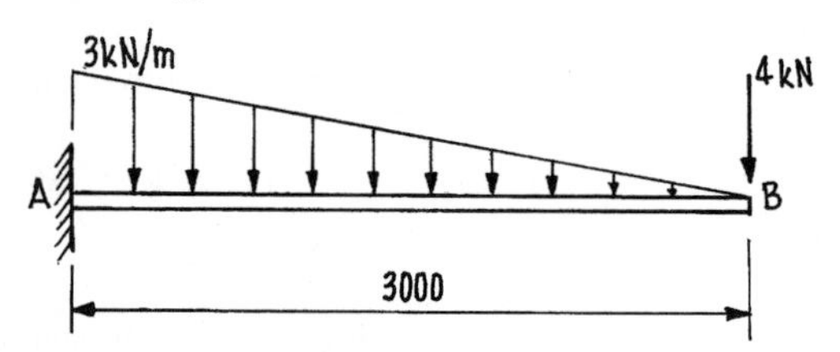

Solution: The beam AB is removed as a free body. The resultant of the hydrostatic load is entered on the sketch and its line of action located. Reactions at A are shown in their positive sense.

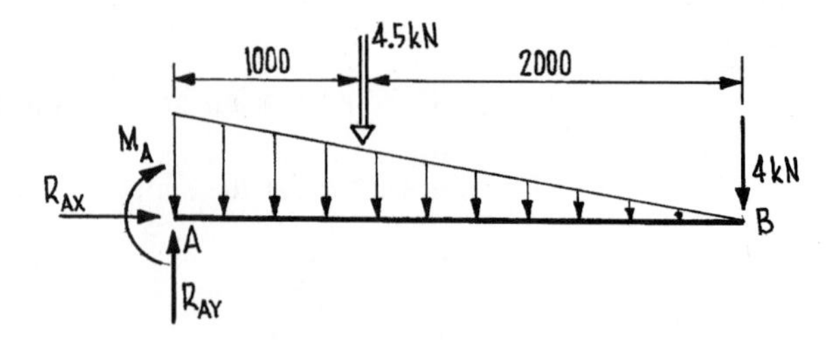

The mathematical laws of equilibrium are now applied. Moments are first summed about A:

$$\Sigma M_A = 0; \quad M_A + 4.5(1000) + 4(3000) = 0$$
$$M_A = -16{,}500 \text{ kN (counterclockwise)}$$
$$= 16.5 \text{ kN·m} \uparrow$$

Forces are summed vertically:

$$\Sigma F_V = 0; \quad R_{AY} - 4.5 - 4 = 0$$
$$R_{AY} = 8.5 \text{ kN}$$

Forces are summed horizontally:

$$\Sigma F_X = 0; \quad R_{AX} = 0$$

Example 7-4

Reactions on a cantilever.

Given: Cantilever beam as shown.

To Find: Reactions at support.

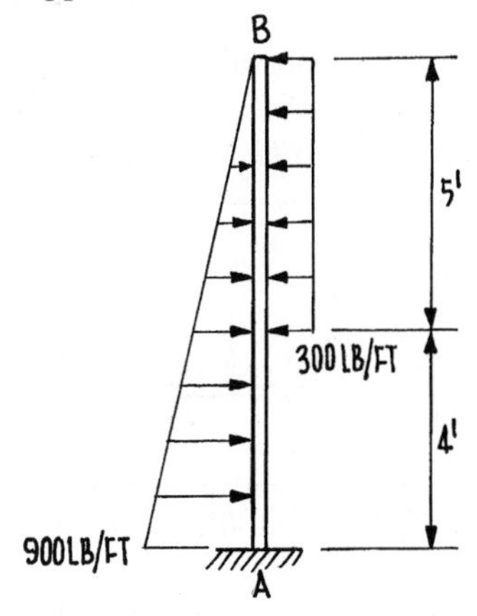

Solution: The beam AB is removed as a free body. The resultants of the distributed loads are entered and their lines of action located.

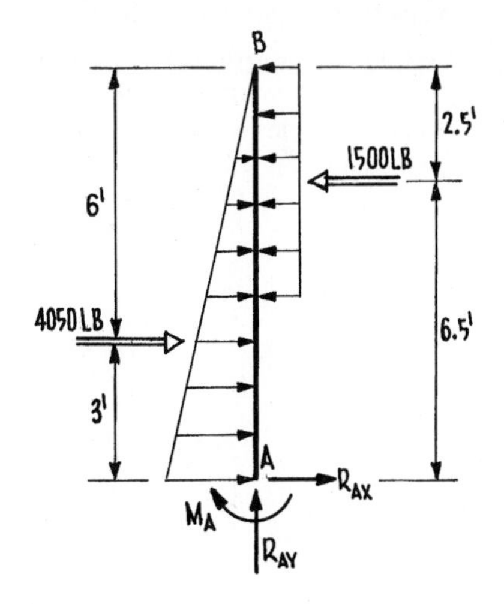

Moments are summed about *A*:

$$\Sigma M_A = 0; \quad M_A + 4050(3) - 1500(6.5) = 0$$
$$M_A = -2400 \text{ lb·ft (clockwise)}$$
$$M_A = 2.4 \text{ kip·ft} \downarrow$$

Forces are summed vertically:

$$\Sigma F_Y = 0; \quad R_{AY} = 0$$

Forces are summed horizontally:

$$\Sigma F_X = 0; \quad -1500 + 4050 + R_{AX} = 0$$
$$R_{AX} = -2550 \text{ lb (to the left)}$$

As suggested by Example 7-4, cantilevers can be oriented in any direction. Some of the more common cantilevers we see around us every day are tall buildings. These buildings act as cantilevers, fixed to their foundations at their bases. The fact that they are large does not change their identity; they act as cantilever beams, subject to lateral wind loads and vertical gravity loads.

7.4 Reactions on Simple Beams

A simply supported beam is one that is anchored by two hinged supports. Some examples of simple beams are shown in Figure 7-8. A simply supported beam may have overhangs at one or both ends and still be classed as a simply supported beam.

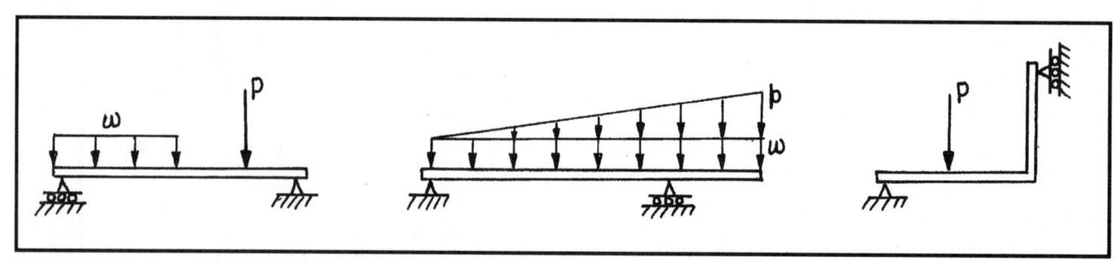

Figure 7-8 Simply supported beams.

It is noted that the beams of Figure 7-8 have one hinged support and one roller. While not previously stated, all simple beams will be supported such that only one of the supports can resist lateral motion. The reason is a practical one; the supports must not resist thermal growth of the beam. Also, if two fixed hinges were to be used, there would be four unknown reactions and the beam would be statically indeterminate.

Reactions for several simple beams have been calculated in earlier discussions. Some examples will illustrate the calculation of reactions when distributed loads and hydrostatic loads occur.

Example 7-5

Reactions on a simple beam.

Given: Simple beam loaded as shown.

To Find: Reactions at supports.

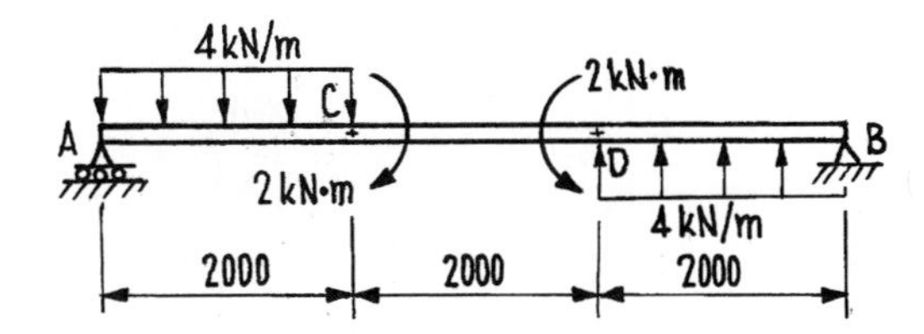

Solution: The beam *AB* is removed as a free body. Resultants of the uniformly distributed loads are shown, along with the position of their lines of action.

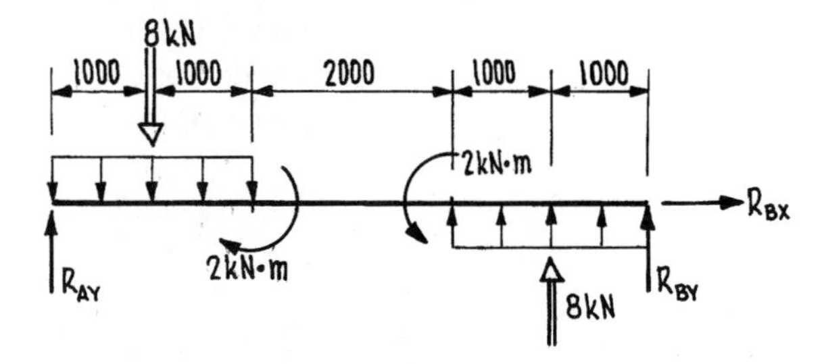

The alternative laws of equilibrium will be used in this solution, using the sum of moments twice and sum of forces once.

Moments are summed about point *B*:

$$\Sigma M_B = 0; \quad R_{AY}(6000) - 8(5000) + 2000 - 2000 + 8(1000) = 0$$
$$R_{AY} = 5.33 \text{ kN}$$

Moments are summed about point *A*:

$$\Sigma M_A = 0; \quad 8(1000) + 2000 - 2000 - 8(5000) - R_{BY}(6000) = 0$$
$$R_{BY} = -5.33 \text{ kN (downward)}$$

Forces are summed in a direction parallel to points *A* and *B*:

$$\Sigma F_X = 0; \quad R_{BX} = 0$$

Forces are summed vertically as a check on the mathematics:

$$\Sigma F_Y = 0; \quad +5.33 - 8 + 8 - 5.33 = 0$$
$$0 = 0 \text{ (OK)}$$

The check shows the arithmetic to be correct.

Example 7-6

Reactions on simply supported beams.

Given: Simply supported beam as shown.

To Find: Reactions at the supports.

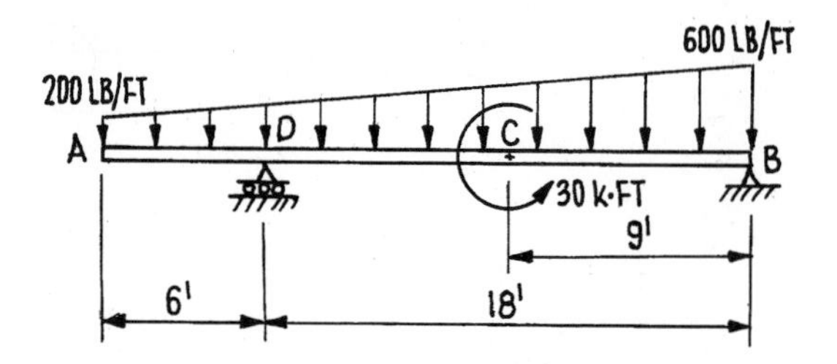

Solution: The beam AB is removed as a free body. All the reactions that can occur at a support are shown, but only the reactions that can occur at a support are shown. The trapezoidal load is broken into two loads, a uniform load and a hydrostatic load. The resultants of these two loads are shown, and their lines of action are located.

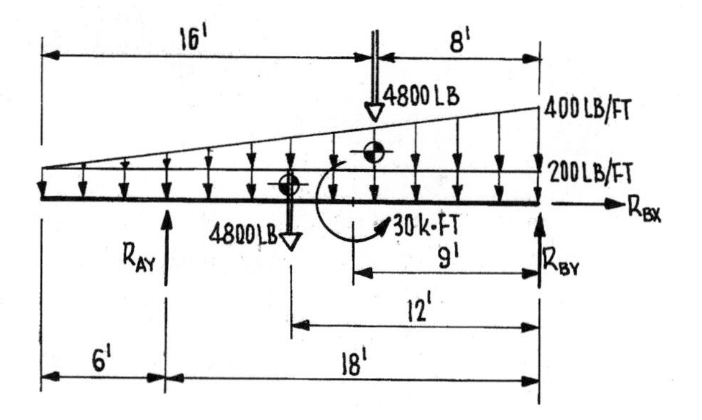

It is noted that there are three unknown reactions, and that there are three equations of equilibrium available. An equilibrium solution is therefore possible.

Moments are summed first about support B:

$$\Sigma M_B = 0; \quad R_{AY}(18) - 4800(12) - 30{,}000 - 4800(8) = 0$$
$$R_{AY} = 7000 \text{ lb.}$$

The alternative laws of equilibrium will be used in this solution, using the sum of moments about two points along the x axis and the sum of forces in the x direction only.

Moments are now summed about point A. The reaction R_{BX} passes through A and therefore drops out of the equation:

$$\Sigma M_A = 0; \quad 4800(6) + 4800(10) - 30{,}000 - R_{BY}(18) = 0$$
$$R_{BY} = 2600 \text{ lb}$$

Forces are now summed in the direction of line AB.

$$\Sigma F_X = 0; \quad R_{BX} = 0$$

The sum of vertical forces in this solution will not yield an independent equation. It will, however, afford a valuable check on the arithmetic in the other equations.

$$\Sigma F_Y = 0; \quad 7000 - 4800 - 4800 + 2600 = 0$$
$$0 = 0 \text{ (OK)}$$

The check shows the sum of forces to be zero.

It should be noted in Example 7-6 that the position of the applied moment never entered into the calculations for reactions. As observed earlier, a moment may be applied anywhere in the plane and there will be no effect on the rigid body reactions. It will be found later in the study of strength of materials, however, that the point of application of the moment is quite important in the way that stresses and strains are produced inside the beam itself.

Example 7-7

Reactions on a simple beam.

Given: Bent simple beam, supported as shown.

To Find: Reactions at supports.

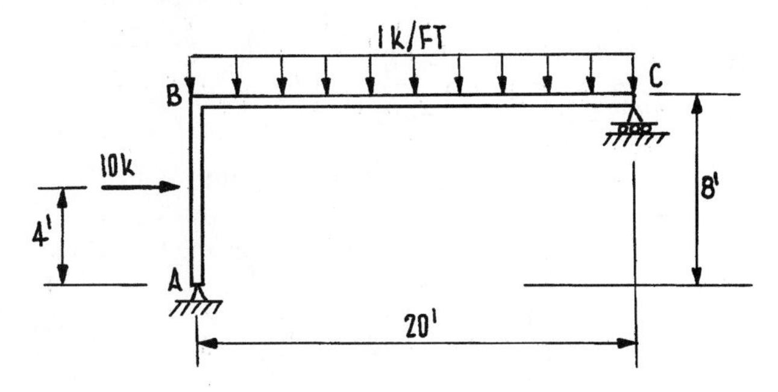

Solution: The beam *ABC* is removed as a free body. The resultant of the distributed load is shown along with its location.

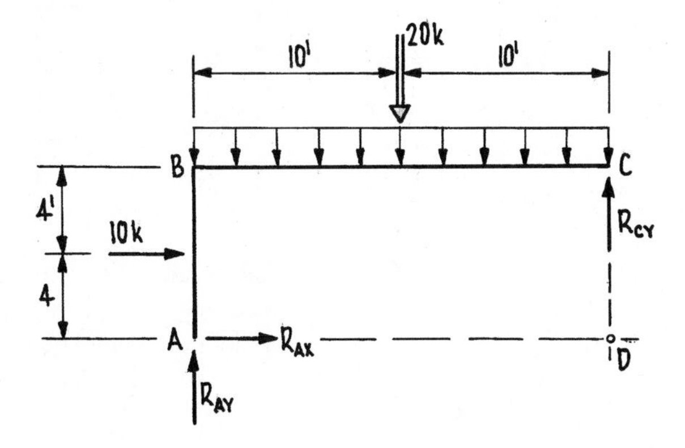

Moments are summed about point *A*:

$$\Sigma M_A = 0; \quad 10(4) + 20(10) - R_{CY}(20) = 0$$
$$R_{CY} = 12 \text{ kips}$$

In this solution, it is seen that there is no benefit in taking moments a second time (unless one takes moments about point D in order to eliminate both R_{AX} and R_{CY}).

Forces are summed vertically, using the value for R_{CY} just obtained:

$$\Sigma F_Y = 0; \quad R_{AY} - 20 + 12 = 0$$
$$R_{AY} = 8 \text{ kips}$$

Forces are summed horizontally:

$$\Sigma F_X = 0; \quad 10 + R_{AX} = 0$$
$$R_{AX} = -10 \text{ kips (to the left)}$$

As a check on the arithmetic, moments are summed about point C:

$$\Sigma M_C = 0; \quad 8(20) + 10(8) - 10(4) - 20(10) = 0$$
$$0 = 0 \text{ (OK)}$$

The check shows the arithmetic to be correct.

It is the practice in engineering always to show loads on their horizontal projection, never along a sloping surface. The reason for such a practice is that positions of the lines of action are much more easily identified. The next example illustrates such a case.

Example 7-8

Reactions on a simply supported beam.

Given: Simply supported beam as shown.

To Find: Reactions at the supports.

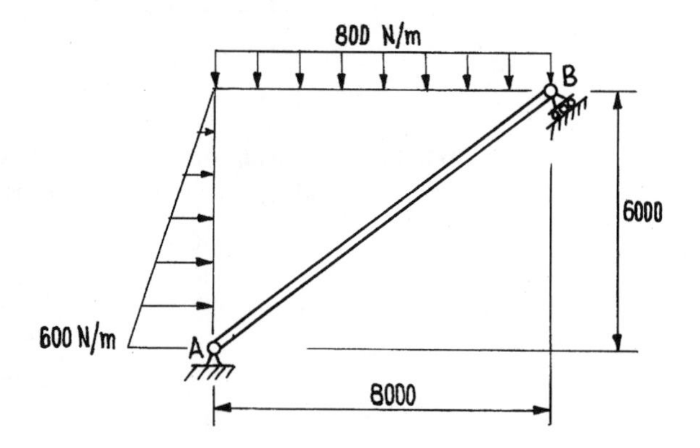

Solution: The beam AB is removed as a free body. The resultants of the distributed load and the hydrostatic load are shown in the free body and their lines of action located. The reaction at B is shown first in its known direction, then its x and y components are entered.

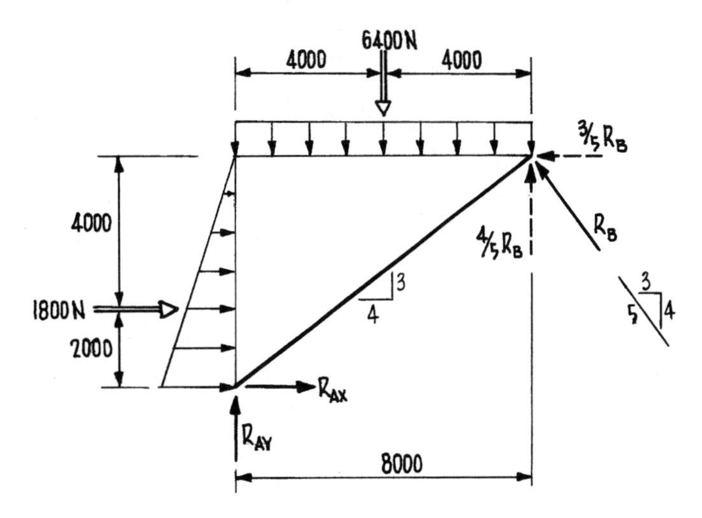

Moments are sumed about point *A*:

$$\Sigma M_A = 0; \quad 1800(2000) + 6400(4000) - {}^3/_5\, R_B(6000) - {}^4/_5\, R_B(8000) = 0$$
$$R_B = 2920 \text{ N}$$

Forces are summed vertically:

$$\Sigma F_Y = 0; \quad R_{AY} - 6400 + {}^4/_5(2920) = 0$$
$$R_{AY} = 4064 \text{ N}$$

Forces are summed horizontally:

$$\Sigma F_X = 0; \quad 1800 + R_{AX} - {}^3/_5(2920) = 0$$
$$R_{AX} = -48\text{N (to the left)}$$

As a check, moments are summed about point *B*:

$$\Sigma M_B = 0; \quad 4064(8000) + 48(6000) - 1800(4000) - 6400(4000) = 0$$
$$0 = 0 \text{ (OK)}$$

The check shows the arithmetic to be correct.

It should be observed from Example 7-8 that expressing all loads and all reactions in their *x* and *y* components considerably simplified the geometry of the problem. All lines of action then became the *x* and *y* distances; there was never any need to compute slope distances.

7.5 Reactions on Three Hinged Arches

One of the more commonly used structures in today's industry is the three hinged arch. It is easy to fabricate and erect, it is insensitive to temperature change and is unaffected by foundation settlements. Some typical examples of three hinged arches are shown in Figure 7-9.

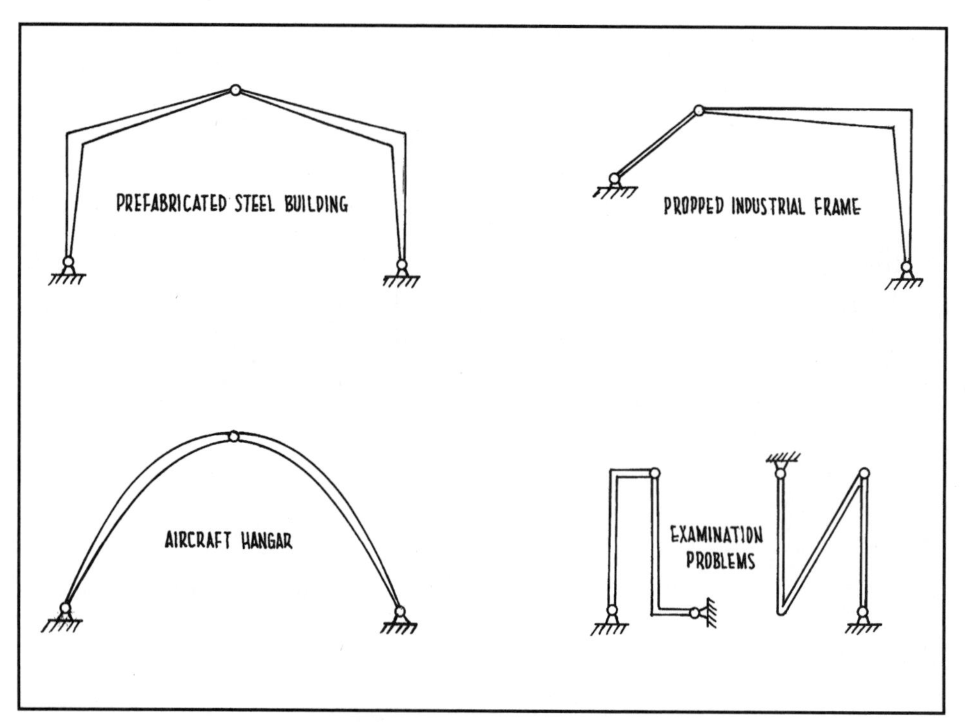

Figure 7-9 Typical three hinged arches.

Consider the building frame shown in Figure 7-9 for a prefabricated steel building. If the frame were subject to a large temperature change, both of the segments would increase in size, but the only effect on the structure is that the top hinge would move upward or downward slightly; there would be no loads induced into the structure as a result of the temperature change. Similarly, if one of the foundations were to settle more than the other, the only effect on the structure is that it would tilt slightly; there would be no loads induced into the structure as a result of the unequal settlements.

Because of their importance in the industry, a closer examination of three hinged arches is appropriate at this point. It should be noted in Figure 7-9 that all of the configurations are composed of two beams having three hinged supports. The beams themselves may be straight, curved or bent, as shown. Supports may be at a single level, or at two levels. The three hinges, however, must form a discrete triangle, as shown in Figure 7-10.

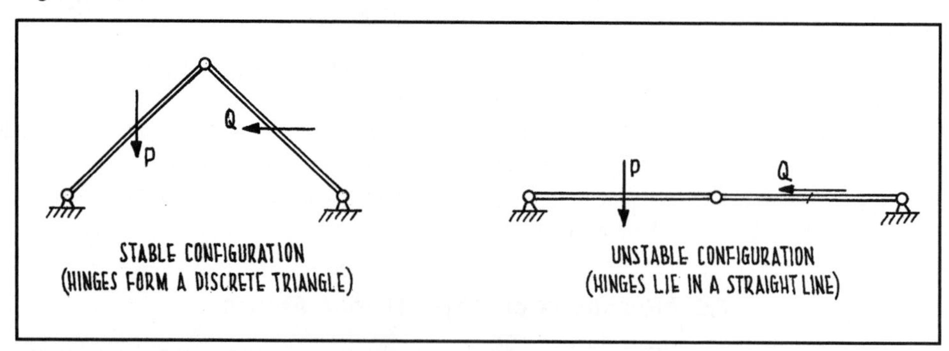

Figure 7-10 Stable and unstable three hinged arches.

As indicated in Figure 7-10, the three hinged arch is a stable form as long as the hinges do not fall into a straight line. If the hinges are in a straight line, the structure becomes a *mechanism*, or *link mechanism*, and will collapse under load.

The reactions on a three hinged arch are found by simple statics. It should be noted, however, that there are four reactions on a three hinged arch but there remains only three equations of equilibrium. A fourth condition must be introduced if a solution is to be found; the third hinge provides that fourth condition.

There are two distinctive cases of three hinged arches, one in which the supports are at the same level and one in which the supports are at different levels. Some examples will illustrate the solutions for the two cases.

Example 7-9

Reactions on a three hinged arch.

Given: Three hinged arch loaded as shown.

To Find: Reactions at the supports.

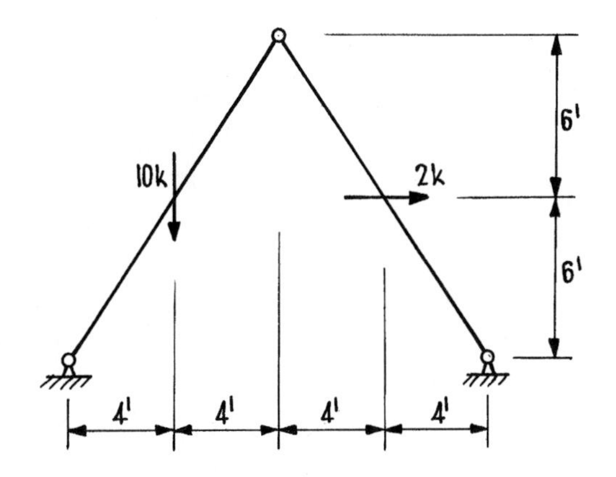

Solution: The entire structure is taken as a free body.

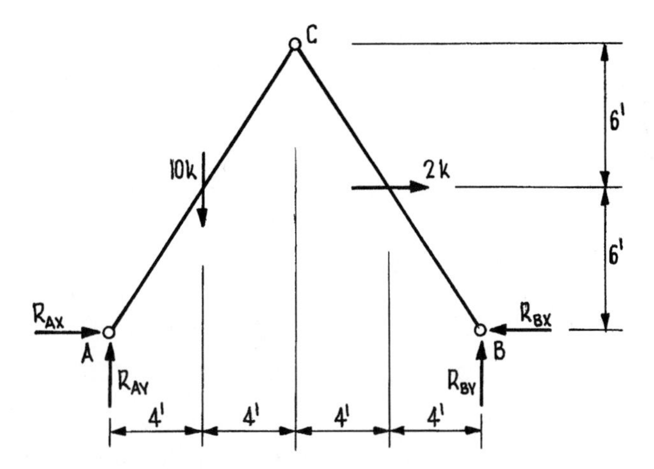

It is noted that there are four reactions and only three equations of statics. It is also noted that summing moments either about *A* or about *B* will eliminate three of the four unknowns, allowing the vertical reactions to be found:

$\Sigma M_A = 0;$ $10(4) + 2(6) - R_{BY}(16) = 0$

$R_{BY} = 3.25$ kips in direction shown

$\Sigma M_B = 0;$ $R_{AY}(16) - 10(12) + 2(6) = 0$

$R_{AY} = 6.75$ kips in direction shown

At this point, there is no way to sum forces or moments that will yield the values for the two horizontal reactions.

The two segments are separated into two free bodies as shown in the following sketch, introducing two more unknown forces at *C*.

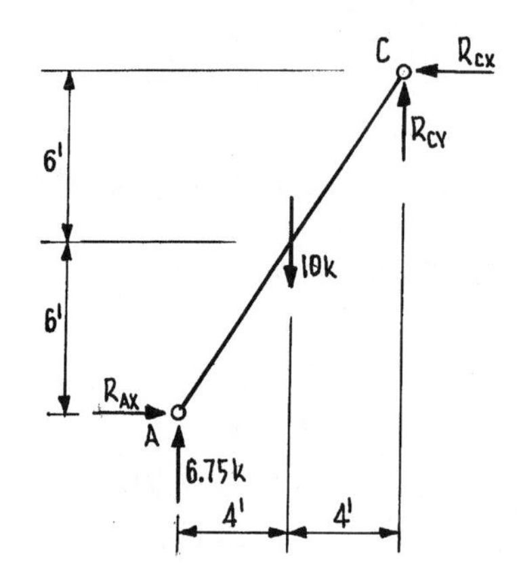

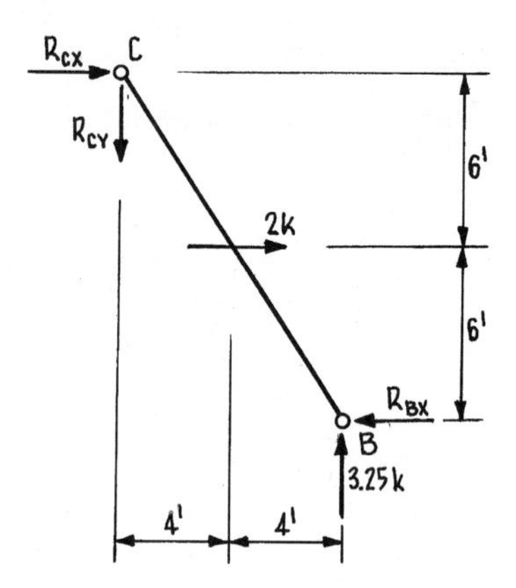

The left segment is considered first. Summing moments about *C* eliminates the two new unknowns, permitting a solution for R_{AX}:

$$\Sigma M_C = 0; \quad -R_{AX}(12) - 10(4) + 6.75(8) = 0$$
$$R_{AX} = 1.167 \text{ kips in direction shown}$$

The right segment is considered next. Summing moments about *C* eliminates the two new unknowns, permitting a solution for R_{BX}:

$$\Sigma M_C = 0; \quad -3.25(8) + R_{BX}(12) - 2(6) = 0$$
$$R_{BX} = 3.167 \text{ kips in direction shown}$$

As a check, vertical and horizontal forces are summed:

$$\Sigma F_Y = 0; \quad 6.75 - 10 + 3.25 = 0$$
$$0 = 0 \text{ (OK)}$$

$$\Sigma F_X = 0; \quad 1.167 + 2 - 3.167 = 0$$
$$0 = 0 \text{ (OK)}$$

If desired, the forces acting on the hinge at *C* could now be found, simply by summing forces on the two segments.

Final reactions are shown on the following sketch.

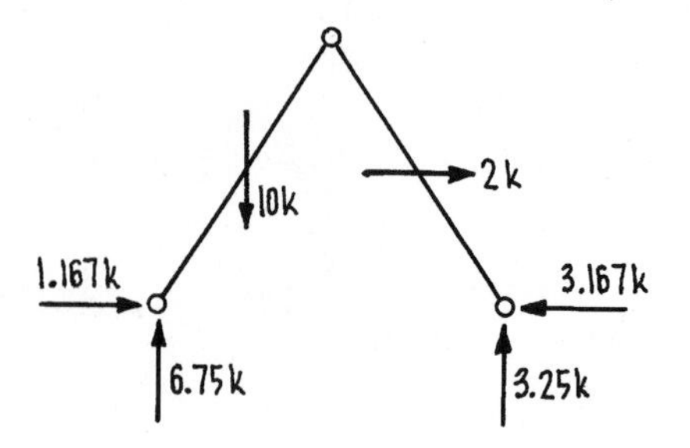

It should be noted in Example 7-9 that having both supports at the same level simplifies the solution somewhat. Summing moments about either support eliminates three of the four unknowns, allowing the two vertical reactions to be computed directly. When the supports are at different levels, the solution is not so neat. That case is shown in the next example.

Example 7-10

Reactions on a three hinged arch.

Given: Three hinged arch loaded as shown.

To Find: Reactions at the supports.

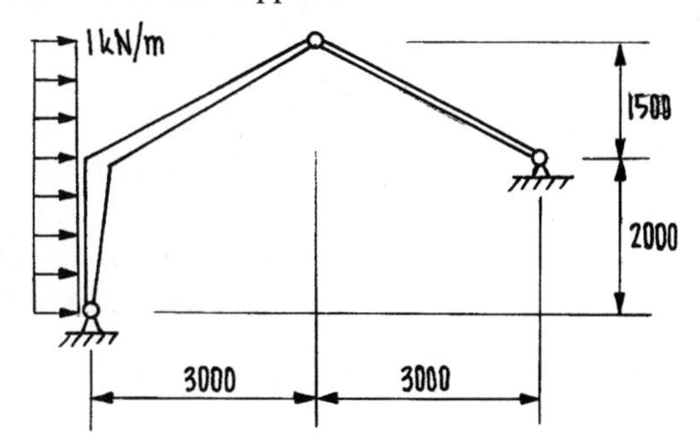

Solution: The entire structure is taken as a free body.

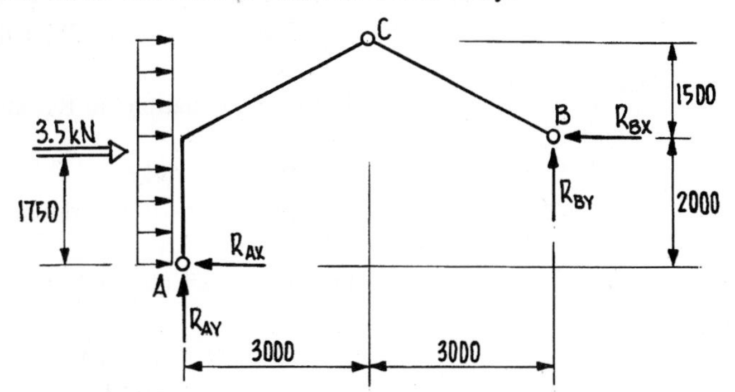

It is elected to solve first for the two unknowns at *B*.

Moments are summed about *A*, yielding an equation in the two unknowns at *B*:

$$\Sigma M_A = 0; \quad 3.5(1.75) - R_{BX}(2) - R_{BY}(6) = 0$$

The two segments are now separated into two free bodies, introducing two new unknowns at *C*.

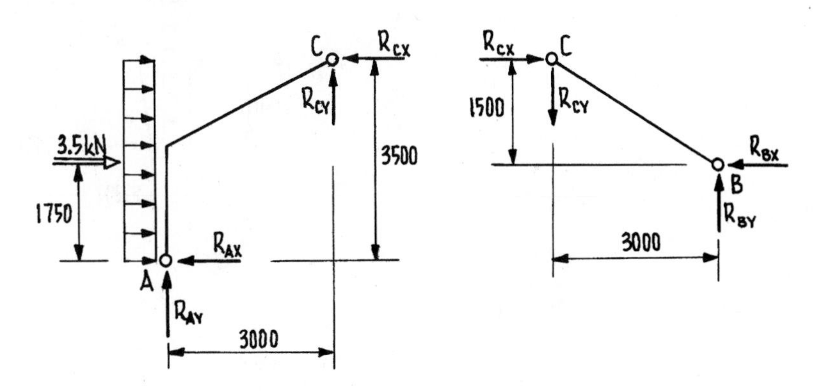

Moments are summed about C on the right segment yielding another equation in the two unknowns at B:

$$\Sigma M_C = 0; \quad R_{BX}(1.5) - R_{BY}(3) = 0$$

This equation is solved simultaneously with the first equation in R_{BX} and R_{BY}:

$$3.5(1.75) - 2R_{BX} - 6R_{BY} = 0$$
$$1.5\,R_{BX} - 3R_{BY} = 0$$

The solution yields:

$$R_{BX} = 1.225 \text{ kN}$$
$$R_{BY} = 0.6125 \text{ kN}$$

The two unknowns at A are solved in the same way. Moments are summed about B on the entire truss, yielding:

$$\Sigma M_B = 0; \quad -3.5(0.25) + R_{AX}(2) + R_{AY}(6) = 0$$

Moments are summed about C on the left segment:

$$\Sigma M_C = 0; \quad -3.5(1.75) + R_{AX}(3.5) + R_{AY}(3) = 0$$

These two equations in R_{AX} and R_{AY} are solved simultaneously, yielding:

$$R_{AX} = 2.275 \text{ kN}$$
$$R_{AY} = -0.6125 \text{ kN (downward)}$$

The results are checked by summing forces vertically and horizontally:

$$\Sigma F_Y = 0; \quad R_{AY} + R_{BY} = 0$$
$$-0.6125 + 0.6125 = 0 \text{ (OK)}$$

$$\Sigma F_X = 0; \quad -R_{AX} + 3.5 - R_{BX} = 0$$
$$-2.275 + 3.5 - 1.225 = 0$$
$$0 = 0 \text{ (OK)}$$

The results are shown on the following sketch.

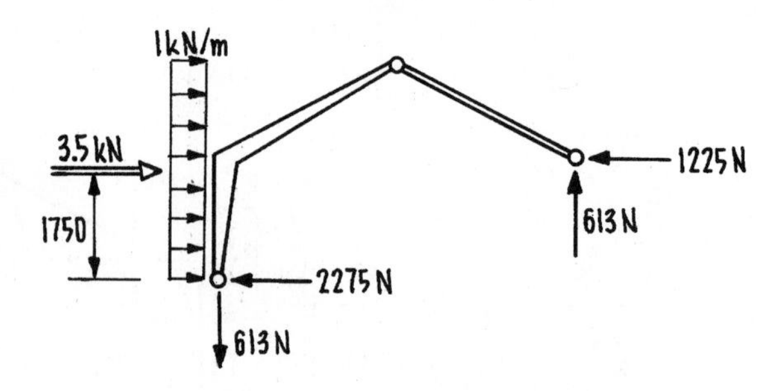

Example 7-11

Reactions on a three hinged arch.

Given: Trussed three hinged arch loaded as shown.

To Find: Reactions at the supports.

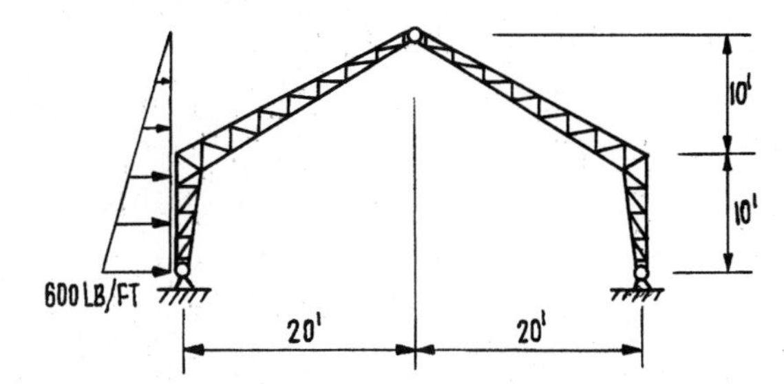

Solution: The truss is recognized as a three hinged arch with supports at the same level.

The entire truss is shown as a free body.

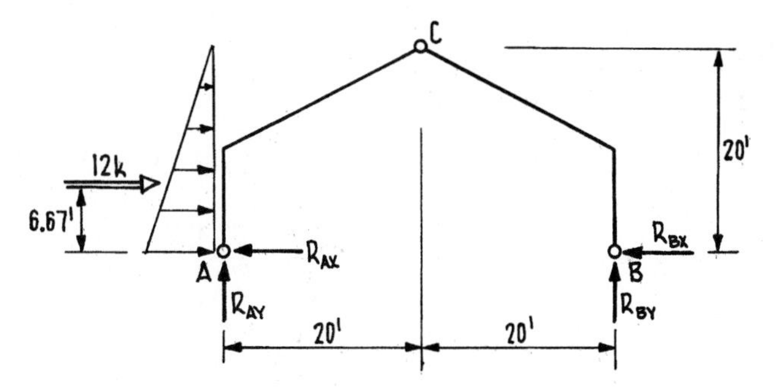

Moments are summed about A, eliminating all unknowns except R_{BY}:

$$\Sigma M_A = 0; \quad 12(6.67) - R_{BY}(40) = 0$$
$$R_{BY} = 2 \text{ kips (in direction shown)}$$

Moments are summed about B, eliminating all unknowns except R_{AY}:

$$\Sigma M_B = 0; \quad 12(6.67) + R_{AY}(40) = 0$$
$$R_{AY} = -2 \text{ kips (in opposite direction)}$$

The two segments are separated into two free bodies.

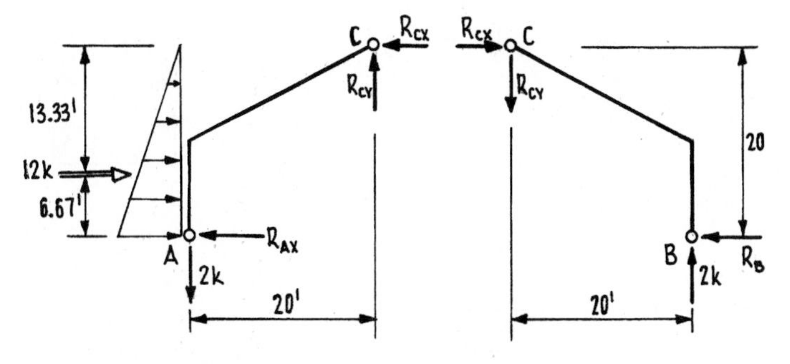

Moments are summed about C on the left segment to find R_{AX}:

$$\Sigma M_C = 0; \quad -12(13.33) - 2(20) + R_{AX}(20) = 0$$
$$R_{AX} = 10 \text{ kips}$$

Moments are summed about C on the right segment to find R_{BX}:

$$\Sigma M_C = 0; \quad -2(20) + R_{BX}(20) = 0$$
$$R_{BX} = 2 \text{ kips}$$

Results are checked by summing forces vertically and horizontally:

$$\Sigma F_Y = 0; \quad -2 + 2 = 0 \text{ (OK)}$$
$$\Sigma F_X = 0; \quad 12 - 10 - 2 = 0 \text{ (OK)}$$

Final results are shown on the following sketch.

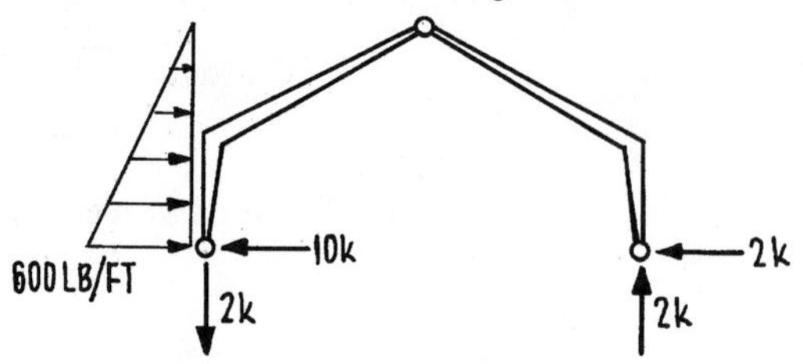

Example 7-12

Reactions on a three hinged arch.

Given: Trussed three hinged arch loaded as shown.

To Find: Reactions at supports.

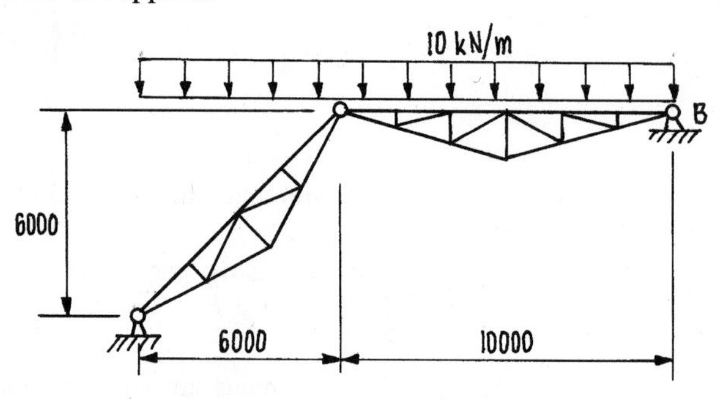

Solution: The structure is recognized as a three hinged arch having supports a two levels.

The entire truss is taken as a free body.

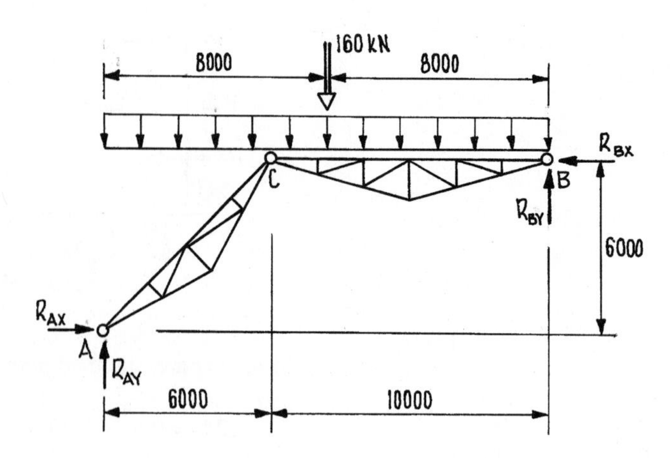

Moments are summed about A, yielding one equation in the two unknowns R_{BY} and R_{BX}:

$$\Sigma M_A = 0; \quad 160(8) - R_{BY}(16) - R_{BX}(6) = 0$$

A piece of scratch paper is held over the left segment, leaving the right segment as a free body. Moments are summed about C, yielding a second equation in the two unknowns R_{BY} and R_{BX}:

$$\Sigma M_C = 0; \quad 100(5) - R_{BY}(10) = 0$$
$$R_{BY} = 50 \text{ kN}$$

The first equation is now solved for R_{BX}:

$$R_{BX} = 80 \text{ kN}$$

$$\Sigma M_B = 0; \quad -160(8) - R_{AX}(6) + R_{AY}(16) = 0$$

A piece of scratch paper is held over the right segment, leaving the left segment as a free body. Moments are summed about C, yielding a second equation in the same two unknowns:

$$\Sigma M_C = 0; \quad -60(3) - R_{AX}(6) + R_{AY}(6) = 0$$

These two equations are solved simultaneously to find:

$$R_{AX} = 80 \text{ kN}$$
$$R_{AY} = 110 \text{ kN}$$

These results are checked by summing forces vertically and horizontally:

$$\Sigma F_Y = 0; \quad 50 - 160 + 110 = 0$$
$$0 = 0 \text{ (OK)}$$

$$\Sigma F_X = 0; \quad 80 - 80 = 0$$
$$0 = 0 \text{ (OK)}$$

Final results are shown on the following sketch.

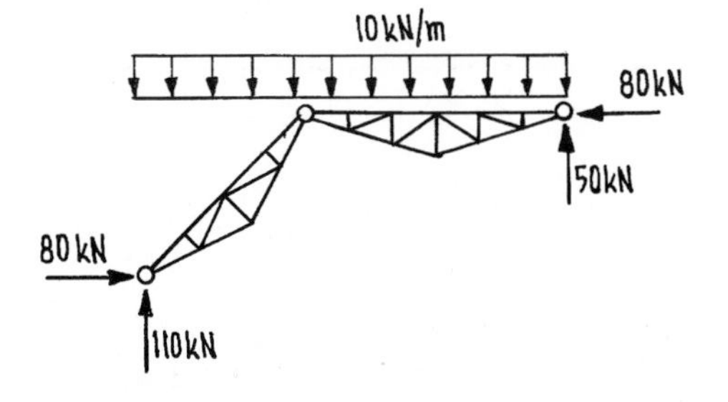

It should be noted that in the last four examples, the configuration of the members had no effect on the calculations. The two trusses might have been solid members and the two solid members might have been trusses; there would have been no change in the calculations. In rigid body mechanics, only the location and direction of the loads are used in the calculations; the actual make-up of the member is of no consequence.

Review Questions

1. Name three of the more common types of loads on a structure, typed according to the way they are distributed on the structure.
2. Where is the resultant of a hydrostatic load located?
3. What is a cantilever beam?
4. What is a simple beam?
5. Why is it necessary that a simple beam have one hinged support and one roller support?
6. Why are all loads on a sloping member shown on their vertical or horizontal projection rather than along the slope?
7. What is a three hinged arch?
8. What key feature concerning the hinges of a three hinged arch determines whether the structure is stable or unstable?

PART

2

STRENGTH OF MATERIALS

CHAPTER

8

DIRECT STRESS AND STRAIN

8.1 Introduction to Strength of Materials

Probably no other subject impacts every study in civil engineering as much as does strength of materials. Regardless whether the study is in theoretical mechanics, structures, soils, materials, or any of the many other specialties in civil engineering, the dependence on strength of materials is evident in every study. A very firm grasp of the principles of strength of materials is essential to anyone who wishes to work in civil engineering.

Up to this point, the study of mechanics has been focused on finding the forces that act on a structural member from the outside. There has been no concern with the effects of those forces on the structural material, nor with the effects inside the materials as they resist those forces. Such a study of the material as it resists externally applied forces is called *mechanics of materials*, or, more commonly, *strength of materials*. The next few chapters deal with this study of strength of materials.

8.2 General Properties of Materials

As usual, the study begins with defining the terms that will be used in the study. Many of these terms will have a generic meaning as well, but when used in strength of materials, they will have a very specific, very narrow meaning. It is those specific narrow meanings that are of interest here.

A material that returns to its *exact original position* after being deformed is said to be *elastic*. The heart of the definition is in the phrase "exact original position". Under this definition, rubber is not elastic; a rubber band, for example, may be formed into an ellipse or a circle and will not try to return to some exact original configuration. One of the more elastic materials commonly available to us is glass. Following any deformation (so long as the glass does not break), glass will return to its *exact* original configuration.

A material that can undergo large deformations without rupture is said to be *tough*. Rubber is tough. Another measure of toughness is in the ability of the material to absorb large amounts of energy without rupture. In this aspect, both timber and steel rank high as tough materials.

A material that can be drawn into wire is said to be *ductile*. Silver, copper and aluminum are all examples of ductile materials. Steel is ductile also, but not as much as the other named materials.

A material that can be formed into thin sheets without breaking apart is said to be *malleable*. Gold is quite malleable, as is aluminum. Gold leaf and aluminum foil are quite common products in use in today's industry.

A material that resists penetration is said to be *hard*. The best-known example of hardness is probably diamonds, but chromium and steel are also quite hard. Steel has the distinct advantage, in engineering, that its hardness can be increased considerably by appropriate alloying and heat treatment.

A material that will rupture rather than undergo a permanent deformation is said to be *brittle*. Steel, for example, is *not* a brittle material; steel can be bent and formed rather severely into permanent shapes without breakage. Glass, however, is brittle, as is concrete, masonry and some of the aluminum alloys; these materials will break before they accept a permanent "set."

A material that has the same properties in all directions is said to be *isotropic*. Steel is an isotropic material, having the same properties in all directions both in tension and compression. In contrast, timber has distinctly different strength along the grain than across the grain, and concrete has very different strength in compression than in tension. Timber and concrete are therefore not isotropic materials.

A material in which every molecule is identical to every other molecule is said to be *homogeneous*. Steel and aluminum are both homogeneous materials. Timber, however, is a nonhomogeneous material due to its having "grain" in one direction only. Concrete is also a nonhomogeneous material, being composed of discrete particles of stone dispersed in a paste of sand and cement. Additionally, reinforcing steel is commonly used in structural concrete which further changes its homogeneity.

The foregoing properties of materials are covered in detail in courses on engineering materials, along with methods of measuring and comparing these properties. The general definitions are repeated here for immediate reference; these terms will be needed in succeeding discussions.

In earlier discussions, a member of a structure would often be removed as a free body, along with the forces and moments that were acting on it. A part of a member (rather than the entire member) may also be removed as a free body, with the member undergoing an imaginary "cut" such that the internal forces may be exposed to view. Such a cut is called a *section*; a typical section is cut from a cantilever in Figure 8-1, with the forces acting inside the member shown on the section.

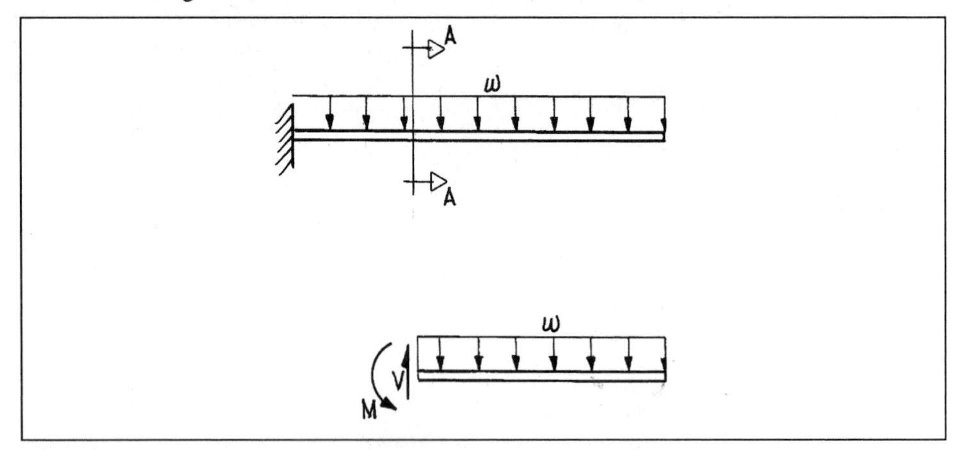

Figure 8-1 Section of a structural member.

The forces inside a loaded member such as that of Figure 8-1 are distributed across the section in some pattern. Each fiber of the material is undergoing some degree of load. Finding the distribution of load and its magnitude at every point in the section is the topic of the next few chapters.

8.3 Axial Stress, Strain and Elastic Modulus

An axially loaded bar is shown in Figure 8-2. The bar carries a load of 1000 lb applied at one end, which produces the reaction of 1000 lb at the other end. The bar is square, 2 in. x 2 in. along its entire length.

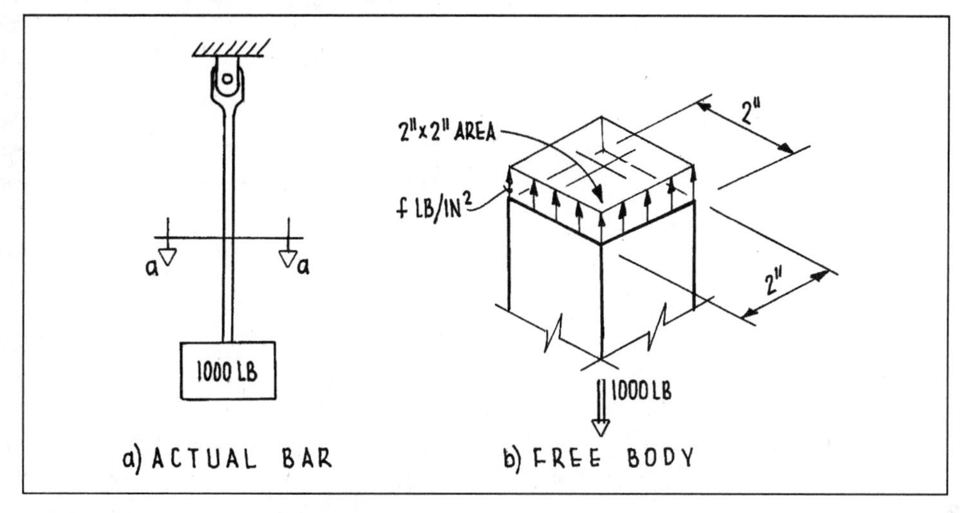

Figure 8-2 Axially loaded bar.

A section of the bar is cut along line a-a and the resulting free body is shown in Figure 8-2b. The force *f* is distributed across the area *A* as shown in Figure 8-2b. It is assumed that at some small distance away from the application of the 1000 lb load, the load has distributed itself uniformly across the section; the force on each fiber is thus equal to that on every other fiber in the section.

Forces are now summed vertically. The fact that the free body contains a cut section does not change the laws of equilibrium; the sum of forces vertically must still equal zero if the body is to remain static:

$$\Sigma F_Y = 0 \; f(A) = P, \text{ or, } f = {}^{P}/_{A} \tag{8-1}$$

$$f(2 \times 2) = 1000 \text{ lb}$$

$$f = 250 \text{ lb/in.}^2$$

The quantity *f* is seen to be force per unit area; it is the axial *stress* normal to the section. Stress is thus seen to be the intensity of load at any point; its direction is normal to the cross section of the bar. The units of stress are lb/in.^{2} or N/mm^2, the same units as pressure.

The type of stress shown in Figure 8-2 is called *direct stress.* Direct stress may occur either in tension or in compression. The distinctive characteristic of direct stress is that it is uniformly distributed across the loaded area; every fiber in the loaded area undergoes the same stress.

Direct stress is often called "the *P*-over-*A* stress" in engineering practice. Regardless how simple the concept may seem, the concept is a very important one.

Some examples will illustrate the calculation of direct stress in some typical members.

Example 8-1

Calculation of direct stress.

Given: Loaded member as shown. The load on each of the steel columns is 100 kips.

To Find: Stress in the loaded material.

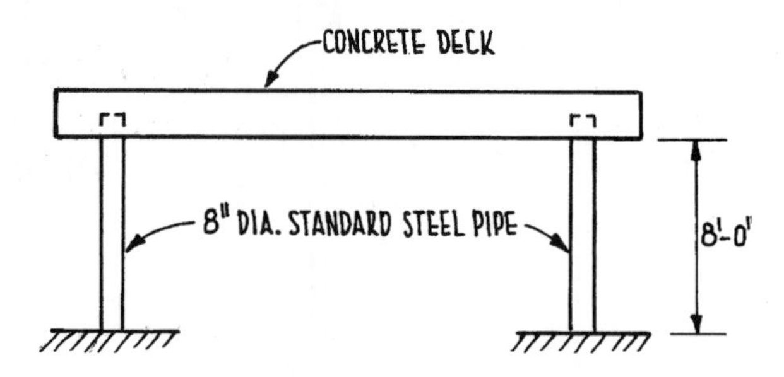

Solution:

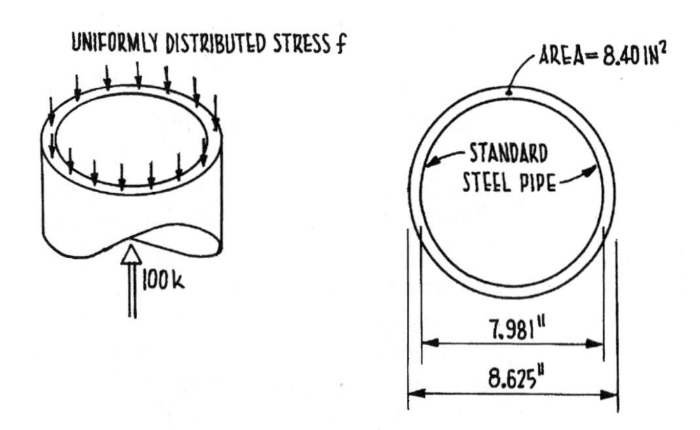

The load of 100 kips is seen to be distributed uniformly on the pipe material. The dimensions for standard steel pipe are found in Table S-8 in the Technical Manual. The stress is computed as force per unit area:

$$f = \frac{P}{A} = \frac{100,000}{8.40} = 11,900 \text{ lb/in.}^2$$

Each square inch of steel is in compression, carrying 11,900 lbs of load.

Example 8-2

Calculation of direct stress.

Given: Stepped pipe sections welded together as shown. Load P = 20k.

To Find: Stress in each segment. Ignore weight of pipe.

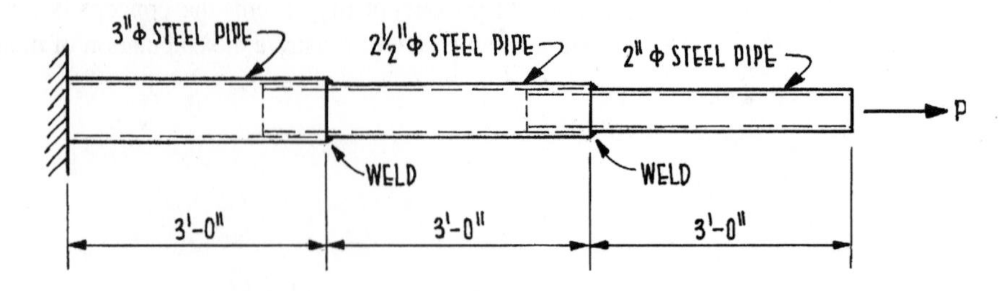

Solution: The total force acting on each segment is seen to be the same 20 kip load.

The cross sectional areas of the three sizes of pipe are found in Table S-8 of the Technical Manual. Those areas are:

Cross-sectional area of 2 in. diameter pipe = 1.07 in.^{2}
Cross-sectional area of $2^1/_2$ in. diameter pipe = 1.70 in.^{2}
Cross-sectional area of 3 in. diameter pipe = 2.23 in.^{2}

Stress on the 2 in. diameter pipe is:

$$f = \frac{P}{A} = \frac{20{,}000}{1.07} = 18{,}700 \text{ lb/in.}^2$$

Stress on the $2^1/_2$ in. diameter pipe is:

$$f = \frac{P}{A} = \frac{20{,}000}{1.70} = 11{,}800 \text{ lb/in.}^2$$

Stress on the 3 in. diameter pipe is:

$$f = \frac{P}{A} = \frac{20{,}000}{2.23} = 8970 \text{ lb/in.}^2$$

It should be noted in Example 8-2 that the same load was carried by each member but that each member had different cross-sectional areas. As the area increased, the stress decreased.

Example 8-3

Calculation of direct stress.

Given: Wire rope consisting of 7 strands of 7 wires each as shown. Wire diameter is 2 mm.

To Find: Load that the wire rope will carry if the stress in the steel is to be limited to 275 N/mm^2.

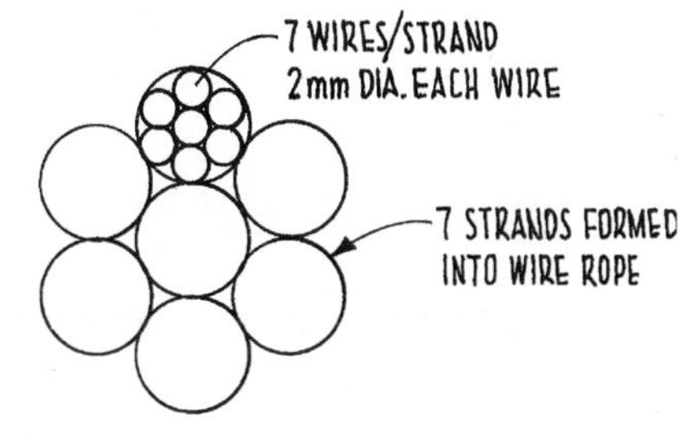

Solution: The cable consists of 7 wires times 7 strands or 49 wires. The area of each wire is:

$$\text{A/wire} = \frac{\pi d^2}{4} = \frac{\pi}{4}(2^2) = 3.14 \text{ mm}^2$$

The total area in 49 wires is:

$$\text{Total A} = 49(3.14) = 154 \text{ mm}^2$$

The total load is found from the definition of direct stress:

$$f = \frac{P}{A}; \quad 275 = \frac{P}{154}$$

$$P = 42{,}300 \text{ N.}$$

Example 8-4

Calculation of direct stress.

Given: A load of 10 kN acts on a 4 in. by 4 in. timber column.

To Find: Compressive stress in the timber.

Solution: As the problem is stated, the units are inconsistent. The timber size will be converted to mm.

The actual size of a 4 in. by 4 in. timber column is $3^1/_2$ in. by $3^1/_2$ in. as shown in Table 4 of the Technical Manual. At a conversion of 25.4 mm/ inch, the 4 in. by 4 in. column is 89 mm by 89 mm. The stress is then:

$$f = \frac{P}{A} = \frac{10{,}000}{(89)(89)} = 1.26 \text{ N/mm}^2$$

Alternatively, the force of 10 kN could have been converted to pounds. At a conversion of 0.225 lb/N, the 10 kN force is 2250 lbs. The stress is then:

$$f = \frac{P}{A} = \frac{2250}{(3.5)(3.5)} = 183 \text{ lb/in.}^2$$

As suggested by Example 8-4, it is unacceptable practice to mix forces from one system of measurements with dimensions from another system.

All materials deform under load. The bar of Figure 8-3, for example, will elongate slightly under the direct axial stress. Such deformations will be very small in most structural materials, so small, in fact, that the use of rather delicate measuring devices are necessary to measure them. It does not matter that the deformations are small; they exist, and they form very precise and predictable patterns.

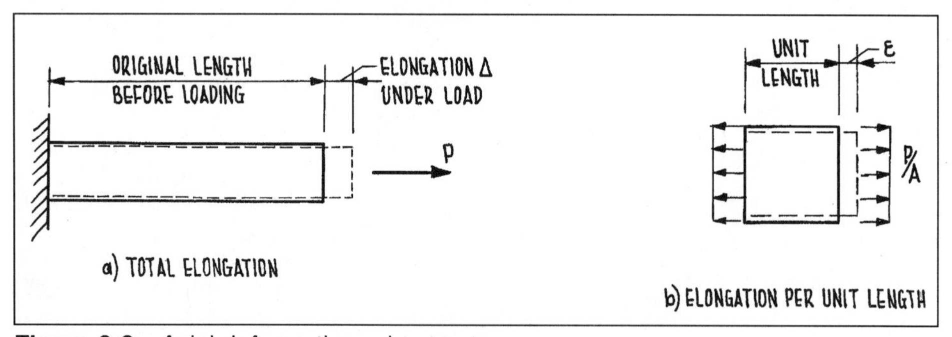

Figure 8-3 Axial deformations due to stress.

The material shown in Figure 8-3 is undergoing a direct axial stress similar to that considered earlier. The elongation of the bar is shown as the deformation Δ. The deformation is exaggerated greatly in the sketch in order that it can be seen.

A piece of the bar 1 unit long is removed from the bar and is shown at larger scale in Figure 8-3b. The elongation per unit length of the bar is shown as ε. The elongation per unit of length is the total elongation divided by the number of units of length,

$$\varepsilon = \frac{\Delta}{L}, \qquad (8\text{-}2)$$

The quantity ε, deformation per unit length, is called *strain;* strain is the inevitable consequence of stress. The units of strain are in./in., mm/mm, ft/ft, M/M, etc. Many engineers simply think of strain as a percent change in length and do not fix a unit of measurement to it. In this text, units will always be used.

Strain is a three-dimensional phenomenon. As indicated in Figure 8-3, when a material undergoes tensile strain in one direction, it will decrease slightly in size in the transverse directions. Conversely, if the material undergoes compressive strain in one direction, it will increase slightly in size in the transverse directions. The strain induced in the transverse direction does not create stress; it is simply an induced strain.

At larger scale, a cube of material one unit in length, depth and thickness is shown in Figure 8-4. The material is loaded uniformly as shown. The longitudinal strain resulting from the axial stress is shown as ε_{LONG} and the induced strain in the lateral direction is shown as ε_{LAT}; it is assumed that the induced strain occurs symmetrically.

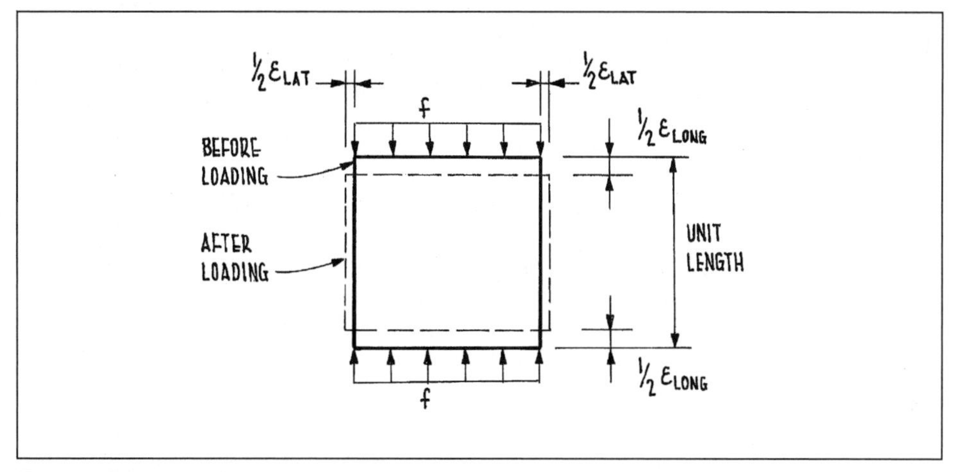

Figure 8-4 Longitudinal and lateral strains.

For any given material, there is a fixed relationship between the axial strain directly caused by a stress and the lateral strain induced by it. The relationship between the two strains is called Poisson's ratio and is denoted μ:

$$\mu = \frac{\text{Unit lateral strain}}{\text{Unit longitudinal strain}} \tag{8-3}$$

Poisson's ratio for some common materials are given in Table 8-1.

Table 8-1 Typical Values of Poisson's Ratio.

Material	Poisson's Ratio
Steel	0.28
Aluminum	0.32
Concrete	0.20
Glass	0.24
Nylon	0.40

The values of Table 8-1 indicate that for most metals, Poisson's ratio is around 0.3, or, for each inch of axial strain created by stress, there is about 0.30 inch of strain induced in the lateral directions. In almost all cases these induced strains create no problems and are usually ignored. In advanced studies (such as flat plate structures), the material may be confined laterally and these strains cannot form; in such cases the effects of such confinement must be included in the analysis.

As one might expect, there is a very fixed relationship between direct stress and its associated strain. Consider the steel bar of Figure 8-5, for example. The bar is $^1/_2$ in. diameter and has been loaded to 7000 lb in increments of 1000 lbs. As each increment is added, the elongation of the bar has been measured and recorded, as shown.

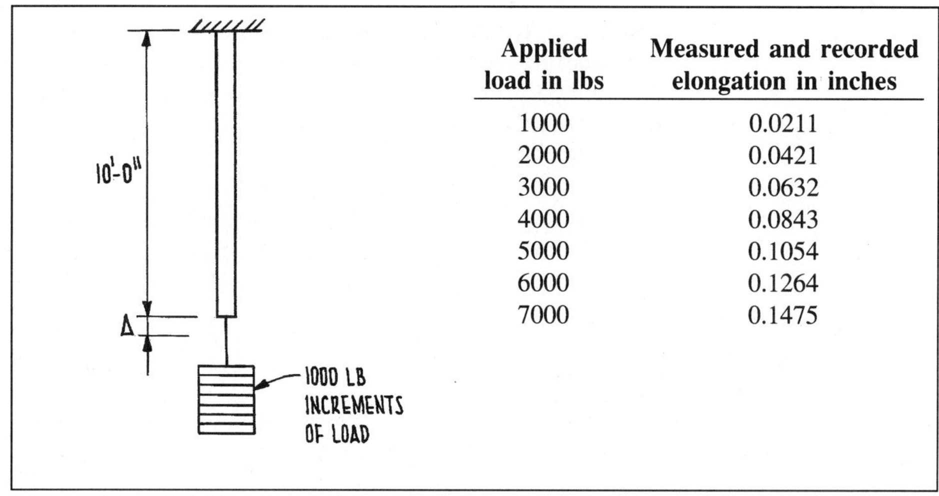

Applied load in lbs	Measured and recorded elongation in inches
1000	0.0211
2000	0.0421
3000	0.0632
4000	0.0843
5000	0.1054
6000	0.1264
7000	0.1475

Figure 8-5 Axial load and deformation.

The data recorded in Figure 8-5 can be plotted to provide a graph of load vs. deformation in a $^1/_2$ in. diameter bar. Far more useful, however, is a plot of the stress in the material vs. the strain in the material at each stage of loading. The result then applies to any steel bar of any size that undergoes stress and the resulting strain. Such a graph is shown in Figure 8-6.

Applied load P lbs	Computed stress, P/A lb/in.^{2}	Measured elongation Δ in.	Computed strain, Δ/L in./in.
1000	5,093	0.0211	0.000176
2000	10,186	0.0421	0.000351
3000	15,279	0.0632	0.000527
4000	20,372	0.0843	0.000702
5000	25,464	0.1054	0.000878
6000	30,557	0.1264	0.001053
7000	35,651	0.1475	0.001229

Figure 8-6 Stress-strain curve.

The plot of stress vs. strain shown in Figure 8-6 is the accepted standard result for an investigation of any material in civil engineering. The approach applies not only to steel but to aluminum, concrete, timber and all other structural materials.

The stress-strain curve shown in Figure 8-6 reveals several important properties of steel. Note for example, that in the range of loading covered by this limited test, the plot is a straight line. The conclusion to be drawn from this straight-line relationship is that *stress is linearly proportional to strain.* It means that if one doubles the load on a member, the deformation will also be doubled. If one reduces the load by 40%, the deformation will similarly be reduced by 40%. This property that stress is linearly proportional to strain is known as *Hooke's Law*, and is one of the most important basic concepts in strength of materials.

Since the relationship between stress and strain is seen to be a straight line, the slope of the straight line will be constant. For steel, the slope is designated E_S and is computed as:

$$E_S = \frac{f}{\varepsilon} \tag{8-4}$$

The slope E is called the *modulus of elasticity* of the material. It defines the relationship between the axial stress in a material (or stress normal to a section) and the deformation that will result from that stress.

For steel, the modulus of elasticity is computed from Eq. 8-4 and the results of the stress-strain curve. It is found to be, for all steels, regardless of ultimate strength:

$$E_S = \frac{35{,}651 \text{ lb / in.}^2}{0.001229 \text{ in./in.}} = 29{,}000{,}000 \text{ lb / in.}^2 \tag{8-5}$$

The units of the modulus of elasticity degenerate to lb/in.^{2} (or N/mm^2). A more accurate unit would be (lb/in.^{2})/(in./in.), since the modulus is a measure of the stress that would be required to produce a strain of 1 in./in., or to double the length of the material. (Only a *very* tough material such as rubber could actually undergo such strain without breaking, but the modulus gives the theoretical stress required to produce such strain.)

The stress-strain relationships for all of the common construction materials have long ago been derived experimentally and the results tabulated. The modulus of elasticity for some of the more common materials is given in Table 3 in the Technical Manual.

The modulus of elasticity E will appear quite frequently in subsequent calculations. One of the most-used values of modulus of elasticity is that for steel, E_S = 29,000,000 psi, or in SI, E_S = 200,000 N/mm^2. Committing these numbers to memory is recommended.

A useful relationship for calculating the axial deflection of a member subject to direct stress may be derived from Eqs. (8-1), (8-2) and (8-3):

$$\Delta = \varepsilon L \tag{8-2}$$

$$\text{where } \varepsilon = \frac{f}{E} \text{ and } f = \frac{P}{A} \qquad \text{(8-3), (8-1)}$$

$$\Delta = \frac{f}{E}L = \frac{P/A}{E}L$$

$$\Delta = \frac{PL}{AE} \tag{8-6}$$

When it is applicable, Eq.(8-6) can be quite useful.

In performing structural calculations, the dimensions of a member are not corrected due to any strains it may undergo. The length of a column that starts at 16 ft-0 in. is considered to be 16 ft-0 in. long in all subsequent calculations; small changes due to deflections or strains are ignored.

Some examples will illustrate the interrelationship between load, stress, deformation and strain in axially loaded members.

Example 8-5

Stress-strain relations.

Given: Steel bar 3m long is loaded to a stress of 120 N/mm^2 in tension.

To Find: Total elongation of the bar.

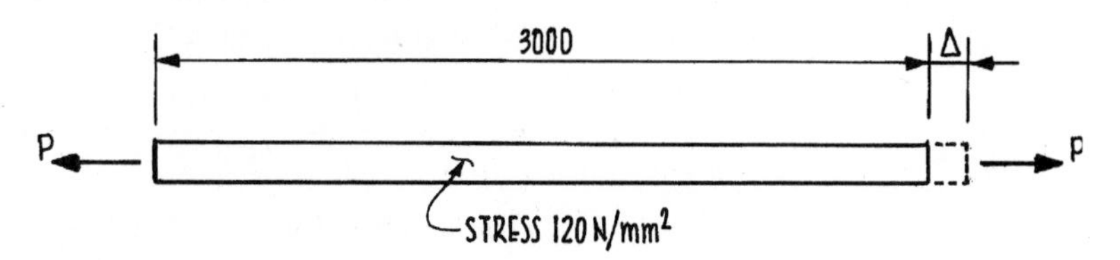

Solution: The strain in the bar can be found from Hooke's law:

$$E = \frac{f}{\varepsilon}, \text{ where } f = 120 \text{ N/mm}^2$$

The modulus of elasticity of steel is found from the design tables: E = 200,000 N/mm².

The strain is calculated directly:

$$\varepsilon = \frac{f}{E} = \frac{120}{200{,}000} = 0.00060 \text{ mm / mm}$$

This result indicates that each mm of the bar elongates 0.00060 mm under the 120N/mm² stress. The total elongation is found by multiplying by the number of mm:

$$\Delta = \varepsilon L = (0.00060)(3000) = 1.80\text{mm}$$

The result of Example 8-5 indicates that the steel bar, loaded to 120N per mm² over its 3 meters of length, will elongate less than 2mm (about 0.06%). Steel is thus seen to be a very rigid material; it deforms very little (but very predictably) under load.

Example 8-6

Stress-strain relations.

Given: 4 in. x 8 in. timber column, 12 ft - 0 in. long, carries an axial load of 12,000 lb. E = 1,400,000 psi. m = 0.22.

To Find: Axial shortening of the column and change in its size due to effects of Poisson's ratio.

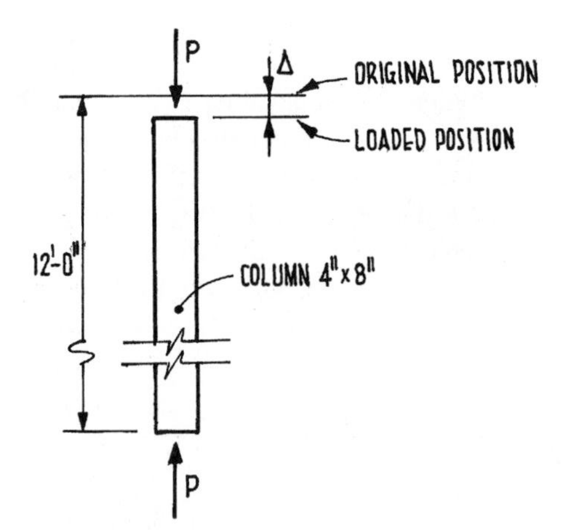

Solution: The stress in the column is found as a direct stress. Actual dimensions for a 4 in. x 8 in. timber member are found from Table T-1 in the Technical Manual to be $3^1/_2$ in. x $7^1/_4$ in.:

$$f = \frac{P}{A} = \frac{12{,}000}{(3\tfrac{1}{2})(7\tfrac{1}{4})} = 473 \text{ psi.}$$

The strain is found from Hooke's law:

$$E = \frac{f}{\varepsilon};\ \varepsilon = \frac{f}{E} = \frac{473}{1{,}400{,}000} = 0.000338 \text{ in./in.}$$

Each inch of the column is shortened by 0.000338 inches. The total shortening is found by multiplying by the number of inches of length:

$$\Delta = \varepsilon L = 0.000338(12)(12) = 0.0486 \text{ in.}$$

This particular problem could also have been solved using the special relationship given by Eq.(8-5):

$$\Delta = \frac{PL}{AE} = \frac{12{,}000(12)(12)}{(3\frac{1}{2})(7\frac{1}{4})(1{,}400{,}000)} = 0.0486 \text{ in.}$$

Under the compressive load, the column will increase slightly in size laterally. The increase is given by Poisson's ratio:

$$\mu = \frac{\text{Unit lateral strain}}{\text{Unit longitudinal strain}} = \frac{\varepsilon_{LAT}}{\varepsilon_{LONG}}$$

$$0.22 = \frac{\varepsilon_{LAT}}{0.000338}$$

$$\varepsilon_{LAT} = 0.0000744 \text{ in./in.}$$

The total increase in size is found by multiplying the transverse strain ε_{LAT} by the transverse dimension:

In the 4 in. direction, $\Delta = \varepsilon_{LAT}\,(3^1/2 \text{ in.})$
$= 0.000260$ in. increase

In the 8 in. direction, $\Delta = \varepsilon_{LAT}\,(7^1/4 \text{ in.})$
$= 0.000539$ in. increase

The final column dimensions will be 3.50026 in. x 7.25054 in.

Example 8-7

Stress-strain relations.

Given: Stepped standard steel pipe sections welded together as shown.

To Find: Total elongation.

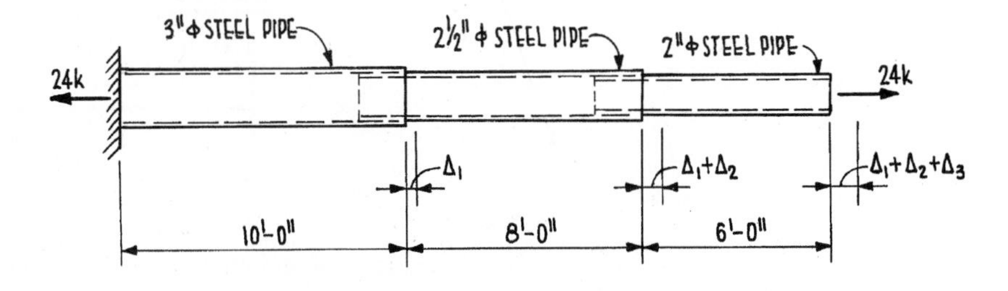

Solution: The total load on each segment is seen to be the same 24 kip load.

The cross-sectional areas of the steel pipe are found in Table S-8 in the Technical Manual.

Area of 3 in. diameter pipe = 2.23 in.^{2}
Area of $2^1/2$ in. diameter pipe = 1.70 in.^{2}
Area of 2 in. diameter pipe = 1.07 in.^{2}

The deflections of the 3 segments are computed separately:

$$\Delta_1 = \frac{PL}{AE} = \frac{24,000(10x12)}{(2.23)(29,000,000)} = 0.0445 \text{ in.}$$

$$\Delta_2 = \frac{PL}{AE} = \frac{24,000(8x12)}{(1.70)(29,000,000)} = 0.0467 \text{ in.}$$

$$\Delta_3 = \frac{PL}{AE} = \frac{24,000(6x12)}{(1.07)(29,000,000)} = 0.557 \text{ in.}$$

The total elongation is the sum of the three:

$$\Delta = \Delta_1 + \Delta_2 + \Delta_3 = 0.0445 + 0.0467 + 0.0557 = 0.1469 \text{ in.}$$

It is interesting to note in the results of Example 8-7 that the longest pipe (the 3 in. diameter pipe @ 10 ft-0 in. long) is elongated least. The smaller pipe sections with their higher stress levels underwent more deformations even though their lengths are shorter.

Example 8-8

Stress-strain relations.

Given: Rigid beam suspended as shown. μ = 0.30.

To Find: a) Rotation due to deflections of supporting wires and
b) change in the diameter of the wires when the 20 kip load is applied. Ignore bending of beam.

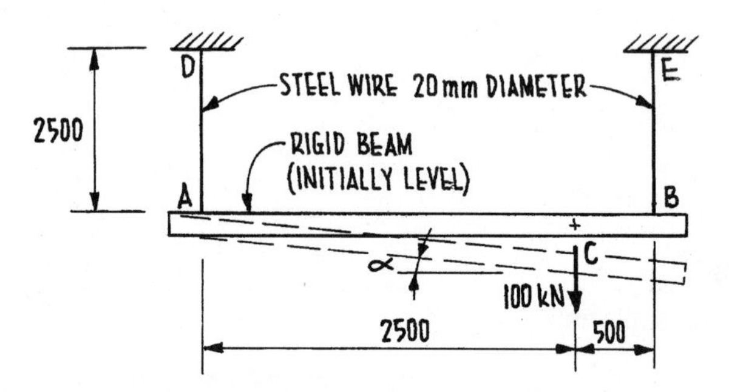

Solution: It is necessary first to find the forces in the wires. These are of course the reactions acting on the beam *AB*.

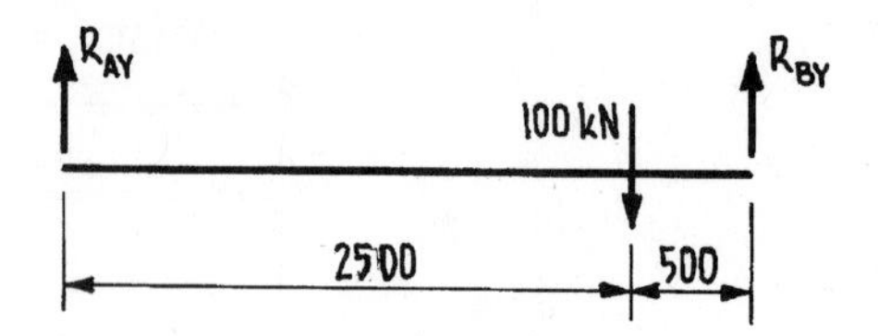

Moments are summed about A to find R_{BY}:

$$\Sigma M_A = 0; \quad 100(2.5) - R_{BY}(3) = 0$$
$$R_{BY} = 83.3 \text{ kN}$$

Moments are summed about B to find R_{AY}:

$$\Sigma M_B = 0; \quad R_{AY}(3) - 100(0.5) = 0$$
$$R_{AY} = 16.7 \text{ kN}$$

Sum of vertical forces indicates 100 kips up, 100 kips down.

The elongation of the wires is found using Eq.(8-5). The area of the wire is found first:

$$A = \frac{\pi d^2}{4} = \frac{\pi}{4}(20)^2 = 314.16\ \text{mm}^2$$

$$\Delta_{AD} = \frac{PL}{AE} = \frac{16{,}666(2500)}{(314.16)200{,}000} = 0.663\ \text{mm}$$

$$\Delta_{BE} = \frac{PL}{AE} = \frac{83{,}333(2500)}{(314.16)200{,}000} = 3.316\ \text{mm}$$

The slope of the bar is shown in the sketch:

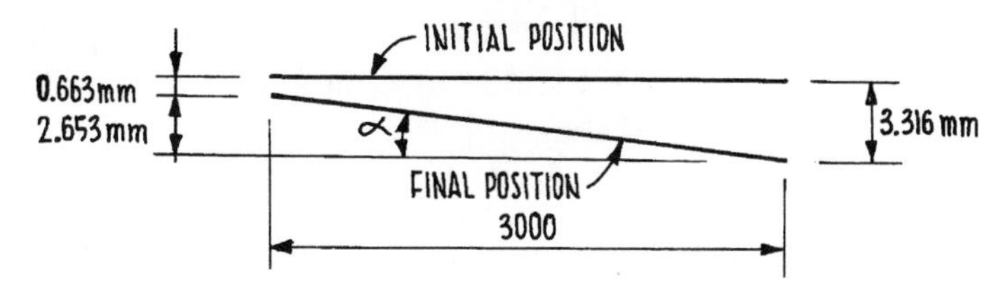

The angle is found from its tangent:

$$\tan\alpha = \frac{2.653}{3000} = 0.000884$$

$$\alpha = 0.0506°$$

The change in the diameter of the wires is found from Poisson's ratio:

$$\mu = \frac{\text{Unit lateral strain}}{\text{Unit longitudinal strain}} = \frac{\varepsilon_{LAT}}{\varepsilon_{LONG}}$$

For wire *AD*:

$$\varepsilon_{LONG} = \frac{\Delta}{L} = \frac{0.663}{3000} = 0.000221\ \text{mm/mm}$$

$$\varepsilon_{LAT} = 0.30\ \varepsilon_{LONG} = 0.0000663\ \text{mm/mm}$$

Change in diameter = 0.001326 mm or 0.0066%.

For wire *BE*:

$$\varepsilon_{LONG} = \frac{\Delta}{L} = \frac{3.316}{3000} = 0.001105\ \text{mm/mm}$$

$$\varepsilon_{LAT} = 0.30\ \varepsilon_{LONG} = 0.0003316\ \text{mm/mm}$$

Change in diameter = 0.00663 mm or 0.033%.

Again, it is seen that structural deformations are indeed small. They exist, however, and their magnitudes, however small, are entirely predictable.

8.4 Bearing Stress

A special case of direct compression stress occurs when one member is supported by another. Such a case occurs in the column and footing arrangement shown in Figure 8-7. The column places a *bearing* stress on the plate, the plate places a *bearing* stress on the concrete footing and the footing places a *bearing* stress on the supporting soil. In all cases, the bearing stress is normal to the contact area.

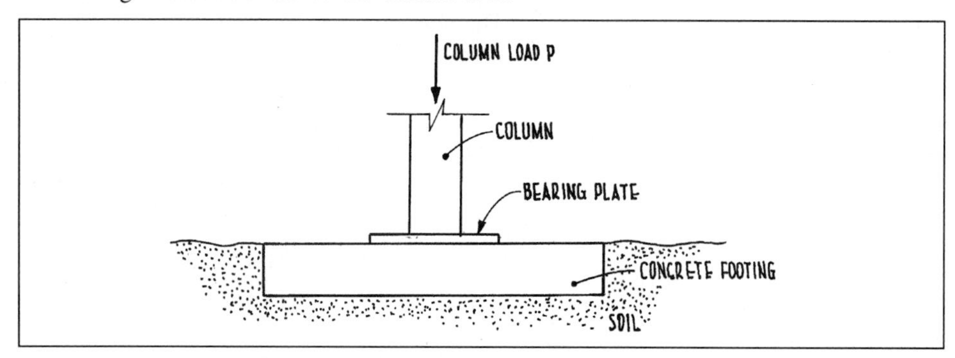

Figure 8-7 Members in bearing.

The bearing stress in each case is a direct stress, computed as a load divided by the bearing area. The bearing stress between the column and the plate shown in Figure 8-12 is computed as:

$$f = \frac{P}{A_{BRNG}} \quad (8\text{-}7)$$

where the bearing area between the two is the contact area, or the area of the column. Similarly, the bearing stress between the plate and the footing is computed as:

$$f = \frac{P}{A_{BRNG}} \quad (8\text{-}7)$$

where the bearing area between the two is the contact area, or the area of the plate. And finally, the bearing stress between the footing and the underlying soil is computed as:

$$f = \frac{P}{A_{BRNG}} \quad (8\text{-}7)$$

where the bearing area between the two is the contact area, or the area of the footing. In all cases, the bearing stress is the stress that occurs as a result of transferring a load from one member to another and the bearing area is the contact area between the two.

Some examples will illustrate the calculation of bearing stress. In soils, it is customary to show stress (pressure) in lb/ft^2 rather than lb/in.^{2}

Example 8-9

Calculation of bearing stress.

Given: Timber column on concrete foundation as shown.

To Find: 1) Bearing stress at top of foundation in lb/in.^{2}
2) Bearing stress on soil in lb/ft^2.

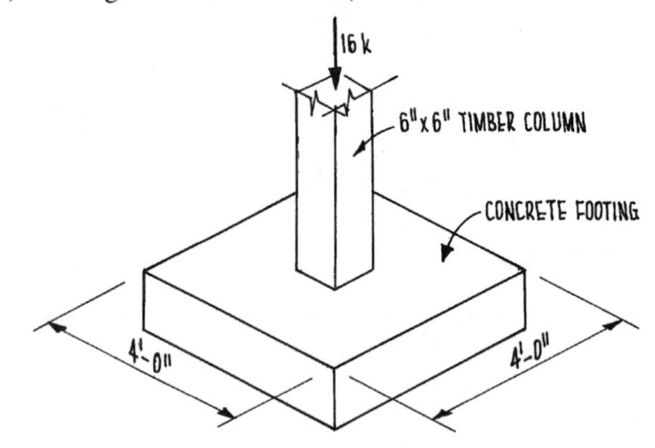

Solution: The bearing stress at the top of the foundation is the force divided by the contact area:

$$f_{BRNG} = \frac{P}{A_{BRNG}} = \frac{16,000}{(5.5)(5.5)} = 522 \text{ lb/in.}^2$$

The bearing stress on the soil is the force divided by the contact area:

$$f_{BRNG} = \frac{P}{A_{BRNG}} = \frac{16,000}{(4)(4)} = 1000 \text{ lb/ft}^2$$

Example 8-10

Calculation of bearing stress.

Given: Steel column on steel base plate as shown. Allowable bearing stress on concrete is 8 N/mm².

To Find: Required size of the bearing plate.

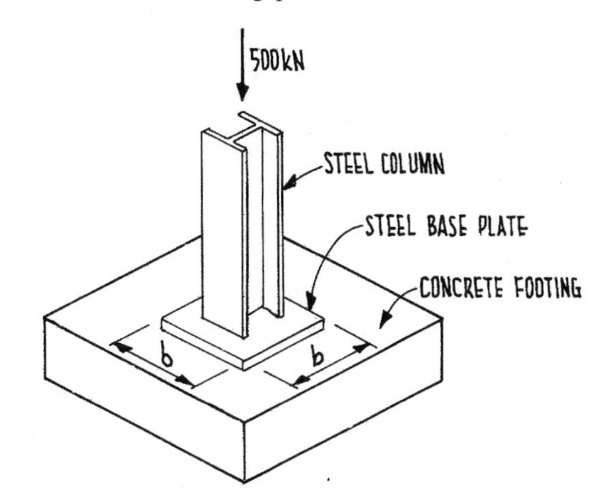

Solution: The bearing stress on the concrete is the force divided by the contact area:

$$f_{BRNG} = \frac{P}{A_{BRNG}}$$

$$\text{Required area} = \frac{P}{f_{BRNG}} = \frac{500,000}{8} = 62,500 \text{ mm}^2$$

For a square base plate $A_{BRNG} = b^2 = 62,500 \text{ mm}^2$:

$$b = \sqrt{62,500} = 250 \text{ mm.}$$

Use base plate 250 mm square.

8.5 Shear Stress, Strain and Modulus

Shear produces a "slicing" effect on a structural member. One of the more easily visualized cases of direct shear stress is that in a bolt or rivet that joins two plates together. Such a connection is shown in Figure 8-8, in which the effect of the load is to slice the bolt into two pieces.

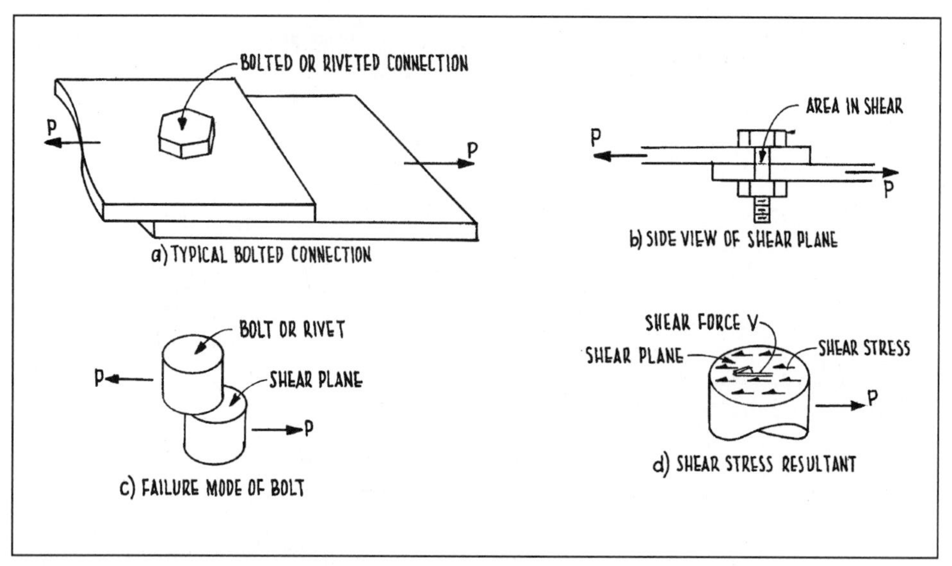

Figure 8-8 Direct shear stress.

The load producing direct shear is usually denoted V. It is assumed that the shearing load is distributed uniformly across the shear plane; every fiber in the shear plane is assumed to be carrying an equal amount of the load. The load over the area is computed as:

$$v = \frac{V}{A_v} \tag{8-8}$$

The load per unit area, denoted v, is the *direct shear stress* on the area; it occurs parallel to the cross section.

Some examples will illustrate the calculation of direct shear stress on fasteners.

Example 8-11

Calculation of direct shear stress.

Given: Bolted connection loaded as shown.

To Find: Shear stress in the three bolts.

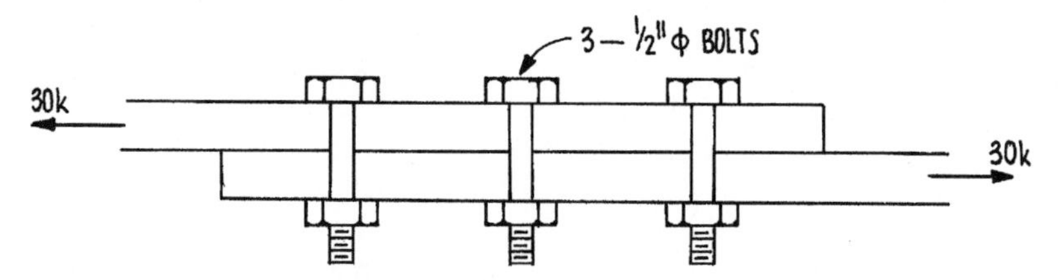

Solution: The shear stress is the shearing force V divided by the area A_v resisting that force:

$$v = \frac{V}{A_v}$$

The shear area consists of 3 bolts, 1/2 in. diameter:

$$A_v = 3\left(\frac{\pi d^2}{4}\right) = 3\left[\frac{\pi}{4}\left(\frac{1}{2}\right)^2\right] = 7.267 \text{ in.}$$

The stress is then:

$$v = \frac{V}{A_v} = \frac{30,000}{7.267} = 4128 \text{ lb/in.}^2$$

Example 8-12

Calculation of direct shear stress.

Given: Connection loaded as shown. Allowable shear stress on the bolts is 100 N/mm². Bolt diameter is 20mm.

To Find: Allowable load on the bolts.

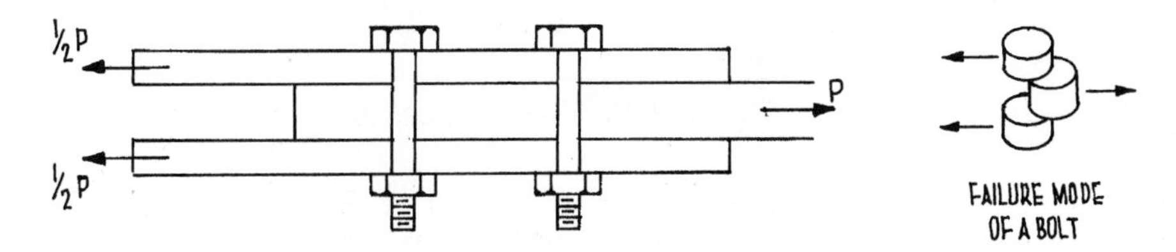

Solution: The shear stress is the shearing force V by the area A_v resisting that force.

The shear area consists of 2 areas in each bolt:

$$A_v = 4\left[\frac{\pi}{4}(d)^2\right] = 4\frac{\pi}{4}(20)^2 = 1257 \text{ mm}^2$$

The maximum allowable load will occur when the stress is at its maximum value of 100 N/mm²:

$$100 = \frac{V}{1257}$$

$$V = 125,700 \text{ N} = 126 \text{ kN}$$

There are other types of direct shear stress, but most of them occur in fastenings of one kind or other. Consider, for example, the welded connection shown in Figure 8-9. The weld lines are undergoing shear stress along their entire length.

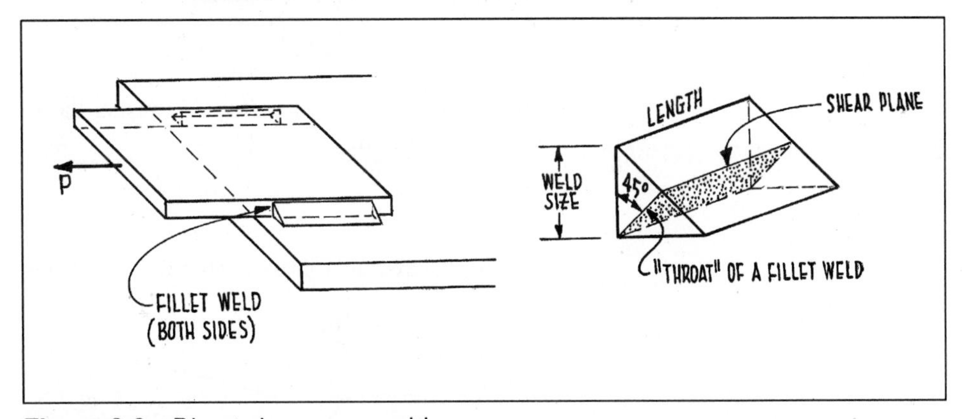

Figure 8-9 Direct shear on a weld.

In fillet welds, the weld size is given as the length of one leg of the weld. The smallest area is that at the *throat* of the weld. The *shear plane* is the rectangle formed by the throat dimension over the entire length of the weld.

In the fillet weld shown in Figure 8-9, the direction of the shear stress is along the longitudinal length of the fillet. The direction of shear need not lie longitudinally; it may also lie across the weld, as shown in Figure 8-9. In both cases, however, the highest stress occurs across the least dimension, or the throat, of the fillet. Again, note that shear stress is parallel to the shear plane.

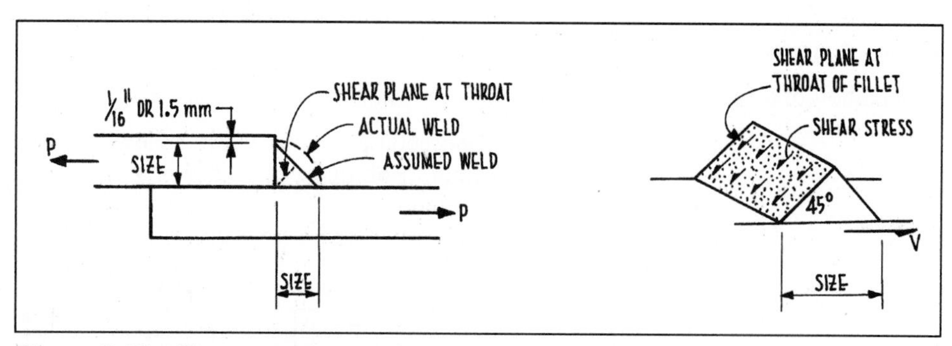

Figure 8-10 Shear stress across a fillet.

A fillet weld is made at a 45° angle and is usually made the full thickness of the plate less 1/16 in. as shown in Figure 8-4. Where the plates are not of equal thickness, the weld size is usually limited by the thickness of the thinner plate. For the standard 45° angle, the thickness of the throat is 0.707 times the weld size.

Some examples will illustrate the calculation of loads and stresses in fillet welds.

Example 8-13

Direct shearing stress in fillet welds.

Given: Connection welded as shown.

To Find: Shearing stress in the weld material.

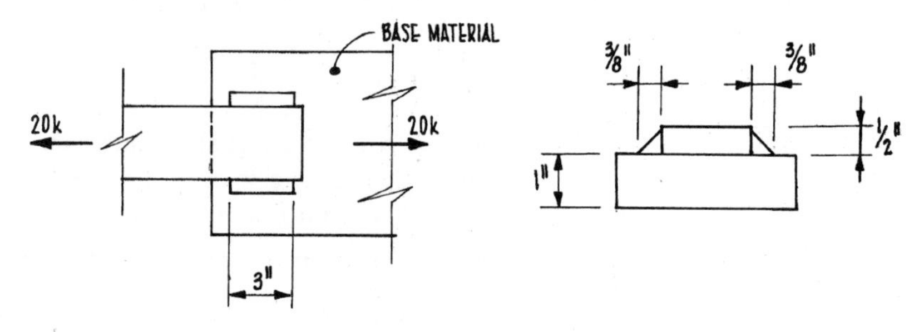

Solution: The shear stress is the force V causing the stress divided by the area A_v being stressed:

$$v = \frac{V}{A_v}$$

The sheared area in each fillet is a plane area as shown:

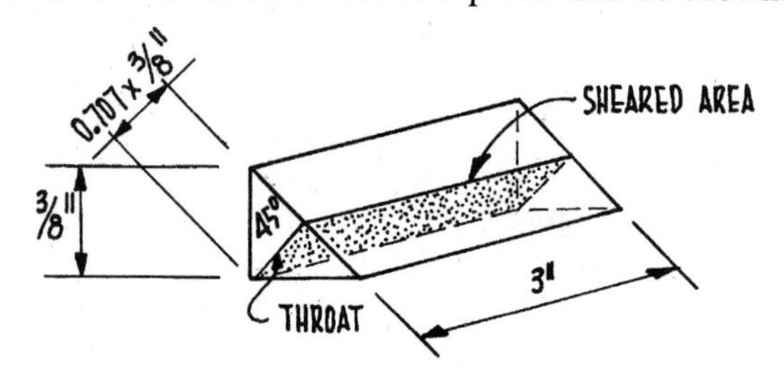

$$A_v = 2[0.707(\tfrac{3}{8})3] = 1.591 \text{ in.}^2$$

The shear stress on this plane is:

$$v = \frac{V}{A_v} = \frac{20{,}000}{1.591} = 12{,}600 \text{ lb/in.}^2$$

Example 8-14

Direct shearing stress in fillet welds.

Given: Fillet weld having configuration shown. All welds 10mm.

To Find: Shear stress in the fillet weld material.

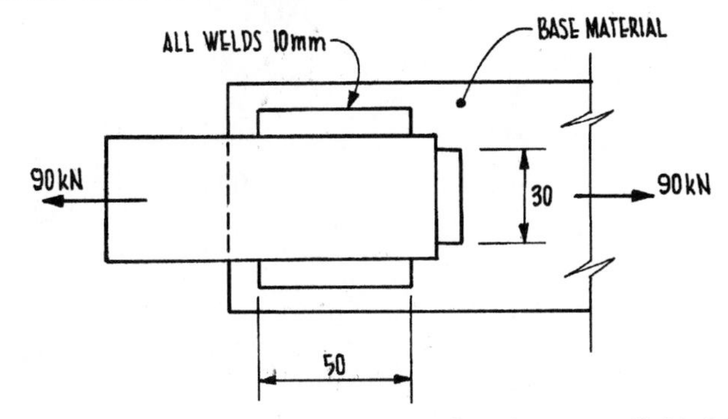

Solution: The shear stress is the force V causing the stress divided by the area A_v being stressed:

$$v = \frac{V}{A_v}$$

The area being stressed consists of 3 plane areas, total length 50 + 30 + 50 = 130 mm and a throat size 0.707(10) mm.

$$A_v = 130(0.707)(10) = 919 \text{ mm.}$$

The shear stress on these 3 planes is:

$$v = \frac{V}{A_v} = \frac{90{,}000}{919} = 98 \text{ N/mm}^2$$

Example 8-15

Direct shearing stress in fillet welds.

Given: Fillet weld configuration as shown. Weld size is $^1/_2$ inch. Allowable weld stress is 15,000 lb/in.^{2}

To Find: Required lengths of the two side welds.

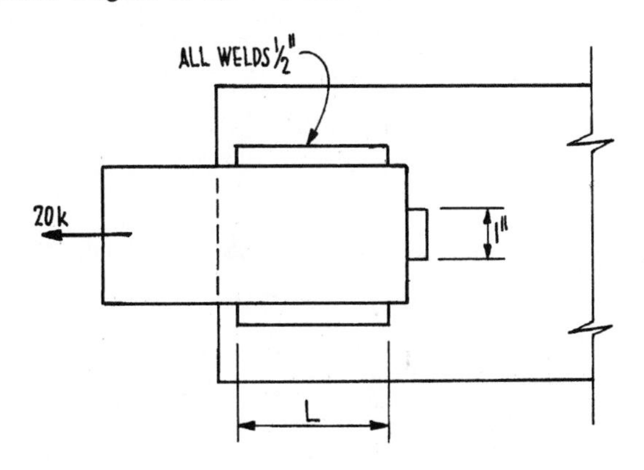

Solution: The shear stress is the shear force V causing the stress divided by the area A_v being stressed:

$$v = \frac{V}{A_v}$$

The area being stressed consists of 3 plane areas, total length 2L + 1 inches, and a throat size 0.707(1/2) in.:

$$A_v = (2L + 1)(0.707)(1/2) = 0.707L + 0.354$$

The length L is determined when the stress reaches its maximum value of 15,000 lb/in.^{2}:

$$v = \frac{V}{A_v}$$

$$15{,}000 = \frac{20{,}000}{0.707L + 0.354}$$

$$L = 1.385 \text{ in.}$$

Use 2 welds, each weld 1½ in. long.

Example 8-16

Direct shearing stress in fillet welds.

Given: Weld configuration as shown. Weld size is 15 mm for both welds.

To Find: Shearing stresses on the throats of both welds.

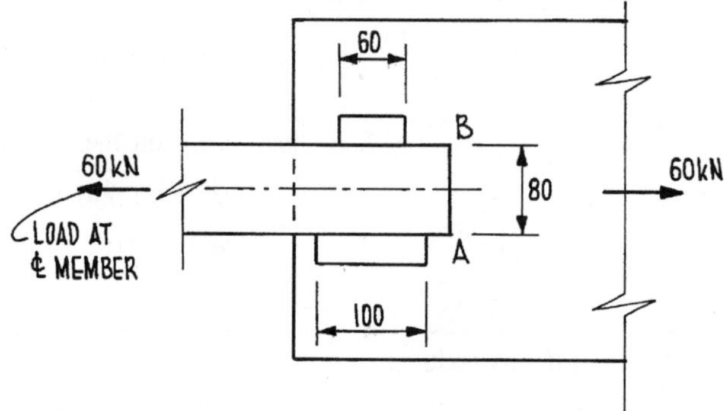

Solution: The force in each weld is found by simple statics. The forces are assumed to be nominally 80 mm apart.

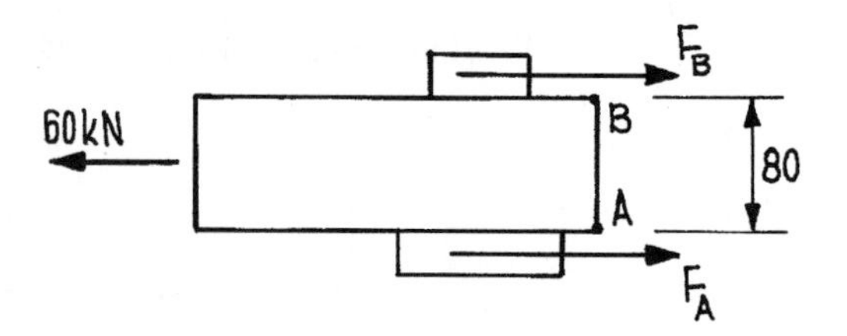

$$\Sigma M_A = 0; \quad -60(40) + F_B(80) = 0$$

$$F_B = 30 \text{ kN}$$

$$F_A = 30 \text{ kN}$$

The shear stress on the weld on side A is:

$$v = \frac{V}{A_v} = \frac{30,000}{100(0.707)15} = 28 \text{ N/mm}^2$$

The shear stress on the weld on side B is:

$$v = \frac{V}{A_v} = \frac{30,000}{60(0.707)15} = 47 \text{ N/mm}^2$$

Up to this point, the shear stresses being considered did not create any deformations; the stressed areas were simply too limited in size to produce any recognizable deformations. In other circumstances, however, shear stress does indeed produce deformations. Such shear deformations can now be introduced.

Consider the shear panel shown in Figure 8-11. The thin panel of thickness t has heavy edge members continuously attached to the panel at all four sides; shear loads may be introduced only at the edge members as shown. A section is taken along line a-a, shown as Figure 8-11b. The shear stress v on the section is computed as before, as the shearing force V acting along the section divided by the area of the section, bt. As before, this direct shear stress occurs parallel to the shear plane.

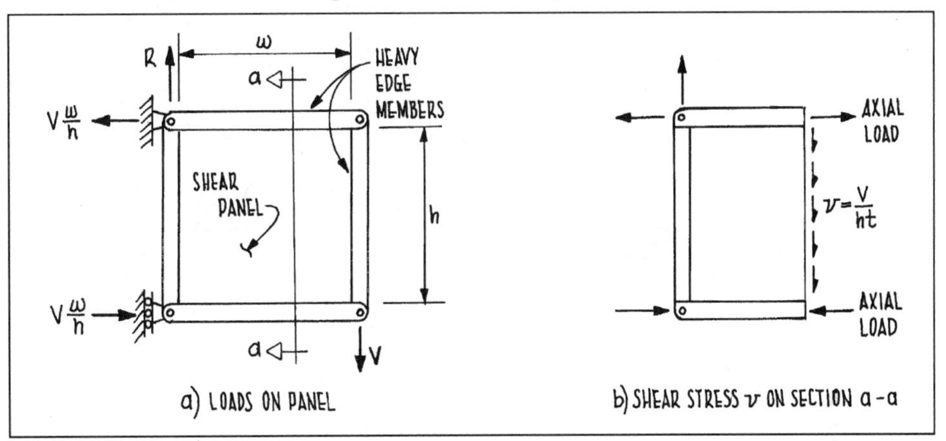

Figure 8-11 Shear stress on a shear panel.

It should be noted that the shear stress on section a-a is assumed to be constant along the full height of the panel and to be uniformly distributed across the thickness t. It is also noted that the only stress in the thin shear panel is the shear stress v.

There is a deformation associated with the shear stress. The deformation is the angle γ as shown in Figure 8-17. The shear deformation is called *detrusion* and occurs wherever shear stress occurs.

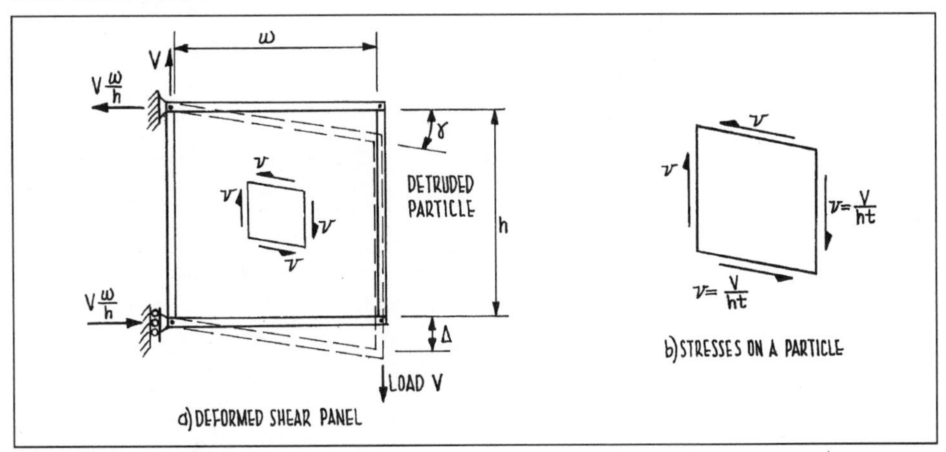

Figure 8-12 Shear deformations.

A particle is removed from the shear panel and is shown in larger size in Figure 8-12b. The four stresses shown on the stressed particle are equal. The vertical stresses are computed as the vertical shearing force V divided by the area resisting the shear, ht. The horizontal stresses are computed as the horizontal shearing force Vw/h divided by the sheared area wt. The end results of the two calculations are identical; the horizontal and vertical shear stresses will always be equal.

The four-sided stress pattern for shear stress shown in Figure 8-12b will occur wherever a material is loaded in shear. The two sets of shear stresses (horizontal and vertical) are seen to form opposing couples that keep the particle in rotational equilibrium.

The detrusion angle γ that accompanies the shear stress is shown in Figure 8-12a. Analogous to axial stress and strain, the ratio of shear stress v to shear strain γ is the shear modulus of elasticity G:

$$G = \frac{v}{\gamma}. \tag{8-9}$$

There is a fixed relationship between the shear modulus G and the axial modulus E. The relationship is derived in advanced books on theory of elasticity:

$$G = \frac{E}{2(1+\mu)} \tag{8-10}$$

where μ is Poisson's ratio for the material.

Some examples will illustrate the interrelationship between shear force, shear stress, shear detrusion and the accompanying linear displacements.

Example 8-17

Direct shearing stress in shear panels.

Given: Shear panel with edge members, loaded as shown. G = 12,000,000 lb/in.^{2} Thickness of the panel is 0.125 inch.

To Find:
1) Shear stress in the panel.
2) The angle of detrusion.
3) Displacement Δ of the 20 kip load.
4) Loads at supports.
5) Distribution of axial force along the edge member CD.

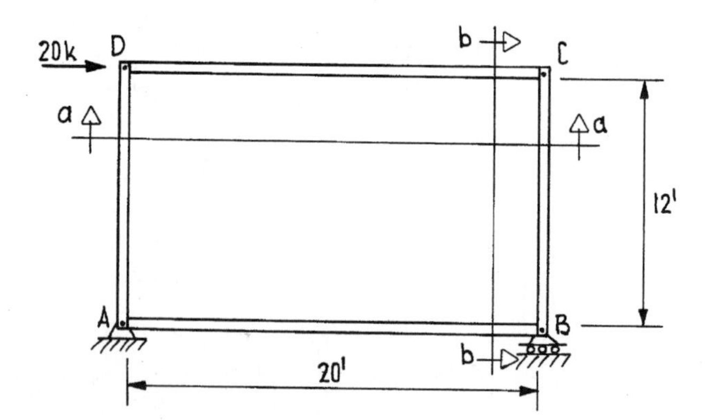

Solution: Shear stress in the panel is the force causing the shear stress divided by the area being stressed:

$$v = \frac{V}{A}$$

A section *aa* is taken as indicated and is shown in the following free body. The shear stress *v* is shown acting parallel to the section.

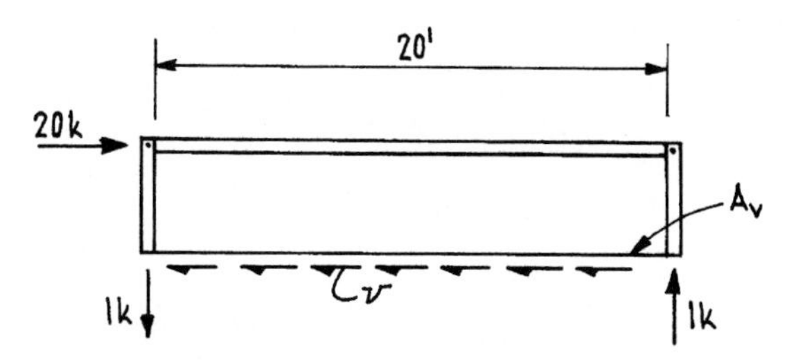

Forces are summed horizontally. The area being sheared is the length times the thickness of the shear panel:

$$\Sigma F_X = 0; \quad 20{,}000 - vA_v = 0$$
$$20{,}000 - v(0.125)(20 \times 12) = 0$$
$$v = 667 \text{lb/in.}^2$$

The angle of detrusion γ is found by definition:

$$G = \frac{\text{Shear stress v}}{\text{Shear strain } \gamma}$$

$$12{,}000{,}000 = \frac{667}{\gamma}$$

$$\gamma = 0.0000556 \text{ radians}$$
$$\gamma = 0.00318 \text{ degrees}$$

The displacement Δ of the 20 kip load is shown in the following sketch. Also shown is the shear angle γ.

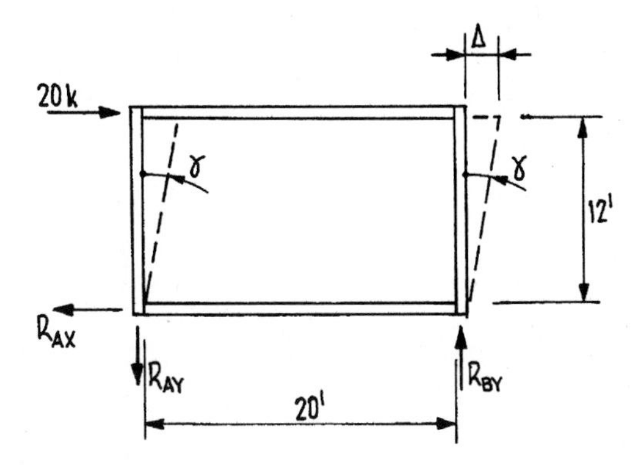

For small angles, tan $\gamma = \gamma$ in radians,

$$\tan\gamma = \frac{\Delta}{(12)(12)} = \tan 0.0000556 \text{ radians} = 0.0000556$$

$$\Delta = 0.0080 \text{ in.}$$

The reactions at *A* and *B*, as indicated in the foregoing sketch, are found by simple statics:

$\Sigma M_A = 0; \quad 20(12) - R_{BY}(20) = 0$
$R_{BY} = 12$ kips (up)

$\Sigma M_B = 0; \quad 20(12) - R_{AY}(20) = 0$
$R_{AY} = 12$ kips (down)

$\Sigma F_X = 0; \quad 20 - R_{AX} = 0$
$R_{AX} = 20$ kips (left)

The edge member *CD* is removed as a free body with all forces shown on it:

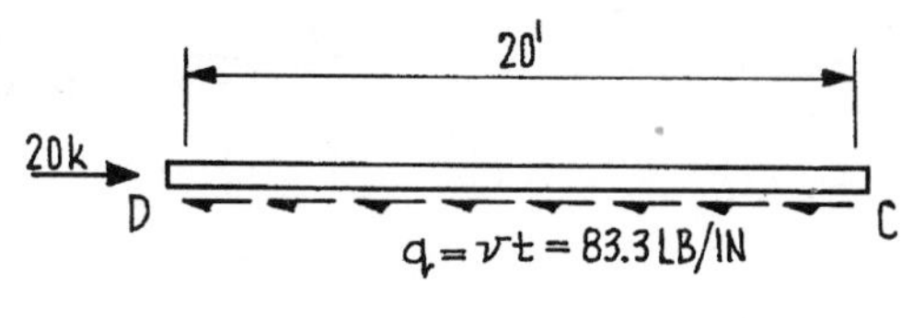

$q = vt = 667(0.125)$
$= 83.33$ lb/in.

The force *q* (called shear flow) shown in the sketch is the force per unit length along the edge member. There is zero force at *C*. Total force at *D* is the shear flow times the length, or 20 kips.

As a matter of interest, the shear stress along section *bb* might also be checked. The section is shown as a free body in the following sketch:

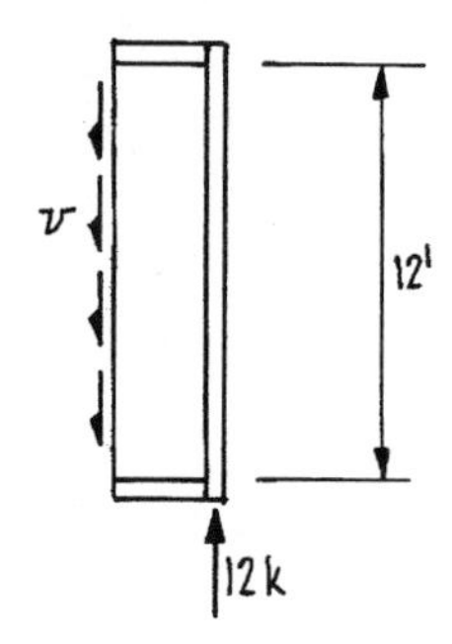

The stress *v* is found by summing vertical forces:

$\Sigma F_Y = 0; \quad -v(0.125)(12 \times 12) + 12{,}000 = 0$
$v = 667 \text{ lb/in.}^2$

The value for shear stress just obtained matches that found in the horizontal direction, as it must. Every particle in the panel will have the same shear stress on its four sides.

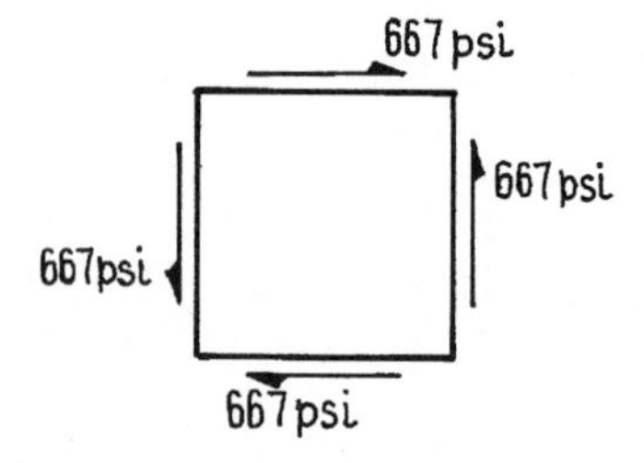

Example 8-18

Direct shearing stress in shear panels.

Given: Shear load on the shear panel as shown. The allowable shear stress on the aluminum material is 40 N/mm^2. G = 40,000 N/mm^2. Note that reactions are given.

To Find: Required thickness of the panel material.

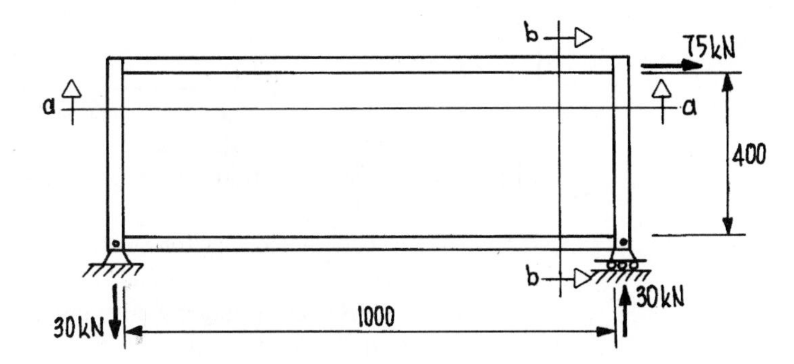

Solution: The shear stress on the panel material is found from a horizontal section such as section *aa*.

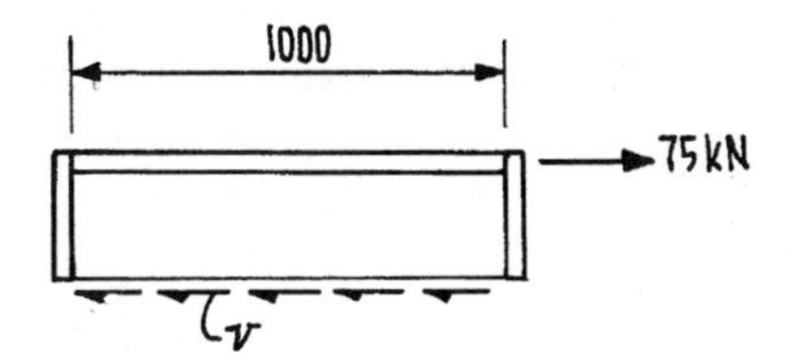

Forces are summed horizontally, with v = 40 kN/mm^2:

$$\Sigma F_X = 0; \quad 75{,}000 - vA_v = 0$$
$$75{,}000 - 40(1000)t = 0$$
$$t = 1.875 \text{ mm.}$$

Use material 2mm thick.

The thickness could also have been found by using the vertical section *bb*.

Forces are summed vertically:

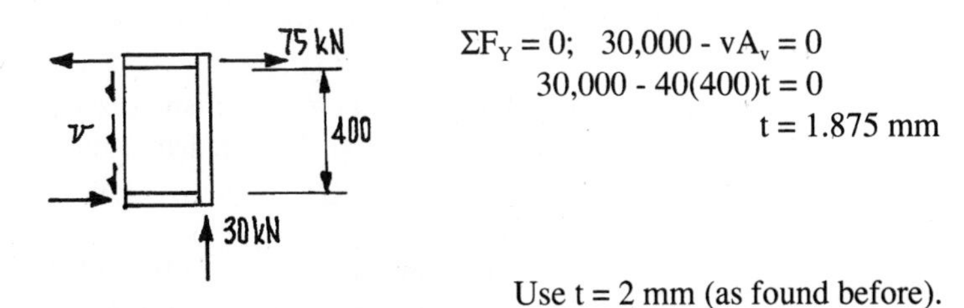

$$\Sigma F_Y = 0; \quad 30{,}000 - vA_v = 0$$
$$30{,}000 - 40(400)t = 0$$
$$t = 1.875 \text{ mm}$$

Use t = 2 mm (as found before).

8.6 Stress-Strain Curves

The stress-strain curve given earlier in Figure 8-6 is only a partial curve of the stress-strain relations for steel. To be complete, the test should be extended until the steel sample is loaded to its maximum strength and ultimate rupture. Such a complete curve for a sample of mild steel is shown in Figure 8-13.

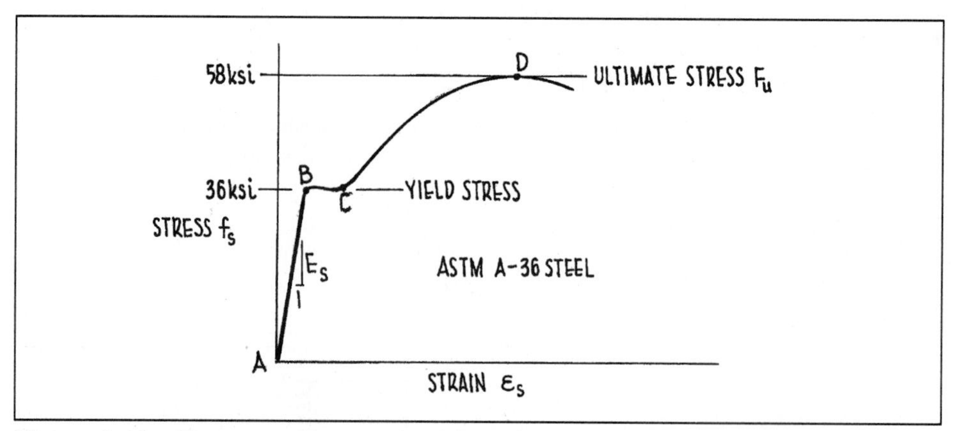

Figure 8-13 Stress-strain curve for mild steel.

It has already been noted that for steel, the portion of the curve between *A* and *B* is a straight line. The range of stresses and strains between *A* and *B* is called the *elastic range* of the material. As stress is increased beyond point *B*, the steel begins to take a permanent "set", that is, if the load is released, the material will not return to its exact original position at *A*, but will retain some permanent deformation. The point *B* is called the *elastic limit* of the material.

The range of stresses between *B* and *C* is an important one. A magnified view of this portion of the curve is shown in Figure 8-14. For the sake of this discussion, the slight "hump" that occurs at *B* has been smoothed into the idealized curve as shown.

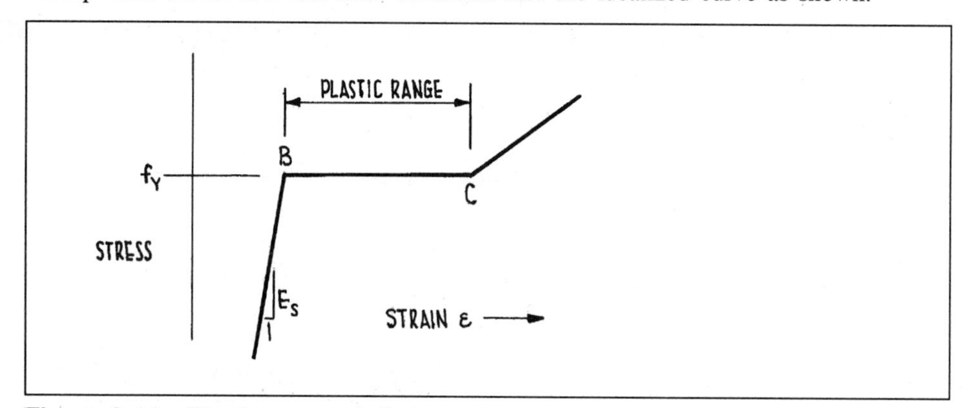

Figure 8-14 Plastic range of strains.

As indicated in Figure 8-14, the steel sample undergoes permanent deformation when the stress exceed f_y. This level of stress is called the *yield stress* of the material. Once deformations progress into this range of strains, the steel becomes permanently deformed.

The range of strains between *B* and *C* is called the *plastic range* or *yield range* of the steel. It is this characteristic plastic range in steel that makes steel such a "forgiving" structural material. Rather than breaking under excess load, the steel simply yields (or bends permanently), giving ample warning of distress long before rupture becomes imminent.

Other materials may not be so forgiving. Cast iron, for example, has no yield range such as that of mild steel. A cast iron machine part will likely undergo fracture without any warning. While durable, strong, hard and functional, cast iron is brittle, and can fail without any indication of distress.

The stress-strain curves for several of the more common construction materials is shown in Figure 8-15. It should be noted immediately, however, that aluminum may exhibit many different stress-strain curves other than the one shown, depending upon the particular alloy. Some aluminum alloys do in fact exhibit a plastic range, similar to that of steel.

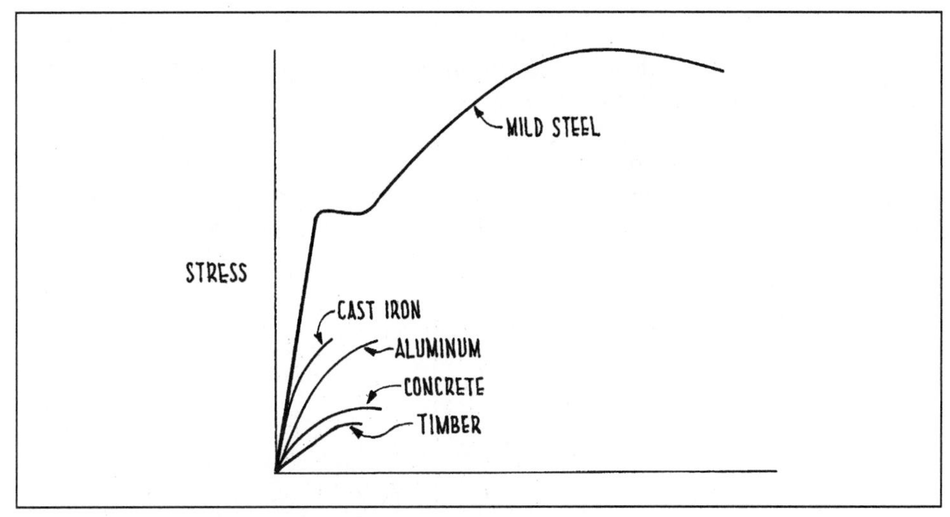

Figure 8-15 Typical stress-strain curves.

In some cases, a material will exhibit very poor elastic properties, so poor, in fact, that it is difficult to assign a modulus of elasticity to the curve. For such materials, the curve may have to be "idealized" such that it conforms to a more recognizable form.

The stress-strain curve for concrete is one such curve that must be idealized if it is to be compared to other elastic materials. A typical but highly exaggerated curve for concrete is shown in Figure 8-16, along with its idealized curve *OAB*. It is this idealized curve that will be used in later chapters for the design of reinforced concrete structural members.

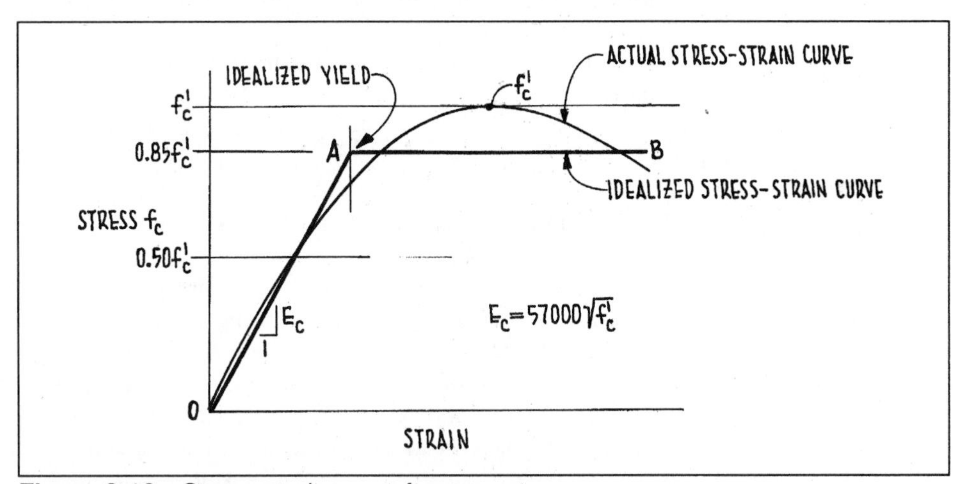

Figure 8-16 Stress-strain curve for concrete.

Unlike steel, concrete has no well-defined straight portion of its stress-strain curve which will define the modulus of elasticity. The line *OA* in Figure 8-16 is therefore drawn as such a straight-line portion of the idealized curve, passing through the point $0.50\,f'_c$ on the actual curve. As indicated, the curve is a close approximation of the actual curve at the lower levels of stress, becoming less accurate as the stress approaches the idealized yield stress of $0.85\,f'_c$. The actual modulus of elasticity of concrete E_c is computed from empirical (test) data:

$$E_c = 57{,}000\sqrt{f'_c} \tag{8-11}$$

The yield range of concrete is shown as line *AB* in the idealized curve. Rupture is arbitrarily set by the design code at a strain of 0.003 in./in. The idealized curve of Figure

8-16 may seem somewhat extreme, but it has been found to yield calculated results in actual concrete members that compare very favorably to laboratory test results; it is difficult to argue with success.

The stress-strain curve for mild structural steel is shown again in Figure 8-17. It is observed that it is highly desirable to keep stresses in a member well below the yield point at *B*. Such a limit on the allowable stress will assure that the steel will never undergo large permanent deformations under day-to-day loads.

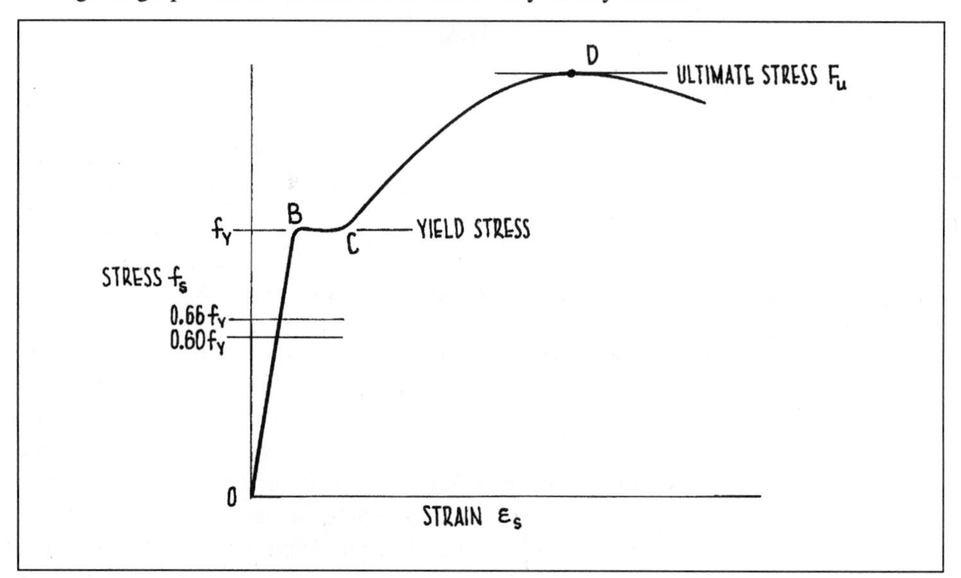

Figure 8-17 Allowable working stresses in steel.

The ratio of the stress at the elastic limit to the allowable stress is called the *factor of safety, FS*:

$$FS = \frac{\text{Stress at elastic limit}}{\text{Allowable elastic stress}} \tag{8-12}$$

For an allowable stress of $0.60f_y$, the factor of safety is 1.7; the material can sustain a 70% overstress to the elastic limit.

For steel, the design code sets the maximum allowable stress in bending at $0.60f_y$, where f_y is the yield stress of the steel. For ASTM A-36 steel, f_y is 36,000 psi and for ASTM A-441 steel, f_y is 50,000 psi; these are the two most common structural steels in use in today's construction. If the steel member meets certain requirements for its shape and for its lateral support, an increase in allowable stress to $0.66f_y$ is permitted by the design code. The cost of steel is so high that providing the lateral support to get this increase in allowable stress is generally well worthwhile.

Other allowable stresses in steel are given in the tables in the Technical Manual. Depending on the type of stress, these allowable stresses range from $0.60f_y$ to $0.75f_y$. These stresses will be reintroduced when appropriate in later discussions of the various types of stress.

The foregoing discussion of stress-strain curves is certainly not intended to be a complete coverage of the properties of construction materials. Complete coverage is presented in separate coursework in engineering materials, which includes work in laboratory testing of the various materials. The discussions here are intended only as the barest introduction into engineering materials for use in later discussions.

Review Questions

1. What is the primary difference between the study of rigid body mechanics and the study of mechanics of materials?
2. What does the term "tough" mean when it is used to describe an engineering material?
3. What does the term "ductile" mean when it is used to describe an engineering material?
4. What does the term "elastic" mean when it is used to describe an engineering material?
5. What is the basis for assuming that direct stress is uniformly distributed across a stressed section?
6. What is direct axial stress?
7. What is direct axial strain?
8. How is direct axial stress related to direct axial strain?
9. State Hooke's law in your own words.
10. What is Poisson's ratio?
11. Why isn't Poisson's ratio of more interest in elementary strength of materials?
12. What is the value of the modulus of elasticity of steel in Imperial units? SI units?
13. Define the modulus of elasticity.
14. What is the physical meaning of the modulus of elasticity?
15. What are the units of the modulus of elasticity?
16. How is bearing stress different from axial stress?
17. How is direct axial stress calculated?
18. How is bearing stress calculated?
19. How is direct shear stress calculated?
20. In view of the answers to questions 17, 18 and 19, how is direct stress distributed across a section?
21. How is shear strain measured?
22. Define the shear modulus of elasticity.
23. What is detrusion?
24. Sketch a detruded particle in a loaded shear panel, having a shear stress of 100 N/mm^2.
25. What is the relationship between axial or normal modulus of elasticity and shear modulus of elasticity?
26. What is meant by elastic limit?
27. What is meant by the term yield stress?
28. What is ultimate stress?
29. What is happening physically to steel when it is in its plastic range?
30. Why are many stress-strain curves "idealized" before use in engineering applications?
31. In concrete, at what percentage of ultimate stress is the yield stress assumed to occur?
32. In steel, at what percentage of yield stress is the allowable working stress usually set?

CHAPTER

9

TORSION, FLEXURE AND BEAM SHEAR

There are types of stress and strain other than direct stress and strain. In these other types of stress, the distribution of the stress across the section is not uniform, as it is in direct stress. Three examples of such nonuniform stresses are torsion, flexure and beam shear.

Torsional stress is the stress created by twisting a member, such as the twist on the driveshaft shown in Figure 9-1a. Torsional stress will be seen to be a shear stress parallel to a cross section of the shaft. Its magnitude will be seen to be maximum at the outer fibers of the shaft and zero at the center of rotation.

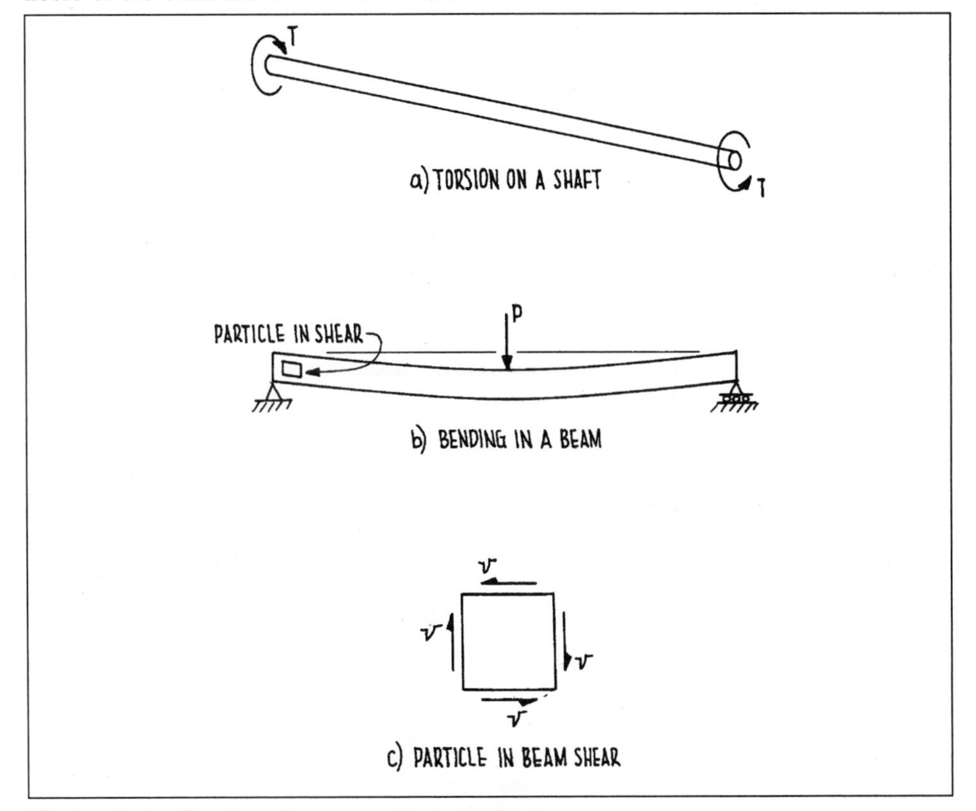

Figure 9-1 Torsion, flexure and beam shear.

Flexural stress is the stress created by bending a member, such as the bending in the beam shown in Figure 9-1. Flexural stress will be seen to be normal to the cross section, similar to axial stresses. Its magnitude is maximum at the outer fibers, in tension on one side of the beam and in compression on the other.

Beam shear stress occurs in a beam as a result of bending, as shown in Figure 9-1. It occurs as two opposing couples on a particle. Its magnitude will be seen to be maximum at the middle of the cross section and zero at the outer fibers.

9.1 Torque on a Section

The twisting moment that causes a shaft to turn against a resistance of some kind is called *torque*. Like moment, torque may be shown in sketches by a couple, or, as indicated in Figure 9-2, it may be shown by a curled arrow. Also like moment, torque is usually applied as a couple, as shown earlier in Figure 3-9, and is then transformed by the shaft back into pure torque.

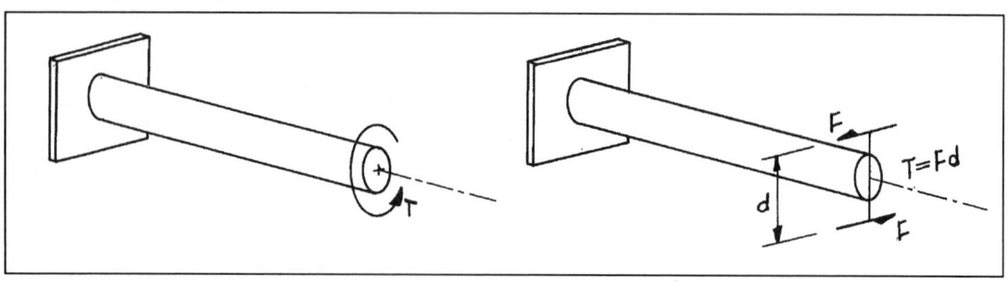

Figure 9-2 Torque on a shaft.

As a point of review, the torque produced by a couple is found as the magnitude of one of the forces times the distance between them. Such a computation is indicated in Figure 9-2. Alternatively, one may simply sum moments about one of the forces to find:

$$T = Fd \tag{9-1}$$

The torque produced by a force about an axis of rotation is found by summing moments about the center of rotation. Examples of such calculations are in Figure 9-3 for several cases of loading. In each case, the torque is found simply as the sum of moments about the axis of rotation.

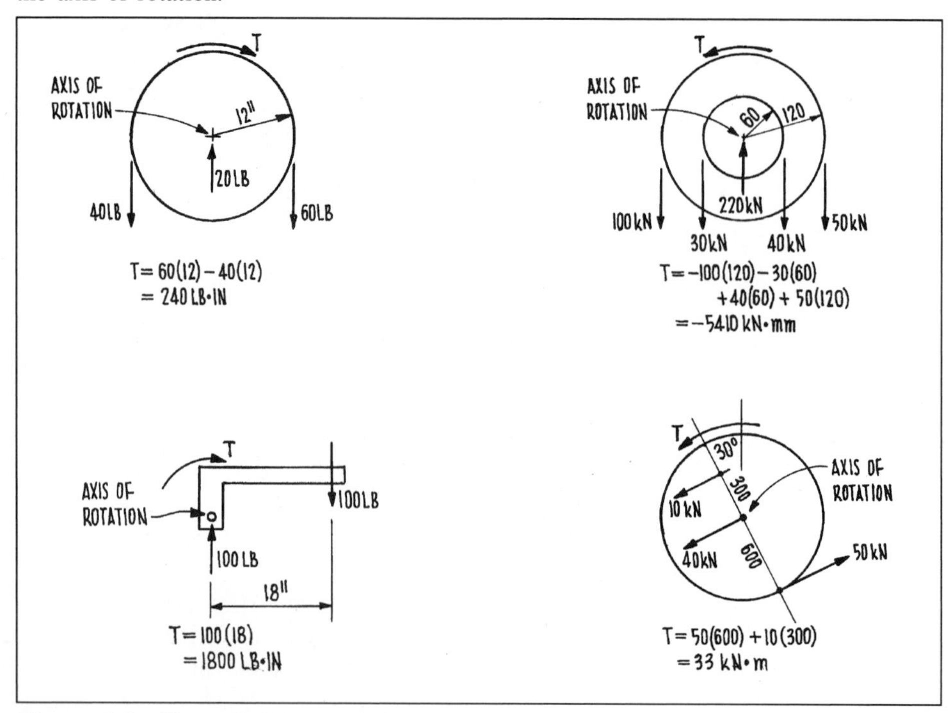

Figure 9-3 Torque about an axis of rotation.

Like moment, the units of torque are force times distance. In the Imperial system, the units may be lb·in., lb·ft, kip·in. or kip·ft. In SI, the units may be N·mm, N·m, kN·mm or kN·m. Occasionally in the literature the distance is given first, such as in.·lb or ft·kips. All these forms of the units are acceptable and all may be used in dimensional analysis.

On a rotating shaft, there may be more than one applied torque. Such a case is shown in Figure 9-4, where a driving torque is applied at the left end of the shaft and power is taken off at three other points. For moment equalibrium of the system about the axis of rotation, the sum of all torques must be equal to zero.

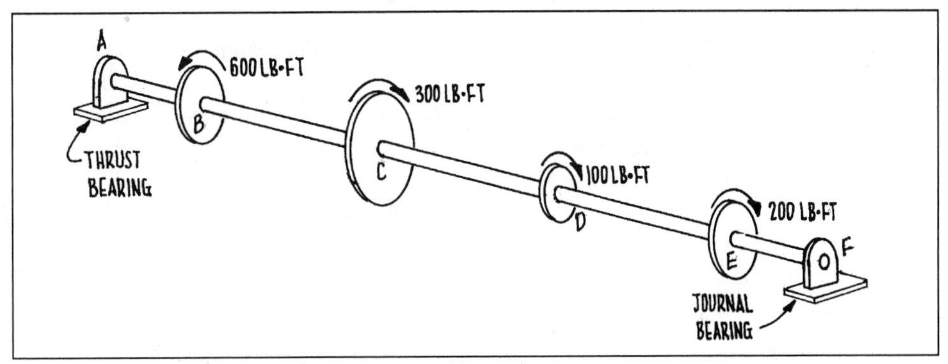

Figure 9-4 Multiple torques on a single shaft.

The torque at any point along the shaft of Figure 9-4 is the sum of all torques to one side of the section. Since there is no torque to the left of *B*, for example, there is no torque in the segment *AB* of the shaft. For the segment *BC*, the sum of torques to the left is 600 lb·ft; that level of torque exists throughout the segment *AB*, the left side being turned counterclockwise with respect to the right. Similarly, the torque in segment *BC* is found by summing torques to either side of the segment, yielding 300 lb·ft, again turning the left side counterclockwise with respect to the right. The torque in the other segments is found similarly.

The torque in the segments *BC*, *CD* and *DE* will produce stresses in those segments. The type and magnitude of those stresses will be determined next.

9.2 Torsional Stress and Polar Moment of Inertia

The effect of torque on a shaft is to create shear; the torque tries to shear one section of the shaft past the other. Such a case of loading is shown in Figure 9-5. The distribution of the shearing stress across a typical section is also shown.

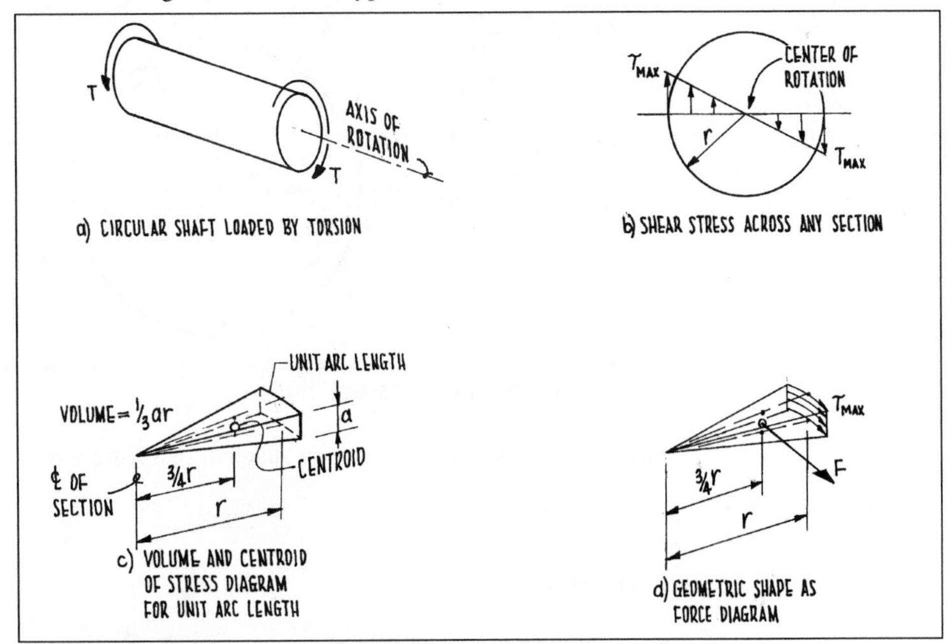

Figure 9-5 Torsion on a circular shaft.

For equilibrium to exist, the torque being applied to the section of Figure 9-5 must be equal to the resisting torque being developed by the material. The resisting torque is the force F times the distance from center of rotation to the centroid of the force diagram:

$$\text{Resisting torque} = F\left(\frac{3}{4}r\right) \tag{9-1}$$

The force F per unit of arc of the circular section is found as the volume of the geometric shape:

$$F = \text{Force/unit of arc} = \frac{1}{3}\tau_{MAX} r \tag{9-2}$$

The torque on the entire circle is this torque per unit of arc times the circumference of the circle:

$$\text{Resisting torque} = \left(\frac{1}{3}\tau_{MAX} r\right)\left(\frac{3}{4}r\right)(2\pi r) = \tau_{MAX}\frac{\pi r^3}{2} \tag{9-3}$$

This resisting torque is equated to the applied torque to find:

$$T = \tau_{MAX}\frac{\pi r^3}{2} \tag{9-4a}$$

Equation (9-4a) is solved for the maximum shear stress τ_{MAX}:

$$\tau_{MAX} = \frac{T}{\left(\frac{\pi r^3}{2}\right)} \tag{9-4b}$$

Equation (9-4b) will yield the maximum shear stress produced by a torque T acting on a circular section of radius r. While correct, the equation is not usually used in this form. Over the years it has been found preferable to express the equation in terms of the shear stress at any point c along the radius rather than at the maximum point.

The shear stress τ_C at some distance c from the center of rotation is shown on the stress distribution diagram of Figure 9-6. The shear stress distribution is seen to be linear, going from zero at the center of rotation to its maximum value of τ_{MAX} at the extreme fibers of the section.

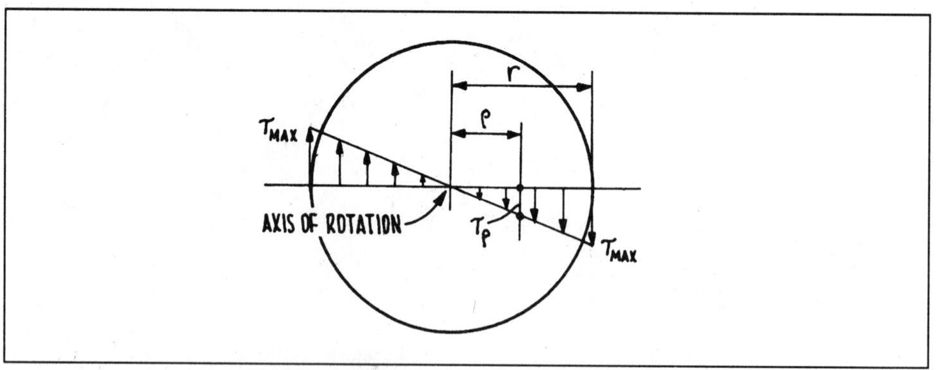

Figure 9-6 Shear stress distribution.

From similar triangles in the stress diagram of Figure 9-6:

$$\frac{\tau_{MAX}}{\tau_\rho} = \frac{r}{\rho} \tag{9-5a}$$

from which:

$$\tau_{MAX} = \tau_\rho \frac{r}{\rho} \tag{9-5b}$$

This value for τ_{MAX} is substituted into Eq.(9-4b) to yield the *torsional stress formula*, in its accepted form:

$$\tau_\rho = \frac{T_\rho}{J} \qquad (9\text{-}6a)$$

$$\text{where } J = \frac{\pi r^4}{2} \qquad (9\text{-}6b)$$

It is very important in using the torsion stress formula to remember that the torsional stress τ_ρ is the shear stress located at a distance ρ from the axis of rotation.

The factor J in Eq.(9-6) is called the *polar moment of inertia* of the cross section; it is a property of the cross section. It is a scalar quantity, having units of inches^4 or mm^4. Numerically, it is the torque required to produce a shear stress of 1 psi at a distance 1 inch from the center of rotation.

Some examples will illustrate the use of the torsion stress formula.

Example 9-1

Torsional stress formula.

Given: Circular drive shaft $2^1/_2$ in. diameter loaded as shown.

To Find: Maximum shear stresses produced by the torques throughout the length of the shaft.

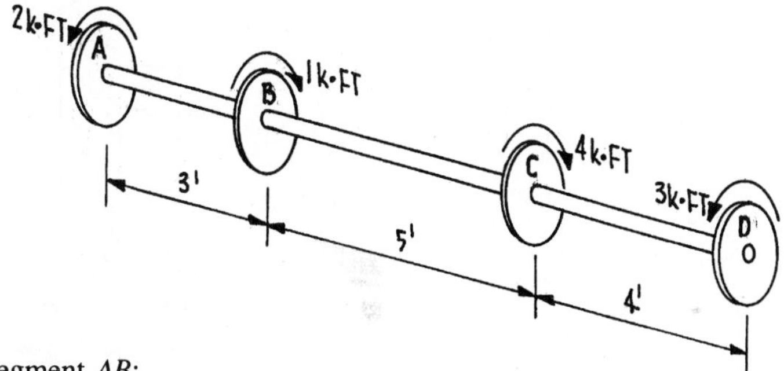

Solution: Segment *AB*:

$$\text{Torsional stress} = \frac{T_\rho}{J}$$

Applied torque = ΣT = 2.0 k·ft

Maximum stress occurs when $\rho = r = 1.25$ in.

$$\text{Polar moment of inertia} = J = \frac{\pi r^4}{2} = \frac{\pi}{2}(1.25)^4 = 3.835$$

$$\tau_{MAX} = \frac{T_r}{J} = \frac{(2000)(12)(1.25)}{3.835} = 7823 lb/in.^2$$

Segment *BC*:

$$\text{Torsional stress} = \frac{T_\rho}{J}$$

Applied torque = $\Sigma T = -2 + 1 = 1.0$ kip·ft

$\rho = r = 1.25$ in., $J = 3.835$

$$\tau = \frac{T_r}{J} = \frac{(1000)(12)(1.25)}{3.835} = 3911\ \text{lb/in.}^2$$

Segment *CD*:

$$\text{Torsion stress} = \frac{T\rho}{J}$$

Applied torque = ΣT = -2 + 1 + 4 = 3.0 kip·ft

ρ = r = 1.25 in., J = 3.835

$$\tau = \frac{T_r}{J} = \frac{(3000)(12)(1.25)}{3.835} = 11734 \text{ lb/in.}^2$$

The torsional stress formula may also be used to determine stresses in hollow drive shafts as shown in Figure 9-7. The torque in a hollow drive shaft may be computed as the torque that would exist if the shaft were solid less the torque lost when the interior is removed.

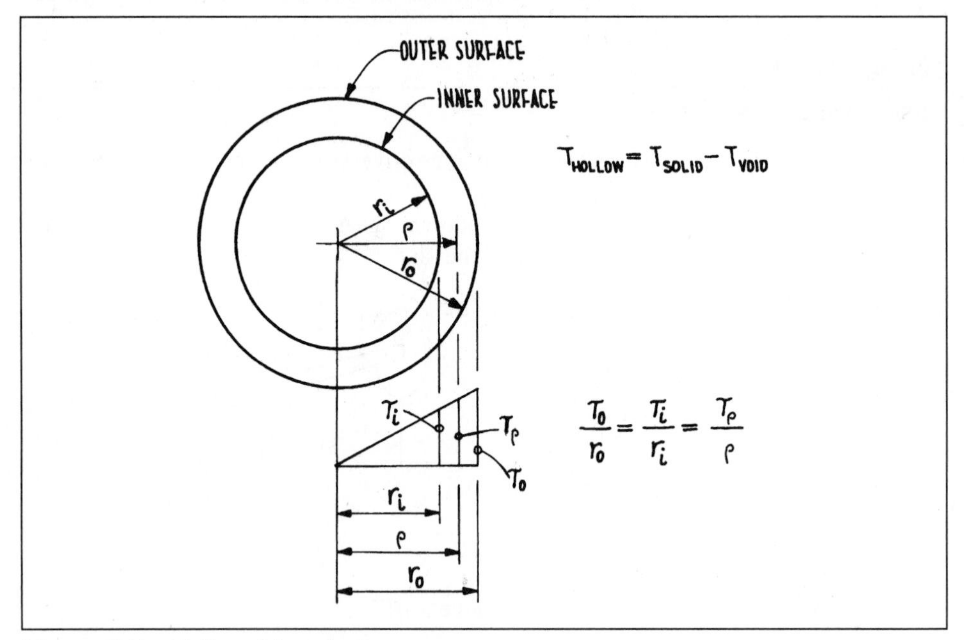

Figure 9-7 Hollow drive shaft.

The torque of the hollow shaft is then:

$$T_{HOLLOW} = T_{SOLID} - T_{VOID} \tag{9-7a}$$

$$= \frac{\tau_0 J_{SOLID}}{r_0} - \frac{\tau_i J_{VOID}}{r_i} \tag{9-7b}$$

From the stress diagram of Figure 9-7:

$$\frac{\tau_0}{r_0} = \frac{\tau_i}{r_i} = \frac{\tau_\rho}{\rho} \tag{9-7c}$$

Hence:

$$T_{HOLLOW} = \frac{\tau_0}{r_0}\left(J_{SOLID} - J_{VOID}\right) \tag{9-8a}$$

$$\tau_\rho = \frac{T\rho}{J_{HOLLOW}}, \tag{9-8b}$$

where $J_{HOLLOW} = J_{SOLID} - J_{VOID}$

The end result is that the polar moment of inertia of a hollow shaft is the polar moment of inertia of the solid shaft less the polar moment of inertia of the area removed. All other features of the torsional stress formula remain the same.

Example 9-2

Torsional stress formula.

Given: Hollow driveshaft having dimensions shown. Applied torque = 3.0 kN·M = 3,000,000 N·m.

To Find: 1) Stress at the outer surface.
2) Stress at the inner surface.

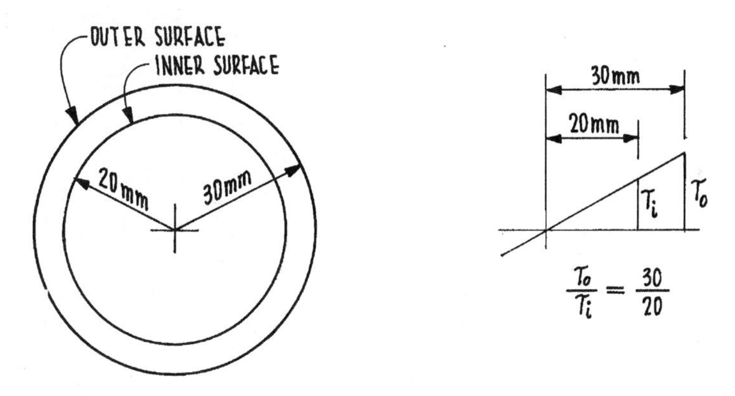

Solution: The stress at the outer surface is:

$$\tau_0 = \frac{Tr_0}{J}$$

$$r_0 = 30 \text{ mm}; \; J = \frac{\pi(30)^4}{2} - \frac{\pi(20)^4}{2} = 1{,}021{,}000\text{mm}^4$$

$$\tau_0 = \frac{(3{,}000{,}000)(30)}{1{,}021{,}000} = 88N/mm^2$$

The stress at the inner surface is:

$$\tau_i = \frac{Tr_i}{J}$$

$$r_i = 20 \text{ mm}; \; J = 1{,}021{,}000$$

$$\tau_i = \frac{(3{,}000{,}000)(20)}{1{,}021{,}000} = 59N/mm^2$$

The value of τ_i could also have been found by the ratio shown with the sketch:

$$\tau_i = \frac{2}{3}\tau_0 = 59 \text{ N/mm}^2$$

9.3 Torsional Deformations

The existence of torsional shearing stress will, of course, create a shearing strain γ. The strain γ is shown on the surface of the shaft of Figure 9-8, along with the angular rotation θ that occurs along the axis of the shaft.

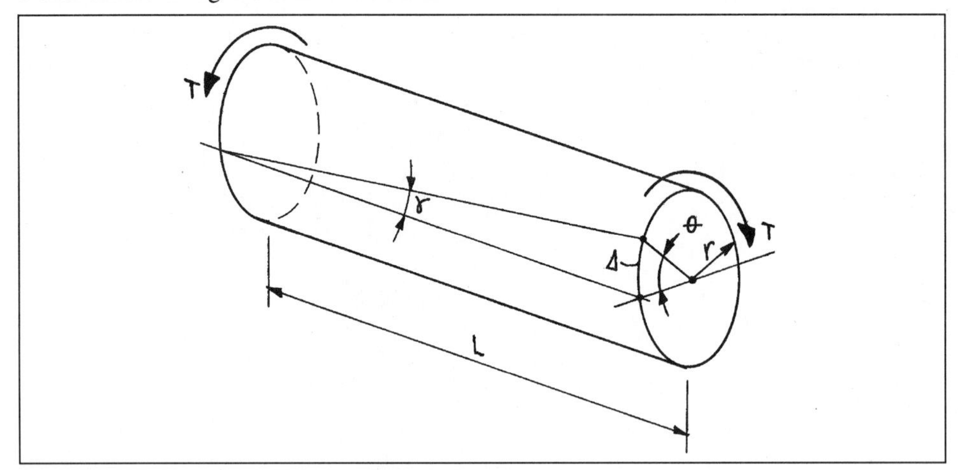

Figure 9-8 Torsional deformations.

It is observed that the torsional arc length Δ is common both to γ and θ. For any small angle, the tangent of the angle is equal to the angle (in radians), hence:

$$L\gamma = \Delta = r\theta. \qquad (9\text{-}9)$$

From the definition of the shear modulus G:

$$G = \frac{\tau}{\gamma} = \frac{Tr}{J\gamma} \qquad (9\text{-}10a)$$

$$\gamma = \frac{Tr}{JG} \qquad (9\text{-}10b)$$

This value of γ is substituted into Eq.(9-9) to find,

$$\theta = \frac{TL}{JG} \text{ (in radians)} \qquad (9\text{-}11)$$

Equation (9-11) yields the angular rotation θ in radians along the axis of a shaft subject to a torque T. The equation is valid over any length L where the torque T is constant. Some examples will illustrate its use.

Example 9-3

Torsional deformations.

Given: Hollow shaft 6 ft-0 in. long, subject to a torque of 10.0 kip·ft.
$G = (12)(10)^6$ lb/in.^{2}

To Find: Angular deformation θ due to the torque.

SOLID
1.5"
2"
VOID

$$J = J_{SOLID} - J_{VOID}$$
$$= \frac{\pi}{2}(2)^4 - \frac{\pi}{2}(1.5)^4$$
$$= 17.18 \text{ IN}^4$$

Solution: The rotation θ is found by Eq.(9-11):

$$\theta = \frac{TL}{JG} = \frac{(10,000x12)(6x12)}{(17.18)(12,000,000)} = 0.0419 \textit{ radians.}$$

$$\theta = 2.401 \text{ degrees}$$

Example 9-4

Torsional deformations.

Given: Solid shaft loaded as shown, 80 mm diameter.
G = 80 kN/mm².

To Find: Total angular deformation from end to end.

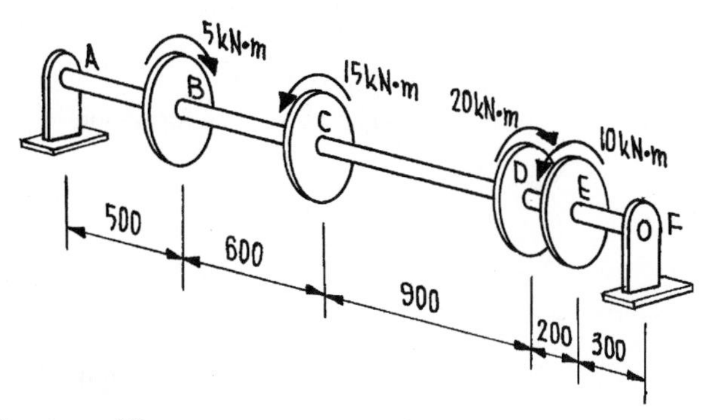

Solution: Segment *AB*:
Angular deformation of segment *AB* is zero since there is no torque on the segment.

Segment *BC*:
The angular deformation is given by:

$$\theta = \frac{TL}{JG}$$

$$T = 5 \text{ kN·m} = 5,000,000 \text{ N·mm (clockwise)}$$

$$L = 600 \text{ mm}$$

$$J = \frac{\pi r^4}{2} = \frac{\pi}{2}(40)^4 = 4.021\text{x}10^6 \text{ mm}^4$$

$$G = 80,000 \text{ N/mm}^2$$

$$\theta = \frac{(5,000,000)(600)}{(4,021,000)(80,000)} = 0.00933 \text{ radians (clockwise)}$$

Segment *CD*:
The angular deformation is given by:

$$\theta = \frac{TL}{JG}$$

T = 10 kN·m = 10,000,000 N·mm (clockwise)

L = 900 mm

J = 4.021x106mm^4

G = 80,000 N/mm^2

$$\theta = \frac{(10,000,000)(900)}{(4,021,000)(80,000)} = 0.02798 \text{ radians}$$

(counterclockwise)

Segment *DE*:
The angular deformation is given by:

$$\theta = \frac{TL}{JG}$$

T = 10 kN.m = 10,000,000 N·mm (clockwise)

L = 200

J = 4.021 x 106mm^4

G = 80,000 N/mm^2

$$\theta = \frac{(10,000,000)(200)}{(4,021,000)(80,000)} = 0.00622 \text{ radians (clockwise)}$$

Segment *EF*:
Angular deformation of segment *EF* is zero since there is no torque on the segment.

Total rotation = +0.00933 - 0.02798 + 0.00622 = -0.01243 radians

$\theta_{TOTAL} = 0.712^0$, end *F* rotates counterclockwise relative to end *A*.

9.4 Shear and Moment on a Beam Section

Force systems create shears and moments on structural members even though these shears and moment may not be readily apparent. Consider, for example, the beam of Figure 9-9. Both shear and moment exist throughout the length of the beam; they occur as a result of the uniform load and the reactions at the supports.

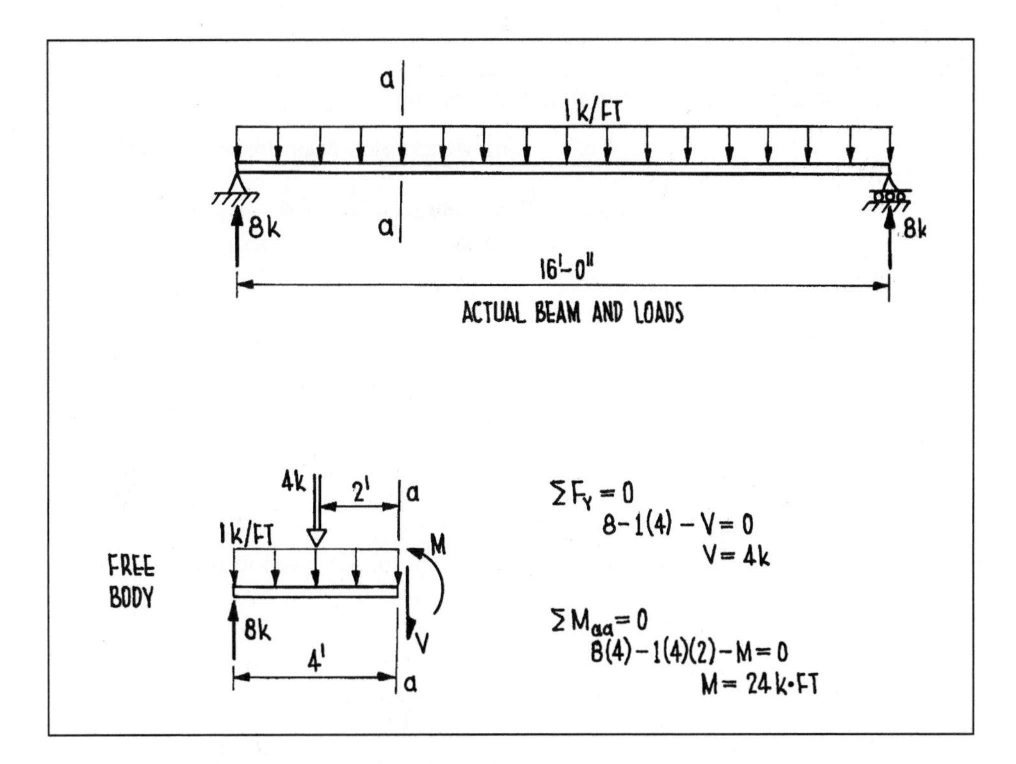

Figure 9-9 Shear and moment on a section.

For the sake of illustration, a section is chosen at a distance 4 feet from the left support and a free body is shown of the left segment of the beam. For equilibrium to exist, a shear force V must exist on the section, as well as a moment M. The shear force V at the section is found by summing forces vertically as shown on the figure. Similarly, the moment M at the section is found by summing moments about the section, as indicated.

From the procedure indicated in Figure 9-9, two important observations are drawn:

1) The shear force V acting on a particular section is computed as the sum of the shearing forces to one side of that section.
2) The moment acting on a particular section is computed as the sum of all moments to one side of that section.

These observations will be used repeatedly as a time-saving device in subsequent chapters.

Neither the shear V nor the moment M that exist at section *aa* are visible. They exist internally as a result of the external system of loads. Further, their magnitudes at any point along the beam varies. Their magnitudes at any section are not readily apparent; they must be calculated.

Some examples will illustrate the calculation of shear and moment at various points on a beam.

Example 9-5

Calculation of shear and moment on a beam section.

Given: Simply supported beam loaded as shown.

To Find: 1) Shear and moment at section *aa*.
2) Shear and moment at section *bb*.

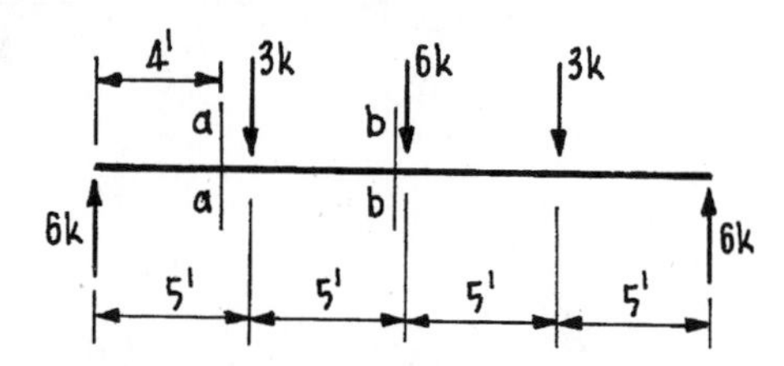

Solution: The segment of the beam to the left of section *aa* is removed as a free body:

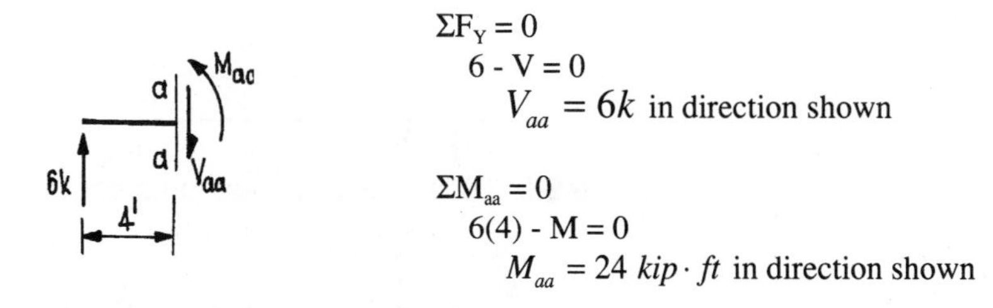

$\Sigma F_Y = 0$

$6 - V = 0$

$V_{aa} = 6k$ in direction shown

$\Sigma M_{aa} = 0$

$6(4) - M = 0$

$M_{aa} = 24\ kip \cdot ft$ in direction shown

The segment to the left of section *bb* is removed as a free body:

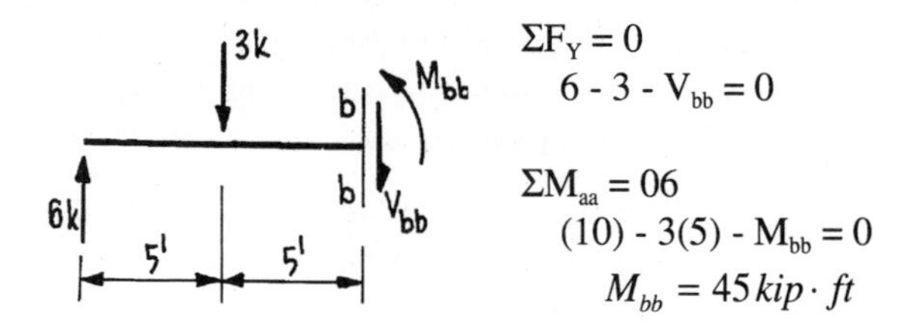

$\Sigma F_Y = 0$

$6 - 3 - V_{bb} = 0$

$\Sigma M_{aa} = 06$

$(10) - 3(5) - M_{bb} = 0$

$M_{bb} = 45 kip \cdot ft$

Example 9-6

Calculation of shear and moment on a beam section.

Given: Beam with overhangs loaded as shown.

To Find: 1) Shear and moment at section *aa*.
2) Shear and moment at section *bb*.
3) Shear and moment at midspan, section *cc*.

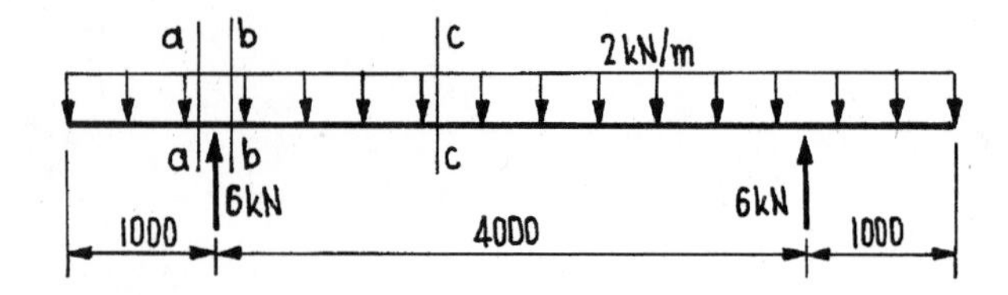

Solution: The segment to the left of section of *aa* is removed as a free body. The resultant of the uniform load is shown as a double-lined arrow, as usual:

$$\Sigma F_V = 0$$
$$-2 - V_{aa} = 0$$
$$V_{aa} = -2kN \text{ in opposite direction}$$

$$\Sigma M_{aa} = 0$$
$$-2(0.5) - M_{aa} = 0$$
$$M_{aa} = -1kN \cdot m \text{ in opposite direction}$$

The segment to the left of section *bb* is removed as a free body. Again, the resultant of the uniform load is shown as a double-lined arrow.

$$\Sigma F_Y = 0$$
$$-2 + 6 - V_{aa} = 0$$
$$V_{aa} = +4 \; kN \text{ as shown}$$

$$\Sigma M_{aa} = 0$$
$$-2(0.5) - M_{aa} = 0$$
$$M_{aa} = -1.0 \; kN \cdot m$$

The segment to the left of midspan is removed as a free body, with the resultant of the uniform load shown as a double-lined arrow.

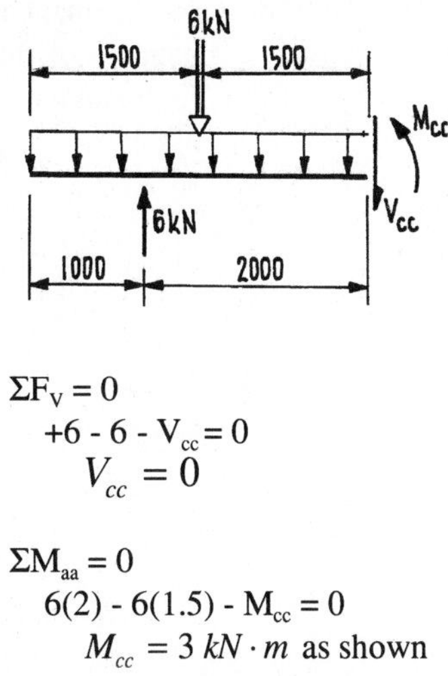

$$\Sigma F_V = 0$$
$$+6 - 6 - V_{cc} = 0$$
$$V_{cc} = 0$$

$$\Sigma M_{aa} = 0$$
$$6(2) - 6(1.5) - M_{cc} = 0$$
$$M_{cc} = 3 \; kN \cdot m \text{ as shown}$$

In the foregoing solutions, the free body could have been taken to either side of the section. In all of the given problems, the free body happened to be simpler if it was taken to the left of the sections.

Though not used in the examples so far, shear and moment on a beam do have algebraic signs. Shear is positive if the left side moves up with respect to the right. Moment is positive if it puts compression on the top fibers and tension on the bottom fibers. Beam segments under positive shear and moment are shown in Figure 9-10.

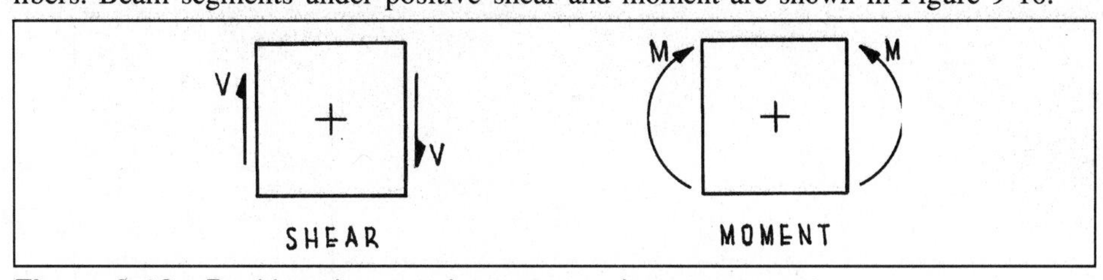

Figure 9-10 Positive shear and moment on beam segments.

In view of these algebraic signs, the free body sketches of examples 9-5 and 9-6 should now be reexamined. Note that the unknown shear and moment were always shown in their positive sense, that is, shear on the right side of a segment is shown downward and moment is shown putting tension on the bottom fibers. Automatically, the numerical solution then yields the correct sign.

Some additional examples will further illustrate the calculation of shear and moment on a beam section.

Example 9-7

Calculation of shear and moment on a beam section.

Given Cantilever beam loaded as shown.

To Find: 1) Shear and moment at section *aa*.
2) Shear and moment at section *bb*.

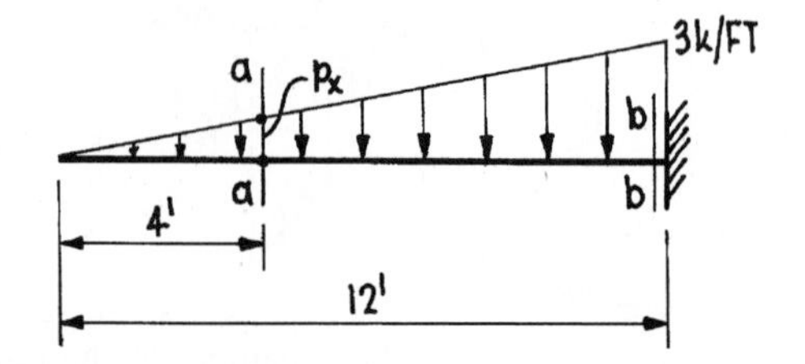

Solution: The segment to the left of section *aa* is removed as a free body. The intensity of the load p_x at that section is calculated by similar triangles. The resultant of loads is then computed as the area of the load diagram:

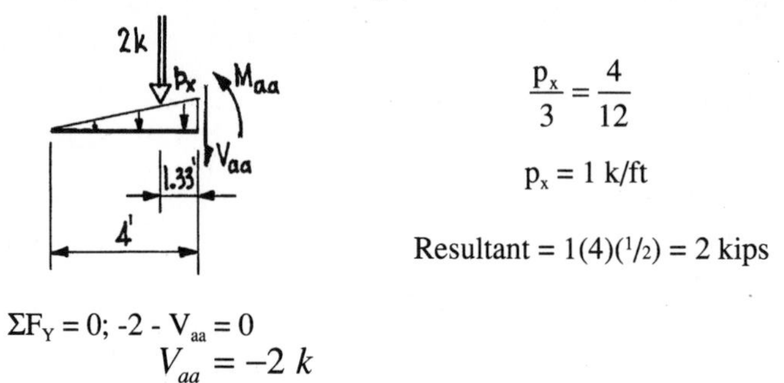

$$\frac{p_x}{3} = \frac{4}{12}$$

$$p_x = 1 \text{ k/ft}$$

Resultant = 1(4)(1/2) = 2 kips

$\Sigma F_Y = 0;\ -2 - V_{aa} = 0$

$$V_{aa} = -2\ k$$

The shear at section *aa* is -2k; the left side moves *down* with respect to the right:

$\Sigma M_{aa} = 0;\ -2(1.33) - M_{aa} = 0$

$$M_{aa} = -2.66\ kip \cdot ft$$

The moment at section *aa* is -2.66 k·ft; the moment puts tension on the top fibers.

The segment to the left of section *bb* is removed as a free body.

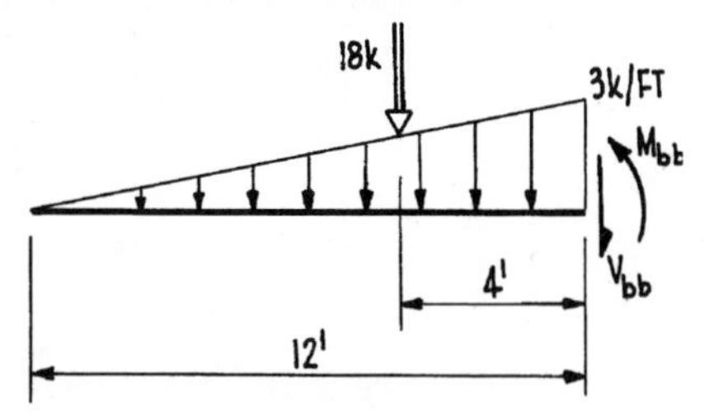

$\Sigma F_Y = 0$; $-18 - V_{bb} = 0$

$V_{bb} = -18\ k$, left moves down with respect to right.

$\Sigma M_{bb} = 0$; $-18(4) - Mbb = 0$

$M_{bb} = -72\ k \cdot ft$, putting tension on top fibers.

Though not a part of this problem, it should be observed that the *maximum* shear and moment that can occur on this beam occur at the section *bb*. The beam must therefore be selected of such size and strength that it can sustain 18 kips in shear and 72 kip·ft in moment.

Example 9-8

Calculation of shear and moment on a beam section.

Given: Simple beam loaded as shown.

To Find: Shear and moment at midspan.

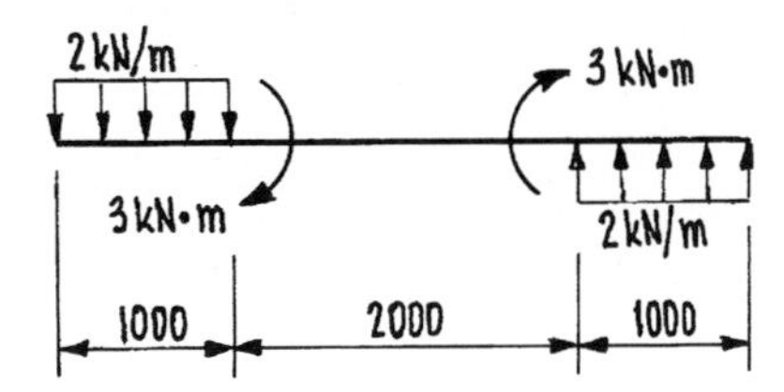

Solution: The segment to the left of midpoint is removed as a free body.

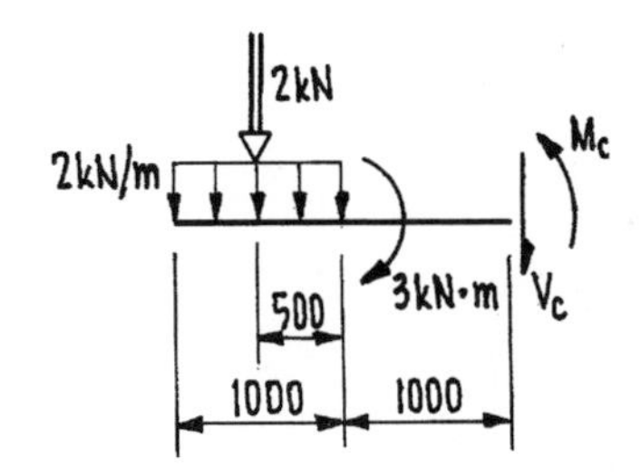

$\Sigma F_Y = 0$; $-2 - V_c = 0$

$V_c = -2\ k$, left moves down with respect to right.

$\Sigma M_c = 0$; $-2(1.5) + 3 - M_c = 0$

$M_c = 0$

The 3 kN·m moments on the sketch were deliberately shown here in their most confusing positions. A less confusing but equivalent position is shown in the following sketch. This confusing type of antisymmetrical loading shows up frequently on engineer licensing exams.

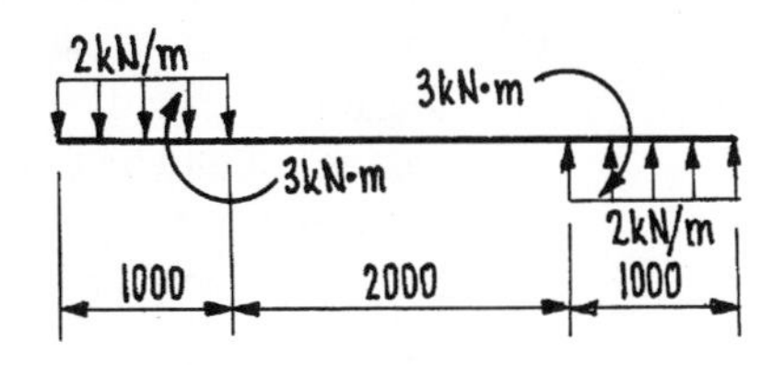

9.5 Flexural Stress and Planar Moment of Inertia

The shears and moments computed in the preceding discussions were in all cases produced by external loads. The beams themselves could have been steel *I* sections, aluminum tees or rectangular timber beams and the calculated shears and moments would have been exactly the same. The shears and moments computed there were simply the external loads that the beam must sustain at the chosen sections.

The beam resists those shears and moments through internal patterns of stress that exactly oppose those external loads. The stresses produced by the applied moment are called *flexural* stresses, or *bending* stresses. It is these flexural stresses that are the subject of this section.

The beam shown in Figure 9-11a is to be examined under flexural loading. It is etched with two parallel straight lines before it is loaded. The lines are carefully measured and marked to be sure they are exactly parallel. The distance between the lines is measured precisely.

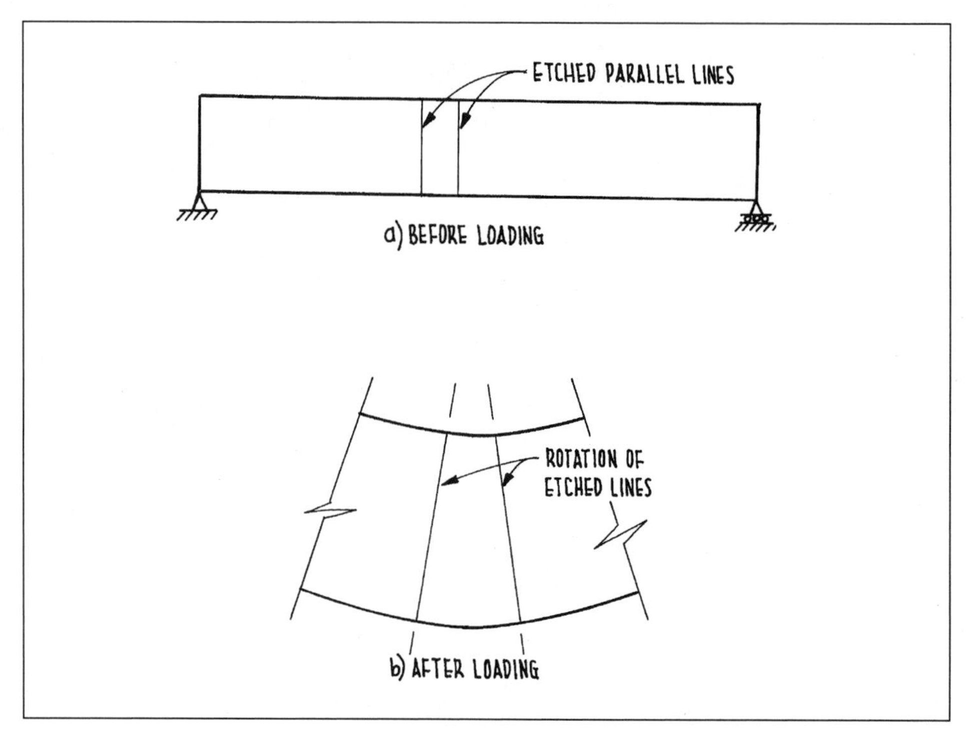

Figure 9-11 Rotations in a flexural section.

The beam is now loaded by a system of loads that produce moment. An expanded (and exaggerated) view showing the two lines after the beam is loaded is shown in Figure 9-11b. The lines are again carefully measured and examined; the following general observations are made as a result of those measurements.

1) The lines remain exactly straight.
2) Both lines undergo rotation.
3) One side of the member (the top) undergoes compressive strain, the other (the bottom) tensile strain. For symmetrical cross sections, the tensile elongation is found to be exactly equal to the compressive shortening; for unsymmetrical cross sections, the two deformations are found to be unequal.
4) As load increases, the rotations and strains increase; the increase is found to be linearly proportional to the increase in load.

As a result of these observations, the stress distribution produced inside the member can be deduced. Such a stress distribution is shown in the stress blocks of Figure 9-12a for a symmetrical rectangular section.

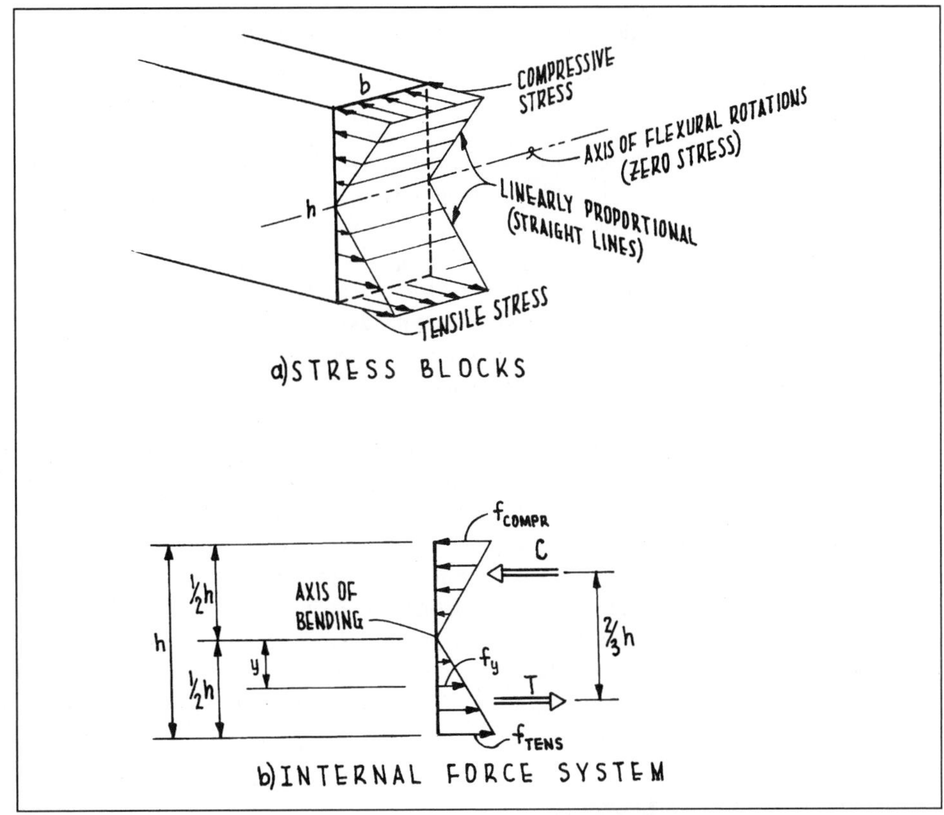

Figure 9-12 Internal stresses and forces on a rectangle.

The pattern of tensile and compressive stresses shown in Figure 9-12b form an internal couple, as shown. For equilibrium to exist, the sum of horizontal forces must be zero:

$$\Sigma F_X = 0 \qquad C = T = {}^1\!/\!{}_4 f_{MAX} bh \tag{9-12}$$

where f is the maximum stress on the section ($f_{COMP} = f_{TENS}$). The moment produced by the internal couple must exactly oppose the externally applied moment on the section:

$$C({}^2\!/\!{}_3 h) = T({}^2\!/\!{}_3 h) = M$$

$$ {}^1\!/\!{}_4 f_{MAX} bh({}^2\!/\!{}_3 h) = M \tag{9-13}$$

Equation (9-13) is solved for the stress f_{MAX} produced by the applied moment M:

$$f_{MAX} = \frac{M}{\left(\frac{bh^2}{6}\right)} = \frac{M}{S} \tag{9-14}$$

where S is the section modulus, $S = bh^2/6$ for the rectangle.

As observed earlier in torsional stresses, it is considered preferable to express the formula in terms of the stress at some distance c from the axis of rotation. From the stress diagram of Figure 9-12, by similar triangles:

$$\frac{f_y}{f_{MAX}} = \frac{y}{{}^h\!/\!{}_2}$$

$$f_{MAX} = f_y \frac{h}{2y} \tag{9-15}$$

This value of f_{MAX} is substituted into Eq.(9-14) to find:

$$f_y = \frac{My}{I} \tag{9-16}$$

where, for a rectangular section, $I = bh^3/12$ and y is measured from the axis of bending.

Equation 9-16 is called the *flexure formula.* It is probably the most widely used mechanics formula in existence. The formula is true for all shapes of cross sections, not just rectangles; it is simply a matter of finding the corresponding value of I for other shapes. It is important to remember, however, that the formula yields the value of stress at some distance y from the axis of bending, which is not necessarily the maximum stress.

Before proceeding into some examples, some observations can be drawn. First, it is emphasized that *a section in flexure rotates*; *there is an axis of rotation for the moment M.* While it is true that the actual angle of rotation is small, it nonetheless does exist. The axis of rotation lies at the point where the stress is zero. The axis is also called the *neutral axis* or the *axis of bending.* It will be shown in later discussions that it passes through the centroid of the cross section; as a consequence, it is sometimes called the *centroidal axis.* All these names are used interchangeably in subsequent discussions.

The planar moment of inertia I that occurs in flexure is quite similar to the polar moment of inertia J that occurs in torsion. The units for planar moment of inertia I are in.^{4} or mm^4. Physically, the moment of inertia I is the moment required to produce 1 psi of stress at a distance of 1 inch from the axis of bending; it is a measure of the section's resistance to flexural rotation.

Example 9-9

Flexure on a rectangular section.

Given: Glued laminated timber beam as shown. Section is under positive moment, M = 15.0 kip·ft.

To Find: Flexural stress at the top and bottom of each lamina.

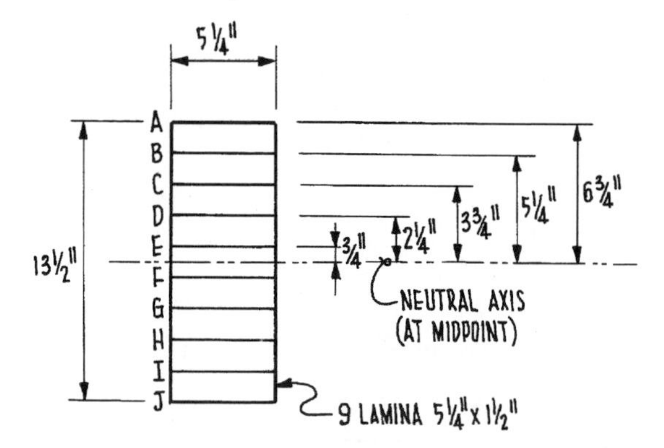

Solution: The stresses are found by the flexure formula:

$$f = \frac{My}{I}, \ M = 15 \text{ k·ft, compression on top.}$$

For a rectangular cross section, bending about its own axis of symmetry:

$$I = \frac{bh^3}{12} = \frac{5.25(13.5)^3}{12} = 1076 \text{ in.}^4$$

At levels A and J, y = 6.75 in.:

$$f = \frac{15{,}000(12)6.75}{1076} = 1129 \text{ lb / in.}^2,$$

compression at A, tension at J.

At levels *B* and *I*, y = 5.25 in.:

$$f = \frac{15{,}000(12)5.25}{1076} = 878 \text{ lb / in.}^2$$

compression at *B*, tension at *I*.

At levels *y* and *H*, y = 3.75 in.:

$$f = \frac{15{,}000(12)3.75}{1076} = 627 \text{ lb / in.}^2$$

compression at *c*, tension at *H*.

At levels *D* and *G*, y = 2.25 in.:

$$f = \frac{15{,}000(12)2.25}{1076} = 376 \text{ lb / in.}^2$$

compression at *D*, tension at *G*.

At levels E and F, y = 0.75 in.:

$$f = \frac{15{,}000(12)0.75}{1076} = 125 \text{ lb / in.}^2$$

compression at *E*, tension at *F*.

Hollow box members in flexure can be treated much like hollow members in torsion. The capacity in moment of the hollow rectangular section shown in Figure 9-13 can be computed as the moment capacity of a solid section less the capacity lost when the interior is removed.

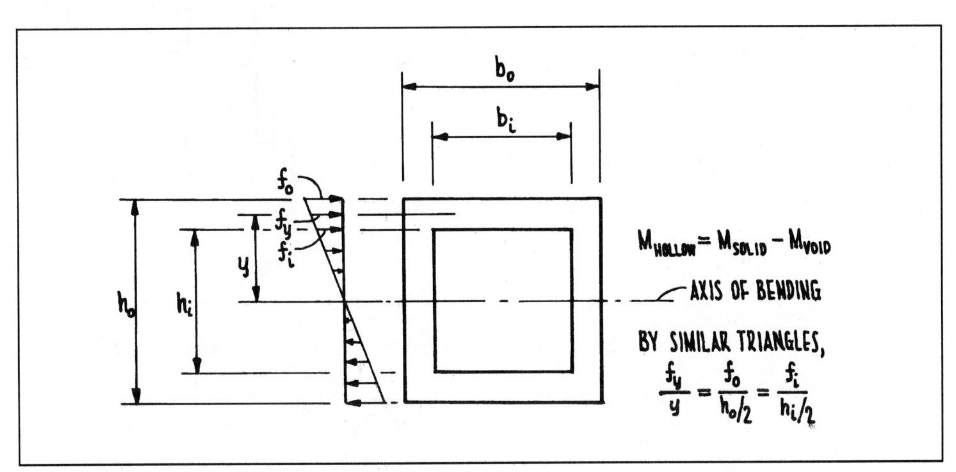

Figure 9-13 Rectangular box section.

The moment capacity of the hollow section is then:

$$M_{HOLLOW} = M_{SOLID} - M_{VOID} \tag{9-17a}$$

$$= f_0 \frac{I_{SOLID}}{h_0/2} - f_i \frac{I_{VOID}}{h_i/2} \tag{9-17b}$$

From the stress triangle shown in Figure 9-13:

$$\frac{f_y}{y} = \frac{f_0}{h_0/2} = \frac{f_i}{h_i/2} \tag{9-17c}$$

This value is substituted into Eq.(9-17b) to find:

$$M_{HOLLOW} = \frac{f_y}{y}(I_{SOLID} - I_{VOID}) \tag{9-18a}$$

Hence:

$$f_y = \frac{My}{I_{HOLLOW}}$$

$$\text{where } I_{HOLLOW} = I_{SOLID} - I_{VOID} \tag{9-18b}$$

The end result is that planar moment of inertia of the hollow box section is the moment of inertia of the solid box less the moment of inertia of the area removed. All other features of the flexure formula remain the same.

Example 9-10

Flexure on a rectangular section.

Given: Built up timber section as shown. Moment is positive, M = 20 kN·m. All members are 50 mm x 250 mm.

To Find: Stress at top and bottom of top member.

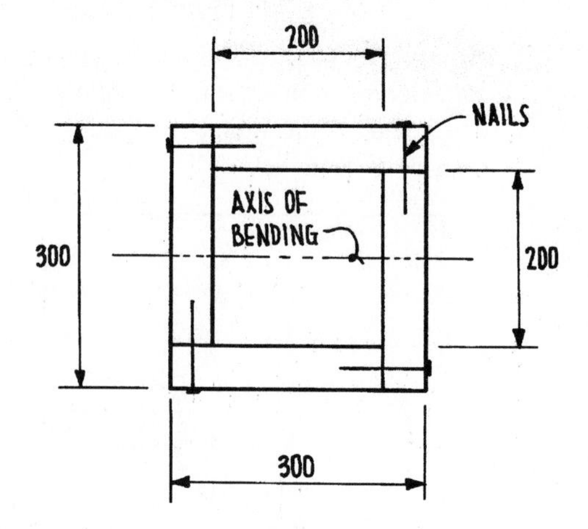

Solution: The stresses will be found by the flexure formula:

$$f_y = \frac{My}{I}$$

$$I = I_{SOLID} - I_{VOID} = \left.\frac{bh^3}{12}\right|_{SOLID} - \left.\frac{bh^3}{12}\right|_{VOID}$$

$$= \frac{300(300)^3}{12} - \frac{200(200)^3}{12} = 542\,x\,10^6\,mm^4$$

At the top surface of the top member, y = 150 mm:

$$f = \frac{(20)(10^6)(150)}{(542)(10^6)} = 5.5 N/mm^2 \text{ compression}$$

At the bottom surface of the top member, y = 100 mm:

$$f = \frac{(20)(10^6)(100)}{(542)(10^6)} = 3.7 N/mm^2 \text{ compression}$$

Example 9-11

Flexure on a rectangular section.

Given: Steel wide flange section as shown. Allowable stress = 20,000 psi.

To Find: Moment capacity of the section in lb·ft.

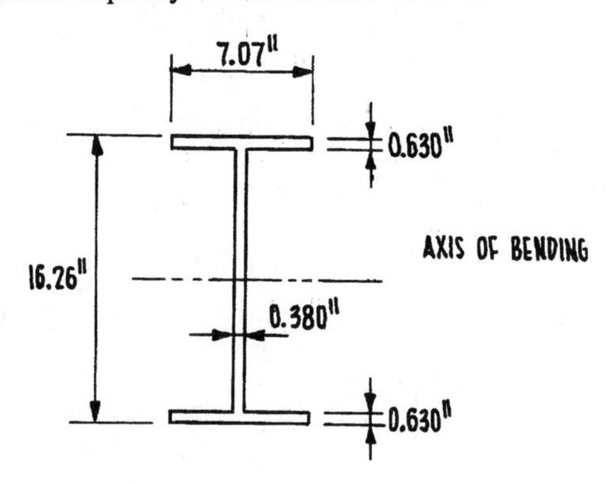

Solution: The moment will be found using the flexure formula:

$$M = f\frac{I}{y};\ f = 20{,}000\text{ psi.}$$

The moment of inertia of the section is found as the moment of inertia of the solid section less the moment of inertia of the voids.

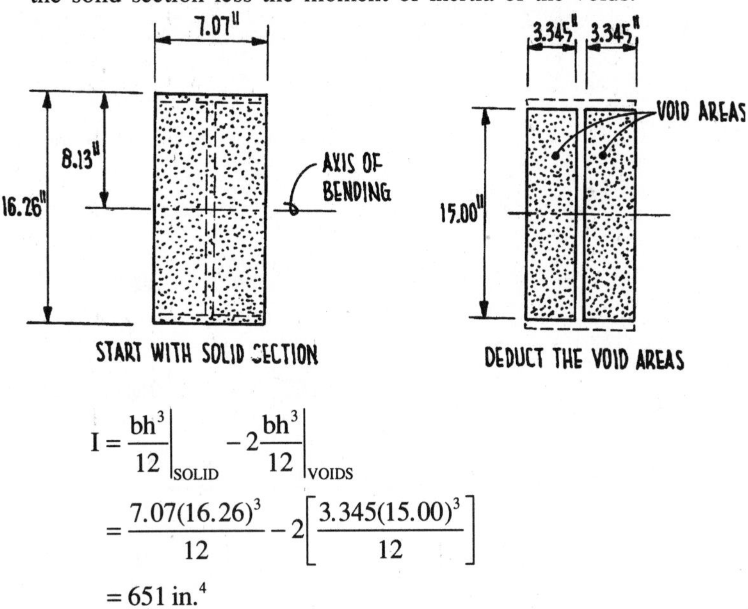

$$I = \left.\frac{bh^3}{12}\right|_{SOLID} - 2\left.\frac{bh^3}{12}\right|_{VOIDS}$$

$$= \frac{7.07(16.26)^3}{12} - 2\left[\frac{3.345(15.00)^3}{12}\right]$$

$$= 651\text{ in.}^4$$

Maximum stress will occur at y = 8.13 in. from axis of bending:

$$M = f\frac{I}{y} = 20{,}000\frac{651}{8.13} = 1602k \cdot in. = 134k \cdot ft$$

The steel section shown in Example 9-11 is a standard steel section, W16x50. The properties of this beam are shown in Table S-1b in the Technical Manual, including its moment of inertia *I*. It should be noted that the moment of inertia is given there as 659 in.^{4} rather than the 651 in.^{4} found in the example. The reason for the discrepancy is the higher numerical accuracy used in preparing the design tables.

The designation W16x50 indicates that the section belongs to a type of beam called a "wide flange" beam. The 16 denotes its nominal depth and the 50 denotes its weight in lbs/ft of length. Steel is bought by the pound; the lightest section is the most economical section. Commercial steel beam sections are discussed further in the next chapter.

Example 9-12

Flexure on a rectangular section.

Given: Built-up timber section as shown. Maximum allowable stress is 7N/mm^2.

To Find: Moment capacity of the section in kN·m.

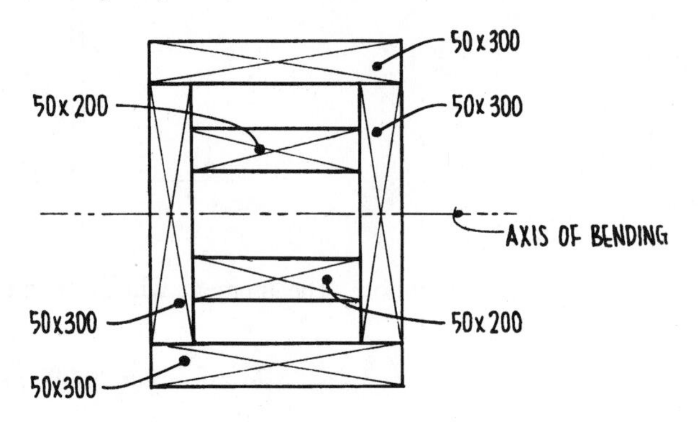

Solution: The moment can be found using the flexure formula:

$$M = f\frac{I}{y};\ f = 7\text{N/mm}^2$$

The moment of inertia of the section is found in four steps:

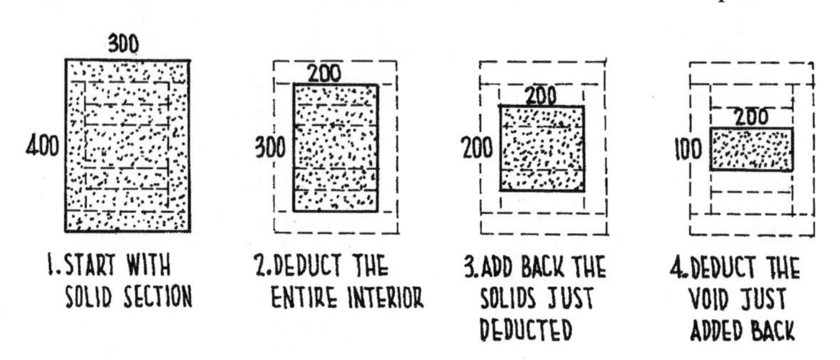

$$I = I_1 - I_2 + I_2 - I_4$$

$$= \frac{300(400)^3}{12} - \frac{200(300)^3}{12} + \frac{200(200)^3}{12} - \frac{200(100)^3}{12}$$

$$= 1267(10^6)(\text{mm}^4)$$

The maximum stress will occur at the extreme fibers, y = 200 mm:

$$M = f\frac{I}{y} = 7\frac{1267(10^6)}{200} = 44{,}300{,}000\ N \cdot mm$$

$$= 44.3kN \cdot m$$

It is of utmost importance to note that in all four of the preceding examples, all of the solid areas and all of the void areas were rectangular and all were symmetrical about the axis of bending; for such areas, $I = bh^3/12$. When a section is not symmetrical about the axis of bending, the formula $bh^3/12$ cannot be applied.

Consider, for example, the composite section shown in Figure 9-14. The section is not symmetrical about the axis of bending. Further, it is not known exactly where the axis of bending lies. It is known only that the variation in strain (and stress) is linear.

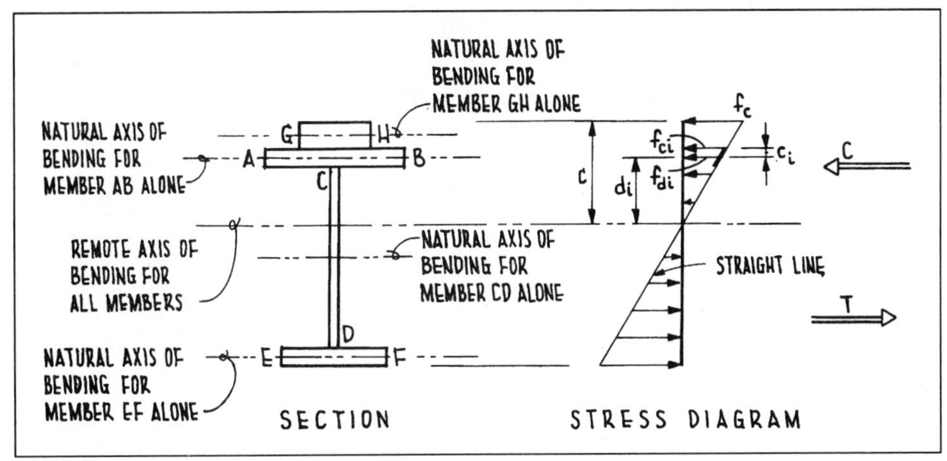

Figure 9-14 Section unsymmetrical about the axis of bending.

For any combined section such as that shown in Figure 9-14, the sum of all forces in the cross section must be zero. The force on any member *i* in the composite section is shown in Figure 9-15.

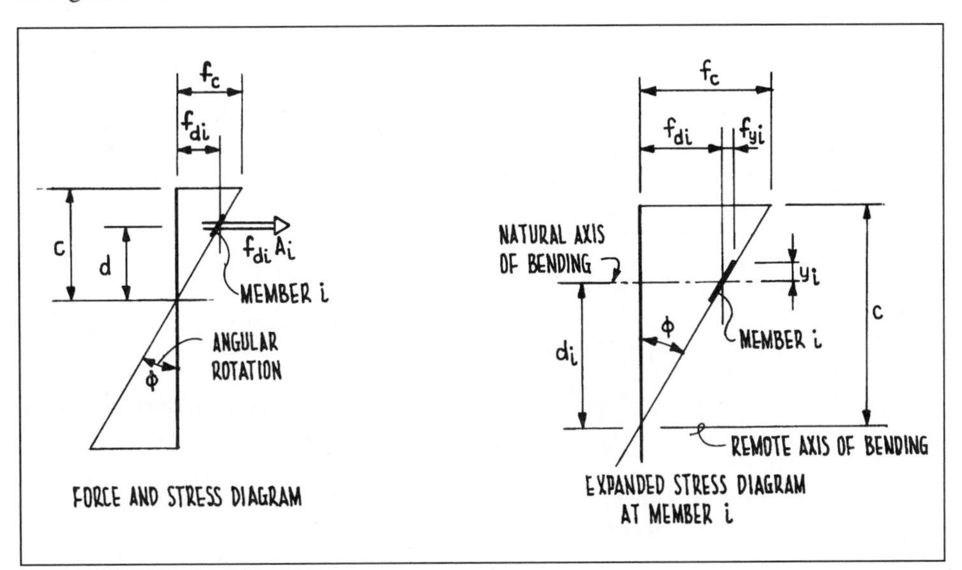

Figure 9-15 Stresses in a combined section.

The sum of all horizontal forces yields

$$\Sigma F_H = 0 = \sum_{i=1}^{n} f_{di} A_i \tag{9-19}$$

It is observed from the stress diagram that for all members:

$$\frac{f_{di}}{d_i} = \frac{f_c}{c}. \tag{9-20}$$

This value of f_{di} is substituted into Eq.(9-14) to find:

$$0 = \frac{f_c}{c}\sum_{i=1}^{n} A_i d_i . \qquad (9\text{-}21)$$

Since the stress f_c is not zero, the summation must be zero:

$$\sum_{i=1}^{n} A_i d_i = 0 . \qquad (9\text{-}22)$$

The only way this summation can be zero is for d_i to be measured from the centroidal axis [see Eq.(3-1)]. It is concluded that the axis of bending of any section in flexure passes through the centroid.

The total moment capacity of the composite section is the sum of the moments carried by each of the n members as they undergo the axial strain and the angular rotation:

$$M_{TOTAL} = M_1 + M_2 + M_3 + ... = \sum_{i=1}^{n} M_i \qquad (9\text{-}23)$$

From the force and stress diagrams of Figure 9-15:

$$M_i = f_{di} A_i d_i + f_{ci}\frac{I_{oi}}{c_i} \qquad (9\text{-}24)$$

where I_{oi} is the moment of inertia of the member i about its own centroidal axis of bending.

By similar triangles on the stress diagram:

$$\frac{f_{di}}{d_i} = \frac{f_{yi}}{y_i} = \frac{f_c}{c} \qquad (9\text{-}25)$$

These values of f_{di} and f_{yi} are substituted into Eq.(9-24) to find, for any component i:

$$M_i = \frac{f_{yi}}{y}[A_i d_i^2 + I_{oi}] \qquad (9\text{-}26)$$

The sum of all these contributing moments M_i is then the total moment on the section. Hence:

$$f_{ci} = \frac{M_{yi}}{I} \qquad (9\text{-}27a)$$

$$\text{where } I = \sum_{i=1}^{n}\left(I_{oi} + d_i^2 A_i\right) \qquad (9\text{-}27b)$$

and all other symbols have been defined or shown in Figure 9-15.

Equation (9-27b) is called the *remote axis theorem* or the *parallel axis theorem*. It is stated as follows:

The moment of intertia of any section about a remote axis of bending that is parallel to its own centroidal axis of bending is given by

$$I = I_o + d^2 A \qquad (9\text{-}28)$$

where I_o is the moment of inertia of the section about its own centroidal axis of bending;
A is the cross section area of the section;
d is the displacement of the centroidal axis of bending of the section to a remote (and parallel) axis of bending.

There are several special cases of the remote axis theorem that are sometimes useful in computing planar moments of inertia. Three such cases are shown in Figure 9-16.

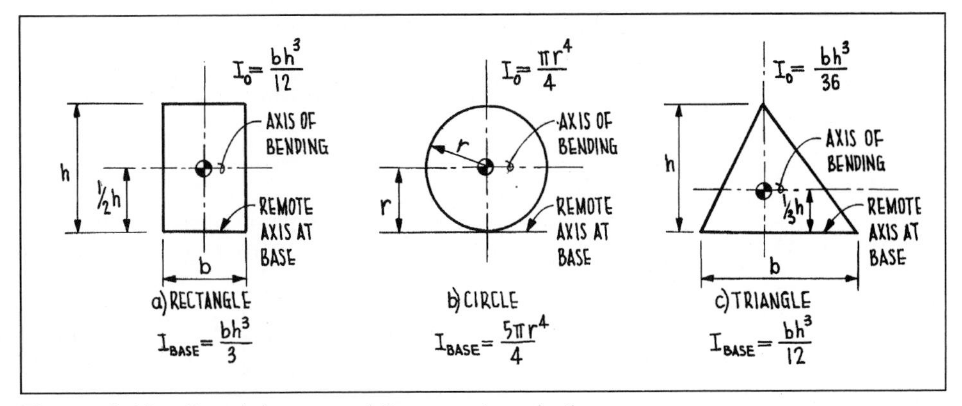

Figure 9-16 Special cases of the remote axis theorem.

For the rectangular section of Figure 9-16a, the moment of inertia of a rectangular section about its own base is given by:

$$I_{BASE} = I_o + d^2A = \frac{bh^3}{12} + \left(\frac{h}{2}\right)^2 bh = \frac{bh^3}{3} \tag{9-29}$$

For the circular section of Figure 9-16b, the moment of inertia of a circular section about its own base is given by:

$$I_{BASE} = I_o + d^2A = \frac{\pi r^4}{4} + (r)^2 \pi r^2 = \frac{5\pi r^4}{4} \tag{9-30}$$

For the triangular section of Figure 9-16c, the moment of inertia of a triangular section about its own base is given by:

$$I_{BASE} = I_o + d^2A = \frac{bh^3}{36} + \left(\frac{1}{3}h\right)^2 \frac{1}{2}bh = \frac{bh^3}{12} \tag{9-31}$$

Some examples will illustrate the use of the remote axis theorem and the special cases shown in Figure 9-16.

Example 9-13

Flexure on a rectangular section.

Given: Section of Example 9-12. Maximum allowable stress is 7 N/mm².

To Find: Moment capacity of the section using the remote axis theorem to compute the moment of inertia.

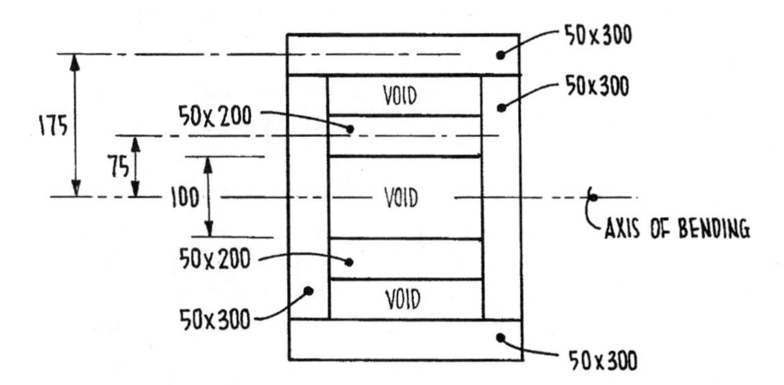

Solution: The moment capacity is found from the flexure formula:

$$M = f\frac{I}{y}; \text{maximum } f = 7\ \text{N/mm}^2 \text{ when } y = 200\ \text{mm}$$

The moment of inertia is found using the remote axis theorem:

$$I = \Sigma(I_o + d^2A)$$

For the two vertical pieces, there is no displacement of their own centroidal axis from the axis of bending of the composite section:

$$I = 2(I_o + d^2A) = 2\left[\frac{50(300)^3}{12} + (0)(50)(300)\right]$$
$$= 225(10^6)(\text{mm}^4)$$

For the two horizontal pieces at top and bottom:

$$I = 2(I_o + d^2A) = 2\left[\frac{300(50)^3}{12} + 175^2(50)(300)\right]$$
$$= 925(10^6)(\text{mm}^4)$$

For the two intermediate pieces, 50(200mm):

$$I = 2(I_o + d^2A) = 2\left[\frac{200(50)^3}{12} + 75^2(50)(200)\right]$$
$$= 117(10^6)(\text{mm}^4)$$

The sum of the three values is the total I:

$$I = 225(10^6) + 925(10^6) + 117(10^6) = 1267(10^6)(\text{mm4})$$

The maximum stress will occur at the extreme fiber, c = 200 mm:

$$M = f\frac{I}{c} = 7\frac{1267(10^6)}{200} = 44{,}300{,}000 N \cdot mm$$
$$= 44.3 kN \cdot m, \text{ as before.}$$

Example 9-14

Flexure on a combined section.

Given: Unsymmetrical section as shown. Dimensions shown are exact dimensions. Moment on the section is +5.0 kip·ft.

To Find: Maximum tensile and compressive stresses.

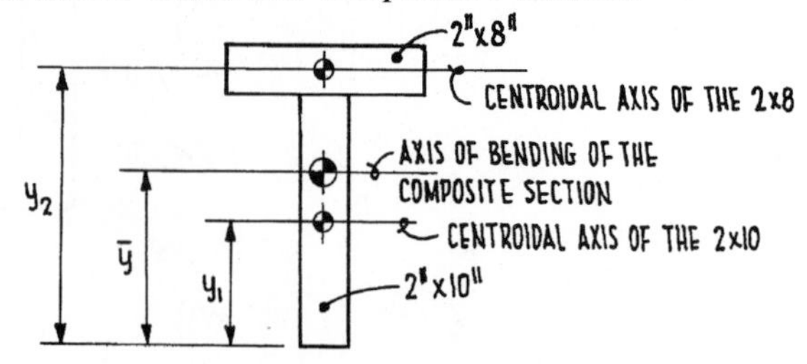

Solution: The centroidal axis of bending for the composite section is determined first:

$$\bar{y} = \frac{\Sigma Ay}{\Sigma A} = \frac{A_1 y_1 + A_2 y_2}{A_1 + A_2}$$

$A_1 = (2)(10) = 20 \text{ in.}^2 \; y_1 = 5 \text{ in.}$
$A_2 = (2)(8) = 16 \text{ in.}^2 \; y_2 = 11 \text{ in.}$

$$\bar{y} = \frac{(20)(5) + (16)(11)}{16 + 20} = 7.67 \text{ in.}$$

The section is shown in the following sketch with the distances of the displaced axes indicated.

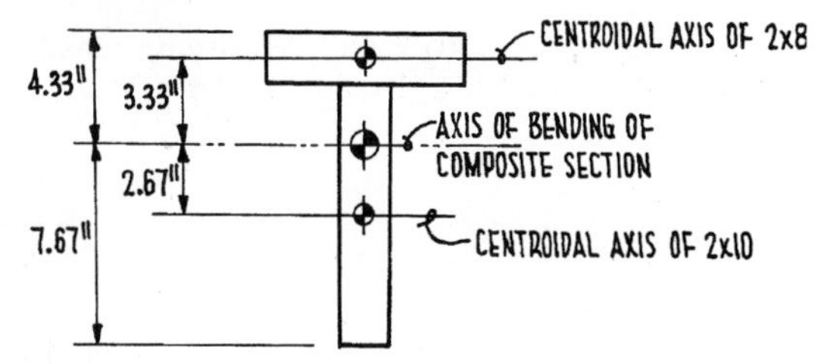

The moment of inertia is computed using the remote axis theorem:

$$I = \Sigma(I_o + d^2A)$$

$$= \left(\frac{bh^3}{12} + d^2A\right)_1 + \left(\frac{bh^3}{12} + d^2A\right)_2$$

$$= \left[\frac{(8)(2)^3}{12} + 3.33^2(2)(8)\right] + \left[\frac{2(10)^3}{12} + 2.67^2(2)(10)\right]$$

$$= 492 \text{ in.}^4$$

The moment is given as +5 k·ft; the maximum tensile stress occurs at the bottom fibers, c = 7.67 in.:

$$f_t = \frac{Mc}{I} = \frac{(5000)(12)(7.67)}{492}$$

$$= 935 lb/in.^2$$

The maximum compressive stress occurs at the top fibers, c = 4.33 in.:

$$f_c = \frac{Mc}{I} = \frac{(5000)(12)(4.33)}{492}$$

$$= 528 lb/in.^2$$

As a matter of interest, the moment of inertia of the section could also have been determined using the special case shown in Figure 9-16 for a rectangle about its own base. The section is shown again in the following sketches.

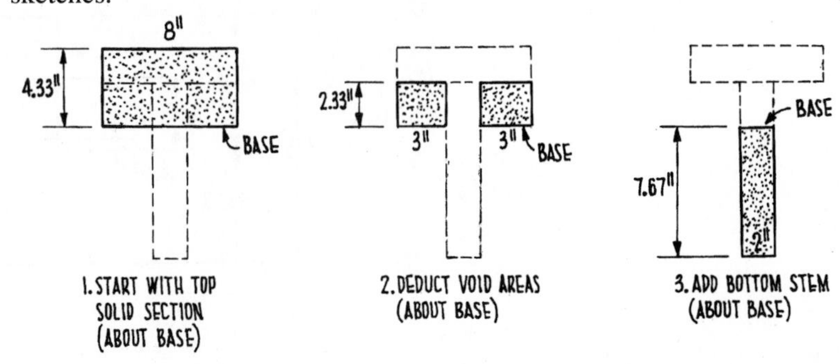

$$I = \left.\frac{bh^3}{3}\right|_{SOLID} - 2\left.\frac{bh^3}{3}\right|_{VOID} + \left.\frac{bh^3}{3}\right|_{STEM}$$

$$= \frac{8(4.33)^3}{3} - 2\frac{3(2.33)^3}{3} + \frac{2(7.67)^3}{3}$$

$$= 492 \text{ in.}^4 \text{ as before.}$$

Example 9-15

Flexure on a combined section.

Given: Section as shown. M = +35 kN·m.

To Find: Maximum tensile and compressive stresses.

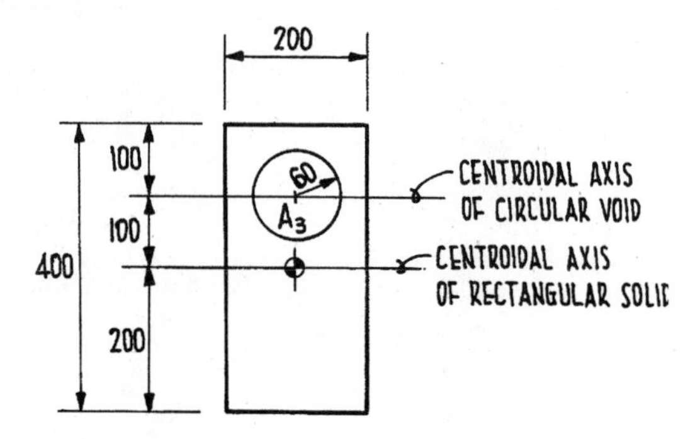

Solution: The centroidal axis of bending of the composite section is determined first. Find $\bar{y}$ from bottom edge:

$$\bar{y} = \frac{\Sigma Ay}{\Sigma A} = \frac{A_1y_1 - A_2y_2}{A_1 - A_2}$$

$$A_1 = (200)(400) = 80{,}000 \; y_1 = 200$$
$$A_2 = \pi(60)^2 = 11{,}310 \; y_2 = 300$$

$$= \frac{(80{,}000)(200) - (11{,}310)(300)}{80{,}000 - 11{,}310}$$

= 183.53 mm from bottom edge.

The moment of inertia is found by the remote axis theorem. Dimensions are shown in the following sketch.

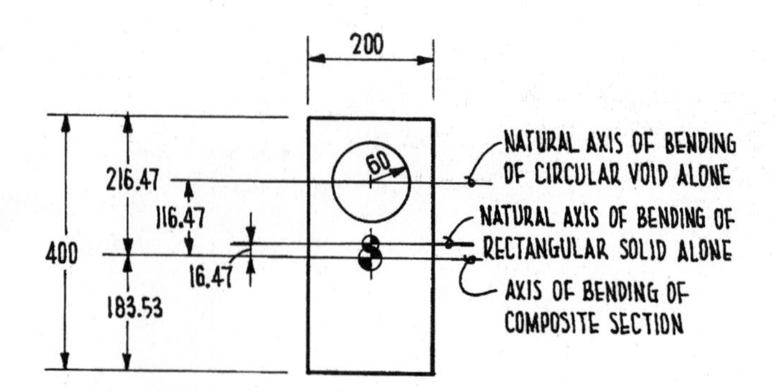

$I = \Sigma I_o + d^2A$

$$\text{Rectangle: } I = \frac{bh^3}{12} + d^2A$$

$$= \frac{200(400)^3}{12} + 16.47^2(200)(400)$$

$$= 1088(10^6)(mm^4)$$

$$\text{Circle: } I = \frac{\pi r^4}{4} + d^2A$$

$$= \frac{\pi(60)^4}{4} + 116.47^2(\pi)(60)^2$$

$$= 164(10^6)(mm^4)$$

$I = 1088(10^6) - 164(10^6) = 925(10^6)(mm^4)$

Maximum tensile stress occurs at the bottom face, c = 183.53:

$$f_t = \frac{Mc}{I} = \frac{(35)(10^6)(183.53)}{(925)(10^6)}$$

$$= 6.94 N/mm^2$$

Maximum compressive stress occurs at the top face, c = 216.47:

$$f_c = \frac{Mc}{I} = \frac{(35)(10^6)(216.47)}{(925)(10^6)}$$

$$= 8.19 N/mm^2$$

Example 9-16

Flexure on a combined section.

Given: Built-up section as shown. Properties of the steel section are shown. Moment is +60 kip·ft.

To Find: Stresses at points *A*, *B* and *C*.

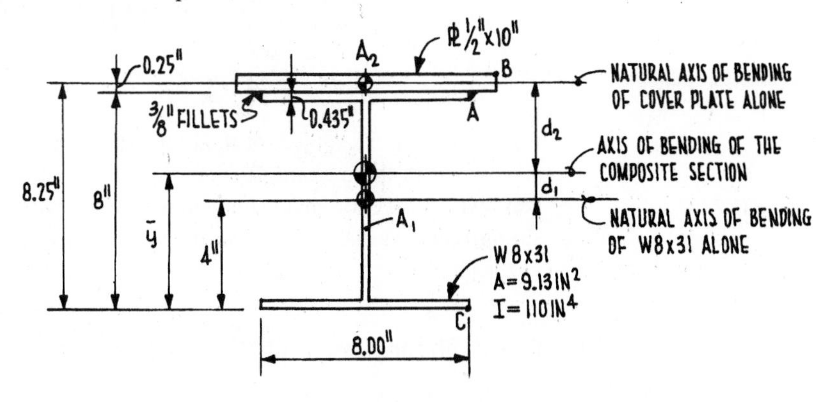

Solution: The centroidal axis of bending for the composite section is determined first:

$$\bar{y} = \frac{\Sigma Ay}{\Sigma A} = \frac{A_1y_1 + A_2y_2}{A_1 + A_2}$$

$$A_1 = 9.13 \; y_1 = 4.00$$
$$A_2 = 5.00 \; y_2 = 8.25$$

$$= \frac{(9.13)(4.00) + (5.00)(8.25)}{9.13 + 5.00} = 5.50 \text{ in.}$$

The moment of inertia about the composite axis of bending is determined next:

$$I = \Sigma(I_o + d^2A)$$

$$\text{W8 x 31: } I = I_o + d_1^2A = 110 + 1.50^2(9.13)$$
$$= 130.54 \text{ in.}^4$$

$$\text{Plate: } I = I_o + d_2^2A = \frac{10(\tfrac{1}{2})^3}{12} + 2.75^2(4.00)$$
$$= 30.35 \text{ in.}^4$$

$$I = 130.54 + 30.35 = 161 \text{ in.}^4$$

Stress at point *A* is compressive, c = 8 - 5.50 - 0.435 = 2.065 in.

$$f_A = \frac{Mc}{I} = \frac{(60{,}000)(12)(2.065)}{161}$$
$$= 9230 lb/in.^2 compression$$

Stress at point *B* is compressive, c = 8 - 5.50 + 0.50 = 3.00 in.

$$f_B = \frac{Mc}{I} = \frac{(60{,}000)(12)(3.00)}{161}$$
$$= 13{,}400 lb/in.^2 compression$$

Stress at point *C* is tensile, c = 5.50 in.

$$f_C = \frac{Mc}{I} = \frac{(60{,}000)(12)(5.50)}{161}$$
$$= 24{,}600 lb/in.^2 tension$$

Before leaving the subject of flexural stress, it is well to emphasize that all of the sections considered in these examples were symmetrical about their vertical axis. The subject of bending on a section that is unsymmetrical on both axes is presented in detail in advanced strength of materials. A few introductory cases of such bending are, however, presented in Chapter 12.

9.6 Beam Shear Flow and Shear Stress

A particular type of shear occurs in beams. It exists wherever moment is changing. It is an important consideration in beam design, especially for materials that are weak in shear, such as timber and concrete.

Consider the beam shown in Figure 9-17 and the segment of unit length cut from the beam and shown as a free body. The shear and moment at both sides of the segment have been computed and found to be V_l and M_l on the left side and V_2 and M_2 on the right side. Both shear and moment are changing even over the short length being examined; it is assumed that both shear and moment are increasing to the right, that is, $V_2 > V_1$ and $M_2 > M_1$.

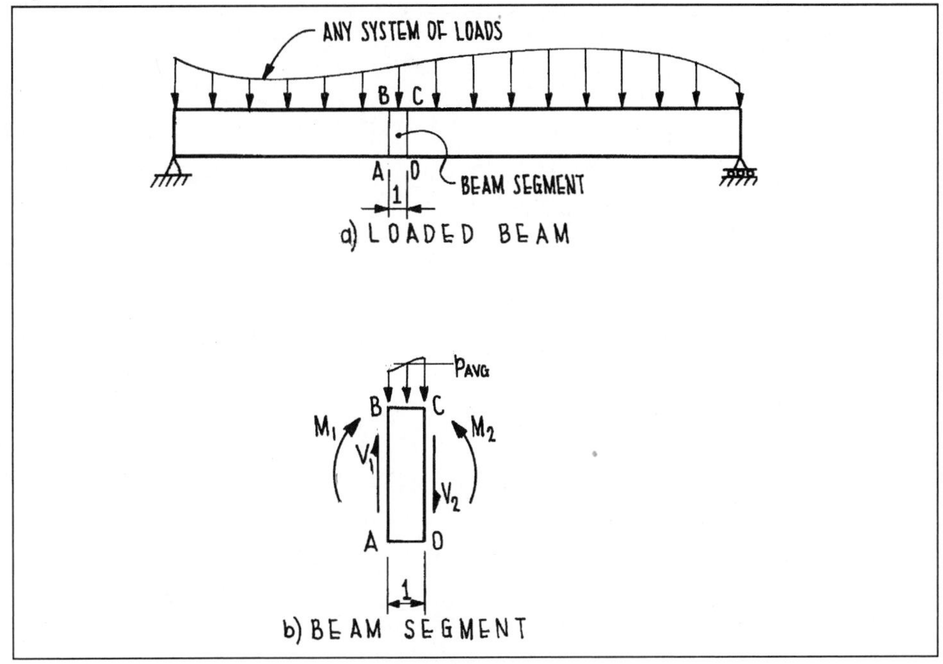

Figure 9-17 Loads on a beam segment.

Forces are summed vertically on the segment.

$$V_1 - p_{AVG}(1) - V_2 = 0$$

$$\frac{V_2 - V_1}{1} = -p_{AVG} \tag{9-32}$$

Equation (9-32) states an important principle: at any point along the length of a beam, the change in shear per unit length of beam is equal to the negative intensity of load at that point.

Moments are now summed about the point O:

$$M_1 + V_1(1) - p_{AVG}(1)(\tfrac{1}{2}) - M_2 = 0$$

$$M_1 - M_2 = -V_1(1) + p_{AVG}(1)(\tfrac{1}{2}) \tag{9-33}$$

The value of $p_{AVG}\Delta$ in Eq.(9-32) is substituted to find:

$$M_1 - M_2 = -V_1(1) - \tfrac{1}{2}(V_2 - V_1)(1)$$

$$= -\frac{V_1 + V_2}{2}(1)$$

$$\frac{M_2 - M_1}{1} = V_{AVG} = V \tag{9-34}$$

Equation (9-34) also states an important principle: at any point along the length of a beam, the change in moment per unit length of beam is equal to the shear at that point.

Refer again to the beam segment in Figure 9-17. A piece off the top of the segment is cut off and shown in larger scale in Figure 9-18, along with its internal stresses. This "cut" face will be called the "cut line" in all discussions to follow.

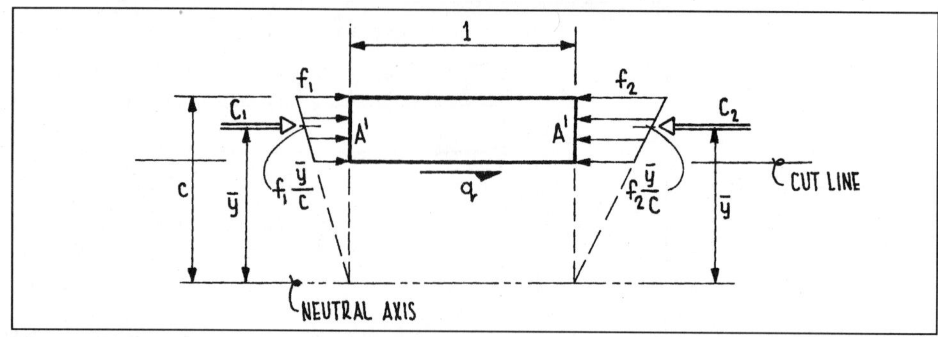

Figure 9-18 Beam shear segment.

Since the moment is known to be changing and $C_2 > C_1$, then for equilibrium to exist, an additional horizontal force must exist at the cut line. The shear force q is shown as that equilibrium force; its units are force/unit length.

The forces C_1 and C_2 are located at the centroid of area A'. Forces are summed horizontally on the free body:

$$\Sigma F_x = 0; \qquad C_1 + q - C_2 = 0 \tag{9-35}$$

where $C_1 = f_1 \frac{\bar{y}}{c} A'$

and $C_2 = f_2 \frac{\bar{y}}{c} A'$

and A' is the area beyond the cut line, extending to the outer fibers.

The expressions for C_1 and C_2 are substituted into Eq.(9-35) to find:

$$q = (f_2 - f_1)A' \frac{\bar{y}}{c} \tag{9-36}$$

It is recognized that f_2 and f_1 are flexural stresses:

$$f_2 = \frac{M_2 c}{I} \text{ and } f_1 = \frac{M_1 c}{I}$$

which, when substituted yields

$$q = (M_2 - M_1)\frac{A'\bar{y}}{I} \tag{9-37}$$

From Eq.(9-34) it is recognized that (M2 - M_1) = V. Also, it is recognized that the term $A'\bar{y}$ is the moment of the area A' about the centroidal axis of bending, hence:

$$q = \frac{VA'\bar{y}}{I} \tag{9-38}$$

where V is the shear force on the section;

A' is the vertical area lying between the cut line and the outer fibers;

$A'\bar{y}$ is the moment of the area A' about the neutral axis of the section; and

I is the planar moment of inertia of the section.

Equation (9-38) is called the *beam shear* equation. The shear q is called shear flow; it is not a stress but a force per unit length, lb/in. or N/mm. Like the flexure formula, it is one of the most important equations in mechanics.

The beam shear equation can be used to find the distribution of shear stress across a section in bending. The rectangular beam of Example 9-9 is shown in Figure 9-19 with graphs of the variation of flexural stress and the variation of shear stress on the section. Maximum shear stress always occurs at the axis of bending; zero shear stress occurs at the outer fibers, where A' = 0.

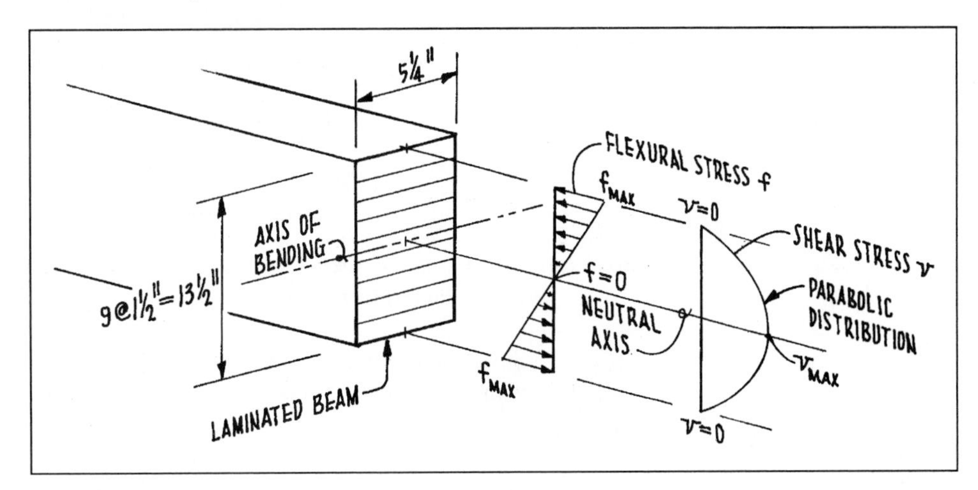

Figure 9-19 Distribution of shear and flexural stresses.

It is observed that the glue joints in the laminated beam are parallel to the axis of bending. Since $A'\bar{y}$ is constant across the entire width, the shear stress across the width b of the beam must also be constant. For this special case, the shear stress v across the width of the joints can be calculated from the shear flow q, to produce a special form of the beam shear equation:

$$v = \frac{q}{b} = \frac{VA'\bar{y}}{Ib} = \frac{VQ}{Ib} \qquad (9\text{-}39)$$

where v is shear stress in lb/in.^{2}

$$Q = A'\bar{y}$$

The two forms of the shear stress equation given by Eq.(9-39) are both commonly used to find shear stress. It must be remembered, however, that the shear stress v can only be found on a plane that is parallel to the axis of bending, where stress is constant across the width of the beam.

It is again emphasized that the shear flow q on a beam section will exist only because the moment (and flexural stress) is changing. The details of the stress diagram of Figure 9-18 is well worth remembering when one is calculating shear flows, particularly regarding the location of the area A'.

Some examples will demonstrate the use of the beam shear equation.

Example 9-17

Applications of the beam shear equation.

Given: Section of Example 9-14. V = 1200 lb.

To Find: Maximum shear stress on the section.

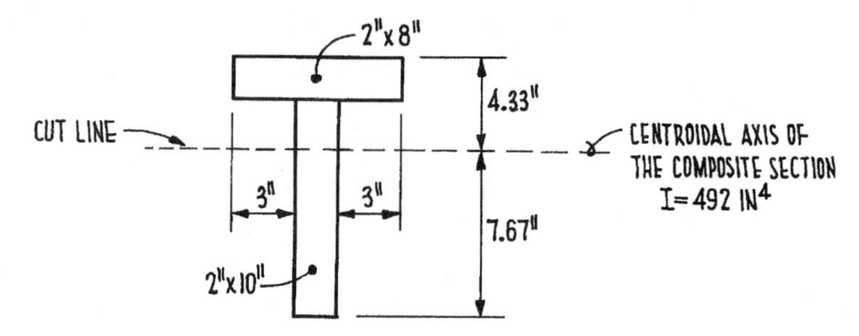

Solution: The maximum shear stress occurs at the centroid of the section. The cut line is therefore positioned there.

Since the cut line is parallel to the axis of bending (it actually coincides with it), the shear stress can be found using the special form of the shear stress equation:

$$v = \frac{VA'\bar{y}}{Ib}$$

The quantity $A'\bar{y}$ is the moment about the neutral axis of the area lying outboard of the cut line. In this case, $A'\bar{y}$ is computed for the area above the neutral axis. It is calculated as the moment of the solid area 8 in. x 4.33 in. about the neutral axis less the moment of the two void areas, 2(2.33 x 3):

$$A'\bar{y} = (8 \times 4.33)^1/_2(4.33) - 2(2.33 \times 3)^1/_2(2.33) = 58.7 \text{ in.}^3$$

Alternatively, $A'\bar{y}$ could be computed for the area below the neutral axis,

$$A'\bar{y} = (2 \times 7.67)^1/_2(7.67) = 58.8 \text{ in.}^2$$

The shear stress is now computed:

$$v = \frac{(1200)(58.8)}{(492)2} = 72 \text{ lb / in.}^2$$

Example 9-18

Applications of the beam shear equation.

Given: Section of Example 9-17. V = 1200 lb.

To Find: 1) Shear flow at the glued joint.
2) Shear stress at the glued joint.

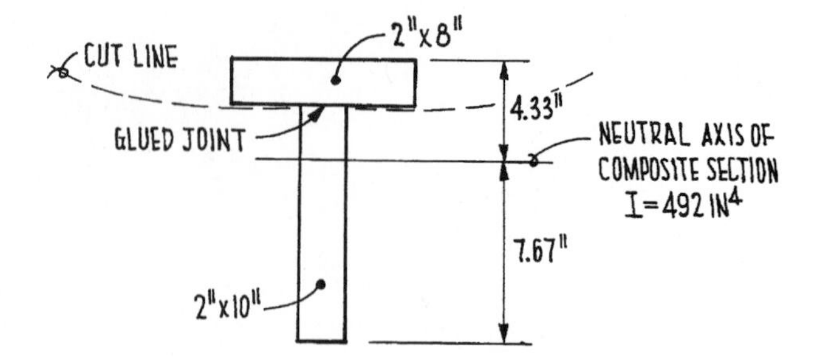

Solution: A cut line is made at the glued joint as shown on the sketch. The shear flow that is to be calculated is shown in the following sketch, looking upward at the glued joint. The area *A′* is the area beyond the cut line, in this case the area *A′* is the 2 in. by 8 in. component.

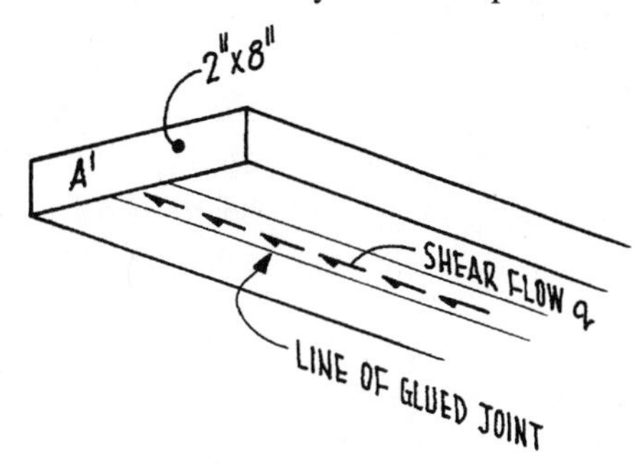

The shear flow is calculated from the beam shear equation:

$$q = \frac{VA'\bar{y}}{I}$$

$V = 1200$ lbs.
$A'\bar{y} = (2)(8)(4.33 - 1) = 53.3$ in.^{3}
$I = 492$

$$q = \frac{(1200)(53.3)}{492} = 130 lb / in. \text{ of length}$$

The shear flow *q* is seen to be distributed over a width of 2 in. Further, the joint is parallel to the axis of bending. Consequently, the shear stess *v* can be found as:

$$v = \frac{q}{b} = \frac{130}{2} = 65 lb / in.^2$$

Example 9-19

Applications of the beam shear equation.

Given: Glued timber member as shown. All dimensions are exact. V = 20 kN.

To Find: Maximum shear stress.

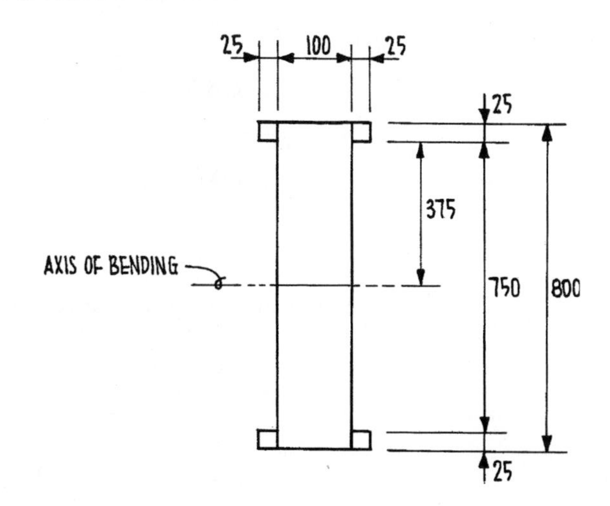

Solution: The maximum shear stress occurs at the neutral axis. The cut line is therefore taken along the neutral axis.

Because the cut line is parallel to the neutral axis, the special form of the shear equation can be used to find the stress directly:

$$v = \frac{VA'\bar{y}}{Ib}$$

The quantity $A'\bar{y}$ is the moment about the neutral axis of the area outboard of the cut line. In this case, it is computed as the moment of the solid area 150 x 400 less that of the two void areas, 2(25 x 375):

$$A'\bar{y} = (150 \times 400)^1/_2(400) - 2(25 \times 375)^1/_2(375)$$
$$= 8.48(10^6)(mm^3)$$

The moment of inertia is similarly computed:

$$I = \left.\frac{bh^3}{12}\right|_{SOLID} - \left.\frac{bh^3}{12}\right|_{VOID} = \frac{150(800)^3}{12} - 2\frac{25(750)^3}{12}$$
$$= 4642(10^6)(mm^4)$$

The stress is now computed:

$$v = \frac{(20{,}000)(8.48x10^6)}{(4602x10^6)(100)} = 0.37N/mm^2$$

Example 9-20

Applications of the beam shear equation.

Given: Glued timber member of Example 9-19. N = 20 kN.

To Find: Shear flow along any one of the glue joints.

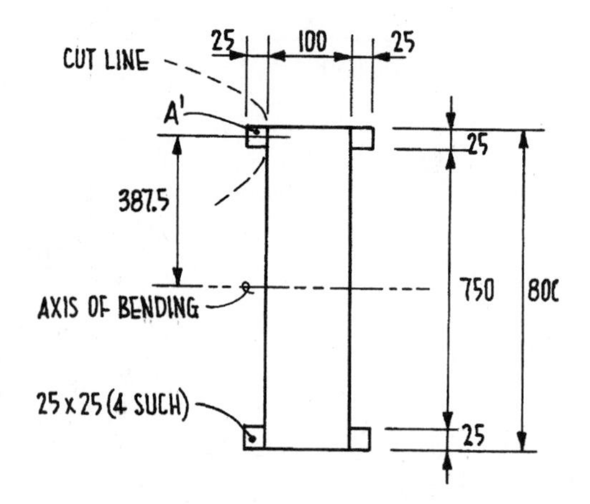

Solution: The moment of inertia is taken from Example 9-19.

$$I = 4642(10^6)(mm^4)$$

A cut line is made as shown, exposing the shears along the glue joint. The shear flow q is shown in the following sketch.

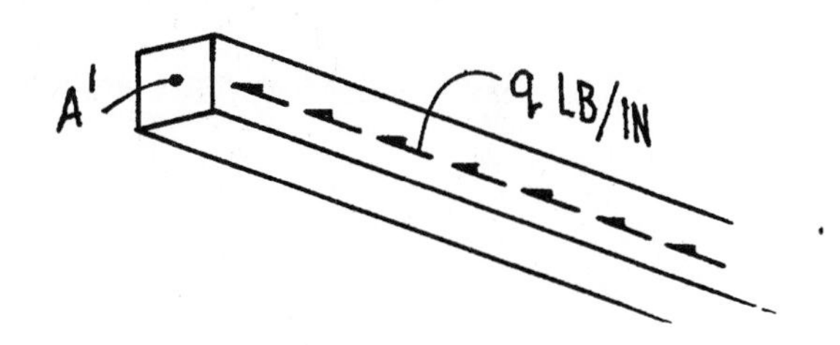

The shear flow is calculated by the beam shear equation:

$$q = \frac{VA'\bar{y}}{I}$$

$$V = 20{,}000 \text{ N}$$
$$A'\bar{y} = (25 \times 25)(387.5) = 242{,}000 \text{ mm}^3$$
$$\text{x } I = 4642(10^6)(\text{in.}^4)$$

$$= \frac{20{,}000(242{,}000)}{(4642)(10^6)} = 104 N/mm$$

Several points in the solution of Example 9-20 warrant discussion. The cut line, for example, is not symmetrical about the vertical axis. Further, the cut line is not horizontal. It should be recalled that there was no requirement in the derivation that the area A' be symmetrical nor that the exposed shear area at the cut line be horizontal. The only requirement was that strains (and stresses) must be linear across the axis of bending.

Note also in the solution of Example 9-20 that it is not possible to find the shear stress v; only the shear flow q can be found. The shear stress varies vertically, as shown in Figure 9-20, going parabolically from zero at the top fibers to a maximum at the bottom fibers. The shear flow q is thus seen to be the resultant of the shear stress over the 25 mm height.

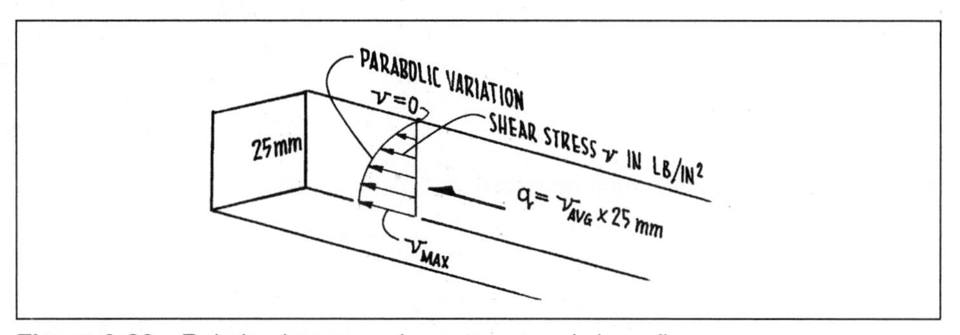

Figure 9-20 Relation between shear stress and shear flow.

Example 9-21

Applications of the beam shear equations.

Given: Built-up steel section of Example 9-16. V = 20 kips.

To Find: Shear stress on the fillet welds.

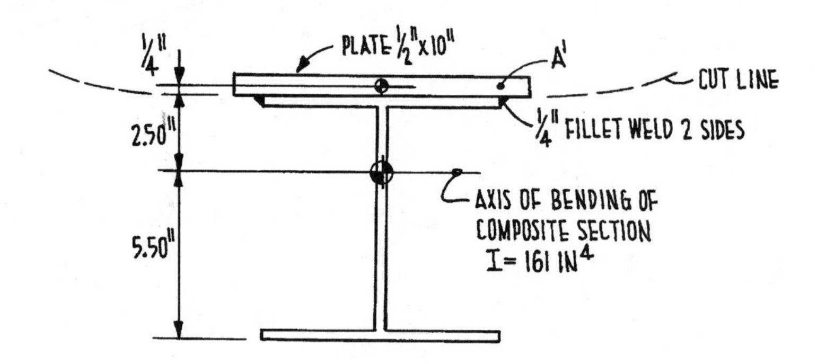

Solution: Shear flow at the fillets is found by the beam shear equation:

$$q = \frac{VA'\bar{y}}{I}$$

$$V = 20 \text{ kips}$$
$$A'\bar{y} = (1/2 \times 10)(2.75) = 13.75 \text{ in.}^3$$
$$I = 161 \text{ in.}^4$$

$$q = \frac{(20{,}000)(13.75)}{161} 1710 \text{ lb/in. on 2 welds}$$

Shear flow on each weld:

$$q/\text{side} = 1710/2 = 855 \text{ lb/in. on 1 weld}$$

Shear stress at the throat:

$$v = \frac{q}{throat} = \frac{855}{0.707(0.25)} = 4840 lb/in.^2$$ on the throat of the fillet.

Example 9-22

Applications of the beam shear equation.

Given: Built-up box beam as shown. V = 5 kN.

To Find: 1) Shear on each nail along line A.
2) Shear on each nail along line B.

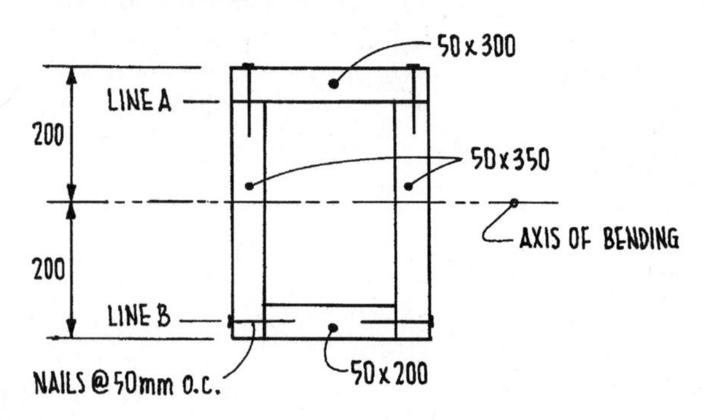

Solution: The section is seen to be symmetrical about its axis of bending. In this determination, only the silhouette of the beam is considered. The means used to fasten the pieces together has no bearing on whether or not a section is symmetrical.

The centroidal axis of bending is at the midpoint. The moment of inertia is found as I_{SOLID} - I_{VOID}:

$$I = I_{SOLID} - I_{VOID} = \left.\frac{bh^3}{12}\right|_{SOLID} - \left.\frac{bh^3}{12}\right|_{VOID}$$

$$= \frac{300(400)^3}{12} - \frac{200(300)^3}{12} = 1150(10^6)(mm^4)$$

The shear flow on the nails at line *A* can be found by taking a cut line along line *A* as shown in the following sketch. For the nails along line *B*, however the cut line must be taken differently; the cut line at *B* is taken as shown in the sketch, cutting the two vertical planes and exposing the shears on the nails.

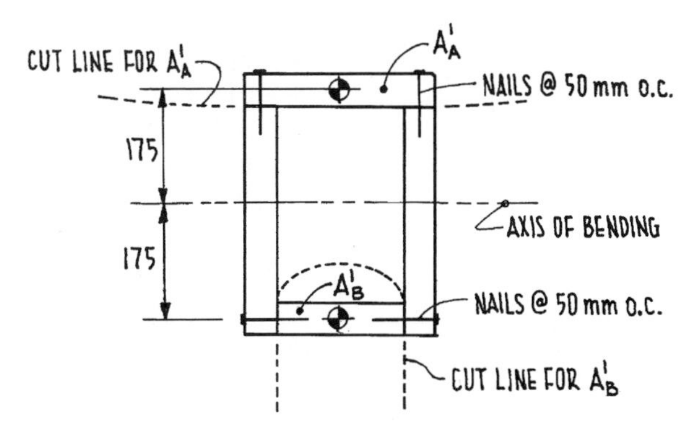

The shear flow along the line of nails on line *A* is shown in the following sketch. The area A'_A is the 50 x 300 member.

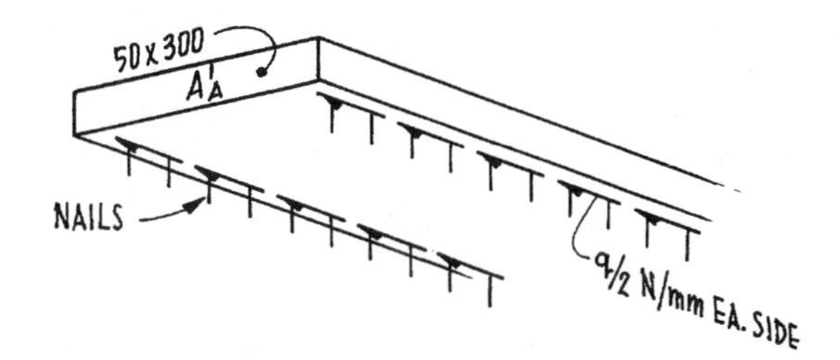

The total shear flow *q* along the two surfaces that have been exposed is found by the beam shear equation:

$$q = \frac{VA'\bar{y}}{I}$$

$$V = 5 \text{ kN}$$
$$A'\bar{y} = (50 \text{ x } 300)(175) = 2.625(10^6)$$
$$I = 1150(10^6)$$

$$q = \frac{(5000)(2.625)(10^6)}{(1150)(10^6)} = 11.4 \text{ N/mm.}$$

The shear flow is seen to be symmetrical, half going to each side.

q/side = 11.4/2 = 5.7 N/mm each side

Each nail must sustain the buildup in shear flow over a distance of 50 mm:

Force/Nail = (5.7)(50) = 285N per nail at line *A*.

For the second part of the solution, the shear flow along the lines of nails on line *B* is shown in the following sketch.

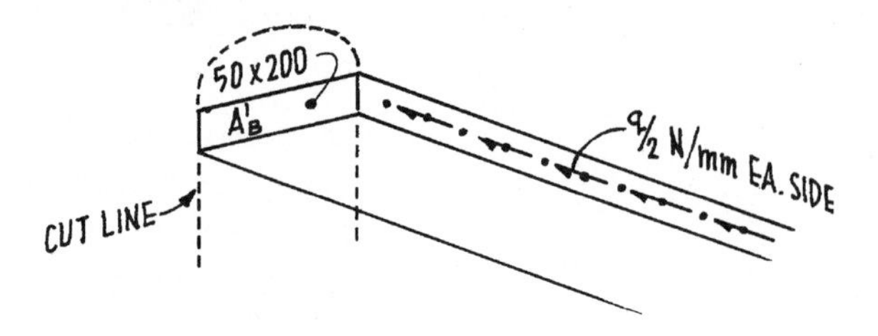

The total shear flow *q* along the two surfaces that have been exposed is found by the beam shear equation:

$$q = \frac{VA'\bar{y}}{I}$$

$$V = 5000$$
$$A'\bar{y} = (50 \times 200)(175) = 1.75(10^6)(\text{in.}^3)$$
$$I = 1150(10^6)$$

$$q = \frac{(5000)(1.75)(10^6)}{(1150)(10^6)} = 7.61 \text{ lb/in.}$$

The shear flow is again seen to be carried on two sides:

q/side = 7.61/2 = 3.80 N/mm each side.

Each nail must sustain a buildup occurring over a distance of 50 mm:

Force/Nail = (3.80)(50) = 190N /nail at line *B*.

In summary, the beam shear equation is an essential tool in designing fasteners in all types of beams. It is used extensively in designing fasteners in composite steel sections and in developing nailing schedules for built-up timber sections. It will appear again and again in the discussions on steel design and timber design.

Review Questions

1. How is torsional stress created?
2. What kind of stress is torsional stress?
3. How is flexural stress created?
4. What kind of stress is flexural stress?
5. How is beam shear stress created?
6. What is torque?
7. How is torque calculated?
8. What are the units of torque?
9. How is torque computed at a particular place along a shaft?

10. How does torsional stress vary across the section?
11. State the torsional stress formula and define each symbol.
12. At what point on the section is torsional stress zero?
13. What is the polar moment of inertia?
14. How is the polar moment of inertia computed for a solid circular shaft?
15. How is the polar moment of inertia computed for a hollow circular shaft?
16. State the formula for computing angular rotation due to strain for a circular shaft and define each symbol.
17. How is the shear force acting on a section computed?
18. How is the moment acting on a section computed?
19. Define positive shear.
20. Define positive moment.
21. How do strains vary across a section in flexure?
22. State the flexure formula and define each symbol.
23. In a symmetrical section, where is the axis of bending?
24. What are the units of planar moment of inertia?
25. How is the planar moment of inertia computed for a solid rectangular section?
26. How is the planar moment of inertia computed for a hollow rectangular box section?
27. When one computes the moment of inertia for a steel section using the dimensions given in the tables, there will usually be a slight difference between that and the tabled value of moment of inertia. Why?
28. What is the nominal depth of a W24 x 68? How much does it weight?
29. Where is the axis of bending for a section that is unsymmetrical about the axis of bending?
30. How does stress vary across a flexural section that is unsymmetrical about the axis of bending?
31. State the remote axis theorem and define each symbol.
32. What is meant by the term "composite section"?
33. The change in shear per unit length along a beam is equal to what?
34. The change in moment per unit length along a beam is equal to what?
35. State the beam shear formula and define each symbol.
36. Under what circumstances can shear stress be computed from the solution for shear flow?
37. On the flexural section, where is flexural stress maximum? Minimum?
38. On the flexural section, where is beam shear stress maximum? Minimum?
39. Why can't shear stress be computed from the solution for shear flow when the cut line is vertical?

CHAPTER

10

DESIGN OF BEAMS AND COLUMNS

Two of the most numerous structural members in any structure are the beams and columns, with floor slabs or floor systems being a distant third. Because of the sheer number of such members, even in small structures, the selection of beams and columns becomes an important procedure in the structural design. The development of special skills for such a frequently-used procedure is well worthwhile. This chapter is devoted to developing such special skills; it is directed toward fast, accurate and thorough investigation of beams and columns.

10.1 Shear and Moment on a Section

In earlier discussions, the shear and moment at any section along the length of a beam was found, using a procedure that involved only simple statics:

1) The shear force V acting on a particular section is computed as the sum of all shearing forces to one side of that section.
2) The moment M acting on a particular section is computed as the sum of all moments to one side of that section.

Such calculation does indeed yield the shear and moment on a particular section, but it does not indicate the section where shear and moment are maximum. Finding the points along the beam where shear and moment are maximum would be a time-consuming process using this procedure; some special aids are warranted.

A very useful aid in finding the maximum shear and maximum moment acting on a beam has been found to be a set of graphs of the shear and moment along the entire length of the beam. From such a set of graphs, the maxima and minima can be found quickly just by visual inspection. A typical set of such graphs is shown in Figure 10-1 for a simply supported beam, loaded by a uniform load over its entire length.

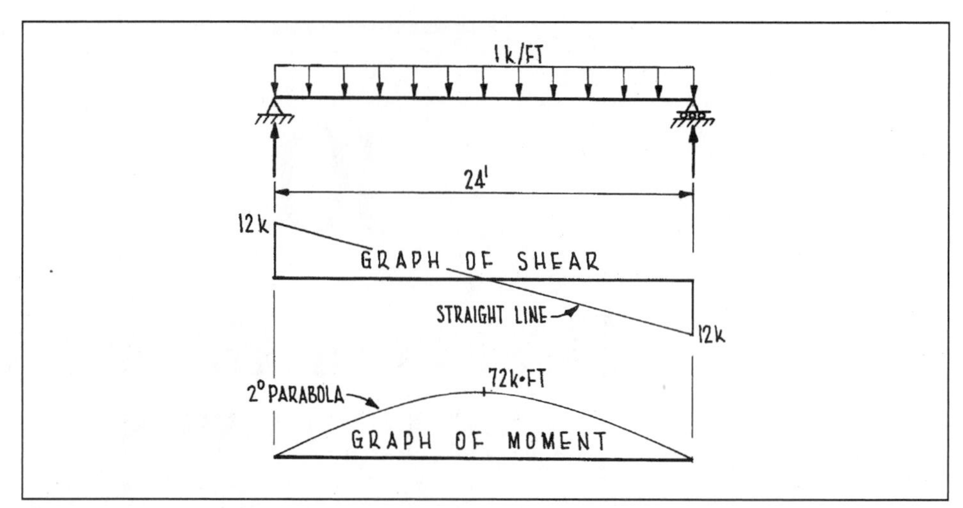

Figure 10-1 Graphs of shear and moment on a beam.

Just a glance at Figure 10-1 reveals that the beam must be able to sustain a maximum shear of 12 kips and a maximum moment of 72 k·ft. If it can sustain these maxima, it can sustain all loads elsewhere in the span. The graphs also reveal that maximum shear and maximum moment do not occur at the same place in the span; such details could bear heavily on the design of the beam itself.

It can be concluded from the sketches of Figure 10-1 that a great deal of accuracy is not required in sketching these graphs; a reasonable level of accuracy will produce the information desired. Note also that the graphs show only the peak values; the lesser values along the graphs are not needed and need not be computed.

A set of graphs such as those of Figure 10-1 is the standard starting point for beam design. A set is prepared for each individual beam with its individual loads and reactions; there are far too many combinations of load of varying magnitudes to permit a "blanket" approach. (An exception to this statement occurs in the design of a particular type of concrete frame, presented in Chapter 16). Over the years, fast and efficient techniques have been developed for sketching these graphs; those techniques are presented in subsequent discussions.

The graphs are called *shear and moment diagrams*. It is strongly recommended that anyone expecting to work in structures or construction become skillful in developing and sketching these diagrams.

10.2 Shear and Moment Diagrams

A typical beam and its loading system is shown in Figure 10-2. Such a beam might be found at a stairwell in a multistory building. Reactions have been computed and are shown on the sketch.

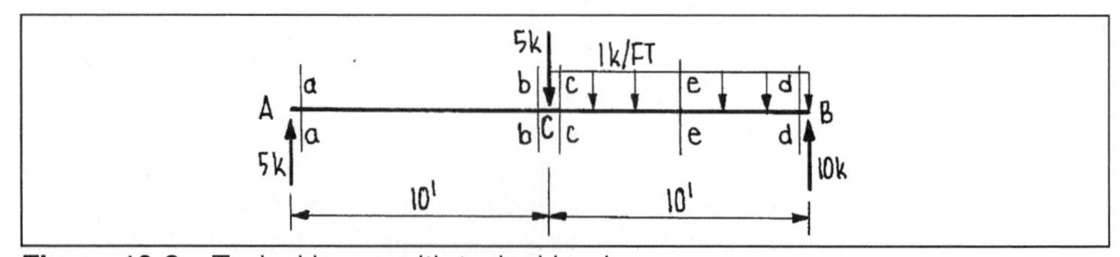

Figure 10-2 Typical beam with typical loads.

The graphs of the shear and moment for this beam can be found without any special techniques, simply by finding the shear and moment at several points along the beam and connecting the values. The sections shown as *aa, bb, cc* and *dd* provide four such points.

A piece of scratch paper is held over the sketch at section *aa*, just to the right of the reaction, hiding all of the beam to the right of section *aa*. The remaining part, the part that is visible, shows the shear forces to the left of section *aa*. The forces and moments are summed:

$\Sigma F_{aa} = V_{aa} = +5k$ (left moves up with respect to right)
$\Sigma M_{aa} = 5(0) = 0$ (section *aa* is too close to provide an arm)

The scratch paper is moved to section *bb*, which is just to the left of the concentrated load. The forces and moments are summed:

$\Sigma F_{bb} = V_{bb} = +5k$ (left moves up with respect to right)
$\Sigma M_{bb} = M_{bb} = +5(10) = +50k\cdot ft$ (puts tension on bottom)

The scratch paper is now moved to section *cc*, just to the right of the concentrated load, but too close to the load to provide it a moment arm. The forces and moments are summed:

$\Sigma F_{cc} = V_{cc} = +5 - 5 = 0$
$\Sigma M_{cc} = M_{cc} = +5(10) - +50k\cdot ft$ (puts tension on bottom)

The scratch paper is now moved to section *dd*, but this time it is held such that all of the beam to the left of the reaction is hidden. Forces and moments are summed:

$\Sigma F_{dd} = V_{dd} = -10k$ (right moves up with respect to left)
$\Sigma M_{dd} = M_{dd} = 10(0) = 0$ (section *dd* is too close to provide an arm)

The values of shear just computed are plotted on the shear diagram of Figure 10-3. Lines are then drawn joining these points to yield the shear diagram as shown. Scale is arbitrary. Any convenient scale may be used.

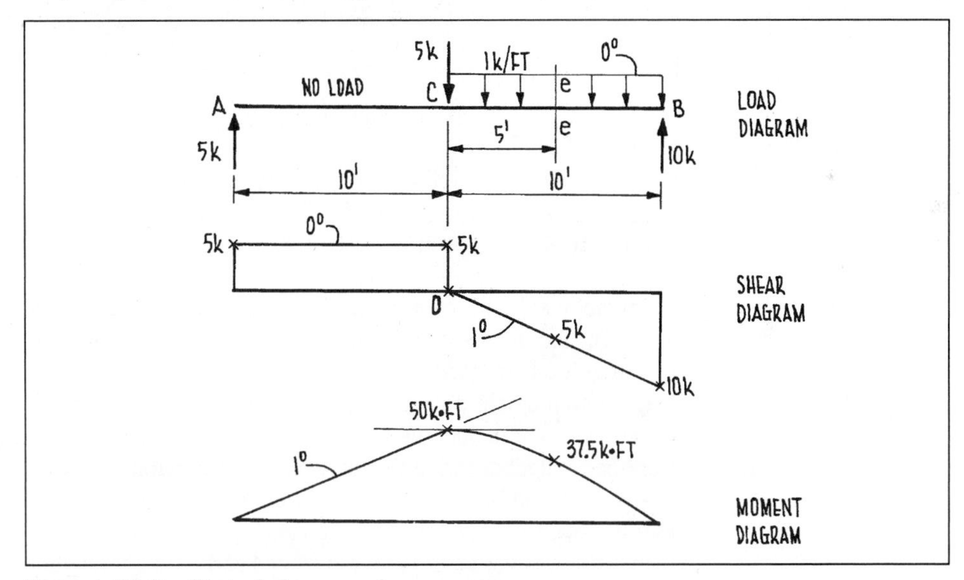

Figure 10-3 Plot of shear and moment.

A question arises about the shape of the shear diagram between points *C* and *B*. So, another section is chosen, section *ee*, halfway between *C* and *D*. The shear and moment are calculated to the right of section *ee*:

$\Sigma F_{ee} = V_{ee} = -10 + 1(5) = -5$ (right moves up with respect to left)
$\Sigma M_{ee} = M_{ee} = +10(5) - 1(5)(5/2) = +37.5k\cdot ft$ (puts tension on bottom)

The shear diagram is now drawn through this additional point as shown, to produce the completed shear diagram.

The moment diagram is constructed similarly. The points just computed are plotted and lines are then added to join those points with smooth curves. The result is the moment diagram as shown.

Several conclusions may be drawn from the foregoing graphs.

1) All points where loads begin and end produce discontinuities in both diagrams.
2) A concentrated load on the load diagram (a spike) shows up as a step on the shear diagram.
3) A step on the shear diagram shows up as a point or a "cusp" on the moment diagram.
4) The shear diagram closes, that is, if forces are summed just to the right of the point *B*, the shear is zero.
5) The moment diagram closes, that is, if moments are summed just to the right of the point *B*, the moment is zero.

The type of curves that appear in the three diagrams seems to be showing a pattern. To find if this is true, the shear and moment is found algebraically in terms of some distance *x*, as shown in Figure 10-4.

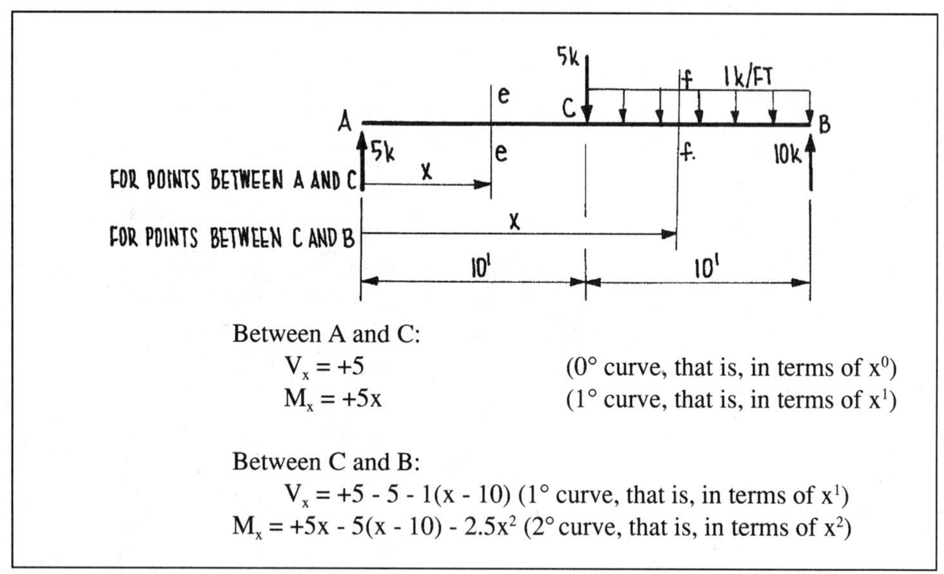

Figure 10-4 Degrees of curvature.

From the results shown in Figure 10-4, it is concluded that the curves do, indeed, follow a pattern: the degree of curvature (the highest power of *x* in the equation) increases by one in going from load diagram to shear diagram and by one more in going from shear diagram to moment diagram. When the load diagram is empty, as it is from *aa* to *bb,* the pattern does not include the load diagram, but starts with the shear diagram. (It is recalled from basic algebra that a 0° curve in *x* is a horizontal line, a 1° curve in *x* is a sloping straight line, and a 2° curve in *x* is a curved parabola.) Such an observation can be a useful tool in developing the diagrams.

Equations 9-32 and 9-34, developed earlier in conjunction with beam shear, can also be useful when applied to shear and moment diagrams. Those equations are, for ready reference:

$$\frac{V_2 - V_1}{1} = -p \qquad (9\text{-}32)$$

$$\frac{M_2 - M_1}{1} = V \qquad (9\text{-}34)$$

Equation 9-32 indicates that at any point along the length of a beam, the change in shear per unit length (the slope of the shear diagram) is equal to the negative intensity of load p at that point. Equation 9-34 indicates that at any point along the length of a beam, the change in moment per unit length (the slope of the moment diagram) is equal to the shear at that point. These slopes are shown in Figure 10-5 along with the convention for positive and negative slopes.

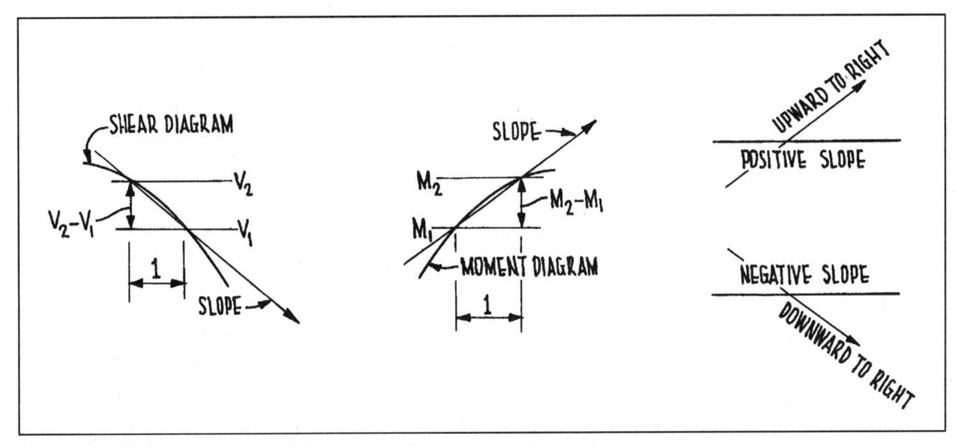

Figure 10-5 Slopes of shear and moment diagrams.

Equations (9-32) and (9-34) also reveal one of the more useful relations between the diagrams. Note that the change in length is indicated only as 1; it could be 1 inch or 1 foot, as needed. Per foot of length of beam, at some point i:

$$V_{i+1} - V_i = p(1) = -A_i \tag{9-32a}$$

In this form, the equation indicates that the *change* in shear between any two points one unit apart is equal to the area under the load diagram between those two points. If all of these areas are summed between two points A and B on the beam, then the *change* in shear between any two points A and B on a beam is equal to the area under the load diagram between those two points, but with a negative sign:

$$V_B - V_A = \sum_{i=1}^{n}(-p_i)(1) \tag{10-1}$$

where n is the number of units between A and B.

Similarly, Eq.(9-34) the change in moment between any two points A and B on a beam is equal to the area under the shear diagram between A and B, with a positive sign:

$$M_B - M_A = \sum_{i=1}^{n} V_i(1) \tag{10-2}$$

where n is the number of units between A and B.

This conclusion is readily checked on the shear and moment diagrams of Figure 10-3.

Between A and C, $V_C - V_A = 0$, area under load diagram is zero.
$M_C - M_A = 50k'$, area under shear diagram is 5(10) = 50
Between C and B, $V_B - V_C = 10$, area under load diagram is 1(10) = 10
$M_B - M_C = -50$, area under shear diagram is $-10(5)^1/_2 = -50$

The foregoing observations are summarized as follows:

1. All points where loads begin and end produce discontinuities in both the shear diagram and moment diagram; the diagrams must therefore be drawn in segments, from one discontinuity to the next.
2. A concentrated load produces a step in the shear diagram. Similarly, a concentrated moment produces a step in the moment diagram.
3. A step in the shear diagram produces a "cusp" (a point) in the moment diagram.
4. The shear diagram must close to zero.

5. The moment diagram must close to zero.
6. The change in shear, $V_B - V_A$, between any two points *A* and *B* along the length of a beam is equal to the area under the load diagram between *A* and *B*, multiplied by -1. (For distributed loads, the positive direction for the load is downward.)
7. The change in moment, $M_B - M_A$, between any two points *A* and *B* along the length of a beam is equal to the area under the shear diagram between *A* and *B*.
8. The slope of the shear diagram at any point is equal to the intensity of load at that point times -1. (For distributed loads, the positive direction for the load is downward.)
9. The slope of the moment diagram at any point is equal to the magnitude of the shear at that point.
10. Where the shear becomes zero, the slope of the moment diagram is zero and the moment is at a maximum or a minimum point.

These observations can now be used to develop sketching techniques in producing shear and moment diagrams. Such techniques are best presented by examples.

In plotting the diagrams in the following examples, the areas under the load diagrams and the shear diagrams will be computed to find the changes in the shear and moment. The formulas used to compute those areas are shown in Table 10-1 for immediate reference.

Table 10-1 Areas of Common Shapes

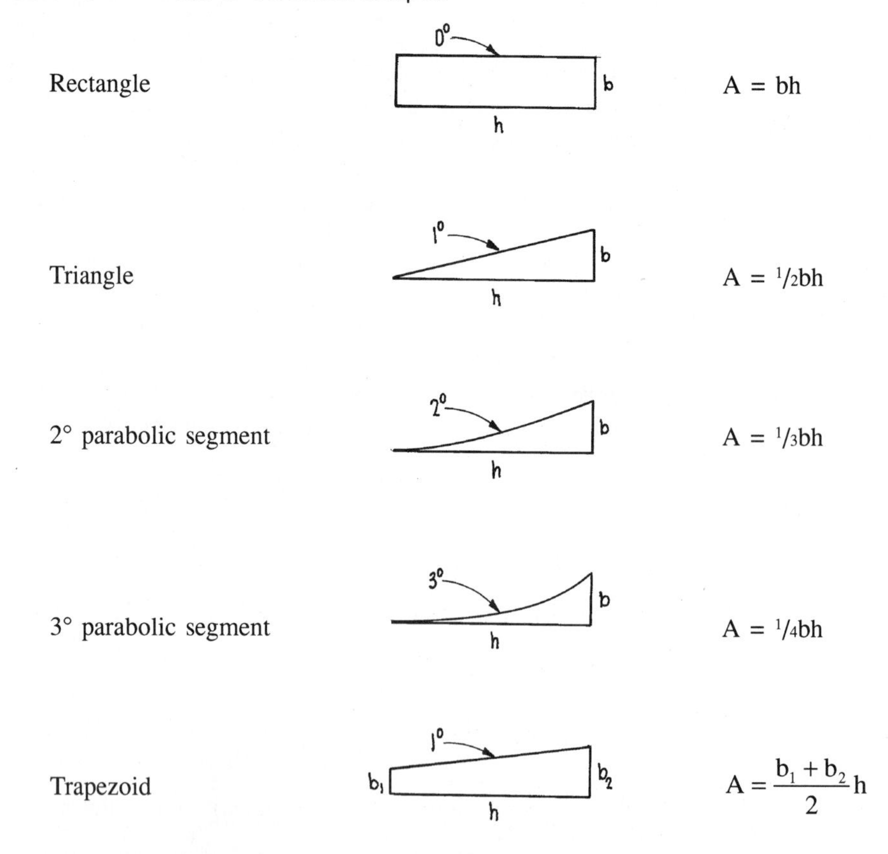

In plotting the examples, some shorthand symbols are used:

- ΔV is read as "change in shear"
- ΔM is read as "change in moment"

Example 10-1

Shear and moment diagrams.

Given: Cantilever beam, loaded as shown.

To Find: Sketch shear and moment diagrams. Show all maxima and minima and their locations.

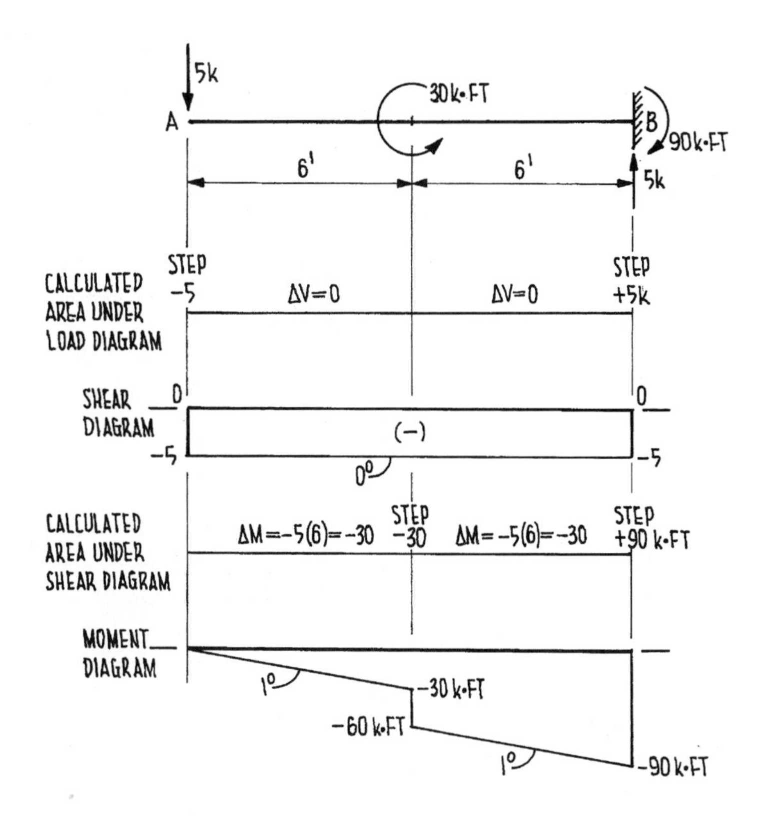

Solution: In finding the starting values at *A* for both the shear and moment diagrams, one need only sum forces just to the left of the 5k load; both shear and moment there are zero.

The shear diagram is drawn by plotting the step at *A*, -5k. Then the change ΔV to *C* is added and the shear at *C* is plotted. Then the change ΔV to *B* is added and the shear at *B* is plotted, to include the 5k step. The plotted points are then connected with straight lines.

The moment diagram is drawn by plotting the value of *M* at *A*, M = 0. Then the change ΔM is added (or subtracted) and the moment at *C* is plotted. Then the step is added (or subtracted) and the point plotted. Then the change ΔM is added and the moment at *C* is plotted. Then the step at *B* is added. The diagram between *A* and *C* is seen to be 1°, so a straight line is drawn connecting the points. The diagram between *C* and *B* is seen to be 1°, so a straight line is drawn connecting the points.

Example 10-2

Shear and moment diagrams.

Given: Cantilever beam loaded as shown.

To Find: Sketch shear and moment diagrams. Show all maxima and minima and their locations.

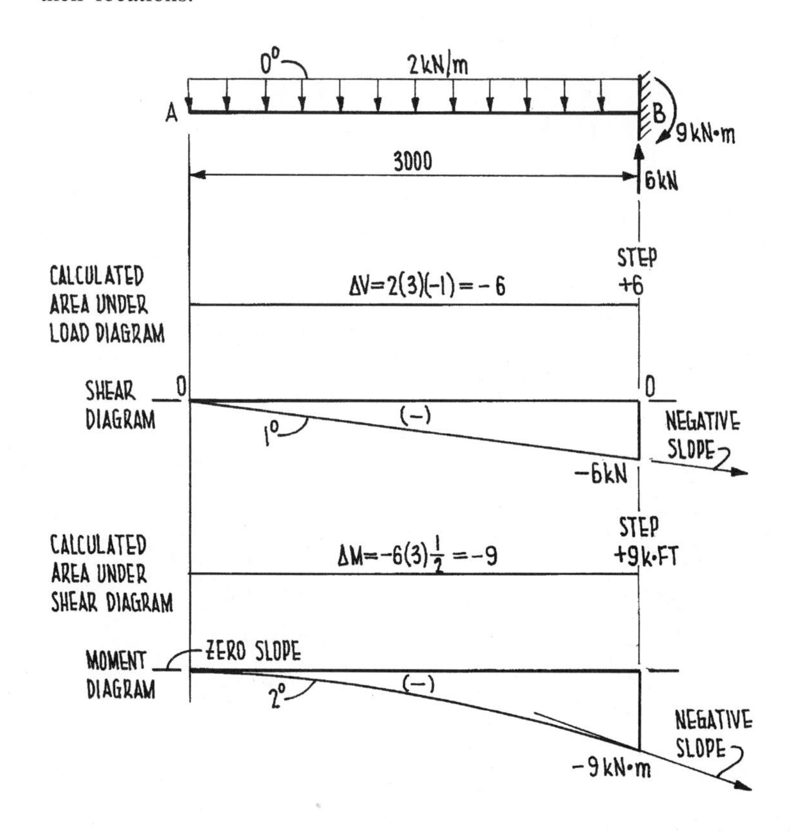

Solution: The shear diagram is drawn by plotting the value of shear at A, which is seen to be zero. Then the change ΔV is added and the shear at B is plotted. Because the load diagram is 0°, it is seen that the shear diagram is 1°, or a straight sloping line. Because the load is downward (positive), the slope of the shear diagram is negative, downward to the right, as shown.

The moment diagram is drawn by plotting the value of moment at A, which is seen to be zero. Then the change ΔM is added and the moment at B is plotted. Because the shear diagram is 1°, it is seen that the moment diagram is a 2° curve, but at this point it is not known whether the curve cups upward or downward. The slope of the moment diagram at A is seen to be zero (since the shear at A is zero) and the slope of the moment diagram at B is seen to be negative (since the shear at B is negative). A zero slope line is drawn at A and a negative slope line is drawn through the plotted point at B. The moment diagram is then drawn through the two plotted points tangent to the two slopes.

Example 10-3

Shear and moment diagrams.

Given: Cantilever beam loaded as shown.

To Find: Sketch the shear and moment diagrams. Show all maxima and minima and their locations.

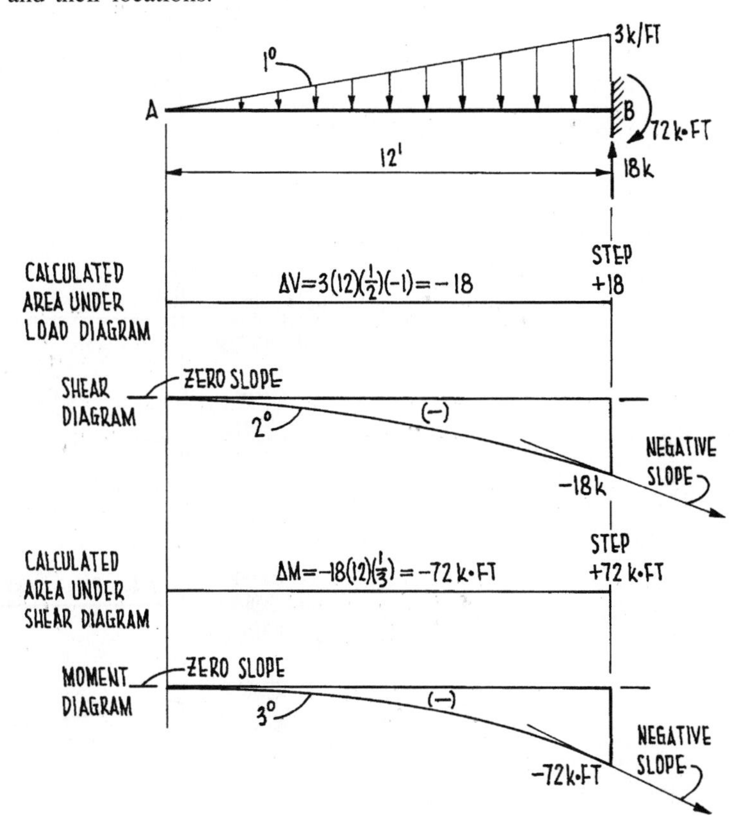

Solution: The shear diagram is drawn by plotting the value of shear at A, which is seen to be zero. Then the change ΔV is added and the shear at B is plotted. Because the load diagram is 1°, it is known that the shear diagram is 3° but at this point it is not known whether the curve cups upward or downward. The slope of the shear diagram at A is seen to be zero (since p is zero) and the slope at B is seen to be negative (p = -3). the two slopes are drawn through the plotted values. The curve is then drawn through the plotted values tangent to the two slopes.

The moment diagram is drawn similarly, but using the values from the shear diagram rather than the load diagram.

Example 10-4

Shear and moment diagrams.

Given: Cantilever beam loaded as shown.

To Find: Sketch the shear and moment diagrams. Show all maxima and minima and their locations.

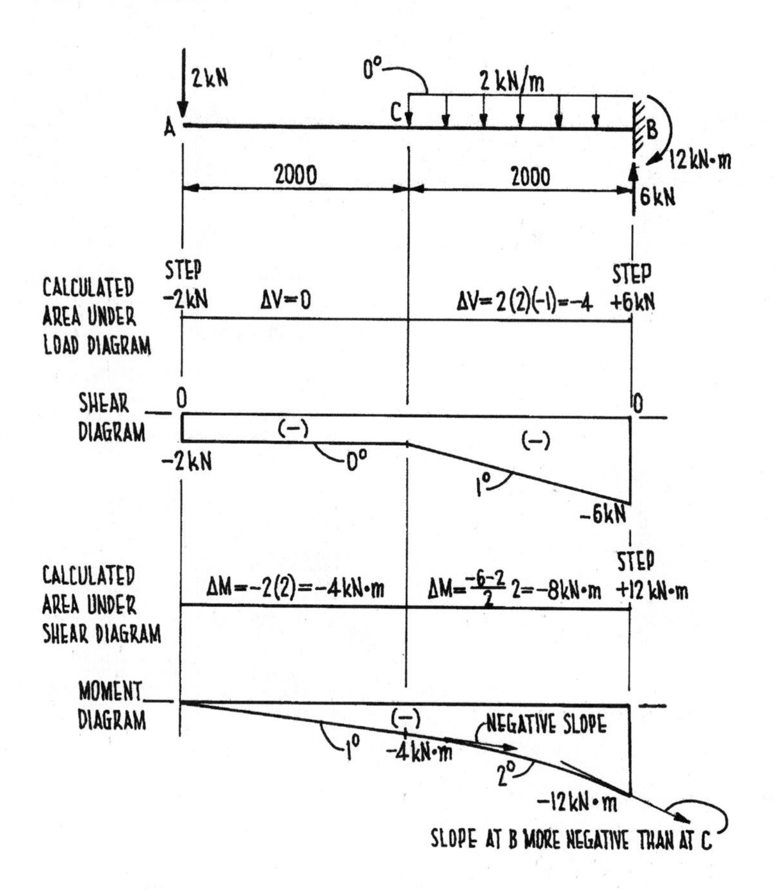

Solution: The shear diagram is drawn by plotting the value of shear at A, which is seen to be stepped to -2kN. Then the change ΔV is added and the shear at C is added. Then the next change ΔV is added and the shear at B is plotted. The shear diagram is then plotted by connecting the three points. The curve between A and C is seen to be 0°, and the curve between C and B is seen to be 1°. The curve is plotted this way.

The moment diagram is drawn by plotting the values of the moment at A, C and B, to include the step at B. The curve from A to C is seen to be 1° so it is drawn as a straight sloping line. The curve from C to B is seen to be a 2° curve. Slopes are drawn through the plotted values of moment at C and B. The curve is then drawn through the plotted values tangent to these slopes.

Example 10-5

Shear and moment diagrams.

Given: Simple beam, loaded as shown.

To Find: Sketch shear and moment diagrams. Show all maxima and minima and their locations.

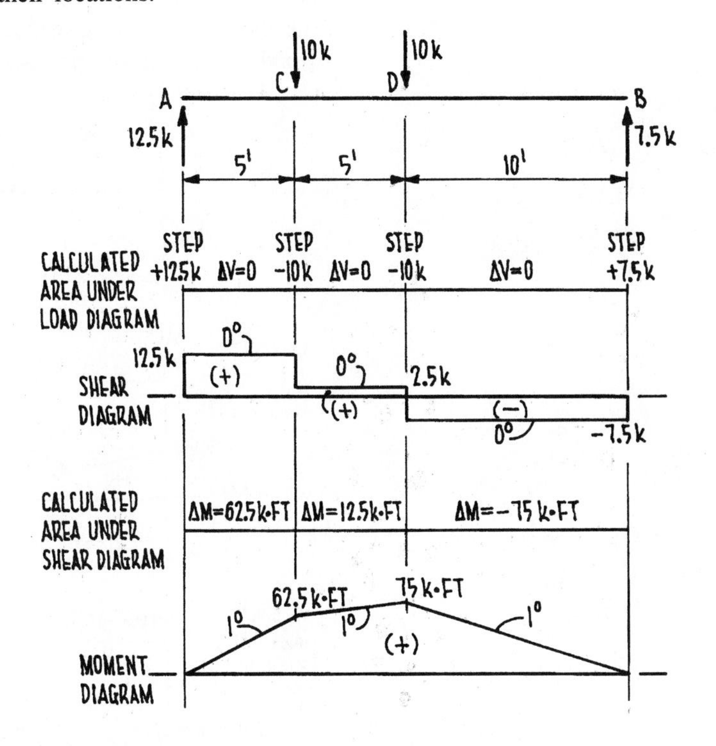

Solution: The shear diagram is seen to be simply a series of steps and is plotted accordingly. All curves are 0°.

The moment diagram is drawn by plotting the values of moment at *A*, *D*, *B* and *B*. All three segments of the moment diagram are seen to be 1° curves, so the plotted points are connected by sloping straight lines.

Example 10-6

Shear and moment diagrams.

Given: Simple beam, loaded as shown.

To Find: Sketch shear and moment diagrams. Show all maxima and minima and their locations.

Solution: The shear diagram is drawn by plotting the values of shear at *A*, *B*, *C* and *D* and connecting the points with straight lines.

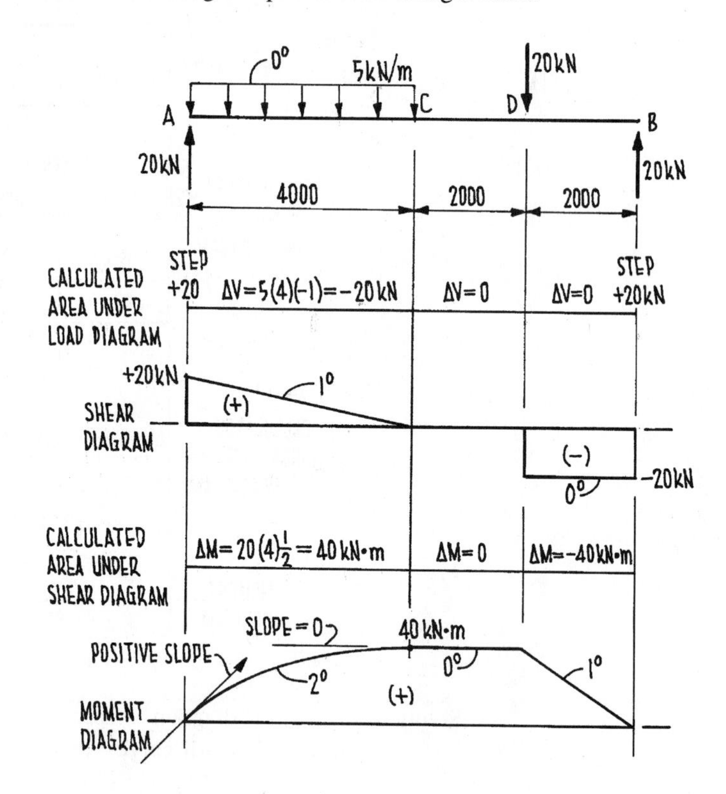

The moment diagram is drawn by plotting the values of moment at *A*, *B*, *C* and *D*. The curve from *A* to *C* is seen to be second degree; slopes are plotted at both ends through the plotted values and the curve is then drawn through the plotted values tangent to these slopes. The curve from *C* to *D* is seen to be a 0° horizontal line and is drawn as such. The curve from *D* to be is seen to 1° sloping straight line and is drawn as such.

Example 10-7

Shear and moment diagrams.

Given: Simple beam, loaded as shown.

To Find: Sketch shear and moment diagrams. Show all maxima and minima and their locations.

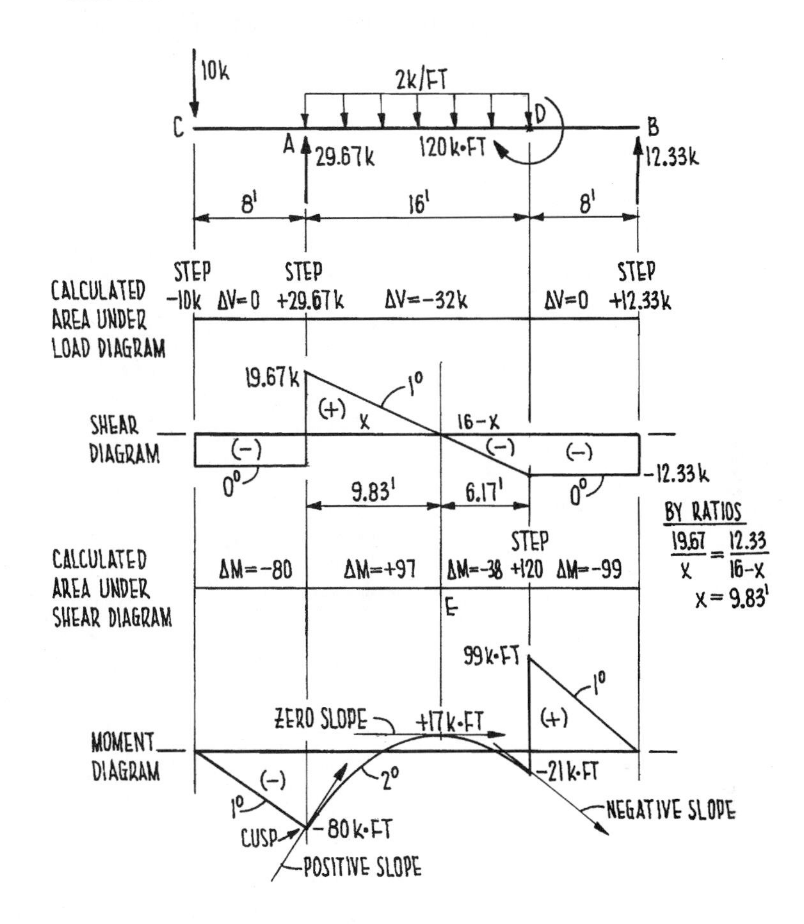

Solution: The shear diagram is drawn by plotting the values of shear at C, A, D and B and connecting the points with straight lines. It is noted that the shear becomes zero between A and D. The location of that point is computed by similar triangles as shown.

The moment diagram is drawn by plotting the values of moment at C, A, D and B, to include the step at D. The curve from C to A is seen to be 1° so it is drawn as a straight sloping line. The curve from A to E to D is seen to be a 2° curve. Slopes are drawn through the plotted values of moment at the three points, A, E and D. The curve is drawn through the three points tangent to the three slopes. The curve from D to B is seen to be 1° so it is drawn as a straight sloping line.

Example 10-8

Shear and moment diagrams.

Given: Simple beam loaded as shown.

To Find: Sketch the shear and moment diagrams.

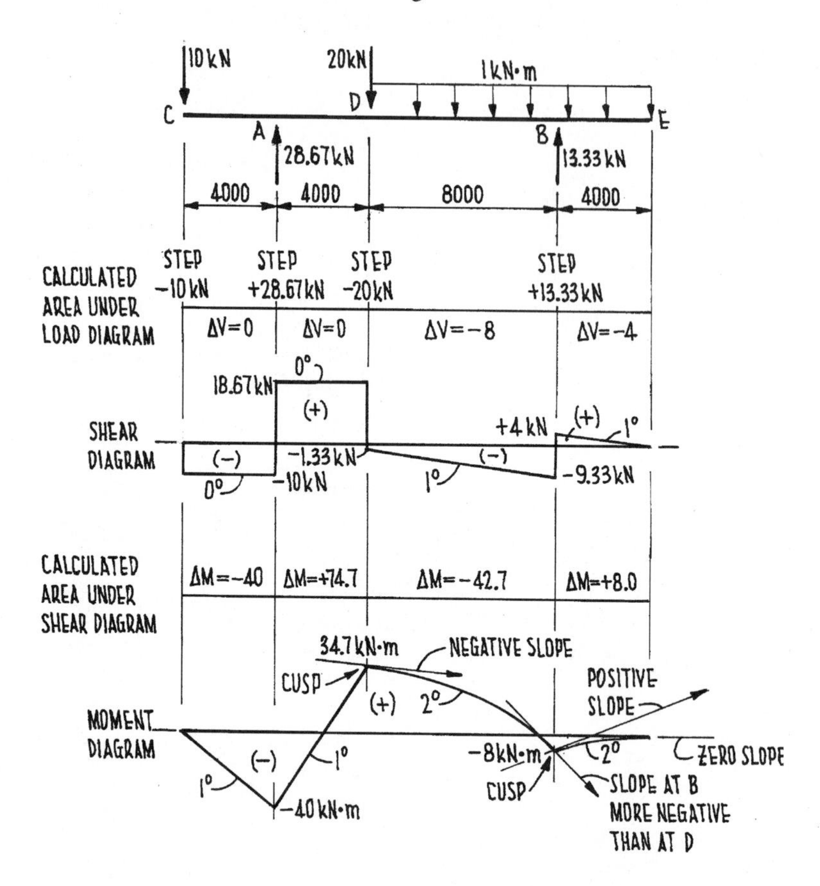

Solution: The shear diagram is drawn by plotting the values of shear at *C*, *A*, *D*, *B* and *E*, to include the steps, and connecting these values with straight lines.

The moment diagram is drawn by plotting the values of moment at *C*, *A*, *D*, *B* and *E*. The curve from *C* to *A* is seen to be 1° so it is drawn as a straight line. The curve from *C* to *D* is seen to be 1° so it is drawn as a straight line. The curve from *D* to *B* is seen to be 2°. The slopes at *D* and *B* are drawn through the plotted values and the curve is drawn through the plotted values tangent to these slopes. The curve from *B* to *E* is seen to be 2°. The slopes at *B* and *E* are drawn through the plotted values and the curve is drawn through the plotted values tangent to these slopes.

When the shear and moment diagram for a particular beam is complete, the maximum design values for shear and moment and their locations are immediately evident, simply by visual inspection. The proper size and shape of a suitable beam can then be selected. The procedures for selecting such a suitable beam section are presented next.

10.3 Design of Beams for Flexure and Shear

It is pointed out that SI units are not used in the remainder of this chapter. The reason is one of simple practicality: the use of two sets of units would require using two supplementary design manuals, learning two sets of materials specifications and applying two sets of design code requirements. The purpose here is to teach design procedures; the procedures presented here in Imperial units will apply equally well when one is working in SI units using materials manufactured to SI standards and design codes written for use with SI units.

The basic procedure for selecting structural beam sections is introduced in the following discussions. The procedure utilizes shear and moment diagrams, the flexure formula and the beam shear equation. Materials considered in these introductory discussions are limited to steel and timber.

Steel beams are considered first, primarily because steel is such an ideal structural material. Steel is remarkably strong, almost completely elastic (up to its yield stress) and is one of the most rigid materials in common use. Because of its high strength, however, member elements can be quite thin; under high compressive stress these thin structural elements can buckle, or "cripple." Any design in steel must be made in full awareness of such complications.

Steel manufacturers and fabricators in the United States have joined together in a trade association called the American Institute of Steel Construction (AISC). The institute promotes the proper use of steel in modern construction by several means, one of which is the dissemination of correct and current design information. Another is maintaining a comprehensive and authoritative design code for steel that is commonly adopted *in toto* into municipal building codes. Such information, along with a wealth of design aids is contained in the AISC *Manual of Steel Construction*, published and sold by the Institute. The design information on steel that is included in the Technical Manual is in fact extracted from this "steel handbook," as the manual is called in the industry.

More than 300 steel beam shapes are commonly being rolled in the American steel industry. Some of the more commonly used of these shapes are listed in the Technical Manual in Tables S-1 through S-9. These tables are reproduced from the *Steel Handbook*, 8th edition. A reproduction of a typical two-page layout is shown for immediate reference in Figure 10-6.

The table heading "W Shapes" in Figure 10-6 refers to a particular shape used for steel beams, the *wide flange* shape. The wide flange shape is by far the most commonly used beam section in use today. In the beam designations in the table, the number following the *W* is the nominal depth of the section in inches and the final number is the weight of the section in lb/ft of length. The section W12x50, for example, has a nominal depth of 12 inches and weighs 50 lbs per foot of length.

On the right-hand side of the pages shown in Figure 10-6 a group of headings is listed under title "Elastic Properties". It is this group of headings that are of immediate interest. Note that the moment of inertia is listed on both the xx and yy centroidal axes, for bending in either direction. (Refer to the sketch in Figure 10-6 for the orientation of the xx and yy axes). Also listed is the section modulus in both directions, where $S = I/c$.

On the left-hand side of the page, the physical dimensions of each section is given, keyed to the defining sketch. It is these dimensions that must be used whenever the remote axis theorem is being applied. Many of the dimensions and properties listed in the table have not yet been encountered in this textbook; they will be introduced as the discussion proceeds.

1 - 28

W SHAPES
Dimensions

Designation	Area A	Depth d		Web Thickness t_w		$\frac{t_w}{2}$	Flange Width b_f		Flange Thickness t_f		Distance T	Distance k	Distance k_1
	In.^{2}	In.		In.		In.	In.		In.		In.	In.	In.
W 12×336[a]	98.8	16.82	16⅞	1.775	1¾	⅞	13.385	13⅜	2.955	2 15/16	9½	3 11/16	1½
×305[a]	89.6	16.32	16⅜	1.625	1⅝	13/16	13.235	13¼	2.705	2 11/16	9½	3 7/16	1 7/16
×279[a]	81.9	15.85	15⅞	1.530	1½	¾	13.140	13⅛	2.470	2½	9½	3 3/16	1⅜
×252[a]	74.1	15.41	15⅜	1.395	1⅜	11/16	13.005	13	2.250	2¼	9½	2 15/16	1 5/16
×230[a]	67.7	15.05	15	1.285	1 5/16	11/16	12.895	12⅞	2.070	2 1/16	9½	2¾	1¼
×210[a]	61.8	14.71	14¾	1.180	1 3/16	⅝	12.790	12¾	1.900	1⅞	9½	2⅝	1¼
×190	55.8	14.38	14⅜	1.060	1 1/16	9/16	12.670	12⅝	1.735	1¾	9½	2 7/16	1 3/16
×170	50.0	14.03	14	0.960	15/16	½	12.570	12⅝	1.560	1 9/16	9½	2¼	1⅛
×152	44.7	13.71	13¾	0.870	⅞	7/16	12.480	12½	1.400	1⅜	9½	2⅛	1 1/16
×136	39.9	13.41	13⅜	0.790	13/16	7/16	12.400	12⅜	1.250	1¼	9½	1 15/16	1
×120	35.3	13.12	13⅛	0.710	11/16	⅜	12.320	12⅜	1.105	1⅛	9½	1 13/16	1
×106	31.2	12.89	12⅞	0.610	⅝	5/16	12.220	12¼	0.990	1	9½	1 11/16	15/16
× 96	28.2	12.71	12¾	0.550	9/16	5/16	12.160	12⅛	0.900	⅞	9½	1⅝	⅞
× 87	25.6	12.53	12½	0.515	½	¼	12.125	12⅛	0.810	13/16	9½	1½	⅞
× 79	23.2	12.38	12⅜	0.470	½	¼	12.080	12⅛	0.735	¾	9½	1 7/16	⅞
× 72	21.1	12.25	12¼	0.430	7/16	¼	12.040	12	0.670	11/16	9½	1⅜	⅞
× 65	19.1	12.12	12⅛	0.390	⅜	3/16	12.000	12	0.605	⅝	9½	1 5/16	13/16
W 12× 58	17.0	12.19	12¼	0.360	⅜	3/16	10.010	10	0.640	⅝	9½	1⅜	13/16
× 53	15.6	12.06	12	0.345	⅜	3/16	9.995	10	0.575	9/16	9½	1¼	13/16
W 12× 50	14.7	12.19	12¼	0.370	⅜	3/16	8.080	8⅛	0.640	⅝	9½	1⅜	13/16
× 45	13.2	12.06	12	0.335	5/16	3/16	8.045	8	0.575	9/16	9½	1¼	13/16
× 40	11.8	11.94	12	0.295	5/16	3/16	8.005	8	0.515	½	9½	1¼	¾
W 12× 35	10.3	12.50	12½	0.300	5/16	3/16	6.560	6½	0.520	½	10½	1	9/16
× 30	8.79	12.34	12⅜	0.260	¼	⅛	6.520	6½	0.440	7/16	10½	15/16	½
× 26	7.65	12.22	12¼	0.230	¼	⅛	6.490	6½	0.380	⅜	10½	⅞	½
W 12× 22	6.48	12.31	12¼	0.260	¼	⅛	4.030	4	0.425	7/16	10½	⅞	½
× 19	5.57	12.16	12⅛	0.235	¼	⅛	4.005	4	0.350	⅜	10½	13/16	½
× 16	4.71	11.99	12	0.220	¼	⅛	3.990	4	0.265	¼	10½	¾	½
× 14	4.16	11.91	11⅞	0.200	3/16	⅛	3.970	4	0.225	¼	10½	11/16	½

[a]For application refer to Notes in Table 2.
Shapes in shaded rows are not available from domestic producers.

American Institute of Steel Construction

1 - 29

W SHAPES
Properties

Nominal Wt. per Ft	Compact Section Criteria $\frac{b_f}{2t_f}$	F_y'	$\frac{d}{t_w}$	F_y'''	r_T	$\frac{d}{A_f}$	Elastic Properties Axis X-X I	S	r	Axis Y-Y I	S	r	Plastic Modulus Z_x	Z_y
Lb.		Ksi		Ksi	In.		In.^{4}	In.^{3}	In.	In.^{4}	In.^{3}	In.	In.^{3}	In.^{3}
336	2.3	—	9.5	—	3.71	0.43	4060	483	6.41	1190	177	3.47	603	274
305	2.4	—	10.0	—	3.67	0.46	3550	435	6.29	1050	159	3.42	537	244
279	2.7	—	10.4	—	3.64	0.49	3110	393	6.16	937	143	3.38	481	220
252	2.9	—	11.0	—	3.59	0.53	2720	353	6.06	828	127	3.34	428	196
230	3.1	—	11.7	—	3.56	0.56	2420	321	5.97	742	115	3.31	386	177
210	3.4	—	12.5	—	3.53	0.61	2140	292	5.89	664	104	3.28	348	159
190	3.7	—	13.6	—	3.50	0.65	1890	263	5.82	589	93.0	3.25	311	143
170	4.0	—	14.6	—	3.47	0.72	1650	235	5.74	517	82.3	3.22	275	126
152	4.5	—	15.8	—	3.44	0.79	1430	209	5.66	454	72.8	3.19	243	111
136	5.0	—	17.0	—	3.41	0.87	1240	186	5.58	398	64.2	3.16	214	98.0
120	5.6	—	18.5	—	3.38	0.96	1070	163	5.51	345	56.0	3.13	186	85.4
106	6.2	—	21.1	—	3.36	1.07	933	145	5.47	301	49.3	3.11	164	75.1
96	6.8	—	23.1	—	3.34	1.16	833	131	5.44	270	44.4	3.09	147	67.5
87	7.5	—	24.3	—	3.32	1.28	740	118	5.38	241	39.7	3.07	132	60.4
79	8.2	62.6	26.3	—	3.31	1.39	662	107	5.34	216	35.8	3.05	119	54.3
72	9.0	52.3	28.5	—	3.29	1.52	597	97.4	5.31	195	32.4	3.04	108	49.2
65	9.9	43.0	31.1	—	3.28	1.67	533	87.9	5.28	174	29.1	3.02	96.8	44.1
58	7.8	—	33.9	57.6	2.72	1.90	475	78.0	5.28	107	21.4	2.51	86.4	32.5
53	8.7	55.9	35.0	54.1	2.71	2.10	425	70.6	5.23	95.8	19.2	2.48	77.9	29.1
50	6.3	—	32.9	60.9	2.17	2.36	394	64.7	5.18	56.3	13.9	1.96	72.4	21.4
45	7.0	—	36.0	51.0	2.15	2.61	350	58.1	5.15	50.0	12.4	1.94	64.7	19.0
40	7.8	—	40.5	40.3	2.14	2.90	310	51.9	5.13	44.1	11.0	1.93	57.5	16.8
35	6.3	—	41.7	38.0	1.74	3.66	285	45.6	5.25	24.5	7.47	1.54	51.2	11.5
30	7.4	—	47.5	29.3	1.73	4.30	238	38.6	5.21	20.3	6.24	1.52	43.1	9.56
26	8.5	57.9	53.1	23.4	1.72	4.95	204	33.4	5.17	17.3	5.34	1.51	37.2	8.17
22	4.7	—	47.3	29.5	1.02	7.19	156	25.4	4.91	4.66	2.31	0.847	29.3	3.66
19	5.7	—	51.7	24.7	1.00	8.67	130	21.3	4.82	3.76	1.88	0.822	24.7	2.98
16	7.5	—	54.5	22.2	0.96	11.3	103	17.1	4.67	2.82	1.41	0.773	20.1	2.26
14	8.8	54.3	59.6	18.6	0.95	13.3	88.6	14.9	4.62	2.36	1.19	0.753	17.4	1.90

American Institute of Steel Construction

Figure 10-6 Typical headings from AISC manual.

Of interest at the moment is the section modulus, *S*. The section modulus is a part of the flexure formula, with *c* being taken to the outermost fibers of the section:

$$f = \frac{M}{S}, \text{ where } S = I/c \qquad (10\text{-}3a)$$

Note that the section modulus is a property of the section; it depends only on the size, shape and dimensions of the cross section. In the steel tables, it always corresponds to the maximum value of stress.

The flexure formula given in Eq.(10-3a) can be solved for the section modulus:

$$S = \frac{M}{f} \qquad (10\text{-}3b)$$

The applications of Eq.(10-3b) are quite direct. Given, for example, a maximum moment of 60 kip·ft that a wide flange steel beam must carry with an allowable stress not to exceed 24,000 lb/in.^{2}, it is found from Eq.(10-3b) that the required section modulus for the steel section would have to be at least 60,000(12)/24,000, or 30. It is then found from the steel tables (such as Figure 10-6) that the lightest-weight wide flange beam which has a section modulus of 30 or more is a W12x26; it is the lightest section that will sustain the given moment without exceeding the allowable stress.

The reason for choosing the lightest section is simply economics. Steel is purchased by the pound, and steel is heavy. For economy, the lightest steel sections that will adequately sustain the loads are the ones chosen.

The preceding example, regardless of how simplistic, illustrates the general procedure by which flexural members are selected:

1. The maximum moment to be sustained is found from the moment diagram.
2. The allowable stress in the material is established.
3. The minimum required magnitude of the section modulus is computed: S = M/f.
4. The lightest section that has a section modulus at least this large is selected.
5. The section thus selected is reviewed to see that it is adequate in shear.

Step 5 in the foregoing procedure introduces a consideration that has not yet been discussed. Whenever flexure exists, beam shear exists. Whenever a beam is selected to sustain the maximum moment (taken from the moment diagram) the member so selected must also sustain the maximum shear (taken from shear diagram).

The shear stress distribution for a wide flange beam is shown in the graph of Figure 10-7. To obtain the graph, the shear stress was computed at short intervals along the height of the section using the shear stress formula, given in Chapter 9 as Eq.(9-39):

$$v = \frac{VA'\bar{y}}{Ib} \qquad (9\text{-}39)$$

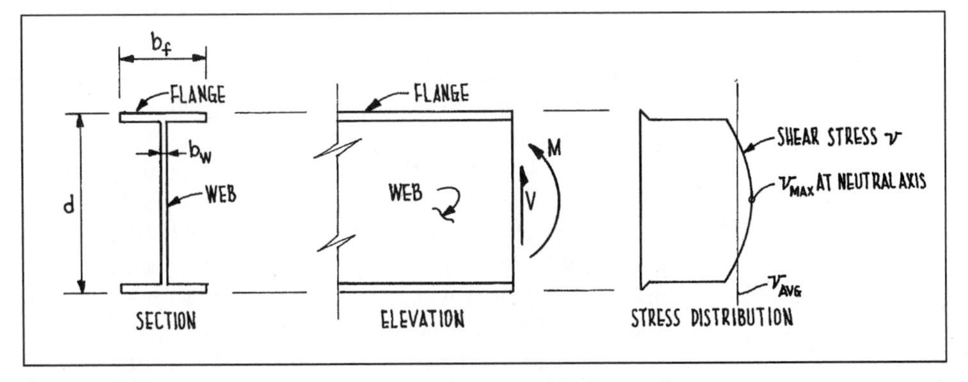

Figure 10-7 Shear stress distribution on a wide flange beam.

The jump in shear stress indicated in Figure 10-7 occurs when the width *b* jumps in Eq.(9-39) from the thin width of the web to the much wider width of the flange.

The computation of the shear stress at numerous levels along the height of the section is a somewhat tedious procedure. The value of $A'\bar{y}$ is of course different at each level, being maximum at the neutral axis. The calculation reveals, however, that the distribution of the shear stress along the web of the section is relatively "flat", varying but little from the average stress v_{AVG}, as indicated in Figure 10-7.

Over the years, it has been found that the average shear stress is an adequate indicator of shear stress in steel beams, and that it is not necessary to use Eq.(9-39) to find the actual maximum stress. The "average" stress on the section is found as the shear force *V* divided by the area of the web, where the web area is that shown in Figure 10-8. (Note that the web height in this approximate formula is taken as the *full height* of the section.)

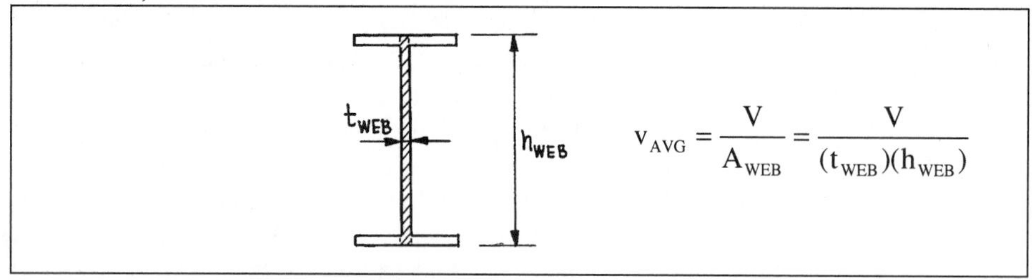

Figure 10-8 Average shear stress on a wide flange web.

The need to choose the lightest steel section suggests that a more ordered approach be developed than just searching the tables at random. The data given in Table S-18 in the Technical Manual provides one such ordered approach. The table lists selected wide flange beams arranged according to their weight. Listed in the table is the section modulus S_{xx} of each section, the maximum allowable spacing L_C along the compression flange for lateral support points, and the maximum allowable moment on A36 steel if these conditions are met.

The requirement to support the compression flange laterally comes as a direct result of the high stresses and the thin elements that are common to steel sections. The thin compression flange of the beam has a strong tendency to "roll" or to buckle under the compressive forces. The allowable stress which the member may safely sustain depends on having closely-spaced lateral supports along the compression flange. If lateral supports are provided no farther apart than the length L_C given in Table S-18, the allowable stress may be taken at 0.66 F_y; for ASTM A36 steel, this allowable stress is commonly taken at 24,000 lb/in^2.

To use Table S-18, simply compute the required section modulus from Eq.(10-3b). Enter Table S-18 with this number, starting with the smallest and lightest sections at the lower right-hand corner. Proceed upward along the S_{xx} column until the first member is reached that has a section modulus at least as large as that required. This member is the lightest member available that will sustain the given moment at the allowable stress of 24,000 lb/in^2.

Alternatively, Table S-18 may be entered with the maximum value of the design moment taken from the moment diagram. Again starting with the smallest sections at the lower right-hand corner, proceed upward along the M_C column until the first member is reached that will sustain this much moment (if properly braced on its compression flange). The member so selected is the lightest section that will sustain the design moment.

A third alternative is indicated in Table S-18 in the column headed by the load constant *WL*. This alternative is often used by builders, but is not commonly used by engineers. It has its widest usage in residential and light commercial timber structures, when a steel beam is occasionally used (instead of timber) to support a long span.

The load constant *WL* is computed by finding all dead and live load (in kips) tributary to the beam, then multiplying that value by the span *L* in feet; the result is the load constant $WL = wL^2$ for that beam. The table is then entered as usual, at the lower right corner. As one moves up the table, the first beam encountered that has a load constant WL at least as large as the required value is the lightest section that will carry that much load on that long a span, with lateral supports no farther apart than the distance L_C.

An example will illustrate the selection of a wide flange steel beam and the computation of the average shear stress to check for adequacy in shear.

Example 10-9

Selection of a wide flange beam section.

Given: The maximum moment from the moment diagram is 69 kip·ft. The maximum shear from the shear diagram is 33 kips. Allowable flexure stress is 24,000 lb/in.^{2} Allowable shear stress is 14,000 lb/in.^{2} ASTM A-36 steel, f_y = 36,000 lb/in.^{2}

To Find: Suitable wide flange section.

Solution: The required magnitude of the section modulus is computed for bending about the *xx* centroidal axis:

$$S_x = \frac{M}{f} = \frac{69{,}000(12)}{24{,}000} = 35 \text{ in.}^3$$

Table S-18 is entered with this value of section modulus.

For a section modulus of 35, the column S_{xx} indicates that a W14x26 is the lightest section that will sustain a moment of 69 kip·ft. This section is therefore selected as the trial section. If it is adequate in shear, it will be the final choice.

(It is again noted that the columns headed M_C in Table S-18 give the resisting moment M_C of all the listed sections at an allowable flexure stress of $0.66F_y$).

The section just chosen is now reviewed for shear. From Table S-1c, the overall depth of the W14x26 beam section is found to be 13.91 in. and the web thickness is found to be 0.255 inches. The average web shear stress is then:

$$v_{AVG} = \frac{V}{A_{WEB}} = \frac{33{,}000}{(0.255)(13.91)} = 9303 \text{ lb/in.}^2 < 14{,}000 \text{ (OK)}$$

Since this stress is well below the allowable stress of 14,000 lb/in.^{2}, the section is seen to be adequate both in flexure and in shear.

Several points arose in the foregoing example that warrant discussion. The designation ASTM A-36 used in the example for the type of steel is a specification for a particular kind of steel. ASTM is an abbreviation for the American Society for Testing and Materials, a private organization of manufacturers and industrial concerns. ASTM prepares thousands upon thousands of materials specifications and test procedures for all types of materials, including steel. Their designation A-36 is a specification for mild structural steel having a yield stress of 36,000 psi and an ultimate stress of 58,000 psi (see Figure 8-13).

ASTM A-36 steel is probably the most common structural steel in use in American practice, followed probably by ASTM A-441 for high-strength steel. The number 36 in the designation A-36 has nothing to do with the yield stress of 36,000 psi; it is a coincidence of numbers. For simplicity in presentation, all applications in this textbook are for ASTM A-36 steel.

The allowable flexural stress in steel used in the example is specified by AISC. It bears repeating that the allowable stress is dependent on the amount and type of lateral bracing that has been provided along the compression side of the beam. Under high stresses, the compression side of steel beams tries to "roll" laterally; the compression flange of the beam must be supported laterally along the length of the beam to prevent such "rolling" from occuring.

Where the compression flange is continuously supported (such as the lateral support provided by a floor), the allowable flexural stress is specified by the AISC design code at $0.66f_y$. For the sake of simplicity, all steel beams considered in this chapter will be assumed to be continuously supported. Other cases of lateral support are considered in later chapters on steel design. An allowable stress of $0.66f_y$ in A-36 steel is taken to be 24,000 psi.

Similarly, the allowable shear stress in steel is specified by the AISC design code at $0.4f_y$. An allowable shear stress of $0.4f_y$ in A-36 steel is taken to be 14,000 psi.

It was also stated in Example10-9 that the section modulus was chosen about the *xx* centroidal axis. In steel beam sections, the section will have a "strong" axis and a "weak" axis. In the beam section W14x26, for example, the section modulus about the *xx* axis is given in Table S-1c in the Technical Manual to be 35.3 and about the *yy* axis to be 3.54; the section is thus 10 times stronger in bending about its *xx* axis than about its *yy* axis. One must use care when using the tables to select from the correct columns of numbers.

The idea of "averaging" in steel sections carries into flexure as well as shear. Consider the wide flange section in Figure 10-9, for example, where the flexural stress distribution is shown alongside the section. It is evident that the greater part of the steel in the section has been concentrated at the top and bottom of the section where stresses are highest. The result is, of course, a more efficient section.

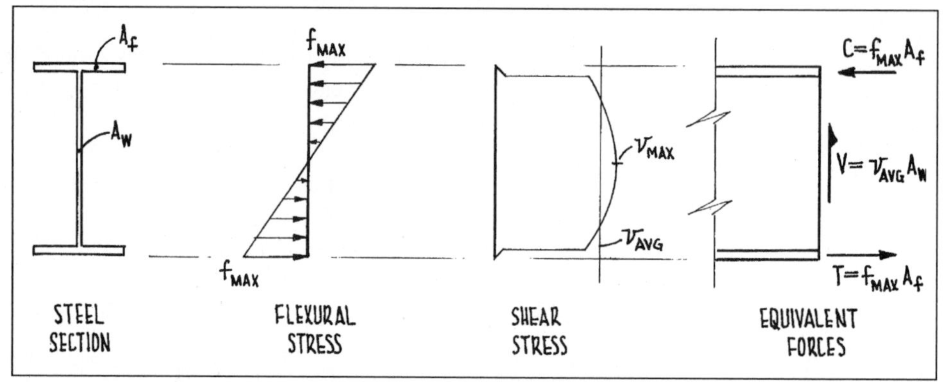

Figure 10-9 Equivalent forces in a wide flange section.

The forces developed in the two flanges form a couple that sustains the moment on the section; the amount of moment carried by the thin web is essentially negligible. The shear force, however, is carried almost entirely by the web; the amount of shear carried by the flanges is essentially negligible. The equivalent forces shown in Figure 10-9 thus present an accurate interpretation of the way that a wide flange beam carries its loads.

There are numerous steel sections other than wide flange sections. These other sections, such as channels, I's, tubing and angles, are deferred to the later chapters on steel design. Two shapes that warrant discussion here, however, are the circular pipe section and the structural tee section, simply because they are in such common use.

The dimensions and properties of circular pipe are given in Table S-8 in the Technical Manual. Note that there are three standard grades of steel pipe: standard, extra strong and double extra strong. One of the more appealing properties of pipe (and square tubing) is that there is no "weak" axis; the member has equal flexural strength in all directions. Also appealing is the property that circular pipe has no tendency to "roll" laterally under load.

Structural tees are widely used in construction falsework and formwork. Structural tees are made by cutting wide flange shapes in half. When the W14x26 section is cut into structural tees, for example, the designation of the tees becomes WT7x13. Structural tees are listed in Table S-5 in the Technical Manual. Note that there are two values of c for structural tees, as shown in Figure 10-10. In the tables, the value of c used to compute the section modulus S is the longer one, the one which yields maximum stress.

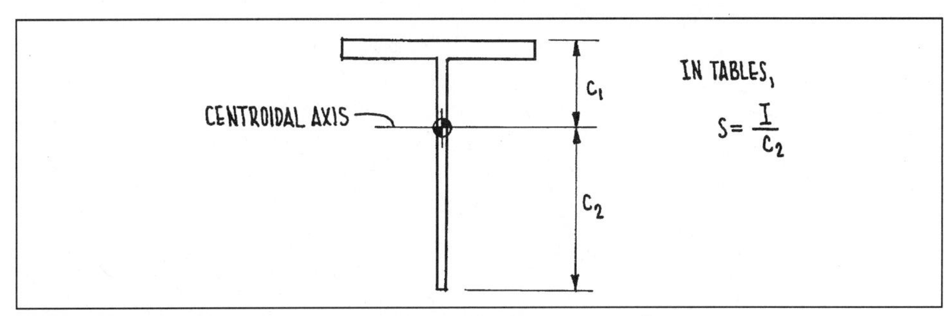

Figure 10-10 Maximum section modulus for structural tees.

Some examples will illustrate the selection of some steel sections.

Example 10-10

Selection of a wide flange beam section.

Given: Loading conditions of Example 10-1. ASTM A-36 steel. Fully laterally supported.

To Find: Suitable wide flange section.

Solution: The required magnitude of the section modulus is computed:

$$S = \frac{M}{f} = \frac{(90{,}000)(12)}{(0.66)(36{,}000)} = 45.5 \text{ in.}^3$$

From Table 10-2 and Table S-1b of the Technical Manual,

Try W16x31, $h = 15.88$ in., $t_{WEB} = 0.275$ in.

Review for shear:

$$v_{AVG} = \frac{V}{A_{WEB}} = \frac{5000}{(15.88)(0.275)}$$

$$= 1145 \text{ lb/in.}^2 \ll 0.4f_y \text{ (O.K.)}$$

Use W16x31.

Example 10-11

Selection of a pipe section in flexure.

Given: Load conditions of Example 10-3, ASTM A-36 steel.

To Find: Suitable pipe section, standard strength.

Solution: The required magnitude of the section modulus is computed:

$$S = \frac{M}{f} = \frac{72{,}000(12)}{(0.66)(36{,}000)} = 36.4 \text{ in.}^4$$

From Table S-8 in the Technical Manual,

Try pipe 12 in. diameter.

Review for shear. In this case, the idea of an "average" web stress is not applicable. The maximum shear stress is known to occur at the centroid so the maximum shear stress at the centroid will be found. The centroid of a half circle is at 4R/3π, as given in Table A-1 in the Technical Manual:

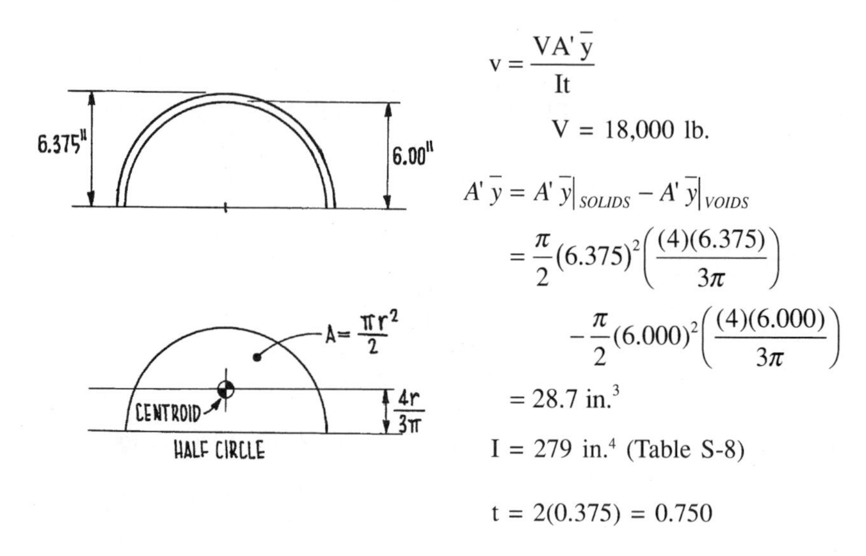

$$v = \frac{VA'\bar{y}}{It}$$

V = 18,000 lb.

$$A'\bar{y} = A'\bar{y}\big|_{SOLIDS} - A'\bar{y}\big|_{VOIDS}$$

$$= \frac{\pi}{2}(6.375)^2\left(\frac{(4)(6.375)}{3\pi}\right)$$

$$-\frac{\pi}{2}(6.000)^2\left(\frac{(4)(6.000)}{3\pi}\right)$$

$$= 28.7 \text{ in.}^3$$

I = 279 in.^{4} (Table S-8)

t = 2(0.375) = 0.750

$$v = \frac{(18{,}000)(28.7)}{(279)(0.75)}$$

$$= 2470 \text{ lb/in.}^2 << 0.4\, f_y \text{ (O.K.)}$$

Use standard pipe 12 in. diameter.

Example 10-12

Selection of a structural tee section.

Given: Load conditions of Example 10-5. ASTM A-36 steel. Fully laterally supported.

To Find: Suitable tee section.

Solution: The required magnitude of the section modulus is computed:

$$S = \frac{M}{f} = \frac{(75{,}000)(12)}{(0.66)(36{,}000)} = 37.9 \text{ in.}^3$$

In this case, there is no table conveniently listing the section modulus of structural tees as there is for wide flange beams. From Table S-5 for structural tees, one simply starts going up the tables of tees in the $S_{x\,x}$ column, beginning with the smallest sizes. When an adequate section is found, its size is noted. Among the available sections, choose the lightest one.

Try WT16.5x59.

Review for shear. In this case, the "average" web stress is again not applicable. The maximum web stress is known to occur at the centroid of the tee, so the maximum shear stress at the centroid will be found. In this case, it is easier to find A' $\bar{y}$ for the lower part of the tee than for the upper part:

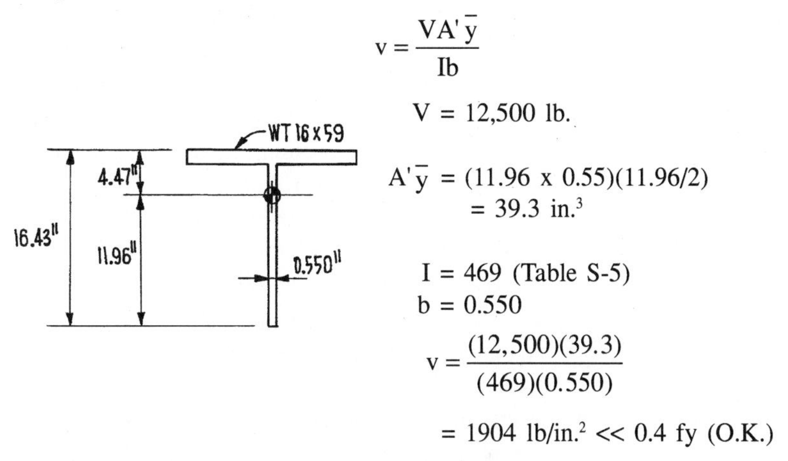

$$v = \frac{VA'\bar{y}}{Ib}$$

$V = 12{,}500$ lb.

$A'\bar{y} = (11.96 \text{ x } 0.55)(11.96/2)$
$= 39.3 \text{ in.}^3$

$I = 469$ (Table S-5)
$b = 0.550$

$$v = \frac{(12{,}500)(39.3)}{(469)(0.550)}$$

$= 1904 \text{ lb/in.}^2 << 0.4 \text{ fy}$ (O.K.)

At this point, it should be evident that steel is so strong in shear that shear stress is rarely a problem. In most cases of routine structures, the shear stress would not even be checked. Until the novice develops a "sense" of design for steel sections, however, it is recommended that the shear stress be checked.

Such a property is not true in timber, however, which is notoriously weak in shear. In fact, the most difficult problems to be overcome in the design of timber members will usually involve its capacity in shear. In the following discussions of timber beams, shear will always be a prominent item.

Comparable in purpose and scope to the American Institute of Steel Construction (AISC), the fabricators and manufacturers of timber products in the United States have joined together in a trade association called the American Institute of Timber Construction (AITC). The *Timber Construction Manual* published by AITC contains the design standards, design codes and corresponding allowable stresses recommended for use in more than 40 species of timber. The manual also includes authoritative guidelines in using timber as a structural material, as well as numerous design aids and recommended design procedures.

While there are more than 40 species of timber listed in the timber construction manual, the discussions in this textbook are limited to three of the most common varieties:

1) Douglas Fir-Larch
2) Southern Pine
3) Spruce-Pine-Fir

The limitation to these three species of timber is done only to simplify the discussions. The analysis of other species follow the same procedures used for these three species; the only difference is that the allowable stress levels (listed in the design tables) will be somewhat different.

All timber is visually graded within broad groupings of structural quality. At least 95% of the timber members produced by a sawmill or lumber manufacturer must be stamped, indicating its structural grade. It is these grades that appear in the tables of design values in the Technical Manual, such as Table T-3a, b, c.

Refer to Tables T-3a, band c in the Technical Manual for the following discussions. The various broad grades of structural quality are listed in the first column. Within a grade, the allowable stress can vary considerably, depending on the size of the member or the purpose for which it is being used. Typically, members 4 inches or less in their least dimension will have one set of allowable stresses while members 5 inches or more will have another.

The allowable stress in bending, F_b, is indicated in the first sets of values. For thicknesses of 4 in. or less, two allowable stress levels are indicated: one if the member is used essentially alone and the other if the member is used in closely spaced repetitive applications, such as joists. In the larger member sizes, 5 in. or more, the column under repetitive uses is usually omitted.

In addition to flexure, there are four other types of design stress which a timber member must be able to sustain:

1) Tension parallel to grain, F_t, which occurs in truss members or hangers, where the entire cross section is placed in tension.
2) Horizontal shear, F_V, or beam shear, which occurs as a result of flexure.
3) Compression parallel to grain, F_C, which occurs in truss members or columns, where the entire cross section is placed in compression.
4) Compression perpendicular to grain, $F_{c\perp}$, which occurs at beam supports.

The values listed in the tables indicate the allowable stresses to which the particular species may be subjected, within the particular size grouping and within the particular visual grade. Once the allowable stress is established, the design procedure for timber beams parallels that for steel:

1. Determine the maximum moment and shear to be sustained from the shear and moment diagrams.
2. Establish the allowable stress within the use and size classifications.
3. Compute the required magnitude of the section modulus, $S = M/F_b$.
4. Select a timber member having a section modulus at least as large as the computed value.
5. Review for shear.
6. Review for bearing at load points and at end supports.

The section modulus for timber sections is that for a rectangular section in flexure about its own centroidal xx axis:

$$S_x = \frac{I_{xx}}{c} = \frac{bh^3/12}{h/2} = \frac{bh^2}{6} \quad (10\text{-}4)$$

A problem arises, however, in that the actual size of b and h in a timber member is less than its nominal size. A member rough-sawn to dimensions 6x12, for example, is actually $5\frac{1}{2}$ x $11\frac{1}{2}$ after being dried and finished. Nonetheless, it is still called a 6x12.

There are rules for remembering the loss in dimensions in finished timber. It is far easier, however, (and surer) to use a table of properties such as those given in Table T-1 in the Technical Manual. Listed there for each nominal size is the dressed size, the actual area, the section modulus and moment of inertia.

Note, however, that a timber member can be used in either of two directions, with the long dimension vertical or the short dimension vertical. In the tables, a 6x12 used with the 12 in. dimension vertical would have a section modulus of 121.2 in.^{3} Used as a 12x6 with the 6 in. dimension vertical, the member would have a section modulus of 57.98, a significant difference.

Before proceeding into some examples, it is well to note in the design Tables 3a, b, and c, that the allowable shear stress in timber is typically quite low, usually less than 10% of the flexural stress. Further, the allowable shear stress does not vary significantly regardless of the grade. For southern pine, for example, the allowable shear stress typically ranges from 90 to 100 psi where the bending stress ranges from 800 psi to 1600 psi or even more. Very often in timber design, it is the allowable shear stress that is the limiting stress.

The beam of Figure 10-11 shows a typical shear crack in a rectangular timber beam. It will of course occur where shears are highest, usually at a support. And it will occur at the point of highest shear stress, at the centroidal axis. And it will occur in the weakest direction for shear which, in a timber member, is the horizontal direction.

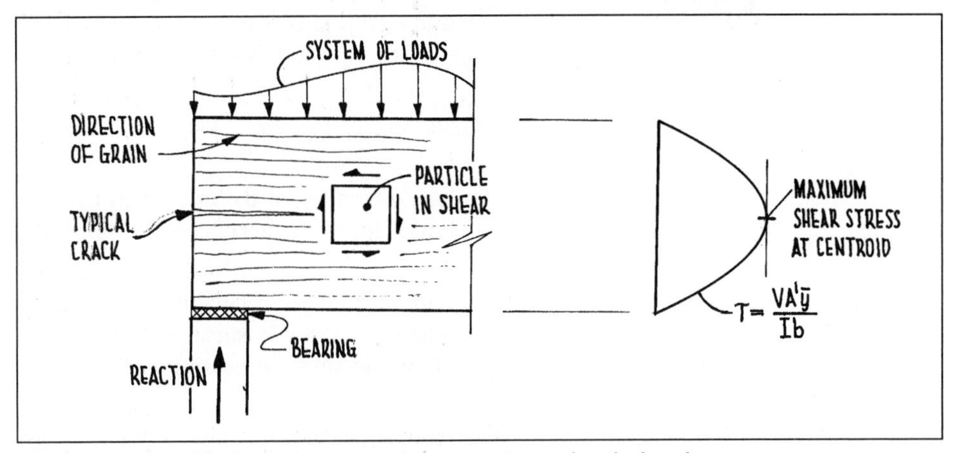

Figure 10-11 Typical shear crack in a rectangular timber beam.

In timber, essentially all sections are rectangular. The shear stress in the rectangular member can be found as a special case of the shear stress formula. As shown in Figure 10-12, the maximum shear stress occurs at the neutral axis.

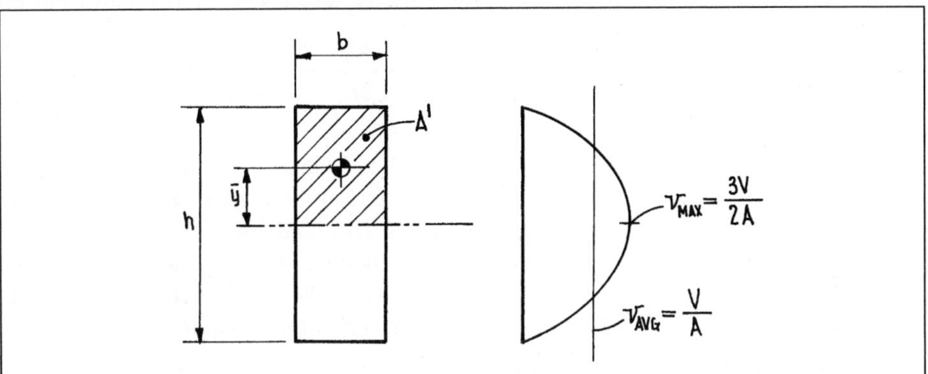

Figure 10-12 Special case of the shear stress formula.

For the beam of Figure 10-12:

$$v_{MAX} = \frac{VA'\bar{y}}{Ib},$$

$$\text{where } A'\bar{y} = \left(b\frac{h}{2}\right)\left(\frac{h}{4}\right)$$

$$I = \frac{bh^3}{12}$$

$$b = b$$

$$v_{MAX} = \frac{3V}{2A}. \qquad (10\text{-}5)$$

It is seen that the maximum shear stress in a rectangular cross-section is some 50% larger than the average stress. The simplified special formula given by Eq.(10-5) will prove useful in selecting timber sections.

Some examples will illustrate the selection of timber beams.

Example 10-13

Selection of a timber member in flexure.

Given: From the shear and moment diagrams, the maximum shear on a beam is found to be 5.0 kips at the end support. The maximum moment is found to be 20 kip·ft. The beam bears on a support 4 inches wide.

To Find: Suitable timber member. Douglas Fir-Larch, Commercial grade No. 2.

Solution: The least dimension of the member is assumed to be greater than 5 in. so the stresses for No. 2 timbers will be used. (Technical Manual, Table T-3a).

The allowable stress in bending is 875 psi.
The allowable stress in shear is 85 psi.
The allowable stress in bearing is 625 psi.

The required section modulus is found as usual:

$$S = \frac{M}{F_b} = \frac{(20,000)(12)}{875} = 274 \text{ in.}^3$$

The required area for shear is found from Eq.10-5:

$$A = \frac{3V}{2F_V} = \frac{(3)(5000)}{(2)(85)} = 88 \text{ in.}^2$$

Table T-1 is entered with these required values for section modulus and area. Starting at the lowest values with a small straightedge, move down the list of sizes until a section is found that has an area at least 88 in.^{2} and a section modulus at least 274 in.^{3} (The most economical section will be the one having the smallest cross-sectional area.) The first beam encountered that meets these requirements for size is the 6x18.

Try 6x18, actual width $5^1/_2$ in.

Review for bearing at the 5 kip reaction:

$$f_{c\perp} = \frac{P}{A} = \frac{5000}{(4)(5.5)} = 227 \text{ psi} < 625 \text{ psi (O.K.)}$$

The section is adequate for bending, shear and bearing. No other section is found that has a smaller area.

Use 6x18 section.

Example 10-14

Selection of a timber member in flexure.

Given: From the shear and moment diagrams, the maximum shear on a beam occurs at the support and is found to be 6.25 kips. The maximum moment is found to be 11 kip·ft. The beam bears on a steel support $1^1/_2$ in. wide.

To Find: Suitable timber member. Southern Pine, commercial grade No. 2.

Solution: The member is assumed to be larger than 5 in.
From Technical Manual Table T-3b for No. 2 timbers,
the allowable bending stress is 850 psi;
the allowable shear stress is 100 psi;
the allowable bearing stress is 375 psi.

The required section modulus is found as usual:

$$S = \frac{M}{F_b} = \frac{(11{,}000)(12)}{850} = 155\ in.^3$$

The required area is found from Eq.10-5:

$$A = \frac{3V}{2F_v} = \frac{(3)(6250)}{(2)(100)} = 94\ \text{in.}^2$$

From Table T-1 it is seen that sections having very large (and inefficient) values of S must be used in order to get enough area. Such is often the case.

Try 6x18, bearing width 5.5 in.

Check for end bearing:

$$f_{c\perp} = \frac{P}{A} = \frac{6250}{(1.50)(5.5)} = 758\ \text{psi} > 375\ \text{(N.G.)}$$

The section is inadequate for bearing. It is noted, however, that a section could be turned the other way, with the short dimension vertical. A 12x10 section in this position is seen to be adequate both in shear and flexure. Its bearing width in this position becomes 11.5 in.

Check for end bearing with the beam in this orientation:

$$f_{c\perp} = \frac{P}{A} = \frac{6250}{(1.50)(11.5)} = 360\ \text{psi} < 375\ \text{(O.K.)}$$

Use 12x10 section, short dimension vertical.

A more complete treatment of both steel and timber beams is presented in later chapters. Reinforced concrete beams are also included there; the approach to reinforced concrete will be seen to be somewhat different than that for steel and timber.

10.4 Euler Columns and Radius of Gyration

Columns can fail in either of two ways: buckling or crushing. Long slender columns will buckle laterally before the material is crushed, while short heavy columns (pedestals) will be crushed before buckling can occur. Intermediate length columns fail by a mixture of the two mechanisms. The three types of columns are shown in Figure 10-13.

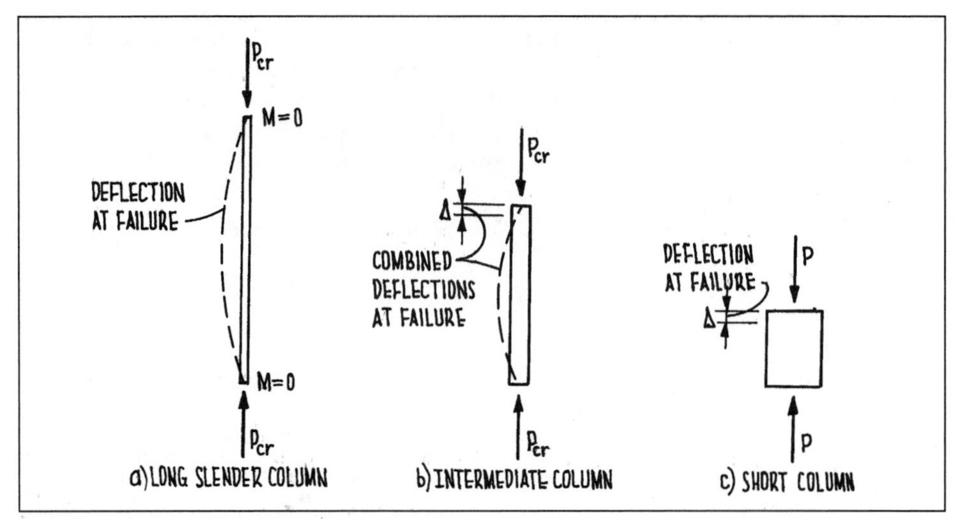

Figure 10-13 Types of column failure.

The type of failure that is of interest here is that of buckling, which occurs in long, slender columns. The type of failure indicated in Figure 10-13a for long columns is an elastic failure; the material itself has not yielded, nor has it failed. This type of elastic buckling is easy to demonstrate, simply by loading a yardstick axially until it buckles under the load. As a column, the yardstick has failed, yet if the load is released, the yardstick will return to its original position, undamaged.

Pursuing the idea of the yardstick, one notes that there are two axes of bending, one much weaker than the other. If the yardstick is braced at its midpoint on its weak axis only, it will buckle under a higher load, but this time it will buckle in the double curve shown in Figure 10-14b. Similarly, if it is braced at the third points on its weak axis only, it will buckle under a yet higher load, but in the triple curve shown in Figure 10-14c.

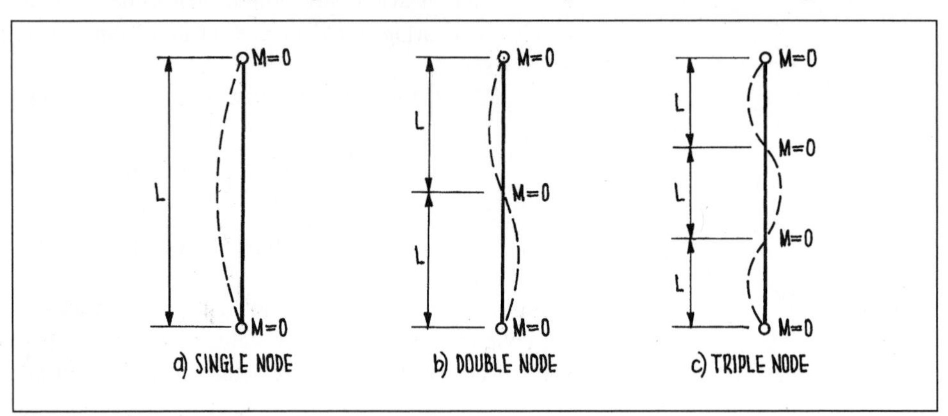

Figure 10-14 Column buckling nodes.

If the yardstick continues to be braced at shorter and shorter intervals, but only on its weak axis, the column loads will eventually become so high that the yardstick will either buckle on its other axis (which was not braced), or it will eventually undergo some sort of crushing failure.

Note especially in Figure 10-14 that the deflection curve at the buckling load always has zero moment at the ends. The length L is always measured from point of zero moment to point of zero moment. These points where the curvature changes direction are called *points of inflection* or *points of contraflexure*.

The critical load at which buckling impends on a long column is given by the well known Euler column formula:

$$P_{cr} = \frac{\pi^2 EI}{L^2} \tag{10-6}$$

where P_{cr} is the critical load at which buckling impends.
E is the modulus of elasticity of the material.
I is the moment of inertia about the axis of bending.
L is the length between adjacent points of zero moment.

The form of Eq.(10-6) is in terms of load. It is oftentimes preferable to express the Euler column formula in terms of the critical stress. The critical stress at which buckling impends is found by dividing both sides of Eq.(10-6) by the cross-sectional area A, yielding:

$$\sigma_{cr} = \frac{\pi^2 E}{(L/r)^2} \tag{10-7}$$

where σ_{cr} is the critical axial stress at which buckling impends.

$r = \sqrt{I/A}$ about the axis of bending.

The symbol r is called the *radius of gyration*. It is an artificial number, computed simply as $\sqrt{I/A}$. It is directional, in that it corresponds to whichever axis the column buckles about. There will, of course, be two values of the radius of gyration for any section, one usually being much smaller than the other. (See the two columns listed r in Figure 10-6; they give the radii of gyration about the two axes of bending.)

The term L/r in Eq.(10-7) is called the *slenderness ratio* of the column. It is a significant and reliable indicator of a column's susceptibility to buckling. It appears in one form or another in all empirical (experimentally derived) column formulas developed for intermediate columns. Note that it is squared in Eq.(10-7); if the slenderness ratio is doubled, the critical stress at buckling is reduced to one fourth its previous value.

End conditions other than hinges can be accommodated in the Euler column formula. Some typical end conditions are shown in Figure 10-15. In each case, the length L to be used in the Euler column formula is the length between adjacent points of zero moment.

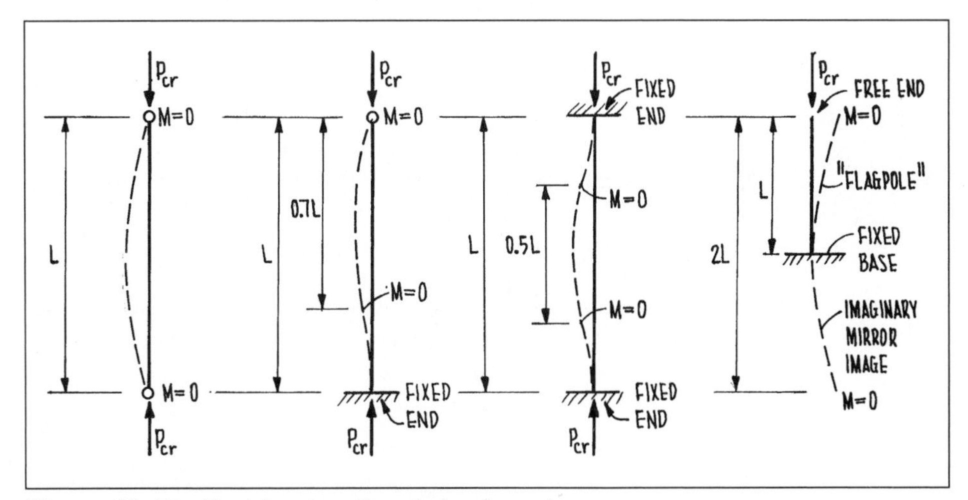

Figure 10-15 Buckling lengths of slender columns.

Some examples will illustrate some uses of the Euler column formula.

Example 10-15

Critical buckling load on long columns.

Given: Steel column W10x49, hinged both ends, 40'-0" long.

To Find: 1) Axial load as buckling impends.
2) Stress as buckling impends.

Solution: Critical load is given by the Euler column formula:

$$P_{cr} = \frac{\pi^2 EI}{L^2}$$

Buckling will occur on the weaker of the two axes. The lesser value of I is found from Table S-1e to be 93.4 in.^{4} Length is the distance between points of zero moment:

$$P_{cr} = \frac{(\pi^2)(29x10^6)(93.4)}{(40x12)^2} = 116\ kips$$

The stress as buckling impends is the direct axial stress. The cross-sectional area is found from Table S-1e to be 14.4 in.^{2}

$$\sigma_{cr} = \frac{P_{cr}}{A} = \frac{116{,}000}{14.4} = 8060\ lb/in.^2$$

Example 10-16

Critical buckling load on long columns.

Given: Column and conditions of Example 10-15. Bracing provided at midpoint in weak direction only.

To Find: 1) Axial load as buckling impends.
2) Stress as buckling impends.

Solution: Critical load is given by the Euler formula:

$$P_{cr} = \frac{\pi^2 EI}{L^2}$$

Buckling on the weak axis will now occur over length of 20 ft as shown:

$$P_{cr} = \frac{(\pi^2)(29x10^6)(93.4)}{(20x12)^2}$$
$$= 464 \text{ kips}$$

$$\sigma_{cr} = \frac{P_{cr}}{A} = \frac{464{,}000}{14.4}$$
$$= 32{,}200 \text{ lb / in.}^2$$

Buckling on the other axis could also occur, for which the length between points of zero moment remains 40 ft.

On the strong axis, I is found from Table S-1e to be 272 in.[4]:

$$P_{cr} = \frac{\pi^2 EI}{L^2} = \frac{(\pi^2)(29x10^6)(272)}{(40x12)^2} = 333\ kips$$

This value is seen to be less than the critical load of 44 kips on the braced axis. Buckling will therefore occur on this axis first. The stress as buckling impends is then:

$$\sigma_{cr} = \frac{P_{cr}}{A} = \frac{338,000}{14.4} = 23,500 lb/in.^2$$

Example 10-17

Critical buckling load on long columns.

Given: Steel column, W12x58, fixed at one end, hinged at the other. Unsupported length 36'-0".

To Find: 1) Critical buckling load.
2) Stress as buckling impends.

Solution: Length between points of zero moment is shown in the following sketch.

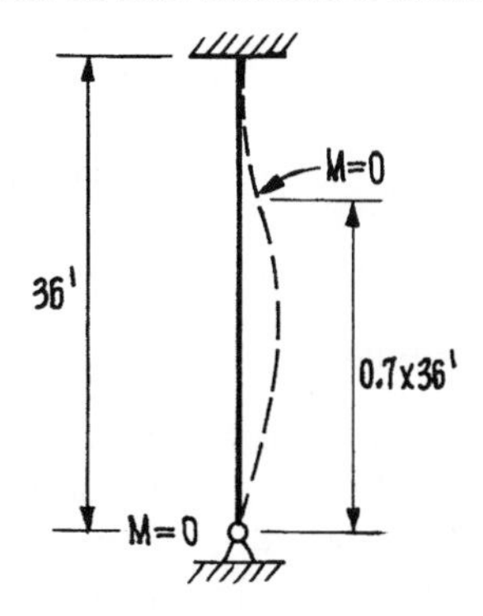

Critical load is given by the Euler column formula the moment of inertia on the weak axis is found from Table S-1d to be 107 in.[4]:

$$P_{cr} = \frac{\pi^2 EI}{L^2} = \frac{(\pi^2)(29x10^6)(107)}{(0.7x36x12)^2} = 335 kips$$

The stress on the cross section as buckling impends is the direct axial stress. The cross-sectional area is found from Table S-1d to be 17.0 in.[2]:

$$\sigma_{cr} = \frac{P_{cr}}{A} = \frac{335,000}{17} = 19,700 lb/in.^2$$

Example 10-18

Critical buckling load on long columns.

Given: Standard steel pipe column, 8 in. diameter, fixed both ends. Unsupported length 42'-0". ASTM A-36 steel.

To Find: Whether column material will yield before the column buckles.

Solution: The length between points of zero moment is shown in the following sketch.

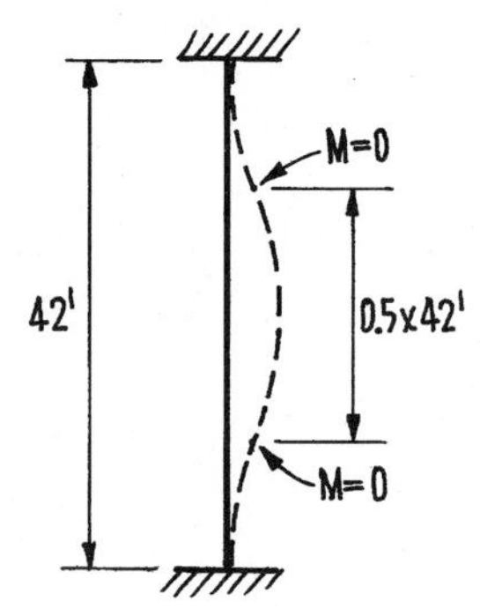

The column will buckle when the cross-sectional stress reaches its critical level. Minimum radius of gyration is found from Table S-8 to be 2.94 in.

$$\sigma_{cr} = \frac{\pi^2 E}{(L/r)^2} = \frac{\pi^2(29x10^6)}{[(0.5)(42)(12/2.94)]^2}$$

$$= 38{,}960 \text{ lb/in.}^2 > 36{,}000 \text{ lb/in.}^2$$

Since the yield stress in ASTM A-36 steel is 36,000 psi, the material will reach its yield point before the column reaches its critical buckling stress.

It is concluded that yield will occur before the column buckles.

Review Questions

1. What is a shear diagram? A moment diagram?
2. Why are shear and moment diagrams necessary in beam design?
3. How is the shear at a section computed?
4. How is the moment at a section computed?
5. What does it mean when it is said that the shear diagram "closes"?
6. What does it mean when it is said that the moment diagram "closes"?
7. What produces the discontinuities in shear and moment diagrams?
8. Define the "slope" of the moment diagram.
9. How does one quickly determine the slope of the moment diagram at any point?
10. How does a concentrated load appear in the moment diagram?
11. How does a concentrated moment appear in the shear diagram?
12. How is the change in shear computed between to points along the axis of a beam?
13. How is the change in moment computed between two points along the axis of a beam?
14. What happens to the moment diagram where shear is zero?
15. What critical bits of information in beam design are found from the shear and moment diagrams?
16. What is the "steel handbook"?
17. A beam is designated W8x31. What does each of these letters and numbers mean?
18. What is a section moduus?
19. Where is flexural stress maximum on a beam section?
20. Where is flexural stress minimum on a beam section?
21. Where is shear stress maximum on a beam section?

22. Where is shear stress minimum on a beam section?
23. Why is it possible to use an average shear stress on a wide flange beam rather than use the actual maximum shear stress?
24. In using the average shear stress on a wide flange beam, how is the area of the web computed?
25. What is the yield stress of ASTM A-36 steel?
26. If a beam made of A-36 steel is continuously supported along its compression flange, what is the allowable flexural stress in the material?
27. In steel beams, why is it necessary to support the compression flange laterally?
28. What is the allowable beam shear stress in ASTM A-36 steel?
29. Why is a steel beam shaped like it is, with the major part of the material lumped at the outer edges?
30. How is the section modulus of a structural tee computed, when it has two values of c ?
31. What are the five types of allowable stress in timber that are specified by AITC?
32. State the special formula for calculating the section modulus of a rectangular section.
33. State the special formula for calculating the maximum shear stress in a rectangular section.
34. Why doesn't a timber member that is designated 4x6 have dimensions 4 inches by 6 inches?
35. Why is a timber beam so likely to crack horizontally at midheight of the section at an end support?
36. State the Euler column formula and define each symbol.
37. What is radius of gyration? How is it computed?
38. How does one determine the strong axis and weak axis of a column section?
39. How is buckling length of a column determined for use in the Euler column formula?
40. What is the slenderness ratio? Why is it so important?
41. What is a point of inflection in a beam?
42. What is a point of inflection in a column?

CHAPTER

11

STATE OF STRESS AT A POINT

To this point, only one type of stress has been considered at a time. Flexural stress was considered by itself, for example, even though it was acknowledged that the existence of flexure stress creates shear stress. It is the purpose of this chapter to look at combinations of stress when shear, flexural stress and axial stress all occur at a point at the same time.

11.1 Combined Orthogonal Stresses

The bar of Figure 11-1 is subject both to flexure and to torsion. Particle A at the top of the bar is therefore subject to a torsional stress plus a tensile flexural stress as shown. Particle B at the bottom of the bar is subject to the same torsional stress, but in this case the flexural stress is in compression.

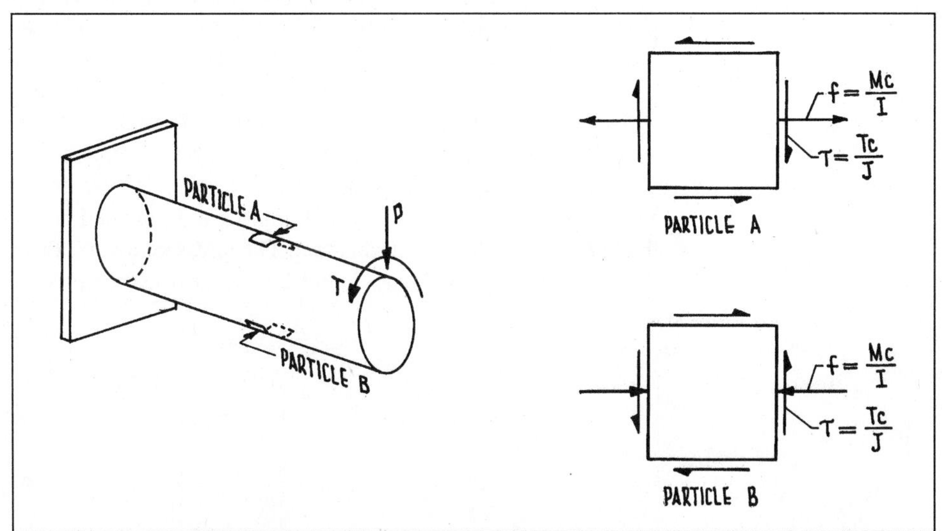

Figure 11-1 Combined stress on a particle.

The existence of these combined stresses suggests that at some angle other than the x and y axes shown, the state of stress may be significantly different. The existence of axial stress in one direction, for example, could (and does) create shear stress at some other angle. Such a phenomenon will be used to explain why a clay soil subject only to a foundation bearing stress will in fact fail in shear at some angle away from the contact surface. It will also be used to explain why a concrete beam subject to a vertical shear at its supports will actually fail in tension at some angle away from vertical. Combined stresses will be seen to have far-reaching ramifications in many areas.

11.2 General State of Stress at a Point

A general state of stress on a particle is shown in Figure 11-2. The particle is small, in order that there will be no variation in stress across the particle; the stresses on one side of the particle are identical to those on the other side. Note that all stresses are shown in their positive sense. (It is convenient to think of shear stress as positive if the stresses on the x axis form a clockwise couple.) The angle θ from the x face to the n-face is positive if it is measured counterclockwise from x face to n face. Note that θ can be measured either face-to-face or axis-to-axis.

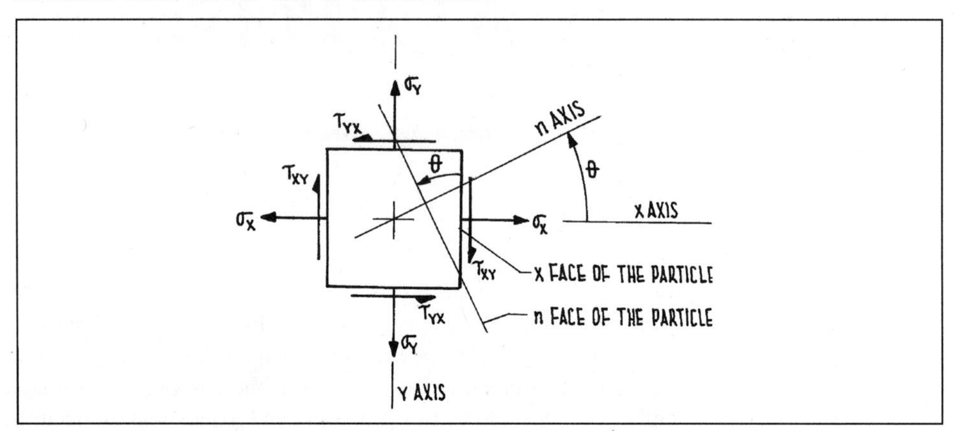

Figure 11-2 Defining state of stress.

Note also that the x face is normal to the x axis, the y face is normal to the y axis and the n face is normal to the n axis. The distinction becomes important in subsequent applications.

The shear stress τ_{xy} is read "shear stress on the x face in the y direction" and τ_{yx} is the "shear stress on the y face in the x direction." The difference is only academic since their magnitudes are equal. The axial stresses σ_x and σ_y are positive if in tension, negative if in compression. Shear stress is positive if the left side moves up with respect to the right, or if the shear stresses on the x axis form a clockwise couple.

Remember that the stresses σ_x, σ_y, τ_{xy} and τ_{yx} have been computed on the x and y faces using the flexure formula, the torsion formula or the shear formula. The purpose here, however, is to find the stresses they produce on some other face such as the n face.

The stresses on the n face at some angle θ from the x face are shown in Figure 11-3. The stresses exposed at that angle are designated σ_n and τ_n. It is assumed that the thickness of the particle is constant. The stressed area on the hypotenuse is designated A; the other stressed areas are found by simple trigonometry.

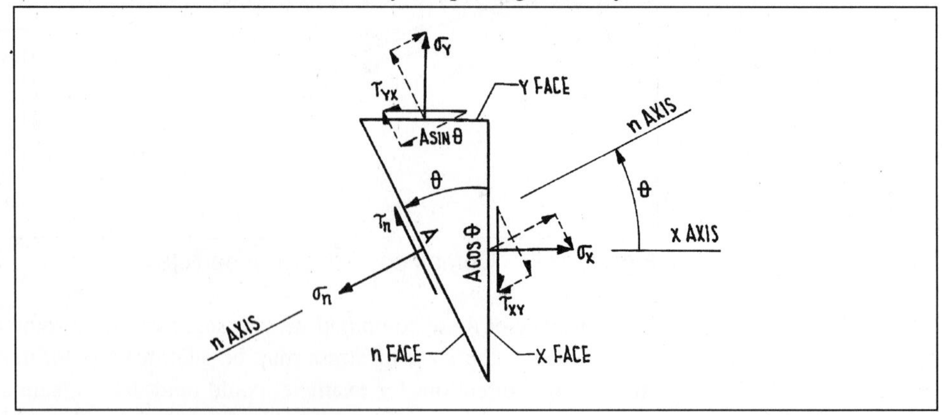

Figure 11-3 Stresses at the n face.

The forces parallel to σ_n are summed:

$$-\sigma_n(A)-\tau_{yx}\cos\theta(A\sin\theta)+\sigma_y\sin\theta(A\sin\theta)$$
$$+\sigma_x\cos\theta(A\cos\theta)-\tau_{xy}\sin\theta(A\cos\theta)=0$$

Forces parallel to τ_n are summed:

$$\tau_n(A)+\tau_{yx}\sin\theta(A\sin\theta)+\tau_y\cos\theta\,(A\sin\theta)$$
$$-\sigma_x\sin\theta\,(A\cos\theta)-\tau_{xy}\cos\theta\,(A\cos\theta)=0$$

The area A in these equations cancel out, indicating that the state of stress is true regardless of the size of the particle. The two equations are now solved for σ_n and τ_n, with $\tau_{xy} = \tau_{yx}$:

$$\sigma_n = \sigma_x\cos^2\theta - \tau_{xy}(2\sin\theta\cos\theta) + \sigma y\sin^2\theta \qquad (11\text{-}2a)$$
$$\tau_n = \sigma_x\sin\theta\cos\theta + \tau_{xy}(\cos^2\theta - \sin^2\theta) - \tau_y\sin\theta\cos\theta \qquad (11\text{-}3b)$$

The trigonometric identities for double angles are now recalled:

$$\cos^2\theta = {}^1/_2(1+\cos 2\theta) \qquad \sin^2\theta = {}^1/_2(1-\cos 2\theta) \qquad \sin\theta\cos\theta = {}^1/_2\sin 2\theta$$

When these values are substituted, the solution for σ_n and τ_n becomes:

$$\sigma_n = {}^1/_2(\sigma_x+\sigma_y) + {}^1/_2(\sigma_x-\sigma_y)\cos 2\theta - \tau_{xy}\sin 2\theta \qquad (11\text{-}3a)$$
$$\tau_n = {}^1/_2(\sigma_x-\sigma_y)\sin 2\theta + \tau_{xy}\cos 2\theta \qquad (11\text{-}3b)$$

Equations 11-3 afford a direct means to compute stresses at some angle other than that at which the stresses σ_x, σ_y and τ_{xy} have been computed. Note, however, that they have been derived using a very rigid set of algebraic signs, directions and faces; the calculations must conform to those constraints. Some examples will demonstrate the use of the equations.

Example 11-1

State of stress at a point.

Given: Computed normal and shear stresses as shown.

To Find: Stresses on the n face at 45°.

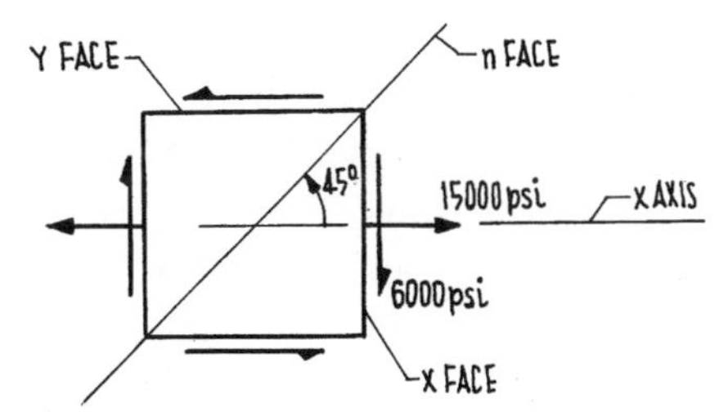

Solution: The angle as shown is improper for use in the equations; it is shown from the x axis to the n face. The particle is redrawn, showing the angle measured from face-to-face or axis-to-axis.

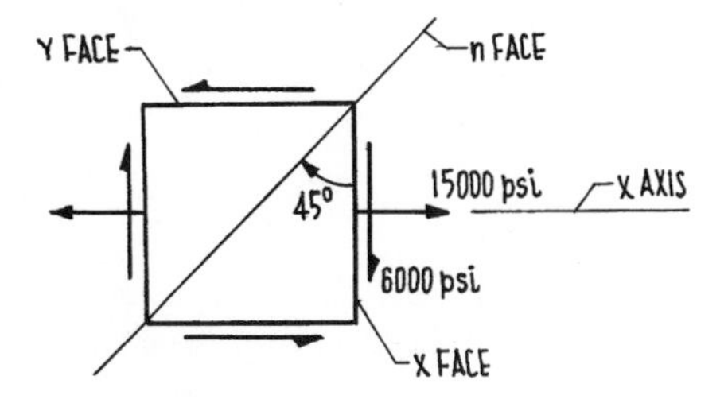

The angle θ when measured from x face to the n face (or the x axis to the n axis) is seen to be clockwise, so θ = -45°. The normal stress on the n face is found from Eq.(11-3a):

$$\sigma_n = \tfrac{1}{2}(15{,}000 + 0) + \tfrac{1}{2}(19{,}000 - 0)\cos(-90)$$
$$-6{,}000 \sin(-90)$$
$$= +13{,}500 \text{ psi.}$$

The shear stress on the n face is found from Eq.(11-3b), again with σ = -45°:

$$\tau_n = \tfrac{1}{2}(15{,}000 - 0)\sin(-90) + 6{,}000\cos(-90) = -7.500 \text{ psi.}$$

The stressed subparticle is shown in the following sketch.

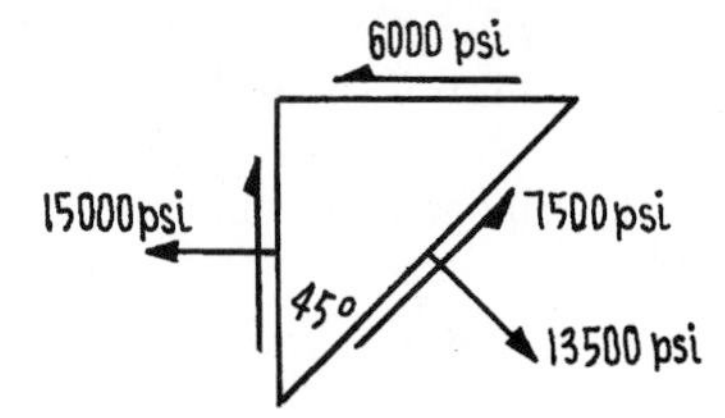

It is interesting to note that the shear stress on the n face is markedly larger than on the x and y faces, while the normal stress is smaller.

Example 11-2

State of stress at a point.

Given: Computed normal and shear stresses at a point as shown.

To Find: Stresses on the n face at 45° clockwise from horizontal.

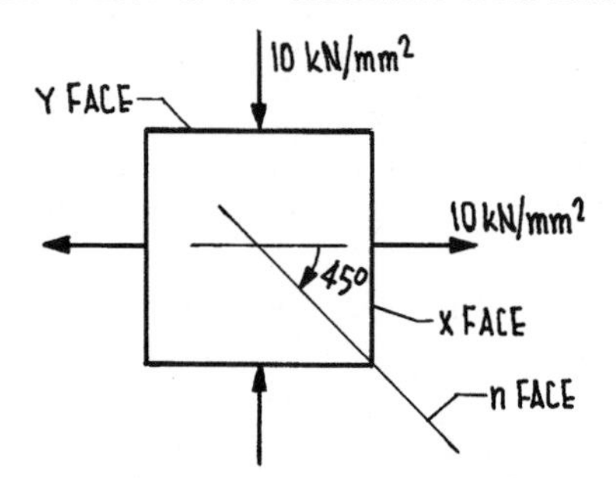

Solution: The angle is shown improperly for use in Eqs.(11-3). The particle is redrawn with the angle measured from the x face to the n face.

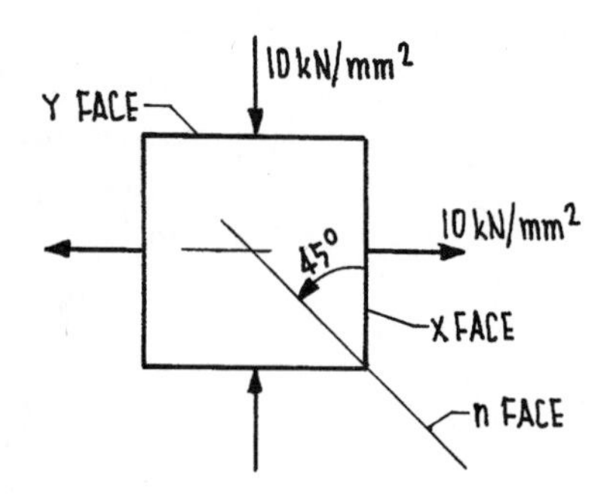

The angle θ when measured from the x face to the n face is seen to be +45°. The normal stress on the n face is found from Eq.(11-3a):

$$\sigma_n = \tfrac{1}{2}[10 + (-10)] + \tfrac{1}{2}[10 - (-10)] \cos(90) - (0)\sin(90)$$
$$= 0$$

The shear stress on the n face is found by Eq.(11-3b):

$$\sigma_n = \tfrac{1}{2}[10 - (-10)] \sin(90) + (0)\cos(90) = +10 \text{ n/mm}^2.$$

The stressed subparticle is shown in the following sketch.

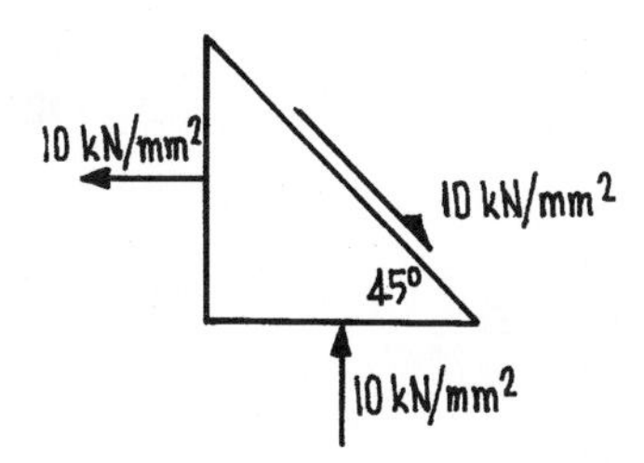

This rather surprising result indicates that a particle having no computed shear stress on its x and y axes can have significant shear stress on another plane.

While investigations such as those of Examples 11-1 and 11-2 may be interesting, such random investigations serve little purpose. It is usually the maximum stresses that are of interest, not the stresses at some arbitrary angle. Equations 11-3a and b can provide such a solution if they are put into a different form.

11.3 Mohr's Stress Circle for Combined Stresses

Equations(11-3) are rearranged and squared to obtain:

$$[\sigma_n - \tfrac{1}{2}(\sigma_x + \sigma_y)]^2 = [\tfrac{1}{2}(\sigma_x - \sigma_y \cos 2\theta - \tau_{xy} \sin 2\theta]^2 \qquad (11\text{-}4a)$$
$$\tau_n^2 = [\tfrac{1}{2}(\sigma_x - \sigma_y) \sin 2\theta + \tau_{xy} \cos 2\theta]^2 \qquad (11\text{-}4b)$$

The bracketed terms on the right are expanded and the two equations are summed to find:

$$[\sigma_n - \tfrac{1}{2}(\sigma_x + \sigma_y)]^2 + \tau_n^2 = [\tfrac{1}{2}(\sigma_x - \sigma_y)]^2 + \tau_{xy}^2 \qquad (11\text{-}5)$$

Equation (11-5) is recognized from analytic geometry as the equation of a circle, having the form:

$$(x - h)^2 + y^2 = R^2$$

where the axes of the circle are the stresses σ_n and τ_n. The center of the circle is seen to lie on the σ_n axis at a distance $\tfrac{1}{2}(\sigma_x + \sigma_y)$ from the origin. Its radius is given by:

$$\sqrt{[(\tfrac{1}{2})(\sigma_x - \sigma_y)]^2 + \tau_{xy}^2}.$$

The stress circle defined by Eq.(11-5) was developed by Professor Otto Mohr in Germany about 1850; it is called Mohr's circle. It provides a convenient graphic means to solve for the state of stress at a point. A very important point to remember in using Mohr's circle is that the angle θ on the particle becomes 2θ in the circle.

A plot of Mohr's circle is shown in Figure 11-4, along with a sketch of the particle from which it was drawn.

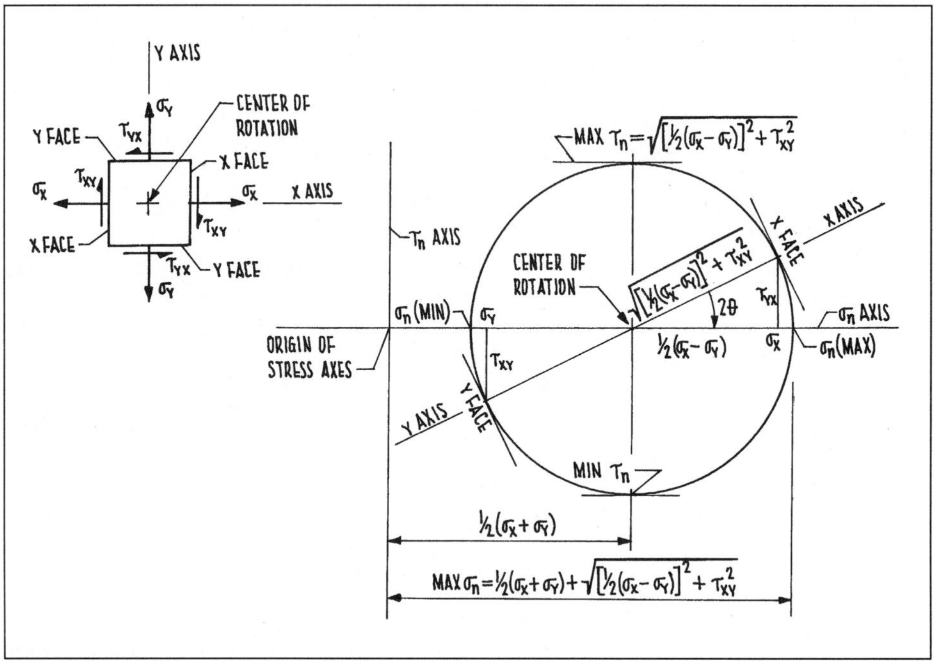

Figure 11-4 Mohr's stress circle.

In its algebraic form, as shown in Figure 11-4, the circle appears complicated. It can be constructed from numerical data quite simply, however. An example will demonstrate the procedure.

Example 11-3

Sketch of Mohr's stress circle.

Given: Computed state of stress at a point as shown.

To Find: Completed Mohr's stress circle from this state of stress.

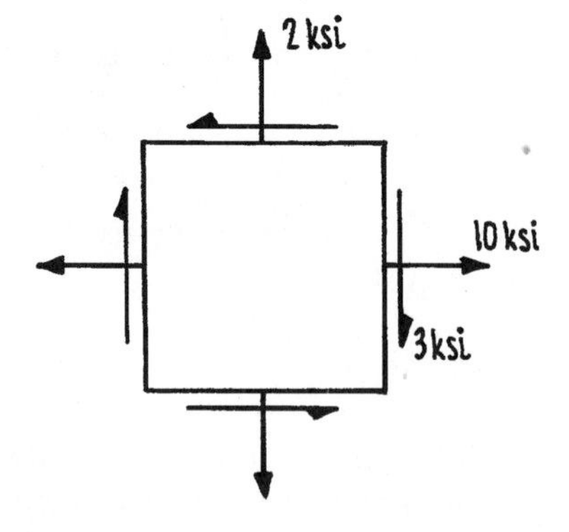

Solution: For the sake of illustration, separate sketches will be used to show the step-by-step procedure.

Step 1: Lay out the σ_n and τ_n axes to a convenient scale.

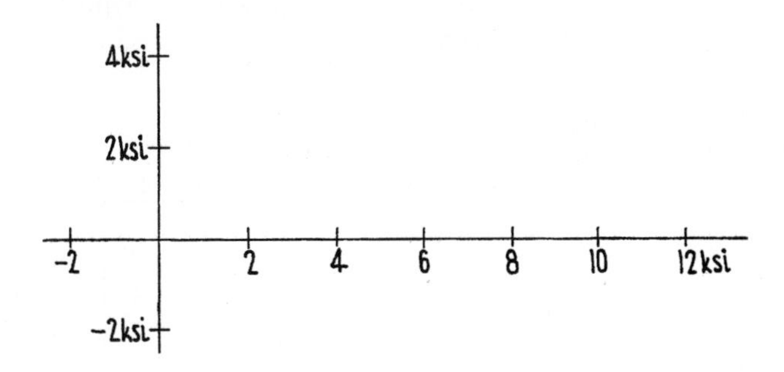

Step 2: Plot the stresses on the x face with their correct signs and label them.

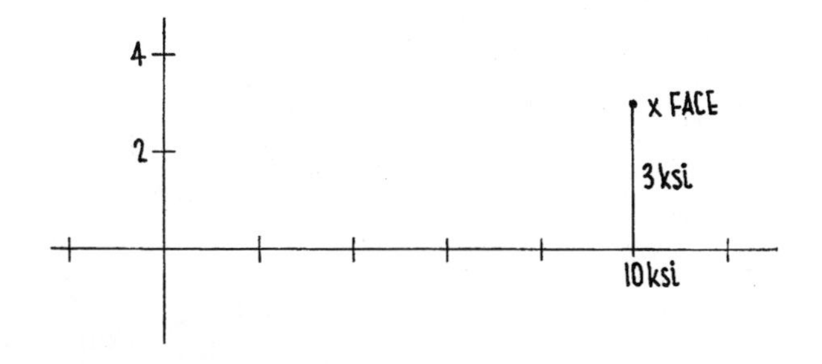

Step 3: Plot the stresses on the y face with their correct signs and label them. (The shear on the y face is always plotted in the opposite direction to the shear on the x face.)

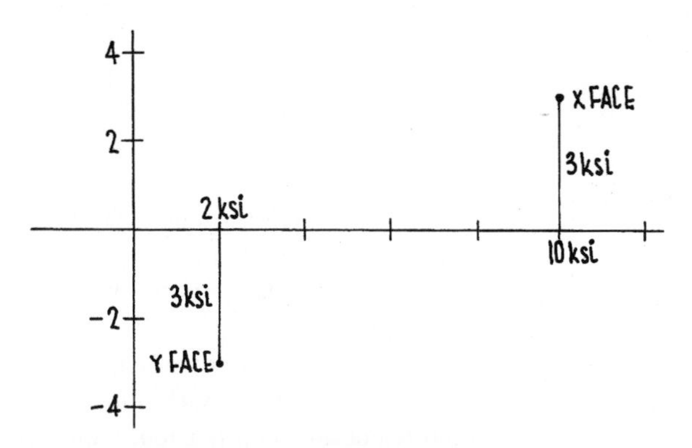

Step 4: Connect the two points, thus creating a diameter of Mohr's circle. Enter the stress at the center of the circle (the average of σ_x and σ_y).

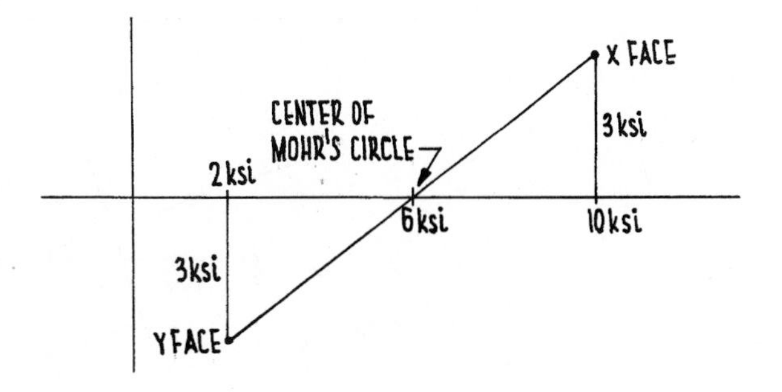

Step 5: Enter the size of the legs of the triangle adjacent to the x face, including the hypotenuse.

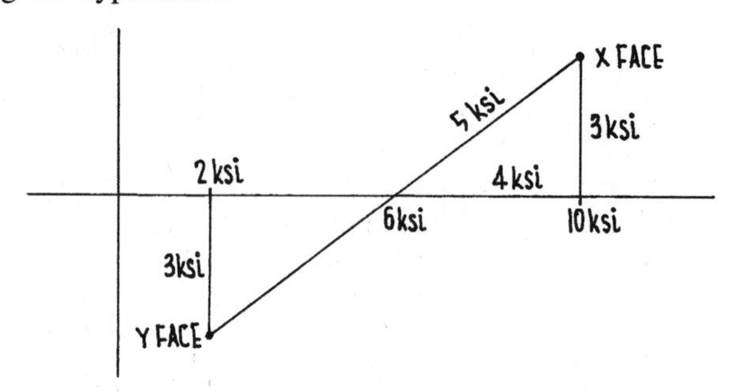

Step 6: Draw the circle. Enter maximum and minimum values of σ_n and τ_n. Compute and enter the angles.

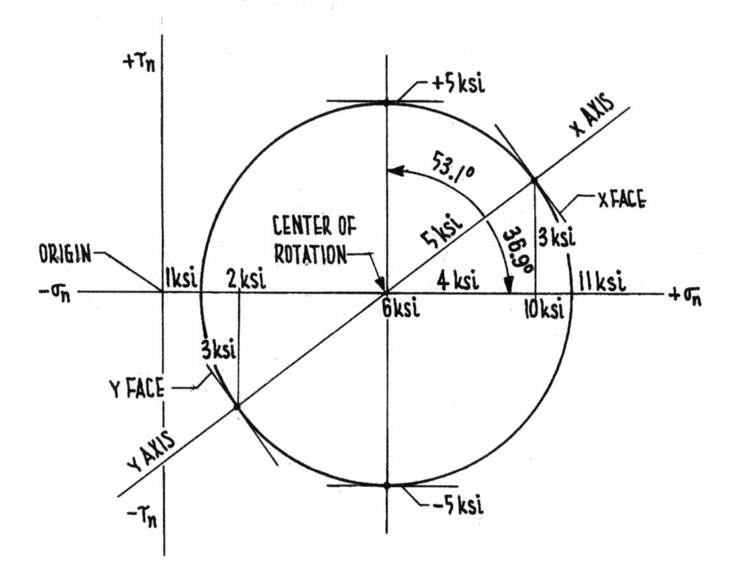

The Mohr's circle just sketched defines every state of stress that can exist at any angle (any n face) within this particular particle. The two states of stress that are of most interest are of course those that contain the maximum stresses. Those are readily found from the circle.

If the diameter containing the x and y faces is rotated 36.9° clockwise on the circle (the particle rotates 18.45° clockwise), the new stress on the x face will be at its maximum value of 11ksi tension, with zero shear. On the y face, the new stress will be at its minimum value of 1 ksi tension. with zero shear. This state of maximum and minimum normal stresses with zero shear is called the "principal" state of stress. The principal state of stress for the particle of Example 11-3 is shown in Figure 11-5.

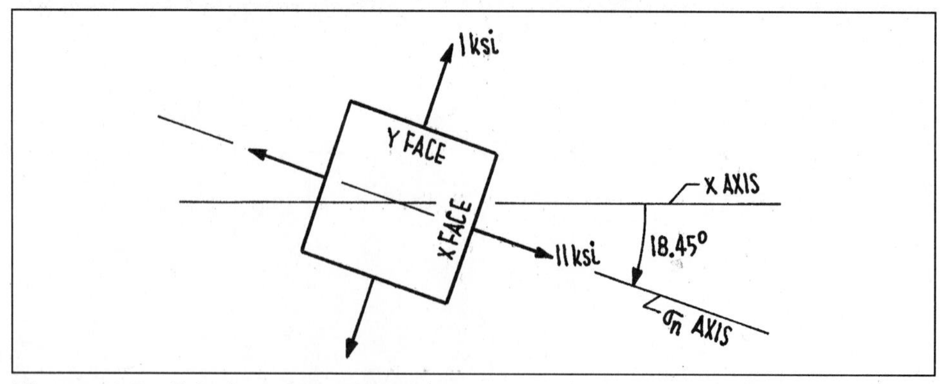

Figure 11-5 Principal state of stress.

The other case of maximum stress occurs when the shear stress reaches its maximum. If the diameter containing the x and y faces is rotated 53.1° counterclockwise (the particle rotates 26.55° counterclockwise), the new stresses on the x face are 6 ksi tension and 5 ksi positive shear (a clockwise couple). On the y face, the new stresses will be 6 ksi tension and 5 ksi negative shear (a counterclockwise couple). This state of stress where σ_x and σ_y are equal and τ_{xy} is maximum is called the "maximum shear" state of stress. The maximum shear state of stress for the particle of Example 11-3 is shown in Figure 11-6.

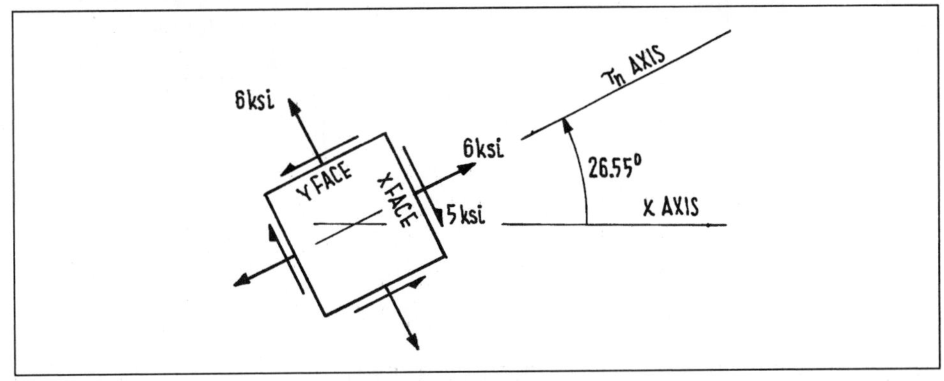

Figure 11-6 Maximum shear state of stress.

Several observations can now be made concerning the solutions for the state of stress at a point.

1. Mohr's circle is a plot of normal stress vs. shear stress on any n axis and its corresponding n face.
2. The x and y faces are 90° apart on the particle; they are therefore 180° apart on Mohr's circle.
3. The sum of $\sigma_x + \sigma_y$ is a constant; $\sigma_x + \sigma y = \sigma_{nMAX} + \sigma_{nMIN}$.
4. The angle between maximum normal stress and maximum shear stress is 90° on Mohr's circle; the angle is therefore 45° on the particle. (In Figures 11-6 and 11-7, note that the two angles sum to 45°.)
5. The maximum shear stress is always equal to the radius of the circle.
6. At the principal state of stress, the shear stress is zero.
7. At the maximum shear state of stress, the two normal stresses are equal.
8. Rotations are always measured from the xy diameter on Mohr's circle to the final position; corresponding rotations of the particle will be in the same direction but only half as large.
9. It is critically important to keep track of the x and y faces in order that proper directions and signs can be assigned.

Some examples will further illustrate the use of Mohr's circle in investigating the state of stress at a point.

Example 11-4

State of stress at a point.

Given: Computed state of stress as shown.

To Find: 1) Principal state of stress, with sketch.
2) Maximum shear state of stress, with sketch.

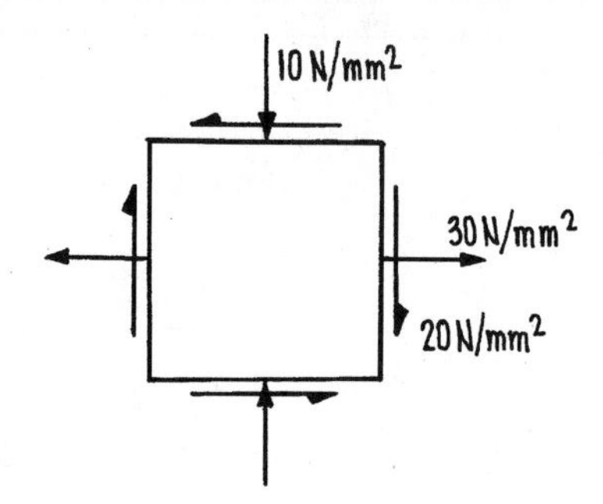

Solution: Mohr's circle is constructed for the given state of stress.

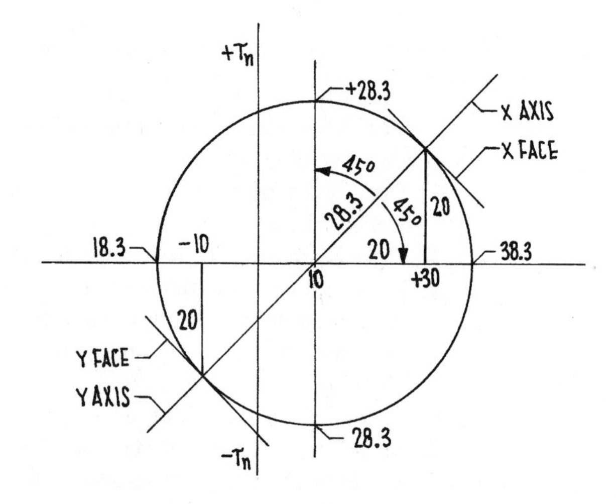

The xy axis in Mohr's circle is rotated 45° clockwise (the particle rotates 22.5° clockwise) to obtain the principal state of stress. The xy axis is rotated 45° counterclockwise (the particle rotates 22.5° counterclockwise) to obtain the maximum shear state of stress.

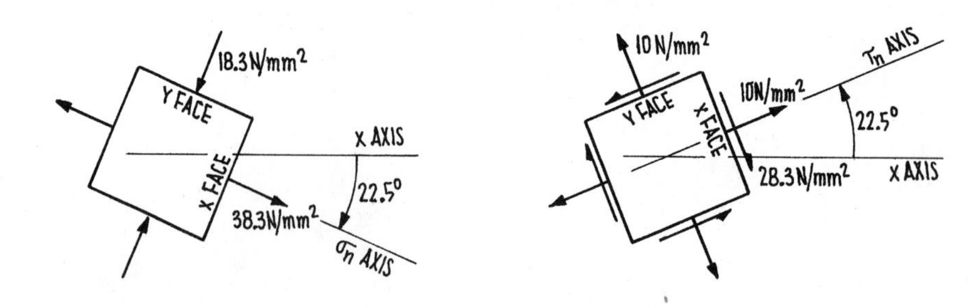

1) Principal stresses. 2) Maximum shear stress.

Example 11-5

State of stress at a point.

Given: Computed state of stress as shown.

To Find: 1) Principal state of stress, with sketch.
2) Maximum shear state of stress, with sketch.

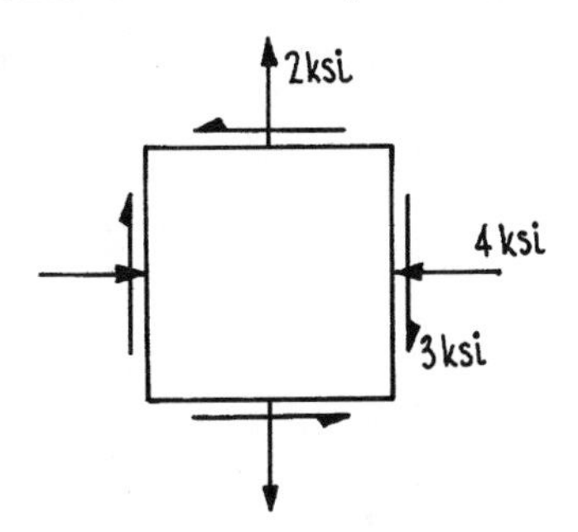

Solution: Mohr's circle is constructed for the given state of stress.

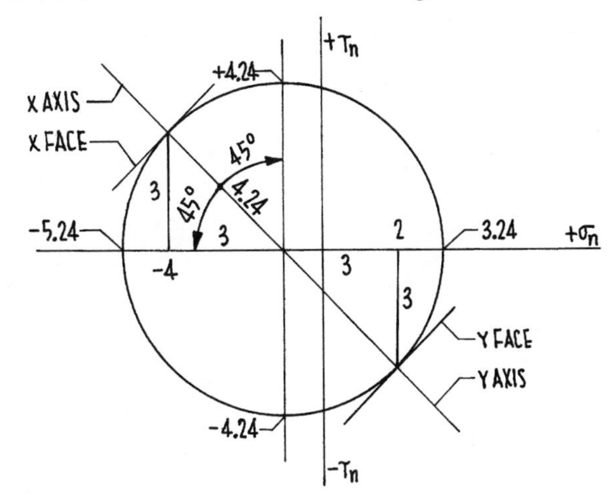

The xy axis in Mohr's circle is rotated 45° counterclockwise (the particle rotates 22.5° counterclockwise) to obtain the principal state of stress. The xy axis is rotated 45° clockwise (the particle rotates 22.5° clockwise) to obtain the maximum shear state of stress.

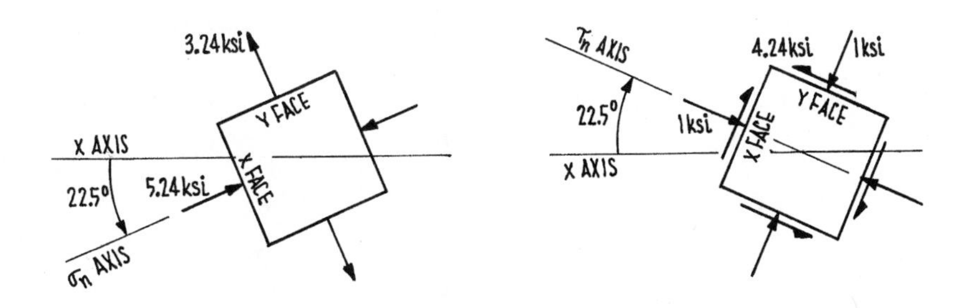

1) Principal stresses. 2) Maximum shear stress.

Example 11-6

State of stress at a point.

Given: Computed state of stress as shown.

To Find: 1) Principal state of stress, with sketch.
2) Maximum shear state of stress, with sketch.

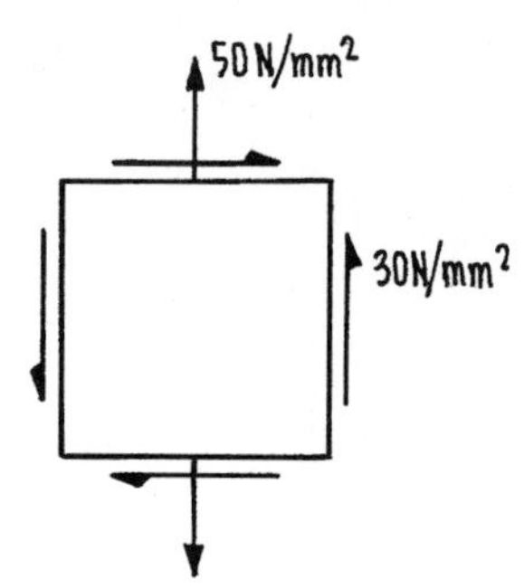

Solution: Mohr's circle is constructed for the given state of stress.

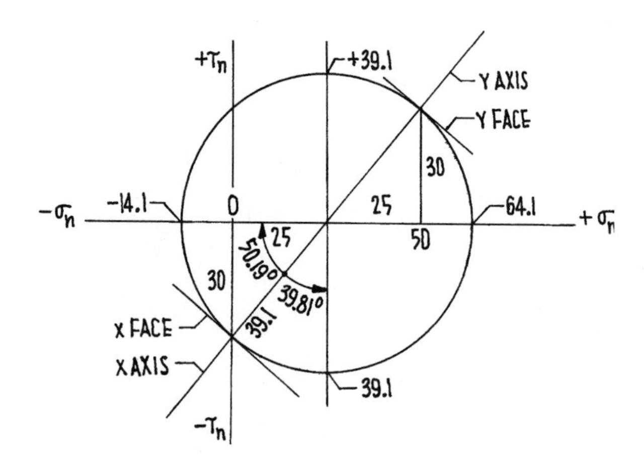

The xy axis in Mohr's circle is rotated 50.19° clockwise (the particle rotates 25.1° clockwise) to obtain the principal state of stress. The xy axis is rotated 39.81° counterclockwise (the particle rotates 19.9° counterclockwise) to obtain the maximum shear state of stress.

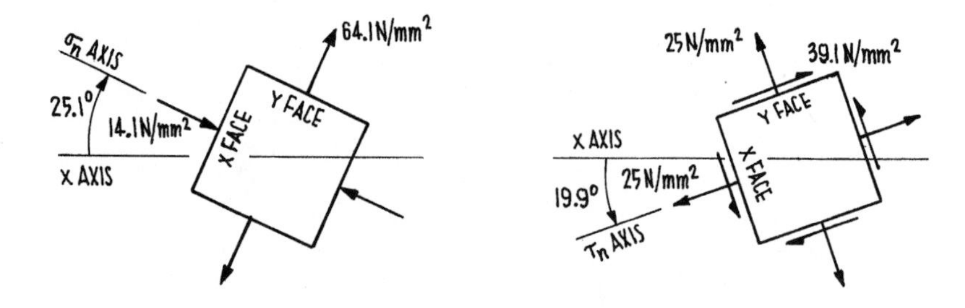

1) Principal stresses. 2) Maximum shear stress.

Example 11-7

State of stress at a point.

Given: Stressed particle of Example 11-1.

To Find: Stress on the *n* face using Mohr's circle.

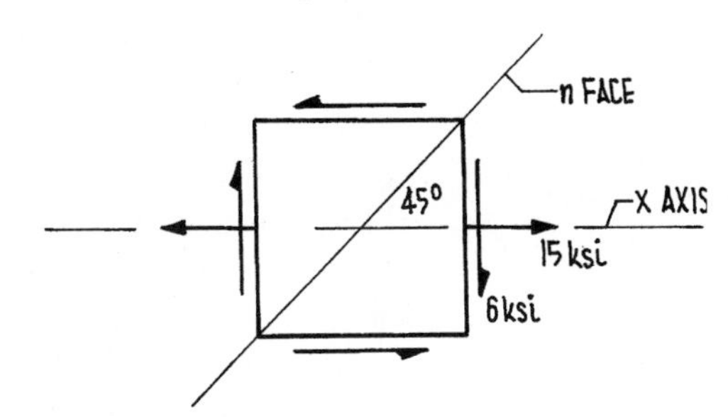

Solution: As shown, the angle is improperly measured. The particle is redrawn with the angle measured properly, either from face-to-face or axis-to-axis. It is seen to be clockwise.

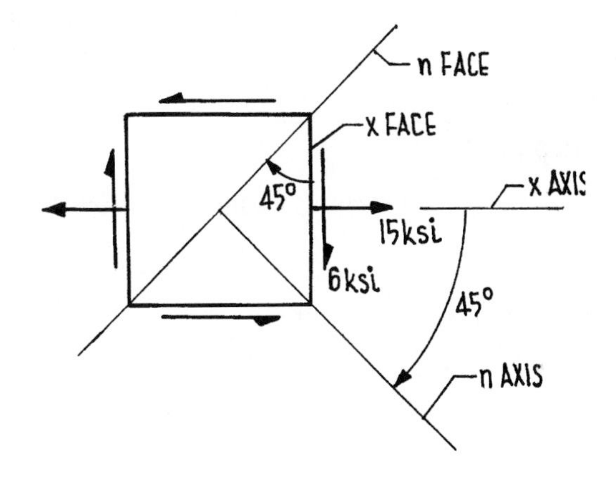

Mohr's circle is constructed for the given state of stress.

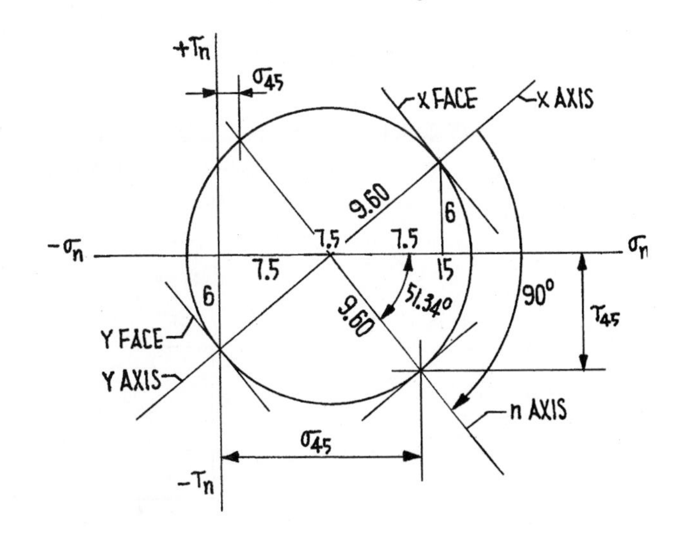

The solution is made by rotating the x face until it is parallel to the specified n face and then finding the stresses on it. The particle is rotated 45° clockwise (90° on Mohr's circle). The 90° angle is drawn on the circle and the angles determined. Stresses are then computed:

At x face, $\sigma_{45} = 7.5 + 9.6 \cos 51.34 = +13.5$ ksi
At y face, $\sigma_{45} = 7.5 - 9.6 \cos 51.34 = +1.5$ ksi
At x face, $\tau_{45} = 9.60 \sin 51.34 = -7.5$ ksi

The particle at 45° clockwise rotation is shown in the following sketch. The results are of course the same as those of Example 11-1. Note that the x face is parallel to the specified n face.

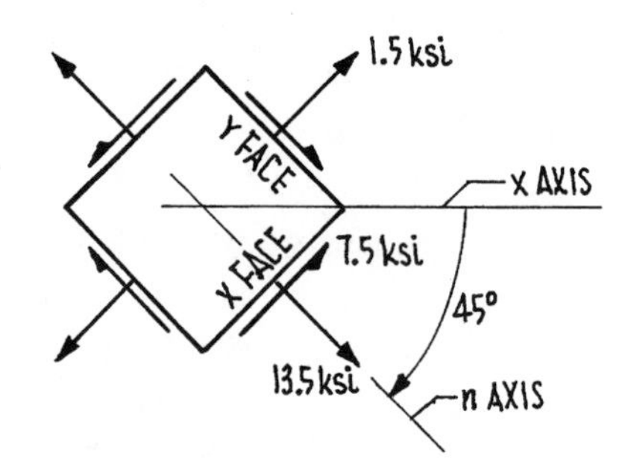

Example 11-8

State of stress at a point.

Given: Computed state of stress as shown. Weld line occurs at 60° off horizontal.

To Find: State of stress on the weld.

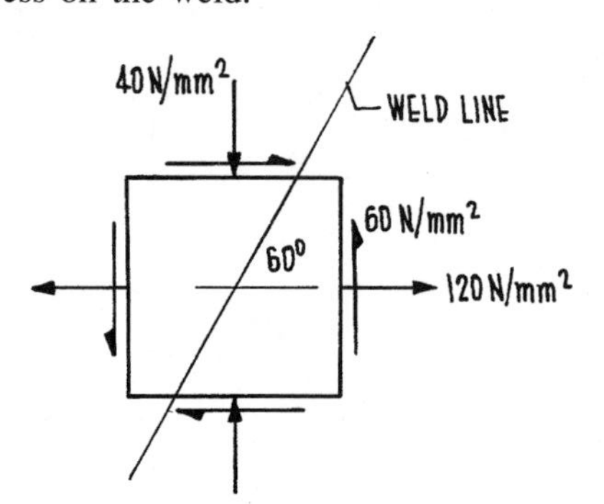

Solution: Again, the angle is improperly shown. The particle is redrawn with the angle measured properly, either face-to-face or axis-to-axis. The angle is 30° clockwise.

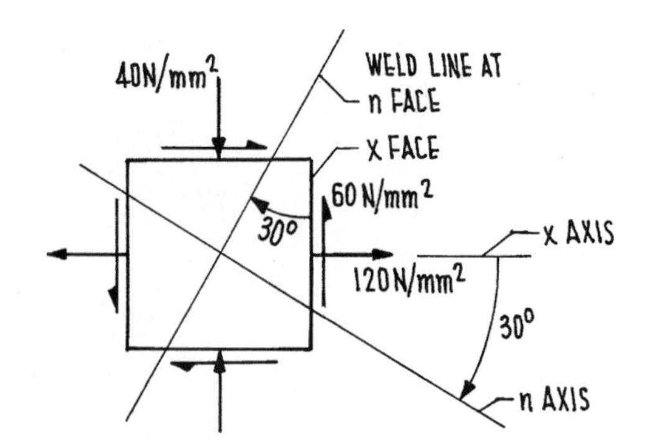

Mohr's circle is constructed for the given state of stress.

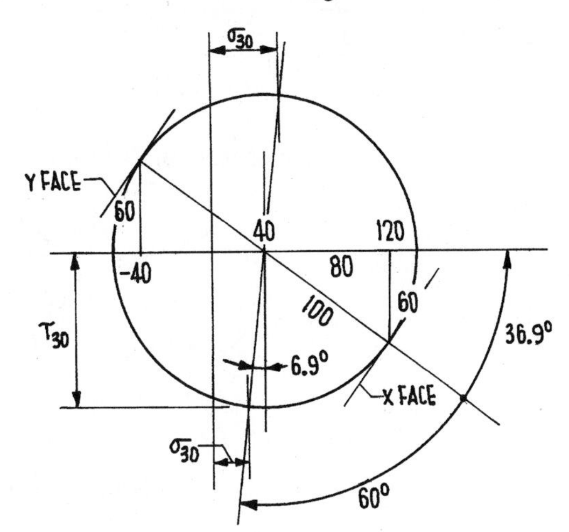

The solution is made by rotating the x face until it becomes parallel to the weld line and then finding the stresses on it. The angle of 30° clockwise on the particle corresponds to an angle of 60° on Mohr's circle. The 60° angle is drawn on the circle and the angles determined. Stresses are now computed:

At x face, $\sigma_{30} = 40 - 100 \sin 6.9° = 23.0$ N/mm^2
At y face, $\sigma_{30} = 40 + 100 \sin 6.9° = 52.0$ N/mm^2
At x face, $\tau_{30} = -100 \cos 6.9° = -99.3$ N/mm^2

The particle at 30° clockwise rotation is shown in the following sketch. Note that the x face is parallel to the weld line.

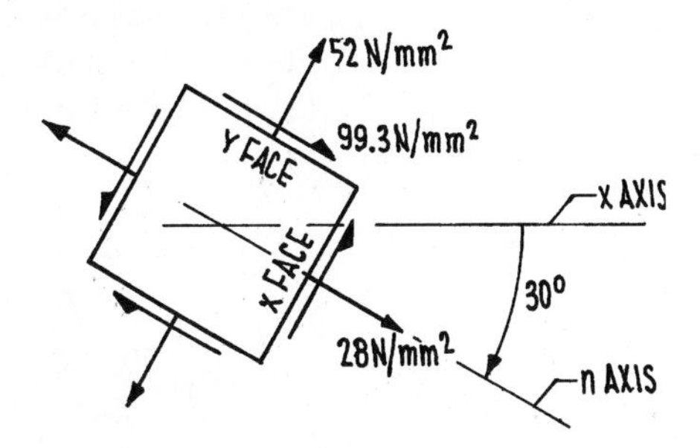

11.4 Maximum Stress Under Combined Loads

General cases of loads and stresses can now be undertaken, where several cases of loading occur on a member at the same time. Under such loading, the stressed particle is drawn for a particular point and the maximum stresses occurring at that point are found from Mohr's circle. It may be necessary to investigate several such points before the point is located where the highest numerical values of stress occur.

There is no new theory to be developed in this section. The investigations presented in this section require only the stress formulas and Mohr's circle. Both of these topics have already been presented.

The procedure is best demonstrated by examples.

Example 11-9

Stresses under combined loads.

Given: Torsion bar under axial load as shown.

To Find: Maximum stress in the material and its location.

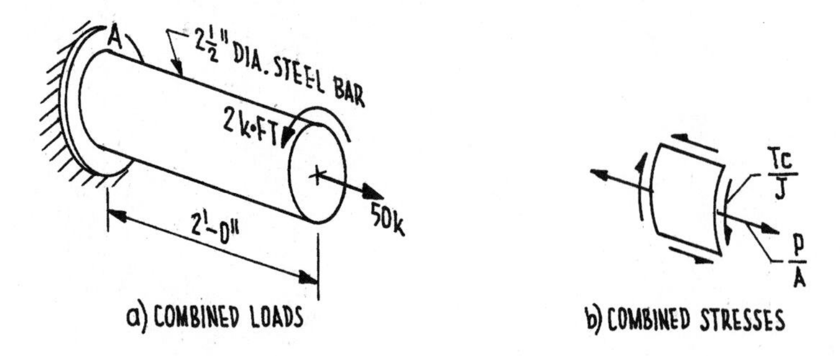

Solution: The torsion stress is known to be at its maximum value on the surface of the bar. Since torque is constant along the length of the bar, the stress is also constant:

$$\tau = \frac{Tc}{J}, \quad T = (2000)(12)\ \text{lb} \cdot \text{in}$$

$$c = r = 1.25\ \text{in.}$$

$$J = \frac{\pi r^4}{2} = 3.83\ \text{in.}^4$$

$$= \frac{(2000)(12)(1.25)}{3.83} = 7830\ \text{psi}$$

The axial stress is known to be uniform across the section, to include the fibers at the surface of the bar. Since axial force is constant along the length of the bar, the stress is also constant:

$$f = \frac{P}{A}, \quad P = 50{,}000\ \text{lb}$$

$$A = \pi r^2 = 4.91\ \text{in.}^2$$

$$f = \frac{50{,}000}{4.91} = 10{,}200\ \text{psi}$$

A stressed particle at any point on the surface is shown in the following sketch.

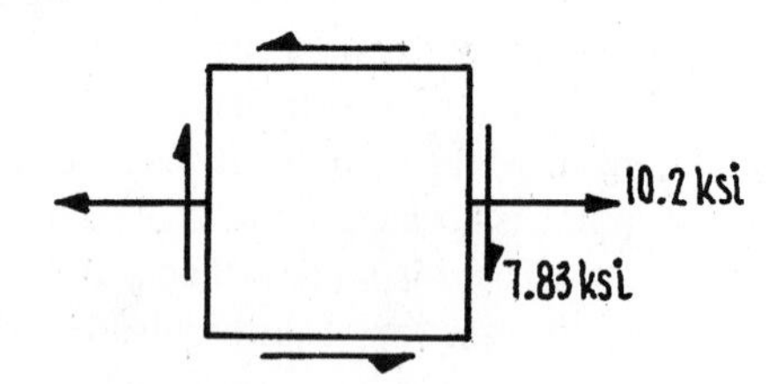

Mohr's circle is constructed for this state of stress.

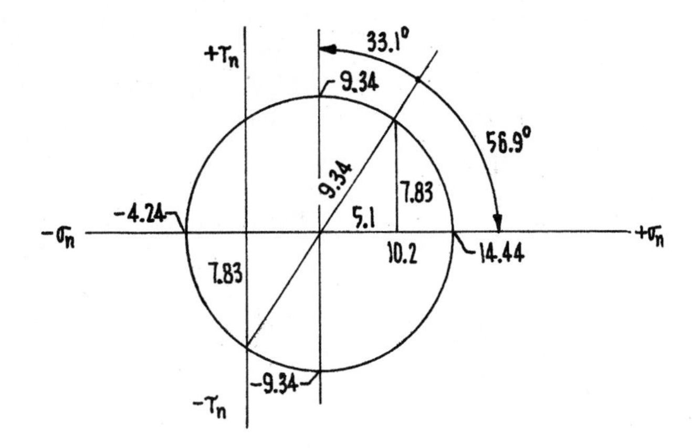

The principal stresses occur at 56.9/2 = 28.5° clockwise rotation. The maximum shear stress occurs at 39.1/2 = 16.6° counterclockwise rotation.

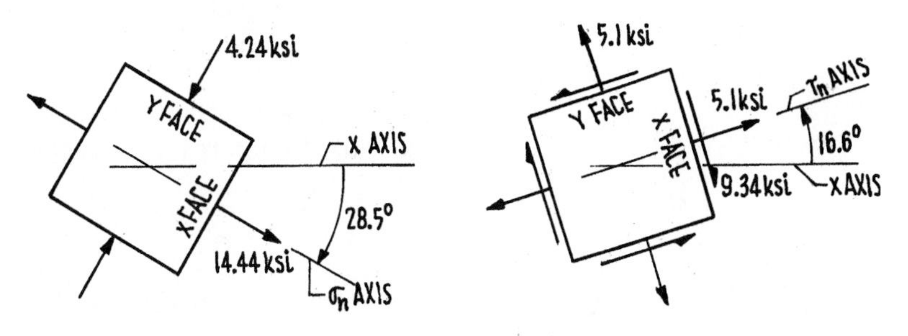

a) Principal stresses. b) Maximum shear stress.

The maximum normal stress is thus seen to be some 40% higher than the calculated axial stress, and the maximum shear stress is some 20% higher than the calculated shear stress.

Example 11-10

Stresses under combined loads.

Given: Axially loaded bar with flexural load as shown.

To Find: Maximum stress in the material and its location.

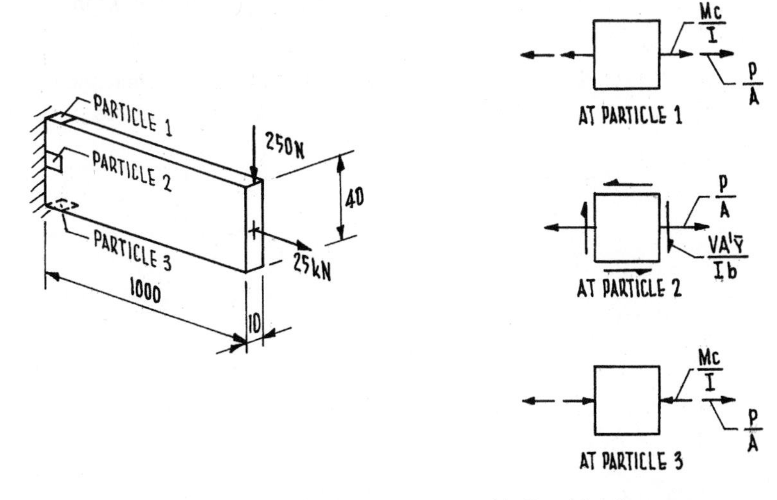

a) Combined loads. b) Combined stresses.

Solution: The axial stress due to flexure is known to be at its maximum value at the top and bottom surfaces of the bar (particles 1 and 3) and zero at the centroid (particle 2). The shear stress due to flexure is known to be zero at the top and bottom surfaces of the bar (particles 1 and 3) and maximum at the centroid (particle 2). The axial stress is known to be uniform across the section, to include all fibers at all surfaces (all particles).

The flexural stress is found by the flexure formula:

$$f = \frac{Mc}{I}$$

$$M = 250,000 \text{ N} \cdot \text{mm}$$

$$c = \frac{h}{2} = 20 \text{ mm}$$

$$I = \frac{bh^3}{12} = \frac{(10)(40)^3}{12} = 53,300 \text{ mm}^4$$

$$f = \frac{(250,000)(20)}{53,300} = 94 \text{ N/mm}^2$$

The maximum beam shear stress at the centroid is calculated from the specialized formula for rectangles:

$$v = \frac{VA'\bar{y}}{Ib} = \frac{3V}{2A}$$

$$V = 250 \text{ N}$$

$$A = (10)(40) = 400 \text{ mm}^2$$

$$= \frac{(3)(250)}{(2)(400)} = 1 \text{ N/mm}^2 \quad \text{(negligible)}$$

The axial stress is a normal stress:

$$f = \frac{P}{A}$$

$$P = 25 \text{ kN}$$

$$A = (10)(40) = 400 \text{ mm}^2$$

$$= \frac{25,000}{400} = 62.5 \text{ N/mm}^2$$

By inspection, it is seen that the stresses at particle 1 will produce the most severe case. The stresses are shown in the following sketch.

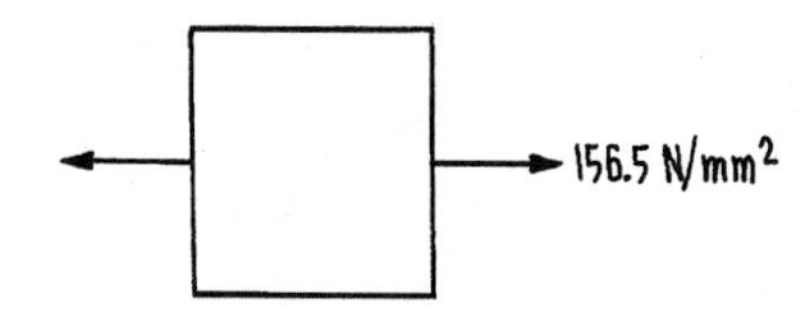

The stress case is already the principle state of stress (shears are zero). Mohr's circle is constructed to find the maximum shear stress.

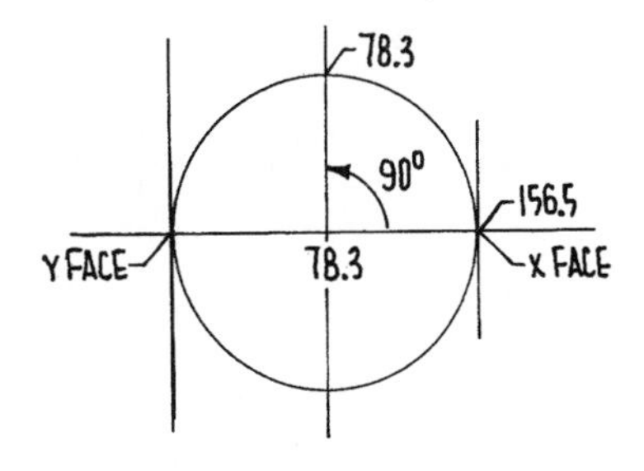

The maximum shear stress occurs at 90/2 = 45° counterclockwise rotation.

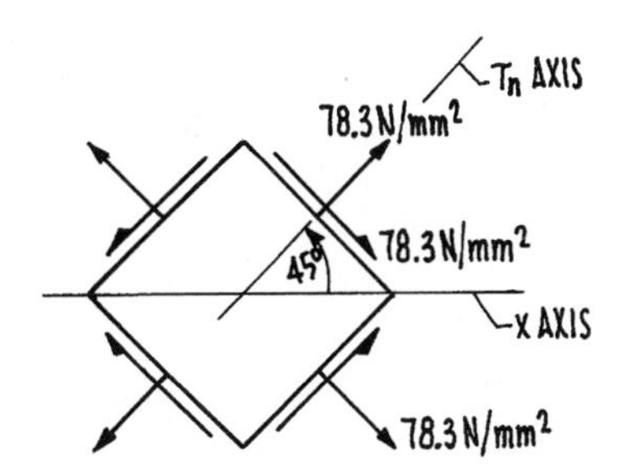

From the results, it is observed that a case of loading showing but little shear stress on the usual axes can have significant shear stress on other surfaces.

Example 11-11

Stresses under combined loads.

Given: Torsion bar of Example 11-9 with added flexural load.

To Find: Maximum stress in the material and its location.

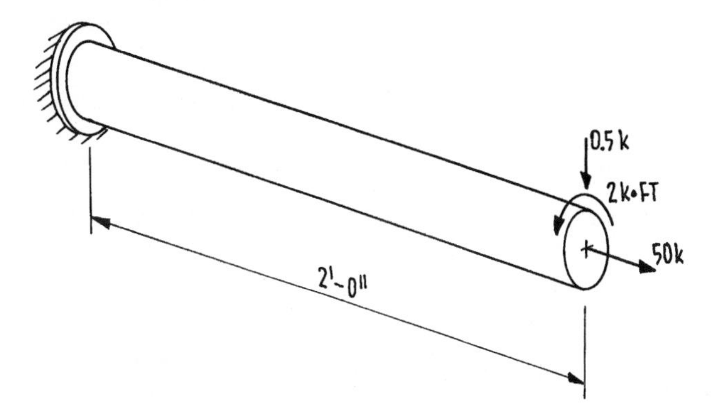

Solution: Maximum flexural stress will occur at the fixed end. Since both axial stress and torsion stress are constant, the location of the maximum stress is therefore taken to be at the fixed end.

There are four potentially maximum cases of load at the fixed end:

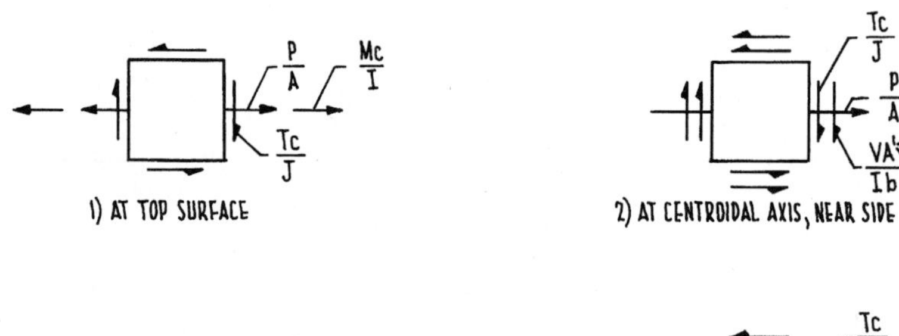

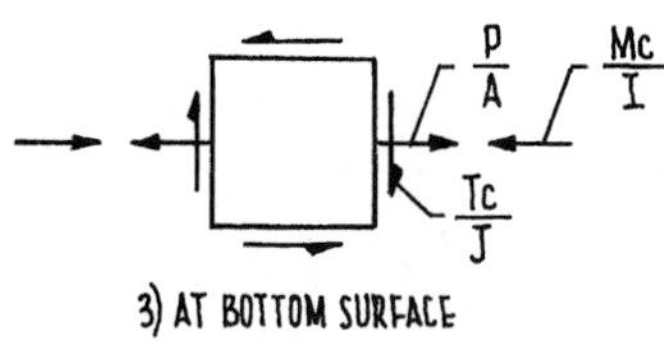

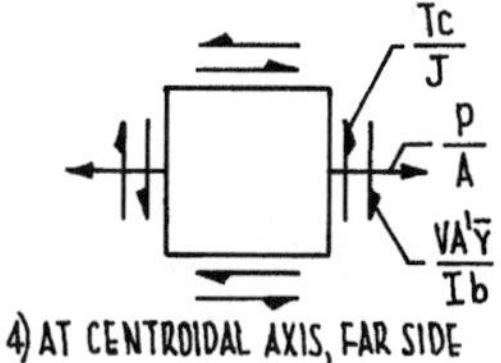

Examination of the four cases indicates that Case 1 will always be more severe than Case 3, and that Case 2 will always be more severe than Case 4. The investigation will therefore be limited to Case 1 and Case 2.

The flexural stress is found from the flexure formula:

$$f_b = \frac{Mc}{I}$$

$$M = (500)(2)(12) = 12{,}000 \text{ lb} \cdot \text{in}$$

$$I = \frac{\pi r^4}{4} = 1.917$$

$$c = r = 1.25$$

$$= \frac{(12{,}000)(1.25)}{1.917} = 7.80 \text{ ksi}$$

The beam shear stress is found at the centroidal axis:

$$v = \frac{VA'\bar{y}}{Ib}$$

$$V = 0.5 \text{ kips}$$

$$A'\bar{y} = \left(\frac{\pi(1.25)^2}{2}\right)\left(\frac{4(12.5)}{3\pi}\right) = 1.302 \text{ in.}^3$$

$$I = 1.917 \text{ in.}^4$$

$$b = 2r = 2.50 \text{ in.}$$

$$= \frac{(500)(1.302)}{(1.917)(2.50)} = 0.14 \text{ ksi} \quad \text{(negligible)}$$

The stresses for torsional shear and axial stress are taken from the solution of Example 11-9:

$$\tau = 7.83 \text{ ksi}$$
$$f = 10.20 \text{ ksi}$$

The stressed particles for Case 1 and Case 2 are shown in the following sketches.

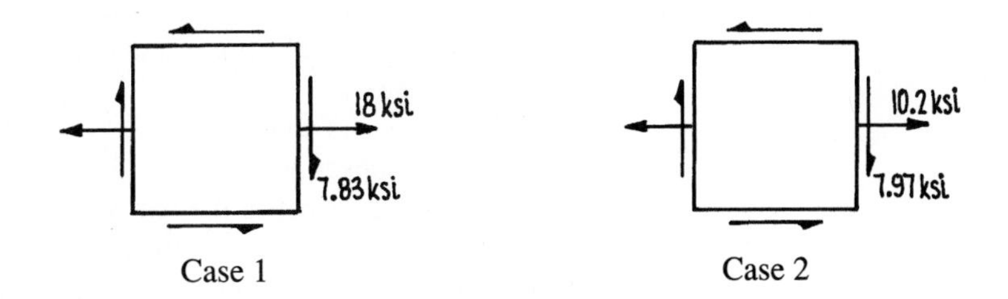

Case 1 Case 2

Case 2 is so much smaller than Case 1 that it will not be investigated further.

Mohr's circle is constructed for Case 1.

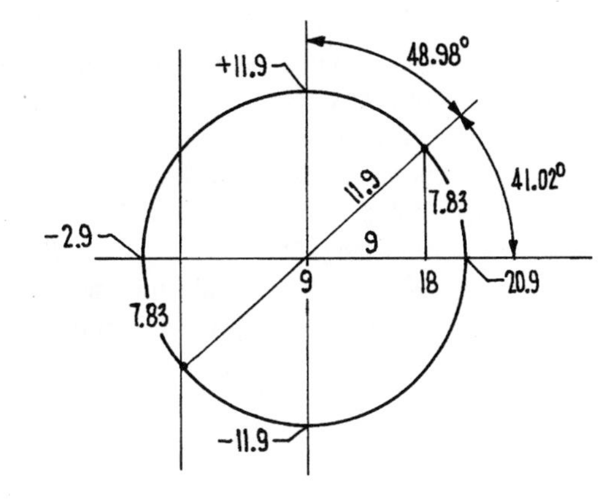

The principal stresses occur at 41.02/2 = 20.51° clockwise rotation.
The maximum shear stress occurs at 48.98° = 24.49° counterclockwise rotation.

Principal stresses. Maximum shear stress.

The addition of the flexural load is seen to cause a distinct increase in shear stress at the top fibers.

Review Questions

1. Why is it necessary to keep such close track of axes, faces and directions when working with state of stress at a point?
2. How is the sign of the angle θ determined when rotating a particle from one state of stress to another?
3. How is the sign of the shear stress determined?
4. What do the subscripts mean on the shear stress τ_{yx}?
5. Given σ_x and σ_y, what is the stress at the center of Mohr's circle?
6. Given the radius of Mohr's circle, what is the maximum shear stress?
7. Given the stress at the center of Mohr's circle and given the maximum shear stress, what will be the maximum and minimum normal stresses?
8. On a stressed particle, what is the angle between the principal state of stress and the maximum shear state of stress?
9. Why are the x and y axes 180° apart on Mohr's circle?
10. What is known about the two normal stresses when the particle is oriented in the maximum shear state of stress?
11. In a group of sketches of stressed particles, how can a particle in its principal state of stress be immediately recognized?
12. How can Mohr's circle be used to find the stress along some specified n face which is not a max./min. face?
13. When combining load cases, how are the potential points of maximum stress selected?
14. What is the formula for finding the planar moment of inertia of a circle?
15. What is the formula for finding the polar moment of inertia of a circle?

CHAPTER

12

RELATED TOPICS IN STRENGTH OF MATERIALS

The topics presented in this chapter are a series of peripheral topics related to, and in support of, the topics presented in earlier chapters. Some of these topics are not "problem" topics. Rather, they are background information. Other topics are problem topics but as a rule they are topics that will be encountered only occasionally.

12.1 Creep and Relaxation Under Stress

Under stress, materials undergo a very slow permanent deformation in the direction of the stress. A concrete column in compression, for example, will actually shorten in length over a period of years. Such a column is shown in Figure 12-1, along with a graph of the deformation it would undergo at various levels of stress.

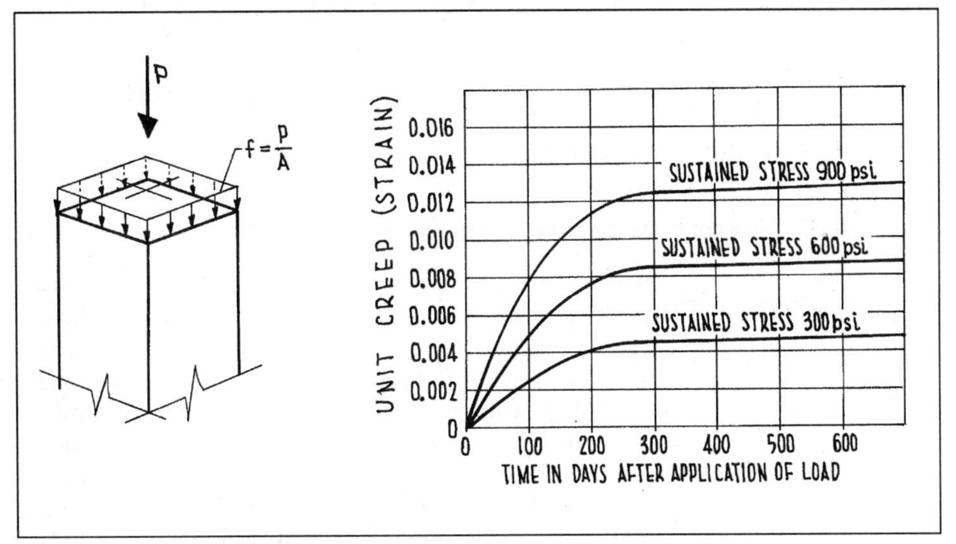

Figure 12-1 Rate of creep in concrete.

This type of permanent change in size due to stress is called *creep*, or *plastic flow*. All materials are subject to creep, some more than others; soils and concrete are two of the worst offenders. The total deformation due to creep divided by the length of the member is a strain; it is that strain that is plotted in the graph of Figure 12-1.

Creep varies both with time and with level of stress. It occurs at all levels of stress, but the rate of creep diminishes sharply after a few months. If after a time the stress is increased, the creep associated with that increase will simply begin anew and will be superimposed on the existing creep.

Creep in metals is aggravated by temperature. At high temperatures, creep rates increase; if the temperature and stress levels are high enough, failure of the material could occur several months in the future. Such a case of high temperature and high stress is shown in Figure 12-2, where the primary stage of creep and deformation corresponds to the curves of Figure 12-1.

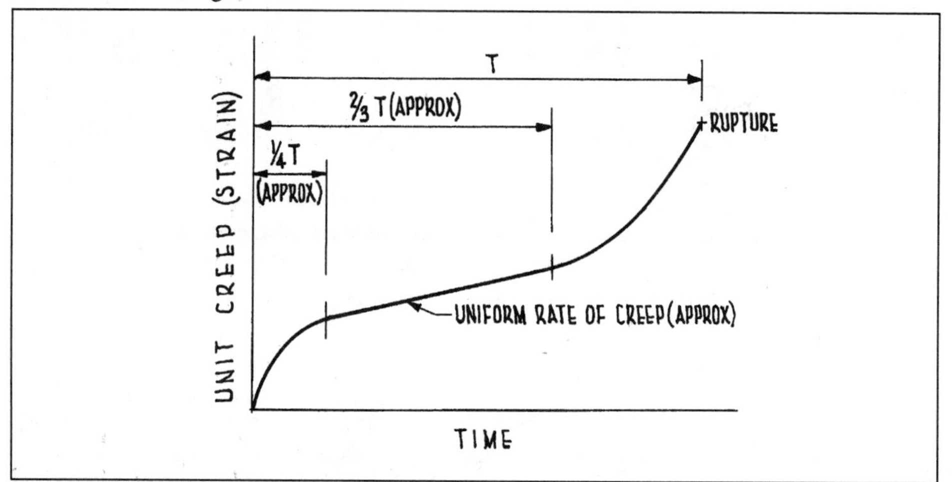

Figure 12-2 Typical creep-failure curve.

The creep-failure curve shown in Figure 12-2 exists only at high temperatures and high stresses. At ordinary atmospheric temperatures under day-to-day loadings, only the primary stage would ever occur. In machine parts under high temperatures and high sustained overloads, however, the possibility of creep failure cannot be ignored.

For metals under high tensile stress, the material undergoes a similar permanent elongation called *relaxation*. Such elongation will produce a loss in the tensile force in high strength bolts and prestressed steel, where the tensile force is a very necessary part of the design. In prestressed concrete members, the concrete is placed under a high compressive stress by steel wires placed under a high tensile stress; the combination of creep in the concrete combined with the relaxation in the steel will produce a loss of about 15% in the tensile force in the steel, a serious consideration both structurally and economically.

12.2 Fatigue in Metals

Probably everyone has broken a piece of wire by repeatedly bending it back and forth into its yield range until it breaks. It is not necessary, however, to stress the material so highly in order to make it break. The same wire undergoing a stress reversal of 100,000 cycles can also be broken the same way, even though stresses might remain elastic.

This type of failure under cyclical (but elastic) stress reversals is called *fatigue*. It seems to be limited to metals. It is a serious consideration wherever metals are subject to large stress reversals, such as those in rotating elements in machines. It can also be a serious consideration even when the load is not completely reversed, but is repeatedly applied and released, such as in bridge beams.

Historically, fatigue in metals became an engineering problem with the advent of high-strength alloys created by modern technology. It had not been a common problem with the low-strength metals in use to that time. Very simply, the low-strength materials of earlier years could not be worked at stress levels high enough to produce fatigue.

A particular alloy can be tested for its resistance to fatigue by placing a sample of the material in a test machine at some predetermined high level of stress at a predetermined temperature. The sample is then loaded in cyclical stress reversals until it fails, or until the number of stress reversals exceeds some limit (such as 1,000,000 cycles). The stress and the number of cycles are recorded.

The test is repeated for successive samples, each at a progressively lower stress. Eventually the sample will not fail, but will apparently take an infinite number of cycles of load reversals without undergoing fatigue failure. The test is then stopped and the results of the tests are plotted on a curve called an *S-N* curve, as shown in Figure 12-3.

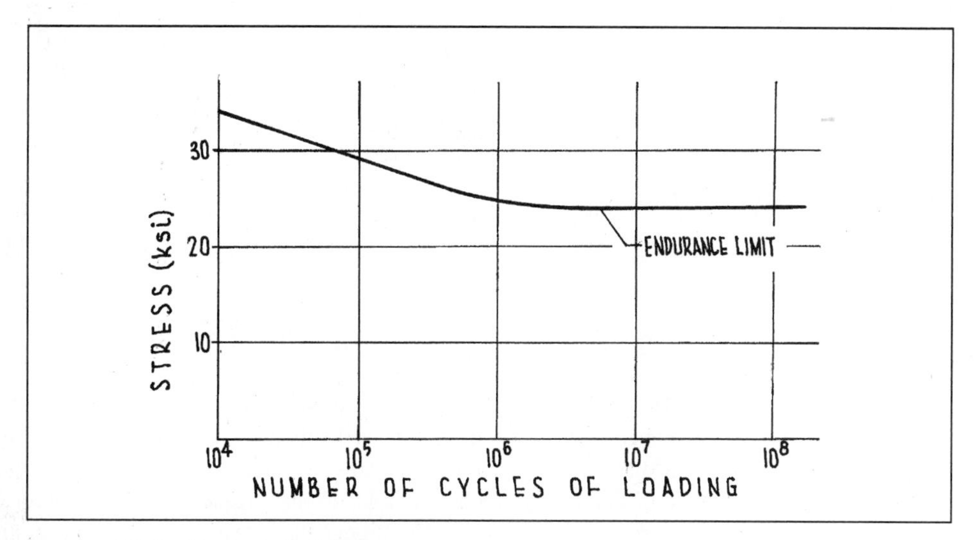

Figure 12-3 Typical *S-N* fatigue curve.

The highest stress at which a material is no longer susceptible to fatigue failure at a given temperature is called the *endurance limit.* The endurance limit does increase as the strength of the material increases, but not proportionally; it increases at a much lower rate. Endurance limit seems to be heavily influenced by microscopic surface defects in the material.

The conclusion to be drawn is that there may not be much gain in using high strength materials (with their commensurately high cost) when the endurance limit increases so little. Since the allowable stress will have to be limited to the endurance limit in any event, it may be more economical to use the lower strength material.

In most metals, the reduction in allowable stress to stay within the endurance limit is severe. For ASTM A-36 steel, for example, the allowable stress in flexure is usually taken at 22,000 to 24,000 lb/in.^{2} If the steel is subject to 1,000,000 cycles or more of load reversals, the allowable stress may be prescribed as low as 12,000 lb/in.^{2}, a serious penalty.

Even at low design levels of the number of repetitions of cyclical loading (10,000 cycles or even less) the consequences of fatigue are so severe that some reduction in stress levels is often justified. Such reductions do include cyclical loading due to earthquake.

12.3 Stress Concentrations

In earlier discussions, it was assumed that stress is uniformly distributed across the loaded area. The assumption is not exactly true, but it is approximately true even if the area in question is only a short distance away from the point of application of a load. The stress distributions shown graphically in Figure 12-3 illustrate the stress patterns to be expected when introducing a load into a member.

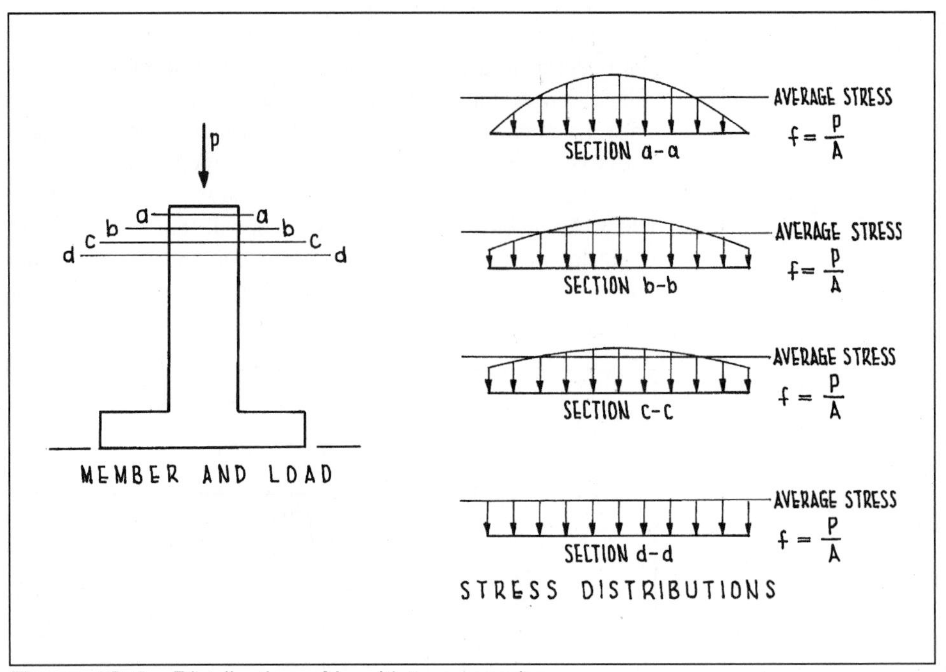

Figure 12-4 Distribution of load into a member.

The high peak of stress shown in section *aa* is called a stress concentration. Such stress concentrations occur whenever loads are introduced into a member or whenever there is a discontinuity (such as a change in size) in the stressed member or whenever there is a discontinuity (such as a hole) in the stressed area. It is almost axiomatic that the more abrupt a discontinuity, the higher the stress concentration around the discontinuity.

Consider, for example, the stressed plate shown in Figure 12-5a. The stress at the continuous part of the plate is a uniformly distributed stress, P/A_1. At the hole, the cross sectional area has been reduced. The average area at that section can be computed as P/A_2, which assumes that the stress is uniformly distributed across the remaining material. In actuality, the stress distribution will be similar to that shown in Figure 12-5b, where the stress reaches a sharp peak at the discontinuity.

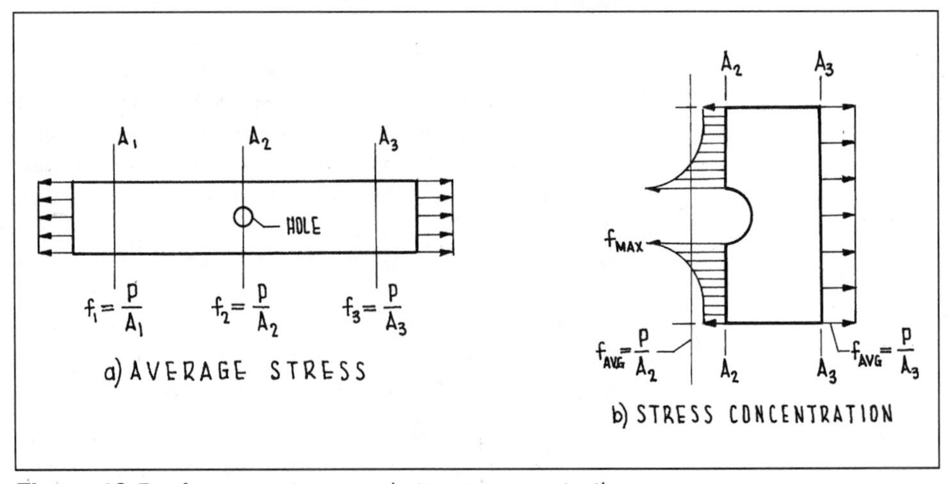

Figure 12-5 Average stress and stress concentration.

The stress concentrations introduced at a discontinuity can easily overstress a material. It has already been observed that the allowable stress on a material is commonly taken at 60% of its elastic limit. Stress concentrations, however, can easily double or even triple the computed average stress, as shown in Figure 12-5. The result is a stress in excess of the elastic limit of the material which can lead to premature failure. The problem can be seriously aggravated if the stress is cyclical.

The abruptness of the discontinuity sharply increases the stress concentration. The plate of Figure 12-6, for example, has three types of discontinuities, one a square hole, one a small round hole and the third large round hole. The difference in the stress concentrations in such cases is quite sizeable. The stress f_3 next to a large round hole might be 1.5 to 1.6 times the average stress, the stress f_2 next to a small round hole might be 2.0 to 2.2 times the average stress and the stress f_3 next to a reentrant sharp corner might be 2.5 to 3 times the average stress.

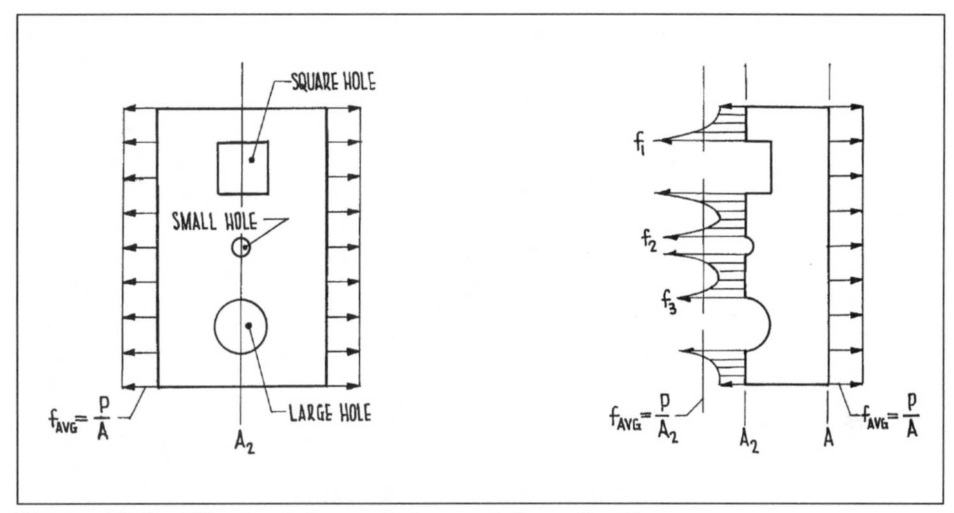

Figure 12-6 Effects of size and shape of discontinuities.

The stress concentrations shown in Figure 12-6 suggest that any discontinuities or transitions that must be introduced into stressed members should be kept smooth, with no sharp edges or sharp interior corners. Where sharp discontinuities become unavoidable in a design (and they often do), then it will be prudent to reduce the stress levels accordingly. The same logic applies to surface defects in highly stressed machine parts, even microscopic ones; if the defects cannot be controlled, the stress levels must be reduced.

The amount of the stress concentration to be expected under a wide variety of conditions has been found experimentally through laboratory testing. The results of such tests are available throughout the technical literature.[1] In general, the better results are presented graphically such as the graph shown in Figure 12-7.

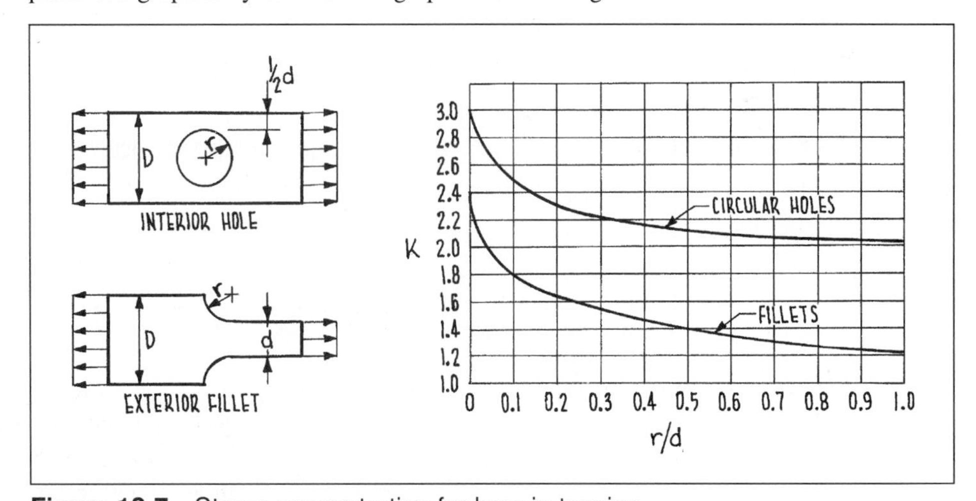

Figure 12-7 Stress concentration for bars in tension.

[1] R. J. Roark and W. C. Young, *Formulas for Stress and Strain*, 5th ed., McGraw Hill, New York, 1975.

The stress concentration factor K given by Figure 12-7 is used as a multiplier times the average P/A stress to find the peak stress:

$$f_{PEAK} = K\frac{P}{A_{NET}} \tag{12-1}$$

where A_{NET} is the net area being stressed (after holes are deducted). Note that as the discontinuity becomes sharper, the stress concentration factor becomes disproportionately larger. Large smooth transitions do a great deal toward reducing the size of stress concentrations.

The literature concerning stress concentrations generally is focused on machine parts and similar mechanical engineering problems. Such problems also occur in civil engineering structures, however. A concrete floor slab 4 inches thick in a multistory building 100 feet square, for example, has the same scale as a 19 gauge sheet metal machine part 12 inches square. Stairwells and elevator holes (with their square sharp corners) can produce stress concentrations fully as damaging to a structural floor as the bolt holes and fillets to a machine part. The difference is only in scale, not in the final effects.

A further application in civil engineering structures occurs in bolted connections. The extremely sharp reentrant notch created by the threads in a bolt produces a stress concentration factor (for tensile stress) of 2.0 to 3.0. For that reason, bolts should never be placed in tension; bolted connections should always be designed such that the bolts are in shear (see Figure 8-8).

12.4 Plasticity and Strain Hardening

The existence of a plastic range in steel was introduced in earlier discussions of the stress-strain curve. The discussions there, however, were directed toward finding a safe allowable stress such that deformations never entered the plastic range. It was concluded that an allowable stress of $0.60f_y$ as shown in Figure 12-8, would assure that even with a major overstress, the material should never enter the plastic range with its large, permanent deformations.

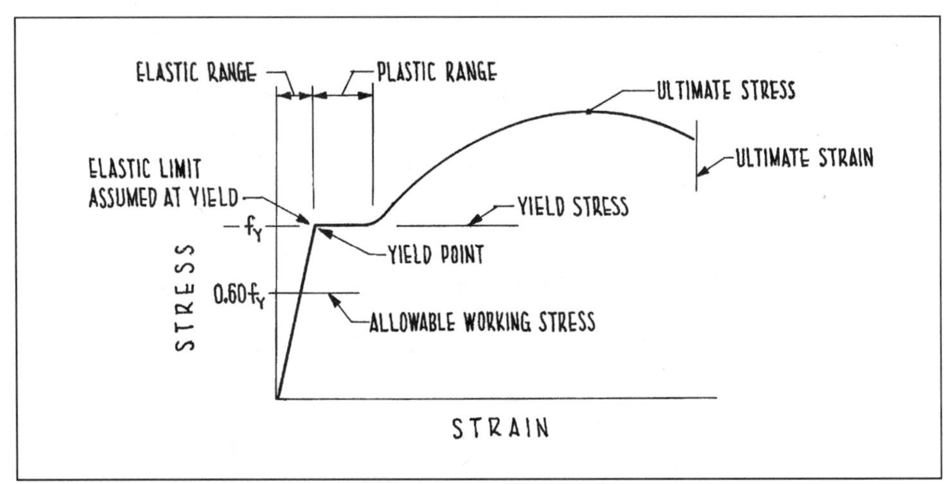

Figure 12-8 Plastic range of stress in steel.

As indicated in Figure 12-8, however, there is an extremely large margin of strength above the working stress. In ASTM A-36 steel, for example, the allowable working stress is 22,000 psi, the yield stress is 36,000 psi and the ultimate stress is 58,000 psi. Only about 38% of the ultimate strength is being used and the rest is margin; unfortunately, the plastic range occurs in that margin along with its unrestrained deformations.

Experimentally, if the stress in the material of Figure 12-8 were to be increased until it exceeded the yield point, the material would enter the plastic range. At that point, the material would continue to deform slowly without any increase in load. If the load were then to be released after only a small "set" had occurred, the strain in the material would return along the line *CD*; the material would retain a permanent set, shown in Figure 12-9 as set 1. Note that the slope of the line *CD* is exactly the same as that of line *OA*.

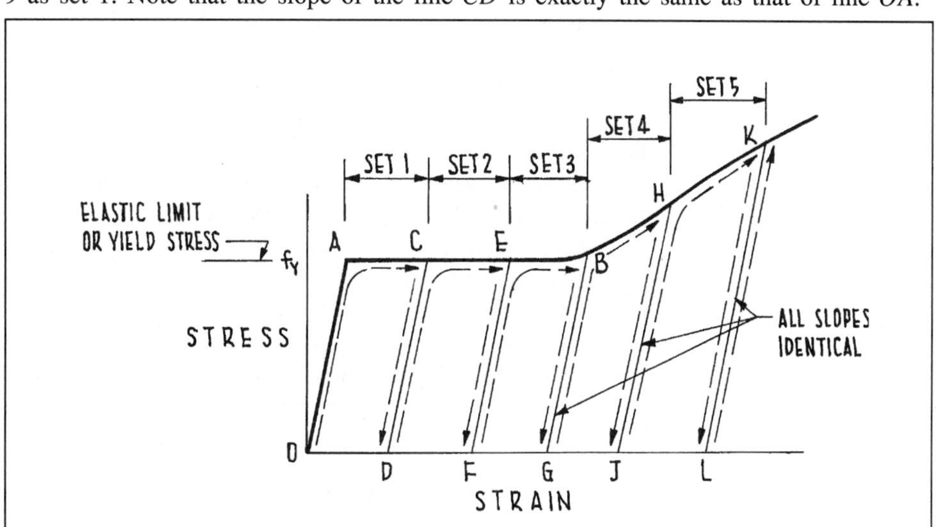

Figure 12-9 Stress-strain behavior.

If loads at working levels were now to be applied without exceeding the yield stress, the material would simply work elastically along line *CD*. The elastic modulus would remain the same as before; the only difference would be the permanent deformation *OD* that has been introduced into the material.

If the stress were again made to exceed the yield stress, the material would reenter the plastic range at *C* and continue to deform slowly without any increase in load, just as before. If the load were again to be released after only a small set (Set 2) had occurred, the material would return to zero stress along line *EF*. If reloaded, the material would work elastically just as before, but it would now work along line *EF*.

The process could continue until the strain reaches point *B*, at which point the material would no longer deform without an increase in load. To continue the experiment, enough additional load must be introduced to cause the material to deform to point *H*. If this higher load were then to be released, the material would simply return to zero stress along line *HJ*, and would then work elastically along line *HJ*.

The process could continue with ever increasing load until the stress is just short of ultimate stress. The stress-strain curve for the material would at this point have been permanently modified from its original form to look like that of Figure 12-10; the plastic range has been completely removed and the elastic limit has been increased considerably.

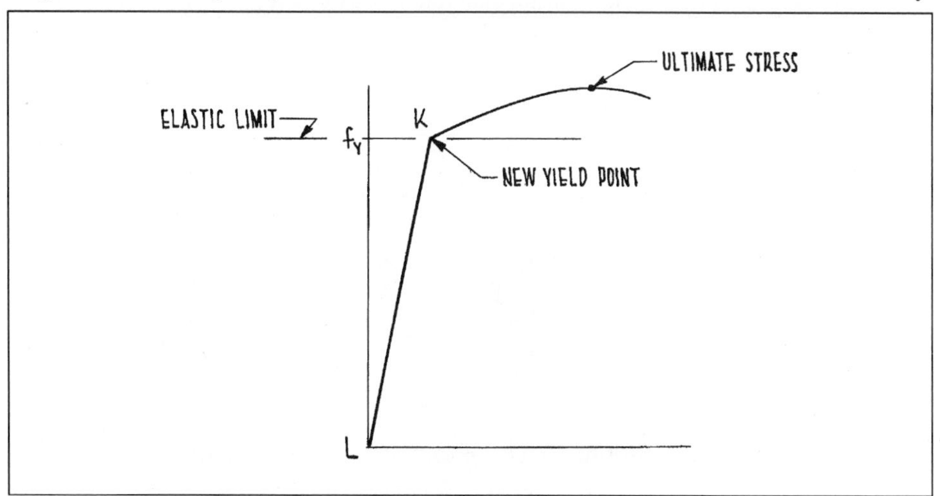

Figure 12-10 Results of strain hardening.

If the material in Figure 12-10 had been A-36 steel, the stress at point K (the elastic limit) might be as much as 50,000 psi. If this steel were to be worked at 60% of its elastic limit, the allowable stress would be 0.60 x 50,000 = 30,000 psi, a 36% increase over the 22,000 psi it started with.

The phenomenon shown in figures 12-9 and 12-10 is called *strain hardening*. The usable strength of the steel has been increased significantly by straining the material until its plastic range is completely removed. The penalty, however, is that the material, though stronger, is no longer "forgiving" of overload; the material shown in Figure 12-10 will rupture abruptly, shortly after the elastic limit is exceeded.

There are other forms of strain hardening. A drive shaft, for example, can be rolled at high pressure between hard rolls until its outer surface has been strain hardened, as shown in Figure 12-11. The outer material can now be stressed to higher levels than the inner material, matching the torsional stress distribution much better; it has been *case hardened.* Its efficiency in carrying torsional stress has been much improved.

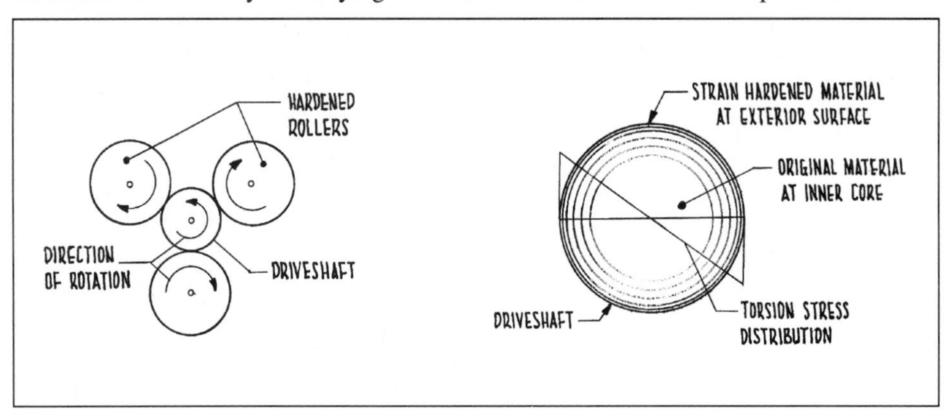

Figure 12-11 Case hardened drive shaft.

In the earlier days of manufacturing, before high strength materials had been introduced and before heat treatment was commonplace, the surface of a mild steel part could be similarly hardened by pelting it at high velocity with hard steel shot. The millions of identations produced by the shot left the surface distinctively marked. The purpose of course was to remove the plastic range at the surface of the part and to produce strains well into the higher stress ranges of the material. The process was called *shot peening*; shot peening is simply another form of strain hardening.

The manufacturing of wire uses a process called *drawing* of a heated but still solid material through small holes. A schematic diagram of the process is shown in Figure 12-12. The combined compressive pressure and tensile force serve to "draw" the hot, almost plastic material into wire. The process is called *cold working*, supposedly because the material is still a solid.

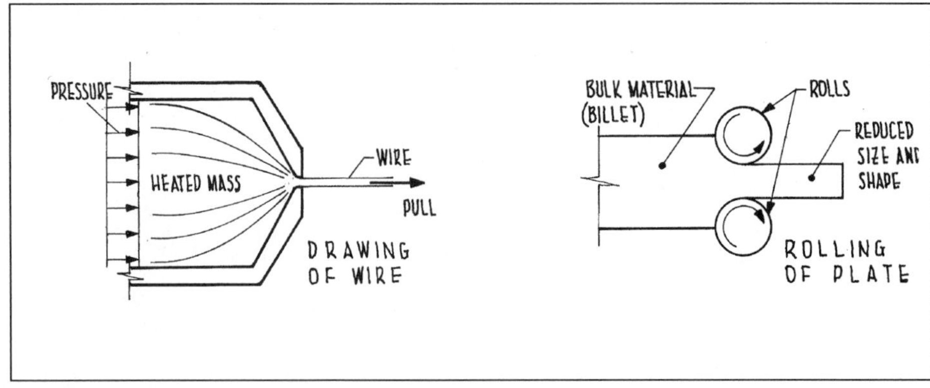

Figure 12-12 Examples of cold working.

Similarly, steel sections of all types are produced by *rolling* a hot but still solid *billet* of bulk material into the final required shape. Even though rolling forces are high, each set of rolls changes the shape of the incoming material only slightly; a steel billet may pass through as many as 20 successive sets of rolls in forming it into its final shape. A typical reduction in size is shown in the schematic diagram of Figure 12-12. When the billet starts through a series of rolls it may be red hot, but the process is still called cold working.

12.5 Shear Center

All of the beam sections considered in earlier discussions were symmetrical about their vertical axes. Further, it was tacitly assumed that the vertical load on the beam lay in that axis of vertical symmetry. Some typical cases of symmetrical beams symmetrically loaded are shown in Figure 12-13.

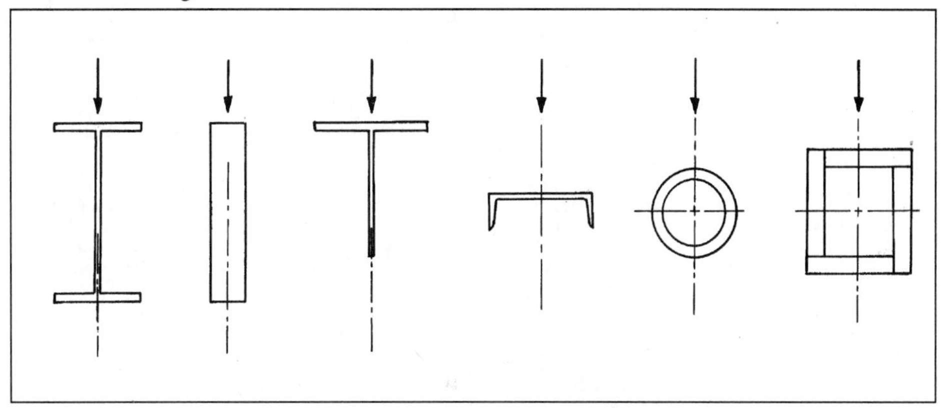

Figure 12-13 Vertically symmetrical beams symmetrically loaded.

In all of the beams shown in Figure 12-13, there is no component of load or section that would cause the section to "roll," or to rotate about its longitudinal axis. Under the vertically symmetrical load, the section will simply translate up or down in its vertical axis of symmetry.

There are many beam sections in common use, however, that are not symmetrical about their vertical axis. Probably the most common, and most familiar, is the channel section. A typical channel section is shown in Figure 12-14 with a vertical load placed in extreme positions either to the left or right of the beam such that "roll" is inevitable.

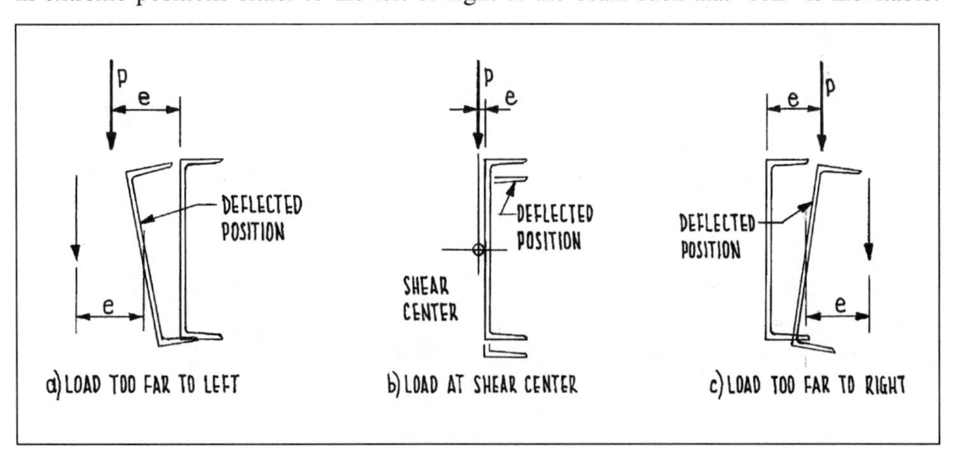

Figure 12-14 Channel beam section under eccentric load.

A load placed in the position shown in Figure 14a will cause counterclockwise rotation of the section. A load placed in the position shown in Figure 14c will cause clockwise rotation of the section. Obviously, there must be a point somewhere between these extremes at which the beam will not rotate at all, but will simply translate vertically. Such a case is shown in Figure 14b; the point of loading at which a load will not cause rotation of the section is called the *shear center* of the section.

The location of the shear center is a property of the section. While the concept of the existence of a shear center is simple, finding its location can be a rather complex calculation. Fortunately, most of the unsymmetrical sections one is likely to encounter are standard shapes and their shear centers have long ago been calculated and tabulated.

The heading of the double-page AISC table on channel sections is given in Table S-3 in the Technical Manual. On the right-hand page is a column headed "shear center location e_o," where the distance e_o is keyed back to the sketch. The shear center is seen to fall generally between 3/8 in. to 3/4 in. from the back of the channel.

If the channel is not loaded through its shear center, the channel will carry sharply less load than it will carry if properly loaded. In most cases, it is a matter of simple detailing to assure that the load falls at the shear center. Some examples of such detailing are shown in Figure 12-15.

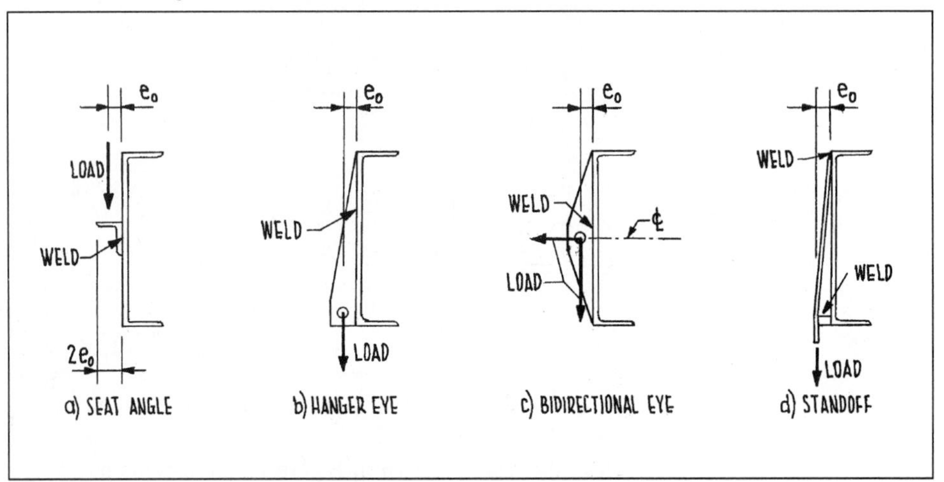

Figure 12-15 Typical loading details on a channel.

For angles, the location of the shear center is at a fixed point; it always falls at the juncture of the two legs. The location of the shear center of an angle is shown in Figure 12-16, along with its actual axes of bending, the u and z axes.

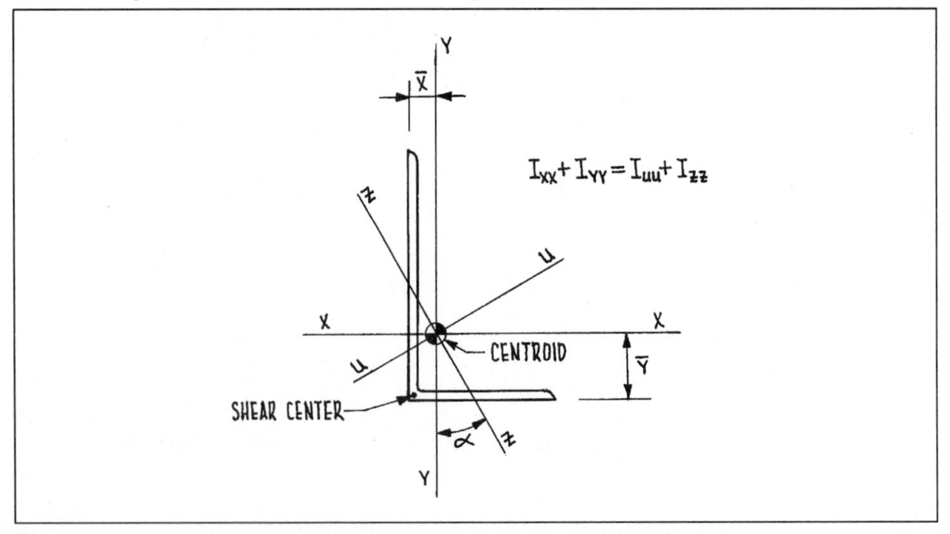

Figure 12-16 Shear center and principal axes of an angle.

An angle does not bend about the x-y axes as does a section that has at least one axis of symmetry. The bending axes of a doubly unsymmetrical angle are the u-z axis as shown in Figure 12-16, with the z axis being the weak axis. The angle α to the weaker zz axis is given in the AISC table of properties for angles, along with the radius of gyration about the zz axis (for column design).

Unless deliberately constrained to do otherwise, an angle is going to bend about the u-z axes, not the x-y axes. The x-y axes are shown in the sketches primarily to locate the centroid, since both sets of axes have their origins at the centroid. The u-z axes shown in Figure 12-16 are called the principal axes of the section. They are found by a Mohr's circle solution similar to that used to find the principal stresses on a particle. It is a property of moments of inertia that $I_{xx} + I_{yy} = I_{uu} + I_{zz}$, where I_{uu} is the maximum moment of inertia the angle can develop and I_{zz} is the minimum.

Bending in beams that are unsymmetrical on both axes is beyond the scope of this text, not due to any unusual level of difficulty but due simply to lack of space.

12.6 Membrane Stresses

Membranes are a type of structure in which there is no bending. A balloon is an excellent example of a membrane. One can readily envision many forms of balloons, from long cylindrical ones to round ones to tapered hot air passenger balloons.

A balloon requires internal pressure to maintain its shape. A structural membrane, however, is stiff enough to maintain its shape without such internal pressure. That stiffness immediately invites problems with unwanted bending stresses unless the membrane is carefully designed to prevent (or accommodate) such bending stresses.

Thin-walled steel pressure vessels are a typical type of membrane. A common pressure vessel (tank) is cylindrical along its length, with domed ends. Such a pressurized tank is shown in Figure 12-17. It might hold anything from air to steam to hydrogen.

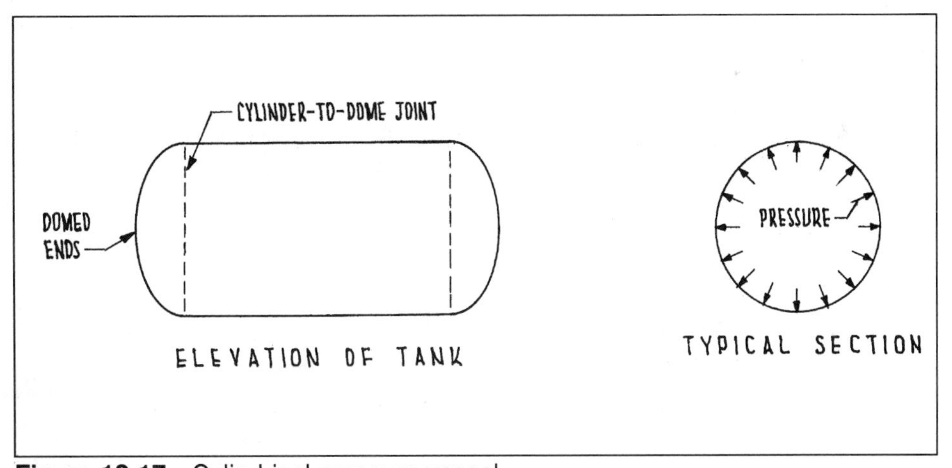

Figure 12-17 Cylindrical pressure vessel.

The pressure vessel of Figure 12-17 is rigid. Nonetheless it may be analyzed as if it were a balloon; the bending stresses in such a tank are so small they can safely be ignored. It should be noted early, however, that bending stresses can be serious wherever a change in geometry occurs, such as the joint where the membrane geometry changes from cylinder to sphere.

A "hoop" is taken out of the cylinder and cut in half. It is shown as a free body in Figure 12-18. The pressure is shown on the projected area.

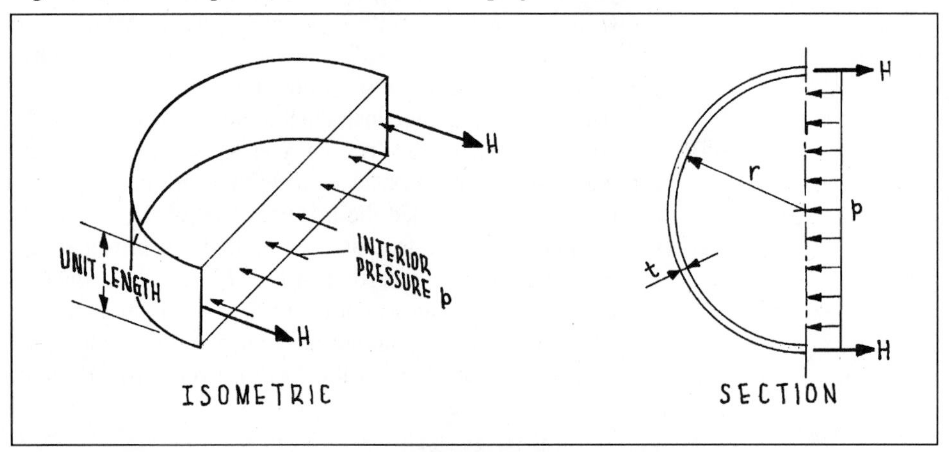

Figure 12-18 Hoop stress in a pressure vessel.

The hoop force in the membrane is found by summing horizontal forces:

$$-p(2r)(1) + H + H = 0$$

$$H = pr \tag{12-2}$$

The wall of the vessel will have a discrete thickness *t*. The hoop stress in the wall is a direct stress:

$$f = \frac{H}{A} = \frac{pr}{t(1)}$$

$$= \frac{pr}{t} \tag{12-3}$$

The longitudinal force in the vessel is found by taking a transverse section. The free body of such a section is shown in Figure 12-19. The internal gas pressure is again shown on the projected area.

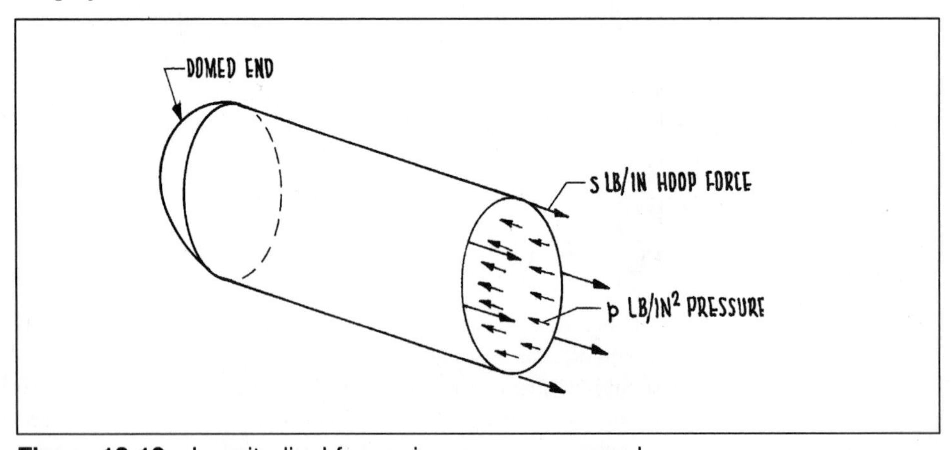

Figure 12-19 Longitudinal forces in a pressure vessel.

The longitudinal force per inch is found by summing horizontal forces:

$$s(2\pi r) - p(\pi r^2) = 0$$

$$s = \frac{pr}{2} \tag{12-4}$$

The stress in the wall in the longitudinal direction is again a direct stress per unit of length of wall:

$$f = \frac{s}{A} = \frac{pr}{2t} \tag{12-5}$$

The final state of stress of a particle taken anywhere along the wall of the cylinder is shown in Figure 12-20.

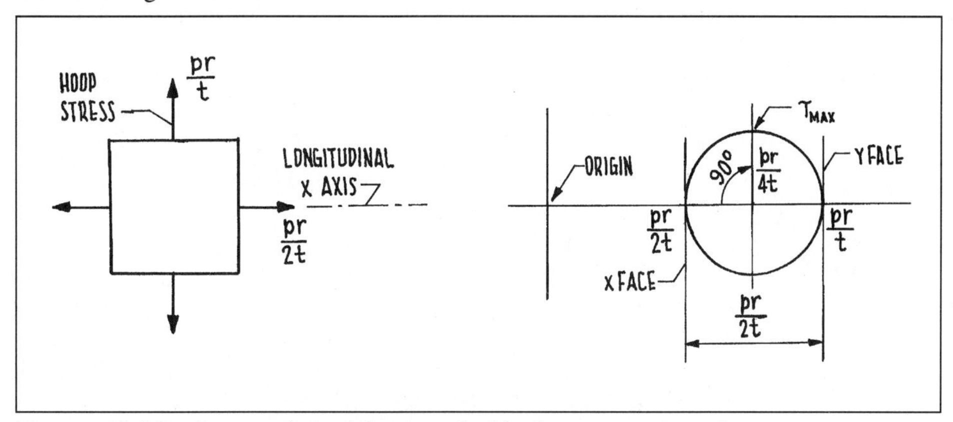

Figure 12-20 Stressed particle on cylindrical pressure vessel.

The state of stress of the particle in Figure 12-20 is immediately recognized as the principal state of stress. Maximum shear stress is readily found from Mohr's stress circle, as shown in Figure 12-20:

$$\tau_{MAX} = \frac{pr}{4t} \tag{12-6}$$

The stresses in the domed ends of the cylindrical tank are best found by finding the stresses in a complete sphere. Such a sphere is shown in Figure 12-21, with a free body taken along a great circle.

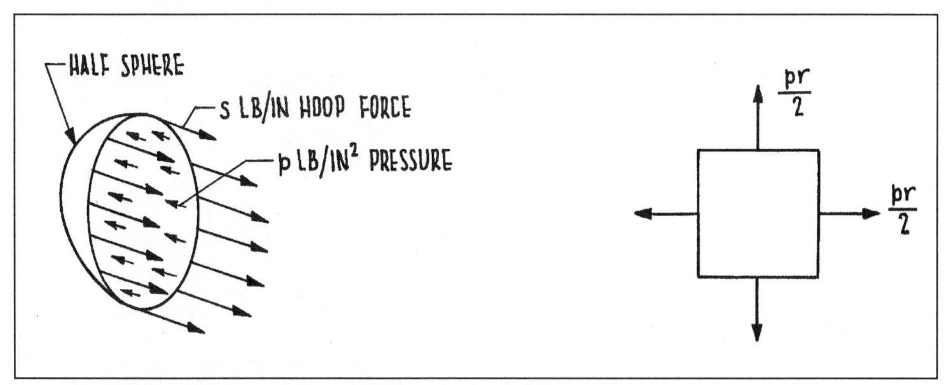

Figure 12-21 Sphere under internal pressure.

Forces are summed horizontally to find the force *S* per unit length of the membrane:

$$s(2\pi r) = p(\pi r^2)$$

$$s = \frac{pr}{2} \tag{12-7}$$

In a pressurized sphere, the force *S* is the same on any two mutually perpendicular great circles, producing the state of stress shown on the particle in Figure 12-21. Note that Mohr's circle for this state of stress is reduced to a point; there is no shear in any direction in such a state of stress.

Some examples will illustrate a few solutions of problems in thin-walled pressure vessels. In these examples, there is no pretense that there is no bending; the bending is simply ignored.

Example 12-1

Forces in pressure vessels.

Given: Pressure vessel with capped ends, as shown. Internal pressure is 60 lb/in.^{2}

To Find: Tensile force in each of the 12 bolts.

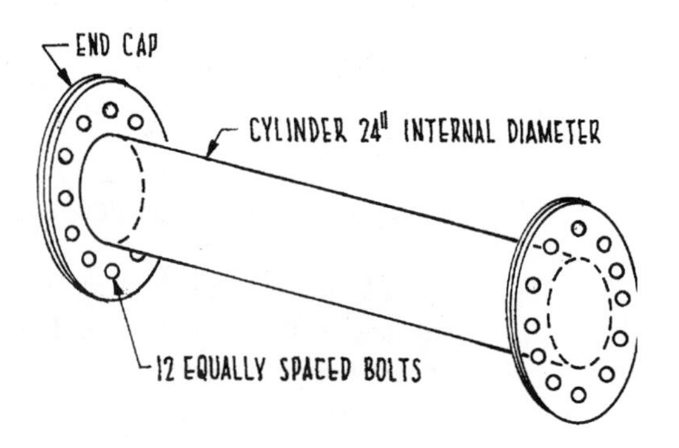

Solution: A free body of the end cap is shown in the following sketch.

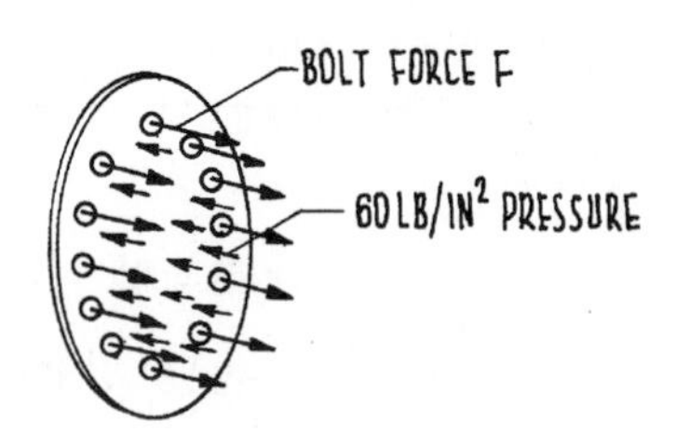

The sum of horizontal forces yields:

$$12F - 60[\pi(12)^2] = 0$$

$$F = 2262 \text{ lbs/bolt.}$$

It is interesting to note that the force produced by the pressurized gas places a load of more than 1 ton on each of the 12 bolts. Such huge forces occur commonly in pressure vessels; they are not to be treated casually.

Steel pipe is commonly made by wrapping a steel strap tightly around a mandrel, forming a spiral as shown in Figure 12-22; the joint is then machine welded. With this process, steel pipe of any diameter and any length can be produced. It has the advantage that shipping is limited to solid heavy rolls of strap; the exhorbitant cost of shipping huge volumes of empty pipe is avoided.

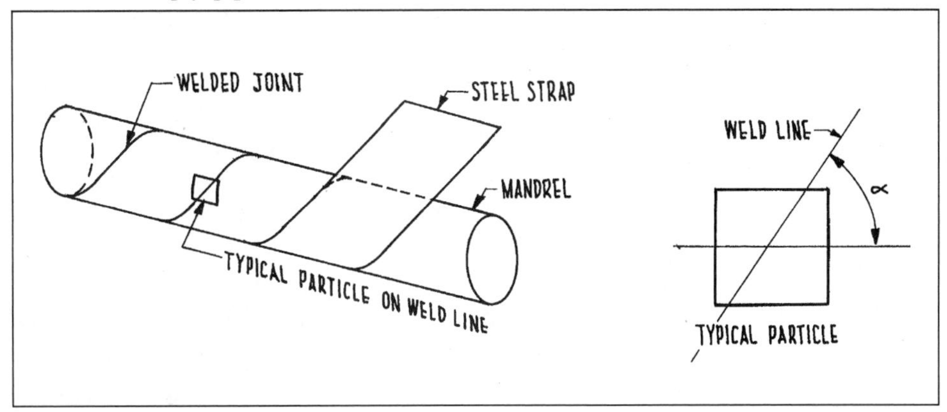

Figure 12-22 Welded steel pipe.

Example 12-2

Forces in pressure vessels.

Given: Welded steel pipe shown in Figure 12-22.
Design pressure is 0.3 N/mm^2.
Internal diameter is 300 mm.
Wall thickness is 10 mm.
Angle α is 30°.

To Find: Stress along the weld line.

Solution: The principal stresses are given by equations (12-3) and (12-5):

$$\text{Hoop stress} = \frac{pr}{t} = \frac{0.3(150)}{10} = 4.5\text{N / mm}^2$$

$$\text{Longitudinal stress} = \frac{pr}{2t} = \frac{0.3(15)}{2(10)} = 2.25\text{N / mm}^2$$

Mohr's circle is drawn for the given state of stress.

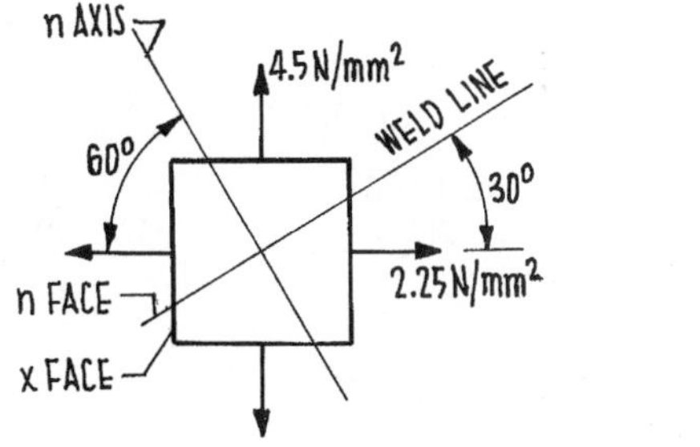

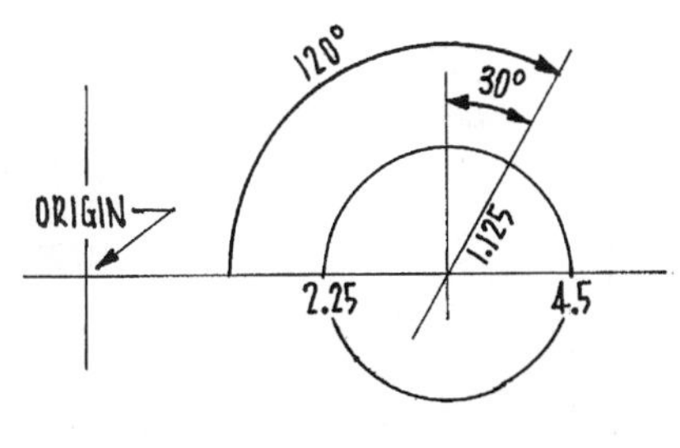

The particle is rotated clockwise until the x face is parallel to the weld. The angle on the particle is 60°; it is therefore 120° on Mohr's circle. The stresses on the x face at that angle are:

$$\sigma_x = 3.375 + 1.125 \sin 30 = 3.9 \text{ N/mm}^2$$
$$\tau_x = 1.125 \cos 30 = 0.97 \text{ N/mm}^2$$

The stresses on the y face are:

$$\sigma_y = 3.375 - 1.125 \sin 30 = 2.8 \text{ N/mm}^2$$
$$\tau_x = -1.125 \cos 30 = 0.97 \text{ N/mm}^2$$

A stressed particle of the weld is shown on the following sketch.

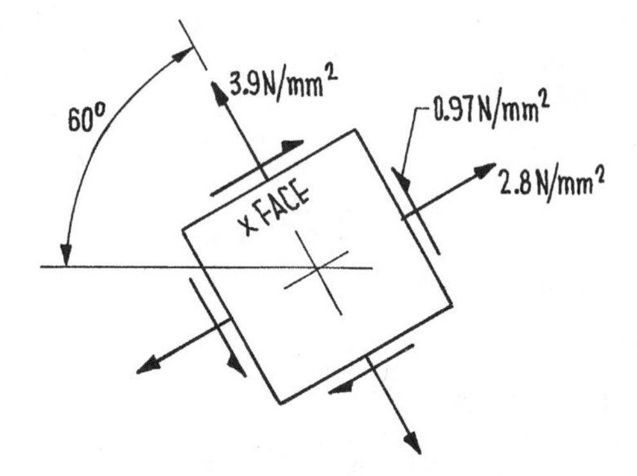

12.7 Bending on Two Axes

All of the loadings on beams and columns considered in previous discussions were presumed to occur one load at a time. In reality, of course, two or even three loadings can occur on a member at the same time. Such a general case of combined loading is shown in Figure 12-23, where a rectangular section is subject to an axial load P and moments M_{xx} and M_{yy} about both centroidal axes at the same time.

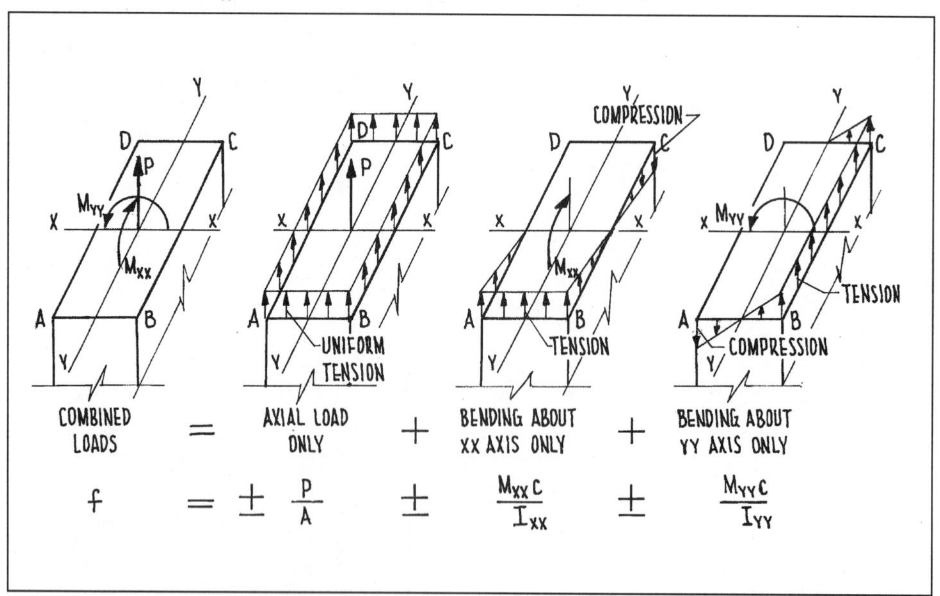

Figure 12-23 Combined axial stress and flexure stress.

The stresses produced by the combined loadings are directly additive. The general form of the solution for stress is shown in Figure 12-23 as:

$$f = \pm\frac{P}{A} \pm \frac{M_{xx}c}{I_{xx}} \pm \frac{M_{yy}c}{I_{yy}} \tag{12-8}$$

The difficulty in using Eq.12-8 is that all signs are ±. As always, positive stress is tension and negative stress is compression. One must establish the point where the stress is to be found and then choose the correct signs individually. At point A in the section of Figure 12-23, for example, the signs under the given directions of load would be:

$$f = +\frac{P}{A} + \frac{M_{xx}c}{I_{xx}} - \frac{M_{yy}c}{I_{yy}} \tag{12-9a}$$

At point *B*, the signs would be:

$$f = +\frac{P}{A} + \frac{M_{xx}c}{I_{xx}} + \frac{M_{yy}c}{I_{yy}} \tag{12-9b}$$

At point *C*, the signs would be:

$$f = +\frac{P}{A} - \frac{M_{xx}c}{I_{xx}} + \frac{M_{yy}c}{I_{yy}} \tag{12-9c}$$

At point *D*, the signs would be:

$$f = +\frac{P}{A} - \frac{M_{xx}c}{I_{xx}} - \frac{M_{yy}c}{I_{yy}} \tag{12-9d}$$

Obviously, for the given case of loading, the maximum stress on the section will occur where all the signs are alike. For the section of Figure 12-23, that point is point *B*, where all the given loads produce tensile stress.

Some numerical examples will illustrate the solution to cases of combined stress.

Example 12-3

Combined axial and flexural stress.

Given: Wide flange section loaded as shown (short pedestal).

To Find: 1) Maximum tensile stress and its location.
2) Maximum compressive stress and its location.

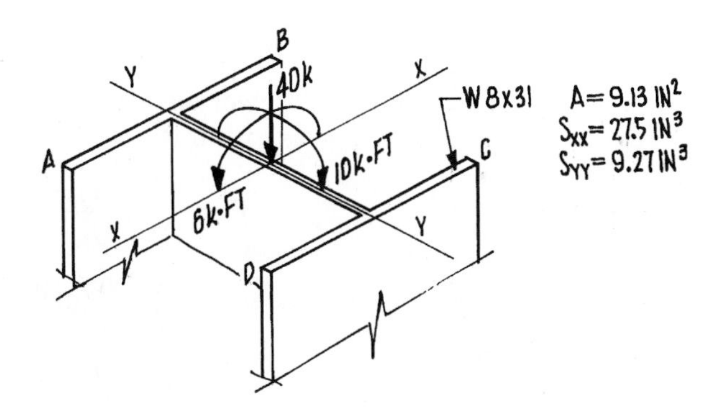

Solution: The location of the maximum compressive stress is relatively easy to locate visually; all three loads produce compressive stress at point D:

$$f_D = -\frac{P}{A} - \frac{M_{xx}}{S_{xx}} - \frac{M_{yy}}{S_{yy}}$$

$$= -\frac{40,000}{9.13} - \frac{10,000(12)}{27.5} - \frac{6000(12)}{9.27}$$

$$= -16,500\ lb/in.^2$$

The location of the maximum tensile stress is also found by visual examination. Since the axial stress is always compressive, the maximum tensile stress will occur where both of the moments produce tensile stress; that point is point B:

$$f_B = -\frac{P}{A} + \frac{M_{xx}}{S_{xx}} + \frac{M_{yy}}{S_{yy}}$$

$$= -\frac{40,000}{9.13} + \frac{10,000(12)}{27.5} + \frac{6000(12)}{9.27}$$

$$= +7750\ lb/in.^2$$

Example 12-4

Combined axial and flexural stress.

Given: Tee section loaded as shown.

To Find: 1) Maximum tensile stress and its location
2) Maximum compressive stress and its location.

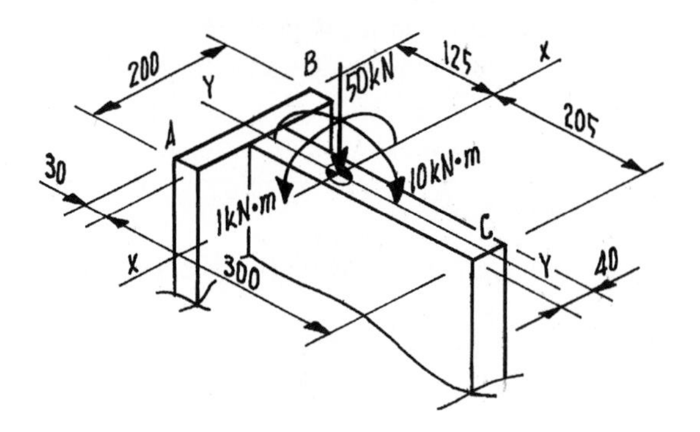

Solution: Maximum compressive stress could occur at point A or at point C. Both stresses will be found:

$$f_A = -\frac{P}{A} + \frac{M_{xx}c}{I_{xx}} - \frac{M_{yy}c}{I_{yy}}$$

$$= -\frac{50,000}{18,000} + \frac{10x10^6(125)}{199x10^6} - \frac{1x10^6(100)}{21.6x10^6}$$

$$= -13.1\ N/mm^2 (\text{maximum})$$

Maximum tensile stress will occur at point B, where both M_{xx} and M_{yy} produce tension:

$$f_B = -\frac{P}{A} + \frac{M_{xx}c}{I_{xx}} + \frac{M_{yy}c}{I_{yy}}$$

$$= -\frac{50,000}{18,000} + \frac{10x10^6(125)}{199x10^6} + \frac{1x10^6(100)}{21.6x10^6}$$

$$= +8.13N/mm^2(\max imum)$$

The combined stresses on a structural member can come from any number of loadings. Some typical cases of loadings that result in combined stresses are illustrated in the following examples.

Example 12-5

Combined axial and flexural stress.

Given: 250x250 pedestal loaded by an inclined load as shown. Allowable stress in the material is $\pm 7 N/mm^2$.

To Find: Maximum allowable load F.

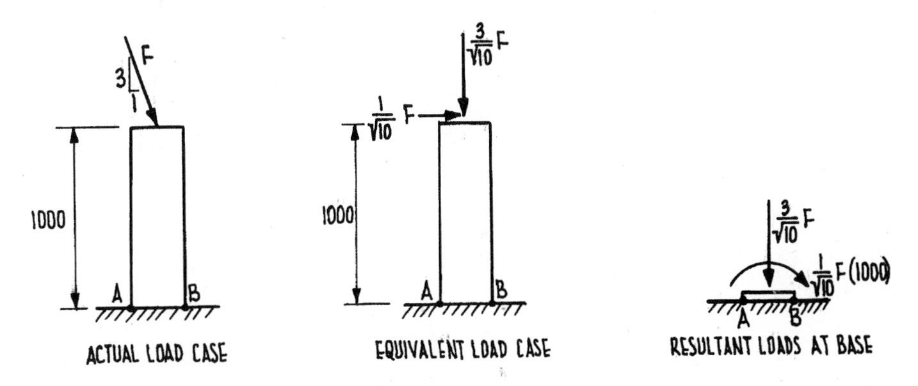

Solution: The given loads produce resultant force and moment at the base as shown in the final sketch.

Maximum stress is seen to be compressive, occurring at point B:

$$f_B = -\frac{P}{A} - \frac{Mc}{I}; \ A = 250 \text{ x } 250 = 62,500 \text{ mm}^2$$

$$I = \frac{250x250^3}{12} = 326 \text{ x } 106 \text{ mm}^4$$

$$c = 125 \text{ mm}$$

$$-7 = -\frac{0.949F}{62,500} - \frac{0.316F(1000)(125)}{326x10^6}$$

$$F = 51.3kN$$

Example 12-6

Combined axial and flexural stress.

Given: Standard steel pipe 6 in. diameter loaded as shown.

To Find: Maximum stress in the pipe.

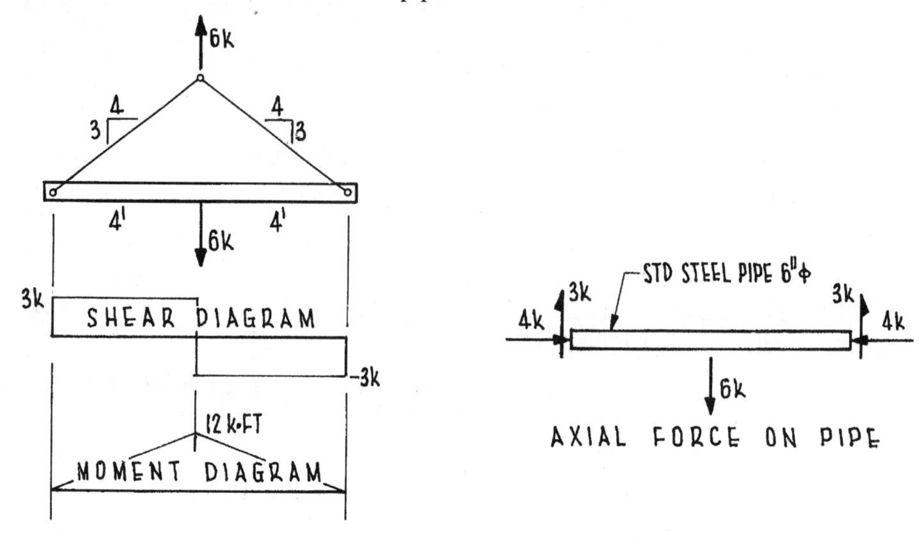

Solution: The shear and moment diagrams are found independently of the axial force, as shown in the sketch.

Since the axial force is negative, the maximum stress will be compressive, occuring in the top fibers of the pipe at the center of the beam:

$$f_c = -\frac{P}{A} - \frac{M}{S};\ A = 5.58\ \text{in.}^2$$

$$S = 8.50\ \text{in.}^3$$

$$f_c = -\frac{4000}{5.58} - \frac{12{,}000(12)}{8.50}$$

$$f = 17{,}700\ psi\ (compression)$$

A particular way of looking at combined loadings is used in column design, where axial loads are usually large and moments are usually small. It is based on the principle that any force may be resolved into a force and a couple, and conversely, any force and moment may be combined into a single force (see Chapter 3, figures 3-10 and 3-11). Such equivalent systems of force and moment on a section are shown in Figure 12-24.

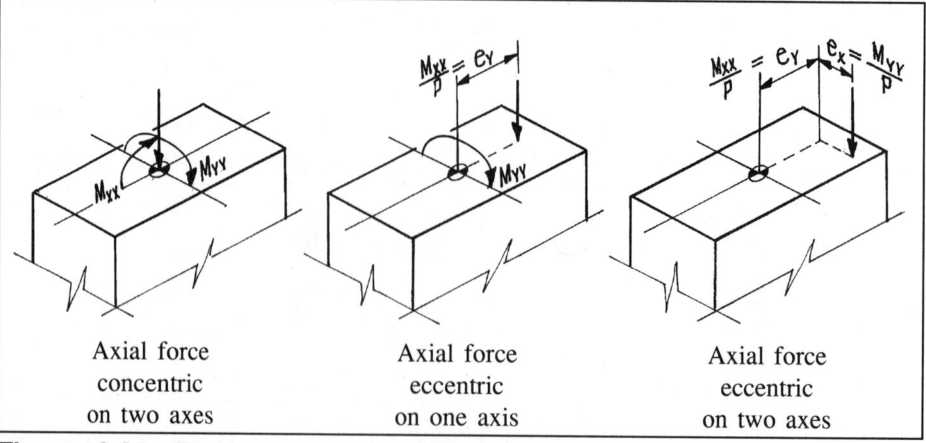

Figure 12-24 Equivalent systems of force and moment.

The three systems of load shown in Figure 12-24 are all equivalent; each will produce the same stresses in the cross section. The eccentricities e_x and e_y are always measured from the centroidal x and y axes. These eccentricities are useful parameters in investigations of combined stresses, such as columns.

The load cases of Examples 12-3 and 12-4 can readily be put into this format as shown in Figure 12-25. The solutions for stress given in the examples, however, would be identically the same.

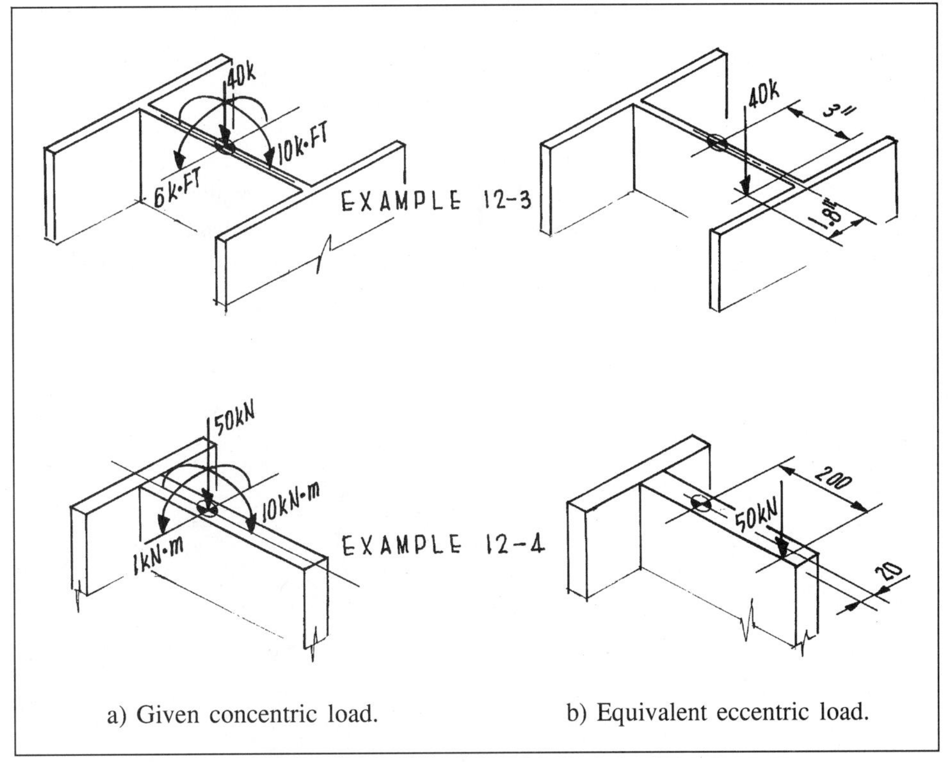

a) Given concentric load. b) Equivalent eccentric load.

Figure 12-25 Equivalent loading formats.

The concept of eccentric loading shown in Figures 12-24 and 12-25 permits the analysis of a special case of loading that will be useful in many future applications.

It is frequently desirable to load a member such that no tension occurs anywhere in the stress diagram. A typical example of such a case is the bearing stress under a footing; since soil cannot resist "uplift," it is desirable that no tension occurs in the stress diagram.

The load case for a rectangular block under eccentric loading is shown in Figure 12-26. The eccentricity of the load from the centroidal axis is shown as e, where $e = M/P$. The load is placed at the eccentricity e that produces zero stress at one edge.

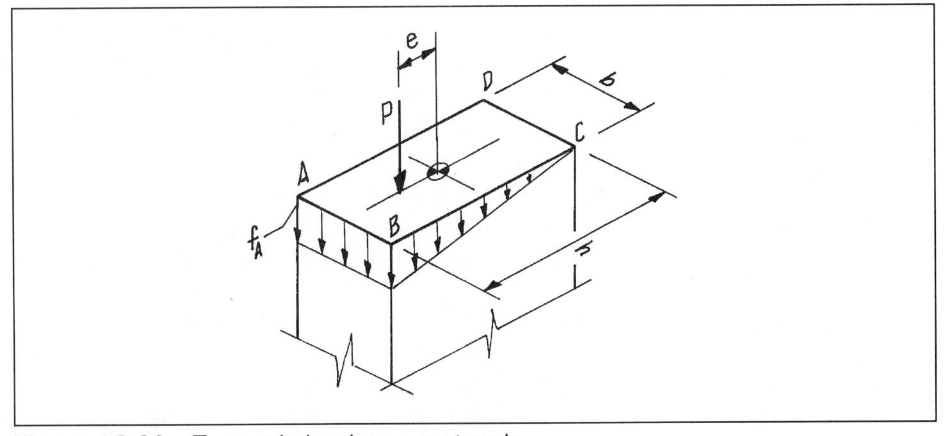

Figure 12-26 Eccentric load on a rectangle.

The eccentricity e is found from the stress computation:

$$f_c = 0 = \pm\frac{P}{A} \pm \frac{M}{S};\ A = bh$$

$$S = bh^2/6$$

$$M = Pe$$

$$0 = \frac{P}{bh} \pm \frac{Pe}{bh^2/6}$$

$$e = \frac{h}{6} \qquad (12\text{-}10)$$

The calculation will produce the same result for bending on either axis. The conclusion is drawn that if an axial load on a rectangle is kept within the middle third of the rectangle, no tension stress will occur. A sketch of such a position of loading is shown in Figure 12-27.

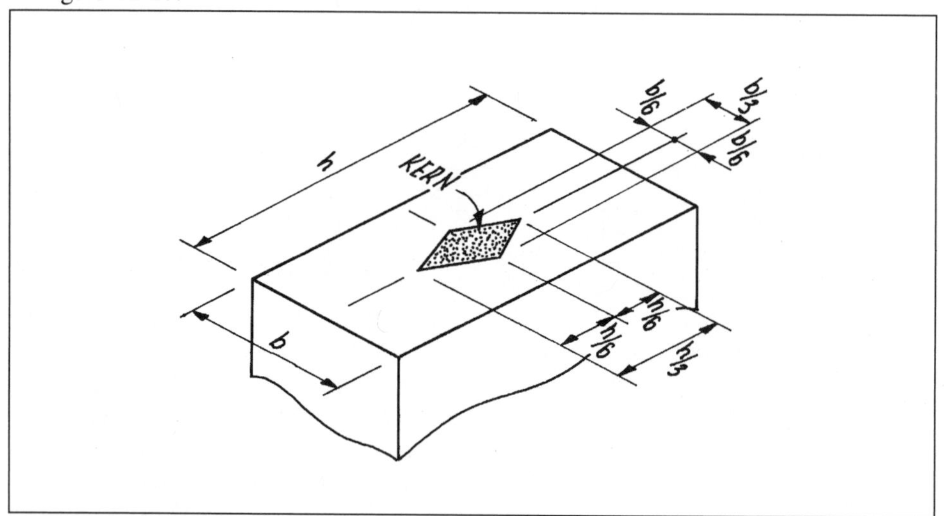

Figure 12-27 Kern of a rectangular section.

The position in a section where a load may be placed without producing tension is called the *kern* of the section. For a rectangular section, the kern is the middle third of the section as shown in Figure 12-27. For a circular cross section, the kern is the middle fourth of the cross section; the proof of this statement is given as an outside problem.

Review Questions

1. At what level of stress does creep begin?
2. How long does creep continue once a material is loaded?
3. How does temperature affect creep?
4. What materials develop creep?
5. What materials develop relaxation?
6. What materials develop fatigue?
7. What is meant by the term "endurance limit" of a material?
8. Does the endurance limit of a material increase or decrease as the ultimate strength is increased?
9. Name two primary causes of stress concentration.
10. Which would produce a higher stress concentration factor in a plate, a small hole, a large hole, or a reentrant corner?
11. What is the general rule to follow for keeping stress concentrations low?

12. When stress concentrations are unavoidable, what must be done to accommodate them?
13. What is the stress concentration factor around a 20 mm diameter hole in a plate 100 mm wide?
14. What is the stress concentration factor around a 5 mm diameter hole in a plate 100 mm wide?
15. How can the stress concentration at a reentrant corner be reduced?
16. In computing peak stress at a stress concentration, how is the average stress computed?
17. Name two places along a bolt in tension where stress concentrations will occur.
18. Name two common construction materials that exhibit a plastic range.
19. How does overloading into the plastic range affect the modulus of elasticity?
20. Describe strain hardening in your own words.
21. What benefit is realized through the strain hardening of a material?
22. What is case hardening?
23. What is shot peening?
24. What is the shear center of a section?
25. Where is the shear center of an angle?
26. Given the information in the *Steel Handbook*, how can the minimum moment of inertia of an angle I_{zz} be calculated? The maximum moment of inertia I_{uu}?
27. What is distinctive about a membrane insofar as its response to loading is concerned?
28. A column 18 in. square carries an axial load of 50 kips and a moment M_{xx} of 25 kip·ft. If this axial load is to be shown as an eccentric load, where would it be located?
29. From what coordinates is the eccentricity of an axial load measured?
30. What is the kern of a section?
31. Where is the kern of a rectangular section?
32. Derive mathematically the size of the kern of a circle.

PART

3

STRUCTURAL ANALYSIS

CHAPTER

13

LOADS ON STRUCTURES

This chapter begins the presentation of structural analysis. In this chapter and succeeding chapters, consideration shifts from individual members to systems of members. The systems of members to be considered may be sets of beams and their interaction with each other or they may be an entire multistory structure and the way the entire structure responds to an external load.

The starting point of the presentation is the definition of loads that can occur on structures. In past discussions, a load was simply assumed to exist on a member and the member was then analyzed for its response to that load. It was never necessary to start with a load condition (such as wind) and then find the specific load on a specific member due to that load condition. That chain of events, or "load path" begins with this chapter.

All of the loads, forces and dimensions used in this chapter and in the remainder of this textbook are in Imperial (British) units. The reason is quite simple: in the United States, the loads are prescribed by building codes and the building codes prescribe the loads in Imperial units. At present, there is no SI edition of either of the two major U.S. building codes, the Uniform Building Code or the Standard Building Code.

There are two major categories of load: gravity loads and lateral loads. Each of these two major categories has two major subcategories:

1. Gravity loads
   a) Dead load
   b) Live load
2. Lateral loads
   a) Wind load
   b) Earthquake load

There are many environmental loads that can occur on a structure, such as snow, ice, drifting sand, ponding water, and so on. These loads are treated simply as variations of the major loads listed above; for the sake of simplicity, they are not treated individually in the following discussions.

13.1 Conventions and Practices

Over the years, certain conventions and practices have come into existence concerning the way that loads are treated in structural analysis. Such "standard" practices exist because over long periods of time and usage, these standard practices have been found to work better than other practices. A few of those standard practices are presented here. Other standard practices are presented in later chapters in the context of a particular material or a particular design concept.

Loads are always given on the projected length or area, never on a slope. A typical example of such a loading is shown in Figure 13-1 for a sloping beam loaded both by gravity loads and lateral loads. In all cases, the load is converted into an equivalent load on the projected length or the projected area.

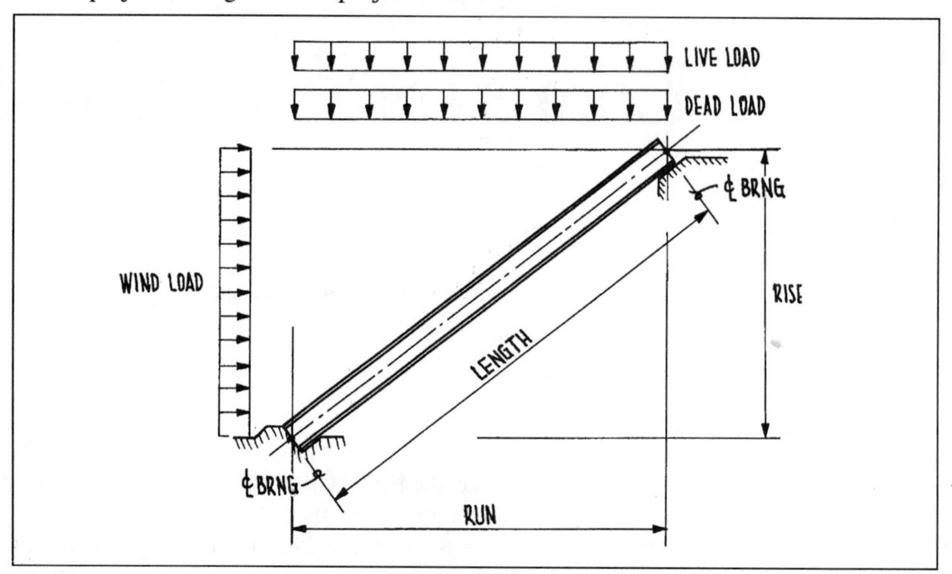

Figure 13-1 Loads on projected dimensions.

The reason for such a convention lies in the way the shears and moments will be computed later. The gravity loads used to determine shear and moment will occur in the vertical (y) direction while the lateral loads will occur in the horizontal (x) direction. It is quite natural and direct to compute shears and moments and to draw the shear and moment diagrams using these vertical and horizontal components. In later problems in design, it will be seen to be a fairly simple procedure to convert these shears and moments into those along the axis of the sloping member.

Similarly, thermal growth of a sloping member is much easier to handle in terms of its x and y components rather than along its sloping axis. Such an approach can greatly simplify the calculations where several sloping members intersect at a point. An example of such thermal growth on a single member is shown in Figure 13-2.

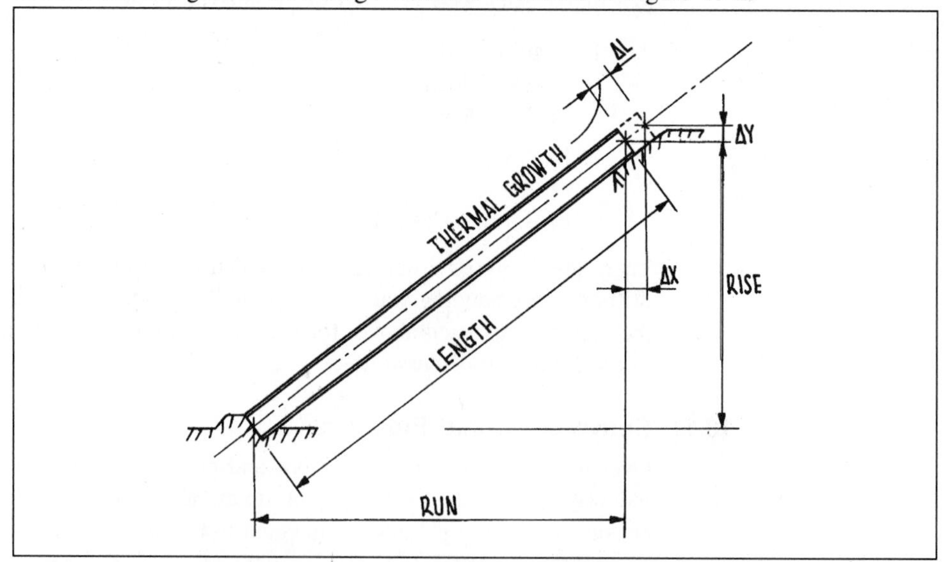

Figure 13-2 Thermal growth on a sloping member.

Dimensions used in structural analysis are always taken to the centerline of the members or to the centerline of supports. Some typical examples of actual dimensions being at variance with centerline dimensions are shown in Figure 13-3.

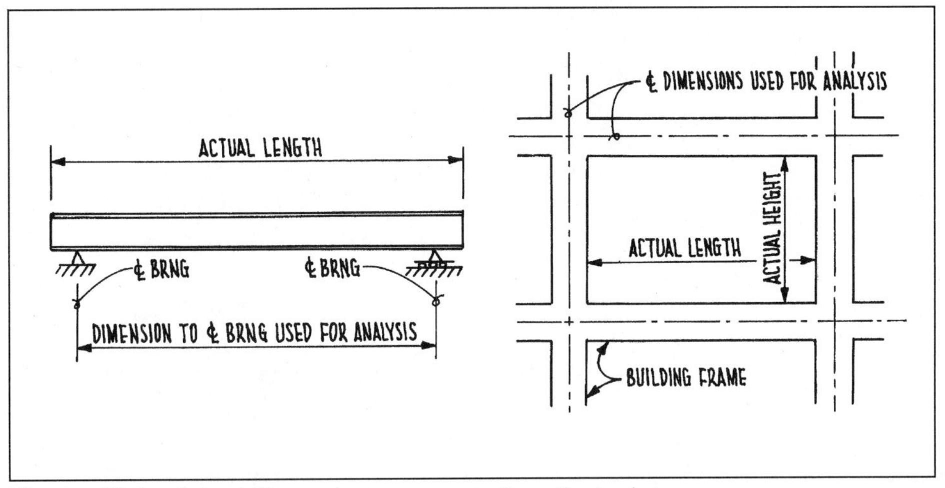

Figure 13-3 Actual dimensions vs. centerline dimensions.

Loads are always treated in standard categories, even when the category does not fit very well. A heavy filing cabinet, for example, will be treated as a concentrated point load in spite of the fact that the footprint of the load is probably $1^1/_2$ feet by 3 feet. Of all possible standard categories, however, it fits best as a concentrated point load and is therefore treated as such in structural analysis.

In structural analysis, a series of closely spaced identical loads (such as joist loads) will be treated as a uniformly distributed load rather than as discrete loads. Such a case is shown in Figure 13-4 for a series of closely spaced joists. The shear and moment diagrams for the supporting beam would be drawn as if the load were a uniformly distributed load.

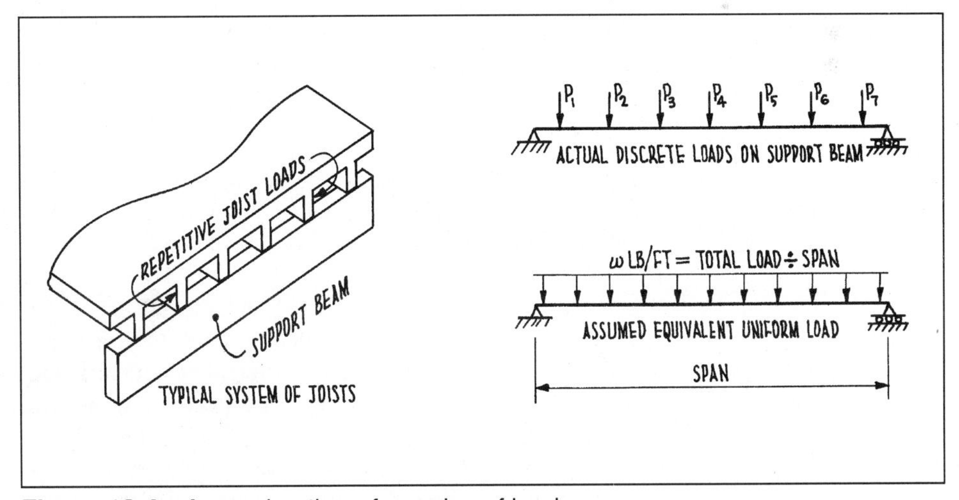

Figure 13-4 Approximation of a series of loads.

The approximation shown in Figure 13-4 would likely be used even for rather widely spaced loads, provided that the load arrangement is similar to that of Figure 13-4. The shear and moment diagrams for such loads spaced at the $^1/_4$ points along the span is not far different from those for a uniformly distributed load, provided, of course, that the total load is the same in both cases. Proof of the accuracy of this approximation is assigned as one of the outside problems in this chapter.

When dealing with repetitive members such as those of Figure 13-4, it is the practice to assume that each of the repetitive members will carry all the load halfway to the next "like" member. A joist, for example, will carry all the load halfway to the adjacent joists at either side. Similarly, the supporting beams and girders will carry all the load halfway to the adjacent beams and girders at either side. This approximation of load distribution is developed more fully in the next chapter.

It has already been noted that beam supports must allow for thermal growth and contraction. A beam firmly restrained against thermal growth can be seriously damaged by thermal growth even at common atmospheric temperature changes. Allowing one end of the beam to move, as shown in Figure 13-5, will prevent such thermal stresses from occurring.

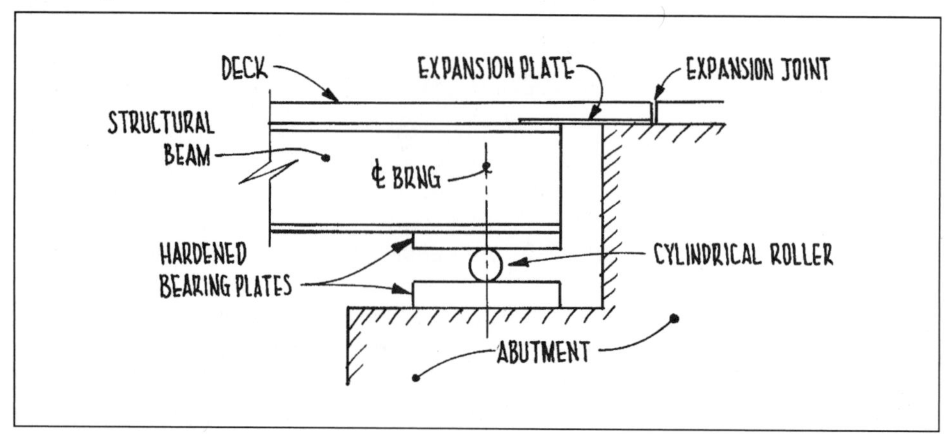

Figure 13-5 Expansion bearings.

The expansion roller bearing shown in Figure 13-5 is an idealized friction-free bearing that offers no resistance to longitudinal movement. Such ideal roller bearings are not commonly used in buildings, though they are often used in bridges. In buildings, the expansion bearings will likely be friction bearings that can develop considerable amounts of resistance but such resistance is commonly ignored in the structural analysis.

Foundations in smaller structures will often consist of isolated spread footings at each column or each bearing wall. Any differential settlement between any of these footings will cause stress in the structural members. Even in small structures, however, there can be hundreds of combinations of differential settlements that might occur in the foundation. A separate analysis of each such possibility would be impractical; a "blanket" approach to such multiplicity of load cases is obviously warranted.

It is the practice in designing foundations to limit the total settlement of every isolated footing to a maximum of 1 inch or 25 mm. If no footing can settle more than 1 inch, then the maximum differential settlement that can occur between any two adjacent footings will be somewhat less than 1 inch; this maximum differential settlement is usually taken to be $^3/_4$ inch. When differential settlements are thus limited to $^3/_4$ inch, it has been found that the overall increase in stress in the structure will not exceed about 15%. For such an increase, the stresses introduced by random foundation settlements are considered to be negligible and are rarely investigated as separate load cases.

In addition to the foregoing list of practices, there are many other "standard" practices that are commonly observed in the analysis and design of structures. The foregoing brief summary, however, will permit this introduction to structural analysis to proceed. In later discussions, other practices will be introduced as appropriate in the context of a particular point in the analysis.

13.2 Gravity Loads on Structures

Gravity loads consist of loads created by gravity as it acts on all objects that the structure supports, whether they are a fixed part of the structural system or whether they are loose and free to move around. Technically speaking, gravity loads are not exactly parallel; their lines of action must eventually intersect at the earth's center. Within the small scope of a building size, however, gravity loads are treated as a parallel load system in all of structural analysis.

There are two major categories of gravity loads: dead load and live load. The dead load of a structure is the weight of all the components that make up the structure. It includes the floors, beams, walls, windows, mullions, columns, plaster, cable trays, plumbing and all other components that are rigidly fixed to or part of the structural frame. Dead load does not include furnishings, carpets, file cabinets, books, electrical wiring, movable partitions or other loose items; such loose items are classified by default as live loads.

Of all the loads that may occur on a structure, both vertical and lateral, only the dead load can be determined with any accuracy. The live load (the loose items) can change daily, while the wind and earthquake loads are necessarily short-term highly variable transient loads. Dead load, in contrast, is composed of fixed definable objects with known computable dead weights.

Because the dead load can be so readily and so accurately determined, the factor of safety for dead load may be set lower than for other, more uncertain loads. Such a reduction has in fact been permitted in reinforced concrete for many years and is currently being extended into other materials. It is important, therefore, that the dead load be accurately determined in order that such reduced factors of safety can be properly assigned; in such circumstances the integrity of the structure actually depends on an accurate determination of dead load.

Further, it is the long-term permanent loads (primarily dead loads) that produce foundation settlements; foundation settlements are by their nature a long-term phenomenon and are affected only slightly (if at all) by short-term loads. If an accurate assessment of foundation settlements is to be made, it is necessary that all of the permanent long-term loads be accurately identified. These long-term loads are, of course, the dead loads; the successful prevention of structural damage due to foundation settlements will therefore depend heavily on having an accurate determination of dead load.

And further, in an earthquake it is the dead loads fixed to the structural frame that will be accelerated laterally and vertically with the frame and will therefore produce force ($F = ma$). Loose or partially fixed items are not accelerated at the same rate as the building frame and will contribute little or nothing to earthquake forces. If an accurate assessment of earthquake forces is to be made, it is essential that these fixed dead loads be identified. A low assessment of these fixed dead loads can produce dangerous underdesign for earthquake, while a high assessment can produce wasteful (and expensive) overdesign; an accurate determination of dead loads is again seen to be essential.

While the foregoing descriptions may seem to define the dead load rather well, the definition is still unacceptably vague; it is left to the bias of the individual designer to determine what is "permanent," what is "long-term" and what is "fixed." Because so much of the structural integrity depends on an accurate and consistent determination of the dead load, the following definition is adopted for all applications in this textbook:

A dead load is defined as any gravity load that is so rigidly fixed to the building frame that in an earthquake it will be accelerated at the same rate as the building frame.

All other gravity loads are by default defined as live loads.

In applying the foregoing definition, it is not necessary that the structure actually be subject to earthquake loads. It is essential only that two designers computing the dead load of a structure within their own personal biases will arrive at consistently similar values; their adhering to the foregoing definition will help considerably in providing such consistency.

Consider, for example, an air conditioning compressor mounted on the roof of a building. Many times, such items of mechanical equipment are mounted on vibration isolators (springs) in order to stop any possible vibration noise from propagating into the building. The equipment is permanent, and it is long-term, but because of the isolators it will not be accelerated at the same rate as the roof in an earthquake; the equipment is therefore classified as a live load.

As another example, consider a heavy safe sitting on the floor in an office. If the safe is not rigidly attached (bolted) to the floor, it is simply a piece of loose furniture, regardless how heavy it is, and regardless how long-term its placement; it is therefore classified as a live load. If, however, the safe is rigidly bolted to the floor, it will be accelerated at the same rate as the building floor and will then be classified as a dead load.

One might argue (successfully) that the foregoing definition could exclude many long-term loads that would be in place long enough to affect settlements. When computing the loads that exist long enough to produce settlements, it is the practice, therefore, to include a portion of the live load, such as dead load plus 50% live load. Such a practice recognizes that a significant but undefined portion of the live load would likely be in place for the several months that are required to produce settlements. It also allows inclusion of unusually heavy long-term live loads as a part of the settlement-producing loads.

When computing dead load, all of the actual items and components that make up the dead load are identified and their weights determined. There is no attempt, however, to identify live loads in such detail. Live load is simply all the loose items, whatever they may be, after all the fixed items have been accounted for.

Live load is generally taken as a blanket load per square foot that will likely occur on a particular structure. In an apartment building, for example, it has been found that the weight of the furnishings, carpets and miscellaneous loose items in a typical apartment will not likely exceed 40 lb/ft^2. The minimum *allowance* for live load in an apartment building is therefore given by the building code as 40 lb/ft^2. There is no attempt to identify any item of live load; it is simply estimated that the total will not likely exceed 40 lb/ft^2.

Obviously, the live load that might occur on a structure is heavily dependent on the usage, or *occupancy*, of the structure. Office buildings will likely need a much lower allowance for live load, for example, than a factory or shop building. And even within an office building, a larger allowance would be necessary for corridors and meeting rooms than for other rooms.

In general, the minimum live load allowance for various functions, or occupancies, are given by the building codes. These minimum allowances have evolved over many years of monitoring and revision, and may be regarded as reliable starting points under most circumstances. In buildings having unusual loading conditions, however, the designer may have to increase these code minimums to suit the circumstances.

Some types of live load may be partially dynamic. Some examples are the foot traffic in corridors, the floor loading in a gymnasium, and floor loadings where forklifts operate, lifting (and dropping) loads. Consistent with the overall approach used in establishing live loads, the dynamic effects are included by an *impact factor* to be applied to the live load. In most cases, a floor live load that is partially dynamic will be increased by $^1/_3$ to account for such dynamic effects; the impact factor in such cases is then $33^1/_3\%$.

13.3 Calculation of Dead Loads

There are many materials that might be used in the construction of a building, and the weights of all such materials must be included when establishing the dead load. An abbreviated list of building materials and their nominal weights is given in Table 13-1; more complete lists may be found in design handbooks.

As indicated earlier, the dead weight of a structure is calculated rather accurately. Some examples will illustrate such calculations.

Example 13-1

Determination of dead load.

Given: Segment of a floor system as shown.

To Find: Dead load per square foot of projected area.

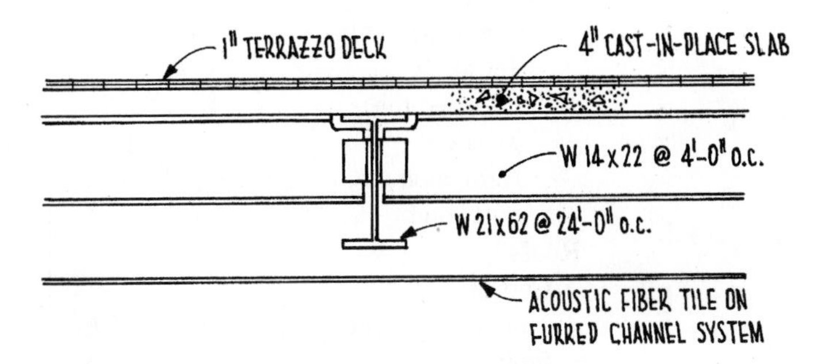

Solution: The dead loads for the various components are found in Table 13-1:

1" terrazzo	13 x 1	= 13.0 psf
4" concrete slab	$12^1/_2$ x 4	= 50.0 psf
W 14 x 22	22/4	= 5.5 psf
W 21 x 62	62/24	= 2.6 psf
Acoustic tile		= 1.0 psf
Furring system		= 1.0 psf
		Σ = 73 psf

Note that the weights of the steel beams are given in pounds per linear foot. To convert this weight to pounds per square foot (average), it is necessary to divide by their spacings.

Example 13-2

Determination of dead load.

Given: Floor system of Example 13-1.

To Find: Design dead load per linear foot to be supported by the W21 x 62.

Table 13-1 Weights of common building materials

Material	psf	Material	psf
Ceilings		**Partitions**	
Furred channel system	1	Clay tile:	
Acoustic fiber tile	1	3 inch	17
Floors		4 inch	18
Concrete, per inch:		6 inch	28
Stone	$12\frac{1}{2}$	8 inch	34
Slag	$11\frac{1}{2}$	10 inch	40
Lightweight	6 to 10	Gypsum block:	
Fills, per inch:		2 inch	$9\frac{1}{2}$
Gypsum	6	3 inch	$10\frac{1}{2}$
Sand	8	4 inch	$12\frac{1}{2}$
Cinders	4	5 inch	14
Mortar bedding	9	6 inch	21
Finishes, per inch:		**Plaster, per inch:**	
Terrazzo	13	Cement	10
Quarried tile	$12\frac{1}{2}$	Gypsum	5
Mastic	$11\frac{1}{2}$	**Lathing**	
Hardwood	5	Expanded metal	$\frac{1}{2}$
Softwood	4	Gypsum	2
Roofs		**Walls**	
Copper	1	Brick:	
3-ply felt and gravel	$5\frac{1}{2}$	4 inch	40
5-ply felt and gravel	6	8 inch	80
Shingles:		12 inch	120
Wood	2	Hollow concrete block:	
Asphalt	3	Heavy aggregate:	
Clay tile	9 to 15	4 inch	30
Slate, $\frac{1}{4}$ in.	10	6 inch	44
Sheathing, per inch:		8 inch	56
Wood	4	12 inch	80
Gypsum	4	Light aggregate:	
Insulation, per inch:		4 inch	21
Loose	$\frac{1}{2}$	6 inch	30
Poured in place	2	8 inch	38
Rigid	$1\frac{1}{2}$	12 inch	56
Corrugated asbestos, $\frac{1}{4}$ in. thick	3	Clay tile:	
Corrugated steel deck:		4 inch	25
16 gauge	2.7	6 inch	30
18 gauge	2.2	8 inch	33
20 gauge	1.6	12 inch	45
24 gauge	1.1	Structural glass, 1 inch	15
28 gauge	0.7	**Timber, nominal weight**	42 pcf
		Concrete, nominal weight	145 pcf

Adapted from the *Manual of Steel Construction,* American Institute of Steel Construction, Ninth Edition.

Solution: The load to be supported by the W21 x 62 beams is the load halfway to the W21 x 62 beams to either side:

Dead load = 73 psf x 24 = 1752 lb/ft.

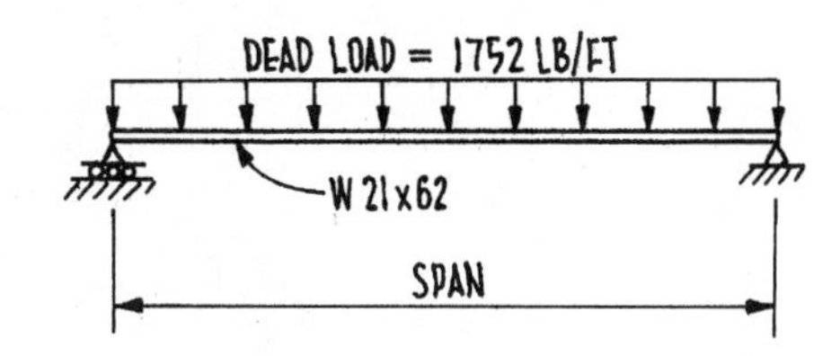

Note that the dead load is actually delivered to the W21 x 62 at 4'-0" intervals. For closely-spaced loads such as these, however, the load is taken as an equivalent (but approximate) uniform load.

Example 13-3

Determination of dead load.

Given: Concrete tee beam roof structure as shown. Concrete weight is 150 pcf.

To Find: Dead load on projected area.

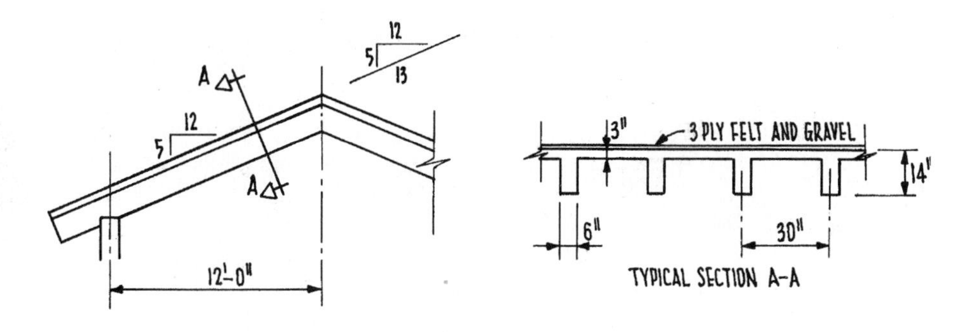

Solution: Dead load per square foot of roof is computed first:

Felt and gravel roof	= 5.5 psf
3" concrete deck 12.5 x 3	= 37.5 psf
11" x 6" stem (11/12)(6/12)(150)/2.5	= 27.5 psf
	Σ = 70.5 psf

The load on the projected area is:

w_{DL} = 70.5(13/12)
= 76.4 psf on the projected area.

Example 13-4

Determination of dead load.

Given: Concrete floor beam at perimeter wall as shown.
Concrete weight is 150 pcf.

To Find: Dead load per foot of beam.

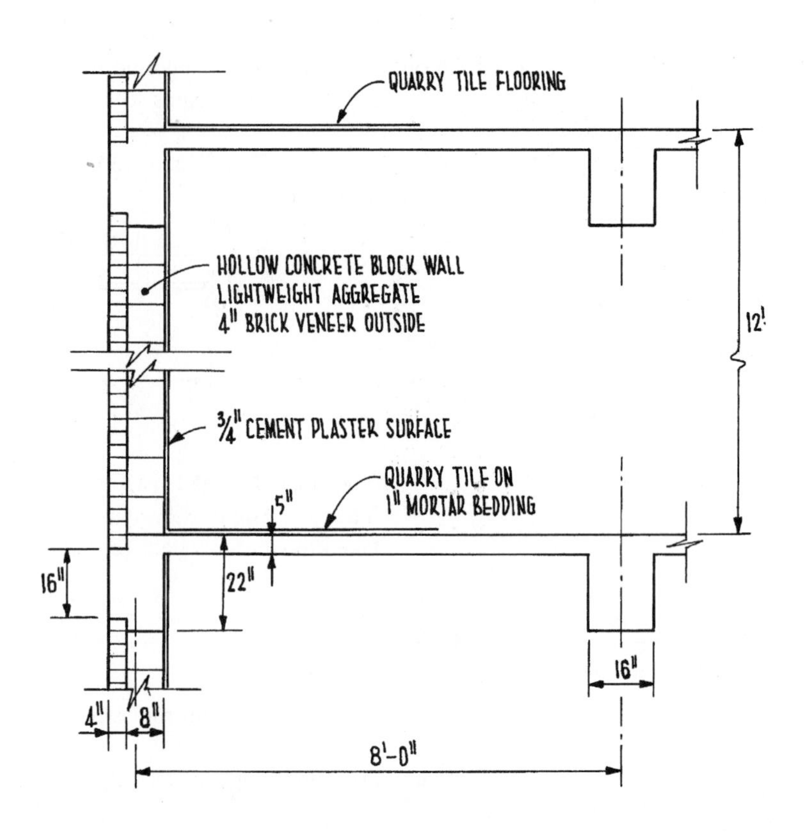

Solution: Assume that the entire weight of the masonry wall is carried by the beam below. Plaster is assumed to adhere to the backing material:

Weight of brick veneer 40 psf (144 - 16)/12	= 427.7 plf
Weight of concrete blocks 38 psf (144 - 22)/12	= 386.3 plf
Weight of plaster 10 psf (3/4)(144 - 5)/12	= 86.9 plf
Weight of concrete beam	
wt = [(8 x 22 + 4 x 16)/144]150	= 250.0 plf
Weight of slab (12.5)(48 - 4)/12	= 229.2 plf
Total dead load	= 1380 plf

13.4 Calculation of Live Loads

Live loads have been defined as those loose items that will not be accelerated at the same rate as the building frame in an earthquake. Further, there has been no effort to identify items of live load; live load is so changeable during the life of a structure that any attempt to identify particular items would be futile. Rather, an *allowance* for live load is included in the design, with the minimum allowance being that stipulated by the building code.

Some typical minimum allowances for live load are given in Table 13-2. These live load allowances will not necessarily be those given by a particular code, since there is some variation between the codes. Before using these values in final design, one should check the building code in effect at the particular building site.

Note that live load allowance in Table 13-2 is given as a uniformly distributed load. In buildings, the live load is identified in section *a* by the occupancy of the building as a whole, with subheadings for particular areas. For particular *usage* of an area, regardless of the occupancy, some floor loadings are specified in more detail in section *b*; the heavier loads of section *b* take precedence over the more general values listed in section *a*.

Some examples will illustrate the use of the live load tables in selecting the proper live load for a particular occupancy and usage.

Table 13-2 Minimum design live loads.

a. Uniformly distributed live loads based on general occupany.

Occupancy	psf	Occupancy	psf
Armories and drill rooms	150	Residential:	
Assembly halls, theatres:		Multifamily units:	
Fixed seats	60	Private apartments	40
Moveable seats	100	Public rooms	100
Balconies, exterior	100	Corridors to public rooms	100
Bowling alleys	75	Single-family units:	
Corridors, first floor	100	First floor	40
Dance halls	100	Habitable attics	30
Dining areas	100	Storage areas	30
Gymnasium floors	100	Hotels:	
Hospitals:		Guest rooms	40
Operating rooms	60	Corridors to private rooms	100
Private rooms	40	Public rooms	100
Wards	40	Corridors to public rooms	100
Corridors above first floor	80	Schools:	
Libraries:		Classrooms	40
Reading rooms	60	Corridors above first floor	80
Stack rooms	150	Stairs and fire escapes	100
Corridors above first floor	80	Stands and bleachers	100
Manufacturing	125	Stores, retail:	
Marquees	75	First-floor rooms	100
Office buildings:		Upper floors	75
Offices	50	Stores, wholesale	125
Lobbies	100	Warehouse, storage	
Penal institutions:		Light	125
Cell blocks	40	Heavy	250
Corridors	100		

b. Uniformly distributed live loads based on specific use.

Use	psf	Use	psf
Air-conditioning equipment	200	Garages, ramps, drives:	
Amusement-park structures	100	Trucks, 3 to 10 tons	150
Bakeries	150	Trucks above 10 tons	200
Boathouse floors	100	Greenhouses	150
Boiler rooms, framed	300	Hangars	150
Broadcasting studios	100	Incinerator floors	100
Catwalks	25	Kitchens, commercial	150
Dormitories:		Laboratories, science	100
Partitioned	40	Laundries	150
Nonpartitioned	80	Libraries, corridors	100
Elevator machine rooms	150	Morgues	125
Fan rooms	150	Public Rooms	100
File rooms:		Rest rooms	60
Letter	80	Rinks, ice skating	250
Card	125	Storage, hay or grain	300
Addressograph	150	Telephone exchanges	150
Foundries	600	Toilet rooms	60
Fuel rooms, framed	400	Transformer rooms	200

Adapted from ASCE Standard 7-93 *Minimum Design Loads for Buildings and Other Structures*.

Example 13-5

Determination of live load.

Given: Commercial hotel.

To Find: Allowance for live load in the kitchen area.

Solution: From Table 13-2, the allowance for live load in public rooms of a hotel is 100 psf based on occupancy. Based on usage, however, the allowance for live load in a commercial kitchen is 150 psf.

Use live load of 150 psf.

Example 13-6

Determination of live load.

Given: Secondary school, single story

To Find: Allowance for live load in:
a) classrooms
b) corridors
c) toilets
d) biology laboratory

Solution: From Table 13-2:
For classrooms, use 40 psf (based on occupancy)
For corridors, use 100 psf (based on occupancy)
For toilets, use 60 psf (based on usage)
For laboratories, use 100 psf (based on usage)

Example 13-7

Determination of live load.

Given: Municipal library, single story

To Find: Allowance for live load in the corridors where the corridors are subject to impact loading.

Solution: From Table 13-2 the allowance for live load is found to be 100 psf based only on usage. With an impact factor of 33%:

Use live load = 100 x 1.33 = 133 psf.

Example 13-8

Determination of live load.

Given: Crowded corridor near the elevators in an office building. Allow standing room of 18 inches x 30 inches for each person. Use nominal weight of 180 lbs per person.

To Find: Live load attributable to each person.

Solution: Wt/unit area = 180/(1.5 x 2.5) = 48 psf.

It is noted that Table 13-2 allows 100 lbs for such areas, indicating that human loading is not the critical case of loading in such areas. Rather, the corridors are more likely designed for freight, carts or other such heavily loaded utility vehicles, plus the associated impact.

It should be noted that the type of construction was never a factor in the preceding examples of live loads. The structures could have been built of concrete, masonry, timber or steel and the live load allowance would remain the same. Live load depends only on occupancy and usage, not on materials.

13.5 Lateral Loads on Structures

The two major subcategories of lateral load are wind and earthquake; while completely different types of load, these loads produce similar effects on a structure. In most of the United States, wind loads will be more severe than earthquake, but it should be recognized that more than 95% of the area of North America is subject to earthquake loads. In areas away from the major earthquake faults, earthquake loads in the past have largely been ignored; current trends require that they be included.

It is emphasized that neither of two major types of lateral load is static; both wind and earthquake produce dynamic loads. High wind does not produce a constant pressure, but a buffeting, whirling, gusting, dynamically varying pressure. Similarly, earthquake is not a single movement, but is a random, physical, violent shaking at the base of the structure. Both wind and earthquake loads come from all directions, vertically and laterally, without order or pattern. Obviously, some rational means to assess the effects of these dynamic loads is in order if a rational design is to be made.

In current practice, however, structures are not designed dynamically. The maximum dynamic deformations are found (by dynamicists) for the given dynamic conditions. A set of static loads are then determined that will reproduce statically those maximum dynamic deformations; the structure is then designed to sustain these equivalent static loads. A highly simplified sketch of this concept is shown in Figure 13-6. Over the years, dynamic loading has thus been refined and reduced into a rational, easily understandable system of static load cases.

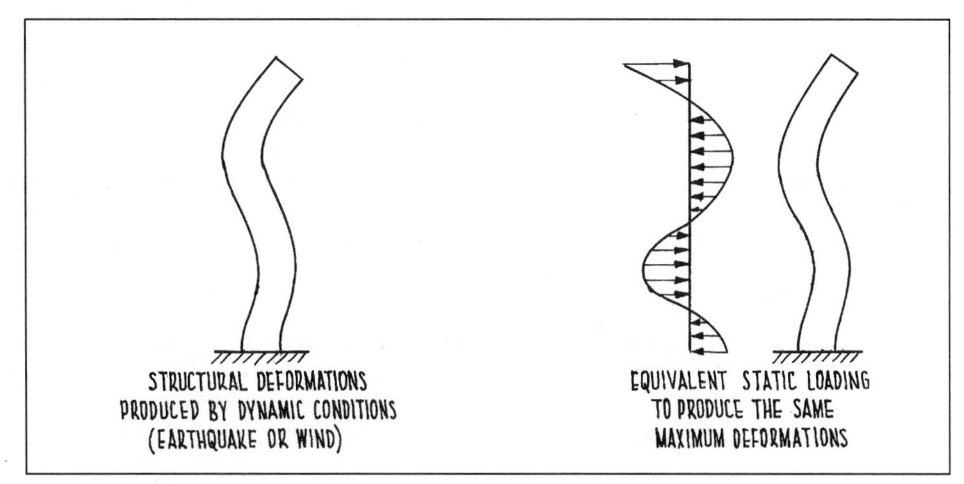

Figure 13-6 Equivalent static loads to reproduce dynamic deformations.

As a beneficial side effect of this approach to wind and earthquake analysis, it is not necessary in today's practice for a structural designer to have a detailed knowledge of dynamics; it is necessary only that the designer be able to understand and apply the prescribed set of equivalent static loads. So far, the approach has been found to produce acceptable results.

Wind forces produce a lateral shear force between a structure and the supporting soil as the wind tries to push the structure across the surface of the earth. The shear produced at the base of the structure is called the *base shear*, V_B. A typical example of such a base shear is shown in Figure 13-7a.

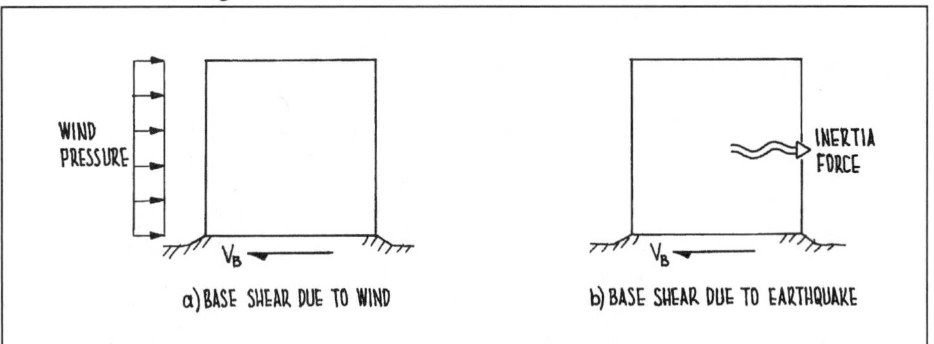

Figure 13-7 Base shears due to wind and earthquake.

In contrast to wind, an earthquake produces extremely fast-moving waves in the surface material of the earth, which in turn produce extremely sharp back-and-forth lateral motions of the earth's surface. (There is also an up-and-down motion but the effects produced are so small they are ignored.) There is a shearing force produced at the base of the structure by this sharp back-and-forth motion of 4 to 8 inches or more underneath the structure. That shear is called base shear, V_B. A typical example of such a base shear is shown in Figure 13-7b.

Both wind and earthquake thus produce a base shear under a structure, but here the similarity between the two loadings ends. Wind is a physical pressure (or suction) acting on the outside wall surfaces of a structure, those surfaces then transfer their loads to the supporting structural frame. In contrast, when a structural frame is accelerated by an earthquake, every particle of dead load mass everywhere in the structure undergoes the acceleration, producing an inertia force in every one of these particles as it opposes the acceleration.

Wind forces have no effect on the interior walls of a structure; wind "sees" only the projected area, or silhouette, of a structure as the resisting surface. In contrast, earthquake inertia forces occur in every particle of every dead load component of the structure regardless of the location of the component; interior and exterior walls are affected identically. The design of exterior walls will therefore include the effects either of wind or of earthquake, whichever is larger, while interior walls will be designed only for earthquake loads.

In recent years, the design of structures for wind and earthquake has undergone profound advances. In today's practice, the design of structures for lateral loads can be performed with a degree of confidence considered impossible a generation ago. Further, these advances have come with a distinct simplification of the procedures; the procedures now in use are both direct and readily understandable.

13.6 Calculation of Wind Loads

As one might expect, the wind force on a structure is a function of the velocity of the wind. The maximum wind velocity that may be expected at any location in the United States has been under observation for many years. Current wind velocity charts are given in the building codes; a typical wind velocity chart is shown in Figure 13-8. (This wind chart accompanies the primary design method in the Standard Building Code.)

Wind velocities vary with height above ground, becoming higher as height increases. The velocities shown in Figure 13-8 are those to be expected at a standard height of 30 feet above the surface of the ground. It is necessarily assumed in developing such charts that the area being examined is generally clear of obstructions, trees or tall buildings that would influence wind velocities at the 30 ft level.

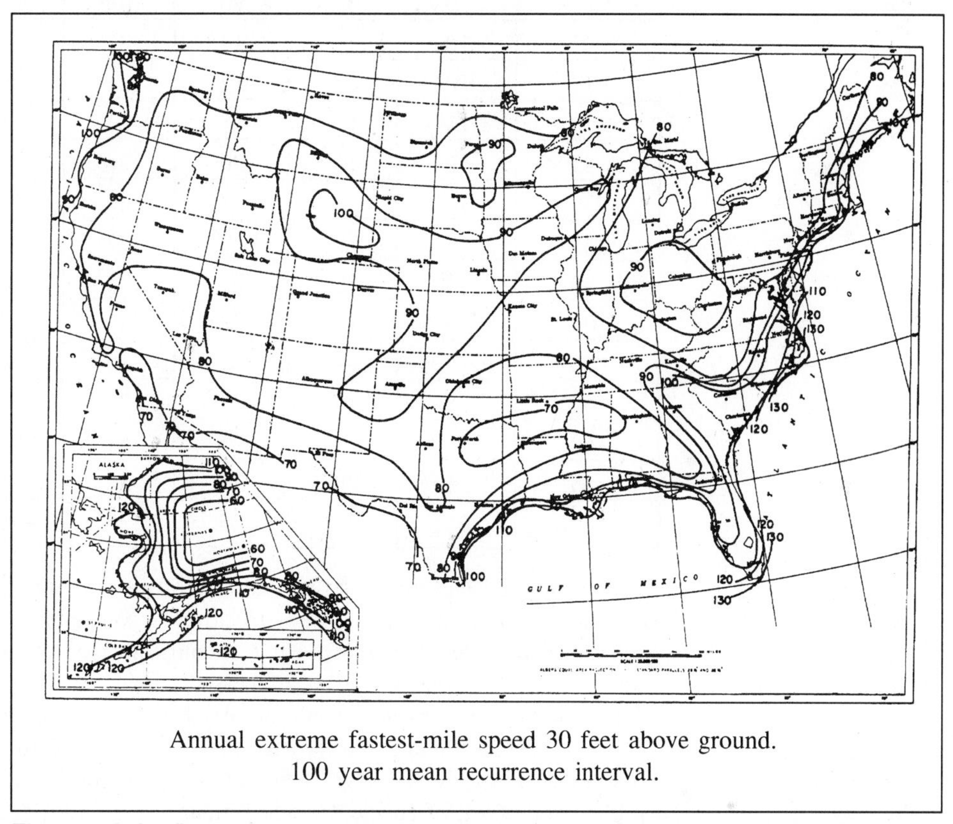

Annual extreme fastest-mile speed 30 feet above ground.
100 year mean recurrence interval.

Figure 13-8 Basic wind speeds in miles per hour. *(Courtesy Southern Building Code Congress, International)*

For calculating the wind pressure at the standard height of 30 feet, the concept of a hypothetical *wind stagnation pressure* is used. The wind stagnation pressure is the pressure that results when all of the kinetic energy in the moving mass of air ($\frac{1}{2}mv^2$) is converted to static pressure. The reference wind stagnation pressure p_{REF} at 30 ft above ground is given by the equation:

$$p_{REF} = 0.00256V^2 \tag{13-1}$$

where V is the wind velocity in miles per hour and p_{REF} is the stagnation pressure in lbs/ft^2.

The stagnation pressure p_S at any height H above the ground is found by multiplying Eq.(13-1) by a height factor,

$$p_s = 0.00256V^2\left(H/30\right)^{\frac{2}{7}} \tag{13-2}$$

where the minimum allowable value of H is 15 feet, that is, wind stagnation pressures below 15 feet cannot be taken less than the pressure at 15 feet. Note that at H = 30 ft, the height factor becomes 1 and Eq.(13-2) degenerates into Eq.(13-1).

Wind stagnation pressures are shown in Table 13-3 for the usual range of wind velocities and heights above ground. It is emphasized that the pressures listed in Table 13-3 are stagnation pressures; they are not the actual pressures exerted on a structure. To convert the stagnation pressures to actual wind pressures, they must be multiplied by a *shape factor*.

Table 13-3 Basic wind stagnation pressures in psf.

Height Above Ground (feet)	Wind Velocity in Miles Per Hour						
	70	80	90	100	110	120	130
0	10	13	17	21	25	30	36
15	10	13	17	21	25	30	36
20	11	15	18	23	28	33	39
25	12	16	20	24	29	35	41
30	13	16	21	26	31	37	43
35	13	17	22	27	32	39	45
40	14	18	23	28	34	40	47
45	14	18	23	29	35	41	49
50	15	19	24	30	36	43	50
55	15	19	25	30	37	44	51
60	15	20	25	31	38	45	53
65	15	20	26	32	39	46	54
70	16	21	26	33	39	47	55

Shape factors depend on the shape and size of the component receiving the wind pressure, as well as its location in the structure. A component on the windward side, for example, may undergo pressure, while a component on the leeward side may undergo suction. Or, a component such as a recessed window frame may undergo serious localized buffeting pressures that would not exist if the surface were smooth and unbroken.

Typical shape factors to be applied to the primary structural frame are given in Table 13-4. These shape factors have been extracted from the Standard Building Code. Other building codes will of course provide similar values. They are the factors to be applied to the wind stagnation pressures given by Eq.(13-2) to convert stagnation pressures to actual pressures.

It is observed that the shape factors given in Table 13-4 include such effects as shape, openness, and inclination from vertical. They do not, however, include recesses, setbacks, steps or other surface irregularities. The reason for this omission is that the wind "sees" only the projected area (silhouette) of the structure. A typical example of such a concept is shown in Figure 13-9.

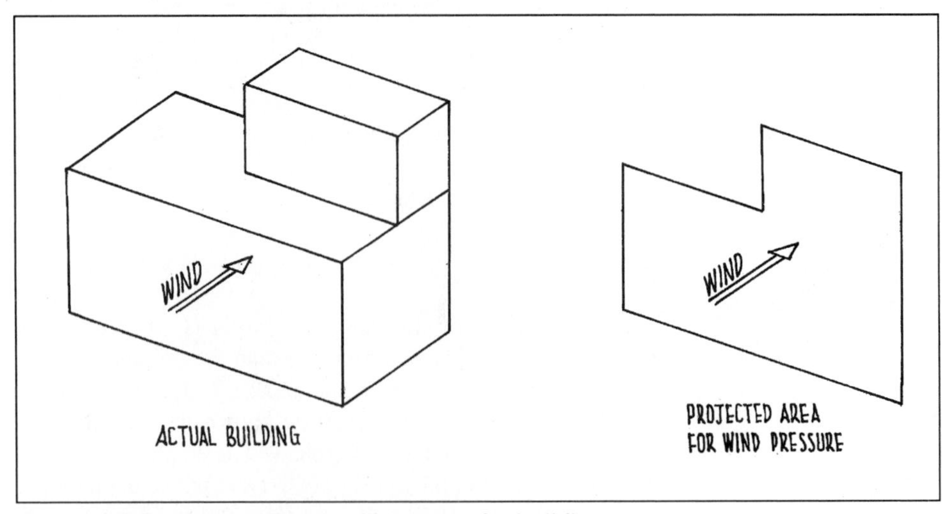

Figure 13-9 Wind pressure silhouette of a building.

Table 13-4 Shape Factors for Primary Frames and Systems

Vertical Surfaces

Shape of vertical surface	Shape factor normal to projected surface area
Rectangular prismatic structures[1]	1.3
Cylinders (chimneys, tanks, etc.)	0.7
Flat planes (signs, fences, billboards)	1.4
Partially open surfaces[2]:	
10% solid	0.35
20% solid	0.55
40% solid	0.80
60% solid	1.00
80% solid	1.20
100% solid	1.30

Inclined Surfaces[3]

Inclination of surface from horizontal[4]	Shape factor normal to an inclined windward surface	Shape factor normal to an inclined leeward surface
80° – 90°	Treat as a vertical surface	
70° – 80°	0.80 pressure	0.70 suction
60° – 70°	0.65 pressure	0.70 suction
50° – 60°	0.55 pressure	0.70 suction
40° – 50°	0.25 pressure	0.70 suction
30° – 40°	0.25 suction	0.70 suction
20° – 30°	0.75 suction	0.70 suction
10° – 20°	0.93 suction	0.70 suction
0° – 10°	Treat as a horizontal surface	
Overhands and eaves[5]	1.50 suction	1.50 suction

Horizontal Surfaces

Type of surface	Shape factor normal to windward third of surface area	Shape factor normal to leeward two-thrids of surface area
Enclosed building	1.0 suction	0.75 suction
Building having one or more sides open	1.5 suction	1.25 suction
Overhands and eaves[5]	1.5 suction	1.50 suction

[1]Distributed 0.8 pressure at windward side plus 0.5 suction at leeward side.
[2]Shape factor to be applied to gross area of surface.
[3]All pressures are normal to the surface.
[4]For buildings with one or more sides open, add 1.0 suction to all suction factors.
[5]This factor is not additive; it is treated as a separate load in all cases.

The shape factors given in Table 13-9 provide the average overall pressures on the projected area that apply to the primary structure. Some of the components of the primary structural system, however, can be subject to localized increases above this average pressure. Shape factors for some of these components are given in Table 13-5; the localized increases are seen generally to occur around recesses, irregular surfaces or protrusions.

Table 13-5 Shape factors for transfer members. Components transferring wind load to the primary structure.

Components having vertical surfaces[1]	Shape factors if component is on windward side	Shape factors if component is on leeward side
Exterior walls of closed buildings, including fixed glass, glazing, windows, doors, fixed panels, veneer facings and supporting members.	1.1 (pressure)	1.1 (suction)
Exterior walls of buidlings with one or more sides open including fixed glass, glazing, windows, doors, fixed panels, veneer facings and supporting members.	1.1 (pressure)	1.5 (suction)

Reproduced by permission of *Southern Building Code Congress International, Inc.* SBCCI makes no warrants as to the accuracy of the material printed, and won't be responsible for errors contained therein.

[1]For inclined surfaces and horizontal surfaces the shape factors given in Table 13-4 remain valid.

Some examples will illustrate the procedures for calculating wind pressures on structures.

Example 13-9

Determination of base shear due to wind.

Given: Building configuration as shown, located in central Kansas. Dead weight of the building is 3670 kips.

To Find: Base shears in two directions due to wind.

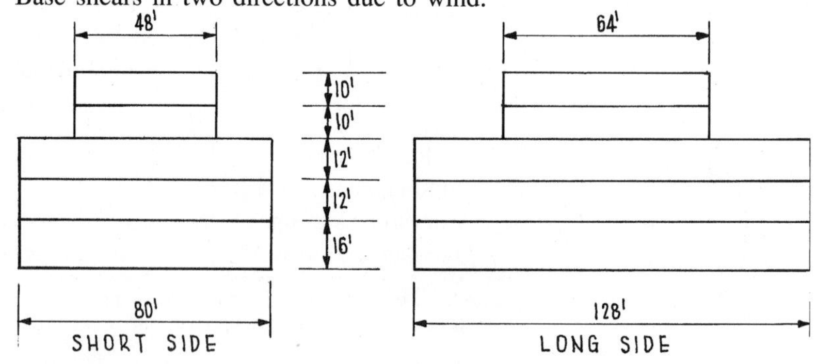

Solution: Design wind velocity in central Kansas is found from the wind velocity map to be 90 mph. The wind stagnation pressures associated with this wind velocity is computed at midheight of each story.

At 8' elevation: $p = 0.00256(90)^2(^{15}/_{30})^{\frac{2}{7}} = 17.0$ psf

At 22' elevation: $p = 0.00256(90)^2(^{22}/_{30})^{\frac{2}{7}} = 19.0$ psf

At 34' elevation: $p = 0.00256(90)^2(^{34}/_{30})^{\frac{2}{7}} = 21.5$ psf

At 45' elevation: $p = 0.00256(90)^2(^{45}/_{30})^{\frac{2}{7}} = 23.3$ psf

At 55' elevation: $p = 0.00256(90)^2(^{55}/_{30})^{\frac{2}{7}} = 24.7$ psf

The stagnation pressures are converted to pressure by multiplying by the shape factor. The shape factor for rectangular structures is 1.3, with 80% of the wind load being applied as pressure on the windward size and 50% being applied as suction on the leeward side. Wind pressures at midheight of each story are shown on the following sketch.

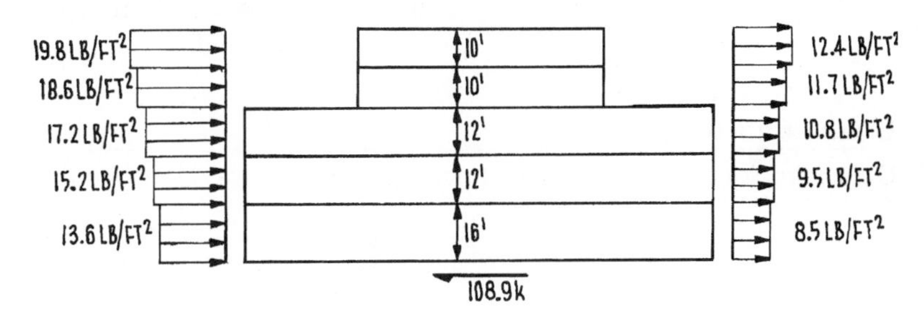

The resulting forces against the short sides of the building are computed as pressure times the area:

Pressure Side:	Suction Side:
P_{55} = (19.8)(48)(10) = 9.5 k	S_{55} = (12.4)(48)(10) = 6.0 k
P_{45} = (18.6)(48)(10) = 8.9 k	S_{45} = (11.7)(48)(10) = 5.6 k
P_{34} = (17.2)(80)(12) = 16.5 k	S_{34} = (10.8)(80)(12) = 10.4 k
P_{22} = (15.2)(80)(12) = 14.6 k	S_{22} = (9.5)(80)(12) = 9.1 k
P_8 = (13.6)(80)(16) = 17.4 k	S_8 = (8.5)(80)(16) = 10.9 k

The forces and the resultant base shear are shown in the following sketch.

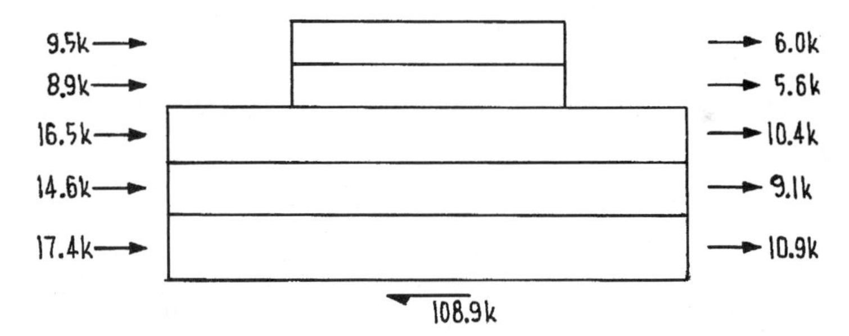

The forces against the long sides of the building are computed similarly:

Pressure Side:	**Suction Side:**
P_{55} = (19.8)(64)(10) = 12.7 k	S_{55} = (12.4)(64)(10) = 7.9 k
P_{45} = (18.6)(64)(10) = 11.9 k	S_{45} = (11.7)(64)(10) = 7.5 k
P_{34} = (17.2)(128)(12) = 26.4 k	S_{34} = (10.8)(128)(12) = 16.6 k
P_{22} = (15.2)(128)(12) = 23.3 k	S_{22} = (9.5)(128)(12) = 14.6 k
P_8 = (13.6)(128)(16) = 27.9 k	S_8 = (8.5)(128)(16) = 17.4 k

The forces and the resultant base shear are shown in the following sketch.

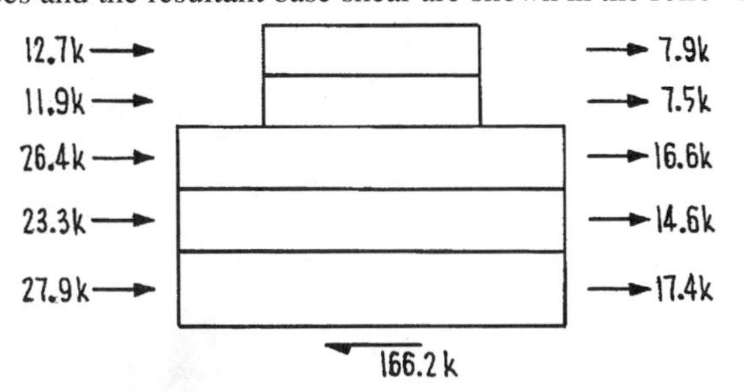

The base shears are seen to be:

V_B = 108.9 k in either direction acting along the long axis of the building.

V_B = 166.2 k in either direction acting along the short axis of the building.

Example 13-10

Determination of base shear and overturning moment due to wind.

Given: Tapered cylindrical smoke stack as shown, located in central Ohio. Dead weight = 7500 kips.

To Find: Base shear and overturning moment on the stack.

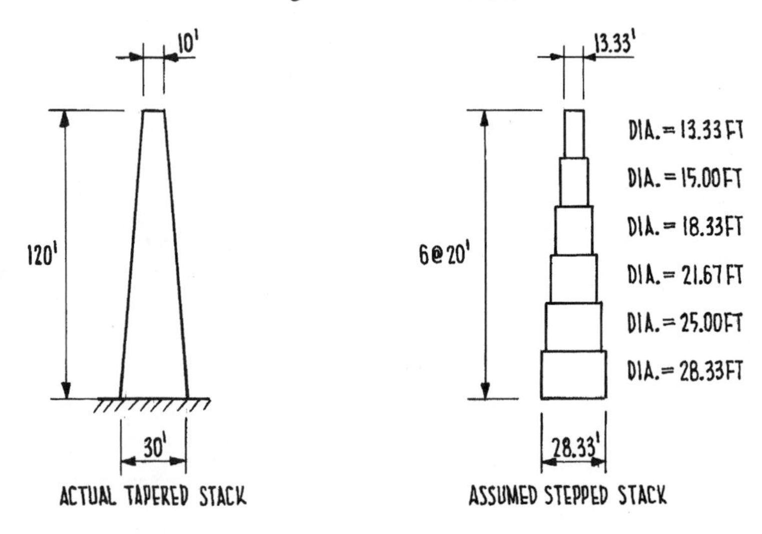

Solution: As indicated in the sketch, the tower has been approximated as a tower having 6 equal steps of 20 ft each. The diameter at each step has been computed and is shown on the sketch.

The wind stagnation pressure is computed at midheight of each step. Wind velocity in Central Ohio is found from Figure 13-8 to be 90 mph.

Height Above Ground	Stagnation Pressure
10'	$0.00256(90)^2(^{15}/_{30})^{\frac{2}{7}} = 17.0$ psf
30'	$0.00256(90)^2(^{30}/_{30})^{\frac{2}{7}} = 20.7$ psf
50'	$0.00256(90)^2(^{50}/_{30})^{\frac{2}{7}} = 24.0$ psf
70'	$0.00256(90)^2(^{70}/_{30})^{\frac{2}{7}} = 26.4$ psf
90'	$0.00256(90)^2(^{90}/_{30})^{\frac{2}{7}} = 28.4$ psf
110'	$0.00256(90)^2(^{110}/_{30})^{\frac{2}{7}} = 30.1$psf

The stagnation pressures are converted to wind pressure by multiplying by the shape factor. For a cylinder, the shape factor is found from Table 13-4 to be 0.70, all of it being positive pressure (with no suction). Computed pressures are shown on the adjacent sketch.

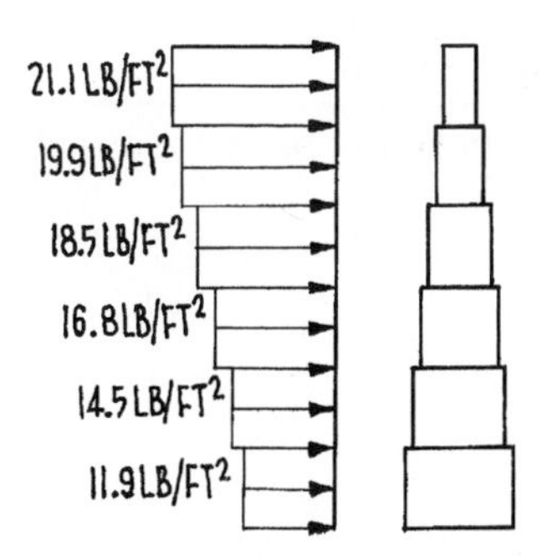

The forces at each step are computed as pressure times projected area:

Height Above Ground	Force
10'	P_{10} = (11.9)(28.3)(20) = 6.7 k
30'	P_{30} = (14.5)(25.0)(20) = 7.3 k
50'	P_{50} = (16.8)(21.7)(20) = 7.3 k
70	P_{70} = (18.5)(18.3)(20) = 6.8 k
90'	P_{90} = (19.9)(15.0)(20) = 6.0 k
110'	P_{110} = (21.1)(13.3)(20) = 5.6 k

The computed forces have been entered on the adjacent sketch.

5.6k DIA.= 13.3 FT
6.0k DIA.= 15.0 FT
6.8k DIA.= 18.3 FT
7.3k DIA.= 21.7 FT
7.3k 7500k DIA.= 25.0 FT
6.7k DIA.= 28.3 FT
V_B M_B
7500k

The base shear is found as the sum of forces,

$$V_B = \Sigma P = 39.7 \text{ k}$$

The overturning moment is the sum of moments due to the various forces,

$$M_B = \sum_{i=1}^{6} P_i h_i = (6.7)(10) + (7.3)(30) + (7.3)(50) + (6.8)(70) + (6.0)(90) + (5.6)(110)$$

$$= 2300 \text{ kip·ft.}$$

Example 13-11

Determination of base shear and overturning moment.

Given: Long A-frame structure as shown, located near Portland, Oregon. Dead load is 6.3 kips per foot of length of the frame.

To Find: Base shear and overturning moment (per foot of length).

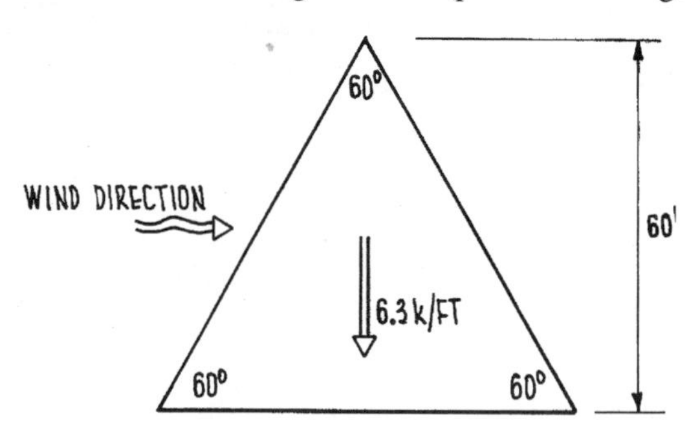

Solution: Wind stagnation pressure is computed for 10 ft segments along the height of the structure. Wind velocity near Portland is found from Figure 13-8 to be 100 mph.

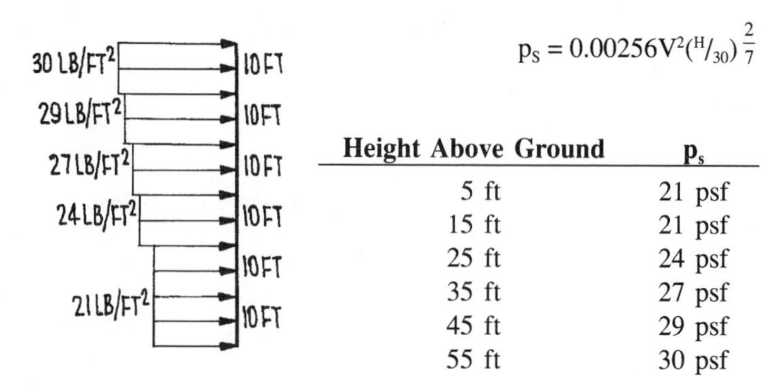

$$p_s = 0.00256V^2(^H/_{30})^{\frac{2}{7}}$$

Height Above Ground	p_s
5 ft	21 psf
15 ft	21 psf
25 ft	24 psf
35 ft	27 psf
45 ft	29 psf
55 ft	30 psf

Stagnation pressure is converted to actual pressure by multiplying by the shape factor. The shape factor for a surface inclined 60° to the horizontal is found from Table 13-4. The table is somewhat vague; the factor for inclined surfaces could be either 0.55 or 0.65. For this case, a value of 0.60 is chosen for positive pressure, with a factor of 0.70 for the suction side.

It is noted in Table 13-4 that the wind pressure acts normal to the inclined surface rather than acting normal to the projected surface.

The pressure and suction diagrams are shown on the following sketch.

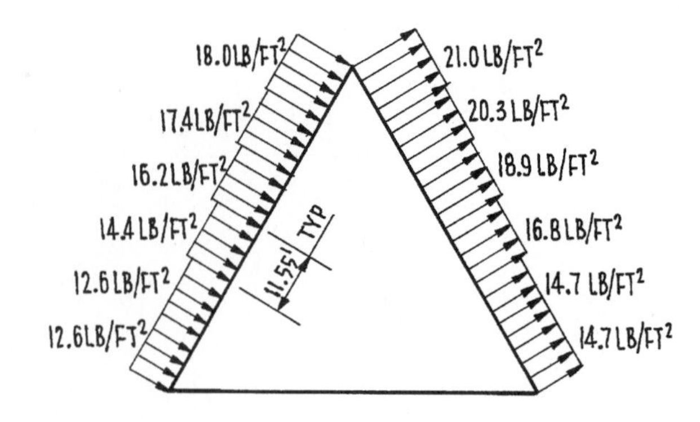

The pressure and suction forces are found by multiplying the pressures times their areas. The results are shown on the following sketch.

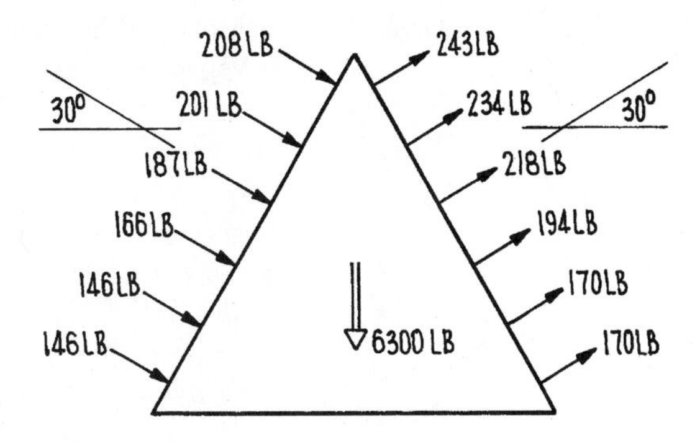

The base shear is found as the sum of all horizontal components,

$$V_B = \sum_{i=1}^{12} P_i \cos 30° = 2280 \cos 30 = 1977 \text{ lb}$$

The overturning moment due to wind is found as the sum of moments due to the wind forces.

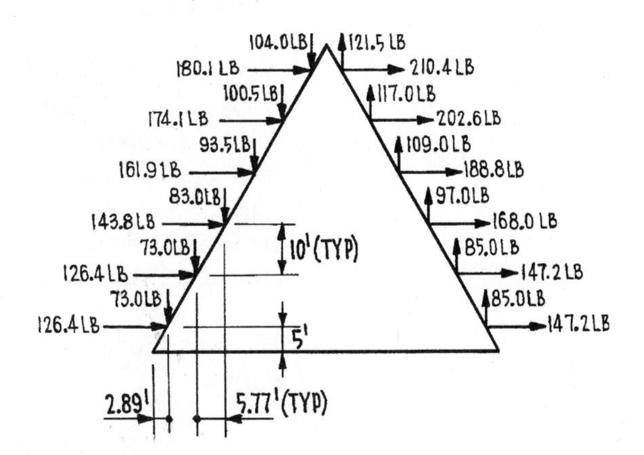

$$\begin{aligned} M_B = {} & (126.4 \times 5 + 73.0 \times 2.89) + (126.4 \times 15 + 73.0 \times 8.66) \\ & + (143.8 \times 25 + 83.0 \times 14.43) + (161.9 \times 35 + 93.5 \times 20.21) \\ & + (174.1 \times 45 + 100.5 \times 25.98) + (180.1 \times 55 + 104.0 \times 31.75) \\ & + (210.4 \times 55 - 121.5 \times 37.53) + (202.6 \times 45 - 117.0 \times 43.30) \\ & + (188.8 \times 35 - 109.0 \times 49.07) + (168.0 \times 25 - 97.0 \times 54.85) \\ & + (147.2 \times 15 - 85.0 \times 60.62) + (147.2 \times 5 - 85.0 \times 66.40) \end{aligned}$$

$$= 42.7 \text{ kip·ft per foot of length of frame.}$$

Final loads are shown in the following sketch.

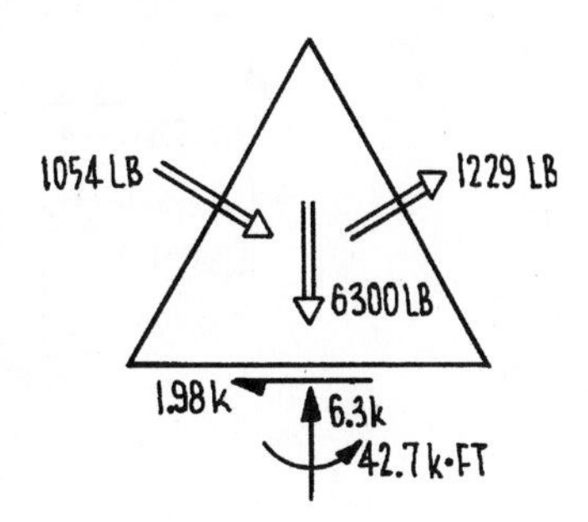

Example 13-12

Determination of base shear.

Given: Four story parking building, all sides approximately 50% open, located in Las Vegas, Nevada.

To Find: Base shear due to wind.

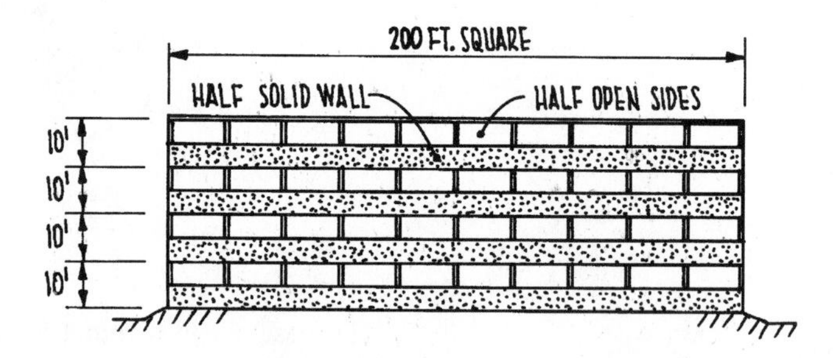

Solution: Design wind velocity in Las Vegas is found from Figure 13-8 to be 80 mph. In order to compute the wind stagnation pressures, it is first necessary to decide how the final wind pressures will be distributed throughout the building.

A key to the distribution of the wind pressure is found in Table 13-4. The shape factor for a building that is 50% open is seen to be reduced to 0.9, but this reduced shape factor is to be applied to the gross surface area (footnote 2). The approach is therefore to apply the wind loads to an equivalent solid surface using a reduced shape factor. As is done with 100% solid buildings, the final wind pressure must still be distributed 80% at the windward side plus 50% at the leeward side.

The wind stagnation pressures are computed as usual at midheight of each story.

Height Above Base	P_s
5'	13 psf
15'	13 psf
25'	16 psf
35'	17 psf

Stagnation pressure is converted to actual pressure by multiplying by the shape factor. For a building that is 50% open, the shape factor is seen to be reduced to 0.9, with 80% applied to the windward side plus 50% applied to the leeward side. The final pressures are shown on the following sketch, along with the base shear. (Base shear is computed as if all sides are solid at this reduced pressure.)

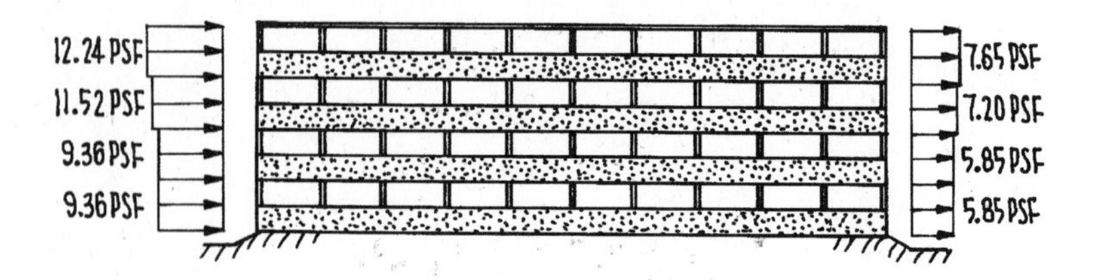

Base shear is computed from the given pressures:

$$V_B = (9.36 + 5.85)(10)(200) + (9.36 + 5.85)(10)(200)$$
$$+ (11.52 + 7.20)(10)(200) + (12.24 + 7.65)(10)(200)$$

$$= 138 \text{ kips (either direction since the building is square).}$$

13.7 Calculation of Earthquake Loads

Earthquakes are produced by slips along faults in the earth's crust. When the slip occurs, shock waves are generated, radiating outward from the slip. The intensity of the shock waves diminishes quickly as the waves spread outward from the source, or epicenter.

The motions of a structure produced by an earthquake are dependent on the proximity of the structure to the epicenter. Near the epicenter, motions will be high, but at a distance from the epicenter, motions will be sharply less. A chart based on this idea of proximity to known faults is given in Figure 13-10, which shows the "risk" areas of high earthquake intensity for the United States.

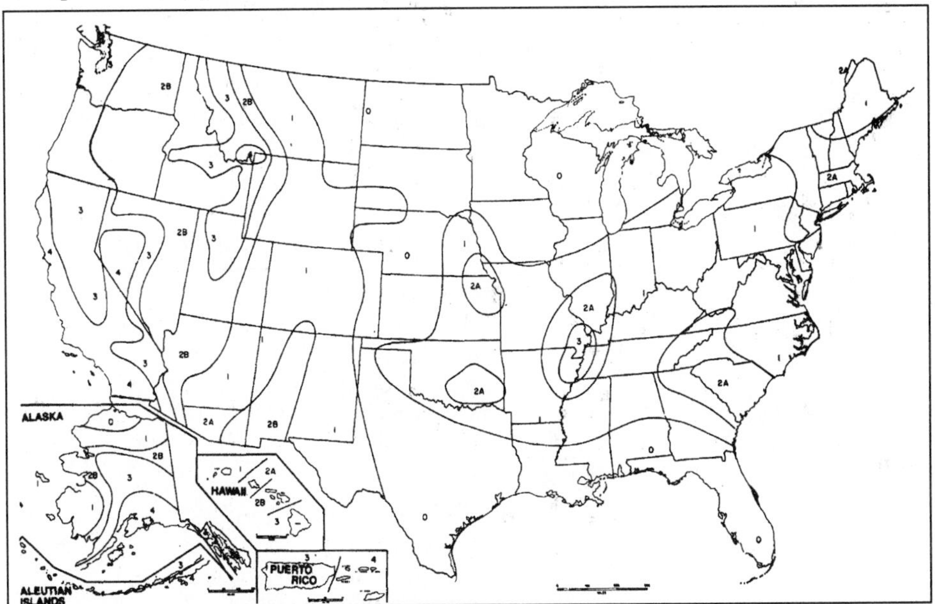

Figure 13-10 Seismic zone map of the United States.

In an earthquake, there is a distinct interaction between the structure and the supporting soil. As a consequence, there can be a magnification of ground motion by the structure, that is, the acceleration of the structure can be up to $2^1/_2$ times as much as the actual accelerations in the ground. In low rigid structures (less than about 70 feet), this magnification is almost certain to occur; in higher more flexible structures, the magnification will diminish somewhat.

Lateral forces are generated in a structure when earthquake ground motions produce accelerations of the individual masses of the structure. Due to their inertia, the masses resist being so accelerated, thus producing *inertia forces* throughout the structure; the direction of these inertia forces acts in opposition to the imposed motion. The amount of force required to accelerate any individual mass is directly proportional to the magnitude of the mass $(F = ma)$.

In the low structures that are of primary interest in this textbook, the lateral inertia force produced by earthquake accelerations of a weight W is, when extracted from the code,

$$V_B = 2.75\left(Z/R_w\right)W \qquad (13\text{-}4)$$

where V_B is the lateral inertia force produced by the acceleration of a mass having a weight W (the 2.75 is a constant ofproportionality).

Z is a risk zone factor, identified by the risk zones of Figure 13-5.

R_W is the interactive response factor, accounting for the response of the type of structural system to base excitation.

W is the dead weight of the mass that is being accelerated.

The values of Z to be used with the risk zones of Figure 13-5 are:

Risk Zone 1: Z = 0.075
Risk Zone 2A: Z = 0.150
2B: Z = 0.200 (13-5a, b, c, d)
Risk Zone 3: Z = 0.300
Risk Zone 4: Z = 0.400

The values of R_W to be used with Eq.(13-4) are set by Code; they are dependent on the stiffness (rigidity) of the structure. The list of typical values of R_W have been extracted from the Code and are given in Table 13-6.

Table 13-6 Values of R_W for buildings[1]

Structures where walls carry both vertical and lateral loads:	R_W
Plywood walls	8
Concrete or masonry walls	6
Steel cross-braced walls	4
Heavy timber walls	4
Structures where walls carry only shear; columns carry all vertical loads:	
Plywood shear panels	9
Concrete or masonry shear panels	8
Concentric braced frames[2]	8
All other shear panels	7
Moment resisting frames:	
Steel frames	6
Concrete frames[2]	5

Values of R_W for nonbuilding structures.

Type of structure:	R_W
Tanks, vessels, spheres	3
Stacks, chimneys, silos	4
Trussed towers	4
Signs and billboards	5
Cooling towers	5
Isolated masses	4

[1] Building heights limited to 65 feet.

[2] Concrete frames are not permitted in risk zones 3 and 4.

The value of W to be used in Eq.(13-4) is the dead load of the structural system plus all other components that will be accelerated at the same rate. Some designers add 20% of live load, but with the procedures used in this text to compute dead load, such an approximation is inappropriate.

In zones of high earthquake intensity, the lateral load imposed on a structure by an earthquake will be about 10% to 12% of the vertical dead load of the structure. In zones of lower intensity, the load decreases to about 3% of the dead load. These lateral loads are commonly called the "g-loads" or "g-forces" on the structure.

The approach to earthquake loads presented here is taken from the Uniform Building Code, one of the most widely-used earthquake codes in the world. For the sake of simplification, the approach has been modified here to apply only to structures less than 65 feet high. For taller structures, the natural period of oscillation of the structure becomes a factor and the procedure becomes exponentially more complex. The analysis of tall buildings subject to earthquake excitation is far beyond the scope of this textbook.

Some examples will demonstrate the calculation of base shears on typical low structures.

Example 13-13

Determination of base shears due to earthquake.

Given: Building of Example 13-9. Building is constructed of reinforced concrete with shear walls that carry only lateral loads.

To Find: Base shear due to earthquake.

Solution: From the risk zone map of Figure 13-10, Central Kansas is seen to be in Risk Zone 1.

The base shear is equal to the intertia force produced by the entire mass as it opposes the motion, given by:

$$V_B = 2.75(Z/R_W)W$$

For Risk Zone 1, $Z = 0.075$.
For concrete building frames, $R_W = 8$.
Dead weight being accelerated has been computed at 3670 k.

$$V_B = 2.75(0.075/8)3670 = 95 \text{ kips in any direction.}$$

For the building of Example 13-9, it is observed that the base shear due to earthquake does not depend on direction, as wind does. The base shears due to wind, however, are in all cases seen to be greater than the base shear due to earthquake. For this building, wind loads rather than earthquake loads will govern the design for lateral loads.

Example 13-14

Determination of base shears due to earthquake.

Given: Smokestack of Example 13-10. Smokestack is constructed of reinforced concrete having walls 15 in. thick. Concrete weight is 145 lb/ft^3.

To Find: Base shear and overturning moments due to earthquake.

Solution: Base shear is readily computed from the given information. From Figure 13-10, it is seen that Ohio is in Risk Zone 1.

The base shear is equal to the intertia force produced by the entire mass as it opposes the motion, given by:

$$V_B = 2.75\left(\frac{Z}{R_w}\right)W$$

For Risk Zone 1, Z = 0.075.
For stacks and chimneys, $R_W = 4$.
Dead weight being accelerated has been computed at 7500 k.

$$V_B = 2.75\left(\frac{0.075}{4}\right)W = 0.0516\ W = 387\ \text{kips.}$$

This value of base shear due to earthquake is seen to be some ten times that due to wind, even in an area as seismically inactive as Ohio. For this structure, earthquake will definitely govern the design.

The overturning moment is not as readily calculated as the base shear. To compute the overturning moment it will be necessary to compute the individual inertia forces for the various segments of the tower. The sum of these individual inertia forces must of course be equal to the total base shear already calculated.

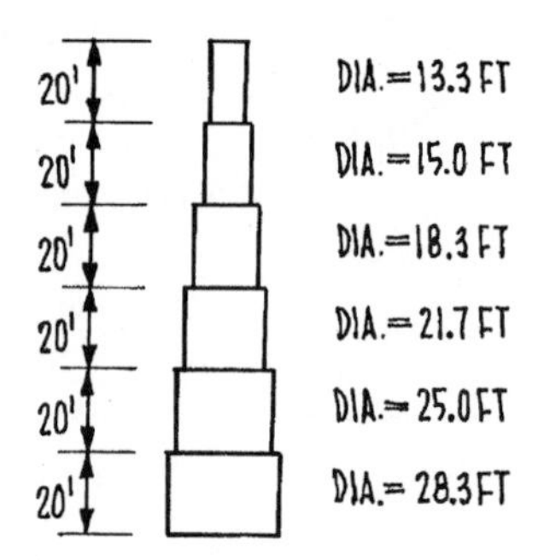

$$V_B = 0.0516[(0.7854)(13.3^2)](1.25)(145)(20) = 26k$$
$$V_B = 0.0516[(0.7854)(15.0^2)](1.25)(145)(20) = 33k$$
$$V_B = 0.0516[(0.7854)(18.3^2)](1.25)(145)(20) = 49k$$
$$V_B = 0.0516[(0.7854)(21.7^2)](1.25)(145)(20) = 69k$$
$$V_B = 0.0516[(0.7854)(25.0^2)](1.25)(145)(20) = 92k$$
$$V_B = 0.0516[(0.7854)(28.3^2)](1.25)(145)(20) = 118k$$

Check: $\Sigma = 387k$

The computed lateral forces for each segment are assumed to occur at midheight of each segment. The result is an approximation of the lateral load induced by the design earthquake.

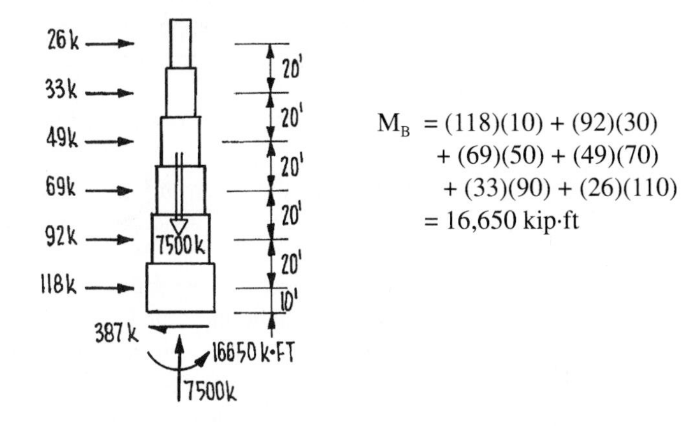

Final loads are shown on the above sketch.

For the stack of Example 13-10, it is seen that the overturning moment due to earthquake is some seven times that due to wind. Even in inactive areas such as Ohio, an investigation of earthquake forces is thus well advised, regardless whether it is required by Code.

13.8 Load Combinations

Up to this point, four loads have been considered: dead load, live load, wind load and earthquake load. These loads do not act individually on a structure; they act in some kind of combination with each other. Such combinations of loads are the subject of this section.

Certainly, one or more times in the life of a structure, the structure will be subjected to the full live load. Since the dead load occurs at all times, the load combination of dead load plus live load becomes

1. Dead Load + 100% Live Load. (13-3)

When combining lateral loads with gravity loads, it is not reasonable to assume that all loads will occur at their maximum values at the same time. Maximum wind load, for example, will not likely occur at the same instant as the maximum earthquake load. It is reasonable, however, that the structure will be subject to part or all of its live load at the time the maximum wind or earthquake occurs.

Further, it is acknowledged that the maximum wind load and the maximum live load are based on long recurrence times; in all probability, the maximum wind load and the maximum earthquake load will occur only once in the life of the structure. For such rarely occurring cases, it is the practice to allow a 33% overstress in the material.

The cases of combined lateral load and gravity loads then become:

2. (0.75)(Dead Load + 100% Live Load + Wind) (13-4)
3. (0.75)(Dead Load + 100% Live Load + Earthquake). (13-5)

A moment's reflection will affirm that designing for 75% of a load case will produce a 33% overstress when (and if) the full load case occurs.

There are other load combinations in common use. One such combination was mentioned earlier, having to do with the loads that are sustained long enough to produce settlements in the supporting soil. (Wind and earthquake are too transient to produce settlements.) The load combination for foundation settlement is commonly taken as:

4. Dead Load + 50% Live Load (13-6)

In addition, however, the strength of the foundation must also be adequate to sustain the total dead plus live load, given by load combination 1.

One last load case deserves attention in this brief discussion. Under wind or earthquake, the worst-case conditions on a foundation may occur because the gravity loads are too light to hold the foundations down. Uplift in such cases becomes the critical design consideration, since soil cannot be placed in tension. Equations 13-4 and 13-5 provide one check for uplift when wind load or earthquake loads are negative. The extreme case occurs, however, when there is no live load at all:

5. Dead Load Plus Wind (13-7)
6. Dead Load Plus Earthquake. (13-8)

(Note that a 33% overstress in uplift is meaningless.)

In summary, the following load cases are those commonly used for structural design. It must be remembered that these load cases are very general; the designer must of course include other loads and load combinations as they apply to the particular project (snow, ice, ponding, etc.).

For primary structural systems:
1. Dead Load + 100% Live Load (13-3)
2. (0.75)(Dead Load + 100% Live Load + Wind) (13-4)
3. (0.75)(Dead Load % 100% Live Load + Earthquake) (13-5)

For foundation strength:
1. Dead Load + 100% Live Load (13-3)
2. (0.75)(Dead Load + 100% Live Load + Wind) (13-4)
3. (0.75)(Dead Load + 100% Live Load + Earthquake) (13-5)

For foundation settlement:
4. Dead Load + 50% Live Load (13-6)

For foundation uplift:
5. Dead Load + Wind (13-7)
6. Dead Load + Earthquake (13-8)

13.9 Building Code Requirements

Earlier discussions have referred to the building code as a source of information on design loads. No mention was made of the source of the building code, nor of its authority nor of the means used for its enforcement. These questions are the topics of this section.

The building code for a municipality establishes minimum standards for all construction within the municipality. When adopted by the municipality, it becomes an ordinance and it has the force of law. Failure to comply with the provisions of the building code can lead to heavy penalties.

The building code includes provisions not only for minimum structural loads, but for light and ventilation, plumbing, electrical wiring and safety and, most extensive of all, provisions for fire safety. In all these areas, the building code establishes minimum standards that must be met if a building permit is to be awarded. In unusual (and extremely rare) cases, the provisions of the building code may be waived where it is shown that other provisions will satisfy the intent of the code.

The enforcement of the building code is delegated to the building official of the municipality, who is usually one of the officials in the city engineer's office. Enforcement is achieved by review of plans and specifications for conformance to the Code; once conformance is assured, the plans are approved and a building permit is issued. Thereafter, periodic inspection by building inspectors during the construction period assures conformance of the construction to the approved plans and specifications.

Producing and maintaining a current and effective building code in today's rapidly changing construction industry would be an expensive process, far out of reach of most municipalities. In recent years, the use of "model" codes has come into common use that allows even small communities to have a modern and effective building code. Model codes are in fact so popular that even large cities use them.

To develop a model code, a group of cities form an organization that will produce and maintain a building code suited to the needs of the member cities. Each city contributes its share of the total cost through annual dues, usually raised by fees on the issuance of building permits. The cost to the city is a small fraction of the total cost of producing and maintaining its own code.

One of the more popular of these model codes is the Uniform Building Code (called UBC), produced and maintained by the International Conference of Building Officials, based in Whittier, California. The provisions for earthquake design in the UBC are widely copied by many other countries of the world. Another popular model code is the Standard Building Code (called Southern Building Code), produced and maintained by the Southern Building Code Congress International, based in Birmingham, Alabama. The wind load provisions of the Southern Building Code have helped immeasurably to improve construction standards on the hurricane-prone Gulf Coast.

In 1987, an earthquake having a magnitude of about 7.0 occurred in Armenia, in an area populated by some 2.3 million people; there were an estimated 25,000 deaths in that earthquake due to collapsing structures. In 1989, an earthquake having a similar magnitude of about 7.0 occurred in San Francisco, California, in an area similarly populated by some 2.1 million people; there were 57 deaths in this earthquake, all but 16 of which were traffic-related. The difference between 25,000 fatalities in Armenia and 16 fatalities in San Francisco lies in the use and enforcement of a modern and effective building code.

Building codes do work.

It is important to note, however, that the building codes establish only minimum standards. These standards may not be adequate for unusual circumstances, in which case the designer must adjust the standards. In the event of a structural failure, for example, a designer may not seek shelter from legal action by showing that the design meets code minimums; meeting code minimums is not in itself a guarantee of structural adequacy.

The provisions of the building code do not apply to the temporary or supporting construction by a contractor, termed *ancillary* construction. Ancillary construction includes all falsework, formwork and access structures designed and built for sole use by the contractor in performing the project construction. For such works, there are no building codes, no plan reviews, no permits and no inspectors; the contractor alone is responsible (and liable) for all aspects of his ancillary construction.

A final point on building codes has to do with terminology. A structure classed as "earthquake resistant" may sustain serious damage in an earthquake, so serious in fact that it may have to be torn down and rebuilt. Under a design basis earthquake, however, it will not collapse, injuring or killing the people inside it. However serious the damage, the structural frame will stand long enough to permit evacuation of its human occupants. (In the same context, a building classed as "fireproof" will in fact burn, but it will stand long enough to permit evacuation of the human occupants.)

Review Questions

1. Name the four major loads that occur on structures.
2. Why is it so essential to make an accurate determination of dead load, rather than use a blanket estimate?
3. Define the two types of gravity loads.
4. How are dead loads determined in areas that are not subject to earthquake loads?
5. How are the sustained loads on a foundation determined when the foundation is subject to settlements?
6. How are live loads established?
7. What is meant by the "occupancy" of a structure?
8. When a particular live load may have dynamic qualities, how is the load evaluated?
9. Between occupancy and usage, which overrides the other in establishing the level of live load?
10. How are dynamic loads treated in a static load design procedure?
11. What is meant by the term base shear?
12. Describe the difference between the way wind delivers its loads to a structure and the way earthquake does.
13. What is meant by "wind stagnation pressure"?
14. How is the theoretical stagnation pressure changed into the actual pressure acting on a structure?
15. At what height is the standard stagnation pressure assumed to occur?
16. How is the stagnation pressure found at heights other than the standard height?
17. What is the design wind velocity in Oklahoma City?
18. What is the shape factor for a cylindrical tower?
19. What is the function of the shape factor?
20. How is the area that is exposed to wind pressure established when the structure has setbacks and recesses?
21. Write the equation for calculating base shear due to earthquake and define each term in your own words.
22. For what size of structure is the equation of question 21 valid?
23. What is meant by the term "g-load" in a structure?
24. Give three commonly used load combinations that apply to the design of structural systems.
25. Why are load combinations necessary?
26. Why is an overstress allowed when lateral loads are included in a load combination?
27. What is meant by a "model" building code?
28. What is the authority of the building code?
29. How is the building code enforced?
30. In the event of a structural failure, what recourse does the designer have if conformance to the code can be established?
31. What is the authority of the building code over the contractor's ancillary construction?
32. What is meant by the term "earthquake-resistant" construction?

CHAPTER

14

DISTRIBUTION OF LOADS WITHIN A STRUCTURE

The preceding chapter deals with the loads that may be applied to a structure. The interactive effects of these loads on all members inside the structure must now be determined in order that these members can be designed. These interactive effects are the subject of this chapter.

14.1 Introduction to Structural Systems

There are two basic structural systems in wide use for building construction:

1. Diaphragm and shearwall systems
2. Rigid frame systems

A comparison of these two systems is shown in Figure 14-1. The sketches in Figure 14-1 represent a "frame" line removed from each of the two basic systems.

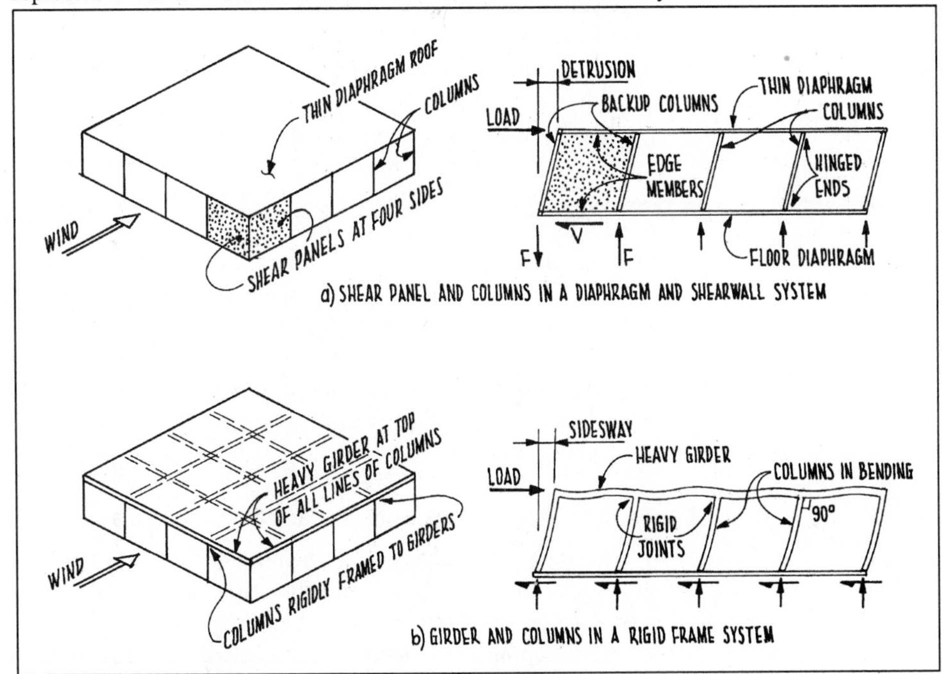

Figure 14-1 Comparison of structural systems.

It should be noted that both of the structural systems shown in Figure 14-1 carry their gravity loads in the same way; the gravity loads are carried entirely by the columns. The feature that makes the two systems different is in the way they resist lateral loads. The names of the two systems are, in fact, derived from the way they resist and sustain lateral loads.

The diaphragm and shearwall system of Figure 14-1a is called a *building frame* system in the design codes. It resists lateral loads through shear at the four sides of the shear panel. (The terms "shearwall" and "shear panel" are used interchangeably.) All columns in the line are hinged at top and bottom; they simply ride along with whatever deformations occur at the shear panel. The applied lateral force V shown in Figure 14-1a tries to roll the thin shear panel. The column loads F thus created in the backup columns oppose and resist that roll. The only stress in the thin shear panel is shear; the edge members and backup columns develop the resisting forces.

In contrast, the rigid frame system shown in Figure 14-1b resists lateral loads entirely through bending in the columns. There are no structural walls anywhere in a rigid frame system. The columns are fixed to the horizontal girder by a rigid fixed connection; as shown in Figure 14-1b, the angle between the girder and each column must remain 90° under all conditions of load. It is the strength of this rigid framed connection that gives the system its ability to resist and sustain lateral loads.

The diaphragm and shearwall system is statically determinate, that is, the forces V and F shown in Figure 14-1a may be found using only simple statics. The gravity loads in all columns may similarly be found using only simple statics. The thin diaphragm receives the lateral load (such as wind) and transmits it through shear to the vertical shear panel; all lateral load is resisted by elements loaded in shear.

In contrast, the rigid frame system is highly statically indeterminate. The solution for reactions involves the use of deformation equations at each span of the girder and at each column (the "slope-deflection" equations). The set of simultaneous equations thus obtained is solved to find the shears and moments at each span of the girder and to find the reaction at the base of each column. As shown in Figure 14-1b, the heavy girders receive the lateral load (such as wind) and transmit it to the columns; all lateral load is resisted by bending in the columns.

In the diaphragm and shearwall system of Figure 14-1a, there are two shear panels in each direction. Such panels are usually (but not necessarily) placed in the perimeter walls. All lateral load in one direction is opposed by the two shear walls and their four foundations; lateral load in the other direction is opposed by the other two shearwalls and their four foundations. Uplift on a foundation can become a serious problem as the height of the building increases. As a practical matter, the height of diaphragm and shearwall structures is usually limited to about six stories.

In contrast, every column and footing on a rigid frame system sustains its share of the lateral load; there is no concentration of load on a few footings. When used in a high-rise building, the rigid frame structure tends to be quite flexible, however, and measures must often be taken to control the vertical angle (drift) that the building as a whole will undergo under lateral load. This lateral displacement in a rigid frame is called *sidesway*. The term sidesway is also used quite loosely to refer to the sway (or drift) of any structure as it opposes lateral loads.

The only structural system presented in this textbook is the diaphragm and shearwall system. It will be seen to be versatile, adaptable and economical. As a consequence of being versatile, adaptable and economical, it is overwhelmingly the most widely used structural system in the world.

14.2 Typical Diaphragm and Shearwall Structure

To illustrate the analysis of a diaphragm and shearwall structure, the much-simplified three-story building shown in Figure 14-2 will be analyzed. The general construction, span lengths and story heights are quite common in today's industry.

Rooftop air conditioning equipment is also common, but when used, it is usually mounted on shock absorbers for the sake of noise suppression. With such mounting, the rooftop equipment in this example is classified as live load rather than dead load. In addition to the rooftop equipment, the *HVAC* system (heating, ventilating and air conditioning system) also includes ductwork, piping, and blowers throughout each story which is not shock mounted. Such rigidly mounted equipment is classified as dead load.

The use of certain "allowances" for dead load is also common. Such allowances are commonly used for arrangements of interior partitions that may be altered periodically during the life of the building. Electrical and plumbing items may also be included in such blanket allowances, since these items are rigidly fixed to the building but their exact location is arbitrarily chosen during construction.

Elevators in low buildings such as that of Figure 14-2 are usually hydraulically operated. Hydraulic elevators have the advantage that they are supported entirely at the ground level, exerting no loads on the structure above. They have the disadvantage that they are slow, and will not likely be used in buildings higher than about five stories.

14.3 Gravity Loads in a Diaphragm and Shearwall Structure

For the building of Figure 14-2, the first investigations will be to determine the gravity loads to be carried by various beams, girders, columns and footings. In all cases, the gravity loads tributary to a structural member are computed as all gravity loads halfway to the next like member. Gravity loads tributary to a joist are the loads halfway to the next joist at either side. Gravity loads tributary to a girder are the loads halfway to the next girder at either side. Gravity loads tributary to a column are the loads halfway to the next column (or other vertical support) at all sides.

The analysis for dead loads in the building of Figure 14-2 is considered first.

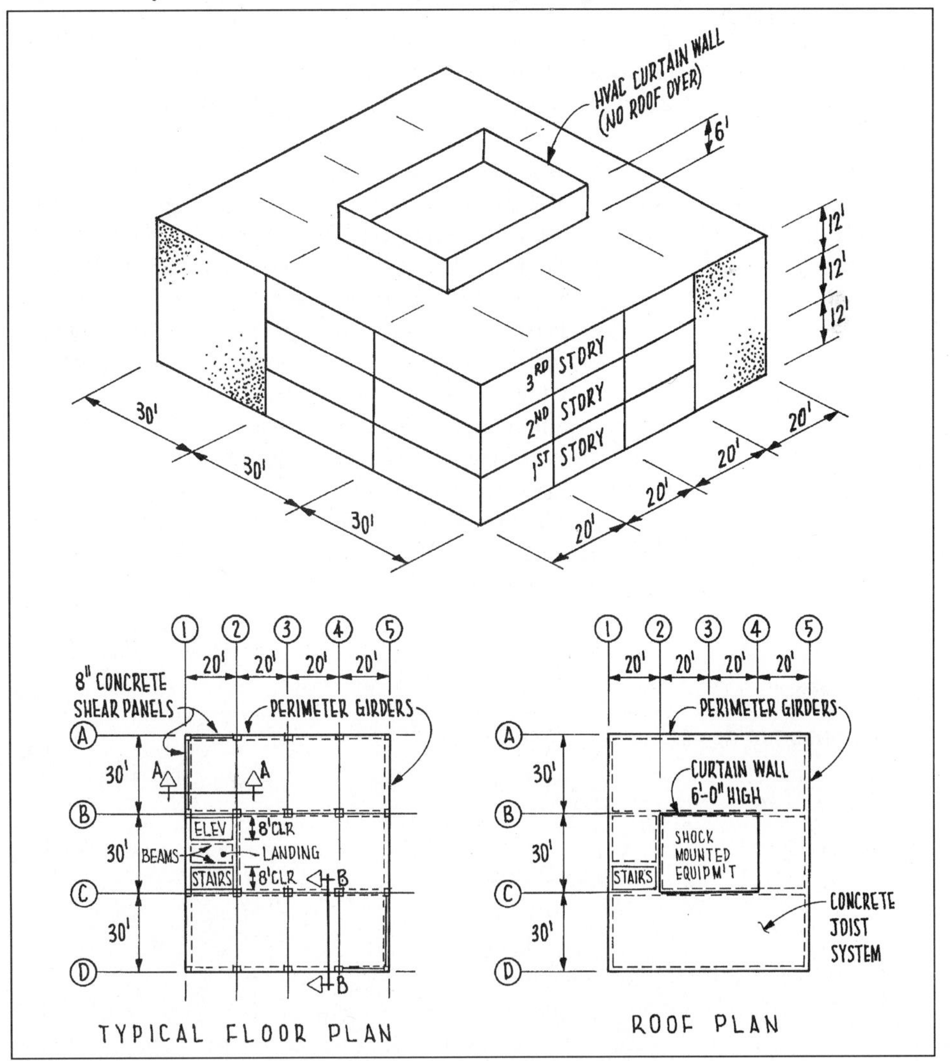

Figure 14-2 Typical diaphragm and shearwall structure. *(cont'd. on next page)*

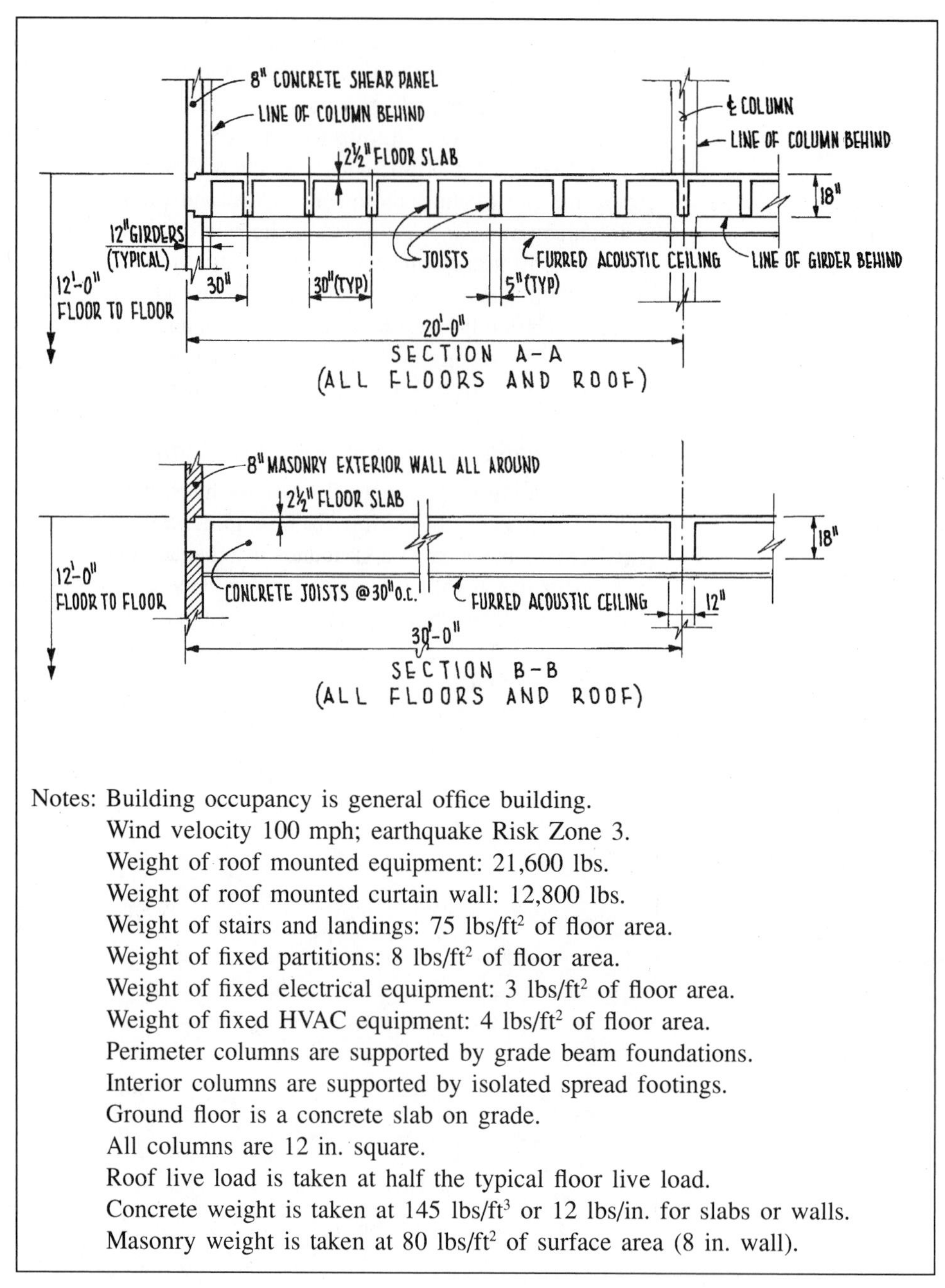

Notes: Building occupancy is general office building.
Wind velocity 100 mph; earthquake Risk Zone 3.
Weight of roof mounted equipment: 21,600 lbs.
Weight of roof mounted curtain wall: 12,800 lbs.
Weight of stairs and landings: 75 lbs/ft^2 of floor area.
Weight of fixed partitions: 8 lbs/ft^2 of floor area.
Weight of fixed electrical equipment: 3 lbs/ft^2 of floor area.
Weight of fixed HVAC equipment: 4 lbs/ft^2 of floor area.
Perimeter columns are supported by grade beam foundations.
Interior columns are supported by isolated spread footings.
Ground floor is a concrete slab on grade.
All columns are 12 in. square.
Roof live load is taken at half the typical floor live load.
Concrete weight is taken at 145 lbs/ft^3 or 12 lbs/in. for slabs or walls.
Masonry weight is taken at 80 lbs/ft^2 of surface area (8 in. wall).

Figure 14-2*(cont'd)* Typical diaphragm and shearwall structure.

Example 14-1

Determination of dead load on a member.

Given: Building configuration of Figure 14-1.

To Find: Dead load per foot of length to be carried by a typical joist.

Solution: Refer to section A-A which shows a typical section of a joist (see Table 13-1 for weights:

Weight of slab (12 lbs/in.)($2^1/_2$)	= 30.0 lb/ft
Weight of stem [(18-$2^1/_2$)(5)/144]145	= 78.0 lb/ft
Weight of acoustic tile (1 + 1)2.5	= 5.0 lb/ft
Weight of fixed partitions (8)(2.5)	= 20.0 lb/ft
Weight of electrical equipment (3)(2.5)	= 8.0 lb/ft
Weight of HVAC equipment (4)(2.5)	= 10.0 lb/ft
Σ	= 151 lb/ft

When computing dead load on a beam due to masonry walls both above and below, the dead load tributary to the beam is assumed to be the load all the way (rather than halfway) to the beam above, with no load coming from below. The masonry is considered to have no tensile strength and cannot "hang" to the bottom of the beam. Reinforced concrete, however, does have tensile strength due to its reinforcement, so it can hang to the bottom of a beam. The tributary dead load due to concrete walls and columns is therefore taken halfway to the next like member both above and below.

Example 14-2

Determination of dead load on a member.

Given: Building configuration of Figure 14-2.

To Find: Dead load per foot of length to be carried by a typical floor girder at line D2-D3.

Solution: Refer to section B-B which shows a typical perimeter girder on the 20 ft span.

Typical weight of the joist system per square foot of floor area (see Table 13-1):

Weight of slab (12 lbs/in.)($2^1/_2$)	= 30.0 lb/ft^2
Weight of stem [(18-$2^1/_2$)(5)(/144]145/$2^1/_2$	= 31.22 lb/ft^2
Σ	= 61.2 lb/ft^2

Weight carried by a typical girder in 20 ft span:

Weight of masonry above [(80)(12-1.5)(1)]	= 840 lb/ft
Weight of girder [(18)(12)/144]145	= 218 lb/ft
Weight of joist system [(30 - 1.5)/2]61.2	= 872 lb/ft
Weight of acoustic ceiling [(30 - 0.67)/2]2	= 29 lb/ft
Weight of fixed partitions [(30 - 0.67)/2]8	= 117 lb/ft
Σ	= 2180 lb/ft

Example 14-3

Determination of dead load on a member.

Given: Building configuration of Figure 14-2.

To Find: Dead load per foot of length to be carried by a roof girder B3-B4.

Solution: Refer to the roof plan and the typical sections:

$$\text{Weight of the curtain wall} = 12{,}800\ (30 + 30 + 40 + 40) = 91.4\ \text{lb/ft}$$

Weight carried by roof girder B3-B4 per foot of length:

Weight of curtain wall	=	91.4 lb/ft
Weight of joist system (61.2)(30)	=	1836.0 lb/ft
Weight of acoustic ceiling (2)(30)	=	60.0 lb/ft
	Σ =	1990.0 lb/ft

The weight of stairs tributary to a beam or to a column is taken as if the stairs were a solid floor rather than a stepped floor. While only an approximation, the approximation does account for stairs going both up and down from a given floor level. Such a calculation occurs in the next example.

Example 14-4

Determination of dead load on a member.

Given: Building configuration of Figure 14-2.

To Find: Dead load per foot of length to be carried by floor girder C1-C2.

Solution: Refer to the floor plan and the typical sections:

Weight of girder [(18)(12)/144]144	=	218 lb/ft
Weight of joist system (61.2)(29)/2	=	887 lb/ft
Weight of stairs (75)(8)/2	=	300 lb/ft
Weight of acoustic ceiling [(29 + 8)/2]2	=	37 lb/ft
Weight of partitions (29/2)(8)	=	116 lb/ft
Weight of electrical equipment [(29 + 8)/2]3	=	56 lb/ft
Weight of HVAC equipment [(29 + 8)/2]4	=	74 lb/ft
	Σ =	1690 lb/ft

Computation of the dead load tributary to a column follows much the same format as that for beams. In addition to the load at each floor, the weight of the column from floor to floor must also be included. The dead load of the column is taken from the midlevel of the story below to the midlevel of the story above.

The load in a column actually varies somewhat between the ceiling and the floor as the dead load of the column is added. For design of the column, the higher load at the floor level is taken as the design load over the entire height of the column at that story. The small error incurred is on the safe side.

At the ground floor, the weight of the floor slab on grade as well as all live loads are assumed to be transmitted directly to the supporting soil. Similarly, the weight of the perimeter walls is assumed to be transmitted directly to the supporting soil by the perimeter grade beams. The only additional load tributary to a ground floor column (and its footing) is the additional weight of the column and shear panels to the midlevel of the story.

In calculating the dead load that is tributary to a member using the method presented here, it must be remembered that the method is an approximation. It is a good approximation, but an approximation nonetheless. In applying any such approximate method, including this one, extreme refinements in the calculations are unwarranted. Commonsense judgements will usually be accurate enough to obtain a reasonable solution.

Example 14-5

Determination of dead load on a member.

Given: Building configuration of Figure 14-2.

To Find: Design dead load on column B-3 at each floor level.

Solution: Refer to the typical plans and sections from earlier solutions:

Weight of curtain wall = 91.4 lb/ft of length
Weight of joist system = 61.2 lb/ft^2 of floor area

At the roof:

Weight of curtain wall (91.4)(20)	= 1828 lb
Weight of girder [(12 x 18)/144](145)(20)	= 4350 lb
Weight of joist system (61.2)(29)(20)	= 35496 lb
Weight of column [(1 x 1)(12 - 1.5)/2]145	= 761 lb
Weight of acoustic ceiling (20)(30)(2)	= 1200 lb
Weight of electrical equipment (20)(30)(3)	= 1800 lb
Weight of HVAC equipment (20)(30)(4)	= 2400 lb
	Σ = 47800 lb

Design dead load for column from third floor to roof:

Add weight of concrete column above (1 x 1)(12 - 1.5)(145)/2	= 760 lb
Design load = 47,800 + 760	= 48560 lb

At the third floor:

Weight of girder [(12 x 18)/144](145)20	= 4350 lb
Weight of joist system (61.2)(29)(20)	= 35496 lb
Weight of column [(1 x 1)(12 - 1.5)]145	= 1523 lb
Weight of acoustic ceiling (20)(30)(2)	= 1200 lb
Weight of partitions (20)(30)(8)	= 4800 lb
Weight of electrical equipment (20)(30)(3)	= 1800 lb
Weight of HVAC equipment (20)(30)(4)	= 2400 lb
	Σ = 51600 lb

Design dead load for columns from second floor to third floor:

Add weight of concrete column above	= 760 lb
Design load = 47,800 + 51,600 + 760	= 100,200 lb

At the second floor:

Same as third floor Σ = 51,600 lb

Design dead load for columns at ground floor level:

Add weight of concrete column above	= 760 lb
Design load = 47,800 + 51,600 + 51,600 + 760	= 151,760 lb

Example 14-6

Determination of dead load on a member.

Given: Building configuration of Figure 14-2.

To Find: Design dead load on column D-4 at each floor level.

Solution: Refer to the typical plans and sections.

From earlier solutions:

Weight of joist system = 61.2 lb/ft^2 of floor area.

At the roof:

Weight of girder [(12 x 18)/144](145)(20)	=	4350 lb
Weight of joist system [(61.2)(29)/2]20	=	17750 lb
Weight of acoustic ceiling [(2)(30-0.67)/2]20	=	590 lb
Weight of concrete wall below (12)(8)(19)/2	=	910 lb
Weight of concrete column below (1 x 1))(12 - 1.5)(145)/2	=	760 lb
Weight of electrical equipment [(20 x 30)/2]3	=	900 lb
Weight of HVAC equipment [(20 x 30)/2]4	=	1200 lb
	Σ =	26460 lb

Design dead load for columns from third floor to roof:

Add weight of concrete column above (1 x 1)(12 - 1.5)(145)/2	=	760 lb
Design load = 26460 + 760	=	27220 lb

At the third floor:

Weight of girder [(12 x 18)/144](145)(20)	=	4350 lb
Weight of joist system [(61.2)(29)/2]20	=	17750 lb
Weight of acoustic ceiling [(2)(30-0.67)/2]20	=	590 lb
Weight of concrete wall above and below [(12)(8)(19)/2]2	=	1820 lb
Weight of concrete column above and below [(1 x 1)(12 - 1.5)(145)/2]2	=	1520 lb
Weight of masonry wall above (80)(12 - 1.5)(19)/2	=	7980 lb
Weight of partitions [(20 x 30)/2]8	=	2400 lb
Weight of electrical equipment [(20 x 30)/2]3	=	900 lb
Weight of HVAC equipment [(20 x 30)/2]4	=	1200 lb
	Σ =	38510 lb

Design dead load for columns from second floor to third floor:

Add weight of concrete column above	=	760 lb
Design load = 26460 + 38510 + 760	=	65730 lb

At the second floor

Same as third floor	Σ =	38510 lb

Design dead load for columns at ground floor level

Add weight of concrete column above	=	760 lb
Design load = 26460 + 38510 + 38510 + 760	=	104240 lb

Example 14-7

Determination of dead load on a member.

Given: Building configuration of Figure 14-2.

To Find: Design dead load on column D-5 at each floor level.

Solution: Refer to the typical plans and sections.

From earlier solutions:

Weight of joist system = 61.2 lb/ft^2 of floor area.

At the roof:

Weight of girder [(12x18)/144](145)(9.5+14.5)	=	5220 lb
Weight of joist system [(61.2)(29/2)(19/2)]	=	8430 lb
Weight of acoustic ceiling [(2)(30 - 0.67)/2](20 - 0.67)/2	=	280 lb
Weight of concrete wall below (12)(8)(19/2 + 29/2)/2	=	1150 lb
Weight of concrete column below (1 x 1))(12 - 1.5)(145)/2	=	760 lb
Weight of electrical equipment [(20 x 30)/4]3	=	450 lb
Weight of HVAC equipment [(20 x 30)/4]4	=	600 lb
Σ	=	16890 lb

Design dead load for columns from third floor to roof:

Add weight of concrete column above (1 x 1)(12 - 1.5)(145)/2	=	760 lb
Design load = 16890 + 760	=	17650 lb

At the third floor:

Weight of girder [(12 x 18)/144](9.5 + 14.5)	=	5220 lb
Weight of joist system (61.2)[(29/2)(19/2)]	=	8430 lb
Weight of acoustic ceiling [2(30-0.67)/2](19 - 0.67)/2	=	280 lb
Weight of concrete wall [(12)(8)(19/2 + 29/2]	=	2300 lb
Weight of concrete column (1 x 1)(12 - 1.5)(145)	=	1520 lb
Weight of partitions [20 x 30/4]8	=	1200 lb
Weight of electrical equipment [(20 x 30)/4]3	=	450 lb
Weight of HVAC equipment [(20 x 30)/4]4	=	600 lb
Σ	=	20000 lb

Design dead load for column from second floor to third floor:

Add weight of concrete column above		760 lb
Design load = 16890 + 20000 + 760	=	37650 lb

At the second floor:

Same as third floor	Σ =	20000 lb

Design load for columns at ground floor level:

Add weight of concrete column above	=	760 lb
Design load = 16890 + 20000 + 20000 + 760	=	57650 lb

It should be noted that no hole is needed in the roof over the hydraulic elevator. Further, there is no additional load on the roof except for some alignment equipment which is negligible. While the elevator makes no contribution to building loads, it does create a void space which must be accounted for. The following example illustrates such a calculation.

Example 14-8

Determination of dead load on a member.

Given: Building configuration of Figure 14-2.

To Find: Design dead load on column B-2 at each floor level.

Solution: Refer to the typical plans and sections.
From earlier solutions:

Weight of joist system = 61.2 lb/ft^2 of floor area.

At the roof:

Weight of curtain wall (91.4)(20/2 + 30/2)	= 2290 lb
Weight of girder [(12 x 18)/144]145(20)	= 4350 lb
Weight of joist system (61.2)(29)(19)	= 33720 lb
Weight of column (1 x 1)(10.5)(145)/2	= 760 lb
Weight of acoustic ceiling (20)(30)2	= 1200 lb
Weight of electrical equipment (20)(30)3	= 1800 lb
Weight of HVAC equipment (20)(30)4	= 2400 lb
	Σ = 46520 lb

Design dead load for column from third floor to roof:

Add weight of concrete column above	= 760 lb
Design load - 46520 + 760	= 47280 lb

At the third floor:

Weight of girder [(12 x 18)/144]145(20 + 29/2 + 19/2)	= 9570 lb
Weight of joist system (61.2)(29)(19) - 61.2(19/2)(8)	= 29070 lb
Weight of column (1 x 1)(10.5)(145)/2	= 760 lb
Weight of acoustic ceiling (20)(30)2 - (19/2)(8)2	= 1050 lb
Weight of partitions (20)(30)8 - (19/2)(8)8	= 4190 lb
Weight of electrical equipment (20)(30)3 - (19/2)(8)3	= 1570 lb
Weight of HVAC equipment (20)(30)4 - (19/2)(8)4	= 2100 lb
	Σ = 48310 lb

Design dead load for column from second floor to third floor:

Add weight of concrete column above	= 760 lb
Design load = 46520 + 48310 + 760	= 95590 lb

At the second floor:

Same as third floor	Σ = 48310 lb

Design load for columns at ground floor level:

Add weight of concrete column above	= 760 lb
Design load = 46520 + 48310 + 48310 + 760	= 143900 lb

The calculation of live load on beams and columns is much more simple than was the calculation of dead load. The live loads will be computed for the same beams and columns used to illustrate the calculation of dead load.

Example 14-9

Determination of live load on a member.

Given: Building configuration of Figure 14-2, to include weights of HVAC equipment.

To Find: Live load per foot of length to be carried by a typical joist (corresponds to Example 14-1).

Solution: Refer to section A-A which shows a typical section of a joist.

From Table 13-2, the live load for the floor of the office building of Figure 14-2 is typically 80 lb/ft^2.

For typical floor joists at 30 in. or $2^1/_2$ ft spacing for floor joists:

$$w_{LL} = 80(2^1/_2) = 200 \text{ lb/ft}$$

For a typical roof joist outside the equipment area, the roof live load is assumed to be half the typical floor load, or 40 lbs/ft^2:

$$w_{LL} = 40(2^1/_2) = 100 \text{ lb/ft}$$

For a typical roof joist inside the equipment area, the roof live load may be taken either at half the typical floor load, or it may be taken at the average weight of the equipment per square foot. The average weight of the roof mounted equipment is readily calculated:

$$w_{HVAC} = 21{,}600 \text{ lb}/(40 \times 30) = 31 \text{ lb/ft}^2$$

Most designers would probably design for the higher "blanket" load of 40 lb/ft^2 than for the lower computed load of 31 lb/ft^2.

In computing live loads, the degree of refinement is usually quite crude. Since the live load itself is at best an approximation, highly refined calculations are inappropriate. Tributary floor areas, for example, will rarely exclude walls from the areas. Some examples will illustrate such rough calculations for tributary live loads.

Example 14-10

Determination of live load on a member.

Given: Building configuration of Figure 14-2.

To Find: Live load per foot of length to be carried by a typical floor girder at line D2-D3 (corresponds to Example 14-2).

Solution: Refer to section B-B which shows a typical perimeter girder on the 20 ft. span.

Typical floor live load for the office building of Figure 14-2 is found from Table 13-2 is seen to be 80 lb/ft^2:

$$w_{LL} = (80)(30/2) = 1200 \text{ lb/ft}$$

Example 14-11

Determination of live load on a member.

Given: Building configuration of Figure 14-2.

To Find: Live load per foot of length to be carried by a typical roof girder at line B3-B4 (corresponds to Example 14-3).

Solution: Refer to the roof plan and the typical sections.

Typical roof live load for the office building of Example 14-2 is found from Table 13-2 is seen to be half of the floor load of 80 lb/ft^2, or 40 lb/ft^2:

$$w_{LL} = (40)(30) = 1200 \text{ lb/ft}$$

Alternatively, the live load within the equipment area might be taken at its actual value of 31 lb/ft^2, in which case:

$$w_{LL} = (40)(30/2) + (31)(30/2) = 1065 \text{ lb/ft}$$

The choice of which load to use is left to the designer.

Example 14-12

Determination of live load on a member.

Given: Building configuration of Figure 14-2.

To Find: Live load per foot of length to be carried by a typical floor girder at line C1-C2 (corresponds to Example 14-4).

Solution: Refer to the floor plan and the typical sections.

Typical floor live load for the office building of Figure 14-2 is found from Table 13-2 is seen to be 80 lb/ft^2 for general floor areas and 100 lb/ft^2 for corridors and stairs:

$$w_{LL} = 80(30/2) + 100(30/2) = 2700 \text{ lb/ft}$$

The dead loads computed for the girders of examples 14-1, 2 3 and 4 are summarized in Figure 14-3. Also shown are the live loads for the same girders computed in examples

14-9, 10, 11 and 12. In a diaphragm and shearwall structure, these are the vertical loads that these girders would have to sustain.

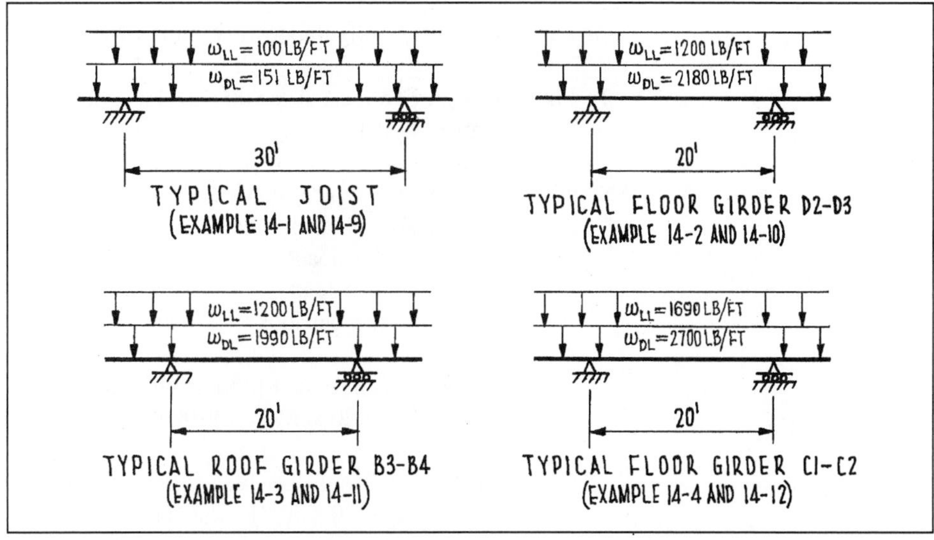

Figure 14-3 Summary of gravity loads on joists and girders.

Live loads tributary to columns follow the same general concepts as live loads tributary to beams. In such calculations, tributary areas are often taken to be quite general. Some examples will illustrate the procedure.

Example 14-13

Determination of live load on a member.

Given: Building configuration of Figure 14-2.

To Find: Design live load on column B-3 at each floor level (corresponds to Example 14-9).

Solution: Refer to the typical plans and sections.

Live loads are taken from Table 13-2 to be:

Roof live load = 40 lb/ft²
Floor live load = 80 lb/ft²
Stair and corridor live load = 100 lb/ft²

At the roof, live load tributary to column B-3 is:

$P_{LL} = 40(20 \text{ x } 30) = 24000$ lb

At the third floor, live load tributary to column B-3 is:

$P_{LL} = 80(20 \text{ x } 30) = 48000$ lb

At the second floor, live load tributrary to column B-3 is:

$P_{LL} = 80(20 \text{ x } 30) = 48000$ lb

At the ground floor, no live load is tributary to column B-3:

Design live load third floor to roof = 24000 lb
Design live load second floor to third floor = 72000 lb
Design live load ground floor to second floor = 120000 lb

Example 14-14

Determination of live load on a member.

Given: Building configuration of Figure 14-2.

To Find: Design live load on column D-4 at each floor level (corresponds to Example 14-10).

Solution: Refer to the typical plans and sections.

Live loads are taken from Table 13-2 to be:

Roof live load = 40 lb/ft^2
Floor live load = 80 lb/ft^2
Stair and corridor live load = 100 lb/ft^2

At the roof, live load tributary to column D-4 is:

$P_{LL} = 40(20 \times 30/2) = 12000$ lb

At the third floor, live load tributary to column D-4 is:

$P_{LL} = 80(20 \times 30/2) = 24000$ lb

At the second floor, live load tributary to column D-4 is:

$P_{LL} = 80(20 \times 30/2) = 24000$ lb

At the ground floor, no live load is tributary to column D-4:

Design live load third floor to roof = 12000 lb
Design live load second floor to third floor = 36000 lb
Design live load ground floor to second floor = 60000 lb

Example 14-15

Determination of live load on a member.

Given: Building configuration of Figure 14-2.

To Find: Design live load on column D-5 at each floor level (corresponds to Example 14-11).

Solution: Refer to the typical plans and sections.

Live loads are taken from Table 13-2 to be:

Roof live load = 40 lb/ft^2
Floor live load = 80 lb/ft^2
Stair and corridor live load = 100 lb/ft^2

At the roof, live load tributary to column D-5 is:

$P_{LL} = 40(20/2 \times 30/2) = 6000$ lb

At the third floor, live load tributary to column D-5 is:

$P_{LL} = 80(20/2 \times 30/2) = 12000$ lb

At the second floor, live load tributary to column D-5 is:

$P_{LL} = 100(20/2 \times 30/2) = 15000$ lb

At the ground floor, no live load is tributary to column D-5:

Design live load third floor to roof = 6000 lb
Design live load second floor to third floor = 18000 lb
Design live load ground floor to second floor = 33000 lb

Example 14-16

Determination of live load on a member.

Given: Building configuration of Figure 14-2.

To Find: Design live load on column B-2 at each floor level (corresponds to Example 14-12).

Solution: Refer to the typical plans and sections.

Live loads are taken from Table 13-2 to be:

Roof live load = 40 lb/ft²

Floor live load = 80 lb/ft²

Stair and corridor live load = 100 lb/ft²

At the roof, live load tributary to column B-2 is:

$P_{LL} = 40(20)(30) = 24000$ lb

At the third floor, live load tributary to column B-2 is:

$P_{LL} = 80(20)(30/2) + 80(20/2)(30/2)$
$+ 100(30/2 - 8)(20/2) = 43000$ lb

At the second floor, live load tributary to column B-2 is:

$P_{LL} = 80(20)(30/2) + 80(20/2)(30/2)$
$+ 100(30/2 - 8)(20/2) = 43000$ lb

At the ground floor, no live load is tributary to column B-2:

Design live load third floor to roof = 24000 lb

Design live load second floor to third floor = 67000 lb

Design live load ground floor to second floor = 110000 lb

The dead loads computed for the columns of examples 14-5, 6, 7 and 8 are summarized in Figure 14-4. Also shown are the live loads for the same columns computed in examples 14-13, 14, 15 and 16. These are the gravity loads that these columns must sustain in addition to any loads that might be imposed by wind or earthquake.

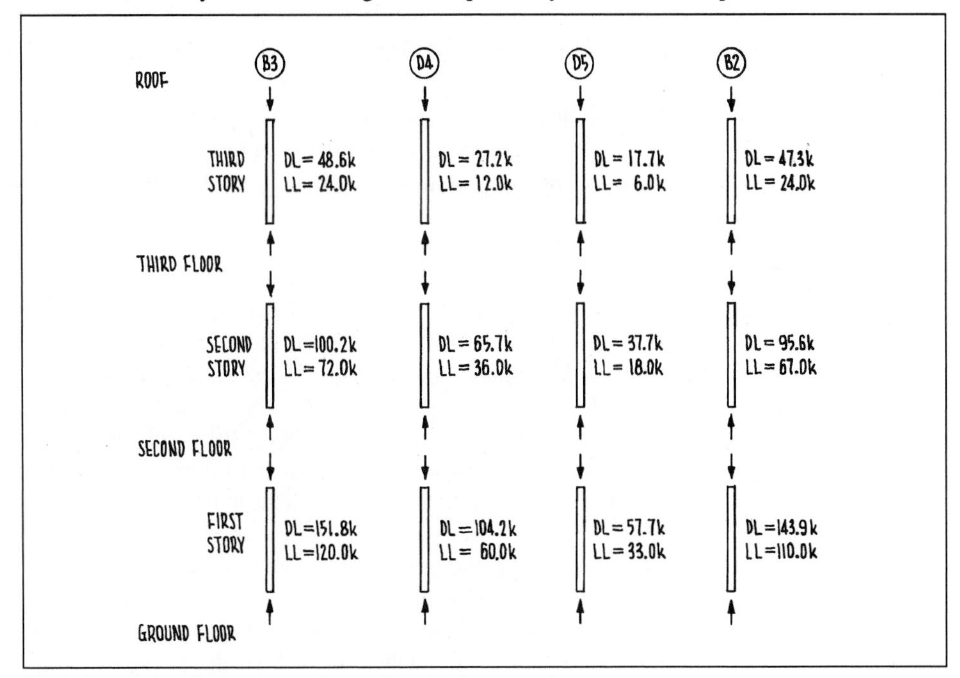

Figure 14-4 Summary of gravity loads on columns.

14.4 Lateral Loads in a Diaphragm and Shearwall Structure

Regardless whether a diaphragm and shearwall system is built of concrete, masonry, timber or steel, it will carry its loads in much the same way. The beams and columns will carry the vertical loads and the diaphragms and shearwalls will carry the lateral loads. The distribution of lateral loads on a multi-story diaphragm and shearwall structure (such as the example building of Figure 14-2) is shown in Figure 14-5. For the sake of clarity, the interior columns are not shown in Figure 14-5.

Wind loads acting on the structure will put pressure on the exterior walls. In sustaining these loads, the exterior walls will act as vertical beams, with the thin diaphragms acting as their supports at top and bottom. The diaphragms receive and transmit the accumulated horizontal loads P_x and P_y to the vertical shear panels, which in turn transmit the load (and the accompanying "roll") to the foundations.

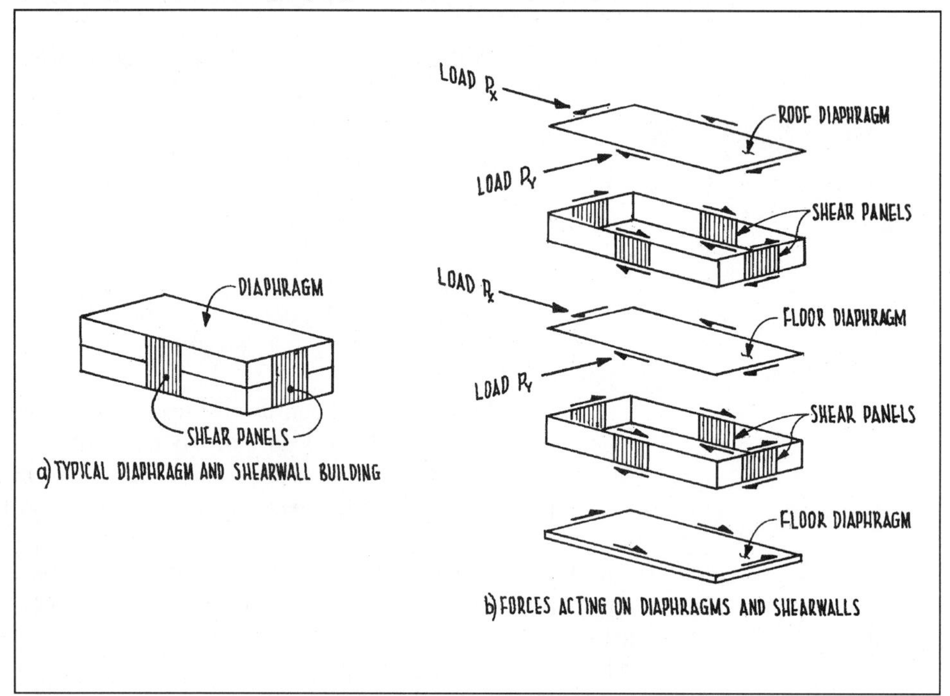

Figure 14-5 Lateral loads on a diaphragm and shearwall structure.

Shear walls can only resist loads that are parallel to them. The set of walls parallel to the force P_x in Figure 14-5, for example, can resist only a force P_x. Under a load P_y in the other direction, they may bend slightly (or tilt) but they will not present any real resistance to the load; the walls parallel to P_y will then be required to resist the entire load P_y.

It is thus necessary to provide two sets of shearwalls, one set to resist loads parallel to the *xx* axis and one set to resist loads parallel to the *yy* axis. In all cases, the weight of the thin diaphragms is supported vertically by the floor and roof beam systems, but they form very rigid membranes in the horizontal plane. All loads coming to the diaphragms are transmitted by shear to the shear panels.

All columns are hinged at top and bottom. Whenever lateral sidesway (or *drift*) occurs, the columns simply ride along; their only loads are the gravity loads that are accumulated and transmitted from floor to floor. The only exceptions to this rule are the backup columns at each side of the shear panels; these columns carry the shears at the vertical edges of the shear panels in addition to carrying their gravity loads.

The thin diaphragm at each floor and roof level serves to maintain the horizontal shape and integrity of the structure at each level. Racking of a diaphragm (allowing it to deform into a parallelogram) cannot be permitted to occur. Except, of course, for its elastic detrusion, the diaphragm must be designed to retain its original shape under all conditions of load.

The thin horizontal diaphragm might be the $2^1/_2$ in. floor slab in a concrete building or it might be the $^3/_4$ in. plywood floor decking in a timber building. In either case, the diaphragm is supported vertically and held in its horizontal plane by the beam and girder system at each level. The beams and girders carry only the vertical loads. The diaphragm acts as a thin membrane, very rigid in its horizontal plane, transmitting all the lateral loads it receives to the vertical shear panels.

Typical diaphragms are shown in Figure 14-6 for various materials. Concrete floors are widely used as diaphragms and can be built of insulating concrete, lightweight concrete or gypsum concrete. These diaphragms often serve a dual or even triple purpose; they can be made to serve as wearing surfaces as well as diaphragms and, in a roof, as the weather barrier.

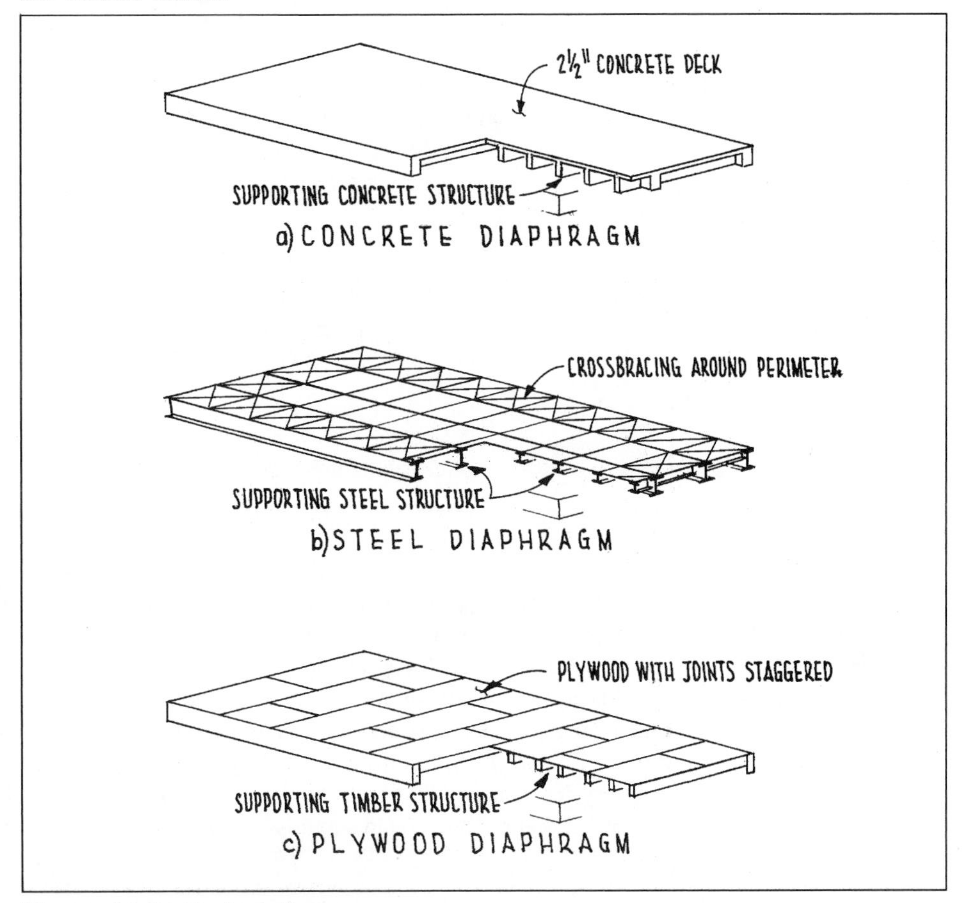

Figure 14-6 Typical diaphragms.

The cross-braced steel floor shown in Figure 14-6 will serve quite well as a diaphragm even though it is not a solid membrane like the others. It is not usually necessary to brace every panel; bracing the perimeter panels as shown will usually be enough to maintain the horizontal shape and integrity of the floor system. Such braced flooring systems are lightweight and functional; they are very useful in areas of high earthquake intensities where every effort must be made to reduce mass.

The plywood decking shown in Figure 14-6 is also very lightweight and functional. All edges of every piece of plywood must be nailed, either to the supporting joists or to added blocking if no support exists along the transverse joints. In recent years, oriented strand board has proven to be an effective and low cost substitute for plywood in such applications.

The discussions so far seem to imply that a structural system may be built of steel or it may be built of timber or it may be built of concrete; mixing of materials has not been suggested. In reality, many structural systems are built using a mixture of materials.

One of the more popular diaphragm systems, for example, is a lightweight concrete deck on steel framing, such as that shown in the sketch of Figure 14-7a.

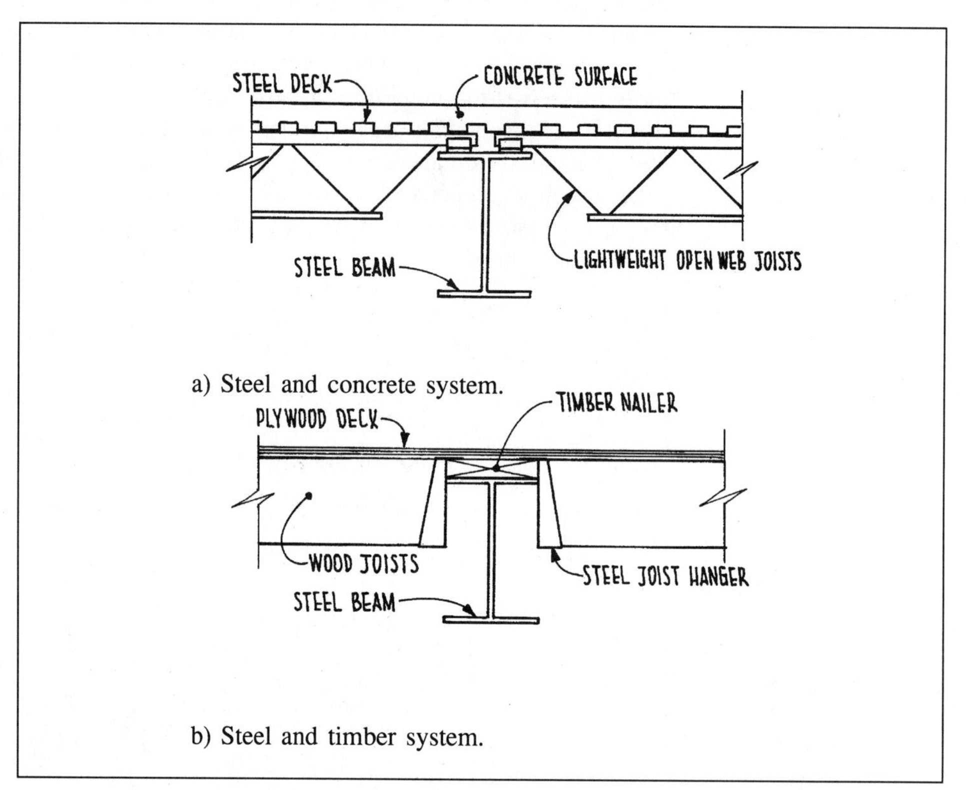

a) Steel and concrete system.

b) Steel and timber system.

Figure 14-7 Mixed concrete and steel system.

Another popular variation is the use of plywood sheathing on steel joists, also shown in Figure 14-7b. While inexpensive and lightweight, its noise suppression properties are unacceptably poor. In most cases such construction is used only for roofs in one-story buildings.

Shear panels function much like diaphragms except that they act in a vertical plane. Like diaphragms, shear panels may also be built of various materials. Some examples are shown in Figure 14-8. Reinforced masonry shear panels are very popular, very functional and very inexpensive. They can also serve double or triple duty as weather barriers, as well as fire walls. Their sound suppression properties are excellent, as one might suppose.

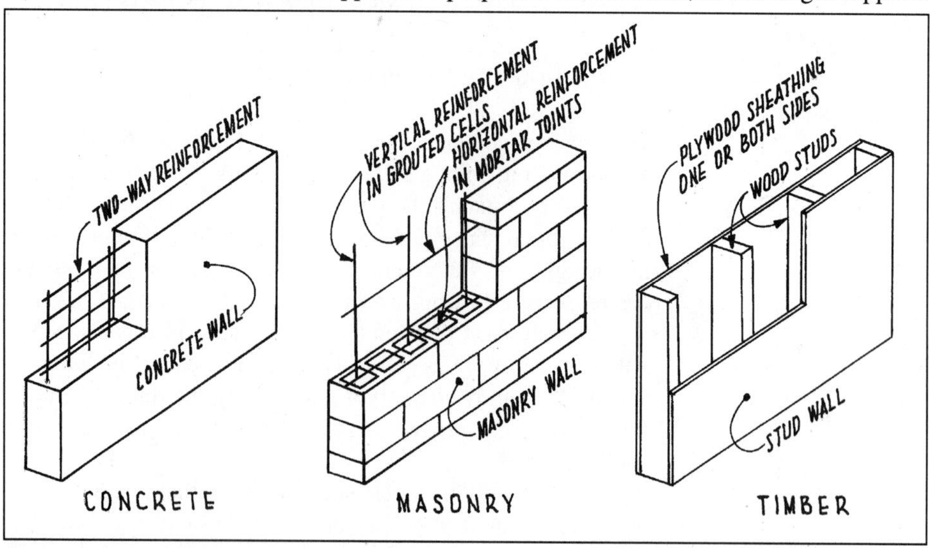

Figure 14-8 Typical shear panels.

The plywood shear panel shown in Figure 14-8 may be sheathed one side or two, depending on the amount of load. In all cases, all four edges of every piece of plywood must be fastened, even if additional blocking members have to be provided in order to do so.

A steel cross-braced panel will also serve quite well as a shear panel even though in reality it is a truss rather than a panel. The lightweight steel rods used as the diagonals will not resist compressive loads. Depending on the direction of load, one of the rods in the panel will be placed in tension, the other in compression. The one in compression simply sags out of the way, leaving the other rod to carry the entire load as a tension member. Such "counterdiagonals" are discussed in the next chapter.

Wind forces acting at the outside of a building were presented in earlier discussions. The distribution of those forces into the diaphragms, shear panels and columns can now be examined. The concepts of the preceding discussions will be used to find the wind forces in the building of Figure 14-2.

Example 14-17

Determination of wind forces in a structure.

Given: Building configuration of Figure 14-2, shown for immediate reference in the following sketch.

To Find: Design wind forces on members due to wind against the long side (the 90 ft side) of the building.

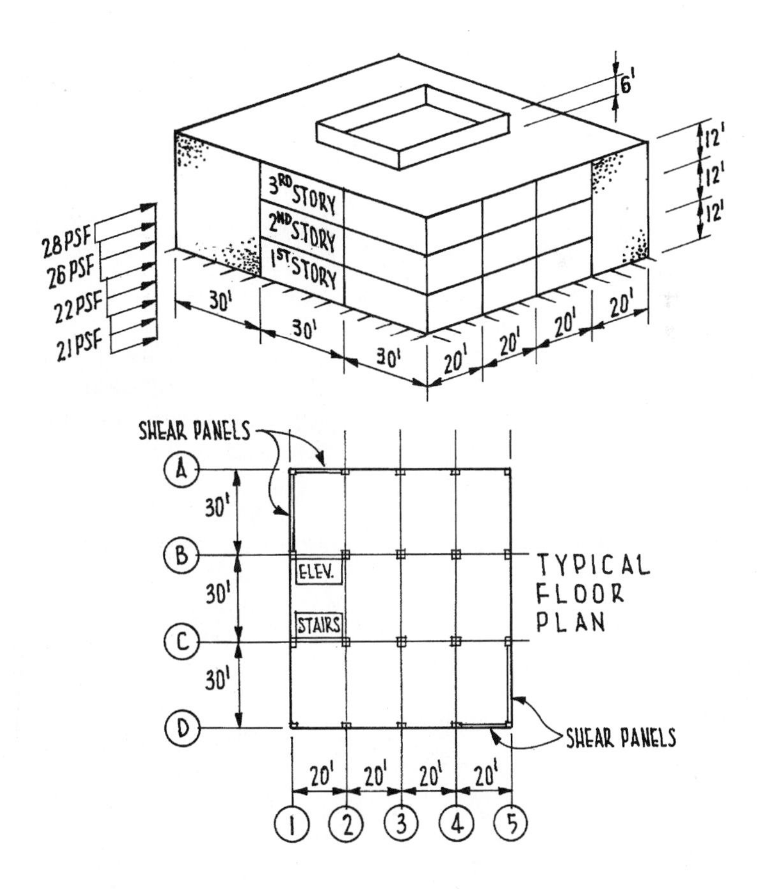

Solution: Wind stagnation pressures are shown in the sketch for a wind velocity of 100 mph.

The wind pressures are found by multiplying the wind stagnation pressures by the shape factor 1.3. Wind pressures are distributed 80% on the pressure side, 50% on the suction side. These pressures are shown in the following sketch.

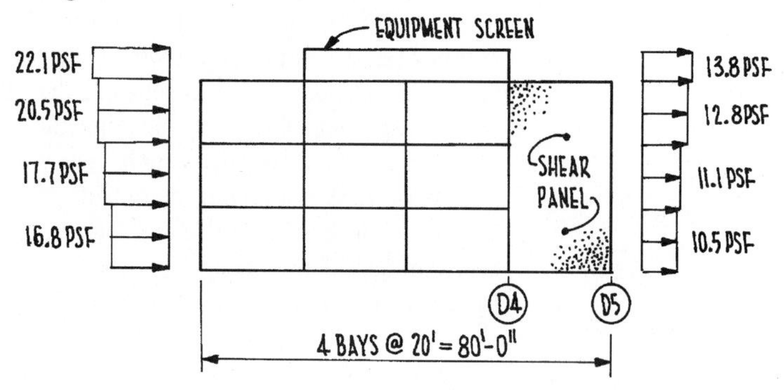

Forces produced by the wind pressures are shown in the following sketch. The forces at each level are computed as pressure times area. The force on each story is then distributed half to the diaphragm above and half to the diaphragm below, where the exterior wall is assumed to act like a vertical beam supported at each end by the diaphragms. The entire wind force on the equipment screen must be transmitted to the roof diaphragm as shown.

EQUIPMENT SCREEN
4.0k 22.1k 19.1k 18.1k
4.0k 2.5k
11.1k 11.1k 9.6k 9.6k 9.1k 9.1k
3RD STORY
2ND STORY
1ST STORY
6.9k 6.9k 6.0k 6.0k 5.7k 5.7k
2.5k 13.8k 12.0k 11.3k
D4 D5

The forces against the diaphragms produce shears in the two vertical shear panels, half of the force being resisted at each shear panel. At each level, the shear to be sustained by the panel is the sum of all shearing forces above that level.

Shear on one shear panel between third floor and roof:

$$V_{3R} = (4 + 2.5 + 11.1 + 6.9)/2 = 12.3 \text{ k}$$

Shear on one shear panel between second floor and third floor:

$$V_{23} = (4 + 2.5 + 11.1 + 6.9 + 11.1 + 6.9 + 9.6 + 6.0)/2 = 29.1 \text{ k}$$

Shear on one shear panel between first floor and second floor:

$$V_{12} = (4 + 2.5 + 11.1 + 6.9 + 11.1 + 6.9 + 9.6 + 6.0 + 9.6 + 6.0 + 9.1 + 5.7)/2 = 44.3 \text{ k}$$

Base shear on foundations of one shear panel:

$$V_B = (4 + 2.5 + 11.1 + 6.9 + 11.1 + 6.9 + 9.6 + 6.0 + 9.6 + 6.0 + 9.1 + 5.7 + 9.1 + 5.7)/2 = 51.7 \text{ k}$$

The resultant horizontal shears on the shear panels along with the vertical shears along the backup columns D-4 and D-5 are shown in the following sketches. The vertical shears may be found by summing moments about any corner of the shear panel.

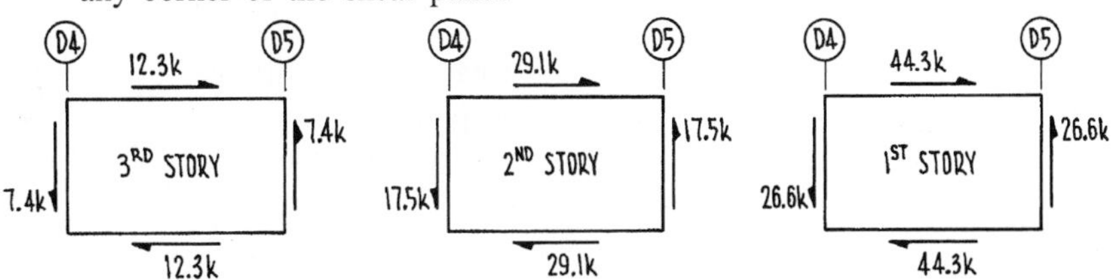

The change in column loads is then:

ΔP on columns from third floor to roof	= ± 7.4 k
ΔP on columns from second floor to third floor	= ± 17.5 k
ΔP on columns from ground floor to second floor	= ± 26.6 k
ΔP on foundations	= ± 26.6 k
Base shear on two foundations (D-4 and D-5)	= ± 57.7 k

The change in forces is shown as plus or minus since the wind can come from either direction.

The wind forces acting on the shear panels in the other directions on lines 1 and 5 are found in the same way as those computed in Example 14-17. The numbers will be slightly different but the procedure is the same. The actual computation of these forces is assigned as an outside problem at the end of the chapter.

Earthquake forces produce shears in the shear panels in much the same way that wind forces do. The primary difference lies in the way that the forces are generated. An example will demonstrate the calculation for earthquake forces on the structure of Figure 14-2.

Example 14-18

Determination of earthquake forces on a structure.

Given: Building configuration of Figure 14-2, shown for immediate reference in the following sketch.

To Find: Design earthquake forces produced by an earthquake acting in the direction of the short axis of the building.

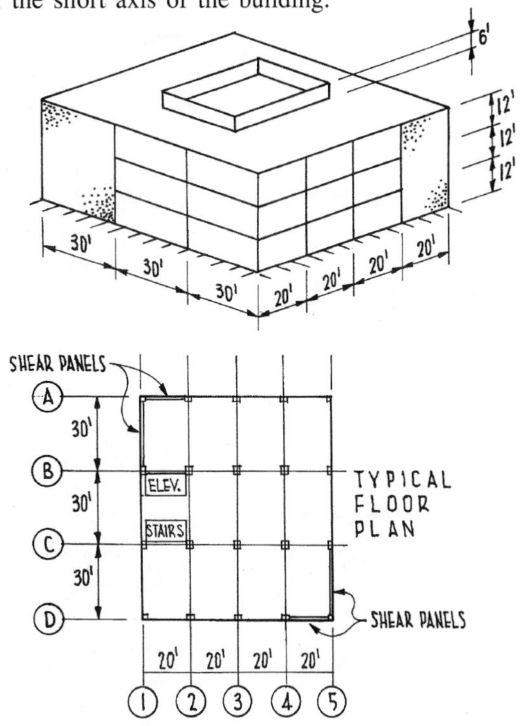

Solution: Earthquake forces will be computed for that portion of the dead load mass of the structure attached to the various diaphragms.

Dead load of all masses attached to and accelerated with the roof diaphragm:

Dead load of curtain wall attached to the roof diaphragm:

Dead load = 12,800 lb

Dead load of joist system in the roof diaphragm:

Dead load
= (61.2)(29)(19)(11) + (61.2)(20)(19) = 394,200 lb

Dead load of girders in the roof diaphragm:

Dead load
= (1 x 1.5)(145)[(80)(4) + (90)(2)
+ (19)(1) + (29)(1)] = 119,200 lb

Dead load of acoustical ceiling attached to the roof diaphragm:

Dead load
= (2)[(80 - 1.67)(90 - 1.67) - (8)(19)] = 135,000 lb

Dead load of electrical equipment attached to the roof diaphragm:

Dead load
= (3)[(80 - 1.67)(90 - 1.67) - (8)(19)] = 20,300 lb

Dead load of HVAC equipment attached to the roof diaphragm:

Dead load = (4)(80 - 1.67)(90 - 1.67) - (8)(19)] = 27,100 lb

Dead load of stairs attached to the roof diaphragm:

Dead load = (75)(8)(19) = 11,400 lb

Dead load of concrete columns attached to the roof diaphragm:

Dead load = (1 x 1)(145)(10.5/2)(20) = 14,800 lb

Dead load of concrete walls attached to the roof diaphragm:

Dead load = (12)(8)(10.5/2)[(19)(2) + (29)(2)] = 48,400 lb

Total dead weight of roof diaphragm Σ = 661,700 lb

Dead load of all masses attached to and accelerated with the third floor diaphragm:

Dead load of joist system in the third floor diaphragm:

Dead load
= (61.2)(29)(19)(11) + (61.2)(11)(19) 383,700 lb

Dead load of girders in the third floor diaphragm:

Dead load
= (1 x 1.5)(145)[(80)(4) + (90)(2)
+ (29)(1) + (12)(2)] = 123,300 lb

Dead load of acoustical ceiling attached to the third floor diaphragm:

Dead load
= (2)[(80 - 1.67)(90 - 1.67) - 2(8)(19)] = 13,200 lb

Dead load of partitions attached to the third floor diaphragm:

Dead load
= (8)[(80 - 1.67)(90 - 1.67) - 2(8)(19)] = 52,900 lb

Dead load of electrical equipment attached to the third floor diaphragm:
Dead load
= (3)[(80 - 1.67)(90 - 1.67) - 2(8)(19)] = 19,800 lb

Dead load of HVAC equipment attached to the third floor diaphragm:
Dead load
= (4)[(80 - 1.67)(90 - 1.67) - 2(8)(19)] = 26,500 lb

Dead load of stairs attached to the third floor diaphragm:
Dead load = (75)(8)(19) = 11,400 lb

Dead load of masonry walls attached to the third floor diaphragm:
Dead load = (80)(10.5)[(19)(6) + (29)(4)] = 193,200 lb

Dead load of concrete columns attached to the third floor diaphragm:
Dead load = (1 x 1)(145)(10.5)(20) = 30,500 lb

Dead load of concrete walls attached to the third floor diaphragm:
Dead load = (12)(8)(10.5)[(19)(2) + (29)(2) = 96,800 lb

Total dead weight of third floor diaphragm Σ = 951,300 lb

Dead load of all masses attached to and accelerated with the second floor diaphragm is the same as the third floor:

Total dead weight of second floor diaphragm Σ = 951,300 lb

At the ground floor, the only mass that will be accelerated by the panel footings (thus producing base shear on these footings) is the mass of the lower half of the concrete panels. All other loads go directly to the supporting soil.

Dead load of concrete walls attached to the panel footings:
Dead load = (12)(8)(10.5/2)[(19)(2)] = 19,200 lb

Total dead weight of ground floor masses = 19,200 lb

The intertia forces generated when these masses are accelerated by a Zone 3 earthquake are calculated as usual:

$$V_B = 2.75\left(Z/R_w\right)W$$

For Risk Zone 3, X = 0.300
For concrete diaphragm and
shearwall structures, $R_w = 8$.

For the roof diaphragm, W = 661,700 lb
$V_B = 2.75\left(0.3/8\right)661{,}700 = 68{,}200$ lb

For the third floor diaphragm, W = 951,300 lb
$V_B = 2.75\left(0.3/8\right)951{,}300 = 98{,}100$ lb

For the second floor diaphragm, W = 951,300 lb
$V_B = 2.75\left(0.3/8\right)951{,}300 = 98{,}100$ lb

At the ground floor footings, W = 19,200 lb

$$V_B = 2.75\left(0.3/8\right)19{,}200 = 1980 \text{ lb}$$

Forces produced on the entire building by earthquake accelerations are summarized in the following sketch.

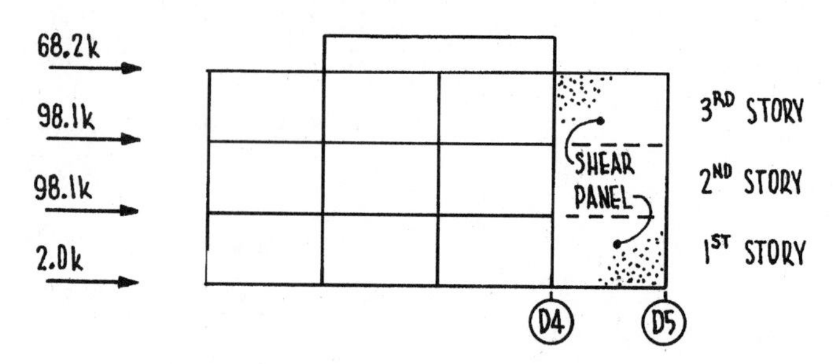

The inertia forces at the diaphragms produce shears in the two shear panels, half the force being resisted at each shear panel. At each level, the shear to be sustained by each panel is the sum of all shearing forces above that level.

Shear on one shear panel between third floor and roof:
$V_{3R} = 68.2/2 = 34.1$ kips

Shear on one shear panel between second floor and third floor:
$V_{23} = (68.2 + 98.1)/2 = 83.2$ kips

Shear on one shear panel between ground floor and second floor:
$V_{12} = (68.2 + 98.1 + 98.1)/2 = 132.20$ kips

Base shear on one shear panel at footing level:
$V_B = (68.2 + 98.1 + 98.1 + 2.0)/2 = 133.2$ kips

The resultant horizontal shears on the shear panels along with the vertical shears along the backup columns D-4 and D-5 are shown in the following sketches. The vertical shears may be found by summing moments about any corner of the shear panel.

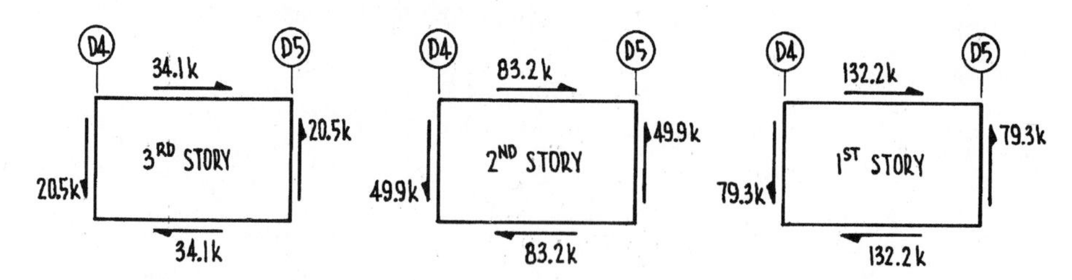

The change in column loads is then:

ΔP on columns from third floor to roof	$= \pm$ 20.5 k
ΔP on columns from second floor to third floor	$= \pm$ 49.9 k
ΔP on columns from ground floor to second floor	$= \pm$ 79.3 k
ΔP on foundations	$= \pm$ 79.3 k
Base shear on two foundations	$= \pm$ 133.2 k

The change in forces is shown as plus or minus since the earthquake can act in either direction.

In the foregoing examples, the loads occurring on four columns have been examined. The dead loads, live loads, wind loads and earthquake loads on these four columns are summarized in Figure 14-9. The final design load on each column can now be computed using the load combinations presented earlier.

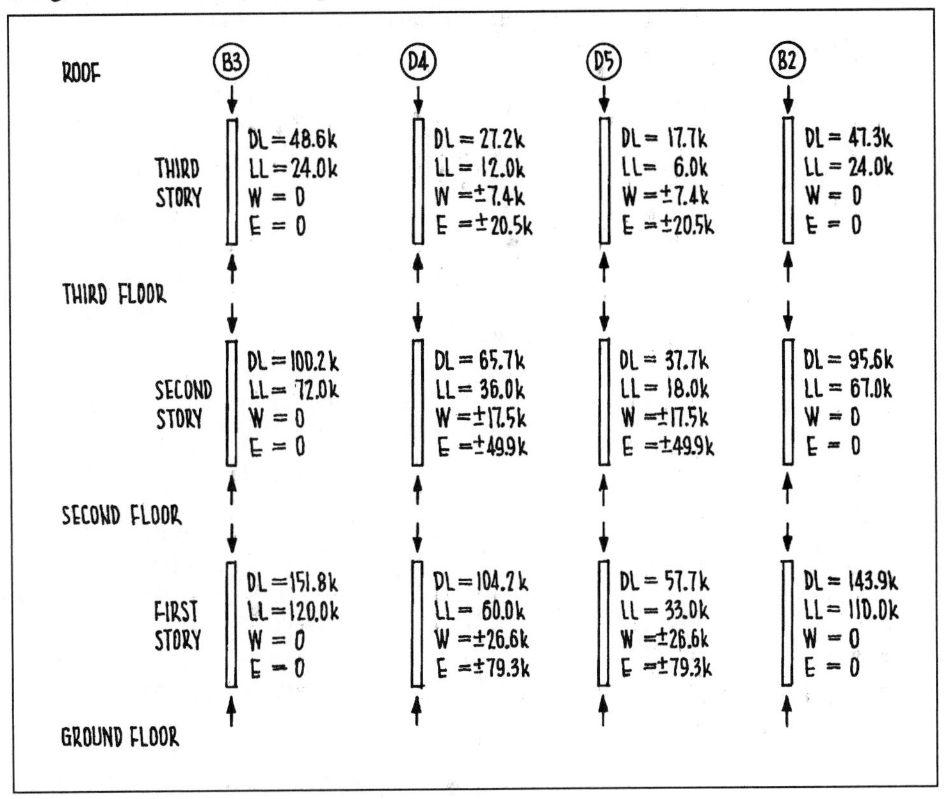

Figure 14-9 Summary of loads on columns.

Final design loads on the four columns of Figure 14-9 (and their footings) are computed using the load combinations given by equations 13-3 through 13-8.

Final design loads at grid point B-3 (not subject to wind or earthquake):

For primary structural systems (columns):

Third story	DL + 100% LL =	48.6 + 24.0 = 72.6 k
Second story	DL + 100% LL =	100.2 + 72.0 = 172.2 k
First story	DL + 100% LL =	151.8 + 120.0 = 271.8 k

For foundations (spread footing):

For strength,	DL + 100% LL = 151.8 + 120.0	= 271.8 k
For settlements,	DL + 50% LL = 151.8 + 0.5(120.0)	= 211.8 k

Final design loads at grid point D-4:

For primary structural systems (columns):

Third story	DL + 100% LL	= 39.2 k
	0.75(DL + 100% LL ± W)	= 35.0 k, 23.9 k (no tension)
	0.75(DL + 100% LL ± E)	= 44.8 k, 14.0 k (no tension)
Second story	DL + 100% LL	= 101.7 k
	0.75(DL + 100% LL ± W)	= 89.4 k, 63.2 k (no tension)
	0.75(DL + 100% LL ± E)	= 113.7 k, 38.9 k (no tension)

First story DL + 100% LL = 164.2 k
0.75(DL + 100% LL ± W) = 143.1 k, 103.2 k (no tension)
0.75(DL + 100% LL ± E) = 182.6 k, 63.7 k (no tension)

For foundations (grade beam):
For strength and uplift DL + 100% LL = 164.2 k
(0.75)(DL + 100% LL + W)
= 143.1 k, 103.2 k (no uplift)
(0.75)(DL + 100% LL + E)
= 182.6 k, 63.7 k (no uplift)
For settlements DL + 50% LL = 134.2 k
For uplift DL - W = 77.6 k (no uplift)
For uplift DL - E = 24.9 k (no uplift)

Final design loads at grid point D-5:
For primary structural systems (columns):
Third story DL + 100% LL = 23.7 k
0.75(DL + 100% LL ± W) = 23.3 k, 12.2 k (no tension)
0.75(DL + 100% LL ± E) = 33.2 k, 2.1 k (no tension)

Second story DL + 100% LL = 5.7 k
0.75(DL + 100% LL ± W) = 54.9 k, 28.7 k (no tension)
0.75(DL + 100% LL ± E) = 79.2 k, 4.4 k (no tension)

First story DL + 100% LOL = 90.7 k
0.75(DL + 100% LL ± W) = 88.0 k, 48.1 k (no tension)
0.75(DL + 100% LL ± E) = 127.5 k, 8.6 k (no tension)

For foundations (grade beam):
For strength and uplift DL + 100% LL = 90.7 k
0.75(DL + 100% LL + W)
= 88.0 k, 48.1 k (no uplift)
0.75(DL + 100% LL + E)
= 127.5 k, 8.6 k (no uplift)

For settlements DL + 50% LL = 74.2 k
For uplift DL - W = ±31.1 k (no uplift)
For uplift DL - E = -21.6 k (uplift)

Final design loads at grid point B-2 (not subject to wind or earthquake):
For primary structural systems (columns):
Third story DL + 100% LL = 71.3 k
Second story DL + 100% LL = 162.6 k
First story DL + 100% LL = 253.9 k

For foundations (spread footing):
For strength DL + 100% LL = 253.9 k
For settlements DL + 50% LL = 198.9 k

The results of the foregoing load combinations indicate that if an earthquake occurs when there is minimal live load, there will be uplift on the footing at the corner column D-5. There simply is not enough dead load on the corner column to offset the overturning effects on the shear panel during an earthquake. In this particular building, the magnitude of the uplift is not large, however, and could probably be handled just by properly designing the grade beam foundation to take the uplift in bending. Alternatively, the shear panel could be moved to an interior bay (bay D-2/D-3) in order to avoid the reduction of dead loads on the corner column D-5. The choice is one of design preference, to be made by the individual designer.

It should also be noted that all columns were checked for tension. In reinforced concrete buildings, tension on columns can produce an undesirable load case on splices in the column reinforcement. The case is discussed further in the chapters on concrete design.

14.5 Effects of Dissymmetry

Implicit in the foregoing analysis for lateral loads was the assumption that the structure was symmetrical about the loads. Such a symmetrical system is shown in Figure 14-10. The structure of Figure 14-10 might be a single-story building or it might be one story of a multistory structure.

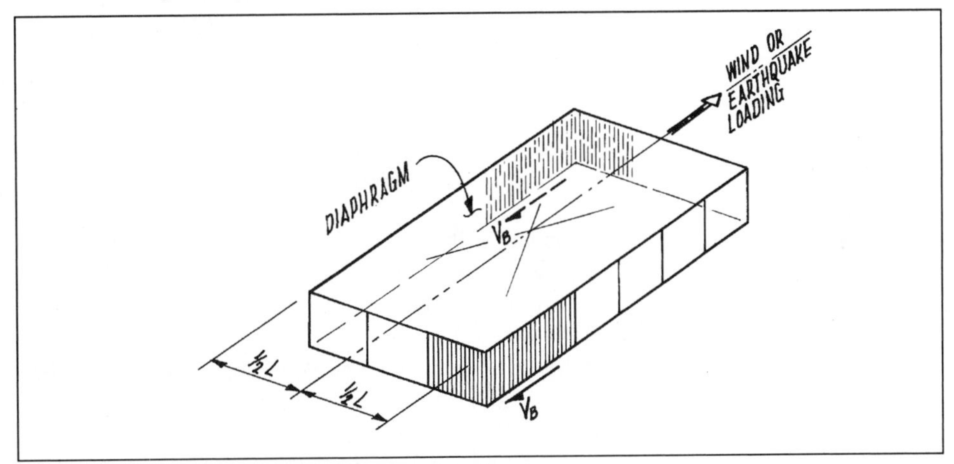

Figure 14-10 Symmetry of loads and structure.

It is important to note that the base shears under the two panels in Figure 14-10 are symmetrical about the loads. As a consequence, the two resisting base shears V_B at the two shear panels will be equal. This assumption that these resisting base shears are equal was a key point in the lateral load analysis presented in the preceeding section.

Some dissymmetry can be permitted without seriously disrupting the lateral load analysis. Consider the structure of Figure 14-11, for example. While the structure itself is not symmetrical, the shearwalls are seen to be generally symmetrical about the load, that is, the shears at the two shearwalls are roughly equal. A difference of 15% to 20% in the two base shears is considered acceptable.

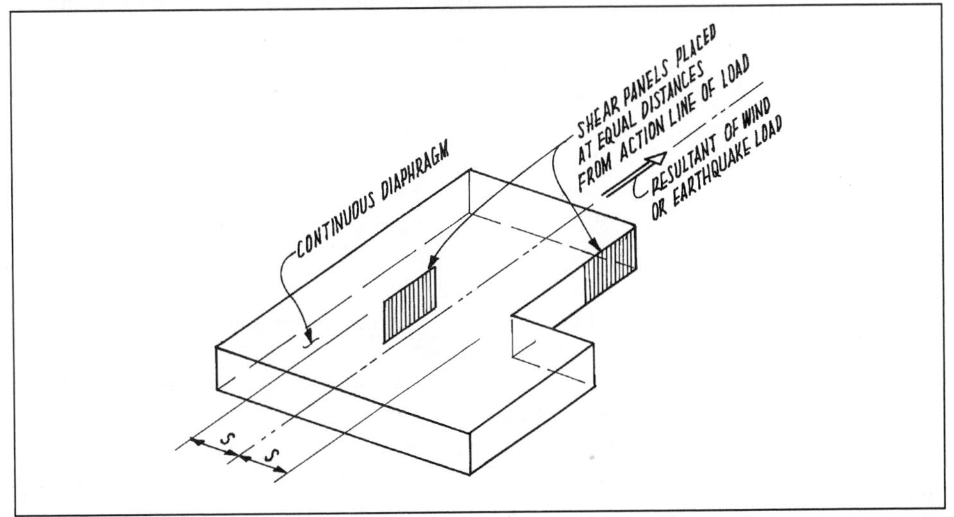

Figure 14-11 Unsymmetrical structure with symmetrical base shears.

Note that one of the two shear panels in Figure 14-11 has been deliberately moved inward to achieve symmetry of resisting loads about the applied load. Such a technique is quite common in unsymmetrical structures.

It should not be inferred that a completely unsymmetrical system of shear panels is incapable of resisting lateral loads. The extreme case of such unsymmetrical systems is the *three-wall system* shown in Figure 14-12.

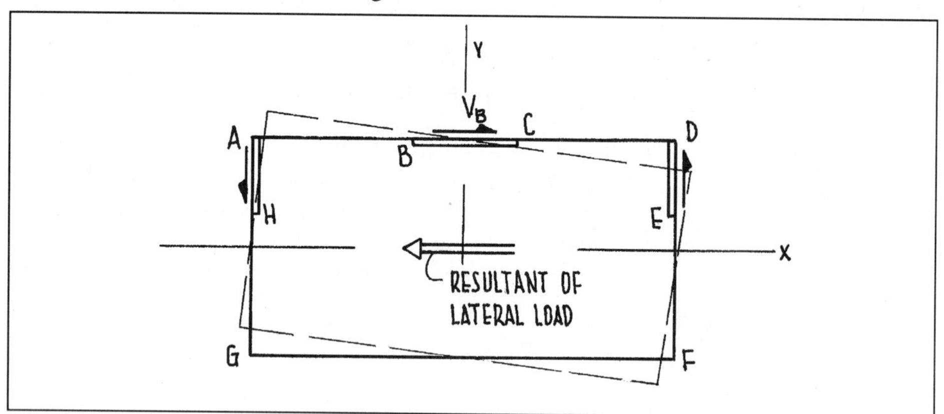

Figure 14-12 Three-wall system.

A load applied in the *yy* direction on the structure of Figure 14-12 will be resisted as usual by the two shear panels *AH* and *DE* oriented in that direction. A load applied in the *xx* direction, however, must be resisted by the single panel oriented in that direction, panel *BC*. A twisting couple results, causing the diaphragm to rotate as shown. The rotation produces shears (and an opposing couple) in the shear panels *AH* and *DE*, which theoretically should provide a stable structural system.

While the load condition shown in Figure 14-12 is indeed theoretically stable, it has been found in practice to be unreliable, depending on soil conditions and relative rigidities of the shear panels. The use of three-wall systems is therefore severely limited by code and is prohibited in Risk Zone 3 or higher. Its use is not recommended. Three-wall systems are not presented in this textbook; such systems are deferred to later studies in advanced structural analysis.

Review Questions

1. Name the two basic structural systems used to resist lateral loads.
2. What is meant in the building codes by the term building frame system?
3. How are gravity loads carried in a building frame system?
4. Why are edge beams and backup columns necessary around a shear panel?
5. How are gravity loads carried in a rigid frame system?
6. How are lateral loads carried in a rigid frame system?
7. How is column bending eliminated in a diaphragm and shear wall system?
8. How are lateral loads carried in a diaphragm and shearwall system?
9. Why must shear walls be used in pairs in a diaphragm and shearwall system?
10. What effect do vibration isolators have on a mass when an earthquake occurs?
11. Why are dead load allowances often used for electrical and mechanical wiring, piping, cable trays and ductwork?
12. Why aren't hydraulic elevators likely to be used in tall buildings?
13. In general, how does one determine the gravity load to be carried by one beam in a series of beams?
14. In general, how does one determine the gravity load to be carried by one column in a group of columns?

15. How are live loads on a concrete floor system treated differently from live loads on a steel or timber floor system?
16. How is it that concrete walls may be supported both from the top or from the bottom but masonry elements must be supported only from the bottom?
17. Describe the blanket method used to distribute the floor-to-floor weigh of stairs.
18. What loads does a hydraulic elevator impose on a building frame?
19. How are wind loads transmitted to the diaphragms in a diaphragm and shearwall system?
20. How is it that the beams and girders supporting the diaphragm are not considered part of the lateral load-carrying system?
21. What is meant by "racking" in a diaphragm?
22. How are wind loads transmitted to the shearwalls in a diaphragm and shearwall system?
23. When combining loads into a design load case for columns, why is tension in concrete columns always checked?
24. When combining loads into a design load case on foundations, why is it necessary both to add and to subtract the lateral loads from the gravity loads, thus getting two loads?
25. Why is it so desirable to have the shear panels roughly symmetrical to either side of the resultant wind force or resultant inertia force?

CHAPTER

15

RELATED TOPICS IN STRUCTURAL ANALYSIS

This chapter is devoted to several peripheral topics in structural analysis that might have been included in other discussions, but which, for the sake of space, were not. Some instructors may insist, however, that one or more of these extended topics should be included in a course in structures. For these instructors, this chapter contains several of the more frequently referenced special topics encountered in structures.

15.1 Hinged Beam Systems

The discussions presented thus far concerning beams have been concentrated on single span beams. Very often, however, it may be advantageous to provide multispan beam systems beyond providing just a series of simple spans. A typical comparison of beam systems is shown in Figure 15-1.

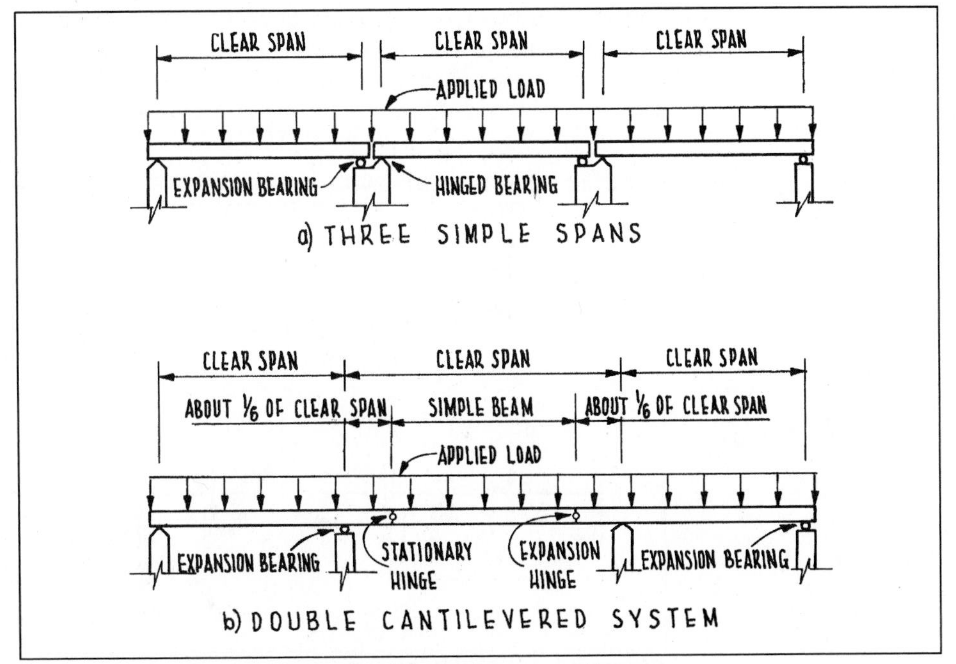

Figure 15-1 Comparison of multispan beam systems.

The double cantilevered system shown in Figure 15-1b is significantly more efficient in usage of materials than the three simple spans of Figure 15-1a. It achieves this efficiency, however, at the expense of some additional fabrication of the two interior hinges in the center span. Such details do increase cost, but often, the cost is more than offset by savings in beam weights.

The interior hinges such as those shown in Figure 15-1b have not yet been encountered. They are fabricated beam-to-beam rather than beam-to-bearing support. Some typical examples of such hinges are shown in Figure 15-2 for steel beams.

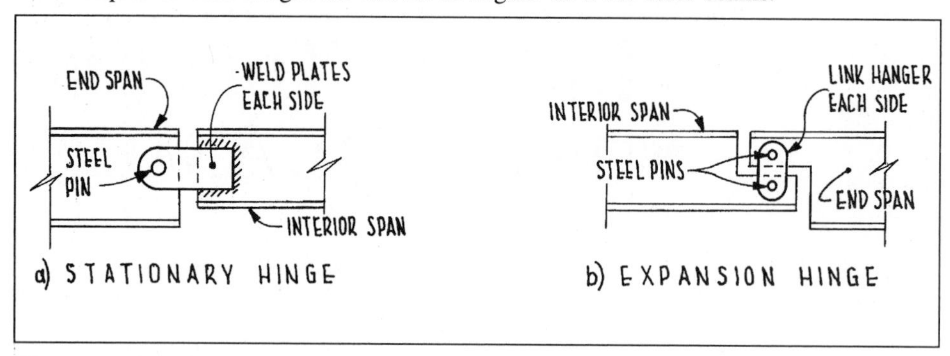

Figure 15-2 Typical interior hinges.

It should be noted that in using interior hinge points, it remains an essential feature in the design that unrestrained thermal growth must be permitted throughout the system. In the case of the double cantilevered beam of Figure 15-1b, the problem of thermal growth is readily handled. In more complex systems the problem of thermal growth can be a real nuisance.

The positioning of the interior hinges in a system of hinged beams such as that of Figure 15-1b is somewhat arbitrary. The increase in efficiency in these systems is derived from the introduction of negative moments at the interior supports; those negative moments should be roughly equal to the positive moments at midspan. Such a balance in positive and negative moments is usually best achieved when the overhanging length of the cantilever lies somewhere between 15% and 20% of the clear span, as shown in Figure 15-1b.

Consider, for example, the hinged beam of Figure 15-3. The system is actually composed of two beams, *AB* and *BCD*. For convenience, the beams are separated into two free bodies as shown, with all unknown reactions entered as appropriate.

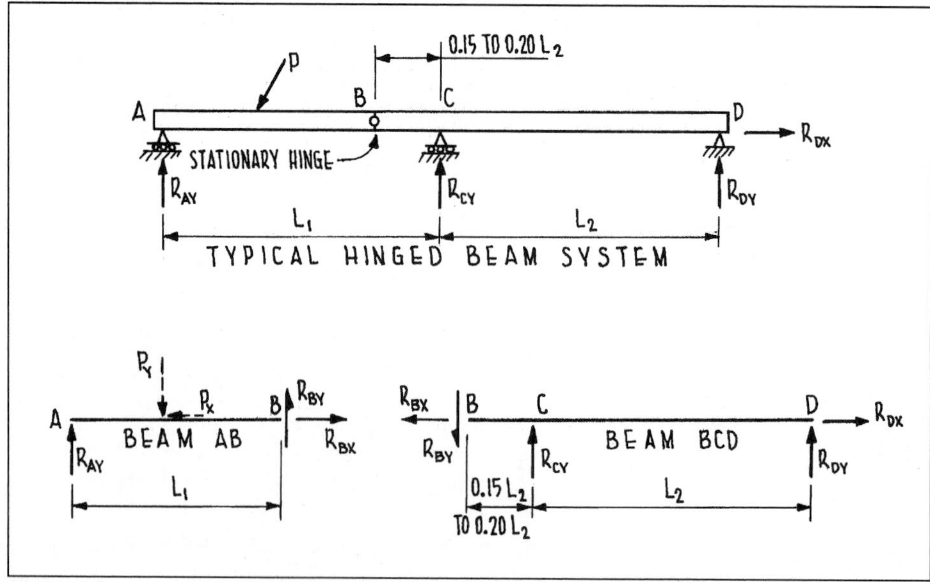

Figure 15-3 Solution for reactions in a hinged beam system.

One may wonder at a seeming inconsistency in solving for the reactions of Figure 15-3. There are four reactions and only three conditions of equilibrium. Obviously, one additional condition must exist if a solution is to be possible.

The additional condition, of course, is that the moment is known to be zero at the additional hinge point. The sum of moments to either side of that extra hinge point is therefore zero. (Such a condition was used earlier in solving for reactions on three-hinged arches.) Each additional hinge in such systems thus adds one additional condition, which in turn permits the system to have one additional reaction.

For the beam system of Figure 15-3, there is seen to be four reactions. There are three conditions of equilibrium plus one additional moment condition at the hinge. The result is four conditions for the four unknowns. The system is therefore statically determinate.

In Figure 15-3, note that the horizontal forces acting at the hinge at *B* are shown in the free bodies either as "pulling" on both sides of the hinge or as "pushing" on both sides, similar to the concept used for hinges in trusses. The vertical (or transverse) forces were not encountered in trusses, however. They are treated in hinged beams as if they were shears, that is, the beam *BCD* pushes up on the beam *AB*, while the beam *AB* pushes down on the beam *BCD*.

The reactions on the beam of Figure 15-3 are determined as usual:

1) Forces are summed vertically on the entire system.
2) Forces are summed horizontally on the entire system.
3) Moments are summed about some point in the beam system other than the interior hinge point.

The foregoing three conditions are those of overall equilibrium. They yield three equations in the four unknown reactions; the additional condition must involve the added hinge point, where it is known that moment is zero.

4) Moments are summed either to the left of the added hinge point or to the right of the added hinge point.

The result of the four steps listed above is four equations in the four unknown reactions. The four equations are then solved simultaneously for the four reactions.

In summing moments about an added hinge, moments may be summed to either side of the hinge, but only one of the two summations may be used as an independent equation; the other then becomes dependent. Only one equation per hinge may be used in the solution.

In practice, one would probably not sketch the two additional free bodies as shown in Figure 15-3. More likely, a piece of scratch paper would be held over the beam to the left of the added hinge or to the right of the added hinge. Moments would then be summed on the visible part of the system and equated to zero, yielding the same end result.

Some examples will illustrate the solution for four reactions in a hinged beam system.

Example 15-1

Determination of reactions in hinged beam systems.

Given: Hinged beam system shown in the sketch. Note that thermal growth can be accommodated.

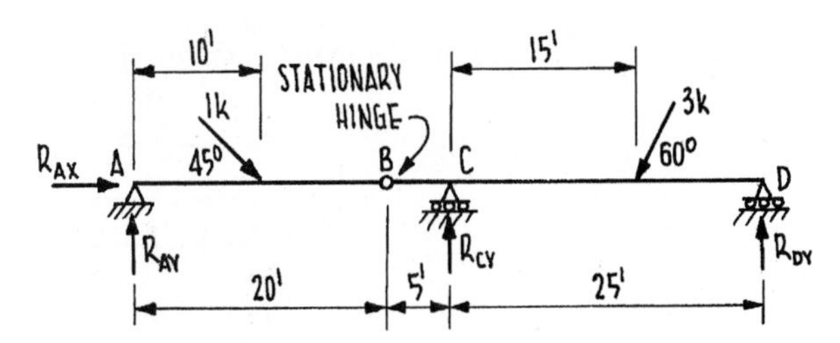

Solution: The four reactions that can occur at the supports have been shown on the sketch. There are three conditions of equilibrium and one additional condition of known moment. With four unknowns and four known conditions, the solution is seen to be statically determinate.

Forces are summed vertically on the entire system:

$$\Sigma F_Y = 0; \quad R_{Ay} - (1)(\cos 45) + R_{Cy} - (3)(\cos 30) + R_{Dy} = 0$$

Forces are summed horizontally on the entire system:

$$\Sigma F_X = 0; \quad R_{AX} + (1)(\cos 45) - (3)(\cos 60) = 0$$

Moments are summed about some arbitrary point such as point C:

$$\Sigma M_C = 0; \quad R_{Ay}(25) - (1)(\cos 45)(15) + (3)(\cos 30)(15) - R_{Dy}(25) = 0$$

A piece of scratch paper is now held over the sketch to the right of point B. Moments are then summed to the left of the hinge at B, yielding:

$$\Sigma M_{BA} = 0; \quad R_{Ay}(20) - (1)(\cos 45)(10) = 0.$$

These four equations are solved simultaneously to find:

$R_{AX} = 0.793$ k (in the direction shown).
$R_{Ay} = 0.354$ k (in the direction shown).
$R_{Cy} = 1.463$ k (in the direction shown).
$R_{Dy} = 1.488$ k (in the direction shown).

Numerical correctness is checked by summing moments for the entire system about some arbitrary point, such as point A:

$$\Sigma M_A = 0; \quad (1)(\cos 45)10 - R_{Cy}(25) + (3)(\cos 30)(40) - R_{Dy}(50) = 0$$

The values of R_{CY} and R_{Dy} are substituted to find: $0 = 0$

The computed values are accepted as numerically correct.

Example 15-2

Determination of reactions in a hinged beam system.

Given: Hinged beam system shown in the sketch. Note that thermal expansion and contraction can be accommodated.

To Find: All reactions at all supports.

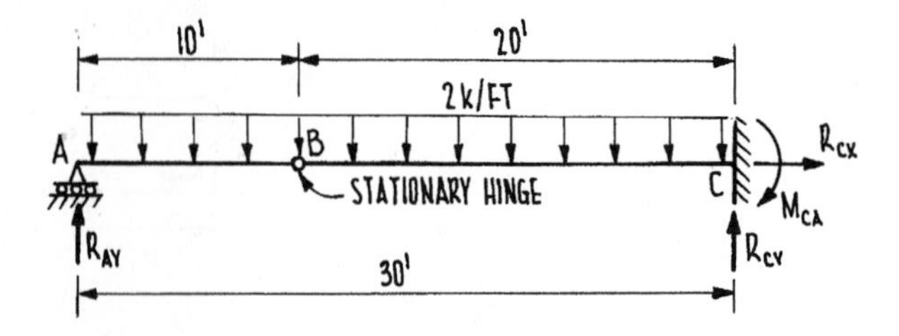

Solution: The four reactions that can occur at the supports have been shown on the sketch. There are three conditions of equilibrium and one additional condition of known moment. With four unknowns and four known conditions, the solution is seen to be statically determinate.

Forces are summed vertically on the entire system:

$$\Sigma F_Y = 0; \;\; R_{Ay} - (2)(30) + R_{Cy} = 0$$

Forces are summed horizontally on the entire system:

$$\Sigma F_X = 0; \;\; R_{CX} = 0$$

A piece of scratch paper is held over the sketch to the right of point B. Moments are summed to the left of the hinge, yielding:

$$\Sigma F_Y = 0; \;\; R_{Ay}(10) - (2)(10)(10/2) = 0$$

Moments are now summed about point C, eliminating the two reactions R_{Cy} and R_{CX}:

$$\Sigma M_{BA} = 0; \;\; R_{AY}(30) - (2)(30)(30/2) + M_{CA} = 0$$

The four equations are solved to find:

$R_{CX} = 0$
$R_{Ay} = 10$ k (in the direction shown)
$R_{Cy} = 50$ k (in the direction shown)
$M_{CA} = 600$ k·ft (in the direction shown)

As a numerical check, moments are summed to the right of the hinge at B:

$$\Sigma M_{BC} = 0; \;\; (2)(20)(10) + M_{CA} - R_{Cy}(20) = 0$$

The values of M_{CA} and R_{Cy} are substituted to find:
$0 = 0$

The computed values are accepted as numerically correct.

More complex systems of beams may have more than four unknowns. Some examples will illustrate the solutions for such systems.

Example 15-3

Determination of reactions in a hinged beam system.

Given: Hinged beam system shown in the sketch. Note that thermal expansion and contraction can be accommodated.

To Find: All reactions in the system.

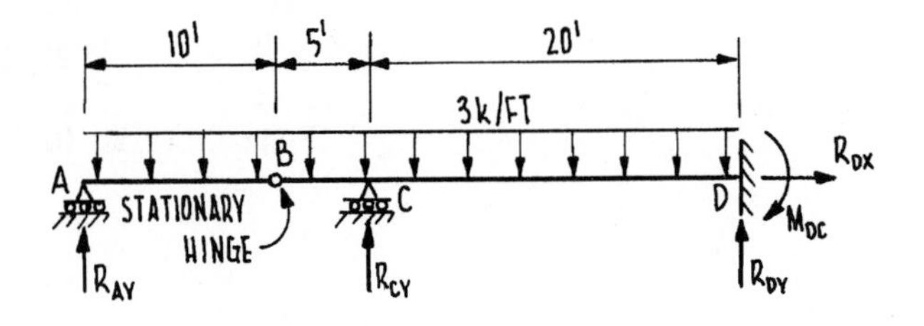

Solution: The five reactions that can occur on this system have been shown on the sketch. There are three conditions of equilibrium and one additional condition of known moment.

There are therefore five unknown reactions in this system and only four conditions of equilibrium. The system is therefore statically indeterminate.

A hinge would have to be placed at point D to make this system statically determinate.

Example 15-4

Determination of reactions in a hinged beam system.

Given: Double cantilevered system shown in the sketch. Note that thermal expansion and contraction can be accommodated.

To Find: All reactions in the system.

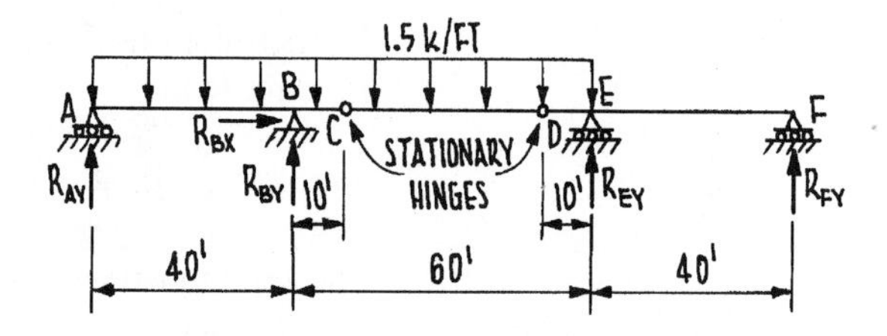

Solution: The five reactions that can occur on this system have been shown on the sketch. There are three conditions of equilibrium and two additional conditions of known moment. There are therefore 5 reactions and five known conditions of equilibrium; the system is thus statically determinate.

Forces are summed vertically on the entire system:

$$\Sigma F_y = 0;\ R_{Ay} + R_{By} - (1.5)(100) + R_{Ey} + R_{Fy} = 0$$

Forces are summed horizontally on the entire system:

$$\Sigma F_X = 0;\ R_{BX} = 0$$

Moments are summed about point B for the entire system:

$$\Sigma M_B = 0;\ R_{Ay}(40) + (1.5)(100)(10) - R_{Ey}(60) - R_{Fy}(100) = 0$$

A piece of scratch paper is held over the system to the right of the hinge at C. Moments are than summed to the left of the hinge at C:

$$\Sigma M_C = 0;\ -(1.5)(50)(50/2) + R_{Ay}(50) + R_{By}(10) = 0$$

The piece of scratch paper is now held over the system to the left of the hinge at D. Moments are then summed to the right of the hinge at D:

$$\Sigma M_D = 0;\ (1.5)(10)(10/2) - R_{Ey}(10) - R_{Fy}(50) = 0$$

(Both of the added conditions at hinges C and D have now been included in the solution.)

The five equations are solved simultaneously to find:

R_{Ay} = +20.6 k (in direction shown)
R_{BX} = 0
R_{Ay} = +84.4 k (in direction shown)
R_{BY} = +54.4 k (in direction shown)
R_{FY} = - 9.4 k (opposite to direction shown)

A check is performed by summing moments to the left of the hinge at D:

$$\Sigma M_D = 0; \ -(1.5)(90)(90/2) + R_{Ay}(90) + R_{BY}(50) = 0$$

The values of R_{AY} and R_{BY} are substituted to find:

$$0 = 0$$

The computed values are accepted as numerically correct.

It is emphasized that although two equations may be written at an added hinge point, one to either side, only one of the two equations can be used as an independent condition. The other equation then becomes a dependent equation. Stated another way, the fact that the moment at a hinge is zero may only be entered once; any additional such entries do not add any new conditions.

15.2 Deflections and Superposition

In most cases in design, it is possible to control deflections of beams by applying blanket limitations on the depths of the beams. Over the years, for example, it has been found that in routine applications, if the depth of a steel beam is not less than the span divided by 23, the deflections of the beam will not likely be a problem. Such blanket controls over deflections is quite common in all the major materials, including steel, concrete and timber.

On occasion, however, it can become necessary to compute the actual deflections of a beam rather than follow such blanket limitations. Such computations can sometimes be quite intricate, particularly when the pattern of loads does not fall into the usual patterns. Simplified methods of handling such calculations are presented in this section.

The deflections at midspan of some simple beams are given in Table A-3, reprinted here for immediate reference. The patterns of load shown in Table A-3 are those most commonly encountered. These cases of loading may be added or subtracted to yield a wide variety of other load patterns. Such addition and subtraction of load cases is called *superposition* of loads.

The deflection curves (or *elastic curves*) of the beams in Table A-3 are included in the sketches. Except for Case VIII, note that these curves do not reverse, that is, they are curved in one direction only. The deformation curves in the sketches are necessarily exaggerated in order that the deflections may be seen. In a real beam, the deflections are so small that they probably could not be seen in a side view.

The elastic curve of a structural member is always a very smooth, very shallow curve. There are no sharp bends or kinks in such curves. As long as the material remains in its elastic range, an elastic beam under load will deform as indicated, in long, smoothly continuous curves having very shallow deflections from the original position.

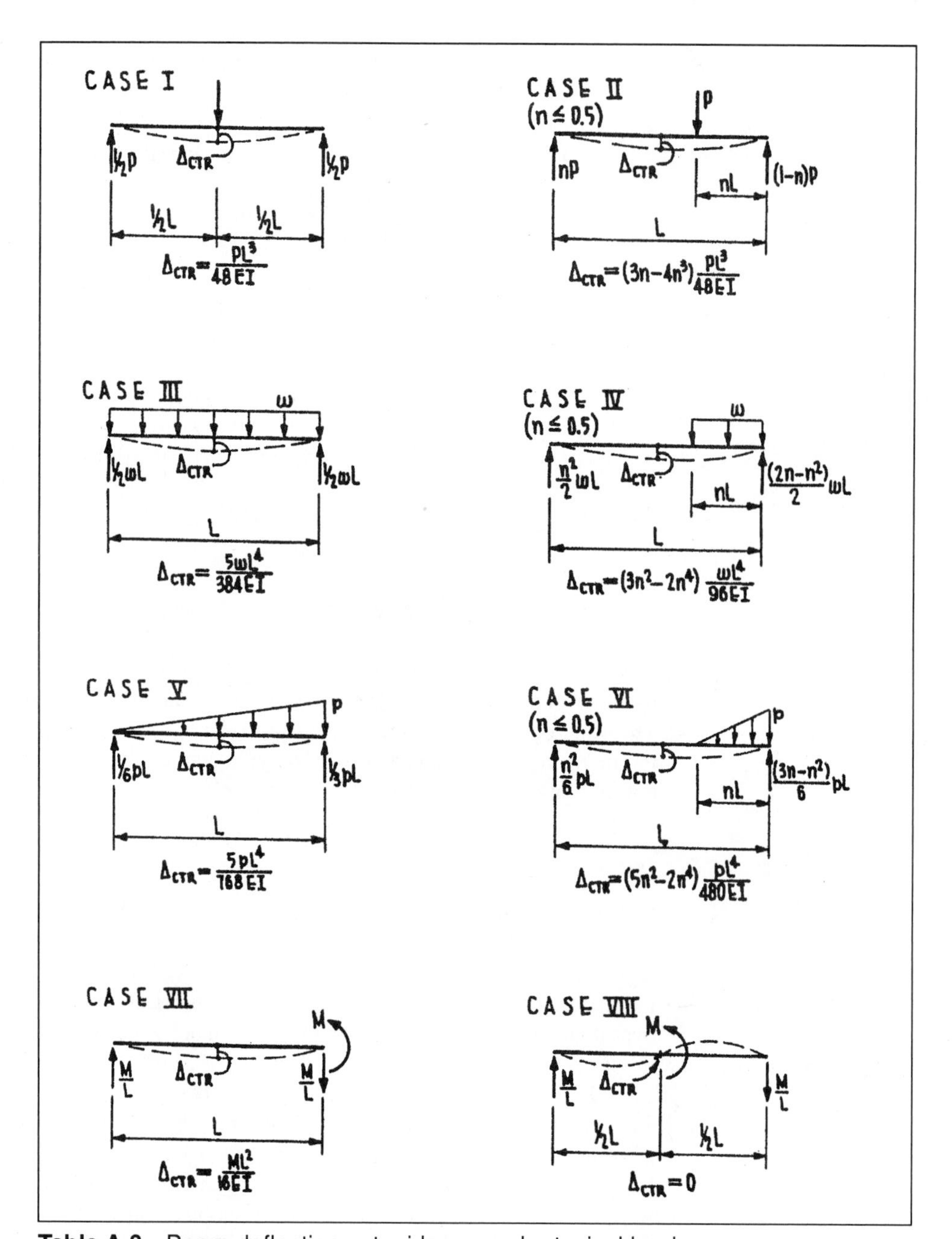

Table A-3 Beam deflections at midspan under typical loads.

For curves as shallow as those of a beam in single curvature, the maximum deflection even for grossly unsymmetrical beams will always be very close to the midpoint between supports. In fact, it may be shown analytically[1] that for beams of single curvature (such as those of Table A-3), the maximum deflection of such unsymmetrically loaded beams will always occur within the center 15.47% of the span. Further, the deflection at midspan in this middle sector of the beam will be within 97.43% of the maximum deflection of the beam. An exaggerated comparison of these unsymmetrical deflections is shown in Figure 15-4.

[1]French, Samuel E., *Fundamentals of Structural Analysis,* West Educational Publishing, Albany, N.Y., 1995.

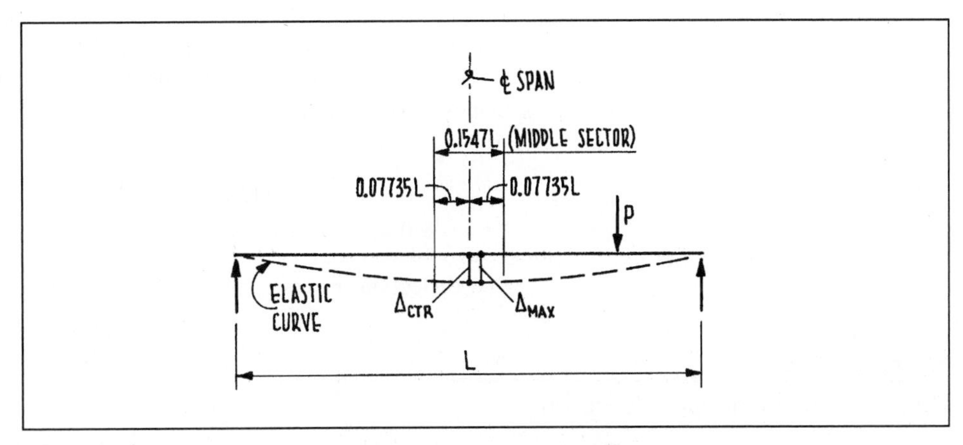

Figure 15-4 Comparative beam deflections at midspan.

The difference between the midspan deflection and the maximum deflection is considered to be negligible in beams of single curvature. In all cases, symmetrical or unsymmetrical, the deflection at midspan is used as the maximum deflection. The extremely tedious and intricate calculation of the absolute maximum deflection thus becomes unnecessary.

The load cases and deflections given in Table A-3 can be used to find deflections in a wide variety of load cases. Some examples, both symmetrical and unsymmetrical, will illustrate the procedure.

Example 15-5

Determination of midspan deflection.

Given: Beam loaded as shown. E = 29,000,000 psi, I = 291 in.^{4}

To Find: Deflection at midspan.

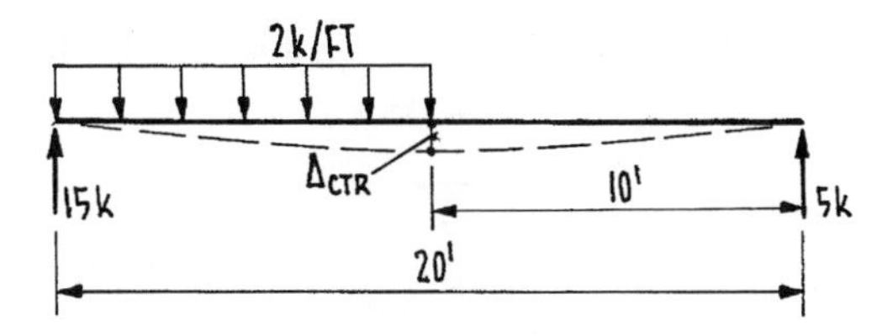

Solution: It is noted that this beam is unsymmetrical but even so, the maximum deflection will be at or near midspan. The load can be reproduced by adding a negative Load Case IV of Table A-3 to Load Case III of Table A-3. Dimensions are changed to pounds and inches in the following calculations.

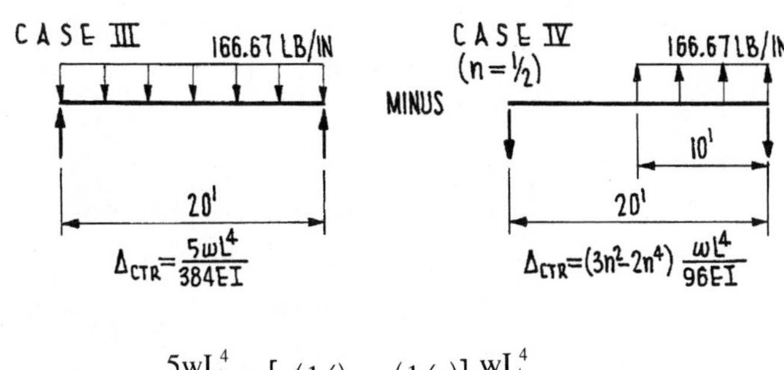

$$\text{Total } \Delta_{CTR} = \frac{5wL^4}{384EI} - \left[3\left(\tfrac{1}{4}\right) - 2\left(\tfrac{1}{16}\right)\right]\frac{wL^4}{96EI}$$

$$= (0.01302 - 0.00651)\frac{(166.67)(20\text{x}12)^4}{(29{,}000{,}000)(291)}$$

$$= 0.427 \text{ in.}$$

Alternatively, this problem could have been solved by recognizing that it is the reverse of Load Case IV; its deflection at midspan will be equal to that of Load Case IV:

$$\Delta_{CTR} = \left[3\left(\tfrac{1}{4}\right) - 2\left(\tfrac{1}{16}\right)\right]\frac{wL^4}{96EI}$$
$$= 0.427 \text{ in., as before.}$$

The deflection in this span of 20 feet is seen to be less than 1/2 in.

Example 15-6

Determination of midspan deflection.

Given: Beam loaded as shown. E = 29,000,000 psi, I = 375 in.^{4}

To Find: Deflection at midspan.

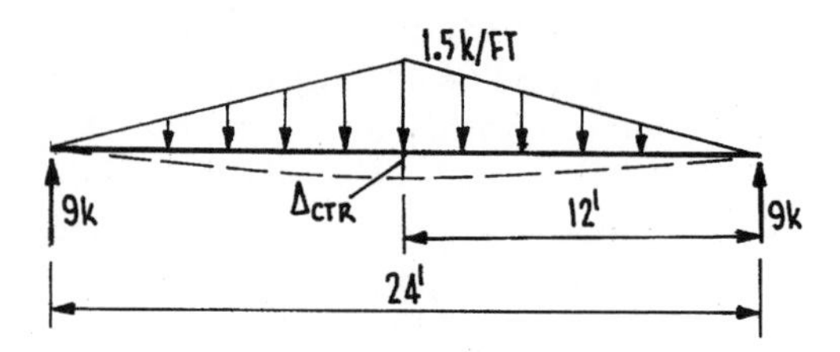

Solution: It is noted that the load case is symmetrical; maximum deflection is at midspan. The load case can be reproduced by adding a negative Load Case VI to Load Case V (Table A-3). Dimensions are kept in kips and feet in the following calculations.

$$\text{In kips / ft}^2\text{, E} = 29{,}000{,}000\left(\text{lb}/_{\text{in.}^2}\right)\left(144\ \text{in.}^2/_{\text{ft}^2}\right)\left(1\ \text{kip}/_{1000\ \text{lb}}\right)$$
$$= 4{,}176{,}000 \text{ kips / ft}^2$$
$$\text{In ft}^4\text{, I} = 375 \text{ in.}^4\left(\frac{1\text{ft}}{12\text{in.}}\right)^4$$
$$= 0.01808\text{ft}^4$$

The load cases are shown in the following sketches.

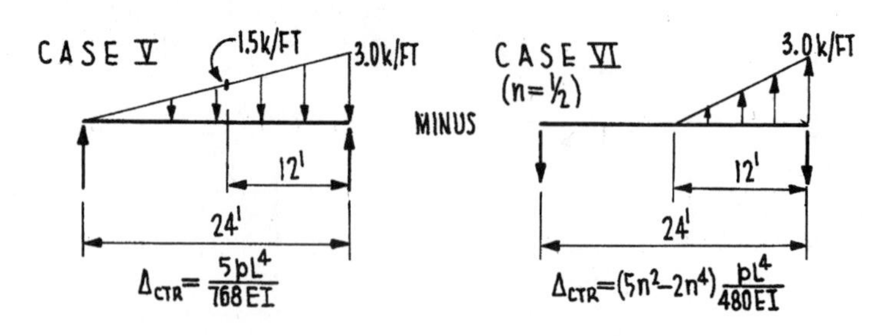

$$\text{Total } \Delta_{CTR} = \frac{5pL^4}{768EI} - \left[5\left(\frac{1}{4}\right) - 2\left(\frac{1}{16}\right)\right]\frac{pL^4}{480EI}$$
$$= (0.00651 - 0.00234)\frac{(3)(24^4)}{(4{,}176{,}000)(0.01808)}$$
$$= 0.0549 \text{ ft}$$
$$= 0.66 \text{ in.}$$

Example 15-7

Determination of midspan deflections.

Given: Beam loaded as shown. E = (29)(10^6)psi, I = 1550 in.^{4}

To Find: Deflection at midspan.

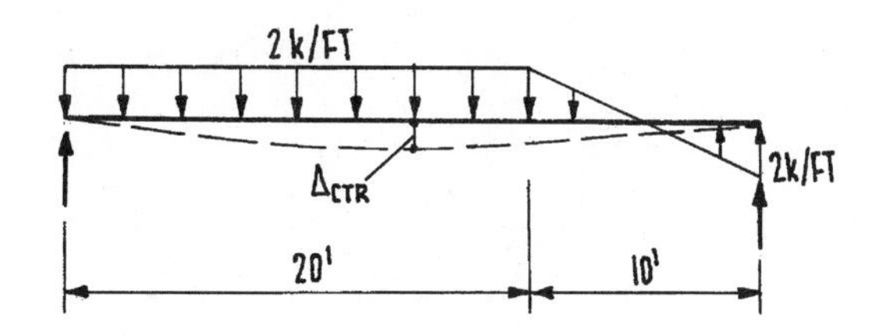

Solution: It is noted that this beam is unsymmetrical but it is assumed to be in single curvature; maximum deflection will be near midspan. The load case can be reproduced by adding a negative Load Case VI to Load Case III (Table A-3). Dimensions are changed to pounds and inches for the calculations.

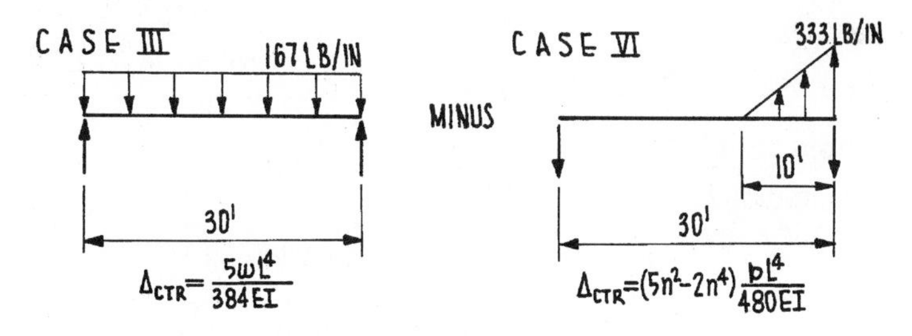

$$\text{Total } \Delta_{CTR} = \frac{5wL^4}{384EI} - \left[5\left(\frac{1}{9}\right) - 2\left(\frac{1}{81}\right)\right]\frac{pL^4}{480EI}$$

$$= [0.01302(166.67) - 0.00111(333.33)]\frac{[(30)(12)]^4}{[(29)(10^6](1550)}$$

$$= 0.673 \text{ in.}$$

Unsymmetrical beams such as that of Example 15-7 may have small load reversals and still be in single curvature. If the load reversal becomes extreme, however, double curvature could result. In that case the computed deflection at midspan, though still correct, may not be within 97.43% of the maximum deflection occurring elsewhere in the beam. Some extreme cases of double curvature are treated in the next section.

Example 15-8

Determination of midspan deflections.

Given: Beam loaded as shown. E = 4,176,000 k/ft^2, I = 0.00752 ft^4.

To Find: Deflection at midspan.

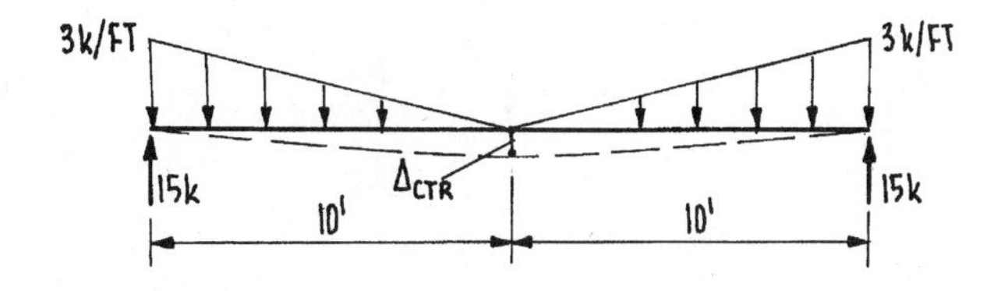

Solution: It is noted that this beam is symmetrical; maximum deflection is therefore at midspan. The load case can be reproduced by adding a negative Load Case V to Load Case III (of Table A-3), then adding back a positive Load Case VI. Dimensions are kept in kips and feet in the calculations.

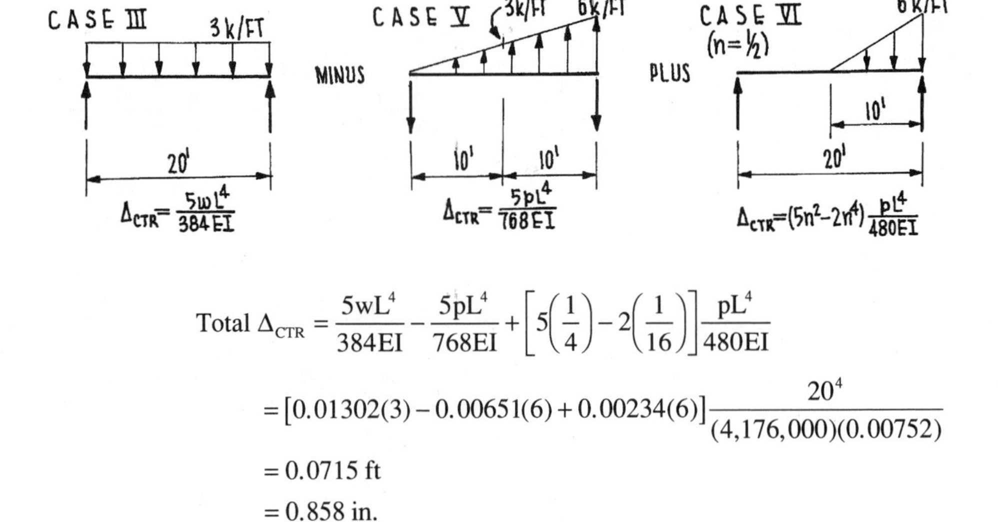

$$\text{Total } \Delta_{CTR} = \frac{5wL^4}{384EI} - \frac{5pL^4}{768EI} + \left[5\left(\frac{1}{4}\right) - 2\left(\frac{1}{16}\right)\right]\frac{pL^4}{480EI}$$

$$= [0.01302(3) - 0.00651(6) + 0.00234(6)]\frac{20^4}{(4{,}176{,}000)(0.00752)}$$

$$= 0.0715 \text{ ft}$$

$$= 0.858 \text{ in.}$$

Example 15-9

Determination of midspan deflections.

Given: Beam loaded as shown. E = 29,000,000 lb/in.^{2}; I = 510 in.^{4}

To Find: Deflection at midspan.

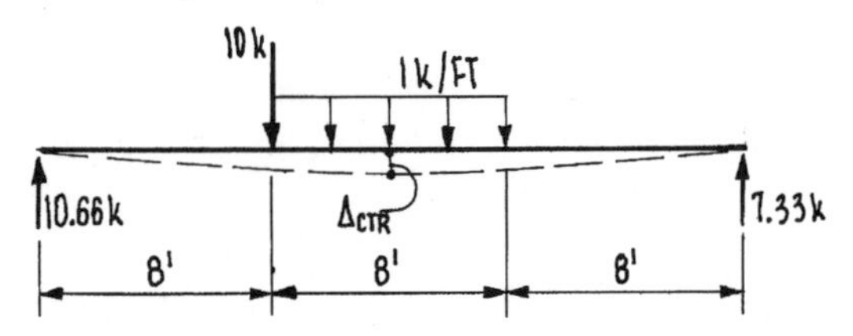

Solution: It is noted that this beam is unsymmetrical but is in single curvature; maximum deflection will be near midspan. The load case may be reproduced by adding three load cases as shown in the following sketches. Dimensions are changed to pounds and inches in the calculations.

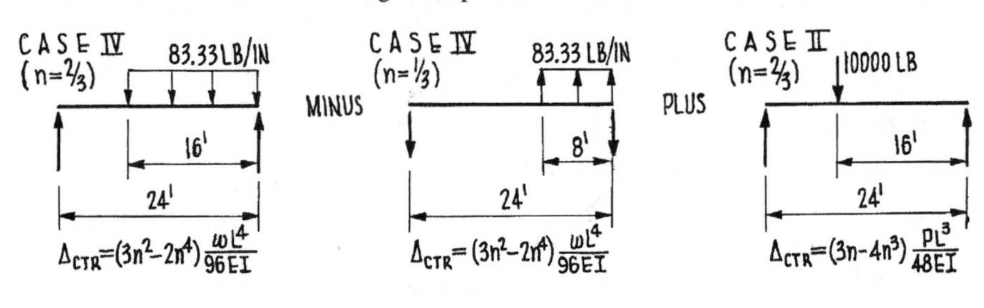

$$\text{Total } \Delta_{CTR} = \left[3\left(\frac{4}{9}\right) - 2\left(\frac{16}{81}\right)\right]\frac{(83.33)(24\text{x}12)^4}{(96)(29\text{x}10^6)(510)}$$

$$+ \left[3\left(\frac{2}{3}\right) - 4\left(\frac{8}{27}\right)\right]\frac{(10{,}000)(24\text{x}12)^3}{(48)(29\text{x}10^6)(510)}$$

$$= 0.3788 + 0.274$$

$$= 0.653 \text{ in.}$$

Example 15-10

Determination of midspan deflections.

Given: Beam with overhangs as shown. E = 4,176,000 lb/ft²; I = 0.025 ft⁴.

To Find: Deflection at midspan.

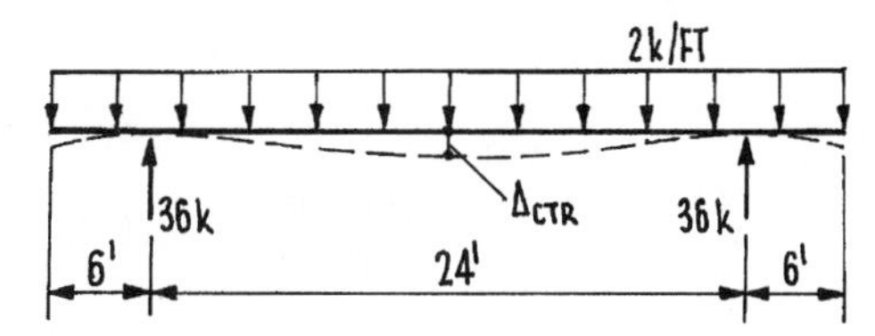

Solution: The beam is redrawn to fit the standard cases presented in Table A-3. It is noted that the deflection curve is symmetrical; maximum deflection is at midspan. Dimensions are kept in kips and feet for the calculations.

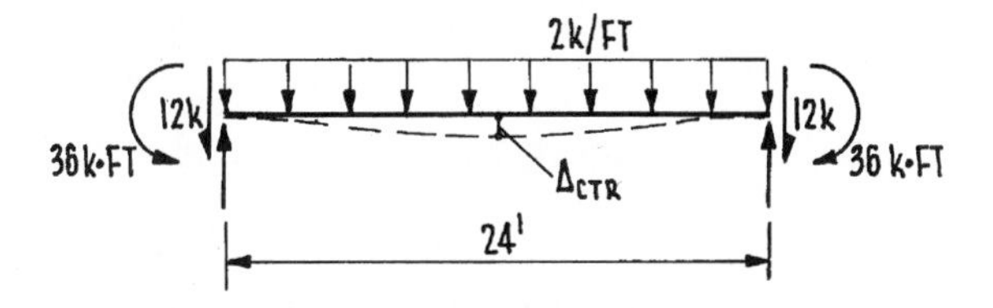

The load cases are reproduced by adding the three following load cases.

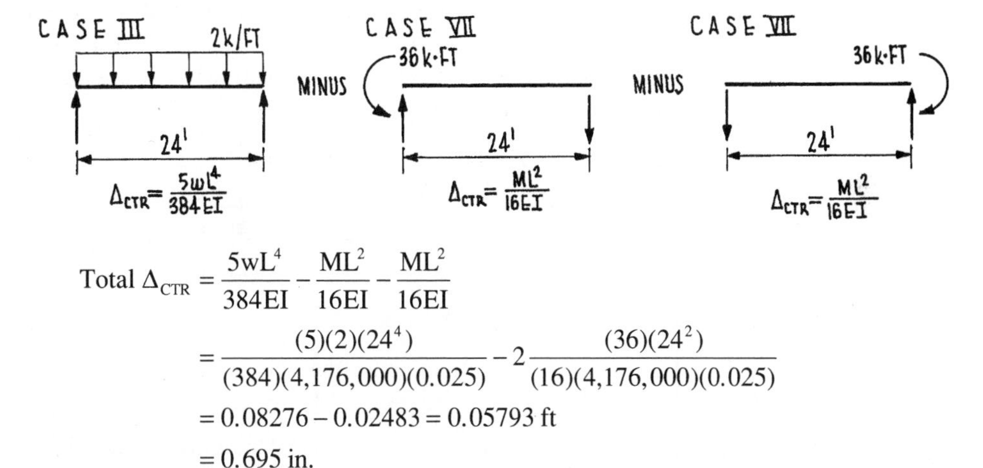

$$\text{Total } \Delta_{CTR} = \frac{5wL^4}{384EI} - \frac{ML^2}{16EI} - \frac{ML^2}{16EI}$$

$$= \frac{(5)(2)(24^4)}{(384)(4{,}176{,}000)(0.025)} - 2\frac{(36)(24^2)}{(16)(4{,}176{,}000)(0.025)}$$

$$= 0.08276 - 0.02483 = 0.05793 \text{ ft}$$

$$= 0.695 \text{ in.}$$

The beam of Example 15-10 is assumed to be in double curvature as shown. But, since the entire load case is symmetrical, the maximum deflection remains at midspan. The calculations in the example for midspan deflection therefore correctly yields the maximum deflection.

15.3 Antisymmetrical Deflections and Superposition

The deflection of beams in double curvature was mentioned briefly in the previous section. The occurrence of double curvature in a beam did not affect the accuracy of the computations for deflection; the computations still yielded the deflection at midspan. The problem arises that the deflection at midspan in such curves may not be a good approximation of the maximum deflection, as it is in beams of single curvature. An exaggerated sketch of such deflections is shown in Figure 15-5.

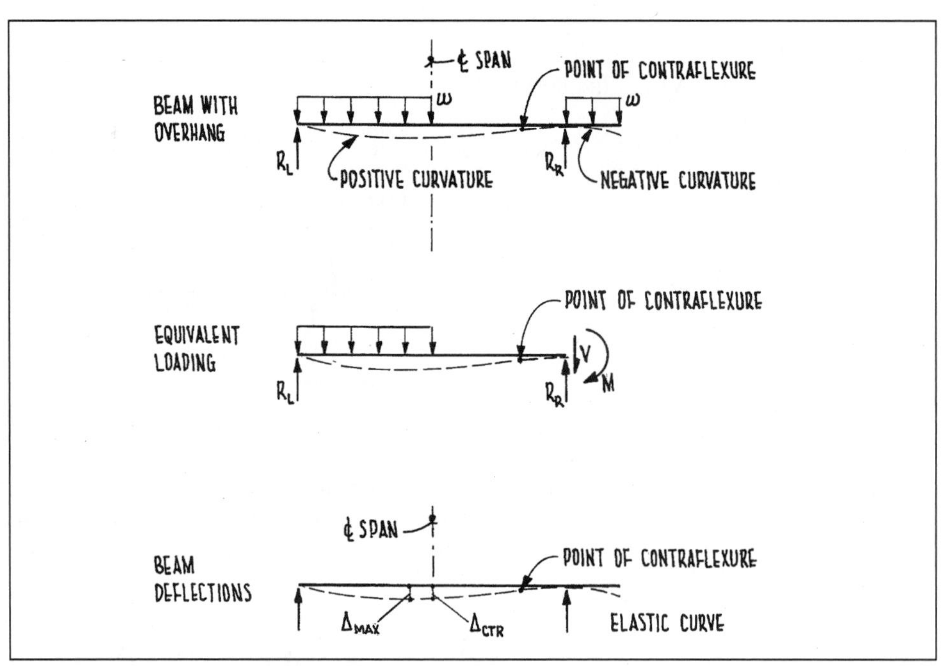

Figure 15-5 Deflections in double curvature.

As long as the reversal in curvature is mild, as in Figure 15-5, the methods given in the previous section will still yield satisfactory results. As the reversal becomes more prominent, the error becomes more marked. The extreme case occurs when the deflection at midspan is zero; that extreme case is the topic of this section.

Loads and deflections in a typical simple beam, antisymmetrically loaded, are shown in Figure 15-6. In all cases of antisymmetry, the resultants of the loads will form a couple. This couple formed by the loads will always be exactly opposed by another couple formed by the reactions.

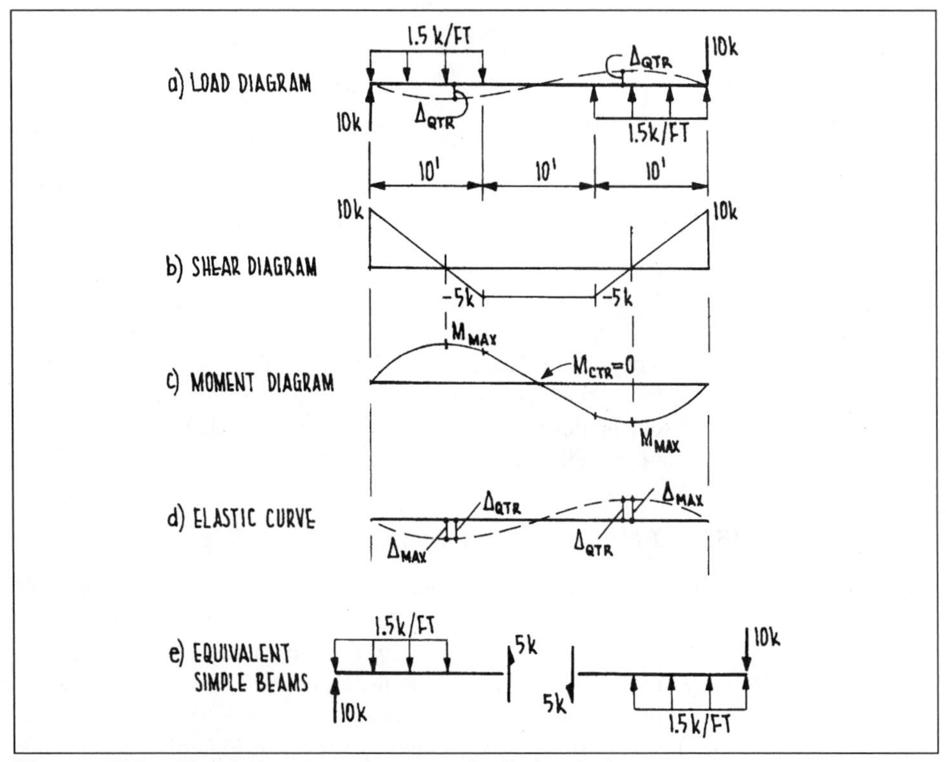

Figure 15-6 Simple beam antisymmetrically loaded.

As indicated in Figure 15-6c and d, the moment at midspan of an antisymmetrically loaded beam is zero, as is the deflection. With its zero deflection and zero moment, the midpoint of the beam is thus identical to a hinge. Insofar as deflections are concerned, an antisymmetrical beam will respond exactly like two simple beams, such as those indicated in 15-6e. And, as shown earlier, the deflections at the quarter points will be within 97.43% of the maximum deflections in either of the two equivalent beams.

There will thus be two deflections of interest in an antisymmetrical beam, one upward and one downward. These two deflections will be equal in magnitude, which simplifies the calculations somewhat. Some examples will demonstrate the solution for some typical cases.

Example 15-11

Determination of deflections in antisymmetrical beams.

Given: Antisymmetrically loaded simple beam, as shown.
$E = 1{,}500{,}000$ lb/in.^{2}, $I = 3400$ in.^{4}.

To Find: Deflections at quarter points.

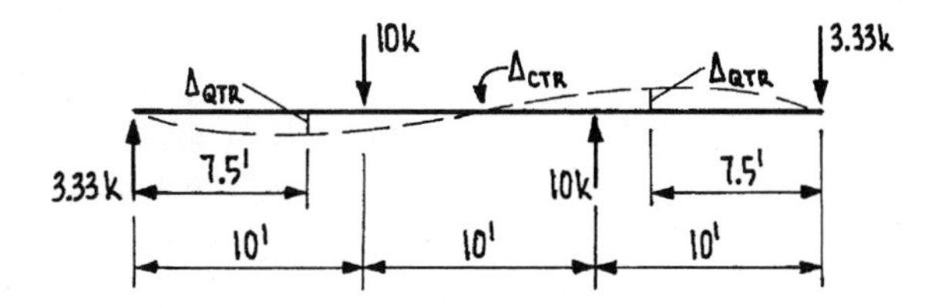

Solution: The left half of the beam is removed as a free body.

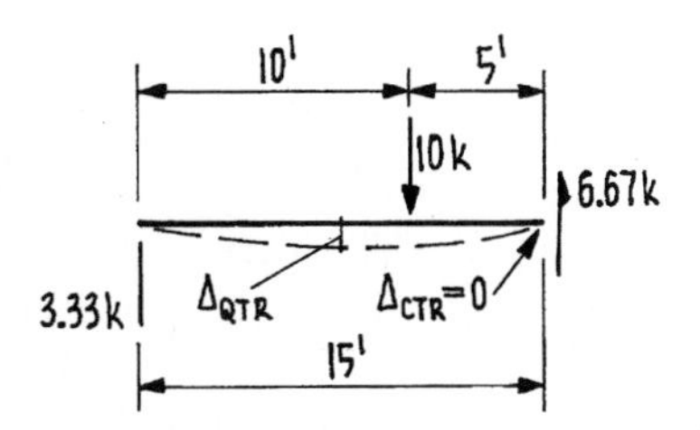

The load case is seen to be that of Case II in Table 15-1, for which $n = {}^1/_3$:

$$\Delta_{QTR} = (3n - 4n^3)\frac{pL^3}{48EI}$$

$$= \left[3\left(\frac{1}{3}\right) - 4\left(\frac{1}{27}\right)\right]\frac{(10{,}000)(15\text{x}12)^3}{(48)(1{,}500{,}000)(3400)}$$

$$= 0.203 \text{ in.}$$

This deflection is, as indicated, downward in the left half and upward in the right half.

Example 15-12

Determination of deflections in antisymmetrical beams.

Given: Antisymmetrically loaded simple beam as shown.
$E = 29,000,000\ \text{lb/in.}^2$, $I = 88.6\ \text{in.}^4$.

To Find: Deflections at quarter points.

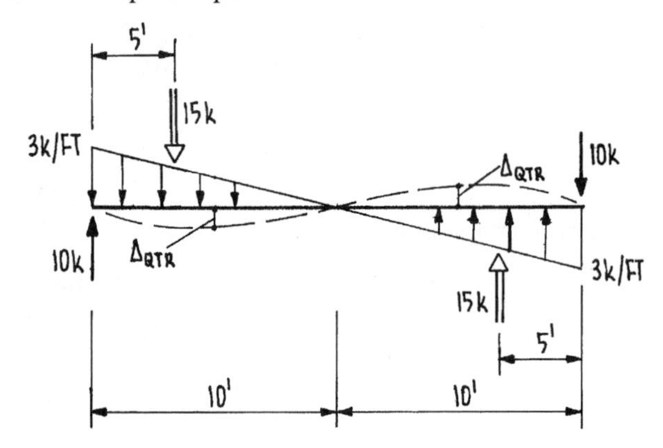

Solution: The right half of the system is recognized as being negative Case V in Table A-3, for which:

$$\Delta_{QTR} = \frac{5pL^4}{768EI}\ \text{(upward)}.$$

For the right half of the beam, length L is 10 ft. Units are kept in pounds and inches, for which p = 250 lb/in.:

$$\Delta_{QTR} = \frac{(5)(250)(10\text{x}12)^4}{(768)(29\text{x}10^6)(88.6)} = -0.131\ \text{in.}\quad \text{(upward)}$$

This deflection is downward in the left half of the beam, upward in the right half, as indicated in the sketch.

The solution for deflections in antisymmetrical beams has been seen to be simply a variation of the solutions in beams of single curvature. Nothing new has been introduced in these solutions.

15.4 Load Reversals and Counterdiagonals in Trusses

A serious problem can occur in trusses when loads are changeable or when they are mobile. Under one set of loads, for example, a particular long slender member may be in tension, in which case the member will act very similar to a wire, becoming ever straighter as stress is increased. But if, as loads change, the load in the member becomes compression, then the member undergoes a dangerous *load reversal*. The member becomes a column in compression, subject to column buckling. As a column in compression, the long slender member will now fail at fairly low levels of load.

A typical case of load reversal is shown in Figure 15-7. Under one case of load, member *GC* is in tension, as indicated. When the load is moved (or moves) to another position, member *GC* goes into a significant level of compression. The member is now subject to column buckling at a level high enough to produce collapse of the truss.

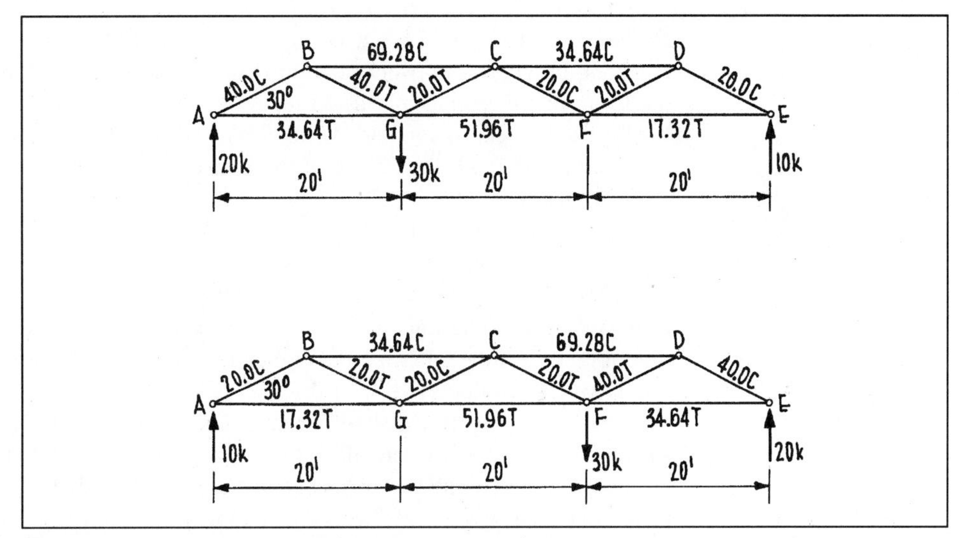

Figure 15-7 Load reversal in a truss member.

One of the major advantages of a truss is that the size of every member can be chosen such that its stresses are high, producing maximum efficiency in every member. That advantage can be a two-edged sword, however. The high compressive stresses caused by a load reversal could easily cause the truss to collapse under the load. Load reversals are indeed a serious possibility in truss design.

One way to investigate the possibility of load reversals in a truss is illustrated in Figure 15-8. A unit load is allowed to move across the truss and the load in each member is then computed for each position of load. The results are then examined to see which members could possibly undergo a load reversal for various positions of load.

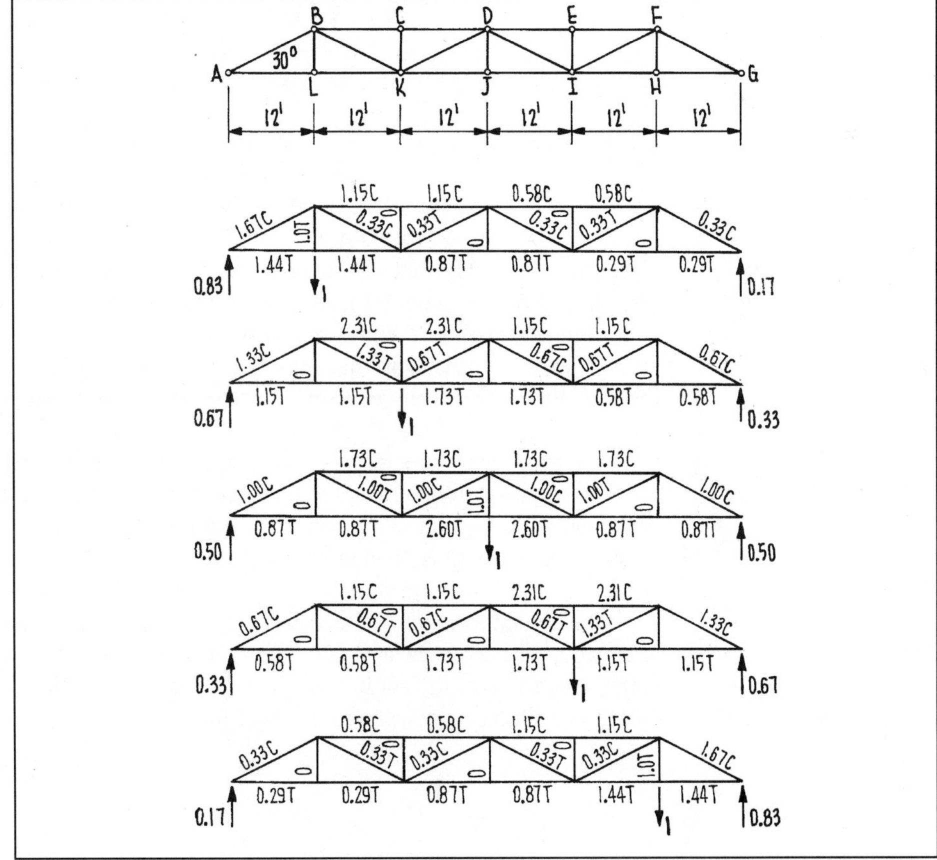

Figure 15-8 Unit load moving across a truss.

In the truss of Figure 15-8 it is noted that all members of the upper chord remain in compression regardless where the downward load is applied. Similarly, all members of the lower chord remain in tension regardless where the downward load is applied. And finally, the two end diagonals, *AB* and *FG*, will be in compression regardless where the downward load is applied. None of these members can ever undergo load reversal under a downward load.

It is also noted, however, that all of the interior diagonals of Figure 15-8, members *BK*, *KD*, *DI* and *IF*, undergo stress reversal as a load moves across the truss. These members are the only ones in this particular truss configuration that are subject to such a stress reversal. The final design of the truss should therefore include a close examination of these members to assure that they can sustain both the maximum tensile load and the maximum compressive load that can occur on them.

Quite often in truss design, all the interior panels in a truss will be cross braced as shown in Figure 15-9, where all of the bracing members are long slender bars or rods (or even cables) that cannot sustain any appreciable compressive load. Whenever a crossbraced panel undergoes a vertical shear, one diagonal is placed in tension, one in compression. Whichever of the diagonals is subjected to a compressive load will simply "sag" out of the way, leaving the other diagonal to take the entire load in tension.

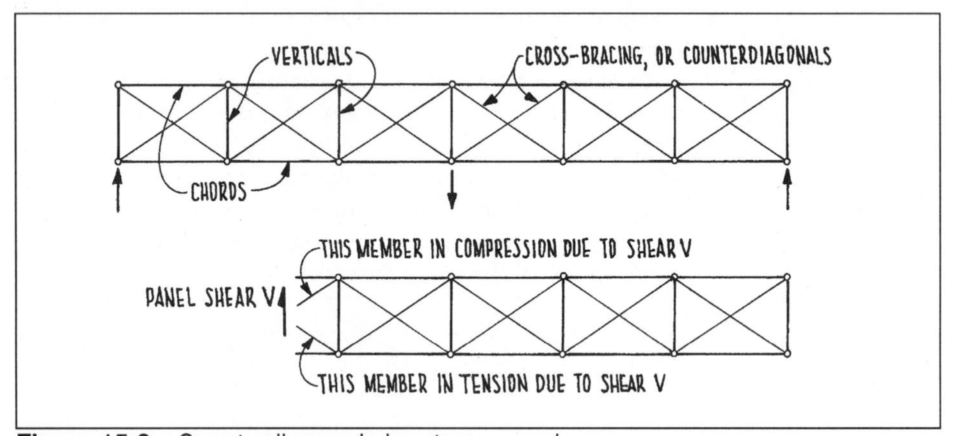

Figure 15-9 Counterdiagonals in a truss panel.

The cross braces shown in Figure 15-9 are called *counterdiagonals*, or more simply, *counters*. They are lightweight and very efficient to use. They are used very commonly in construction falsework. Their primary disadvantage is that they add clutter and can oftentimes block a potential passageway through a panel for the construction labor.

Counters offer one extra reassuring advantage, however. They automatically take care of any load reversals that may occur in the truss due to unforseen or accidental loadings. In construction falsework, this single feature is usually considered to be worth far more than any of the disadvantages they may have.

The truss of Figure 15-9 is shown again in Figure 15-10, with a unit load moving from one end to the other. As the unit load progresses across the span, all the diagonals in compression sag out of the way, leaving the other diagonal to take the entire load in tension. The truss thus changes its physical configuration as the load moves across the span.

The reconfiguration of the truss to keep all of its diagonals in tension is completely automatic; whenever shear occurs across a panel, the diagonal that is placed in tension is the one that takes the entire load. If the shear changes direction, the other diagonal will be the one placed in tension and it will then be the one taking the entire load.

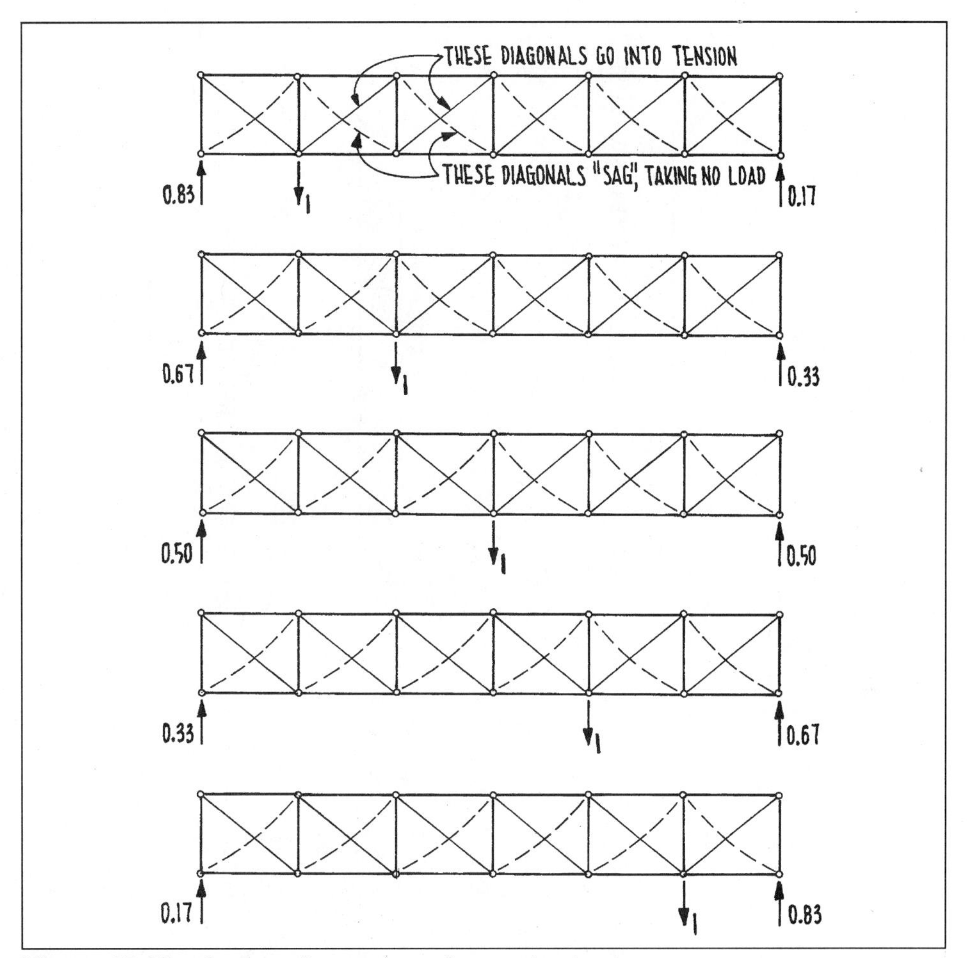

Figure 15-10 Counterdiagonals under moving load.

From the results shown in Figure 15-10, it is evident that the truss does in fact change its configuration to suit the load. If every panel point were to be loaded (rather than a single panel load as in Figure 15-10) it would not be possible routinely to predict the configuration of the truss. The truss would have to be analyzed for each completely final load case in order to find out which of the two diagonals in each panel is under load.

The change in configuration with each position of load affects other members in the truss as well; it is not limited just to the diagonals. Consider, for example, the truss configuration of Figure 15-8, with all of the interior diagonals being replaced by sets of counterdiagonals. Such a comparison is shown in Figure 15-11 for a unit load moving across the span.

In Figure 15-11, it should be noted that the truss configuration does change as expected for each position of load, but that the forces in members other than the counterdiagonals change also. Any analysis of such a truss must include these side effects in other members that will also undergo changes in load with each reconfiguration of the truss.

Since the configuration of the truss can change with each arrangement of load, the use of superposition of load cases is not permissible in a truss that contains counterdiagonals. Such superposition would amount to adding the loads in a truss having one configuration to the loads in another truss having a different configuration. Such an addition cannot be made in elastic structures. Superposition of loads simply cannot be used where counterdiagonals occur.

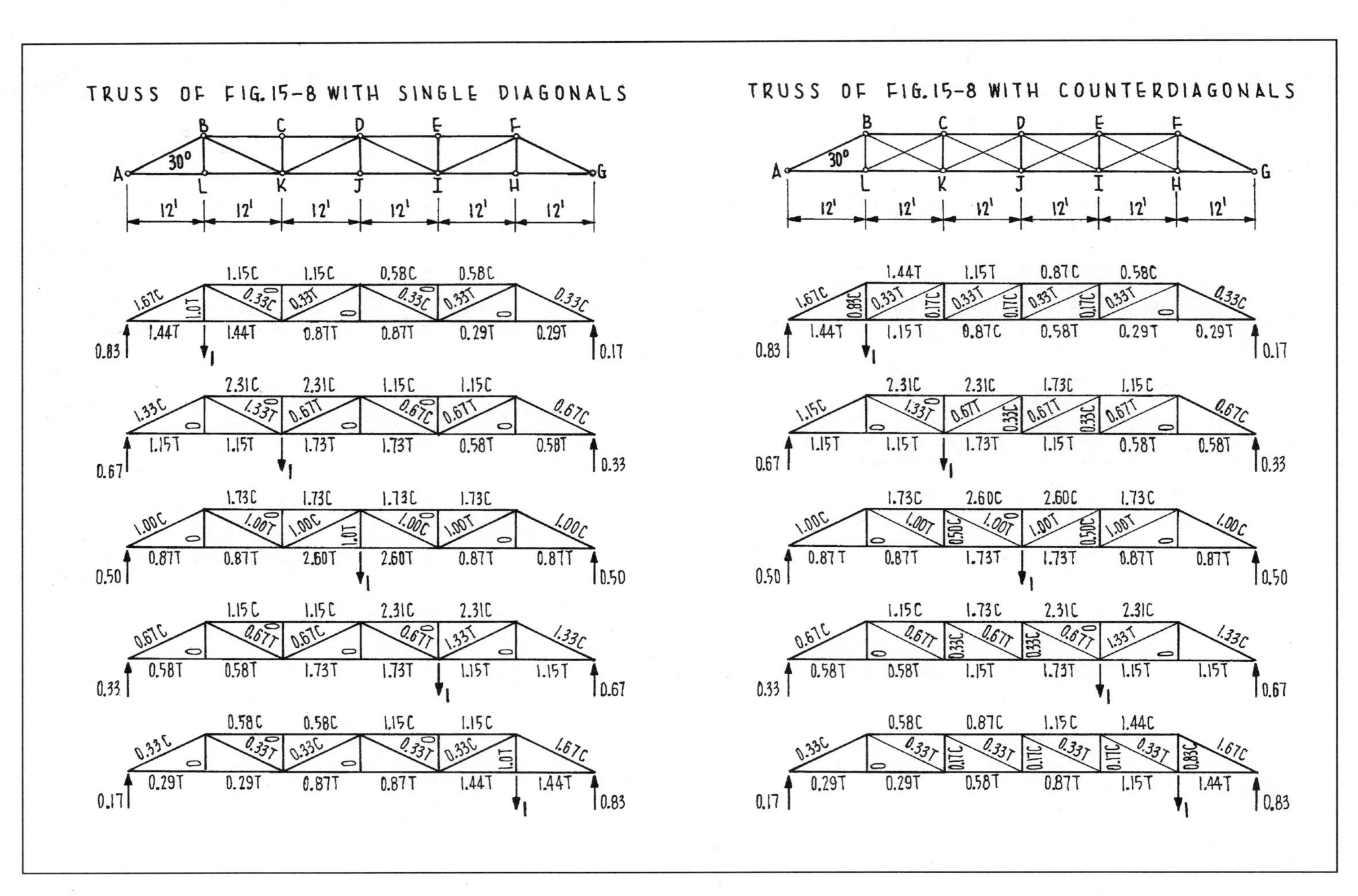

Figure 15-11 Comparison of truss loadings.

Review Questions

1. How is it that a series of interacting beams having 4, 5 or 6 reactions can be solved when there are only three equations of statics?
2. How is thermal growth accommodated in multispan beam systems?
3. In a double cantilever beam system, what is the nominal lengthh of the overhangs of the end beams?
4. In a double cantilever beam, what is the benefit derived from the overhangs?
5. How many additional independent equations are provided by the introduction of an internal hinge into a beam system?
6. What is the usual method of controlling deflections in a system of beams?
7. In what types of beams can the maximum deflection be taken to be generally equal to the deflection at midspan?
8. For the beams of Question 7, where in the span will the maximum deflection occur?
9. For the beams of Question 7, how close to the maximum deflection will the midspan deflection be?
10. Why can't the maximum deflection in beams of double curvature be taken as being approximately equal to the midspan deflection?
11. How is the approximate maximum deflection of antisymmetrical beams computed?
12. For the computation of Question 11, what makes such an approach to antisymmetrical deflections possible?
13. Why are load reversals so serious in trussed beams but of such low consequence in solid beams?
14. Which kind of truss members are most likely to be subject to load reversals?
15. What are counterdiagonals?
16. How is it that a truss having two diagonals in one panel can be treated as a "properly formed" truss?
17. Why can't superposition of loads be used in trusses that have counterdiagonals?
18. What is the distinctive feature of trusses that are provided with counterdiagonals in all panels?

PART

4

ENGINEERING OF CONCRETE AND MASONRY STRUCTURES

CHAPTER

16

CONCRETE AS AN ENGINEERING MATERIAL

To be a good structural material, a material should be homogeneous, isotropic, and elastic. Portland cement concrete is none of these. Naturally, it is very popular.

16.1 Materials and Properties of Concrete

Portland cement concrete is manufactured using a coarse aggregate of stone, a fine aggregate of sand, and a cementing paste of portland cement and water. The end result is a man-made stone that can be shaped while in its plastic state and allowed to harden into its final configuration. Compared to other construction materials, such as steel, aluminum, or timber, portland cement concrete is weak and heavy, but its characteristics of durability, adaptability, and availability have made it a popular material of construction.

Portland cement concrete is quite weak in tension. In most structural applications, its tensile strength is assumed to be zero and steel is provided at all points where the concrete will experience tension. The result is concrete reinforced for tension, or more simply, reinforced concrete.

Consider the beam shown in Figure 16-1, for example. Note that under the given load conditions, the beam of Figure 16-1 will experience tension on the bottom of the section at midspan, a region of positive moment. Note further that the beam will experience tension on the top of the section in the vicinity of the overhang, a region of negative moment. In both regions, a reinforcement area of steel denoted A_s in Figure 16-1 must be provided in the correct amount and located in the correct position to sustain these tensile forces.

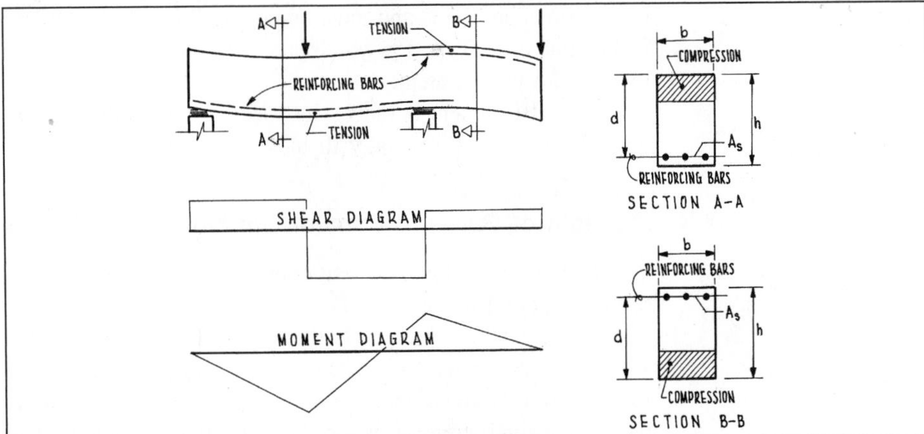

Figure 16-1 Typical reinforcement locations.

It is well to note at this point that the moment diagram of Figure 16-1 is plotted upside down, that is, with positive moment being plotted downward rather than upward. It should be observed that by being plotted this way, the moment diagram will always fall on the tension side of the member. Further, if the moment diagram is drawn accurately to scale, the cutoff points for the reinforcement can actually be determined by scaling the moment diagram, a common practice in the design of reinforced concrete members.

Throughout succeeding chapters, the practice of sketching the moment diagram "on the tension side" will be followed in all design procedures. The practice not only provides a very good method for locating reinforcement but it also provides a reliable suggestion of the deflection pattern of the beam under the given loads.

16.2 Portland Cement

Portland cement is a hydraulic cement, developed in 1824 by an English bricklayer, Joseph Aspdin. The name "portland" was applied because the color of the finished concrete resembled a building stone quarried on the Isle of Portland, off the coast of Dorset, England. The cement is manufactured from a mixture of about 4 parts limestone and 1 part clay, heated almost to the melting point of the mixture (about 2700° F) and then cooled and ground to a fine powder. A small amount of gypsum (about 5% by weight) is added to control set.

Portland cement works by hydration, that is, it forms a chemical bond with the water in the mix and, in doing so, forms a bond to other cement particles, to the aggregate, and to any reinforcement that it contacts. It does not need air to harden or "set"; it will harden as well under water as when exposed to air.

Five standard types of portland cement are manufactured:

Type I: regular portland cement
Type II: increased resistance to sulfate attack
Type III: high early strength
Type IV: lowered heat of hydration
Type V: high resistance to sulfate attack

By itself, Type I portland cement concrete is reasonably resistant to most forms of chemical attack that might occur naturally, but high concentrations of waterborne sulfates can have very deleterious effects on it. Commonly, such concentrations can occur in sewage, in groundwater carrying dissolved gypsum, and in some seawater exposures (from sulfur-producing marine organisms). For castings in a high-sulfate environment, special cements are manufactured, Types II and V, which have an increased resistance to sulfate attack.

Heat is generated by all five types of cement during hydration. For the more common sizes of structural members this heat is readily dissipated and presents no problems. For extremely large castings such as heavy equipment foundations, the trapped heat can pose serious problems and must be provided for. For such large castings a special cement is manufactured, Type IV, which has a lower heat of hydration than other types and helps to alleviate the problem.

Type III cement achieves its specified strength in 7 days rather than the usual 28 days. It does so at a penalty in increased heat of hydration as well as in higher cost.

16.3 Strength of Portland Cement Concrete

The strength of portland cement concrete is dependent on the number of pounds of water used per pound of cement. This ratio of water to cement, shown as the water/cement (W/C) ratio in Figure 16-2, is the single most important parameter used to control the strength of concrete. As indicated in the figure, there is a minimum W/C ratio required for hydration of all cement molecules. Any water in the mix in excess of that amount will reduce the final strength of the concrete. It is assumed, of course, that the aggregate is at least as strong as the sand-cement paste, or matrix.

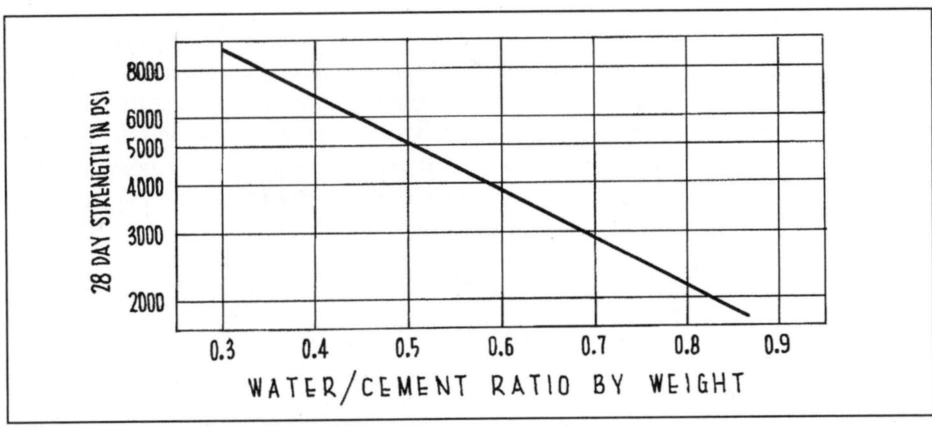

Figure 16-2 Concrete strength.

In condensed and abbreviated comments such as these, it is difficult to overstate the importance of the *W/C* ratio. An excess of water reduces not only strength but hardness, durability, resistance to chemical attack, resistance to freeze-thaw, and all other desirable properties of the concrete. Thus the construction worker who adds water to the mix to make it more workable is, by this single act, significantly reducing all the desirable characteristics of the finished concrete.

As with other structural materials, the strength of a concrete and the configuration of its stress-strain curve form the basis of all structural calculations. The strength of a concrete is gauged at 28 days by its compressive stress at failure. For measuring the stress at failure, a concrete cylinder 12 in. long and 6 in. in diameter is cast from a sample of the concrete. The cylinder is allowed to cure under controlled conditions for 28 days and is then placed in a compression test machine and loaded to failure. The compressive stress computed for the highest load is the "ultimate" stress, or 28-day strength, of that concrete.

A typical strength-time curve is shown in Figure 16-3. It should be noted that the gain in strength after 28 days is not acknowledged, but that concrete continues to gain strength for months or even years after manufacture. It should also be noted that the concrete attains about 60% of its design strength at 7 days, a useful bit of information to know when precast elements are to be lifted or forms are to be removed.

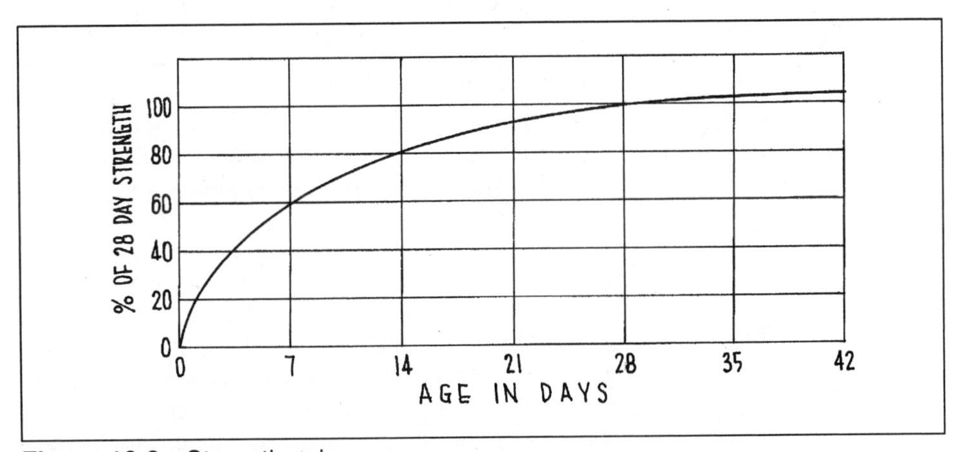

Figure 16-3 Strength gain.

There is no immediate test that can be performed at the time the concrete is being cast to assure that the concrete will reach a certain strength 28 days later. In practice, concrete is sampled periodically and cylinders are made as the concrete is being cast into the forms. These cylinders are tested 28 days later, affording a verification that the concrete had been manufactured properly last month. It is thus apparent that the cylinder test is a "report card," revealing how well a job was done 28 days ago.

To assure that the concrete is of proper strength and quality at the time it is cast, rigorous measures of quality control must be instituted and maintained during its production. Over the years, simple but adequate measures for field quality control have been developed which, with proper enforcement, will assure the production of good-quality concrete. These measures are unique in the industry; no other structural material is sampled for its strength and quality at the time of its final placement in the structure.

16.4 Strengths of Concrete in Common Use

In practice, concrete strengths lower than 3000 psi are rarely used for structural concrete. The design tables have been set up for only the more common concrete strengths: 3000, 4000, and 5000 psi. Beams and girders are commonly cast from concrete having an ultimate strength of 3000 or 4000 psi and columns from 4000 or 5000 psi.

16.5 Stress-Strain Curves for Concrete

The stress-strain curve for concrete can be plotted readily from the load-deflection data of a standard cylinder test. Typical stress-strain curves for various strengths of concrete are shown in Figure 16-4, where ultimate stress is denoted f'_c. It should be noted that there are no distinct "breaks" in these stress-strain curves: they are continuous smooth curves.

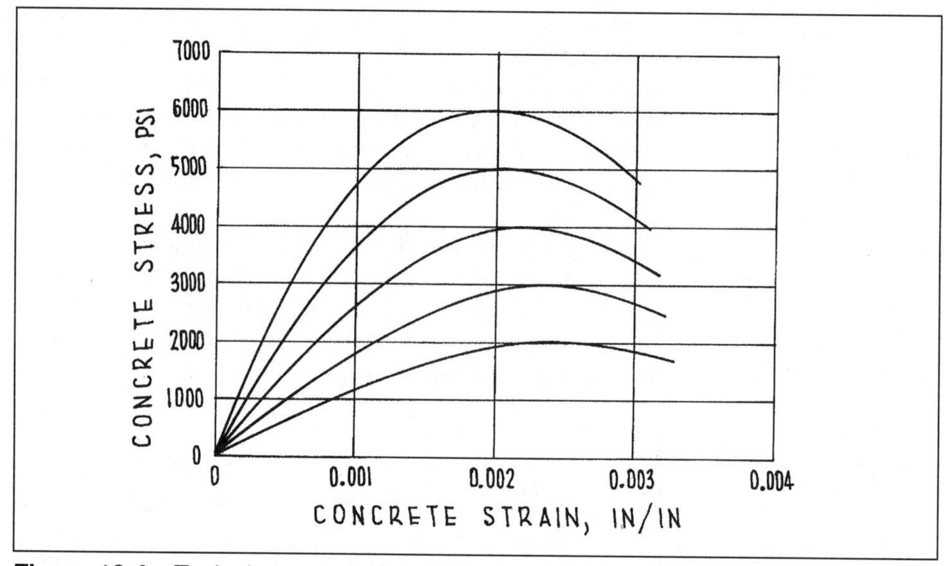

Figure 16-4 Typical stress-strain curves.

By definition, an elastic material under load will deform along a straight line up to its yield point. Within this elastic range, it will resume its exact original configuration upon release of the load. From the curves of Figure 16-4 it is seen that concrete is not a truly elastic material under this definition, although it is reasonably elastic within the lower three-fourths of its ultimate strength. It is noted, however, that the normal range of working stresses for concrete is within the lower half of its ultimate stress. Consequently, with a normal factor of safety and under its day-to-day service loads, concrete can be expected to work at less than half of its ultimate stress and will therefore behave as an elastic material under short-term service loads.

An exaggerated stress-strain curve is shown in Figure 16-5. An approximation of the slope of the initial portion of this curve is usually taken as the modulus of elasticity; its value is the stress divided by the strain at any point. The value of the modulus of elasticity increases as the strength of the concrete increases. The modulus of elasticity E_c in pounds per square inch is computed empirically by the relationship:

$$E_c = 57{,}000\sqrt{f'_c} \tag{16-1}$$

where f'_c is the ultimate strength of the concrete in pounds per square inch. The modulus of elasticity for each of the more common values of f'_c is given in Table C-1 in the Technical Manual.

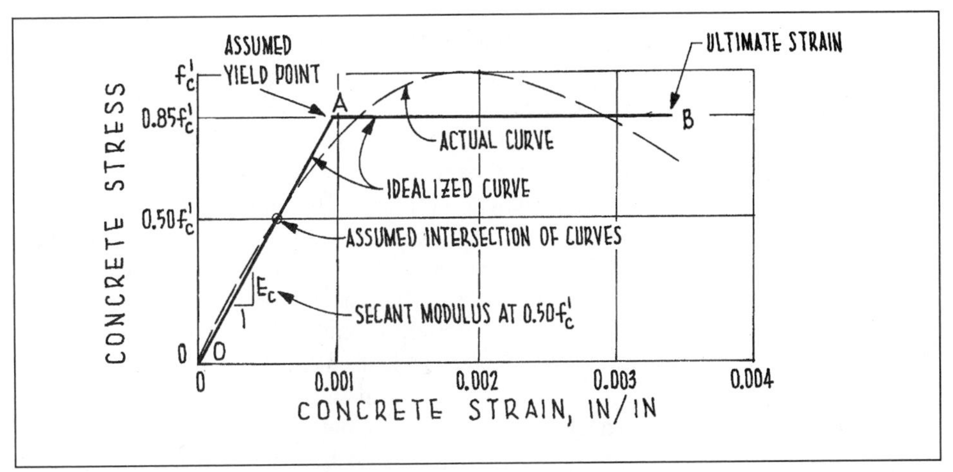

Figure 16-5 Idealized stress-strain curve for concrete.

Since the actual stress-strain curve of Figure 16-5 has no well-defined yield point, an idealized curve is substituted for the top portion of the actual curve. The resultant idealized curve *OAB* forms the basis of the derivations and calculations in the following chapters. The position of line *AB* has been found to provide the best correlation to comprehensive test data when it is taken at $0.85\,f'_c$. The distance *AB* is called the *plastic range* of the material.

16.6 Shrinkage and Creep

Only a relatively small amount of water is required to hydrate all the cement in the concrete mix. Any excess water that is free to migrate can evaporate as the concrete hardens, causing a slight reduction in the size of the member. This reduction in size, called *shrinkage*, can produce undesirable internal stresses and cracking. The concrete may regain much of the shrinkage loss if it is later submerged, but in dry buildings, the shrinkage can be considered to be permanent.

As a very general rule of thumb, the drying shrinkage of a typical structural concrete will produce a dimensional change roughly equal to that of a temperature drop of 40°F. Unlike a temperature drop, however, which affects both the concrete and its reinforcement, shrinkage affects only the concrete. The reinforcement stays at its original dimensions while the concrete shrinks around it, thereby creating compressive stresses in the reinforcement and tensile stresses in the concrete.

It was noted earlier that under sustained loads, concrete is seriously susceptible to creep; the magnitude of these deformations due to creep at any given time is unpredictable. As with creep deformations, shrinkage deformations at any time are also unpredictable. The combined effect of shrinkage and creep is to cause a dimensional change in the concrete that must be accounted for in the design.

The end result of long-term shrinkage and creep in concrete members is to produce an increase in the compressive strain. Such an increase occurs with no accompanying increase in load. The increase does not go on and on without limits, however. At worst, the inelastic strain due to shinkage and creep combined can be expected to be roughly as much as the elastic strain due to applied loads. In effect, therefore, the modulus of elasticity when the long-term effects of shinkage and creep are included can be estimated as half that due only to short-term elastic loading. For calculations, the design codes do exactly that; shrinkage and creep are accounted for by taking the modulus of elasticity due to long-term loads to be half that due to short-term loads.

16.7 Bond Strength

The adhesion of concrete to its imbedded reinforcement is called *bond.* Bond strength between concrete and reinforcement is probably the most highly variable property of concrete that must be used in design. Accordingly, bond strength is assigned a high factor of safety to account for the many uncertainties and variables. The resulting conservative values for bond strength requires that reinforcement be deeply embedded in concrete to assure full development of the steel strength.

Bond strength increases as the ultimate strength of the concrete increases. It can be adversely affected by excess water, by air bubbles, by excessive rust on the reinforcement, by improper consolidation of the concrete, by accidental movement or vibration of the reinforcement after the concrete has started to set, and by the type and number of deformations on the reinforcement. Even with identical placement conditions and practices, two embedded bars can have strikingly different pullout strengths.

It is a design code requirement that the reinforcement used in reinforced concrete must be manufactured with surface deformations to improve bond. Earlier design codes permitted smooth reinforcing bars to be used, allowing half as much bond strength for smooth bars as for deformed bars; many buildings throughout the world are still being built to that provision. In the U.S., however, the design codes require that deformed bars be used.

16.8 Reinforcement and Its Properties

Reinforcement is manufactured under several international specifications for a variety of yield stresses, or grades. In this text, consideration is concentrated on reinforcement grades 40 and 60. For these grades, the yield stress is 40,000 and 60,000 psi, respectively. Grade 50 steel, having a yield stress of 50,000 psi, has fallen out of common use in American practice but is still occasionally found; it is therefore included in this text.

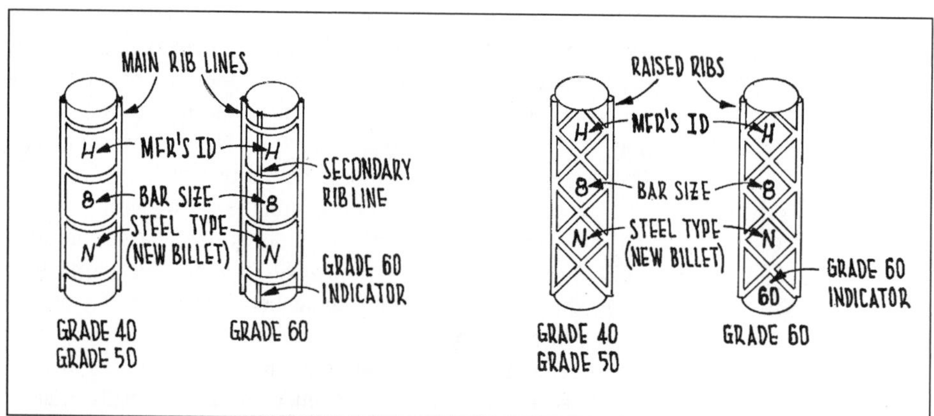

Figure 16-6 Deformed reinforcing bars.

Reinforcement is rolled in round bars, having deformed surfaces designed to improve the connection to the adjacent concrete (see Figure 16-6). In the United States, the identifying number of a reinforcing bar, up to a No. 9 bar, indicates its diameter in eighths of an inch; thus a No. 5 bar has a nominal diameter of $^5/_8$ inch. Bar sizes No. 9, No. 10, and No. 11 are also round, but their diameters are set to provide the same areas as older square bars 1 in., 1 1/8 in., and 1 1/4 inch respectively. A No. 9 bar has a diameter 1.128 in., a No. 10 bar has a diameter 1.27 in., and a No. 11 bar has a diameter 1.41 inch. Bar sizes larger than No. 11 are used primarily in very heavy construction and are not included here.

Although deformed bars are used almost without exception in the United States, smooth bars or drawn wire are frequently used throughout much of the rest of the world. In small diameters (6, 8, 10 and 12 mm), smooth wire can be shipped in rolls occupying a low volume at reduced shipping costs. It should be noted that labor costs are considerably higher to place a large number of small smooth wires in the forms compared to fewer larger deformed bars. Where labor is cheap and shipping is expensive, however, smooth wire will probably remain popular.

Stress-strain curves for steel are treated in detail in elementary strength-of-materials texts. For its applications in reinforced concrete, an idealized curve similar to that of concrete (Figure 16-5) is required. Such idealized curves for steel are shown in Figure 16-7 with the complete stress-strain curve shown alongside for reference. Since steel is such an ideal structural material, the idealized curves of Figure 16-7 are but little different from the same portion of the actual curve.

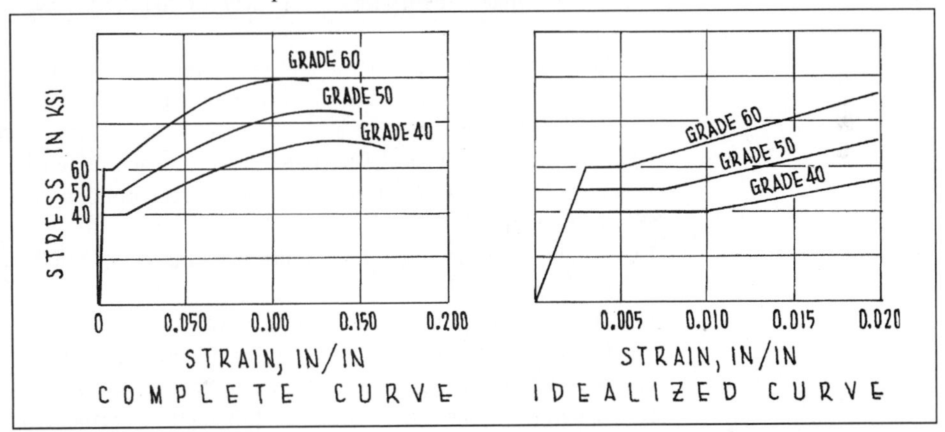

Figure 16-7 Idealized stress-strain curve for steel.

From Table C-1 in the Technical Manual it is noted that the elastic modulus for steel is $29x10^6$ psi. For that value of the modulus of elasticity, the strain at the yield point is 0.00138 in./in. for grade 40 steel, 0.00172 in./in. for grade 50 steel and 0.00207 in./in. for grade 60 steel.

In addition to individual smooth wires and deformed bars, reinforcement is also fabricated into a rectangular mesh of smooth wires, called *welded wire fabric (WWF)* or into a mat of deformed bars called *structural fabric*. These fabrics are made up as a convenience to construction; the structural design is the same regardless whether the reinforcement is placed as individual bars or as a mesh.

16.9 Weight and Density of Concrete

The weight of concrete varies with the density of its aggregates. An average value for unreinforced concrete is 140 pounds per cubic foot (pcf) and for reinforced concrete is 150 pcf. A median weight of 145 pcf is used throughout this text.

The weight of concrete can be reduced significantly by the use of lightweight aggregates. Concretes that weigh as low at 90 pcf are produced this way and are in common use. In such concretes, the decrease in dead load can often offset the higher materials costs, even though the strength of the lighter concrete is also reduced.

It is almost axiomatic that strength is reduced as density is reduced. Whatever causes a decrease in density of concrete, such as entrapped air or lighter aggregates, will almost always produce a reduction in strength.

16.10 Thermal Properties of Concrete

The coefficient of thermal expansion and contraction for concrete varies somewhat with the aggregates. An average value is 0.0000055 in./in. per degree Fahrenheit. Since the corresponding coefficient for reinforcing steel is quite close, 0.0000065 in./in. per degree Fahrenheit, the effects of differential thermal growth between the concrete and its reinforcement is negligible at common atmospheric temperature ranges.

Review Questions

1. Why is it necessary to reinforce concrete?
2. What are the ingredients of portland cement concrete?
3. What does the name "portland" mean in portland cement?
4. Name the five types of portland cement and the distinguishing characteristics of each.
5. In what circumstances can high concentrations of sulphates occur that would have deleterious effects on concrete?
6. Under what circumstances can heat of hydration become a problem in concrete castings?
7. What is the primary factor that controls the strength of a concrete mix?
8. How is the ultimate strength of a concrete mix determined?
9. At what age is Type I portland cement concrete considered to be at full strength?
10. At what age is Type III portland cement concrete considered to be at full strength?
11. What happens to the strength of portland cement concrete over several years after its manufacture?
12. A concrete is designed for an ultimate strength of 4000 psi at 28 days. What will be its strength at 7 days?
13. Why is it necessary to idealize the stress-strain curve for portland cement concrete?
14. How is the modulus of elasticity of concrete computed?
15. At what stress is the idealized yield strength taken?
16. Generally, what is the cause of shrinkage in portland cement concrete?
17. What is the cause of creep in portland cement concrete?
18. How does the design code account for the inelastic strains due to shrinkage and creep in concrete?
19. Are the inelastic strains due to shinkage and creep tensile or compressive strains?
20. What is bond?
21. What is the purpose of putting deformations on the surface of reinforcing bars?
22. What are the three most common grades of reinforcing steel available in the United States?
23. What is the diameter of a No. 7 bar?
24. What is the yield strength of grade 40 steel? Grade 50 steel? Grade 60 steel?
25. What is the modulus of elasticity of grade 40 steel? Grade 50 steel? Grade 60 steel?
26. What is the nominal weight of regular reinforced concrete?
27. What is the thermal coefficient of expansion and contraction for concrete?
28. Why is there no problem with differential thermal growth between concrete and its reinforcement?

CHAPTER

17

DESIGN CODE REQUIREMENTS

The design of structures in reinforced concrete is rigidly governed by codes. One may spend years learning the fine points of these codes, but the major features of design are contained in a surprisingly few paragraphs. It is these major features that are the immediate subject of this text; the fine points are usually learned through exposure, experience, and embarrassment.

17.1 Design Codes

In the United States, those sections of building codes that deal with concrete design are usually based on the *Building Code Requirements for Reinforced Concrete*, American Concrete Institute, 1989. Any reference to a code in the following chapters will mean this code. It is commonly identified as ACI 318-77 or ACI 318-89, where the number following the dash is the year of the edition.

Discussions in the following chapters refer frequently to particular sections of the ACI Code. It is recommended that anyone designing concrete members obtain a current copy of the Code and become familiar with it. Where the meaning of a particular provision becomes clear only after repeated study, a marginal note will save some time several weeks or months hence when the provision is encountered again.

Where appropriate in subsequent discussions, the section number of the Code is given in parentheses following a reference to the Code. For example, in the sentence "Code (10.2.3) requires that ultimate strain in concrete be taken at 0.003 inches per inch.", the referenced provision is stated in Section 10.2.3 of ACI 318-89.

The ACI Code covers much more than just design methods. Among other things, Code prescribes the maximum and minimum sizes of members that may be built of reinforced concrete, as well as minimum required amounts and sizes of reinforcement. It also prescribes limits on allowable deflections and means to predict and control those deflections. Code also prescribes loads, load factors and load combinations to be used in design, as well as means to allow for undercapacity in the event a concrete member is not built exactly as it was intended to be built.

In addition to design requirements, Code prescribes construction requirements. Among the many construction items covered, Code prescribes tolerances to be held in constructing the formwork, in placing the reinforcement and in aligning the members. It prescribes the minimum cover that must be maintained over the reinforcement in order that the steel will be adequately protected from weather, from attack by chemicals in the soil or from corrosion by salts and deicing compounds, as well. Code also prescribes imbedment lengths that must be maintained to assure adequate bond between the concrete and its reinforcement, and Code prescribes the circumstances when reinforcing bars must be placed singly or when reinforcement may be placed in bundles of several bars.

There is much to be learned about Code requirements when one begins the study of reinforced concrete. A few of the more general Code requirements are introduced and discussed in the following sections; other Code requirements are introduced and discussed in later chapters when they are first encountered. The remaining requirements will be encountered by the practicing designer over the years; it will be seen that those remaining requirements are by far the largest part of the design code.

17.2 Minimum Dimensions

The minimum size of some concrete members is set by Code and of others by limitations on forming and casting. The difficulties in forming and casting very thin or very small members in the field should not be underestimated. Labor hours and costs required to cast such members can easily be double or triple those required to cast more conventional sizes.

The following list includes an indication of whether the minimum dimension is fixed by Code and may not be decreased, or whether it is limited by practice and may be decreased if one is willing to pay the price.

- Bearing walls, cast in place, minimum 10 in. thick (practice).
- Bearing walls, precast, minimum 4 in, thick (Code 14.5.3.1).
- Columns, cast in place, minimum dimension 10 in. (practice).
- Foundation walls, minimum 7$^{1}/_{2}$ in. thick (Code 14.5.3.2).
- Nonbearing walls, cast in place, minimum 4 in. thick (Code 14.6.1).
- Slabs on grade, minimum thickness 3$^{1}/_{2}$ in. (practice).

17.3 Minimum and Maximum Reinforcement

The minimum and maximum area of flexural reinforcement given in the following paragraphs is governed by Code. These limits assure that the member will behave properly under extremes of load and that cracking in the concrete will be within acceptable sizes and will follow acceptable patterns.

For slabs having flexural reinforcement in one direction only, temperature and shrinkage reinforcement in the other direction is required. Minimum area of temperature and shrinkage reinforcement is 0.002bh for grades 40 and 50 steel and 0.0018bh for grade 60 steel, where b and h are gross dimensions of the section; bar spacing may not exceed 18 inches. This requirement applies to all one-way slabs, including those of joist systems. This same minimum steel area also applies to the primary flexural reinforement as well (for very lightly reinforced beams).

The steel ratio ρ in flexural members is defined as A_s/bd (see Figure 16-1). For flexural members, the steel ratio may not be less than $200/f_Y$ nor may it be more than 75% of the balanced steel ratio. The balanced steel ratio is defined as that ratio of steel that will allow the reinforcement to enter yield just as the concrete reaches a strain of 0.003; it is discussed further in Chapter 18.

For columns, the area of longitudinal reinforcement may not be less than $0.01bh$ nor more than 0.08bh, where b and h are gross cross-sectional dimensions. In practice, however, congestion at joints becomes so severe with the higher amounts of reinforcement that the use of more than 4% steel is avoided.

For bearing walls reinforced with grade 60 deformed bars not larger than No. 5, the area of reinforcement may not be less than 0.0012bh vertically nor less than 0.0020bh horizontally. These same minimums also apply to mesh reinforcement having the same bar sizes regardless whether the bars are smooth or deformed or whether the bars are grade 40, 50, or 60 steel (smooth bars are permitted in a mesh). For all other reinforcement sizes and grades, the area of reinforcement may not be less than 0.0015bh vertically nor less than 0.0025bh horizontally. As before, b and h are gross dimensions. These requirements are for total area of steel, whether placed in the middle of the wall, on one face, or on both faces.

For floor slabs on grade, Code does not require reinforcement. For crack control, however, it is common practice to meet at least Code requirements for temperature reinforcement (in both directions). For slabs more than 5 in. thick, the reinforcement mesh should be placed in two layers, at top and bottom surfaces.

17.4 Minimum Spacing of Reinforcement

The minimum clear distance between bars is governed by Code (7.6). This minimum limitation permits the wet concrete to flow freely between bars without leaving air pockets or gaps. In earlier years, an additional provision was included to account for the nominal size of the aggregate used in making the concrete, but in more recent Codes, that provision has been dropped.

A typical section of a concrete member is shown in Figure 17-1. The clear cover and clear spacing is shown in Figure 17-1a. Where bars are to be spliced, the bars being spliced will overlap each other as shown in Figure 17-1b; clear distance between adjacent sets of bars must be maintained in such splices.

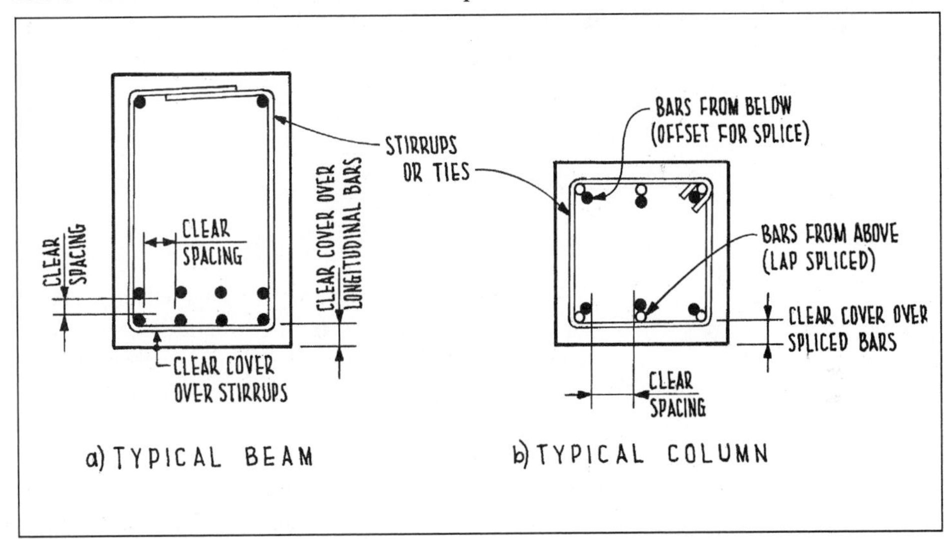

Figure 17-1 Cover and spacing of bars.

The following limits on bar spacing must be maintained:

- The minimum clear spacing between single bars in a layer shall not be less than d_b nor 1 inch, where d_b is the diameter of the bar.
- Where parallel reinforcement is placed in two or more layers, bars in the upper layers shall be placed directly above the bars in the lower layers, with a minimum clear distance between layers of 1 inch.
- In tied columns, clear distance between longitudinal bars shall not be less than $1.5d_b$ nor less than $1\frac{1}{2}$ inches.
- Limitations on clear distance shall apply also to the clear distance between a contact lap splice and adjacent splices.
- In walls or slabs other than concrete joist construction, primary flexural reinforcement shall be spaced not farther apart than three times the wall or slab thickness, with an absolute maximum spacing of 18 inches.

As noted earlier, the foregoing limits are imposed primarily for the sake of casting wet concrete in and around the clusters of reinforcement. These spacings also have a profound effect on the formation of crack lines or "split lines," which progress from bar to bar and which disrupt bonding between the bar and the concrete. Additional limitations on spacing due to such problems with bonding are discussed in Chapter 20.

17.5 Bundling of Bars

When the number of parallel bars in a concrete member is so numerous that it causes placement problems, Code (7.6.6) permits the bars to be collected into "bundles" of 2, 3 or 4 bars. Such bundling of bars is shown in Figure 17-2, in which the congested bar arrangement of Figure 17-2a has been changed into the more open bar arrangement of Figure 17-2b.

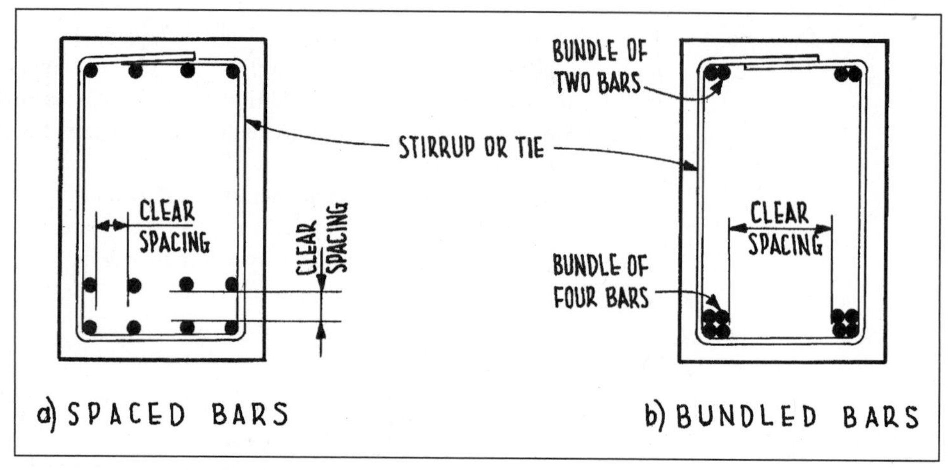

Figure 17-2 Bundling of bars.

The following criteria apply to bundling of bars:

- Parallel reinforcing bars may be bundled in contact to act as a unit, where the maximum number of bars in a bundle is limited to four.
- Bundled bars shall be enclosed within stirrups or ties.
- Bars larger than No. 11 shall not be bundled in beams.
- Individual bars within a bundle that are terminated within the span of flexural members shall be terminated at different points, with at least $40d_b$ staggered between cutoff points, where d_b is the diameter of the bar being cut.
- Where spacing criteria or cover criteria are based on bar diameters d_b, a bundle of bars shall be treated as an equivalent single bar having the same total cross sectional area.

Bundling of bars is a distinct convenience in many circumstances, but the convenience does not come without a penalty. When a group of bars is bundled, it loses surface area and, with the loss in surface area, the bundle loses bond strength with the adjacent concrete. This loss in bond strength is discussed further in Chapter 20, along with measures to correct for such a loss.

17.6 Minimum Cover Over Bars

The amount of clear concrete cover over the outermost reinforcement is governed by Code (7.7.1). It is this cover that provides fire protection. It also prevents the intrusion of salts or oxygen that would cause corrosion of the reinforcement. Code (7.7.5) requires that the cover be increased above Code minimums where conditions are severe.

The following criteria are taken from the ACI Code (7.7). In this summary, any dimension that is based on bar sizes is the same whether the bars are used singly or made into a mesh. Mesh reinforcement may be made of smooth or deformed bars; bars used singly must be deformed.

Minimum cover for concrete cast in place:

Concrete cast against earth and permanently exposed to earth	3 in.
Concrete exposed to earth or weather:	
(a) Bars larger than No. 5	2 in.
(b) Bars No. 5 and smaller	1 1/2 in.
Concrete not exposed to earth or weather:	
1. Slabs, walls and joists	
(a) Bars larger than No. 11	1 1/2 in.
(b) Bars No. 11 and smaller	3/4 in.
2. Beams and columns	1 1/2 in.
3. Shells and folded plates	
(a) Bars larger than No. 5	3/4 in.
(b) Bars No. 5 and smaller	1/2 in.

Minimum cover for precast concrete elements manufactured under plant-controlled conditions:

Concrete exposed to earth or weather:	
1. Wall panels	
(a) Bars larger than No. 11	1 1/2 in.
(b) Bars No. 11 and smaller	3/4 in.
2. Other members	
(a) Bars larger than No. 11	2 in.
(b) Bars larger than No. 5 but smaller than No. 11	1 1/2 in.
(c) Bars No. 5 and smaller	1 1/4 in.
Concrete not exposed to earth or weather:	
1. Slabs, walls and joists	
(a) Bars larger than No. 11	1 1/4 in.
(b) Bars No. 11 and smaller	5/8 in.
2. Beams and columns	
(a) Primary reinforcement:	
One bar diameter, but not less than	5/8 in.
nor more than	1 1/2 in.
(b) Ties or stirrup	3/8 in.
3. Shells and folded plates	
(a) Bars larger than No. 5	5/8 in.
(b) Bars No. 5 and less	3/8 in.

17.7 Limits on Deflections

Within a structure, there are glass, finishes, fillers, and other nonstructural elements that are not themselves part of the load-carying system but which are attached directly to a load-carrying member. Some of these elements may be damaged if the structural members supporting them undergo excessive deflections. Those nonstructural elements that would be subject to such damage are collectively termed herein the *brittle elements.*

The effects of structural deflections on the brittle elements are no different in concrete structures than in structures made of other materials. The nature and timing of the deflections themselves, however, can be quite different in concrete structures due to the inelastic deformations resulting from shinkage and creep. In evaluating the effects of deflections in concrete structures, the designer must distinguish between short-term and long-term loadings and the effect that each could have on the deflections at any given time.

The following limits on deflections specified by Code (9.5) apply only to application of the short-term live load:

1. For flat roofs not supporting or attached to brittle elements; deflections are limited to *L/180*, where *L* is the span.
2. For floors not supporting or attached to brittle elements, deflections are limited to *L/360*, where *L* is the span.

The following limits on deflections apply only to that part of the total deflection following the placing and attaching of the nonstructural elements; earlier long-term deflections may be excluded but subsequent long-term or short-term deflections may not.

1. For roofs or floors supporting or attached to brittle elements, deflections are limited to *L/480*, where *L* is the span.
2. For roofs or floors supporting nonstructural elements that do not include any brittle elements, deflections are limited to *L/240*, where *L* is the span.

Deflections due to sustained loads are known to increase with time and decrease with the amount of compressive reinforcement. Code (9.5.2.5) includes these effects in a factor λ, where:

$$\lambda = \frac{\xi}{1 + 50\rho'}$$

where ξ is a time factor and ρ' is the ratio of compressive reinforcement A_s'/bd. The time factor ξ is prescribed by Code:

For 5 years or more: $\xi = 2.0$
For 12 months: $\xi = 1.4$
For 6 months: $\xi = 1.2$
For 3 months: $\xi = 1.0$

The inelastic deflection is computed by multiplying the elastic deflection due to sustained loads times the factor λ.

Code does not place limits on any deflections other than those due to flexure. Where brittle finishes are fixed to concrete columns, such as mosaic tile, mirrors, or marble, the designer must estimate the long-term deformations by his or her own methods. The foregoing time factors offer a useful guide for estimating such long-term inelastic deformations.

17.8 Control of Deflections

Only the deformations at service levels of loading are of interest to the designer. These are the day-to-day deformations that determine whether the building will perform satisfactorily in service. Such deformations affect cracking of plaster, "springiness" of floors, transmission of vibrations, weather seals at joints, and all other effects that arise from the building's service deflections.

The foregoing Code criteria gave the limits that must be observed for deflections of flexural members under service conditions. The foregoing criteria did not, however, stipulate how the deflections are to be determined. In a separate section, Code (9.5.2) prescribes means to compute or to limit deflections in the strength method of design.

Code (9.5.2) permits a blanket approach to the control of deflections in lieu of a detailed calculation of deflections. In this method, deflections are not computed nor is there any estimate made of their effects. The depths of all members are simply kept above prescribed minimum limits; experience has shown that buildings constructed using such member sizes will perform satisfactorily insofar as deflections are concerned.

In the blanket method, therefore, it is never known what the magnitude of the deflections are; it is only known that they will not be a problem. As one may suppose, this blanket approach to control of deflections is somewhat conservative. Nonetheless, the use of this method produces little or no penalty for smaller buildings. As the building size increases, however, the conservatism becomes increasingly expensive and a detailed calculation of deflections may become worthwhile.

In this textbook, only the blanket method for the control of deflections is included. Consequently, when the depth of a member is selected, the check for deflections consists only of a fast check against the minimum allowable depth for the member. The minimum overall depth h of members is adapted from the Code (Table 9.5a) and presented in Table 17-1.

Table 17-1 Minimum Overall Depth of Flexural Members[1]

	Overall depth of member	
Support condition	Solid slabs, one-way flexure	Beams or ribbed slabs one-way flexure
Simply supported	L/20	L/16
One end continuous	L/24	L/18.5
Both ends continuous	L/28	L/21
Cantilever	L/10	L/8

[1] L is the length of span. Values are for grade 60 steel, f_Y = 60,000 psi. For other grades of steel, these values must be multiplied by $(0.4 + f_Y/100{,}000)$.

17.9 Strength Reduction Factors

Construction and placement tolerances are more numerous and more generous for concrete than for other materials, presumably because concrete members are usually fabricated on-site. All aspects of concrete construction have allowable tolerances, which, under normal circumstances, combine to cancel each other. If only a few of these happen to accumulate, however, a significant loss of strength could result.

Code (9.3) requires that the computed ultimate strength of concrete members be reduced somewhat to account for any accidental adverse buildup in tolerances. The amount of the reduction varies, depending on the type of loading; a higher reduction is required for columns than for beams. The following strength reduction factors, ϕ, apply to the indicated type of loading at ultimate capacity:

Beam flexure, without axial loads:	$\phi = 0.90$
Axial tension, with or without flexure:	$\phi = 0.90$
Axial compression, with or without flexure, square or rectangular tied columns:	$\phi = 0.70$
Shear or torsion:	$\phi = 0.85$
Bearing:	$\phi = 0.70$

17.10 Load Factors and Load Combinations

The strength reduction factor ϕ of the preceding section provides for accidental undercapacity of a section. Its purpose is to provide extra capacity in the event the section is not built exactly as intended; it is not related to improper loading. In arriving at the value of ϕ, it is tacitly assumed that the external loads are properly applied and that no overload occurs.

Overloading can in fact occur, however, and the chances of its occurring are completely independent of construction practices. It has already been noted that small loads may occur due to temperature or settlements that are ignored in the analysis and design of the structure. An allowance for such overload, accidental or planned, is an essential part of the design.

It was noted in Chapter 13 that it is not reasonable to design a structure for every maximum load that can be imagined during its life and to assume that all these maximum loads will occur at the same time. Maximum wind load, for example, will not likely occur during maximum earthquake load. Rather, structures are designed for reasonable combinations of loads compatible with the intended service; a reasonable margin is then provided for unpredictable circumstances.

In the working stress method this margin is provided by the *safety factor*, as discussed earlier. In the strength method, the margin is provided by *load factors*.

In the strength method, load factors are used to project service loads up to an "ultimate" level of load for which the concrete member is to be designed. The member is assumed to be stressed to its absolute maximum capacity under this ultimate load; all materials are assumed to be in yield and at their maximum levels of strain just prior to rupture. Under actual service loads, the member will then work at comfortable levels of stress under much lower levels of load.

Load factors and load combinations are prescribed by Code (9.2). The following requirements are taken from the Code, with D representing the effects for dead load, L for live load, W for wind load, T for settlement or temperature, and E for earthquake. With this notation, the required ultimate load U must be at least equal to the following combinations of loads, termed *factored* loads by ACI:

$$U = 1.40D + 1.7L, \text{ or}$$
$$U = 0.75(1.40D + 1.7L + 1.7W), \text{ or}$$
$$U = 0.90D + 1.3W, \text{ or}$$
$$U = 0.75[1.40D + 1.7L + 1.7(1.1E)], \text{ or}$$
$$U = 0.75(1.4D + 1.7L + 1.4T)$$

Where lateral loads are small, the first equation will usually yield the highest loads.

The ACI Code follows current philosophy in permitting an increase of 33% in overall loads where wind, earthquake and thermal load occur in combination with dead and live loads. That provision is incorporated into the appropriate load combinations in the usual way by making the design value 75% of the total load; the full load (when it occurs) will then produce a 33% overload above this design value. At this point, it is important only to recognize that Code permits an overload of some 33% above ordinary service levels for these occasionally-encountered load cases.

17.11 Nominal Ultimate Loads and Service Loads

In the strength method for the design of concrete, there are thus two sets of factors to be used to project the loads from their actual service level up to their theoretical ultimate level. The first of these are the "load factors" and the second are the "strength reduction factors." Further, a 33% overload is allowed for certain combinations of load. These are the ultimate load conditions prescribed by Code for the design of concrete members.

In the design procedures in current use, the prescribed conditions are met through the use of a nominal ultimate load case U_n. The nominal ultimate load U_n is found by dividing the factored load case U (given in the preceding section) by the strength reduction factor ϕ. For example, for some of the more common load combinations, the nominal ultimate load case is given by:

$$U_n = U/\phi = (1.4D + 1.7L)/\phi \qquad (17\text{-}1a)$$
$$U_n = U/\phi = 0.75(1.4D + 1.7L + 1.7W)/\phi \qquad (17\text{-}1b)$$
$$U_n = U/\phi = 0.75[1.4D + 1.7L + 1.7(1.1E)]/\phi. \qquad (17\text{-}1c)$$

Or, alternatively, the nominal ultimate load case may be written in the form:

$$U_n = U/\phi = 1.7[{}^{1.4}/_{1.7}D + L)/\phi] \qquad (17\text{-}2a)$$
$$U_n = U/\phi = 1.7[0.75({}^{1.4}/_{1.7}D + L + W)/\phi] \qquad (17\text{-}2b)$$
$$U_n = U/\phi = 1.7[0.75({}^{1.4}/_{1.7}D + L + 1.1E)/\phi] \qquad (17\text{-}2c)$$

The combinations inside the brakets of Eqs.(17-2) are designated herein to be the load cases U_{SV} at service levels:

$$U_{SV} = ({}^{1.4}/_{1.7}D + L)/\phi \quad (17\text{-}3a)$$
$$U_{SV} = 0.75({}^{1.4}/_{1.7}D + L + W)/\phi \quad (17\text{-}3b)$$
$$U_{SV} = 0.75({}^{1.4}/_{1.7}D + L + 1.1E)/\phi \quad (17\text{-}3c)$$

At these service levels of load, the reduction in factor of safety for dead loads and the increase in the factor of safety for earthquake loads is recognized simply as a feature of the ultimate strength method of design; it is implicit in the load cases given by Code (9.2).

In terms of moment, shear and axial force,

$$\text{For moment,} \quad M_n = 1.7\ M_{SV} \quad \text{with } \phi = 0.90 \quad (17\text{-}4a)$$
$$\text{For shear,} \quad V_n = 1.7\ V_{SV} \quad \text{with } \phi = 0.85 \quad (17\text{-}4b)$$
$$\text{For axial force,} \quad P_n = 1.7\ P_{SV} \quad \text{with } \phi = 0.70, \quad (17\text{-}4c)$$

where the subscripts $_n$ and $_{SV}$ are used in the same context as before. All service loads therefore have a factor of safety of 1.7 to ultimate load, or conversely, the service loads are some 60% of the ultimate loads.

The following examples will illustrate the computation of design loads for some typical cases.

Example 17-1

Computation of design loads at service levels. Concrete member in flexure, $\phi = 0.9$ for flexure, $\phi = 0.85$ for shear. No wind or earthquake loads occur.

Given: $M_{DL} = 60$ kip-ft, $V_{DL} = 38$ kips, $M_{LL} = 44$ kip-ft, $V_{LL} = 29$ kips

To Find: Maximum service design moment M_{SV}.
Maximum service design shear V_{SV}.

Solution: Since there are no lateral loads, the maximum values for shear and moment are given by the load case of Eq.(17-3a):

$$U_{SV} = ({}^{1.4}/_{1.7}D + L)/\phi$$

For moment:

$$M_{SV} = [{}^{1.4}/_{1.7}(60) + 44]/0.9$$
$$M_{SV} = 104 \text{ kip-ft}$$

For shear:

$$V_{SV} = [{}^{1.4}/_{1.7}(38) + 29]/0.85$$
$$V_{SV} = 71 \text{ kips}$$

These values of M_{SV} and V_{SV} are the values to be sustained at the maximum service level of stress in the concrete member. Note that ultimate loads M_n and V_n can now be found (if needed) simply by multiplying the service loads by 1.7:

$$M_n = 1.7M_{SV} = 177 \text{ kip-ft.}$$
$$Vn = 1.7V_{SV} = 121 \text{ kips.}$$

Example 17-2

Computation of design loads at service levels. Concrete member in flexure, $\phi = 0.90$ for flexure, $\phi = 0.85$ for shear. Wind and earthquake loads included.

Given: $M_{DL} = 86$ kip-ft, $V_{DL} = 40$ kips
$M_{LL} = 77$ kip-ft, $V_{LL} = 27$ kips
$M_W = 36$ kip-ft, $V_W = 12$ kips
$M_E = 48$ kip-ft, $V_E = 18$ kips

To Find: Maximum service design moments M_{SV}.
Maximum service design shear V_{SV}.

Solution: The load combinations given by Eqs.(17-3) will apply:

$$U_{SV} = (^{1.4}/_{1.7}D + L)/\phi$$
$$U_{SV} = 0.75(^{1.4}/_{1.7}D + L + W)/\phi$$
$$U_{SV} = 0.75(^{1.4}/_{1.7}D + L + 1.1E)/\phi$$

Substitute and solve for M_{SV}:

$$M_{SV} = [^{1.4}/_{1.7}(86) + 77]/0.9 = 164 \text{ kip-ft}$$
$$M_{SV} = 0.75[^{1.4}/_{1.7}(86) + 77 + 36]/0.9 = 153 \text{ kip-ft}$$
$$M_{SV} = 0.75[^{1.4}/_{1.7}(86) + 77 + 1.1(48)]/0.9 = 167 \text{ kip-ft}$$

Substitute and solve for V_{SV}:

$$V_{SV} = [^{1.4}/_{1.7}(40) + 27]/0.85 = 71 \text{ kips}$$
$$V_{SV} = 0.75[^{1.4}/_{1.7}(40) + 27 + 12]/0.85 = 70 \text{ kips}$$
$$V_{SV} = 0.75[^{1.4}/_{1.7}(40) + 27 + 1.1(18)]/0.85 = 70 \text{ kips}$$

By inspection of the foregoing results, the maximum design values for M_{SV} and V_{SV} are selected:

Maximum $M_{SV} = 167$ kip-ft.
Maximum $V_{SV} = 71$ kips.

These values of service loads are those that must be sustained at the maximum service level of stress in the concrete member. As before, the ultimate loads M_n and V_n can be found (if needed) by multiplying the service loads by 1.7:

$$M_n = 1.7M_{SV} = 284 \text{ kip-ft.}$$
$$V_n = 1.7V_{SV} = 121 \text{ kips.}$$

Example 17-3

Computation of ultimate design load. Concrete member in flexure, $\phi = 0.90$ for flexure, $\phi = 0.85$ for shear. No wind or earthquake loads occur.

Given: $M_{DL} = 120$ kip-ft, $V_{DL} = 52$ kips, $P_{DL} = 41$ kips
$M_{LL} = 105$ kip-ft, $V_{LL} = 37$ kips, $P_{LL} = 22$ kips

To Find: Ultimate design moment M_n.
Ultimate design shear V_n.
Ultimate design axial load P_n.

Solution: With no lateral loads, the applicable load case is given by Eq.(17-1a):

$$U_n = (1.4D + 1.7L)/\phi$$

For moment:

$$M_n = (1.4 \times 120 + 1.7 \times 105)/0.90$$
$$M_n = 385 \text{ kip-ft.}$$

For shear:

$$V_n = (1.4 \times 52 + 1.7 \times 37)/0.85$$
$$V_n = 160 \text{ kips.}$$

For axial load:

$$P_n = (1.4 \times 41 + 1.7 \times 22)/0.70$$
$$P_n = 135 \text{ kips.}$$

Again, note that the service loads M_{SV}, V_{SV} and P_{SV} may be found (if needed) simply by dividing by 1.7:

$$M_{SV} = M_n/1.7 = 226 \text{ kip-ft}$$
$$V_{SV} = V_n/1.7 = 94 \text{ kips}$$
$$P_{SV} = P_n/1.7 = 80 \text{ kips.}$$

Example 17-4

Computation of ultimate design load. Concrete member in flexure, $\phi = 0.90$ for flexure, $\phi = 0.85$ for shear. Wind and earthquake loads included.

Given:
$M_{DL} = 99$ kip-ft, $V_{DL} = 52$ kips, $P_{DL} = 36$ kips.
$M_{LL} = 66$ kip-ft, $V_{LL} = 31$ kips, $P_{LL} = 26$ kips.
$M_W = 54$ kip-ft, $V_W = 23$ kips, $P_W = 14$ kips.
$M_E = 61$ kip-ft, $V_E = 21$ kips, $P_E = 11$ kips.

To Find: Ultimate design moment M_n.
Ultimate design shear V_n.
Ultimate axial load P_n.

Solution: The applicable load cases are those given by Eqs.(17-1a, b, c):

$$U_n = (1.4D + 1.7L)/\phi$$
$$U_n = 0.75(1.4D + 1.7L + 1.7W)/\phi$$
$$U_n = 0.75[1.4D + 1.7(1.1E)]/\phi$$

Substitute and solve for M_n:

$$M_n = (1.4 \times 99 + 1.7 \times 66)/0.90 = 279 \text{ kip-ft.}$$
$$M_n = 0.75(1.4 \times 99 + 1.7 \times 66 + 1.7 \times 54)/0.90 = 286 \text{ kip-ft.}$$
$$M_n = 0.75(1.4 \times 99 + 1.7 \times 66 + 1.7 \times 1.1 \times 61)/0.90$$
$$= 304 \text{ kip-ft.}$$

Substitute and solve for V_n:

$V_n = (1.4 \times 52 + 1.7 \times 31)/0.85 = 148$ kips
$V_n = 0.75(1.4 \times 52 + 1.7 \times 31 + 1.7 \times 23)/0.85 = 145$ kips
$V_n = 0.75(1.4 \times 52 + 1.7 \times 31 + 1.7 \times 1.1 \times 21)/0.85$
$= 145$ kips

Substitute and solve for P_n:

$P_n = (1.4 \times 36 + 1.7 \times 26)/0.7 = 135$ kips
$P_n = 0.75(1.4 \times 36 + 1.7 \times 26 + 1.7 \times 14)/0.7 = 127$ kips
$P_n = 0.75(1.4 \times 36 + 1.7 \times 26 + 1.7 \times 1.1 \times 11)/0.7$
$= 123$ kips

By inspection of the foregoing results, the ultimate design loads are seen to be:

$M_n = 340$ kip-ft
$V_n = 148$ kips
$P_n = 135$ kips

From these results, the service loads M_{SV} and V_{SV} can be found (if needed) by dividing by 1.7:

$M_{SV} = M_n/1.7 = 179$ kip-ft
$V_{SV} = V_n/1.7 = 86$ kips
$P_{SV} = P_n/1.7 = 79$ kips

17.12 Shear and Moment Envelopes

The concept of shear and moment envelopes is used extensively in the design of concrete structures. The moment envelope, when accurately drawn, may be scaled to determine the cutoff points for longitudinal reinforcement. The shear envelope may be similarly scaled to determine the limiting points where shear reinforcement is required. These envelopes are the subject of this section.

For the sake of simplicity in the following presentation, only uniform loads will be considered, although the same concepts apply regardless of the type of load. Also, only working levels of dead load and live load will be considered throughout the structural analysis. The shears and moments due to dead loads are kept separate from those due to live loads, since they must be used separately later in the design of columns and again in the design of the foundations.

As indicated in Figure 17-3, a beam may be subject to various combinations of load, any one of which may occur in the life of the structure. Each combination of load produces its own shear and moment diagrams, as indicated by the shear and moment diagrams of Figure 17-3. Depending on the circumstances, there could be numerous such combinations. It would indeed be a tedious pursuit to check every load case through every point on the beam to assure that the highest value of load has been accounted for. Rather, the shear and moment diagrams are drawn reasonably accurately to scale, and the outermost values of these diagrams at any point form the *envelope* of shears or moments that the beam must be able to sustain. It should be noted that the envelopes for Figure 17-3 are different for every span.

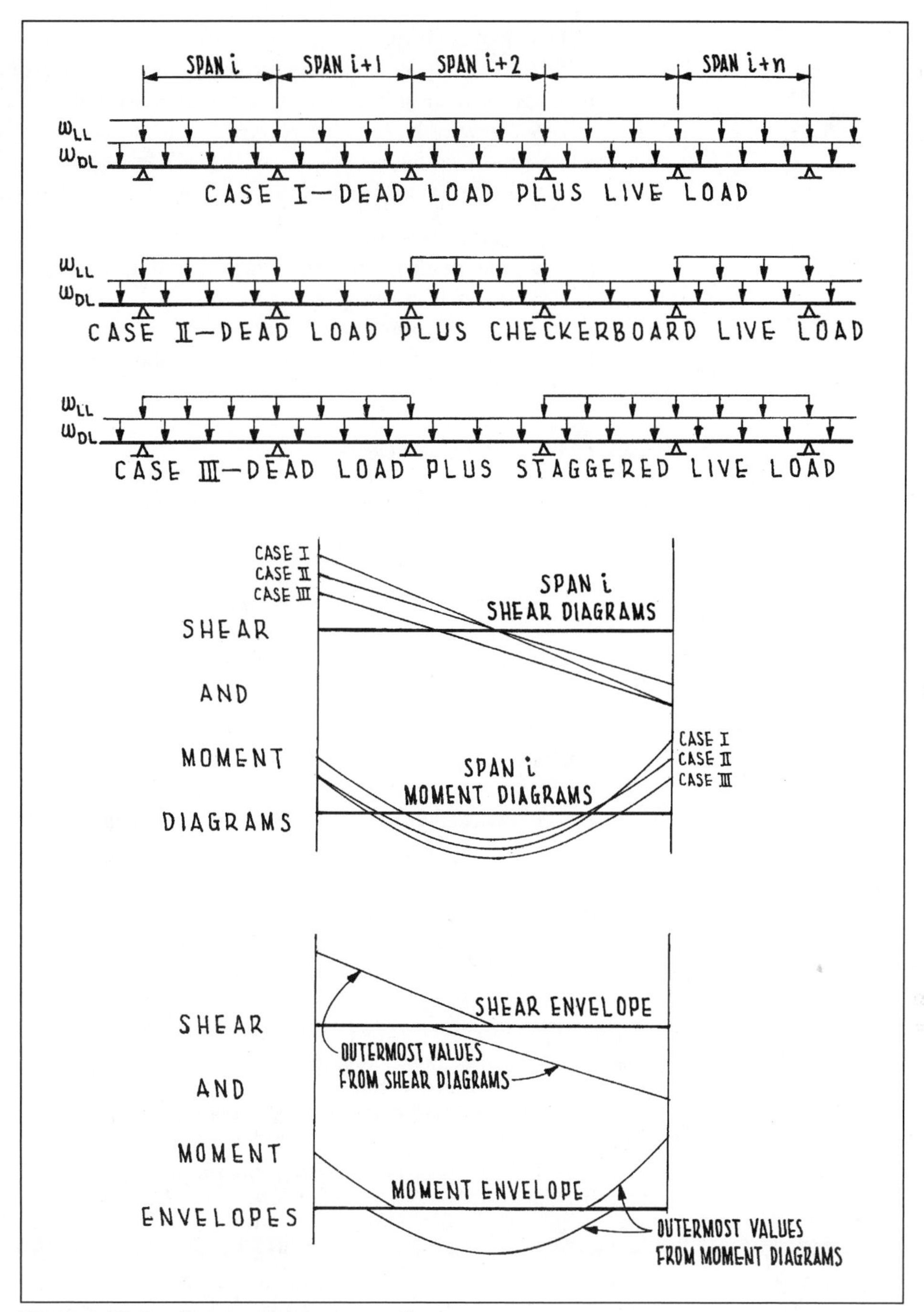

Figure 17-3 Shear and moment diagrams.

Only the more common arrangements of loading are shown in Figure 17-3; maximum values of shear or moment are readily found from the diagrams. There are other arrangements of load, however, which might cause even higher values of shear or moment at some particular point. A complete analysis would therefore include all reasonable arrangements of load which could produce maximum values of shear or moment at some point along the length of the beam.

ACI has in fact performed such an analysis, using a multiplicity of loading arrangements. From its analysis, ACI has arrived at the values given in Table 17-2 for the maximum values of shear and moment on continuous beams and frames. Termed the *ACI Approximate Method*, the use of these coefficients is accepted throughout the practice for the final design of continuous beams and braced frames where sidesway is prevented. The ACI coefficients are valid where the following conditions are met:

1. There are at least two spans.
2. Spans are roughly equal, with the longer of any two adjacent spans not more than 20% longer than the shorter span.
3. Loads are uniformly distributed.
4. Live load is not more than three times the dead load.
5. Members are prismatic.

Table 17-2 ACI Coefficients[1]

Positive moment:	
End spans:	
Discontinuous end simply supported	$wL_n^2/11$
Discontinuous end integral with support	$wL_n^2/14$
Interior spans	$wL_n^2/16$
Negative moment at exterior face of first interior support:	
Two spans	$wL_n^2/9$
More than two spans	$wL_n^2/10$
Negative moment at other faces of interior supports	$wL_n^2/11$
Negative moment at face of supports for slabs with spans not exceeding 10 ft and beams where ratio of sum column stiffnesses $[\Sigma(I/L_n)]$ to beam stiffnesses $[\Sigma(I/L_n)]$ exceeds eight at each end of the span	$wL_n^2/12$
Negative moment at interior face of exterior support for beams or slabs built integrally with supports:	
Where support is a beam or girder	$wL_n^2/24$
Where support is a column	$wL_n^2/16$
Shear in end members at face of first interior support	$1.15wL_n/2$
Shear at face of all other supports	$wL_n/2$

[1]For positive moment, L_n is the clear span. For negative moment, L_n is the average of the two adjacent clear spans. For shear, L_n is the clear span. In all cases, w is the load per unit length.

For timber beams or steel beams, the use of a moment envelope is rarely required since the strength of the beam is constant throughout the span and is equal for both positive and negative moments. Once the peak value is known, either for positive or negative moment, the beam can be sized for that value and it is then known to be adequate for all other points in the span. In concrete, however, where strength of a beam varies across the span and where strength under positive moment need not be equal to strength under negative moment, the capacity of the beam at every point of the span must be examined; the shear and moment envelopes afford a graphic and easily-interpreted means to perform this examination.

It should be noted before proceeding that the use of the ACI coefficients for the final design of concrete structures is one of the more significant simplifications in all of concrete design. The ACI coefficients may be used with confidence on structures that are less than about 70 feet high and which are designed as diaphragm/shearwall structures. In such structures, sidesway due to wind and earthquake produces no bending in the columns. Such structural systems are overwhelmingly the most common type of concrete structure in the industry; this textbook is deliberately concentrated on the design of this type of structural system.

Review Questions

1. State the full name of the ACI Code covering the design of reinforced concrete and the year of its latest revision.
2. What is the minimum dimension for a concrete column?
3. What is "temperature and shrinkage" reinforcement in slabs?
4. What is the maximum spacing of bars used as temperature and shrinkage reinforcement?
5. What is the minimum and maximum percentages of longitudinal reinforcement in columns?
6. What is meant by "steel ratio" in flexural members?
7. What is the difference between the symbols d and h in a concrete section?
8. What is the minimum steel ratio for flexural members reinforced with grade 60 steel?
9. What is the minimum clear spacing between reinforcing bars placed in a single layer?
10. What is the minimum clear spacing between layers of reinforcing bars when reinforcement is placed in two or more layers?
11. What is meant by "bundling" of bars?
12. How much concrete cover is required in an exterior exposure for No. 6 bars in a flexural member?
13. Why is the consideration of "brittle elements" important?
14. For a span of 24 feet, what is the allowable live load deflection for a floor beam carrying brittle elements? For a floor beam not carrying brittle elements?
15. Why is the strength reduction factor ϕ necessary?
16. What value of ϕ is applied to flexural members? To columns? To shear loads?
17. What is the difference between strength reduction factors and load factors?
18. State the three most common load combinations.
19. How is ultimate load related to service load?
20. What is the purpose in drawing shear and moment envelopes?
21. State the conditions under which the ACI coefficients are valid.
22. How are lateral loads accounted for when the ACI coefficients are used to design the structural frame?

CHAPTER

18

FLEXURE IN CONCRETE BEAMS

In the design of a flexural member (beam or girder), there are two levels of loading that are of interest. One level is the elastic level, at which the flexural member will carry its day-to-day loads throughout its service life. The other level is that at ultimate load, at which the member is loaded so highly that collapse is imminent. These two levels of flexural loading and their interrelationship are the subject of this chapter.

18.1 Methods of Flexural Design

The ultimate strength design method prescribed by ACI 318-89 (the "strength method") specifies only the ultimate load condition for the design of concrete flexural members; there are no required conditions of stress or load prescribed by Code for the day-to-day service conditions. There are, however, requirements for serviceability, deflection and crack control that must be imposed at service levels regardless what the ultimate load requirements may be. At this point in the presentation, however, it is emphasized that there is no specified limiting stress that must be observed when designing concrete members for flexure.

Though the ACI strength method does not use elastic stress, ACI recognizes the validity of elastic analysis and design of concrete members; a separate method of designing members for their elastic working stresses is in fact included in the Code as an *alternate design method.* In the U.S., the working stress method (as it is called) is used routinely for the design of prestressed concrete members, for composite steel and concrete members (steel beam with integral concrete deck) and for the analysis of concrete frames subject to transient earthquake loads. Both the elastic stresses and the ultimate loads are, of course, integral parts of a competent design in concrete.

The design method presented in this chapter is completely derived from the *strength design method*, as ACI refers to its ultimate load method; the methods presented here are not related to the alternate design method. It should be noted that the two approaches are not equivalent, that is, a concrete member designed using the strength method will not be the same as a member designed using the alternate design method.

The idealized stress-strain curve for concrete shown in Figure 18-1 forms the basis of the approach used in this text, both at elastic levels of stress and at ultimate levels of load. A full familiarity with this idealized curve is recommended; it will be frequently referenced in succeeding discussions.

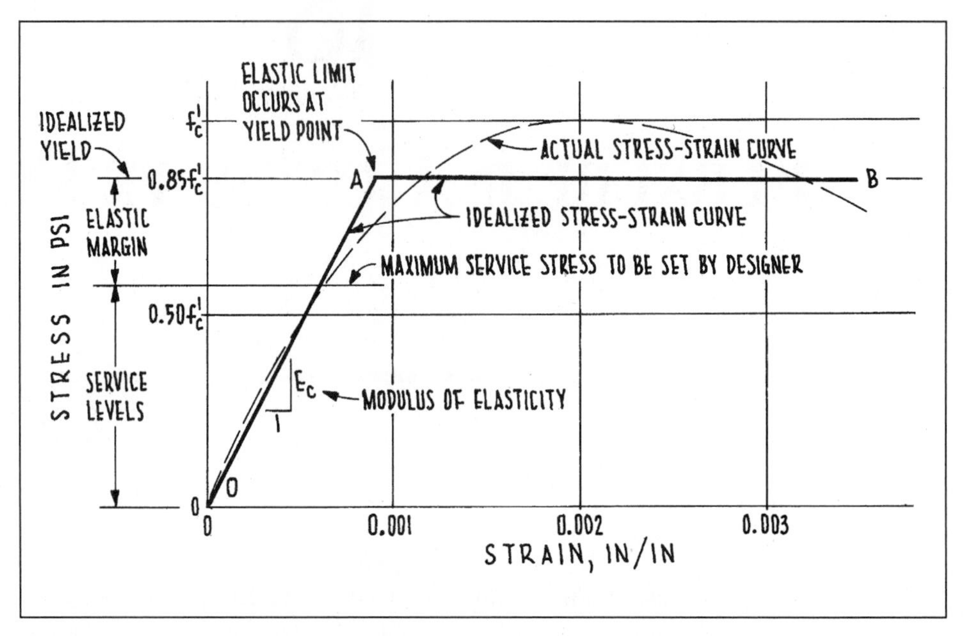

Figure 18-1 Idealized stress-strain curve for strength design.

The analysis and design of concrete members at elastic levels of stress is presented first. As noted in Chapter 16, concrete has been found to be elastic to about 75% of its ultimate stress, or, within acceptable error, up to its idealized yield stress of $0.85f'_c$.

18.2 The Elastic Flexure Formula

The flexure formula is well known from elementary strength of materials. With f_c denoting the stress on the compression side of the beam, the flexure formula is:

$$f_c = \frac{Mc}{I} \tag{18-1a}$$

where M = moment acting on the section
I = moment of inertia about the neutral axis
c = distance from the neutral axis to the level where f_c is computed

Typical sections in steel, timber and concrete are shown in Figure 18-2, with the distance c given for the various configurations.

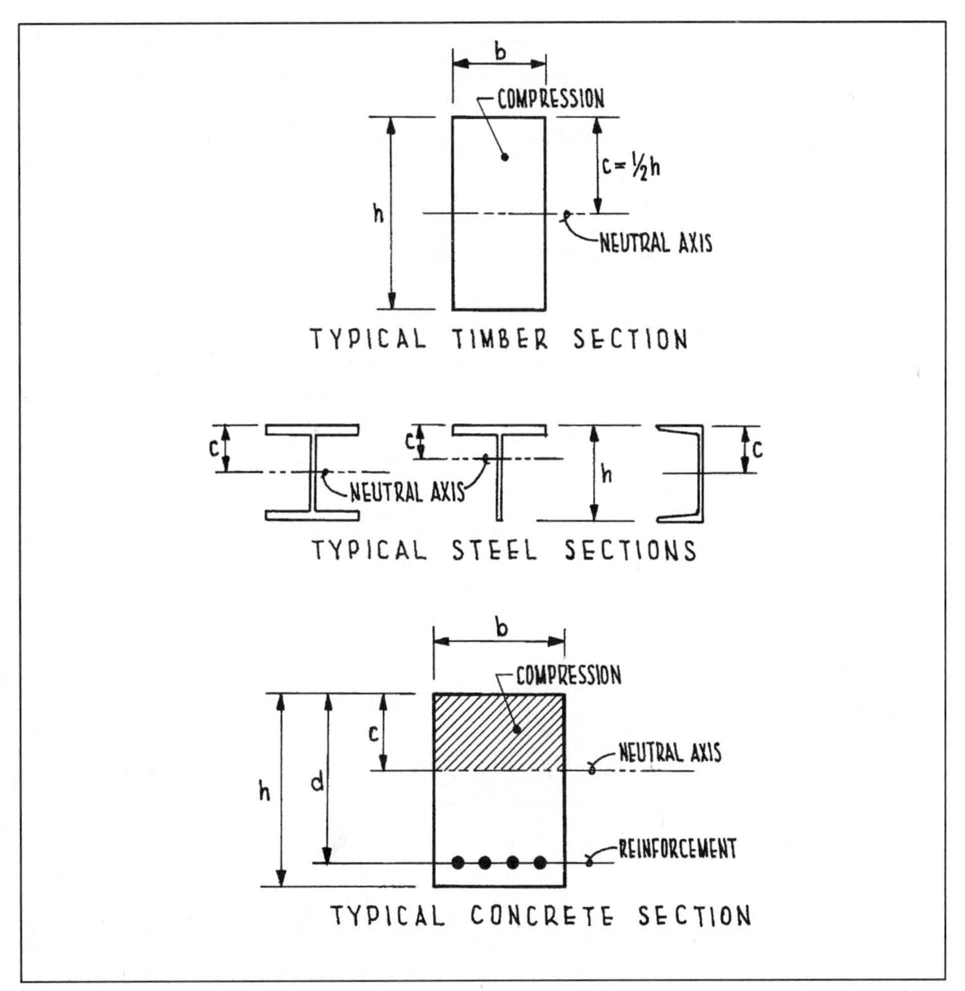

Figure 18-2 Typical flexure sections.

In an alternative form, the flexure formula can also be used to compute the required magnitude of the section modulus S_c, where $S_c = I/c$:

$$\frac{M}{f_c} = S_c \tag{18-1b}$$

The symbol S_c is used to denote the section modulus, taken to the outermost compression fiber. The section modulus is seen to be the ratio between the moment acting on the section and the stress which that moment produces at the outermost fibers. It is a property of the section; its value depends only on the size and shape of the cross section. Its units are moment per unit stress (lb·in./psi or N·mm/MPa) which reduce to in.^{3} or mm.^{3}

For design in steel, the section modulus of a structural steel member is found by looking it up in a table in the steel manual. For American practice, the *Steel Construction Manual* (American Institute of Steel Construction, 1989) lists the section modulus for each of the several hundred steel sections commonly manufactured in the United States. To try to design a steel structure without such a section modulus table would be impractical.

For design in timber, the section modulus may be computed by formula ($S = bh^2/6 = 0.1667bh^2$) or again, it may be looked up in a standard section modulus table for timber sections. It must be remembered that a timber section nominally designated 6 in. x 12 in. is actually 5½ in. x 11½ in. and it is the actual dimensions that must be used in the flexure formula. It is usually more convenient to use a table to find a suitable section modulus in timber than to try to remember the rules for finding the actual dimensions.

For design in concrete, the procedure used herein is no different from that for steel or timber. The section modulus is found from a section modulus table and used in the same way. Admittedly, the existence of the larger number of variables in a concrete section makes the tables somewhat longer than for other materials, but there is no difference in concept. Even with a large number of variables, however, it is a relatively simple matter to develop a table of values for the section modulus of a rectangular concrete section. The derivation of such a table is developed in the following sections.

18.3 Derivation of the Elastic Section Modulus

The flexure formula itself can be adapted readily to beams of two materials, such as reinforced concrete beams. To do so, it is only necessary to derive the moment of inertia and the section modulus for such a beam. In the following derivations, the section modulus is always taken to the compression side of the cross section.

Concrete is assumed to have no tensile strength. Wherever concrete is placed in tension, it is assumed to be cracked and the net tensile stress is zero. Reinforcing steel is provided to take all of the tensile load.

Regardless whether the concrete is cracked or uncracked, when concrete and its reinforcing steel are bonded together in a beam, their strains at any point are equal, as shown in Figure 18-3.

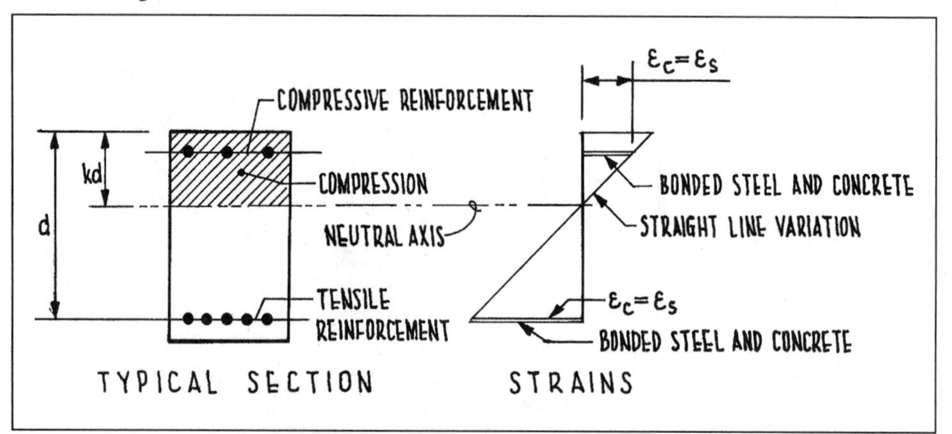

Figure 18-3 Strains in a reinforced section.

The relationship between the stresses is fixed by the equality of strains:

$$\varepsilon_c = \varepsilon_s = \frac{f_{cA}}{E_c} = \frac{f_{sA}}{E_s} \tag{18-2}$$

where ε_c, ε_s = strains in adjacent concrete and steel, respectively
f_{cA}, f_{sA} = stresses in adjacent concrete and steel, respectively
E_C, E_S = moduli of elasticity of concrete and steel, respectively

Equation(18-2) is solved readily for stress in steel:

$$f_{sA} = nf_{cA} \tag{18-3}$$

where $n = E_S/E_C$. It was observed in Chapter 16 that due to shrinkage and creep, the modulus of elasticity of concrete for long-term compressive loads is taken to be half that for short-term loads. For long-term loading, therefore:

$$f_{sA} = 2nf_{cA} \text{ for steel in compression} \tag{18-4a}$$
$$f_{sA} = nf_{cA} \text{ for steel in tension} \tag{18-4b}$$

A cross section of a concrete beam is shown in Figure 18-4 along with its stress diagram. It should be noted that the section contains reinforcement on the compression side of the beam. Such compressive reinforcement is commonly used where the size of the beam is so restricted that the concrete alone is not adequate to carry the compressive load within the specified limits for deflections. Alternatively, it is far less expensive (but not always possible) to make the concrete section bigger and avoid the use of compression steel.

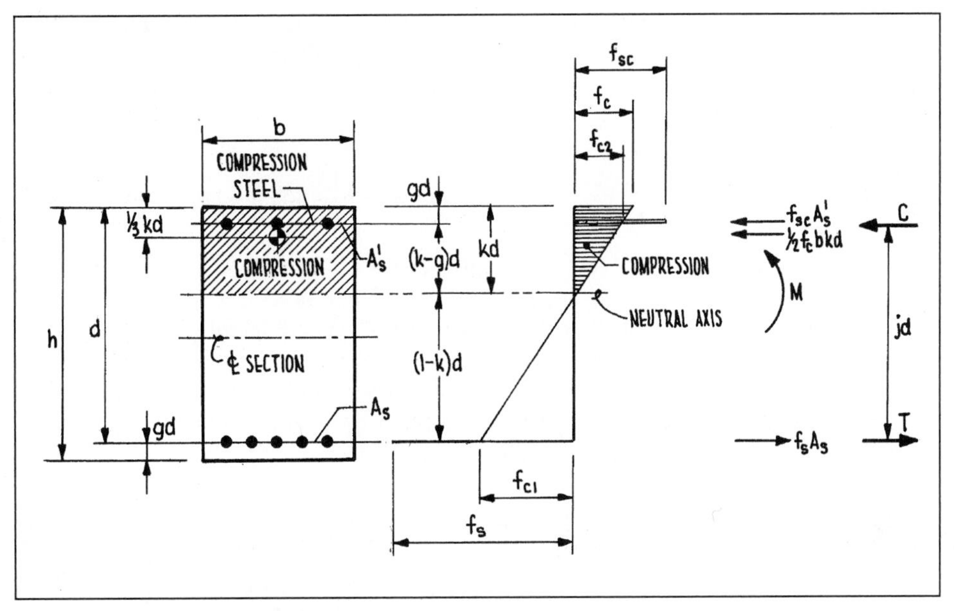

Figure 18-4 Beam section.

By ratio, the stress in the concrete adjacent to the compressive steel is found to be:

$$f_{c2} = \frac{f_c(k-g)}{k} \tag{18-5a}$$

The stress in the compressive steel is, then, from Eq.(18-4a):

$$f_{sc} = 2nf_{c2} = \frac{2nf_c(k-g)}{k} \tag{18-5b}$$

The stress in the tensile steel is found similarly:

$$f_s = nf_{c1} = \frac{nf_c(1-k)}{k} \tag{18-5c}$$

It is observed that the resisting moment of the section can be shown as an internal couple formed by the forces *C* and *T* in Figure 18-4. An average value for the distance between the forces, designated *jd* in Figure 18-4, will be shown later to be about 0.90d. The average distance *jd* is affected but little by the existence of compressive steel.

Refer again to Figure 18-4. The symbol A_s' is used to denote compressive steel and A_S to denote tensile steel. The corresponding steel ratios ρ' and ρ are then:

$$\rho' = \frac{A_s'}{bd} \text{ and } \rho = \frac{A_s}{bd} \tag{18-6a, b}$$

Horizontal forces shown in Figure 18-4 are now summed, yielding:

$$\Sigma H = 0 = \tfrac{1}{2} f_c bkd - f_{c2}A_s' + f_{sc}A_s' - f_s A_s \tag{18-7}$$

The second term in Eq.(18-7) deducts the concrete displaced by the compressive steel. Equations (18-5) and (18-6) are substituted into Eq.(18-7), yielding a solution for *k*:

$$k = \sqrt{[n\rho + (2n-1)\rho']^2 + 2[n\rho + (2n-1)g\rho']} - [n\rho + (2n-1)\rho'] \tag{18-8}$$

Refer again to Figure 18-3. Moments are summed about the neutral axis, yielding:

$$M = \tfrac{1}{2} f_c bkd \frac{2kd}{3} - f_{c2} A_s'(k-g)d + f_{sc} A_s'(k-g)d + f_s A_s (1-k)d \qquad (18\text{-}9)$$

Equations (18-5) and (18-6) are substituted into Eq.(18-9) and the result solved to obtain the section modulus S_c to the outermost compression fiber:

$$\frac{M}{f_c} = S_c \qquad (18\text{-}10)$$

$$\text{where } S_c = \left[\frac{k^2}{3} + (2n-1)\rho' \frac{(k-g)^2}{k} + n\rho \frac{(1-k)^2}{k}\right] bd^2$$

and where the value of k is given by Eq.(18-8).

Equations (18-8) and (18-10) would be rather formidable expressions to solve manually in order to find the elastic (or service) section modulus S_c. Fortunately, it is not necessary to solve them manually. They can be solved readily by a small computer and the results tabulated for ready reference. Such a tabulation is presented in the Technical Manual in Tables C-5, C-6 and C-7.

With the section modulus known, however computed, the moment of inertia of the cracked section for long-term loading, I_{cr}, is readily computed from the definition of the section modulus:

$$S_c = \frac{I}{c} \text{ hence } I_{cr} = S_c kd \qquad (18\text{-}11)$$

For computing the moment of inertia I_{cr} for short-term deflections (for wind and earthquake), the long-term creep and shrinkage effects should not be included. For such computations, the term (2n-1) in Eq.(18-10) becomes (n-1); the value (n-1) was used in calculating the short-term value of Icr listed in tables C-5 through C-7. The coefficient for the moment of inertia I for long-term deflections can be found, if needed, simply by multiplying the coefficient of Sc given in the tables by the value of k_{SV}; the long-term moment of inertia I is then this result times bd^3.

It will also be necessary to know the ratio of stresses f_s/f_c. A diagram showing these stresses is given in Figure 18-5.

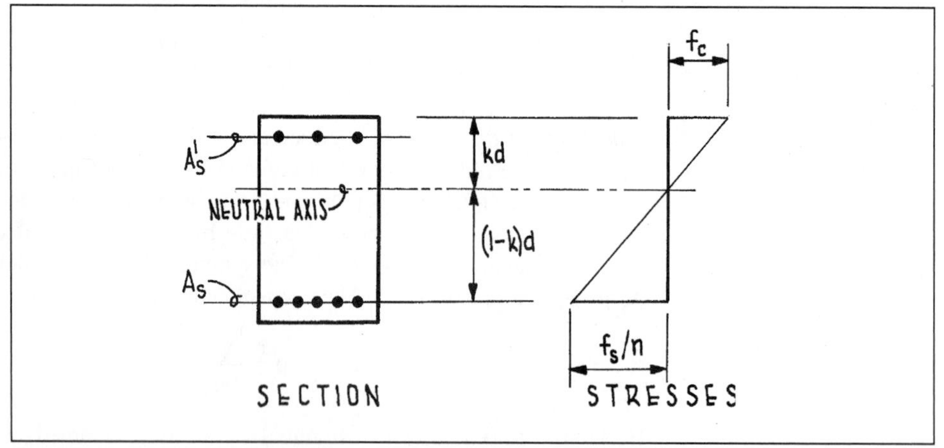

Figure 18-5 Elastic stresses on a concrete section.

The ratio f_s/f_c is found by similar triangles from the stress diagram:

$$\frac{f_s}{f_c} = \frac{n(1-k)}{k} \qquad (18\text{-}12)$$

A table of the foregoing section properties is presented in tables C-5 through C-7 in the Technical Manual. The tables are entered with the allowable values of f_s/f_c and the ultimate strength of the concrete. The columns in the tables with the heading "At Service Loads" reflect the tabulated values of Eqs.(18-8) and (18-10) through (18-12). To distinguish the values of k from those of the ultimate load analysis (presented later), a subscript $_{sv}$ has been added to k in the tables.

Rather than being computed from allowable values of f_s and f_c, the ratio f_s/f_c can be deliberately selected to provide exactly the same factors of safety (to yield) for both steel and concrete. Such a feature produces optimum efficiency throughout the elastic range of the materials, since neither material can then enter yield ahead of the other. For such a "balanced" stress condition, with FS denoting factor of safety:

$$\text{for steel, } f_s = f_y/FS \qquad (18\text{-}13)$$

$$\text{for concrete, } f_c = 0.85f_c'/FS, \qquad (18\text{-}14)$$

which provides a ratio of f_s/f_c of:

$$\frac{f_s}{f_c} = \frac{f_y}{0.85f_c'} \qquad (18\text{-}15)$$

The tables may therefore be entered with the fixed ratio $f_y/0.85f_c'$. The section so chosen will have exactly the same factors of safety and elastic margins for both the steel and the concrete over the entire elastic range of both materials. Both materials will enter their yield ranges at exactly the same time, an efficient and desirable feature in the design.

For convenience, a separate table for the balanced stress condition has been included in the design tables in the Technical Manual. The table, Table C-8, has been prepared utilizing exact values for $f_y/0.85f_c'$; these exact values eliminate the need for interpolation that can occur when using the more general design tables, tables C-5, C-6 and C-7. In developing the table, the fixed stress ratio $f_y/0.85f_c'$ was substituted into Eq.(18-12) and the result solved for k. The value of k thus obtained was used to find the steel ratio ρ from Eq.(18-8). With both k and ρ known, all the remaining section constants were readily computed.

As an alternative means to enter the design tables, the tables may be entered with known values of ρ and ρ'. Such a case will occur when the size and reinforcement of a section are already known, and the section is being investigated to find its capacity for moment.

18.4 Applications at Elastic Levels of Stress

Some examples will illustrate the use of the tables of elastic section constants.

Example 18-1

Determination of elastic stress due to moment.

Given: Section as shown.
Elastic moment = 46 kip·ft.
Grade 50 steel, f_c'=4000 psi.

To Find: Maximum stress in concrete.
Maximum stress in reinforcement.

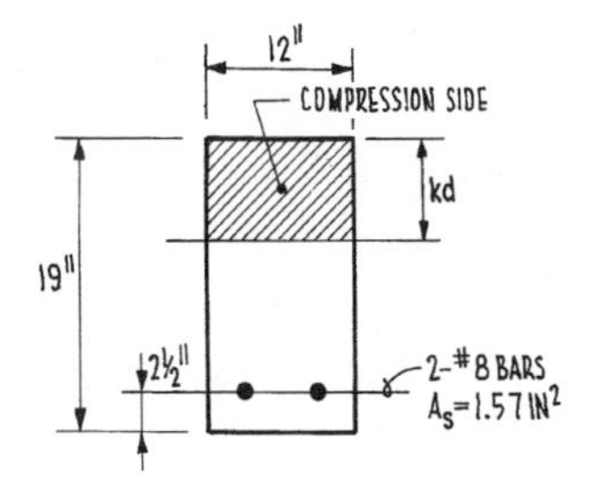

Solution: Calculate the steel ratio ρ for the given section:

$$\rho = \frac{A_s}{bd} = \frac{1.57}{12x16.5} = 0.008.$$

Enter Table C-6 with this steel ratio and find the section constants:

$$\rho = 0.008,\ S_c = 0.135bd^2,\ f_s/f_c = 18.76.$$

Solve for the stress in concrete:

$$f_c = \frac{M}{S_c} = \frac{(46{,}000)(12)}{(0.135)(12)(16.5)(16.5)} = 1250 \text{ psi (compression)}$$

Solve for stress in reinforcement:

$$f_s = 18.76f_c = (18.76)(1250) = 23{,}450 \text{ psi (tension)}$$

Example 18-2

Determination of a suitable section.

Given: Section as shown.
Grade 60 steel, $f_c' = 4000$ psi.
Allowable concrete stress = 1800 psi.
Allowable steel stress = 24,000 psi.
Applied moment = 76 kip·ft.

To Find: Required size of section and reinforcement.

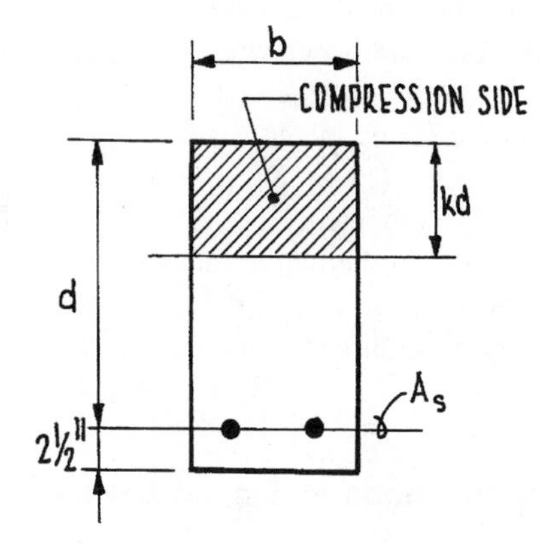

Solution: Desired ratio for steel and concrete stresses:

$$f_s/f_c = 24{,}000/1800 = 13.3.$$

Enter Table C-6 with this ratio of stresses and find the section constants:

$$\rho = 0.014,\ S_c = 0.164bd^2,\ f_s/f_c = 13.44 \text{ (close enough to 13.3 to be acceptable).}$$

Calculate the required magnitude of the section modulus:

$$S_c = \frac{M}{f_c} = \frac{76{,}000(12)}{1800} = 507 \text{ in.}^3$$

Solve for the required size of section, assuming b = 0.6d:

$S_c = 0.164bd^2$; $507 = 0.164(0.6d)(d^2)$

Solve for d = 17.27 in.
Solve for b = 0.6d = 10.36 in.

Solve for the required steel area:

$A_s = \rho bd = (0.014)(10.36)(17.27) = 2.50$ in.^{2}

From Table A-3 select 2 - No. 10 bars,
A_s furnished = 2.53 in.^{2}

Round dimensions up, to nearest 1/2 in.

Use b = 10.5 in., d = 17.5 in., 2-No. 10 bars, as shown at the beginning of the example.

Example 18-3

Determination of capacity of a known section.

Given: Section and reinforcement as shown.
Grade 50 steel, $f_c' = 4000$ psi.
Allowable stress in steel = 20,000 psi.

To Find: a) Allowable moment on section.
b) Whether stress in the section is balanced.

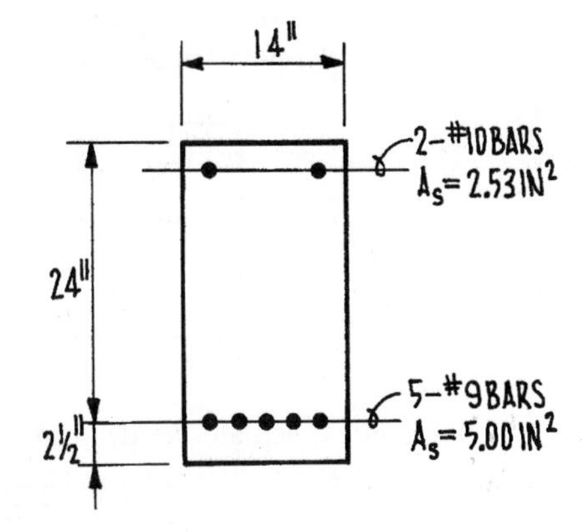

Solution: Calculate the steel ratio for the given section:

$$\rho = \frac{A_s}{bd} = \frac{5.00}{14(24)} = 0.015, \rho' = 0.5\rho(\pm).$$

Enter Table C-6 with $\rho = 0.015$, $\rho' = 0.5\rho$, and find the section constants:

$\rho = 0.015$, $S_c = 0.211bd^2$, $f_s/f_c = 15.94$.

Determine the allowable stress in the concrete:

$$\frac{f_s}{f_c} = 15.94; f_c = \frac{f_s}{15.94} = \frac{20,000}{15.94} = 1254 \text{ psi.}$$

Determine the allowable moment on the section:

$$M = f_c/s_c = 1254(0.211)(14)(24)(24) = 2134 \text{ kip·in} = 178 \text{ kip·ft.}$$

Determine the stress ratio for the balanced stress condition:

At balanced stress, $f_s/f_c = f_y/0.85 f_c' = 50{,}000/0.85(4000) = 14.7$

Actual stress ratio = 15.94 ≠ 14.7; conclude that the stresses are not balanced.

Final results:

Allowable moment = 178 kip·ft.; section is not balanced for stresses.

The elastic section constants may also be used to design members. Some examples will illustrate.

Example 18-4

Design of a beam.

Given: Uniformly loaded beam, simple span of 20 ft.-0in., exterior exposure. Dead load = 2.2k/ft, live load 1.8k/ft. Grade 60 steel, f_c' = 3000 psi. Service stress = 1500 psi for balanced design.

To Find: Service moment M_{sv}. Required size of member with balanced stresses. Required reinforcement.

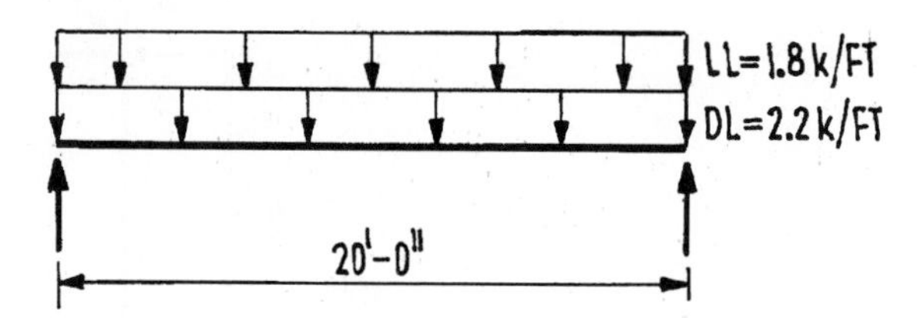

Solution: Calculate the dead load and live load moments:

$$M_{DL} = \frac{wL^2}{8} = \frac{2.2(20^2)}{8} = 110 \text{kip·ft.}$$

$$M_{LL} = \frac{wL^2}{8} = \frac{1.8(20^2)}{8} = 90 \text{kip·ft.}$$

Calculate the service moment $M_{sv} = (^{1.4}/_{1.7} M_{DL} + M_{LL})\phi$
$= (^{1.4}/_{1.7} \times 110 + 90)/0.9$
$= 201$ kip·ft.

Solve for the required magnitude of the section modulus:

$$S_c = \frac{M_{sv}}{f_{sv}} = \frac{201{,}000(12)}{1500} = 1608 \text{ in.}^3$$

For the balanced stress condition f_{sv} = 1500 psi (given). Enter Table C-5, select section constants for a beam with no compressive reinforcement:

$$\rho = 0.0060, S_c = 0.128bd^2, k_{sv} = 0.283, f_s/f_c = 23.53.$$

Determine the required sizes and reinforcement, assuming b = 0.6d:

$$S_c = 0.128bd^2;\ 1608 = 0.128(0.6d)(d^2)$$

Solve for d = 27.6 in., b = 16.5 in.

Steel area = ρbd = (0.0060)(16.5)(27.6) = 2.73 in.^{2}

From Table C-3, select 2-No. 8 and 2-No. 7 bars. A_s furnished = 2.77 in.^{2}

Use b = 16.5 in., d = 28.0 in., 2-No. 8 and 2-No. 7 bars.

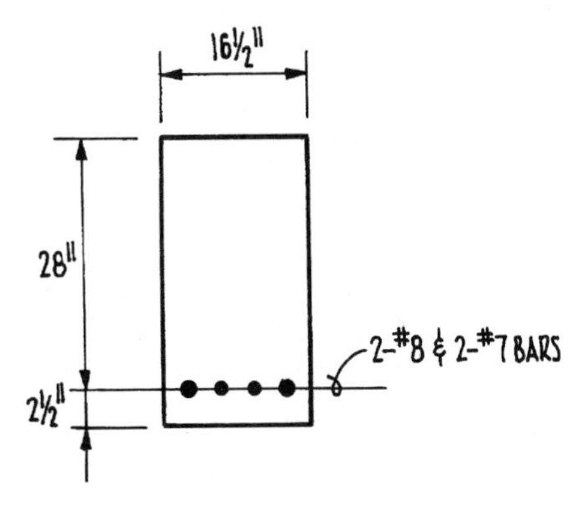

18.5 Common Arrangements of Reinforcement

Some of the more common arrangements of flexural reinforcement were used in the preceding examples. There are other types of reinforcement that occur in beams, however, for which other arrangements become necessary. One such additional type of reinforcement is that for shear, as shown in Figure 18-6; this type of shear reinforcement is called a *stirrup*. Stirrups are placed at a spacing of *½d* or *¼d* along the length of the beam where shears are high.

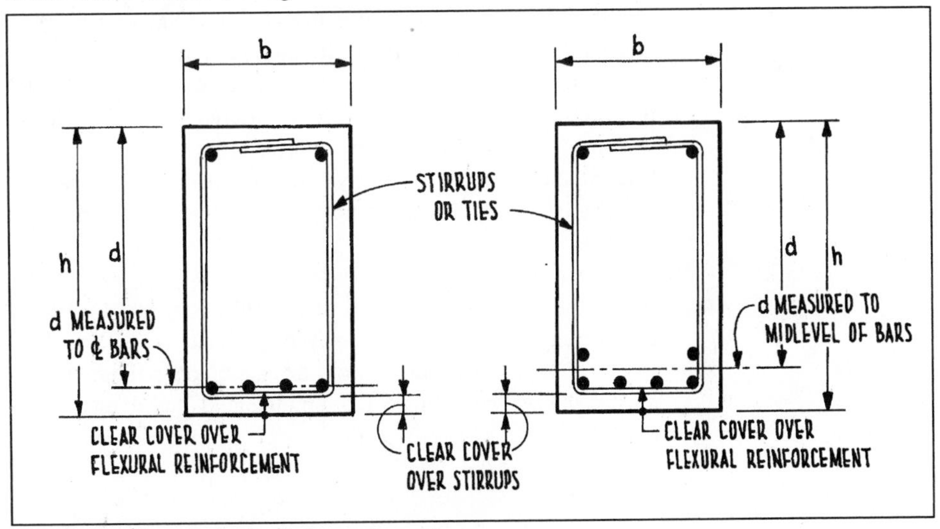

Figure 18-6 Typical reinforced sections.

Reinforcement for shear is presented in detail in chapter 19. At this point, it is necessary only to consider the effects that the existence of shear reinforcement will have on the overall size of the section. Minimum cover must be provided for the shear reinforcement as well as for the flexural reinforcement; the cover over both types of reinforcement must therefore be considered when one is establishing the required depth of section *h*.

Requirements for minimum cover given in Chapter 17 apply also to shear reinforcement, or stirrups. A dimension sketch is shown in Figure 18-7 for typical steel arrangements that include shear reinforcement. For flexural members in interior exposures, the minimum cover is $^3/_4$ in. for bars No. 11 and smaller. In exterior exposures, the minimum cover is $1^1/_2$ in. for bars No. 5 and smaller and 2 in. for bars larger than No. 5. As a matter of interest, stirrups are usually made from No. 4 or No. 5 bars; stirrups larger than No. 5 are uncommon.

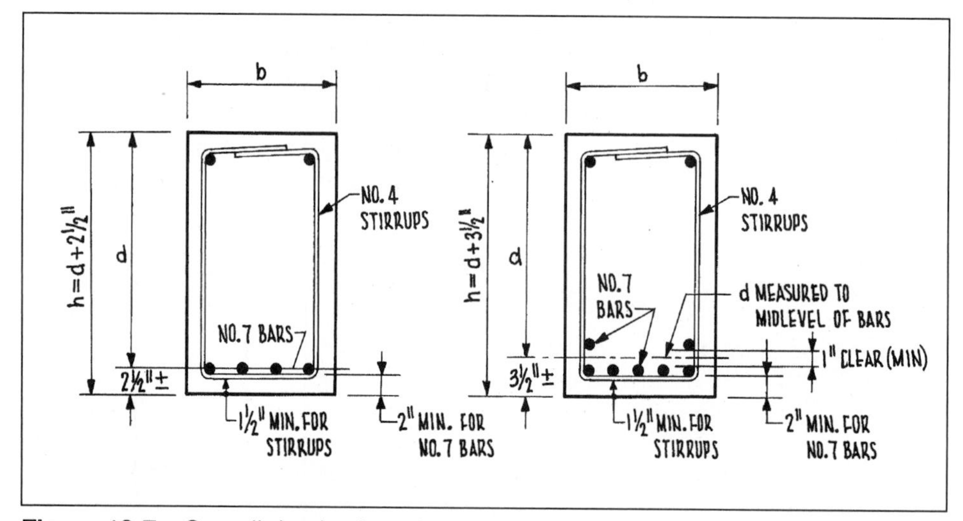

Figure 18-7 Overall depth of section with stirrups.

For flexural reinforcement larger than No. 8 bars or for interior exposures, the dimensions shown in Figure 18-7 will vary somewhat. Such arrangements must be checked individually for proper cover as appropriate. In general, dimensions that include cover are rounded up to the nearest $^1/_2$ in., with the allowances for minimum cover being rather generous.

18.6 Ultimate Flexure

Traditionally, most structural materials (including concrete) have been designed at elastic levels of stress rather than at ultimate load. The reason for such a limitation is that once the stresses enter yield and the strains become inelastic, the deformations become so large that the member is no longer considered to be usable; stresses are therefore held within elastic levels in order to limit large deformations. In addition, once the strains become inelastic, the beam reactions for continuous beams begin to change, sometimes drastically, and the reactions and moments derived from the elastic analysis are no longer valid.

There is, however, a very large reserve of strength in a member after it enters into inelastic strains. That reserve of strength is ignored when the design is limited to the elastic range. It should be remembered that the factor of safety used in elastic theory is based on a maximum yield stress, not on collapse load. If the factor of safety in elastic theory were to be recomputed and based on collapse load, it would increase considerably.

With the 1956 Code, ACI recognized that this large reserve of strength does indeed exist in concrete members and that the design of concrete members, even at elastic levels, can take into account this reserve of strength; the ACI strength method of design in current use has been developed from that viewpoint. The following sections present the ACI strength method of design.

18.7 The Plastic Section Modulus

The ACI Code does not prescribe the methods to be used in achieving an end result; it prescribes only the end result that must be achieved. For concrete members in flexure, for example, Code (10.2) prescribes only the pattern of strains that must exist in a member when it is at its ultimate capacity. The methods for selecting the sizes and reinforcement of a member such that the prescribed pattern of strains do, in fact, occur are not prescribed.

There are numerous approaches to designing a concrete member such that the member will sustain a prescribed ultimate load at a prescribed pattern of strain. Some of the methods are slow but simple, others are faster but more complex. Some are suited to manual solutions, others only to computer applications. The use of a "plastic section modulus", as used in this textbook, is regarded as one of the slower but simpler manual methods; it has the distinct advantage to the intermittent user, however, in that it is much easier to remember and apply over the years than the faster, but more complex, methods.

The plastic section modulus is directly analogous to the elastic section modulus used in the preceding section. Recall that the elastic section modulus S_c is the ratio of moment M to concrete stress f_c where all deformations are elastic:

$$S_c = \frac{M}{f_c}. \tag{18-1b}$$

By analogy, the plastic section modulus Z_c is the ratio of nominal ultimate moment M_n to the idealized yield stress $0.85 f_c'$, with deformations at specified inelastic levels:

$$Z_c = \frac{M_n}{0.85 f_c'}. \tag{18-16}$$

Since the nominal ultimate moment M_n is readily calculated from the ACI load factors and the idealized yield stress $0.85 f_c'$ is known, the required magnitude of the plastic section modulus Z_c can be easily computed from Eq.(18-16). It remains only to find a way to express Z_c in terms of the member's cross section such that the size of the member can be easily computed. Such an expression for Z_c is developed next.

18.8 Derivation of the Plastic Section Modulus

The analysis for the ultimate moment on a concrete section is stringently prescribed by Code (10.2). To begin, it is required by Code (10.2.3) that the maximum strain in the concrete shall be 0.003 at ultimate moment, which is presumed to include all long-term effects of shrinkage and creep. To accompany this prescribed strain in the concrete, the strain in the steel must take whatever value is required to produce equilibrium.

Code (10.2.2) also requires that the variation in strains across the section shall be assumed to follow a straight-line variation. Such a straight-line variation in strain at ultimate load conditions is shown graphically in Figure 18-8. Strain in steel at yield is shown as c_{sy}. The strain in concrete is 0.003 in./in., as required by Code (10.2.3).

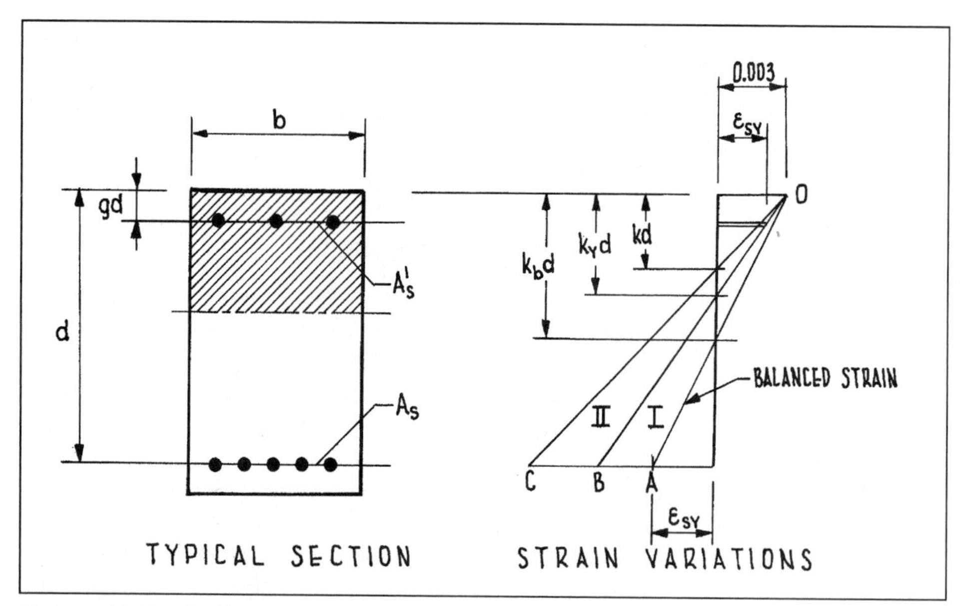

Figure 18-8 Strains at ultimate load.

Strains falling in stress range I of Figure 18-8 are those for a heavily reinforced section, where the neutral axis is low and the stress in the compressive reinforcement is in yield. Strains falling in stress range II are those for lightly reinforced sections, for which the neutral axis is much higher on the section and the compressive reinforcement is elastic. Line *OA* indicates the strains when the tensile steel is just at yield, *OB* when the compressive steel is just at yield, and *OC* at some arbitrarily chosen minimum level of reinforcement.

The complete solution for the plastic section modulus therefore consists of two separate parts. The first part is for stress range I in which the compressive reinforcement is in yield. The second part is for stress range II in which the compressive reinforcement is still elastic. These two parts require two separate solutions.

The variations in stress that accompany the strain diagrams of the two regions shown of Figure 18-8 are shown in Figure 18-9. In Figure 18-9c, the compressive steel is still in yield; in Figure 18-9d it has emerged from yield and is in its elastic range. In both cases, the tensile steel remains in yield, denoted f_y.

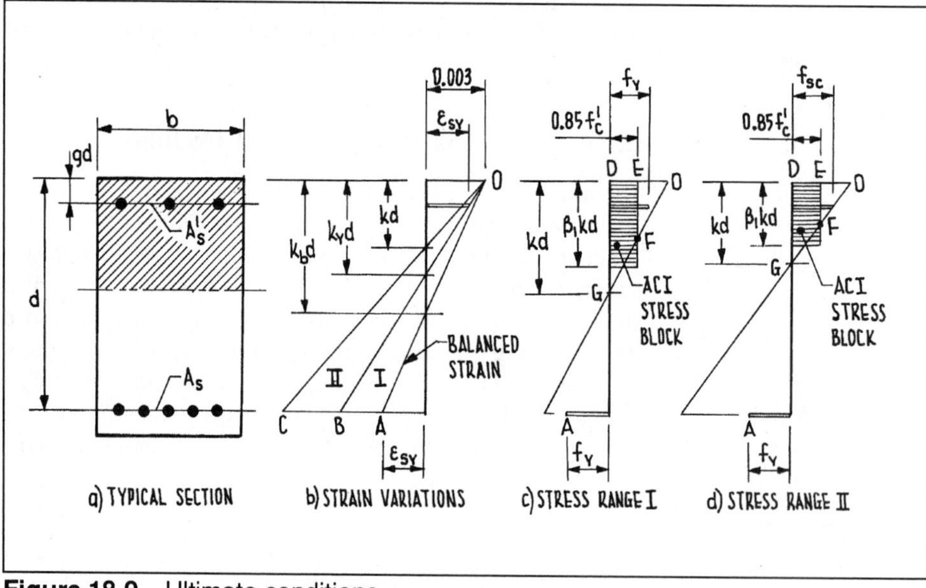

Figure 18-9 Ultimate conditions.

The variations in stress should theoretically follow the stress-strain curve of Figure 18-1, but it does not matter since Code (10.2.7) also specifies an empirically derived "stress block" to be used in computing the compressive force. In all succeeding derivations it is assumed that both the concrete and the tensile steel are well into yield, but that compressive steel may or may not be in yield.

The value of β_1 shown in the stress diagrams for the ACI stress block is prescribed by Code(10.2.7.3). Although the Code permits approaches other than this, the Code value of β_1 is known to provide a close correlation to test data and is accepted here. When the prescribed value of β_1 is used, the force in the compression stress block is found to be $0.85f_c'\,\beta_1 kd$.

In the form of an equation, the factor β_1 is given by Code (10.2.7.3):

$$\beta_1 = 0.85 - 0.05(f_c' - 4);\ f_c' \text{ in ksi.} \tag{18-17}$$

The following detailed derivations of the plastic section modulus is included as a matter of completeness. Those not interested in such details may wish to jump ahead to the summary of results. There will be no loss of continuity in jumping the derivations.

The value of k that occurs when the compressive steel is just at yield, designated k_y, can be computed by similar triangles from the line OB in the strain diagram of Figure 18-9b:

$$\frac{0.003}{k_y d} = \frac{\varepsilon_{sy}}{k_y d - gd} \text{ where } \varepsilon_{sy} = \frac{f_y}{E_s}. \tag{18-18}$$

The solution for k_y is, with E_s = 29,000,000 psi:

$$k_y = \frac{0.003E_s g}{0.003E_s - f_y} = \frac{87{,}000g}{87{,}000 - f_y} f_y \text{ in psi.} \tag{18-19}$$

For all values of k greater than k_y the stress diagram of Figure 18-9c applies; for values of k less than k_y, the stress diagram of Figure 18-9d applies. Taken together, these two stress diagrams define the state of stress in concrete beams throughout the range of interest. The ultimate section modulus (plastic section modulus) can be developed readily from these diagrams.

From Figure 18-10, the sum of horizontal forces yields an expression for $\beta_1 k$ for the first case, where $k > ky$ and the compressive steel is in yield, that is, $f_{sc} = f_y$:

$$\Sigma H = 0 = 0.85 f_c' b\beta_1 kd + f_y\rho' bd - f_y \rho d \tag{18-20}$$

The solution for $\beta_1 k$ is, where $k > ky$ and compressive steel is in yield, $f_{sc} = f_y$,

$$\beta_1 k = \frac{f_y(\rho - \rho')}{0.85f_c'} \tag{18-21}$$

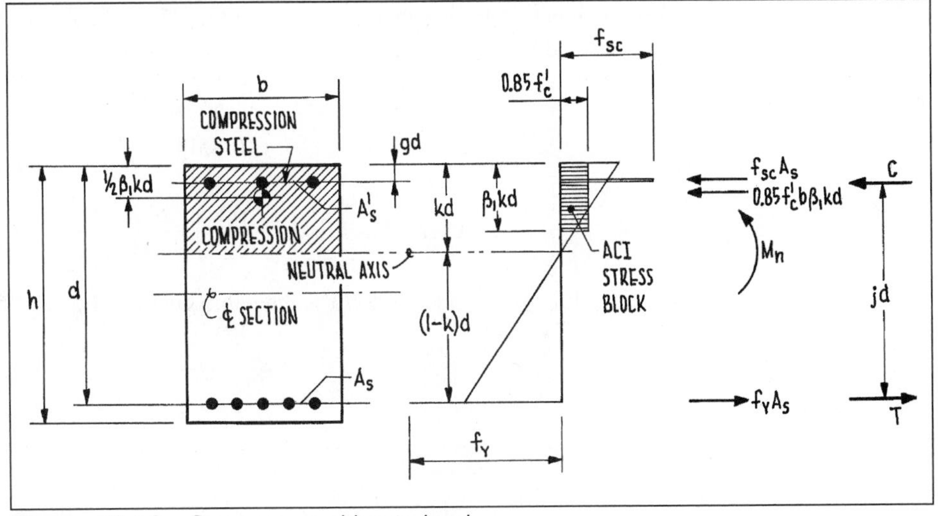

Figure 18-10 Stresses at ultimate load.

Note that since β_1 is governed by Code, it is not appropriate to deduct the compressive steel area from the stress block.

Refer again to the stress diagram of Figure 18-10. The sum of moments about tensile steel yields:

$$M_n = 0.85f_c' b\beta_1 kd(d - \tfrac{1}{2}\beta_1 kd) + f_y A_s'(d - gd). \qquad (18\text{-}22)$$

Solve Eq.(18-22) for $M_n / 0.85f_c'$, substitute f_y from Eq.(18-21), and solve for the plastic section modulus Z_c. For $k>k_y$; with compression steel in yield, the plastic section modulus is found to be:

$$\frac{M_n}{0.85f_c'} = Z_c, \qquad (18\text{-}23)$$

$$\text{where } Z_c = \beta_1 k\left(1 - \frac{\beta_1 k}{2} + \rho'\frac{1-g}{\rho - \rho'}\right)bd^2$$

and where $\beta_1 k$ is the value given by Eq.(18-21).

Equations (18-21) and (18-23) are the values of $\beta_1 k$ and Z_c when the compressive steel is in yield. When the compressive steel emerges from yield and is in the elastic range, its elastic strain ε_s can be found from Figure 18-9b by ratio; where E_s = 29,000,000 psi:

$$\frac{\varepsilon_s}{0.003} = \frac{kd - gd}{kd}, \text{hence } f_{sc} = \varepsilon_s E_s = 87{,}000\frac{k-g}{k}. \qquad (18\text{-}24a,b)$$

For the second case, where values of $k<k_y$, and the compression steel is elastic, the sum of horizontal forces shown in Figure 18-9d yields again an expression for k:

$$\Sigma H = 0 = 0.85f_c' b\beta_1 kd + f_{sc}\rho' bd - f_y \rho bd \qquad (18\text{-}25)$$

Equation(18-24b) is now substituted and the result solved for $\beta_1 k$, where $k<k_y$ and stress in the compression steel is elastic

$$\beta_1 k = \sqrt{\left[\frac{f_y\rho - 87{,}000\rho'}{2x0.85f_c'}\right]^2 + \frac{87{,}000g\rho'\beta_1}{0.85f_c'}} + \frac{f_y\rho - 87{,}000\rho'}{2x0.85f_c'}. \qquad (18\text{-}26)$$

As before, moments are again summed about the tensile steel (Figure 18-10), where f_{sc} is elastic

$$M_n = 0.85f_c' b\beta_1 kd(d - \tfrac{1}{2}\beta_1 kd) + f_{sc}\rho' bd(d - gd) \qquad (18\text{-}27)$$

Equation(18-24b) is substituted into Eq.(18-27) and the result solve for $M_n / 0.85f_c'$. For $k<k_y$, and compression steel is elastic, the plastic section modulus Z_c is found to be:

$$\frac{M_n}{0.85f_c'} = Z_c \qquad (18\text{-}28)$$

$$\text{where } Z_c = \left[\beta_1 k\left(1 - \frac{\beta_1 k}{2}\right) + \frac{87{,}000\rho'}{0.85f_c'}(1-g)\frac{k-g}{k}\right]bd^2$$

and where $\beta_1 k$ is the value given by Eq.(18-26).

The results of the derivation are summarized for the two stress regions:

For stress region I, with heavy tensile reinforcement and with compressive reinforcement in yield:

$$Z_c = \beta_1 k\left[1 - \frac{\beta_1 k}{2} + \rho' \frac{1-g}{\rho - \rho'}\right] bd^2 \qquad (18\text{-}23)$$

$$\text{where } \beta_1 k = \frac{f_y(\rho - \rho')}{0.85 f_c'} \qquad (18\text{-}21)$$

For stress region II, with light tensile reinforcement and with compressive reinforcement in the elastic range:

$$Z_c = \left[\beta_1 k\left(1 - \frac{\beta_1 k}{2}\right) + \frac{87{,}000\rho'}{0.85 f_c'}(1-g)\frac{k-g}{k}\right] bd^2 \qquad (18\text{-}28)$$

$$\text{where } \beta_1 k = \sqrt{\left[\frac{f_y\rho - 87{,}000\rho'}{2\text{x}0.85 f_c'}\right]^2 + \frac{87{,}000 g\rho'\beta_1}{0.85 f_c'}} + \frac{f_y\rho - 87{,}000\rho'}{2\text{x}0.85 f_c'} \qquad (18\text{-}26)$$

The foregoing equations (18-21), (18-23), (18-26), and (18-28) provide the plastic section modulus for a concrete beam throughout its range of interest. As with the elastic analysis, it is not necessary to solve these rather lengthy equations manually. They can be solved by computer and the results tabulated for reference. Such a tabulation is given in tables C-5, C-6 and C-7 in the Technical Manual, with k becoming k_n to distinguish it from k_{sv} in the elastic constants. As in the elastic analysis, the tables may be entered with the values of ρ and ρ', the ultimate strength of concrete and the grade of steel. The columns headed "at ultimate strength" give the tabulated values of equations (18-21), (18-23), (18-26) and (18-28).

The value of k_n at ultimate load is not often of interest, but its value can be obtained from the listed value of $\beta_l k_n$ simply by dividing by β_l; the value of β_l is given by Eq.(18-19) and is also given at the top of each beam table.

For ultimate load design, the Code places limits on both the minimum amount of steel that may be used and the maximum amount as well. Code (10.5.1) gives the minimum steel ratio by a simple formula:

$$\text{minimum}\,\rho = \frac{200}{f_y} \qquad (18\text{-}29)$$

The maximum steel ratio is somewhat more involved. When there is no compressive reinforcement in the section, the maximum steel ratio is given by Code (10.3.3) as 75% of that required to produce the balanced strain* condition (line OA of Figure 18-9b). At the balanced strain condition, the concrete reaches its ultimate strain of 0.003 in./in. just as the tensile steel enters yield. This state of strain is shown again in Figure 18-11, along with the corresponding stresses.

* The "balanced strain" condition used here and prescribed by Code should not be confused with the "balanced stress" condition used earlier as a means to control elastic margins. The two conditions are unrelated.

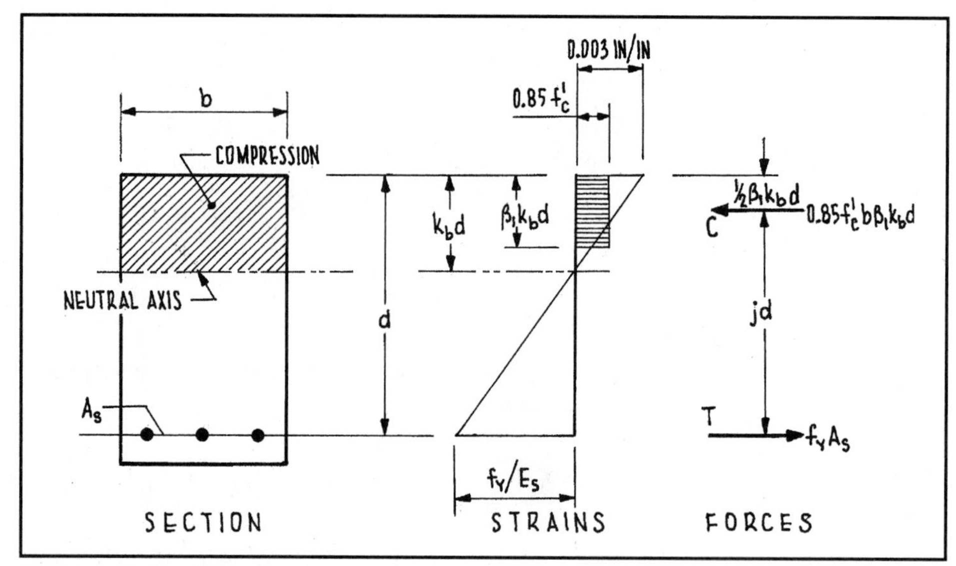

Figure 18-11 Balanced strain condition.

The value of k_b for the balanced state of strain is found by similar triangles, where, with E_s = 29,000,000 psi and with no compressive reinforcement:

$$\frac{f_y / E_s}{0.003} = \frac{d - k_b d}{k_b d}; \quad k_b = \frac{87,000}{87,000 + f_y}. \tag{18-30}$$

Horizontal forces are summed, yielding:

$$0 = 0.85 f_c' b \beta_1 k_b d - f_y \rho_b bd. \tag{18-31}$$

This result is solved for ρ_b where, with the value of k_b given by Eq.(18-30):

$$\rho_b = \beta_1 \frac{0.85 f_c'}{f_y} \left(\frac{87,000}{87,000 + f_y} \right), \quad f_y \text{ and } f_c' \text{ in psi} \tag{18-32}$$

$$\text{and maximum allowable } \rho = 0.75 \rho_b. \tag{18-33}$$

The limitation thus imposed on the area of steel assures that the tensile steel will always enter yield before the concrete reaches its ultimate strain, thereby avoiding the chance of brittle failure in the concrete.

Tables C-5 through C-7 in the Technical Manual reflect the foregoing maximum and minimum values of ρ permitted by Code. Values greater than that given by Eq.(18-33) are not entered. Values less than that given by Eq.(18-29) are those above the interior line in the tables; the reason for including these smaller values is given later with the discussions of concrete tee beams.

Under the ACI strength method, there are no further rules for choosing the steel ratio ρ; it may fall anywhere between the maximum and minimum allowable values. The most economical sections, however, are those where ρ is chosen about midway between the maximum and minimum allowable values. Where appropriate in the following examples, the steel ratio ρ is therefore chosen at about the midpoint in the range of allowable values.

18.9 Applications at Ultimate Load

Some examples will illustrate the use of the plastic section modulus in the design of concrete sections.

Example 18-5

Strength method of design.
Determination of moment capacity.

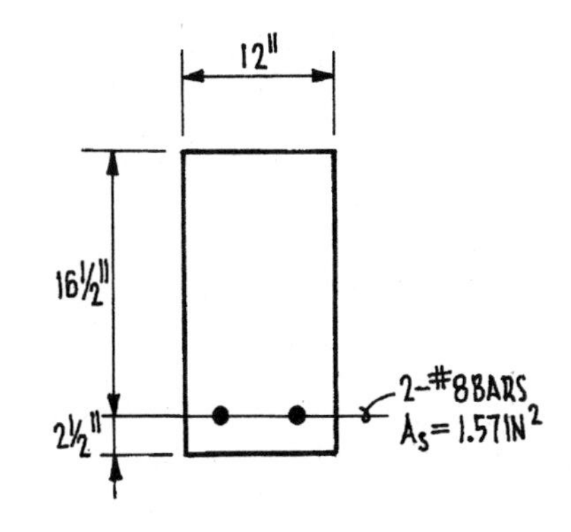

Given: Section as shown.
Grade 50 steel, f_c'=4000 psi.

To Find: Ultimate moment M_n the section will sustain.

Solution: Calculate the steel ratio ρ for the given section,

$$\rho = \frac{A_s}{bd} = \frac{1.57}{(12)(16.5)} = 0.008.$$

Enter Table C-6, and find section constants,

$$\rho = 0.008, Z_c = 0.111bd^2.$$

Solve for the capacity of the section in moment:

$$M_n = 0.85f_c'Z_c = (0.85)(4000)(0.111)(12)(16.5)(16.5)$$
$$M_n = 1233 \text{ kip·in.} = 103 \text{ kip·ft.}$$

The given section will fail at a nominal ultimate moment of 103 kip·ft.

Example 18-6

Strength method of design.
Determination of moment capacity.

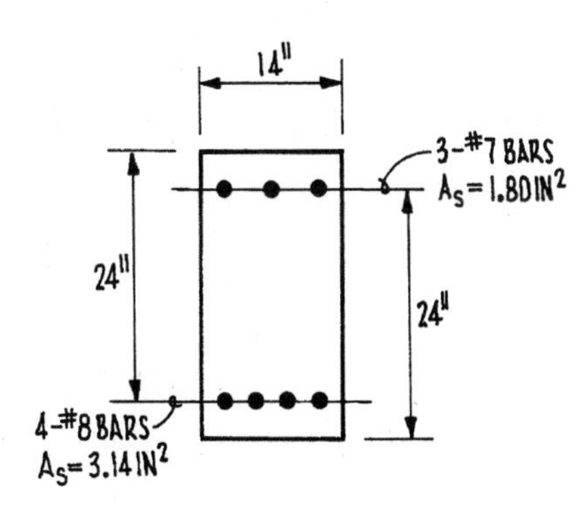

Given: Section as shown.
Grade 60 steel, f_c' = 3000 psi,
ϕ = 0.90.
No wind or earthquake.
Dead load moment = 121 kip·ft.

To Find: Maximum allowable live load moment M_{LL}.

Solution: Calculate the steel ratios ρ and ρ':

$$\rho = \frac{A_s}{bd} = \frac{3.14}{(14)(24)} = 0.0094$$

$$\rho' = \frac{A_s'}{bd} = \frac{1.80}{(14)(24)} = 0.0054$$

$$\frac{\rho'}{\rho} = 0.57, \quad \rho' = 0.57\rho; \quad \text{use } \rho' = 0.60\rho$$

Enter Table C-5; find section constants (by interpolation):

$\rho = 0.0094$, $\rho' = 0.6\rho$, $Z_c = 0.199bd^2$.

Determine the nominal ultimate moment M_n:

$$M_n = 0.85 f_c' Z_c = (0.85)(3000)(0.199)(14)(24)(24)$$
$$= 4092 \text{ kip·in.} = 341 \text{ kip·ft.}$$

Solve for the live load moment:

$$M_n = (1.4M_{DL} + 1.7M_{LL})/\phi$$
$$341 = (1.4 \times 121 + 1.7 \times M_{LL})/0.9$$
$$M_{LL} = 81 \text{ kip·ft.}$$

The section will sustain a live load moment of 81 kip·ft.

Example 18-7

Strength method of design.
Design of a rectangular section in flexure.
No limitations on dimensions.

Given: M_{DL} = 88 kip·ft.; M_{LL} = 68 kip·ft.
Grade 60 steel, f_c' = 4000 psi, ϕ = 0.90.

To Find: Suitable section to sustain the load.

Solution: Calculate the ultimate load moment Mn. With no wind or earthquake, the load case given by Eq.(17-1a) applies:

$$M_n = (1.4M_{DL} + 1.7M_{LL})/\phi = (1.4 \times 88 + 1.7 \times 68)/0.90$$
$$= 265 \text{ kip·ft.}$$

Determine the required magnitude of the section modulus Z_c:

$$Z_c = \frac{M_n}{0.85f_c'} = \frac{265{,}000(12)}{0.85(4000)}$$

$$Z_c = 935 \text{ in.}^3$$

Enter Table C-6; select a section with no compressive reinforcement about midway between minimum and maximum steel ratios:

$\rho = 0.0080$, $Z_c = 0.131bd^2$

Solve for minimum required dimensions:

$Z_c = 935 = 0.131bd^2$, assume $b = 0.6d$,
$d = 22.8$ in., $b = 13.7$ in.

Solve for steel area A_s:

$$A_s = \rho bd = 0.0080(13.7)(22.8) = 2.50 \text{ in.}^2$$

From Table C-3:

Use 6-No. 6 bars, A_s furnished = 2.65 in.^{2}

Round up to nearest inch or half-inch:

Use b = 14 in., d = 23 in., 6-No. 6 bars.

The selected section is shown in the following sketch:

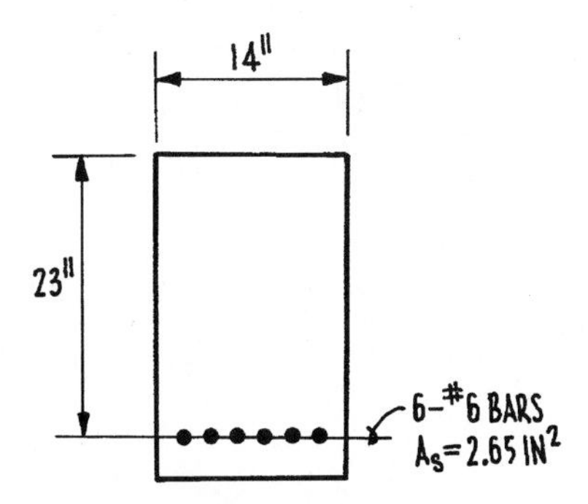

Often, the effective depth of a section must be restricted. Such circumstances commonly occur around air conditioning ductwork, pipe and cable trays and wall openings. Such a case is considered in the next example.

Example 18-8

Strength method of design. Design of a rectangular section in flexure. Depth of section limited.

Given: M_{DL} = 88 kip·ft; M_{LL} = 68 kip·ft.
Grade 60 steel, f_c' = 4000 psi, ϕ = 0.90, depth d ≤ 20".

To Find: Suitable section to sustain the load.

Solution: Calculate the ultimate design moment M_n. With no wind or earthquake:

$$M_n = (1.4M_{DL} + 1.7M_{LL})/\phi = (1.4 \times 88 + 1.7 \times 68)/0.90$$
$$= 265 \text{ kip·ft.}$$

Determine the required magnitude of the section modulus Z_c:

$$Z_c = \frac{M_n}{0.85f_c'} = \frac{265{,}000(12)}{0.85(4000)} = 935 \text{ in.}^3$$

Enter Table C-6; select a section with no compressive reinforcement, about midway between minimum and maximum steel ratios:

$\rho = 0.0080$, $Z_c = 0.131bd^2$.

Solve for minimum required dimensions:

$Z_c = 935 = 0.131bd^2$, use d = 20 in.,
b = 17.8 in., d = 20 in.

Solve for steel area A_s:

$$A_s = \rho bd = 0.008(17.8)(20) = 2.85 \text{ in.}^2$$

From Table C-3:

Use 5-No. 7 bars, A_s furnished = 3.01 in.^{2}

Round up to nearest inch or half-inch:

Use b = 18 in., d = 20 in., 5-No. 7 bars.

Final section is shown in the following sketch.

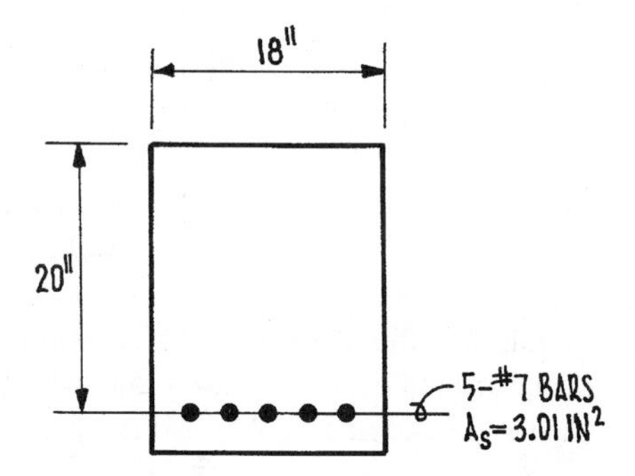

It is pointed out that Example 18-8 has identically the same set of design conditions as the preceding example, Example 18-7, except that the effective depth has been limited. The resulting section in this second case is somewhat wider than desirable, but it still was not found to be necessary to go to heavier amounts of reinforcement. When both the width *b* and the depth *d* are restricted, however, the use of heavier levels of reinforcement may become unavoidable; such circumstances occur in the next example.

Example 18-9

Strength method of design. Design of a rectangular section in flexure. Both width and depth are limited.

Given: M_{DL} = 88 kip·ft; M_{LL} = 68 kip·ft. Grade 60 steel, f_c' = 4000 psi, ϕ = 0.90. Width *b* limited to 12 in. Effective depth *d* limited to 18 in.

To Find: Suitable section to sustain the load.

Solution: Calculate the ultimate design moment M_n. With no wind or earthquake:

$$M_n = (1.4M_{DL} + 1.7M_{LL})/\phi = (1.4 \times 88 + 1.7 \times 68)/0.90$$
$$= 265 \text{ kip·ft.}$$

Determine the required magnitude of the section modulus Z_c:

$$Z_c = \frac{M_n}{0.85f_c'} = \frac{265{,}000(12)}{0.85(4000)} = 935 \text{ in.}^3$$

Since both b and d are restricted, the required coefficient of Z_c may be computed:

$$Z_c = 935 = (\text{coefficient})(b)(d^2),\ b = 12 \text{ in.},\ d = 18 \text{ in.}$$
$$\text{Coefficient} = 0.240$$

From Table C-6, with no compressive reinforcement, select the required steel ratio. (It should be noted that the section selected under these conditions must be chosen near the maximum value for ρ rather than being about midway between the minimum and maximum values.)

$$\rho = 0.0160,\ Z_c = 0.242bd^2.$$

Solve for steel area A_s:

$$A_s = \rho bd = 0.0160(12)(18) = 3.46 \text{ in.}^2$$

From Table C-3:

Use 3-No. 10 bars, A_s furnished = 3.80 in.^{2}

The final section is shown in the following sketch.

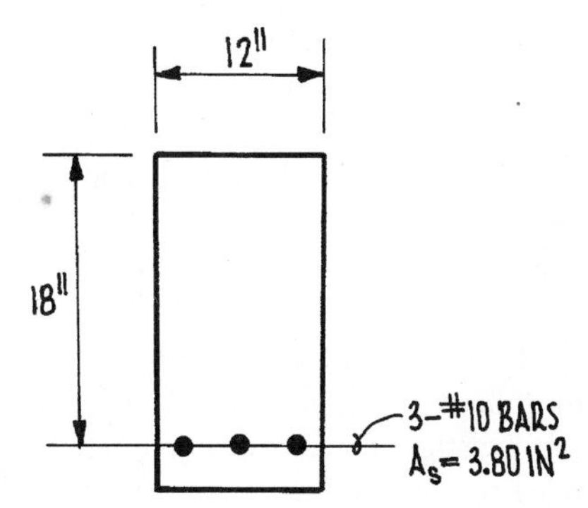

In Example 18-9, the required amount of reinforcement is considerably greater than that in Example 18-7. Such is the penalty to be paid when sizes are restricted. Such restrictions, however, are often unavoidable, arising typically when mechanical equipment must be accommodated in tightly enclosed spaces. In many cases, the cost of additional reinforcement is the most economical alternative.

18.10 Balanced Flexural Design

To this point, the discussions of flexure in concrete have been centered around two independent concepts, elastic stress at service levels of load and inelastic forces at ultimate levels of load. There has been no effort so far to link these two concepts together and to find how one influences the other. They are, of course, intimately interrelated; their interrelationship is one topic to be examined in the following sections.

A second topic to be examined in these sections is the design of members to achieve something approaching optimum efficiency, both at elastic levels of stress and at ultimate levels of load, when the interrelationships between the two are considered. It will be seen that optimum efficiency can be achieved only in certain types of beams; in others one must simply live with inefficient stress levels in the materials.

18.11 Balanced Stress Condition

By definition of the plastic section modulus Z_c, the nominal ultimate moment M_n is computed by:

$$M_n = 0.85 f_c' Z_c. \qquad (18\text{-}34)$$

Similarly, by definition of the elastic section modulus S_c, the service moment M_{sv} is computed by:

$$M_{sv} = f_{sv} S_c \qquad (18\text{-}35)$$

where $M_{sv} = M_n/1.7$ and f_{sv} is the service stress corresponding to this value of M_{sv}.

Equation (18-34) is divided by Eq.(18-35), yielding:

$$\frac{M_n}{M_{sv}} = \frac{0.85 f_c' Z_c}{f_{sv} S_c}. \qquad (18\text{-}36)$$

It is recognized that $M_n/M_{sv} = 1.7$, hence:

$$\text{service } f_{sv} = 0.5 f_c' \frac{Z_c}{S_c}. \qquad (18\text{-}37)$$

It is noted immediately that the service stress f_{sv} defined by Eq.(18-37) is an invariant property of the section, dependent only on section properties and materials properties. It is the elastic stress that will occur in the concrete at 60% of the ultimate moment (or more exactly, at $M_n/1.7$); the service stress f_{sv} thus provides the link between service levels of stress and ultimate levels of load. For reference, the service stress f_{sv} for various steel ratios, steel grades and concrete strengths has been computed and included in tables C-5, C-6 and C-7 in the Technical Manual.

With this addition of f_{sv}, the derivation of tables C-5, C-6 and C-7 is now complete. Each line of these tables defines a valid and usable section under the Code. The tables may be entered with a known value for the ratio f_s/f_c or with a desired value for the service stress f_{sv}. All other properties, both elastic and plastic, may then be read from the line so selected.

The stress ratio f_s/f_c is now deliberately chosen at the balanced stress condition presented earlier, that is:

$$\frac{f_s}{f_c} = \frac{f_y}{0.85 f_c'}. \qquad (18\text{-}15)$$

The elastic section constants S_c, k_{sv} and y_{sv} corresponding to this balanced stress condition have already been introduced; these elastic constants have been computed and tabulated in a special table, Table C-8 in the Technical Manual. To this special table, the plastic section constants Z_c and k_n can now be added, where the steel ratio ρ is that found earlier with the elastic constants. With both Z_c and S_c thus known, the service stress f_{sv} for the balanced stress condition has been found from Eq.(18-37) and listed, thereby completing the special table, Table C-8.

18.12 Transition from Elastic to Plastic Flexure

For the balanced stress condition, the transition from elastic behavior to plastic behavior can now be traced. As indicated in sketches *a* and *b* of Figure 18-12, the stresses remain elastic throughout all the lower values of moment, up to the transition moment M_{TR}. At the transition point, the concrete and the steel are simultaneously on the verge of yield.

At this point, the maximum elastic resistance to moment has been developed; any further rotation will produce inelastic strains.

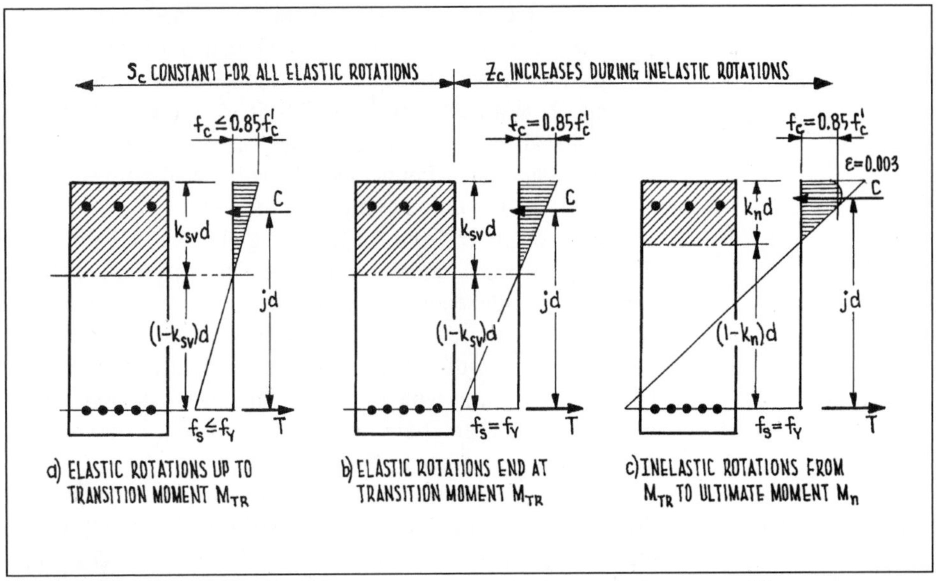

a) ELASTIC ROTATIONS UP TO TRANSITION MOMENT M_{TR}

b) ELASTIC ROTATIONS END AT TRANSITION MOMENT M_{TR}

c) INELASTIC ROTATIONS FROM M_{TR} TO ULTIMATE MOMENT M_n

Figure 18-12 Rotations of a section under balanced stress conditions.

As rotations increase further, the inelastic strains begin; both concrete and steel enter yield. At that point the arm jd begins to increase slightly, which provides a very small increase in moment capacity. Thereafter, a small but steady increase in jd (and moment capacity) will accompany any further inelastic rotations. The inelastic rotations end when the strain in the concrete reaches 0.003. At that point, as indicated in Figure 18-12c, the ultimate moment M_n has been reached and the arm jd is at its maximum, with $M_n = f_y A_s jd$.

Alternatively, the transition may be traced by plotting the rotation of the section against the corresponding moment. As shown in Figure 18-13, rotations of the section remain elastic up to the transition point. As rotations progress past the transition point, both concrete and steel simultaneously enter yield. As yield in the concrete continues to increase, the arm jd also increases slightly, adding a small increase in moment capacity; moment capacity continues to increase slightly until the maximum concrete strain of 0.003 in./in. is reached.

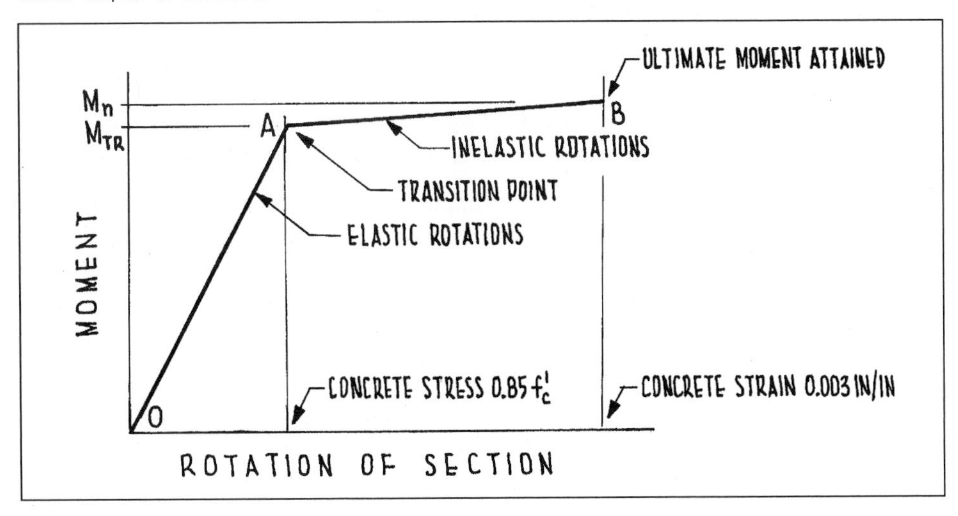

Figure 18-13 Moment vs. rotation at the balanced stress condition.

In Figure 18-13, a comparison between the transition moment M_{TR} and the ultimate moment M_n can be drawn using the relative values of Table C-8. The maximum elastic moment is M_{TR}, at which point the stress in both steel and concrete is just at yield, for which case, $M_{TR} = 0.85f'_c S_c$. For comparison, the ultimate moment is M_n, for which case $M_n = 0.85f'_c Z_c$. The difference between these two moments is a direct consequence of the difference between Z_c and S_c. From Table C-8, it is seen that for the balanced stress condition, Z_c and S_c are always very close to each other; their difference, in fact, is always less than 4%. As indicated in Figure 18-13, therefore, the transition moment M_{TR} will always be within 4% of the ultimate moment M_n.

It is concluded from the foregoing observations that when a member is designed for the balanced stress condition, the inelastic deformations will begin just as the concrete and steel simultaneously reach their yield stresses. At that point, more than 96% of the resistance to flexural load will have been attained. A member designed for the balanced stress condition will therefore behave elastically at all levels of load up to some 96% of its ultimate load, at which point the member will (idealistically) begin its final inelastic deformations. Thereafter, rotations will increase rapidly and inelastically to the final collapse of the member.

It is observed also that the use of the balanced stress condition in combination with the ACI strength method of design will incorporate all the best features of both ultimate load design and elastic stress design. A member so designed will perform smoothly and elastically all the way through its elastic levels of load up to its elastic limits (or yield stresses), at which point it will undergo inelastic deformations smoothly and predictably to ultimate collapse. There is no early failure, no premature inelastic behavior and there will be less than 4% wasted residual strength.

If, however, the service stress f_{sv} is chosen at any other level than at this balanced stress condition, there will be an "imbalance" between the elastic margins for the steel and the concrete; one material will necessarily enter yield before the other. As loads are increased above this level, the member will undergo some sort of nonlinear rotations as it progresses on up to ultimate load; at that point the elastic values used to compute the design moment M_n will no longer be valid. It is important to note, however, that *Code does not require a balanced state of stress*, and that insofar as Code is concerned, the only disadvantage to using such an imbalance in the design is in the inefficient use of materials.

A final observation can be drawn from Tables C-5, 6 and 7 concerning the service stress f_{sv}. It is noted that the service stress is, in all cases, just slightly more than $0.5f'_c$; the maximum variation from this norm is seen to be less than 4%. With only a small error, therefore, the nominal service stress f_{sv} under balanced stress conditions can be thought of as being 60% of the idealized yield stress of concrete, or $f_{sv} = 0.6(0.85f_c')$. Similarly, the corresponding service stress in the steel will also be roughly 60% of yield, or $f_s = 0.6f_y$.

18.13 Applications of Balanced Flexural Design

The following examples will demonstrate the use of the special table, Table C-8, in the design of concrete members.

Example 18-10

Design of a rectangular section in flexure. No limitation on dimensions.

Given: M_{DL} = 36 kip·ft, M_{LL} = 42 kip·ft, f_c' = 3000 psi, Grade 60 steel.

To Find: Suitable section to sustain the load.

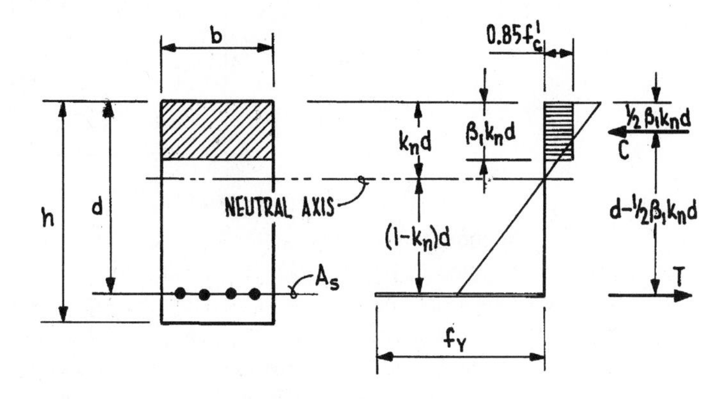

Solution: Calculate the design moment at ultimate load:

$$M_n = (1.4M_{DL} + 1.7M_{LL})/\phi = (1.4 \times 36 + 1.7 \times 42)/0.9$$
$$= 135 \text{ kip·ft.}$$

Determine the magnitude of the required plastic section modulus Z_c:

$$Z_c = \frac{M_n}{0.85f_c'} = \frac{135{,}000(12)}{0.85(3000)} = 635 \text{ in.}^3$$

Select the service stress and section constants for the balanced stress condition (both the steel and the concrete will then have the same elastic margin to yield):

From Table C-8, no compressive reinforcement,
use $\rho = 0.0060$, $f_{sv} = 1539$ psi, $Z_c = 0.132bd^2$, $f_s/f_c = 23.53$.

Solve for minimum required sizes:

$$Z_c = 635 = 0.132bd^2.$$

Assume that b = 0.6d, then $635 = 0.132 \times 0.6d^3$.

Solve for d = 20.0 in., b = 12.0 in.

Steel area = $\rho bd = 0.006bd = 0.006(12.0)(20.0) = 1.44$ in.^{2}

From Table C-3, use 5-No. 5 bars, as furnished = 1.53 in.^{2}

Dimensions are now rounded up to even inches or half inches:

Use b = 12.0 in., d = 20.0 in., A_s = 5-No. 5 bars

The final section is shown in the following sketch.

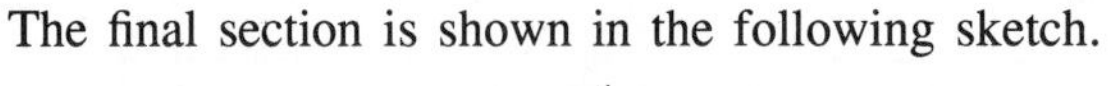

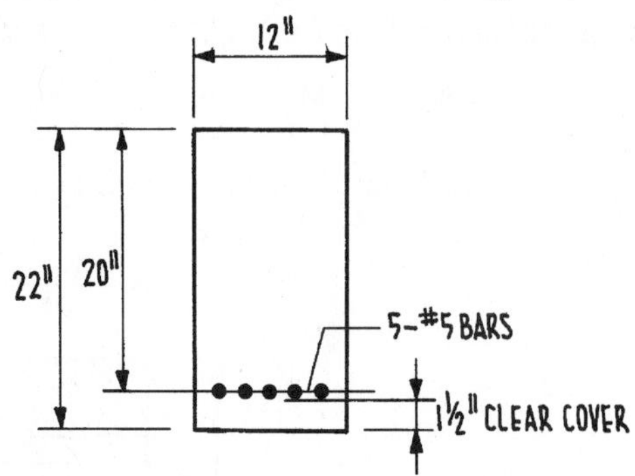

Without making any further investigations, it is known immediately that the beam section selected in Example 18-10 will develop a concrete stress of 1539 psi when subjected to its service moment of $M_n/1.7$ or 79.4 kip·ft. The stress in the Grade 60 steel under that moment will be $1539(f_s/f_c)$ or 36,200 psi. Further, the beam will have the same margins to elastic yield for both the steel and the concrete. And finally, the beam will perform elastically throughout its entire load-carrying range from zero moment all the way up to 96% of its ultimate moment. Inherently, when a section is selected at its balanced stress condition, there is no question what its service performance will be.

On occasion, it becomes necessary to limit the overall depth of a beam. When there is no corresponding limit on the width *b*, one way to design the member is to make it wider and flatter. Such a case is considered in the next example.

Example 18-11

Design of a rectangular section in flexure. Depth of section limited.

Given: M_{DL} = 37 kip·ft, M_{LL} = 25 kip·ft, f_c' = 4000 psi, Grade 50 steel. Depth *h* limited to 16½ in. Interior exposure.

To Find: Suitable section to sustain load.

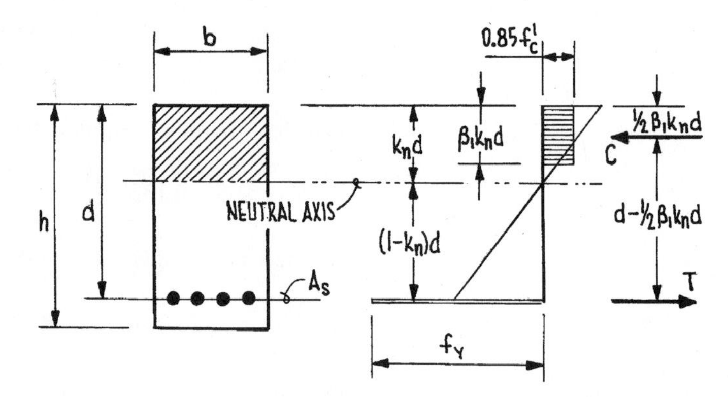

Solution: With overall depth *h* limited, it is necessary to estimate the maximum allowable value for *d*, as shown in the following sketch.

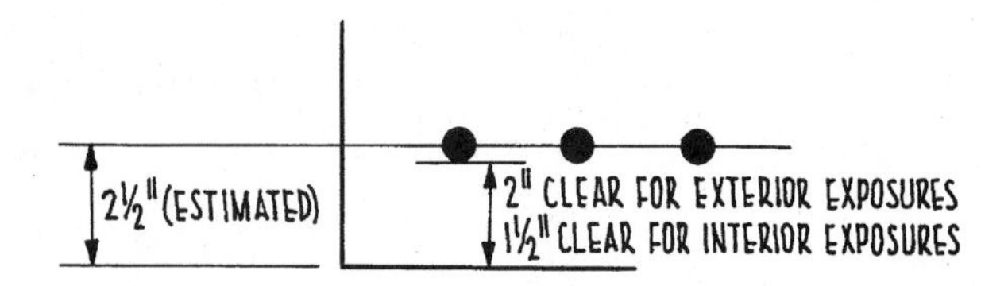

Estimate maximum allowable d = h - 2½ in. = 14 in. Calculate the design moment at ultimate load:

$$M_n = (1.4M_{DL} + 1.7M_{LL})/\phi = (1.4 \times 37 + 1.7 \times 25)/0.9$$
$$= 105 \text{ kip·ft.}$$

Determine the magnitude of the required plastic section modulus Z_c:

$$Z_c = \frac{M_n}{0.85f_c'} = \frac{105{,}000(12)}{0.85(4000)} = 371 \text{ in.}^3$$

Select the service stress and section constants to provide a balanced stress condition.

From Table C-8, no compressive reinforcement:

Try $\rho = 0.0120$, $f_{sv} = 2067$ psi, $Z_c = 0.161bd^2$, $f_s/f_c = 14.71$

Solve for required minimum sizes:

$Z_c = 371 = 0.161bd^2$

For d = 14 in., solve for b = 11.8 in.

Steel area = $\rho bd = 0.0120(11.8)(14) = 1.98$ in.^{2}

From Table C-3, use 2-No. 9 bars, A_s furnished = 2.0 in.^{2}

Use b = 12.0 in., d = 14 in., h = 16½ in., 2-No. 9 bars.

Note that *b* and *d* are used at their exact values for computing A_s, but are rounded off to the nearest inch or ½ inch after all calculations are complete. Note also that this section is wider than would ordinarily be desirable, but the restriction on *d* will not permit a narrower section to be used unless compressive reinforcement is added.

It is again reassuring to note that due to the use of the balanced stress condition, the concrete in the beam of Example 18-11 will work at an elastic stress of 2067 psi when the moment on the section is 105 kip·ft/1.7 or 61.8 kip·ft. The stress in the steel at that point will be $f_{sv}(f_s/f_c)$ or 30,400 psi. Further, both the steel and the concrete will be elastic all the way to 96% of the ultimate moment of 105 kip·ft.

It is emphasized that in selecting section constants from the tables in the Technical Manual, all sections listed in tables C-5, C-6 and C-7 are usable and are within all requirements of the Code. It is simply good practice to avoid the use of compressive steel (where possible) and to keep the section balanced for its elastic margins. Nonetheless, in Example 18-11 a section having a steel ratio of 2.75% (see Table C-6) and its accompanying theoretical service stress of 3200 psi or $0.80f_c'$ is an acceptable section under the Code.

On occasion, both the depth *d* and width *b* of a concrete section may be limited by outside constraints. Such a case is considered in the next example.

Example 18-12

Design of a rectangular section in flexure; both depth *d* and width *b* limited.

Given: M_{DL} = 62 kip·ft, M_{LL} = 35 kip·ft, f_c' = 3000 psi, Grade 40 steel. Overall *h* limited to 20 in. Width *b* limited to 12 in. Exterior exposure, 1/2 in. ties.

To Find: Suitable section to sustain the load.

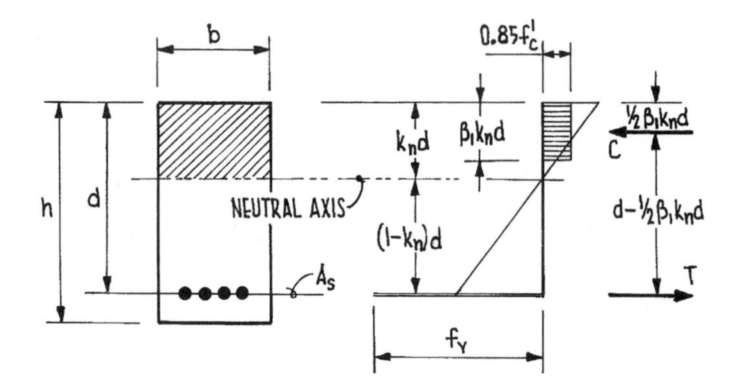

Solution: With overall height *h* limited to 20 in., it becomes necessary to estimate the maximum effective depth *d*, as shown in the following sketch.

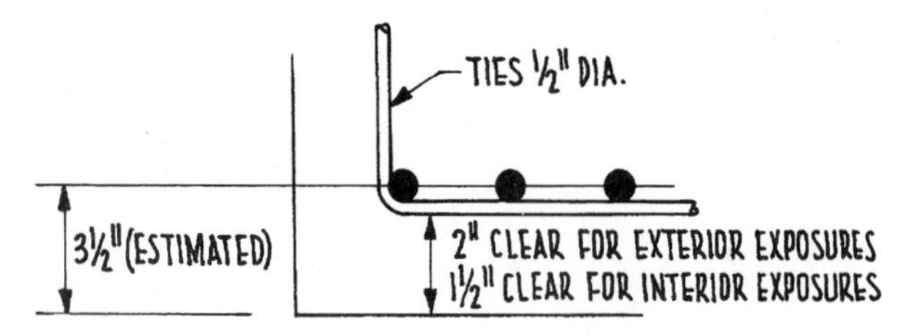

The maximum allowable value for *d* is estimated at 20 in. - 3 1/2 in. = 16 1/2 in.

Calculate the design moment at ultimate load:

$$M_n = (1.4M_{DL} + 1.7M_{LL})/\phi = (1.4 \times 62 + 1.7 \times 35)/0.90$$
$$= 163 \text{ kip·ft.}$$

Determine the magnitude of the required plastic section modulus Z_c:

$$Z_c = \frac{M_n}{0.85f_c'} = \frac{163{,}000(12)}{0.85(3000)} = 767 \text{ in.}^3$$

Since both *b* and *d* are known in this case, the coefficient of the plastic section modulus can be computed directly, where Z_c = (coefficient)(bd^2),

$$Z_c = 767 = (\text{coefficient})(12)(16.5^2)$$
$$\text{coefficient} = 0.235$$

It is now required to find in Table C-8 a section having a coefficient of Z_c at least 0.235. It is seen immediately that a section without compressive reinforcement will not work; the coefficient for that case is only 0.169. Further, providing compressive steel in the amount of 20% of tensile steel is still inadequate; its coefficient is only 0.197. But for a compressive steel ratio of 40% of tensile steel, the section constants are:

$$\rho = 0.0169, Z_c = 0.238bd^2, f_{sv} = 1541 \text{ psi}, f_s/f_c = 15.69.$$

The result is verified:

$$M_n = 0.85 f_c' Z_c = 0.85(3000)(0.238)(12)(16.5^2)/12$$
$$= 165 > 164 \text{ kip·ft (O.K.)}$$

The area of tensile reinforcement is selected:

$A_s = \rho bd = 0.0169(12)(16.5) = 3.35$ in.^{2},
use 4-No. 9 bars in tension.

$A_s' = 0.40; A_s = 0.40(3.335) = 1.34$ in.^{2},
use 2-No. 8 bars in compression.

Use b = 12 in., d = 16.5 in., h = 20 in.

4 - No. 9 bars in tension
2 - No. 8 bars in compression.

The final cross section is similar to that shown at the beginning of his example.

Had it not been a requirement to design for the balanced stress condition, the section of Example 18-12 could have been designed to sustain the moment M_n with no compressive reinforcement at all. For such a design, the required tensile steel ratio is found from Table C-5 to be 0.0174, producing a required steel area of 3.45 in.^{2}; the earlier choice of 4 No. 9 bars for the balanced stress condition is thus seen to be adequate even without the addition of compressive reinforcement. The conclusion is drawn that the inclusion of the two No. 8 bars in compression adds very little to the moment capacity of the section.

It is further noted, however, that the addition of the two No. 8 bars in Example 18-12 reduces the service stress in the concrete from 1920 psi (or $0.64 f_c'$) when no compressive reinforcement is used, down to 1541 psi (or $0.51 f_c'$) if compressive reinforcement is used. Further, the long-term deflections of the beam will be reduced by some 33% if compressive reinforcement is added (see factor λ, Chapter 17). It is concluded that the addition of compressive steel adds little to the moment capacity when the tensile steel ratio is less than $0.75\rho_b$; the primary benefit derived from such reinforcement is in the reduction of the day-to-day service stresses in concrete and in the reduction of long-term deflections.

From such results, one might suspect that there is more involved in the use of compressive reinforcement than just strength. Such suspicions are justified; there is indeed a great deal more involved. Some of the more prominent of these additional factors are treated in more depth in the next section.

18.14 Use of Compressive Reinforcement

There are two reasons to use compressive reinforcement in a flexural section:

1. To reduce the stress in the concrete and thereby reduce the deflections that accompany high stresses in the concrete.
2. To add capacity in moment.

The two effects occur almost independently of each other and may be treated as separate problems.

It has already been observed that the allowable range for the tensile steel ratio ρ is, for a section with no compressive reinforcement:

$$\frac{200}{f_y} \leq \rho \leq 0.75\,\rho_b \tag{18-16}$$

where f_y is the yield stress of the steel:
ρ_b is the steel ratio at balanced strain, that is, the steel is just entering yield when the strain in the concrete is 0.003 in./in.

Anywhere within this allowable range of values for ρ, the major effect of adding compressive reinforcement is to reduce the day-to-day service stress in the concrete and thereby to reduce long-term deflections (see factor λ in Chapter 17).

The use of compressive reinforcement when ρ is within the limits prescribed by Eq.(18-16) does, however, provide a small increase in moment capacity. In the solution of Example 18-12, it was observed that this increase in moment capacity is indeed small but that the increase in moment capacity came with a disproportionate increase in steel area A_s.

When a significant increase in moment capacity is required, Code (10.3.4) permits the area of tensile reinforcement to exceed this level of $0.75\rho_b$ provided that the excess area of tensile reinforcement is matched by a corresponding addition of compressive reinforcement. The extra steel areas are shown schematically in the sketch of Figure 18-14.

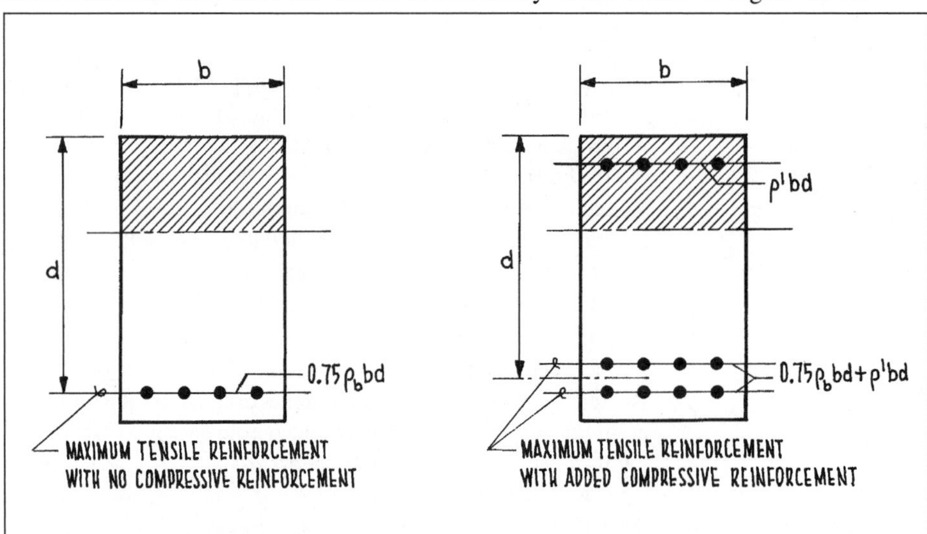

Figure 18-14 Tensile steel area in excess of balanced strain.

Code does not require the excess area of tensile reinforcement to be reduced by the factor 0.75. The total amount of tensile reinforcement permitted by Code is then, when compressive reinforcement is used:

$$\text{maximum}\,\rho \leq 0.75\rho_b + \rho' \tag{18-34}$$
$$\text{or,}\ \rho - \rho' \leq 0.75\rho_b$$

As a practical matter, large amounts of reinforcement can produce serious problems with congestion in placing and holding the steel in the forms. A practical limit on the total area of tensile and compressive reinforcement has been found to be about 8% of gross area; steel areas in excess of this amount produce unacceptable problems in placement.

Sections having these larger values of steel ratio are included in the design tables C-5 through C-7. If a significant increase in moment capacity is required, then the balanced stress condition will not be possible; for such cases the service stress in concrete is allowed to increase to whatever value is necessary.

Example 18-13

Moment capacity with compressive reinforcement.

Given: Section having the dimensions shown. f_c' = 3000 psi, Grade 60 steel.

To Find: Moment capacity for:

1. $\rho = \rho_b = 0.0160$, $\rho' = 0$.
2. $\rho = 0.0200$, $\rho' = 0.0040$.
3. $\rho = 0.0260$, $\rho' = 0.0104$.
4. $\rho = 0.0400$, $\rho' = 0.0240$.

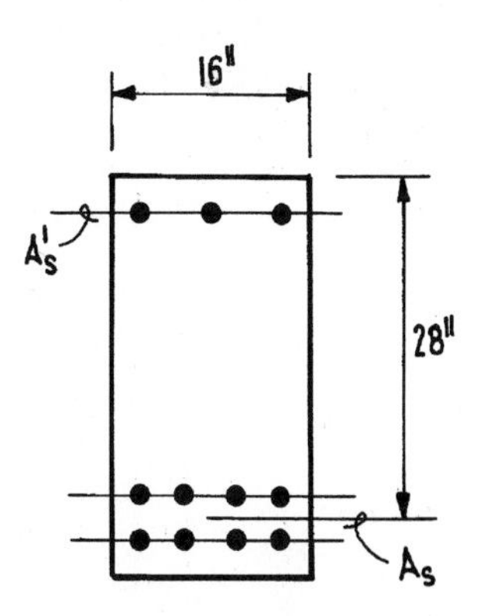

Solution: The maximum steel ratio with no compressive reinforcement is listed in Table C-5 as $\rho_b = 0.0160$:

1) For $\rho = \rho_b = 0.0160$, $\rho' = 0$,

$$M_n = 0.85 f_c' Z_c = 0.85(3000)(0.306)(16 \text{ x } 282)$$
$$= 815 \text{ kip·ft.}$$

2) For $\rho = 0.0200$, $\rho' = 0.0040$, ρ' = 20% of ρ,

Verify that $\rho - \rho' \leq 0.75\rho_b$

$$0.0200 - 0.0040 \leq 0.0160 \text{ (O.K.)}$$
$$M_n = 0.85 f_c' Z_c = 0.85(3000)(0.388)(16 \text{ x } 28^2)$$
$$= 1034 \text{ kip·ft.}$$

3) For $\rho = 0.0260$, $\rho' = 0.0104$, ρ' = 40% of ρ,

Verify that $\rho - \rho' \leq 0.0160$ (O.K.)

$$0.0260 - 0.0104 \leq 0.0160 \text{ (O.K.)}$$
$$M_n = 0.85 f_c' Z_c = 0.85(3000)(0.514)(16 \text{ x } 28^2)$$
$$= 1370 \text{ kip·ft.}$$

4) For $\rho = 0.0400$, $\rho' = 0.0240$, ρ' = 60% of ρ,

Verify that $\rho - \rho' \leq 0.75\rho_b$

$$0.0400 - 0.0240 \leq 0.0160 \text{ (O.K.)}$$
$$M_n = 0.85 f_c' Z_c = 0.85(3000)(0.5800(16 \text{ x } 28^2)$$
$$= 2132 \text{ kip·ft.}$$

Summary of results:

1) $\rho' = 0$ M_n = 815 kip·ft, f_{sv} = 2556 psi or $0.85 f_c'$.
2) $\rho' = 0.2\rho$ M_n = 1034 kip·ft, f_{sv} = 2608 psi or $0.87 f_c'$
3) $\rho' = 0.4\rho$ M_n = 1370 kip·ft, f_{sv} = 2641 psi or $0.88 f_c'$.
4) $\rho' = 0.6\rho$ M_n = 2132 kip·ft, f_{sv} = 2178 psi or $0.91 f_c'$

It is observed from the results of Example 18-13 that the increase in moment capacity from a section with no compressive reinforcement to a section with 60% compressive reinforcement is some 260%, a significant increase. It comes with a penalty, however.

The concrete in all four beams of Example 18-13 will serve its day-to-day service life at a stress near or above its idealized yield stress.

It is again emphasized that all four beams in Example 18-13 are within Code limitations and are usable sections under the Code, regardless of the fact that the concrete service stress is extremely high. But a designer who is inclined to worry may begin to feel uncomfortable with a structure in which stresses are allowed to reach idealized yield under day-to-day service loads; such a designer may wish to control these elastic stresses. The author is one such worrier who chooses to control these stresses, either by increasing the size of the section if possible, or by the use of yet more compressive reinforcement (without a corresponding increase in tensile reinforcement) to reduce the concrete stress.

Review Questions

1. In concrete, at what stress is the idealized yield stress assumed to occur?
2. How is the modulus of elasticity of concrete computed?
3. Describe the "balanced stress condition" at elastic levels of stress in a beam.
4. Given the section modulus S_c and the distance to the neutral axis kd, how is the moment of inertia I computed?
5. In flexural design of concrete, how is the effect of creep and shrinkage accounted for?
6. Define the steel ratios ρ and ρ'.
7. When flexural reinforcement is placed in two levels, to what level is the effective depth d measured?
8. In a particular rectangular beam subject to exterior exposures, the flexural reinforcement consists of No. 5 bars and the shear reinforcement consists of stirrups made from No. 4 bars. What clear cover is required for the flexural reinforcement? For the stirrups? Sketch your result and show the clear cover finally selected.
9. What is the effect of creep and shrinkage on the stress in the tensile reinforcement of a concrete beam?
10. What is the effect of creep and shrinkage on the stress in the compressive reinforcement of a concrete beam?
11. Define the elastic section modulus of a concrete beam in flexure.
12. Define the plastic section modulus of a concrete beam in flexure.
13. What is the maximum value of strain that is assumed to occur in concrete at ultimate load?
14. What is the maximum value of strain that is assumed to occur in the reinforcing steel at ultimate load?
15. At ultimate load, how does strain vary across the section?
16. How is the value of the ACI factor β_l determined?
17. What happens to stress in reinforcing steel once the steel enters yield?
18. How is the minimum stress ratio ρ determined?
19. For low steel ratios, that is, for steel ratios less than the maximum given by Eq.(18-33), what is the primary benefit to be realized in the use of compressive reinforcement?
20. Under what conditions can the maximum tensile steel ratio $0.75\rho_b$ be exceeded?
21. How can the service stress f_{sv} be called the "link" between ultimate levels of load and elastic levels of stress?
22. A section is designed without compressive reinforcement at the balanced stress condition; $f_c' = 4000$ psi, steel is Grade 60. What is the day-to-day service stress in the concrete?
23. At the balanced stress condition, about how much margin of strength is left when the steel and concrete first enter yield?

24. At the balanced condition, what is the nominal day-to-day service stress in the concrete, expressed as a percentage of f_c'?
25. At the balanced stress condition, what is the nominal day-to-day service stress in the tensile reinforcement, expressed as a percentage of the yield stress f_y?
26. When the steel ratio ρ of a particular beam is less than that at the balanced stress condition, which material will enter yield first, the concrete or the steel? How is it that the beam does not collapse completely at this point?
27. Why is the balanced stress configuration inherently an economical configuration?
28. What purpose is served in using compressive reinforcement at the balanced stress condition?
29. Under what conditions should the use of compressive steel be considered when the tensile steel ratio is less than $0.75\rho_b$?
30. What is the penalty in using steel ratios at or near the maximum allowable values?

CHAPTER

19

SHEAR IN CONCRETE BEAMS

In earlier chapters, the subject of flexure in concrete beams was developed along with methods for designing concrete beams to sustain the flexural loadings. It was found that concrete beams could be designed for flexure using the same concepts that were developed in elementary strength of materials for steel or timber. The lack of tensile strength in the concrete was overcome by adding reinforcement wherever tension was expected to occur. The procedures for designing concrete beams thus became somewhat more detailed than for steel or timber, but the concepts and procedures were familiar ones.

19.1 Effects of Shear in Concrete Beams

In addition to its effect on flexural strength, the lack of tensile strength in concrete also has a profound effect on the ability of concrete beams to resist shear. Even the relatively low levels of shear that are encountered in routine buildings can introduce serious tension fields in concrete beams. The design of concrete beams to sustain such shear-induced tension has no counterpart in other common structural materials; no other material is routinely reinforced for the tensions produced by beam shear.

The procedures for designing concrete beams for shear are simple and well developed and their effectiveness has been well proven over the years. Since there are hundreds of combinations of live and dead loads that could vary the shear patterns, the design for shear has evolved into a semiempirical "blanket" method which assures that the member will be capable of carrying the extremes in shear. Although the extremes may not occur in all beams, Code requires that all beams be capable of sustaining them.

A detailed analysis of shear in beams is beyond the scope of this book. Even if it were included, however, it would provide only background information; the actual design is prescibed by Code without requiring a rational analysis. The following sections contain only brief discussions and explanations of shear patterns in beams, intended to identify the sources of the shear problem and the solutions currently being used.

19.2 Shear as a Measure of Diagonal Tension

When a concrete beam is subjected to high shearing forces, tension stresses develop in the beam. It should be noted that using "shear as a measure of diagonal tension" is an accurate summary of the approach used by ACI to predict the magnitude of these tension stresses.

A simply supported rectangular beam subject to applied loadings is shown in Figure 10-1a. A section is removed and shown in Figure 10-1b, showing the shearing force that occurs across the section. Shear on a section is considered to be positive when the left side moves up with respect to the right.

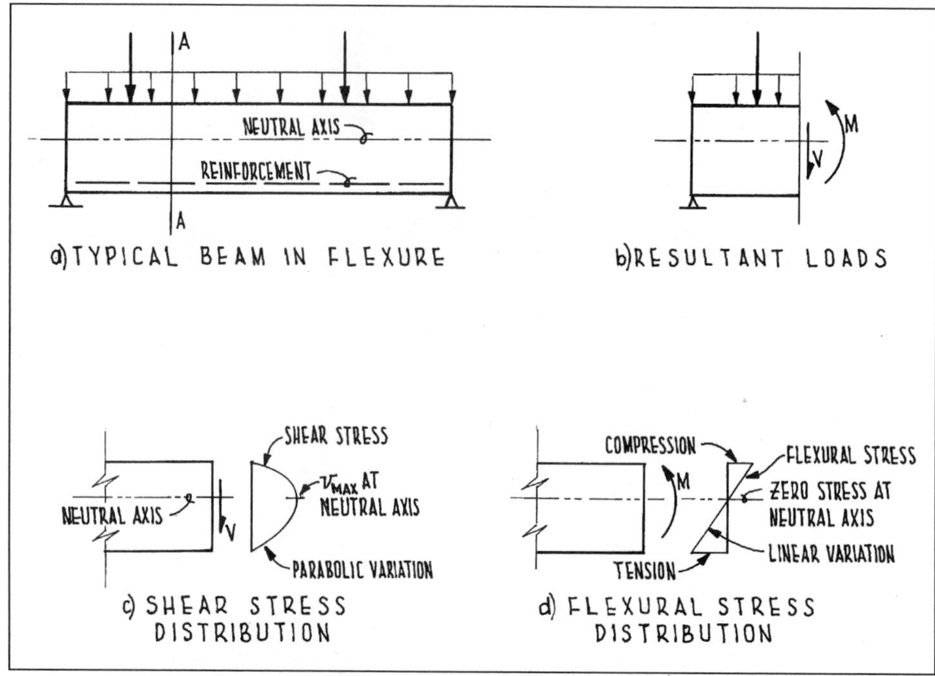

Figure 19-1 Beam under load.

The theory concerning the distribution of shear stress across a beam section was treated in Chapter 9, and the computation of stresses at various angles on a particle was treated in Chapter 11. The typical distribution of shear stress in a rectangular beam is shown in Figure 19-1c. Shear stress is seen to be maximum at the neutral axis and zero at the extreme fibers, just reverse to the distribution of flexure stress, shown for comparison in Figure 19-1d.

At the ends of a simply supported beam where there is no flexural stress and the shear stresses are highest, the shears acting alone will produce tension stresses acting at 45° from horizontal, as shown in Figure 19-2a. Examining the stress pattern from left to right across the span, it is seen that the angle must slowly change across the span toward the center as the shear decreases to zero and the bending moment increases to maximum. At midspan, where there is no shear on the section, the moment acting alone produces a tension stress acting horizontally.

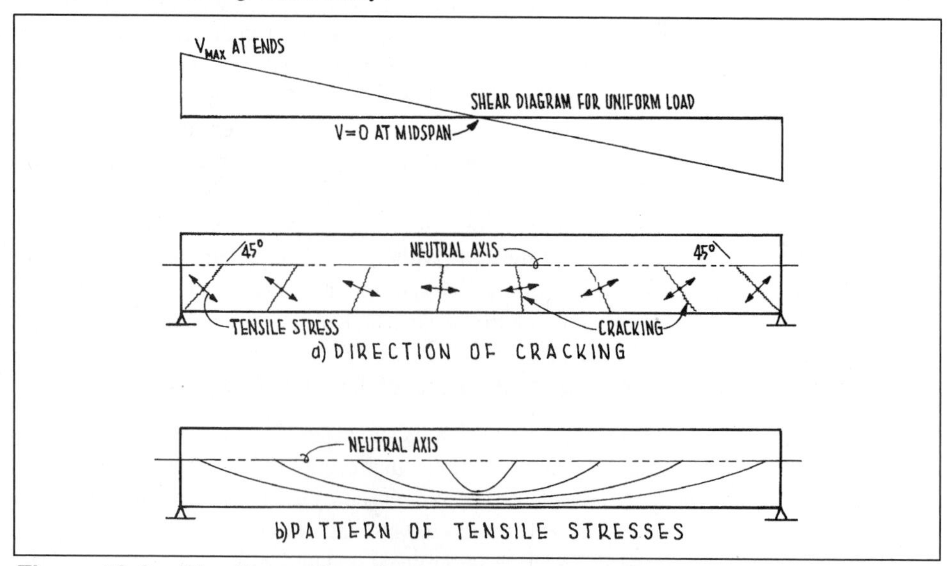

Figure 19-2 Directions of tensile stresses.

The tension cracks that can be expected to accompany the shear and moment stresses are also shown in Figure 19-2a. As stated earlier, these cracks are usually quite small, to the point of being invisible to the naked eye. Regardless how small, however, these cracks must exist if the steel reinforcement is to reach any significant levels of stress.

The general direction of tension stresses in a symmetrically loaded beam is shown in Figure 19-2b. Because concrete is so weak in tension, reinforcement must be provided wherever the diagonal tension reaches significant levels. It should be noted that diagonal tension can occur wherever there is shear stress; it is toward the ends of the beam at the neutral axis where the shear stress is highest that the problem is most serious.

19.3 Types of Effective Shear Reinforcement

Refer again to Figure 19-2. It is apparent that the directions of the cracks shown in Figure 19-2a will always be perpendicular to the direction of the tensile stresses shown in Figure 19-2b. A potential crack would therefore form first at the bottom of the beam, where tensile stresses due to flexure would be highest (Figure 19-1d). At the lowest point, the shear stresses would be zero (Figure 19-1c), so the crack would start as a vertical crack. The crack would then progress upward, turning gradually toward 45° as it nears the neutral axis, where shear stress is maximum and flexural stress is zero. At all points, the direction of the crack would be perpendicular to the direction of the tensile stress, as shown in Figure 19-2b.

The crack pattern just described is typical of a shear crack in beams, as indicated in Figure 19-3a. In this type of failure, the longitudinal steel is largely ineffective in resisting the separation of the beam into an upper piece and a lower piece. To be effective, any additional reinforcement would have to cross the crack and thereby keep the crack from becoming large enough to be detrimental. As noted before, the crack *must* form before the reinforcement can be stressed to any appreciable amount. The crack need be only the size of a hairline, however, for the steel to become effective.

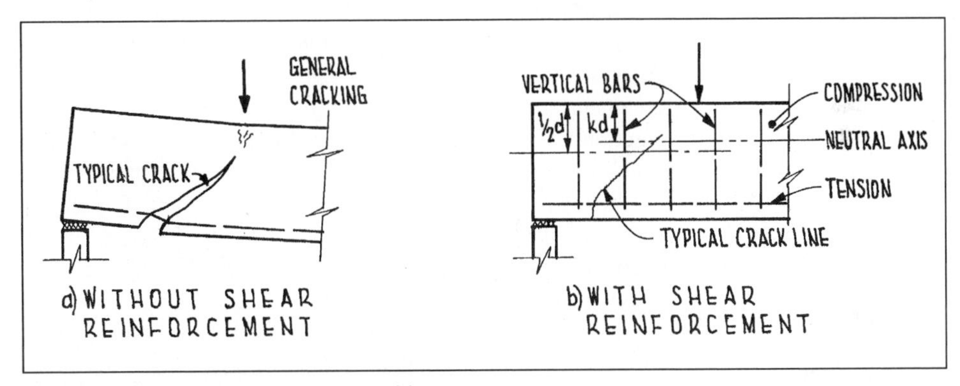

Figure 19-3 Typical shear cracking.

Ideally, the shape of the tensile reinforcement in a beam should follow the general pattern of the tensile stresses, shown in Figure 19-2b. Spaced at some relatively close spacing, the reinforcement would then cross any potential crack that might form, such as those shown in Figure 19-2a. Such a pattern of steel bars would be difficult to bend and nest into such a shape, but an approximate shape can readily be configured.

The schematic pattern of reinforcement shown in Figure 19-4a follows one such approximate configuration. When compared to the directions of stress shown in Figure 19-2b, it is apparent that this approximation is reasonably close to that desired. The longitudinal flexural reinforcement has simply been bent upward across the web after the moment has decreased to the point that it is no longer needed as flexural reinforcement. (The ends of the bars are bent back into a horizontal plane to produce anchorage.)

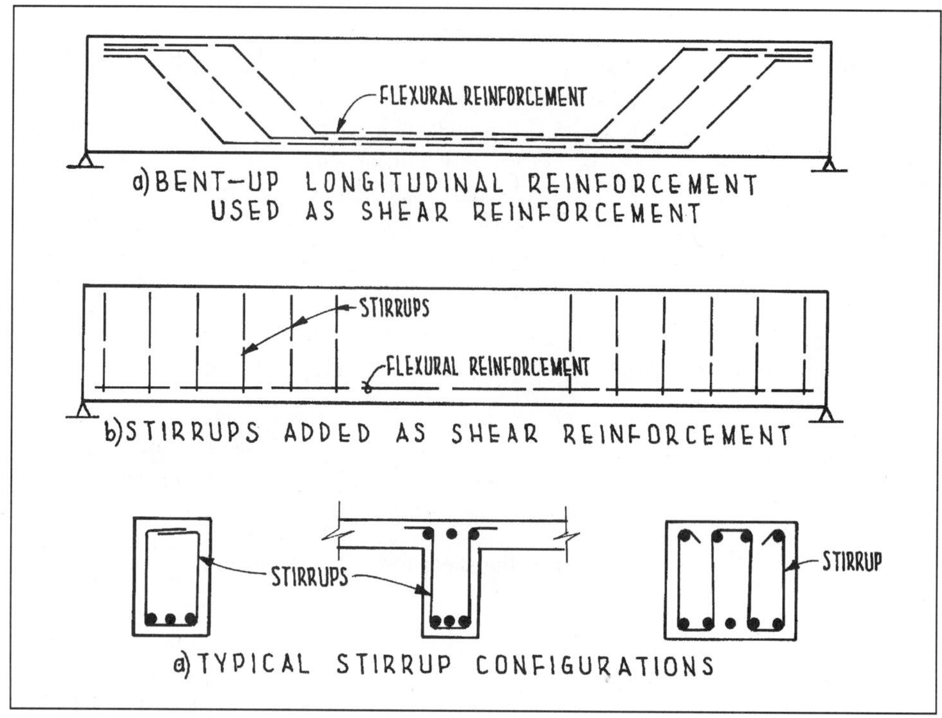

Figure 19-4 Shear reinforcement.

Toward the middle of the span, shear stresses become much lower, and little, if any, shear reinforcement may be required. The crack pattern in this area is shown in Figure 19-2a and is almost vertical; such tension comes as a result of flexural tension rather than shear. Toward the ends of the beam, the diagonal steel of Figure 19-4a intercepts the cracks almost at right angles and becomes effective reinforcement against diagonal tension.

Less efficient, but still effective, the vertical bars of Figure 19-4b also intercept the potential shear cracks. In combination with the separate bars used for longitudinal reinforcement, the configuration of Figure 19-4b provides only a rude approximation of the directions shown in Figure 19-2b. However approximate, the crack patterns have nonetheless been intercepted and the desired purpose has been achieved.

The pattern of diagonal shear reinforcement formed by bending the longitudinal reinforcement, as shown in Figure 19-4a, has been in use for many years. Additional diagonal bars may be added to extend the pattern of diagonal bars both toward the center of the span and toward the ends. In recent years, however, labor costs have increased disproportionately in comparison to materials costs and this method has been replaced by methods requiring less labor.

With few exceptions, the pattern of separate vertical bars shown in Figure 19-4b is used for shear reinforcement in today's practice. The cost of the small additional amount of steel is more than offset by lower labor costs and faster handling times. In this book, only this pattern of vertical shear reinforcement is presented.

Typical configurations of the separate vertical bars are shown in Figure 19-4c. Called *stirrups*, these bars are spaced along the span according to the level of shear stress; where shear stresses are higher, the stirrups are placed closer together. Where shear stresses are nearly zero toward the center of the span, stirrups can theoretically be omitted.

Stirrups offer an additional benefit to the builder, in that they provide a sturdy means of tying and holding the longitudinal steel in position while concrete is being cast. For that reason, the builder will frequently use lightweight stirrups even where none are required, or may extend the stirrups (at a wider spacing) across the middle part of the span even when the drawings show them omitted. The judicious use of stirrups in the design can be applied somewhat generously; they will usually be doubly beneficial.

19.4 Code Requirements for Shear

Where vertical stirrups are used for shear reinforcement, their design is stringently prescribed by Code (11.5). In the strength method, a simplified design is permitted which is based only on the ultimate shear force acting across the section; no consideration is given to any moments acting on the section. Code (11.3.2) also prescribes a more exact refinement of the method in which the moments are included; that refinement is not included in the following discussions.

Code (B.7) also permits the design of shear reinforcement using the alternate method, or working stress method, which will be discussed fully in a subsequent section. As usual in the alternate method, Code prescribes allowable stresses rather than allowable loads. Even so, both the strength method and the alternate method use essentially the same approach, but it is emphasized that one is not an exact multiple of the other.

In the strength method, Code (11.1.1) recognizes that the concrete by itself will take a portion of the total shear force even at failure. The concrete takes this transverse shearing force across the cracked section through friction; remember that the cracks are extremely fine and the rough cracked surface will still develop a friction force. The remainder of the shear force is, of course, taken by stirrups. That part taken by concrete alone, V_c, is computed by

$$V_c = 2\sqrt{f'_c}\,b_w d \tag{19-1}$$

where b_w is the width of the concrete web (or stem of a tee) and all other symbols are the same as defined earlier. For cicular sections, the effective web width b_w is taken as the diameter of the section.

The terms used in Eq.(19-1) are usually interpreted as an "average" ultimate shear stress of $2\sqrt{f'_c}$ acting across the somewhat arbitrary web area (or stem area of a tee) given by $b_w d$. Although this is a convenient interpretation and this "average" ultimate shear stress is a useful parameter, the Code makes no such claim. The equation is simply a highly generalized but proven means to compute the load taken by the concrete; it applies equally to rectangular beams and slabs as well as tee shapes, circular shapes, and irregular shapes.

The remainder of the nominal ultimate shear force V_n is taken by the vertical steel stirrups. That force, V_n-V_c, is designated V_s and is also prescribed by Code (11.5.6), but it is, of course, dependent on the spacing of the stirrups. The horizontal spacing of the stirrups, shown in Figure 19-5, is specified as a portion of the effective depth, such as $^1/_2 d$, $^1/_4 d$, and so on. As the stirrups are spaced closer together, the force V_s is permitted to be higher.

Code (11.5.4) prescribes a maximum spacing of $^1/_2 d$ for stirrups and implies a minimum spacing of $^1/_4 d$, but places no restrictions on the number of intermediate spacings that may be used. Considering the overall level of accuracy of the highly generalized design method, a rigorous calculation using several intermediate stirrup spacings is difficult to justify. In this text, stirrup spacings will be limited to the two Code values, $^1/_2 d$ and $^1/_4 d$.

The force per space V_s that may be taken by a single stirrup is given by Code (11.5.6.2) in terms of the spacing:

$$V_s = V_n - V_c = \frac{A_v f_y d}{s} \tag{19-2}$$

where s is the stirrup spacing, shown in Figure 19-5, and A_v is the total cross-sectional area of steel in the stirrup; other symbols are those used previously.

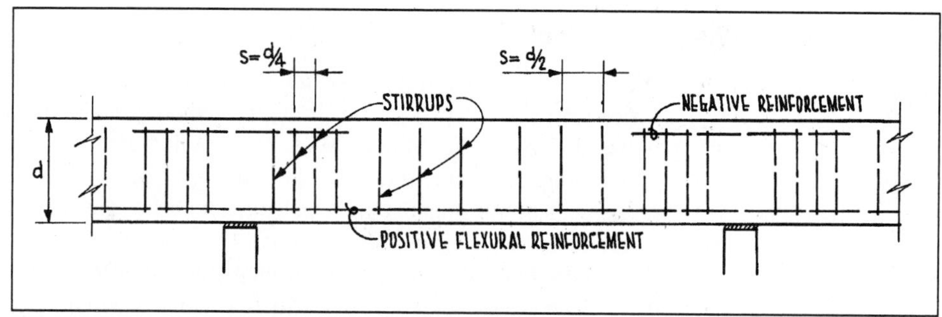

Figure 19-5 Stirrup spacing.

The nominal ultimate shear force V_n that the entire section can develop, including benefits due to stirrups, can be stated as an average ultimate shear stress v_n times the cross-sectional area:

$$V_n = v_n b_w d \tag{19-3}$$

Such an average shear stress is shown in the sketch of Figure 19-6.

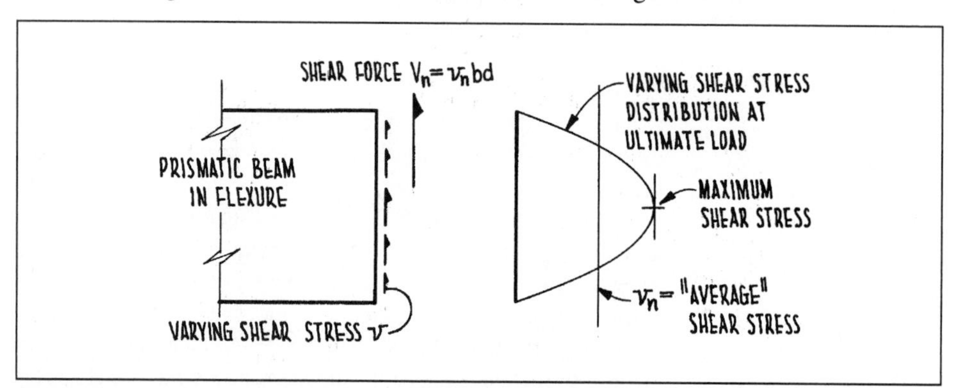

Figure 19-6 Average shear stress on a section.

The maximum values of this average ultimate shear stress v_n that can be developed at various levels of reinforcement are, when extracted from the Code:

$$\text{No stirrups: } v_n \leq 2\sqrt{f'_c} \tag{19-4a}$$

$$\text{Stirrups at } {}^1\!/_2 d\text{: } v_n \leq 6\sqrt{f'_c} \tag{19-4b}$$

$$\text{Stirrups at } {}^1\!/_4 d\text{: } v_n \leq 10\sqrt{f'_c} \tag{19-4c}$$

Code limitations do not permit the average ultimate shear stress to exceed $10\sqrt{f'_c}$.

When the values of Eqs.(19-4) are used to compute the shear forces, it is convenient to use the ratio of the stresses rather than the stresses themselves.

$$\text{For concrete alone: } V_c \leq v_n b_w d = 2\sqrt{f'_c}\, b_w d$$

$$\text{Without stirrups: } V_n \leq V_c \tag{19-5a}$$

$$\text{With stirrups at } {}^1\!/_2 d\text{: } V_n \leq 3V_c \tag{19-5b}$$

$$\text{With stirrups at } {}^1\!/_4 d\text{: } V_n \leq 5V_c \tag{19-5c}$$

The 1:3:5 ratios given in Eqs.(19-5) are easy to remember and apply. One first determines the ultimate shear force V_c that the section can sustain without any shear reinforcement, in which case $V_c = 2\sqrt{f'_c}\, b_w d$. Then, if stirrups are added at a spacing of ${}^1\!/_2 d$, the section can take a total shear force $V_n = 3V_c$. Or, if stirrups are added at a spacing of ${}^1\!/_4 d$, the section can take a total shear force $V_n = 5V_c$. There is thus no need for complex calculations to find the allowable shear force on a reinforced section.

Before proceeding with an example, it is well to list several other requirements and practices:

1. Sections located closer than a distance *d* from the face of support may be designed for a "critical" shear force V_{cr} computed at a distance *d* from the face of support.
2. The first stirrup shall be placed within a distance of $^1/_2d$ from the face of support where the required spacing is $^1/_2d$ and within a distance of $^1/_4d$ from the face of support where the required spacing is $^1/_4d$.
3. Minimum shear reinforcement shall be placed wherever the nominal ultimate shear force V_n acting on the section exceeds one-half the shear strength of the concrete V_c.
4. Minimum total cross-sectional area of shear reinforcement in all legs is designated A_v and is computed by

$$A_v = 50\frac{b_w s}{f_y} \tag{19-6}$$

5. Strength reduction factor ϕ for shear is 0.85.

The third requirement is something of a curiosity. It states that shear reinforcement is not required at all unless the nominal ultimate shear force exceeds V_c, but when the nominal ultimate shear does exceed V_c, the shear reinforcement must begin back at $^1/_2V_c$ rather than at V_c.

In addition to the foregoing requirements, there is a practical matter to be considered concerning the placement of stirrups. Heavy stirrups at close spacing are most likely to be required at the ends of heavily loaded girders. At a module (column) point, it can be expected that two such girders with their heavy negative reinforcement and their stirrups will intersect a column with its heavy vertical reinforcement and ties. The congestion of reinforcement in such locations is often formidable. Wherever reasonable, the size of the girders should be kept large enough that the minimum stirrup spacing of $^1/_4d$ is never required; a spacing not smaller than $^1/_2d$ should be maintained if possible.

It should be recognized that the strength reduction factor ϕ is applied only to external loads, not to any of the computed capacities of the section. For that reason it is recommended that the factor ϕ always be included with the shear diagram when making shear computations; it need never be applied thereafter. By this means, there is no confusion later whether the factor ϕ should or should not be applied to any other loads that may be under consideration.

19.5 Examples in Reinforcing for Shear

The following examples illustrate the procedure; a relatively simple continuous rectangular beam is chosen as the first example. Shear and moment diagrams are given. A more general coverage is presented in Chapter 21 with tee beams, but it should be recognized that in designing shear reinforcement, all sections are considered to be rectangular; the shear capacity is based on a rectangular area $b_w d$ regardless whether the section is a tee or a rectangle or a circle.

Example 19-1

Design of shear reinforcement. Flexural design already completed.

To Find: Determine the shear reinforcement for the symmetrically loaded rectangular beam shown below. Reinforcement for flexure has already been selected as indicated. Shear and moment diagrams include dead load and are drawn from the nominal ultimate values of V_n and M_n; they include the strength reduction factor ϕ. Use Grade 60 steel, $f'_c = 3000$ psi.

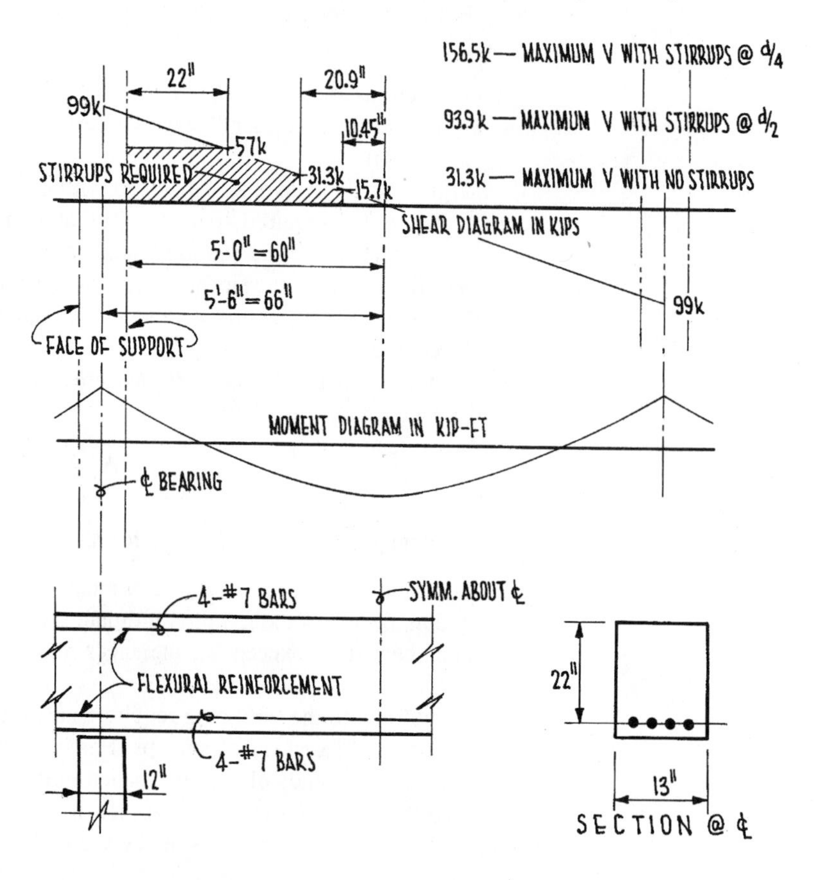

Solution: Calculate (or scale) the critical shear V_{cr} at a distance d from the face of support, by ratio:

$$V_{cr} = \frac{60 - 22}{66} 99 = 57 \text{ kips (includes } \phi)$$

Determine the allowable shear forces for the three levels of reinforcement:

$$\text{For concrete alone: } V_c = 2\sqrt{f'_c}\, b_w d = 2\sqrt{3000}(13)(22) = 31.3 \text{ kips}$$

No stirrups: $V_n = 1(31.3) = 31.3$ kips
Stirrups at $^1/_2 d$: $V_n = 3(31.3) = 93.9$ kips
Stirrups at $^1/_4 d$: $V_n = 5(31.3) = 156.5$ kips

Determine the horizontal distance to V_{cr} (without stirrups) from the centerline of the beam:

$$\text{distance} = \frac{31.3}{99} 66 = 20.9 \text{ in. from the centerline of the beam.}$$

The foregoing shears and distances have been plotted on the shear diagram above. Note that a stirrup spacing of $^1/_2 d$ (11 in.) will be required, beginning within a distance of $^1/_2 d$ from the face of support and extending to within 10.45 in. of the centerline of the beam. Since the stirrups extend so close to the center, it is chosen in this case to use stirrups across the entire span.

The chosen layout of stirrups is shown in the following sketch.

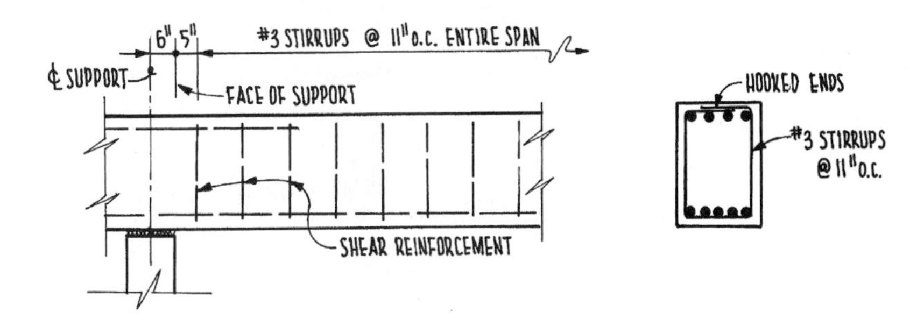

Calculate the required size of the stirrups for the indicated layout, for Grade 60 steel. The maximum shear to be carried by any section is 57 kips:

$$V_s = V_{cr} - V_c = \frac{A_v f_y d}{s}; \quad A_v = \frac{(V_{cr} - V_c)s}{f_y d}$$

$$A_v = \frac{(57 - 31.3)(10^3)(11)}{60{,}000(22)} = 0.214\text{in.}^2 \text{ (in two legs)}$$

Use stirrups, No. 3 bars at 11 in. off center as shown in the sketch.

The stirrups chosen for Example 19-1 are shown with hooks at their upper end. The hooks are an anchorage requirement that is discussed in Chapter 20. It is also a requirement that the stirrups must be anchored within the compression side of the beam. Theoretically, for those parts of the span where the bottom of the beam is in compression, the stirrups would have to be turned upside down, such that the hooks are on the bottom. Such a state of stress occurs at the supports, where the moment is negative, but turning the stirrups is rarely done.

Just as it is possible to vary the stirrup spacing across the span to suit the variations in the shearing force, so is it possible to vary the size of the bar used for stirrups where the load is small enough to justify it. Such refinements are rarely made in small buildings. The tonnage of steel that can be saved by such measures would rarely justify the time and effort spent in engineering, drafting, field layout, and in just keeping track of the additional mark numbers of stirrups.

Where a beam is not quite symmetrically loaded but is nearly so, the shear reinforcement is usually laid out symmetrically to avoid the additional labor hours in drafting and field layout. It also obviates any possibility of the stirrups being installed backwards in the beam. On occasion, however, where a beam is distinctly antisymmetrical, the shear reinforcement must be laid out to suit the actual shear diagram. The procedure is the same, just more complex, as illustrated in the next example.

Example 19-2

Design of shear reinforcement. Flexural design already completed.

To Find: Determine the shear reinforcement for the antisymmetrically loaded rectangular beam shown below. Reinforcement for flexure has already been selected as indicated. Shear and moment diagrams include dead load and are drawn for the nominal ultimate values of V_n and M_n; the indicated loads include load factors as well as the strength reduction factor ϕ. Use Grade 60 steel and f'_c=3000 psi.

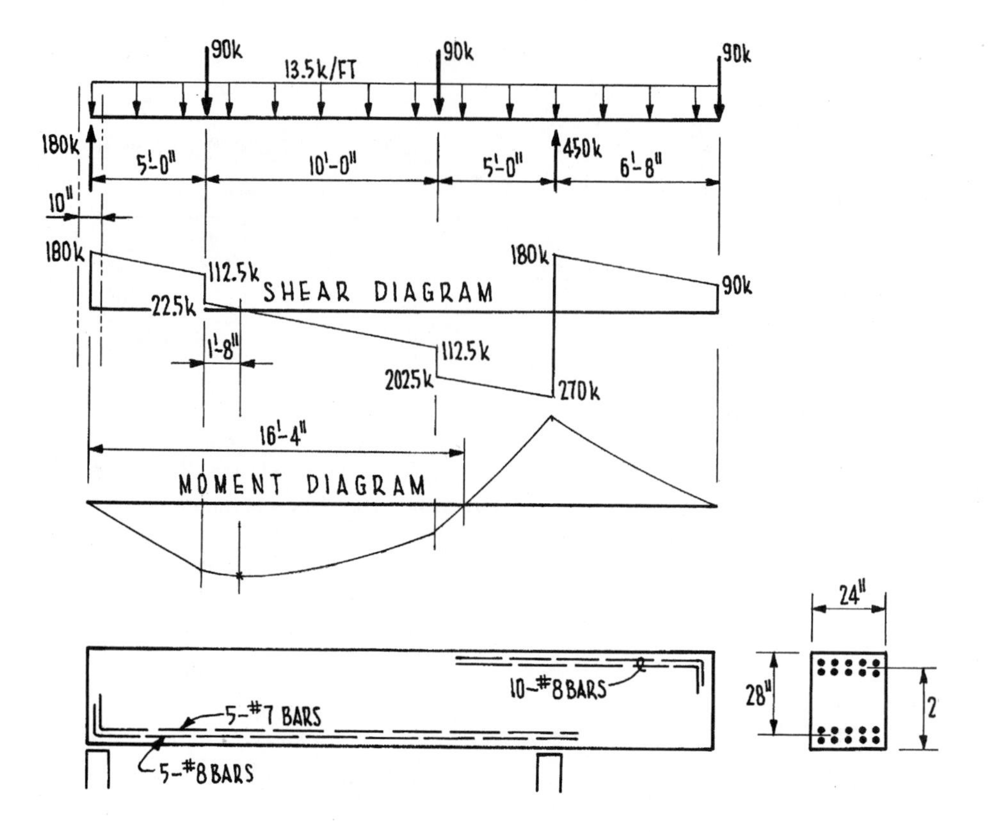

Solution: Calculate (or scale) V_{cr} at a distance d from face of support:

At right side of left support, 33 in. from centerline of support:

$$V_{cr} = 180 - (180 - 112.5)\,{}^{33}\!/_{60} = 143 \text{ kips}$$

At left side of right support, 33 in. from centerline of support:

$$V_{cr} = 270 - (270 - 202.5)\,{}^{33}\!/_{60} = 233 \text{ kips}$$

At right side of right support, 33 in. from centerline of support:

$$V_{cr} = 180 - (180 - 90)\,{}^{33}\!/_{80} = 143 \text{ kips}$$

Determine the allowable shear forces for the three levels of reinforcement:

For concrete alone: $V_c = 2\sqrt{f'_c}\,b_w d = 2\left(\sqrt{3000}\right)(24)(28)$
$= 73.6$ kips

No stirrups: $V_n = 1(73.6) = 73.6$ kips
Stirrups at $^1/_2$d: $V_n = 3(73.6) = 221$ kips
Stirrups at $^1/_4$d: $V_n = 5(73.6) = 1368$ kips

Plot the foregoing values to scale on the shear diagram as shown below.

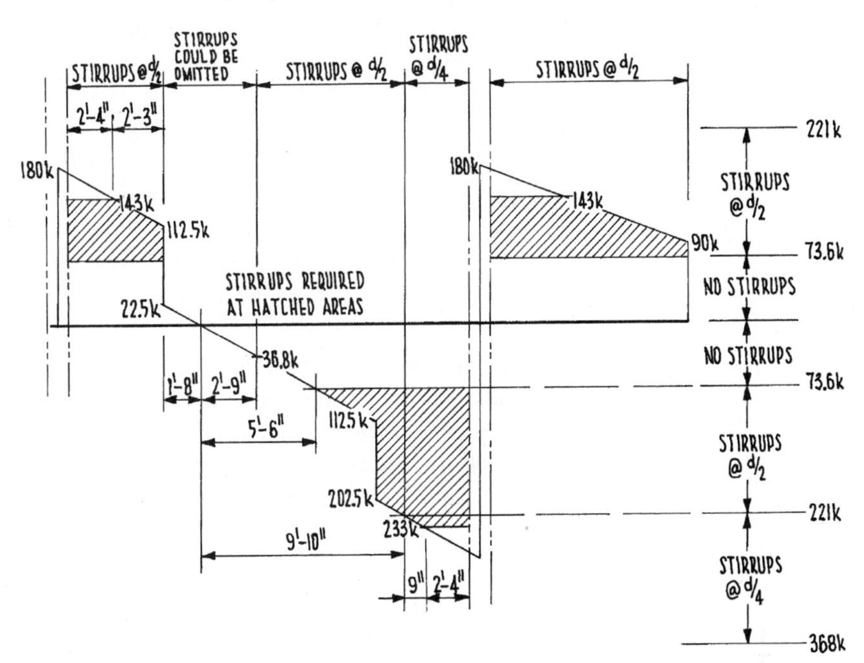

Calculate the required size for the stirrups:

$$V_s = V_n - V_c = \frac{A_v f_y d}{s}; \quad A_v = \frac{(V_n - V_c)s}{f_y d}$$

For spacing at $^1/_4$d: $A_v = \dfrac{(233 - 73.6)(7)}{60{,}000(28)} = 0.664 \text{ in.}^2$

For spacing at $^1/_2$d: $A_v = \dfrac{(221 - 73.6)(14)}{60{,}000(28)} = 1.23 \text{ in.}^2$

Use four legs, No. 5 bars, $A_v = 1.23$ in.^{2}

Final shear reinforcement is shown in the following sketch.

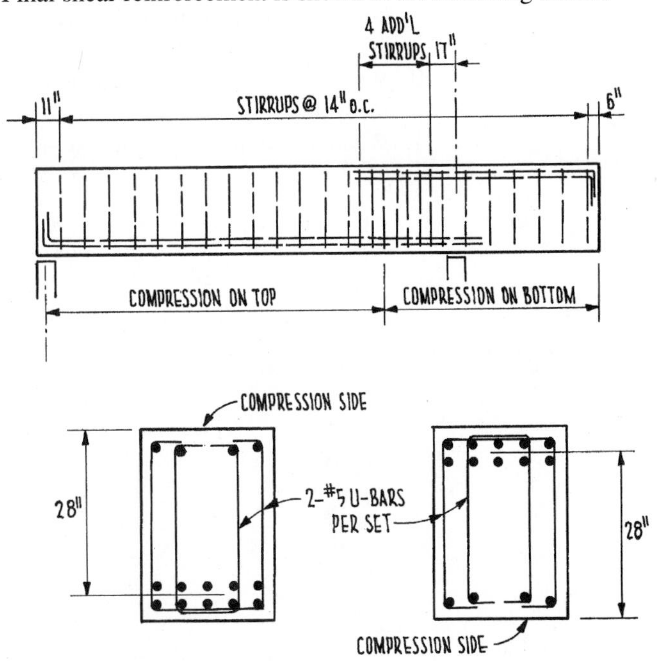

19.6 Shear at Service Levels of Stress

The procedure for the design of shear reinforcement at service levels of stress is identical to that at ultimate levels of load; one is a direct scalar multiple of the other. At service levels of stress:

Unreinforced, $v_{sv} = v_p/1.7 = 1.18\sqrt{f'_c}$ (19-6)

No stirrups, $V_{sv} = 1V_c = 1.18\sqrt{f'_c}\, b_w d$ (19-6a)

With stirrups @ $^1/_2$d, $V_{sv} = 3V_c$ (19-6b)

With stirrups @ $^1/_4$d, $V_{sv} = 5V_c$ (19-6c)

Since one method is simply a direct numerical multiple (or fraction) of the other, there is no particular reason to prefer one method over the other. As a consequence, only the ultimate strength method is included here. If one wishes, however, the entire design for shear could be performed at service levels, simply by using the reduced values for the allowable stresses in concrete and in steel. (It is well to note that design at service levels of stress is *not* the same as the "working stress method" of design; the two are *not* equivalent.)

Review Questions

1. When a particle is subjected to a pure shear, how is it that a tension stress occurs?
2. Where in the cross section of a beam is flexure stress highest? Lowest? Where is shear stress highest? Lowest?
3. Where in the span of a simply supported beam is bending moment highest? Where are shearing forces highest?
4. In view of the answers to Questions 2 and 3, explain why the design for shear in a concrete beam may be treated generally independently from the design for flexure.
5. In view of the answers to Questions 2 through 4, explain why the direction of shear cracks will be close to 45° at the ends of a simple span, becoming more nearly vertical toward midspan.
6. How do vertical stirrups provide reinforcement for a diagonal tension stress?
7. On a beam having a circular cross section, what is the shear width b_w?
8. In view of the answer to Question 7, deteremine an effective width for b_w for a hollow circular beam of reinforced concrete.
9. What is the strength reduction factor ϕ for shear?
10. Where is the strength reduction factor ϕ applied in the ultimate strength design method?
11. Where is the strength reduction factor ϕ applied in the working stress design method?

CHAPTER

20

ANCHORAGE OF REINFORCEMENT

In any use of reinforcement, there must be a capability to transfer stress between the reinforcement and the concrete at every point along the reinforcement. This "fixing" of the reinforcement to the adjacent concrete is called *anchorage*. Such anchorage of reinforcement throughout its length is the subject of this chapter.

20.1 Definitions and Concepts

The term *development length*, denoted ℓ_d, is used frequently in subsequent discussions. The development length of a reinforcing bar is the length of bar that must be bonded to the concrete to develop the full strength of the bar. Ideally, the end of a bar could be embedded in a block of concrete to a depth equal to its development length and when the protruding end is loaded to failure, the bar itself will fail just as it starts to pull out of the concrete block. A typical state of this equilibrium loading is shown on the reinforcing bar of Figure 20-1.

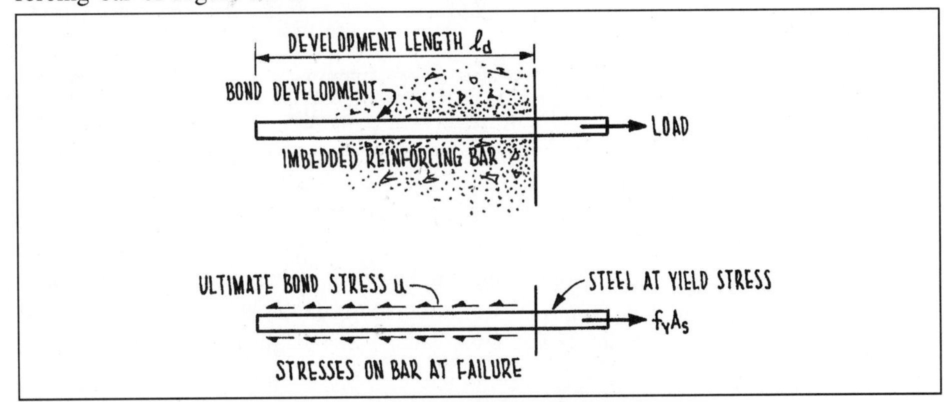

Figure 20-1 Development length of reinforcement.

The adhesion of concrete to its reinforcement is called *bond*. It is pointed out in Chapter 16 that bond strength is one of the more uncertain properties of concrete that must be used in design. To reduce the dependence on theoretical values when using this uncertain property, the development lengths of reinforcement under a wide variety of circumstances have been determined by extensive tests; requirements for embedment have been established from these test results and are prescribed by Code.

There are several special circumstances defined by the Code where the development lengths may be reduced somewhat. Those special circumstances that are encountered frequently enough to justify the time and effort to learn them are included in the subsequent sections. Other cases, infrequently applicable, are omitted to avoid a confusion of special cases. The results herein may therefore be slightly conservative at times.

Present Code requirements are prescribed by empirical formulae, to be used for computing the required embedment length under various circumstances. These lengths have been computed for various bar sizes and are tabulated in Tables C-12 and C-13 in the Technical Manual. The lengths were determined from the criteria given in the following discussions; they are equally applicable whether the design is being done according to the strength method or at elastic stress levels.

The following discussions are limited to bar sizes No. 11 or smaller for flexural reinforcement and to bar sizes No. 5 or smaller for stirrups and ties. Bar sizes larger than these are subject to additional Code requirements requiring additional design considerations and conditional checks. Further, these larger sizes would apply primarily to heavy construction, which is beyond the scope of this book.

In addition, consideration here is limited only to deformed bars; smooth wire and mesh are not included. Code requirements concerning the patterns and sizes of the deformations are quite stringent. Several approved patterns of deformations are shown in Figure 20-2.

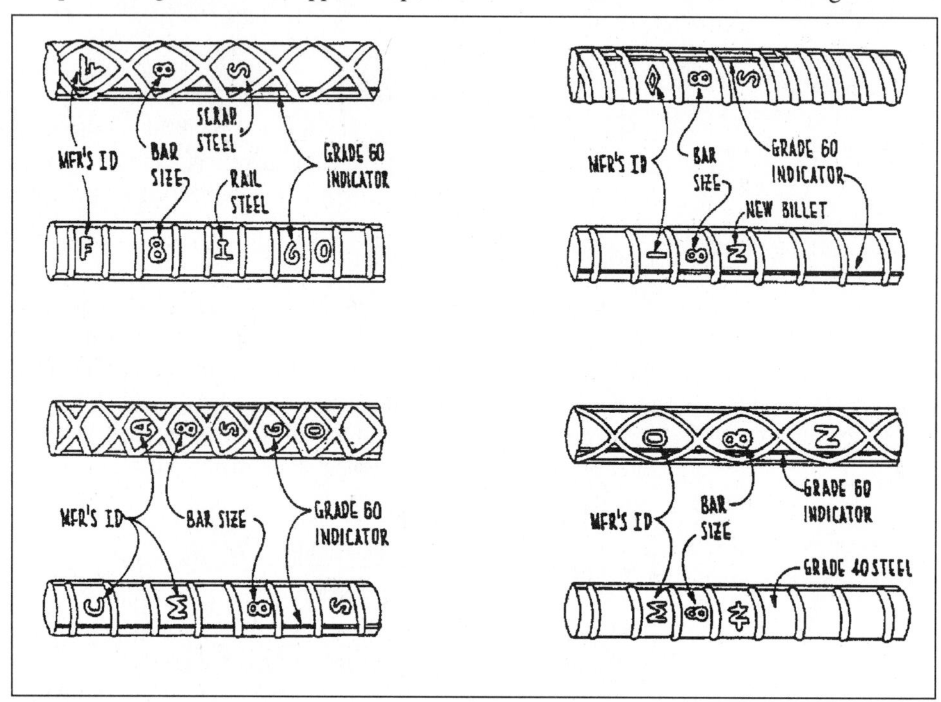

Figure 20-2 Deformation patterns on reinforcement.

The strength reduction factor ϕ is rarely required in determination of development lengths. The empirical formulas adopted by ACI inherently include the effects of placement tolerances and other factors that might affect ultimate strength.

20.2 Effects of Cover, Spacing and Transverse Ties

Even very small cracks in the concrete immediately surrounding reinforcing bars can have detrimental effects on bond and anchorage. Providing a minimum amount of cover and a minimum amount of space between bars can do a great deal toward reduction or elimination of such cracks. Further, placing transverse ties or stirrups at very close spacing around the longitudinal reinforcement will provide a very positive control over potential cracking, even where cover is minimum or bar spacing is close.

Code minimums for cover and spacing are given in Chapter 17. It should be noted immediately, however, that the minimum cover specified in Chapter 17 is the cover that will protect the reinforcement from weather, oxidation and intrusion of salts; the requirement for clear cover given there is unrelated to the development of reinforcement through bond. Similarly, requirements for bar spacing given in Chapter 17 are the minimum distances that will allow free movement of the wet concrete between bars during placement; those requirements for clear spacing are generally unrelated to the development of the reinforcement.

The cracking or splitting of concrete around its reinforcement is shown in Figure 20-3. Where cover over the bars is inadequate, a splitting crack outward to the surface will occur as indicated in Figure 20-3a. Where bar spacing is too close, a splitting crack will propagate between bars as shown in Figure 20-3b. Such splitting may be controlled, however, by providing closely spaced ties at alternate bars as shown in Figure 20-3c.

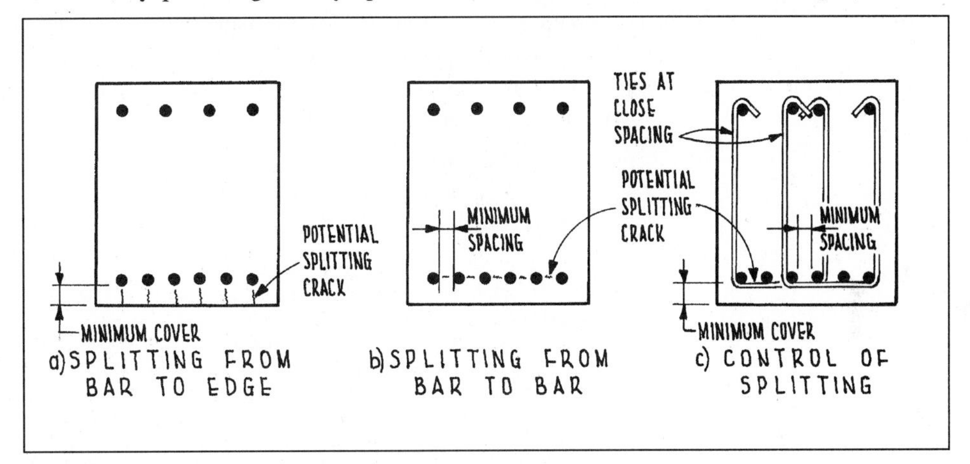

Figure 20-3 Cover, spacing and transverse ties.

The topics of cover, spacing and transverse ties are considered in the following sections. The three items are intimately interrelated; inadequacies in one item can sometimes be corrected by providing excesses in another. The approach, however, is a cookbook approach, using certain configurations that have been tried and tested and are therefore known to work.

20.3 Development Length of Straight Bars in Tension

There are many variables that can have an effect on the required development lengths for reinforcement. The more common variables recognized by Code are:

- Clear concrete cover to the nearest exposed face (for beams, columns, slabs, walls).
- Clear spacing between bars (for beams, columns, slabs, walls).
- Transverse reinforcement (existence of stirrups or ties).
- Distance from bottom of bar to bottom face of member (whether top bars or bottom bars).
- Type of aggregate (whether regular or lightweight).
- Coatings on bars (whether epoxy coated or clean).
- Excess reinforcement at a section (whether A_s provided is greater than A_s required).
- Bundling of reinforcement (whether bars are grouped in bundles of 2, 3 or 4 bars).

Code (12.2.2) establishes a "basic" development length ℓ_{db} based on standard sets of assumed conditions. If any of the assumed conditions is not met, a prescribed multiplier is used to extend the development length, thereby supplying additional length to correct for the inadequacy. In the event the actual conditions are better than the assumed conditions, a reduction of the development length may be permitted; the reduction is similarly obtained by multiplying the basic development length by a prescribed modifier. After all extensions and reductions have been applied, the resulting development length ℓ_d is then checked against the absolute minimum development length required by Code. The end result of such a computation is a development length for deformed bars in tension that closely conforms to the actual design conditions.

Note that in the terminology of the Code, extensions to the basic development length are computed through the use of a "multiplier," while reductions are computed through the use of a "modifier."

Horizontal bars having 12 inches or more of fresh concrete cast below them are called "top" bars in the Code. Top bars can lose a considerable amount of bond strength due to collections of air, water and laitance at their lower side. These impurities rise and collect under the bars during compaction of the concrete. Code (12.2.4.1) requires that additional development length be provided for such bars.

The requirements for computing development lengths of deformed bars in tension are summarized in Table 20-1. A detailed examination of Table 20-1 indicates that as a very general guide, splitting of concrete cover can be controlled by maintaining a minimum cover of $2d_b$ over all reinforcement. Similarly, splitting from bar-to-bar along a line of reinforcement can be controlled by maintaining a minimum spacing of $3d_b$ between bars. If the cover and spacing do not meet these minimums, then additional development length will be required to offset the possibility of splitting.

Two new symbols are used in Table 20-1:

A_{tr} is the area of steel (stirrups or ties) transverse to the steel being spliced or developed.

N is the number of bars in a layer being spliced or developed.

Table 20-1 Development Lengths in Tension.

- Compute basic development length ℓ_{db} for deformed bars in tension under standard conditions of service:

$$\ell_{db} \geq \frac{0.04 A_b f_y}{\sqrt{f'_c}}$$

- The foregoing value of ℓ_{db} is valid if any one of the four following sets of standard conditions is met:

   1. Bars used in beams and columns:
      Clear cover meeting Code minimums.
      Clear spacing $\geq 3d_b$.
      Ties or stirrups meeting Code minimums.

   or 2. Bars used in beams and columns:
      Clear cover meeting Code minimums.
      Clear spacing meeting Code minimums.
      Ties or stirrups having $A_{tr} \geq d_b sN/40$

   or 3. Bars used in slabs or walls:
      Clear cover meeting Code minimums.
      Clear spacing $\geq 3d_b$.

   or 4. Bars used in any type of member:
      Clear cover $\geq 2d_b$.
      Clear spacing $\geq 3d_b$.

- Should an inadequacy exist in the applicable set of standard conditons:
   Multiply ℓ_{db} by a factor of 2 if cover $\leq d_b$.
   Multiply ℓ_{db} by a factor of 2 if spacing $\leq 2d_b$.
   Multiply ℓ_{db} by a factor of 1.4 for any other inadequacy.

- Should a significant excess exist in the applicable set of standard conditions:
   Modify ℓ_{db} by a factor of 0.8 if spacing $\geq 5d_b$ and cover $\geq 2.5\ d_b$.
   Modify ℓ_{db} by a factor of 0.75 if No. 4 ties at 4 in. o.c. exists.

- Check ℓ_{db} against Code minimum: $\ell_{db} \geq 0.03 d_b f_y / \sqrt{f'_c}$

- Multiply ℓ_{db} by a factor of 1.3 for top bars.

- Modify ℓ_{db} by a factor of (A_s required)/(A_s provided) for excess A_s.

- Check final ℓ_d against absolute Code minimum: $\ell_d \geq 12$ inches.

The criteria for development length have been incorporated into the development lengths listed in Table C-13 in the Technical Manual, insofar as possible. Table C-13 was prepared assuming that at least one of the four basic sets of standard conditions has been met. The only multiplier appearing in the table is that for top bars; no other multiplier or modifier has been included.

Other multipliers may be applied as appropriate to extend the development lengths given in Table C-13. For reductions, however, the only modifier that may be applied to the values given in Table C-13 is the modifier to account for excess reinforcement. Development lengths which include excess cover or excess spacing must be recomputed manually in their entirety; such computations must include appropriate checks against the Code minimums, $\ell_{db} \leq 0.03d_bf_y/\sqrt{f'_c}$ and $\ell_d \leq 12$ inches, where appropriate.

Some examples will demonstrate the use of Table C-13 in finding development lengths.

Example 20-1

Determination of development lengths.

Given: Cantilever slab as shown; Grade 60 steel, $\sqrt{f'_c} = 4000$ psi. Structure not exposed to weather.

To Find: Required imbedment length of longitudinal bars.

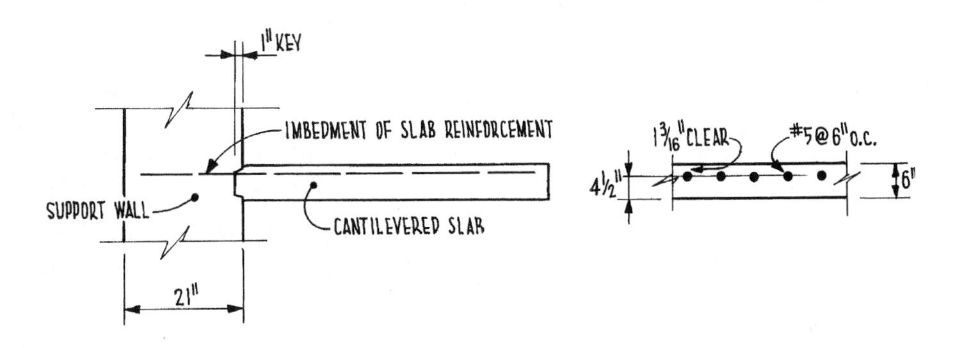

Solution: Clear cover = $1^3/_{16}$" clear or $1.9d_b$.
Clear spacing = $6^5/_8$" or $8.6d_b$.

Conclude that the set of standard conditions given in Table 20-1 as set No. 3 have been met.

With only $4^3/_{16}$" of concrete below the bars, these bars are not top bars.

From Table C-13, find $\ell_d = 18$ in.

Use imbedment 18 in. into support for 100% development.

Example 20-2

Determination of development lengths.

Given: Cantilever slab of Example 20-1 but with No. 7 bars @ 12 in., providing roughly the same A_s per foot of width.

To Find: Whether this selection of reinforcement is permissible with straight bars as shown.

Solution: Clear cover = $1^1/_{16}$" clear or $1.2d_b$.
Clear spacing = $6^7/_8$" = $5^1/_8$" clear or $5.86d_b$.

Conclude that the set of standard conditions given in Table 20-1 as set No. 3 have been met.

From Table C-13 find ℓ_d = 25 in.

Since the support is only 21 in. wide, there is not enough room to anchor these bars so this selection is not permissible.

Example 20-3

Determination of development lengths.

Given: Rectangular section under negative moment, 12 in. x 20 in. Required negative reinforcement is 2.31 in.^{2} Assume clear cover of 2 in. to top face of section. Exterior exposure, Grade 60 steel, f'_c = 3000 psi.

To Find: Required development length at support.

Solution: The bar arrangement is shown in the sketch. Assume 4 - No. 7 bars for reinforcement, A_s = 2.4 in.^{2}

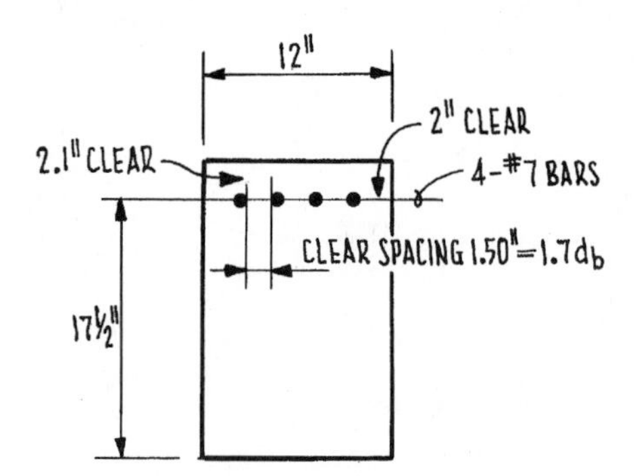

Since spacing of the bars is less than $3d_b$, the standard conditions given in Table 20-1 for set No. 1 or set No. 2 have not been met by this steel arrangement. A multiplier of 2 must therefore be used for the values given in Table C-13.

From Table C-13, find ℓ_d = 37 in. (for top bars).

With multiplier of 2, ℓ_d = 74 in.

Note that the development length required in Example 20-3 is more than 6 feet, half of which is due to the fact that the clear distance is too small. Such a severe penalty often makes it worthwhile to juggle the bar sizes to reduce the development lengths. In Example 12-3, for example, the use of 3 - No. 8 bars will meet the required steel area of 2.31 in.^{2}, but will require a smaller development length of only 63 inches. Such a reduction can sometimes be a worthwhile alternative. Verification of this reduction is left to the reader.

Example 20-4

Determination of development lengths in tension.

Given: Rectangular beam, 16 in. wide, f'_c = 4000 psi, Grade 50 steel. 4 - No. 6 bars in tension, classed as "other than top" bars. Required A_s = 1.01 in.^{2}, exterior exposure. Clear cover 2.5 in. both vertical and horizontal.

To Find: Required development length of bars in tension.

Solution: Compare cover requirements to cover actually provided:

Code minimum cover for No. 6 bars, exterior exposure, must be ≥ 2.0 in.

Required cover if modifier is allowed must be ≥ $2d_b$.

Cover actually provided = 2.50 in. ≥ $2d_b$.

Conclude: cover meets minimum requirements.
cover O.K. for modifier if spacing ≥ $3d_b$.

Compare spacing requirements to actual spacing:

Code minimum spacing ≥ $1d_b$ but not less than 1 in.

Clear spacing actually provided:

$$\text{Spacing} = \frac{b - 2(\text{clear cover}) - \text{No. bars}(d_b)}{\text{No. bars} - 1}$$

$$= \frac{16 - 2(2.50) - 4(0.75)}{4 - 1} = 2.67 \text{ in.} \geq 3d_b.$$

Conclude: Spacing meets Code minimums; no multipliers are required; and spacing and cover permit use of modifier.

Compare required steel area to area actually provided:

Required steel area = 1.01 in.^{2}

Area of steel provided = 1.77 in.^{2}

Conclude: Development lengths may be reduced due to excess steel area.

Calculation of required length of imbedment:

From Table C-13, ℓ_d = 18 in.

No multipliers required due to insufficient spacing.

Apply modifier of 0.8 for excess cover and spacing:

ℓ_d = 18(0.8) = 14.4 in.

Apply modifier for excess steel area:

ℓ_d = 14.4(1.01/1.77 = 8.22 in.

Absolute minimum for No. 6 bars in tension, ℓ_d ≥ 12 in.

Use ℓ_d = 12 in.

20.4 Development Length of Straight Bars in Compression

Development lengths in compression are established much like development lengths in tension: a basic development length is determined, then multipliers or modifiers are applied to correct for any inadequacies; the end result is then checked against an absolute minimum prescribed by Code. The computations for development lengths in compression, however, are much simpler than for those in tension. In compression, there are no circumstances where the development length must be lengthened, and there are only two circumstances where the development length may be reduced.

The requirements for computing development lengths of deformed bars in compression are summarized in Table 20-2.

Table 20-2 Development Lengths in Compression.

- Compute basic development length ℓ_{db} for deformed bars in compression, where minimum cover, spacing and ties as required by Code have been provided:

$$\ell_{db} \geq \frac{0.02 d_b f_y}{\sqrt{f'_c}}$$

- Check ℓ_{db} against Code minimum: $\ell_{db} \geq 0.0003 d_b f_y$.
- Modify ℓ_{db} by a factor of (A_s required)/(A_s provided) for excess A_s.
- Modify ℓ_{db} by a factor of 0.75 if No. 4 ties @ 4 in. o.c. exist.
- Check final ℓ_d against absolute Code minimum: $\ell_d \geq 8$ inches.

The criteria for deformed bars in compression are included in the development lengths given in Table C-13 in the Technical Manual. It should be noted in Table C-13 that there is no Code provision for top bars in compression reinforcement.

Some examples will demonstrate the use of Table C-13 in finding the required development length of deformed bars in compression.

Example 20-5

Determination of development lengths.

Given: No. 8 reinforcing bar imbedded 12 in. vertically in a concrete foundation, protruding $^1/_2$ in. above the concrete, to be loaded by a concentric axial force, Grade 60 steel, $f'_c = 4000$ psi.

To Find: The ultimate compressive load that can be distributed into the concrete by the single reinforcing bar.

Solution: The development length for a No. 8 bar is found from Table C-13 to be 19 inches. At 19 in. of imbedment, the bar will develop its yield stress of 60,000 psi; the load is then $f_y A_s$:

$$P_{19} = f_y A_s = 60{,}000(\pi)(0.5^2) = 47{,}000 \text{ lb.}$$

The bar is not imbedded to the required 19 in., however, but is only imbedded 12 in. The load at 12 inches imbedment is taken to be proportional to the imbedment length:

$$\frac{P_{19}}{19} = \frac{P_{12}}{12};\ P_{12} = P_{19}(^{12}/_{19}) = 29{,}800 \text{ lb.}$$

It is assumed that this bar will, at ultimate load, distribute 29,800 lbs of force into the concrete over its embedment length of 12 inches.

It is pointed out that the assumed ratio of force to imbedment length used in Example 20-5 is not proposed by Code. It is based on the assumption that at full development, the stress in the bar will be entering yield just as the bond between concrete and steel begins to fail. In compression, there is undoubtedly a certain amount of end bearing at the bottom of the bar, suggesting that load is not exactly proportional to length and that the assumption used here is therefore somewhat conservative. (If the load were tensile, however, there would be no end effects and the assumed linear ratio of force to imbedment length would probably be more accurate). In the absence of a Code provision, the designer's judgement becomes the final authority in such matters; some rationale such as that used here to solve Example 20-5 then becomes necessary.

Example 20-6

Determination of development length.

Given: Square pedestal 20 in. x 20 in. x 24 in. high, reinforced with 4 - No. 9 bars at its four corners, Grade 60 steel, f'_c = 5000 psi; the pedestal bears on its foundation pad built of concrete having f'_c = 3000 psi. The pedestal is subject to compressive loads only.

To Find: Required length of imbedment for the No. 9 bars.

Solution: From Table C-13 for f'_c = 5000 psi, ℓ_d = 20 in.

From Table C-13 for f'_c = 3000 psi, ℓ_d = 25 in.

Extend No. 9 bars 20 in. into pedestal, 25 in. into foundation.

In finding the development lengths of Example 20-6, it should be noted that potential loads on the bars were never considered. The bars were simply imbedded far enough to develop their full strength, regardless whether their full strength would ever be needed. Such is the approach commonly used in the industry for anchorage of reinforcement; imbedded reinforcement is detailed to provide full development regardless of loading.

Example 20-7

Determination of development lengths in compression.

Given: Rectangular beam, 14 in. wide, f'_c = 4000 psi, Grade 60 steel, 3 - No. 10 bars in compression, required A_s = 2.20 in.^{2}, exterior exposure. Clear cover 2.5 in. both vertical and horizontal.

To Find: Required development length of bars in compression.

Solution: Compare cover requirements to cover actually provided:

Code minimum cover for No. 10 bars, exterior exposure, must be ≥ 2.0 in.

Cover actually provided = 2.50 in. ≥ 2.0 in.

Conclude: cover meets minimum requirements.

Compare spacing requirements to actual spacing:
Code minimum spacing ≥ $1d_b$ but not less than 1 in. for No. 10 bars.
Clear spacing actually provided:

$$\text{Spacing} = \frac{b - 2(\text{clear cover}) - \text{No. bars}(d_b)}{\text{No. bars} - 1}$$

$$= \frac{14 - 2(2.50) - 3(1.27)}{3 - 1} = 2.60 \text{ in.} \geq 1.27.$$

Conclude: spacing meets Code minimums.

Compare required steel area to area actually provided:
Required steel area = 2.20 in.^{2}
Area of steel provided = 3.80 in.^{2}
Conclude: development lengths may be reduced due to excess steel area.

Calculation of required length of imbedment:
From Table C-13, ℓ_d = 24 in.
No multipliers required due to insufficient spacing.
Apply modifier for excess steel area:
ℓ_d= 24(2.20/3.80) = 13.9 in.
Absolute minimum for No. 10 bars in compression, $\ell_d \geq 8$ in.
Use ℓ_d = 14 in.

20.5 Development Length of Bundled Bars

Bundling of longitudinal reinforcement is discussed in Chapter 17. One of the penalties incurred when bars are bundled together is the loss of surface area for bonding the steel to the concrete. The end result of such a loss is that development lengths must then be extended to compensate for the reduction in surface area.

Code (7.6.6) requirements for the extended lengths are quite simple. The basic development lengths are those computed earlier for single bars in compression or tension, multiplied by a factor to account for the effects of bundling.

> Development length of individual bars in a bundle, whether in tension or in compression, shall be that for the individual bar, increased 20 percent for a three-bar bundle and 33 percent for a four-bar bundle.
>
> For determining the appropriate factors to be applied when computing ℓ_{db}, a unit of bundled bars shall be treated as a single bar having a diameter that produces the same total area.

Example 20-8

Determination of cover and spacing.

Given: Bundle of 4 - No. 6 bars.

To Find: Cover requirements for 2_{db} minimum cover.
Spacing requirements for 3_{db} minimum spacing.

Solution: From Table C-13 for 4 - No. 6 bars, A_s = 1.77 in.^{2} = $\pi D^2/4$.

Equivalent diameter $D = \sqrt{4A_s/\pi}$ = 1.50 in.

For calculating cover and spacing, use $d_b = D = 1.50$ in.
Provide clear cover $2(1.50) = 3.00$ in. outside of bundle.
Provide clear spacing $3(1.50) = 4.50$ in. between bundles.

20.6 Development Length of Standard Hooks

Where high-strength steels are used with low-strength concrete, development lengths of straight bars can become prohibitively long. The amount of steel that is duplicated in these straight development lengths can add considerably to the total tonnage of reinforcement. A more efficient but not always less expensive method of providing development of reinforcement consists of bending the end of the bar into a "hook"; a hook is simply a bend configuration that is known to improve the anchorage of the bar in the concrete.

The two types of hooks prescribed by Code (7.1) are shown in Figure 20-4. Both types of hooks produce full development of the bar and both are used extensively throughout the industry, but the 90° hook is easier to tie in the forms and is probably the more frequently used. As a general rule, the cost of bending the reinforcement into hooks is at least partially offset by the savings in materials. In some cases, however, there simply is not enough room to provide for straight development lengths and the use of a hook becomes necessary regardless of cost.

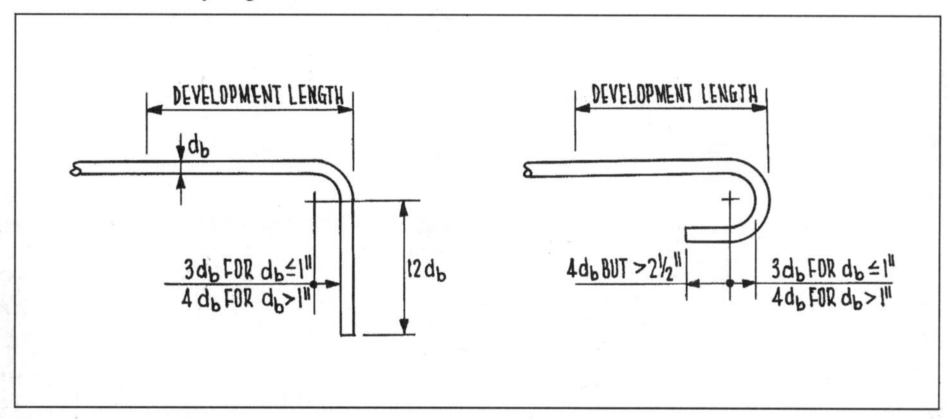

Figure 20-4 Standard tension hooks.

A hook transfers a rather large concentration of load from the steel into the concrete in a relatively small distance. As a consequence, a rather confused stress pattern develops locally around hooks in which there will almost certainly be high tensile stresses. Splitting of the concrete in the vicinity of hooks is likely to occur when cover is small, particularly where several hooks occur together. In all cases, particular care is warranted when detailing hooked bars to assure that the required cover is maintained.

Hooks are not effective in compression.

Development lengths ℓ_{dh} for hooked bars in tension are established much like other development lengths: a basic development length ℓ_{hb} is determined, then multipliers or modifiers are applied to correct for any inadequate conditions. Development lengths for hooks, however, are quite simple. As indicated in subsequent discussions, there are no cases where multipliers must be used to extend the required development length (except for lightweight concrete which is not included here), and there are only two cases where modifiers may be used to reduce the development length. After the modifiers are applied, however, the result must be checked against Code minimums.

The requirements for computing the development lengths of hooked bars in tension are summarized in Table 20-3. The basic development lengths given by Table 20-3 have been tabulated in Table C-12.

Table 20-3 Development Lengths for Hooked Bars.

- Compute basic development length ℓ_{hb} for hooked deformed bars in tension, where minimum cover, spacing and ties as required by Code have been provided:

$$\ell_{hb} \geq \frac{0.02 d_b f_y}{\sqrt{f'_c}}$$

- Modify ℓ_{hb} by a factor of 0.7 for side cover ≥ 2½ inches and, for 90° hook only; cover ≥ 2 in. over the extension beyond the hook.
- Modify ℓ_{hb} by a factor of 0.8 for ties spaced ≤ $3d_b$, but not to include hooks located at discontinuous ends of members having cover ≤ 2½ inches.
- Modify ℓ_{hb} by a factor of (A_s required)/(A_s provided) for excess A_s.
- Check final ℓ_{dh} against Code minimums: $\ell_{dh} \geq 8d_b$,
  $\ell_{db} \geq 6$ inches.

Some examples will demonstrate the use of Table C-12 in finding development lengths of hooked bars in tension.

Example 20-9

Selection of anchorage for reinforcement.

Given: Rectangular beam as shown. Grade 40 deformed steel. $f'_c = 3000$ psi.

To Find: Required anchorage for reinforcement.

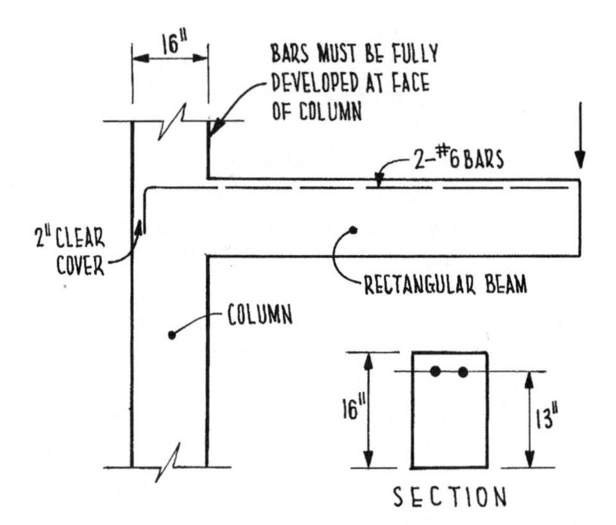

Solution: The required development length for a straight No. 6 bar is given in Table C-12. Since the bars shown in the sketch have more than 12 in. of fresh concrete below them, they are classed as top bars, and $\ell_d = 21$ inches in tension. There is not enough room at the support to provide this development length. If a hook is used, the development length from Table C-12 is 11 in., which can be provided. Use hooked bars with at least 2 in. of cover, as shown; the actual embedment length then becomes 14 in.

Example 20-10

Selection of imbedment for a lifting eye.

Given: Precast tee as shown. Grade 40 steel; f'_c = 3000 psi.

To Find: Required anchorage for the lifting eye.

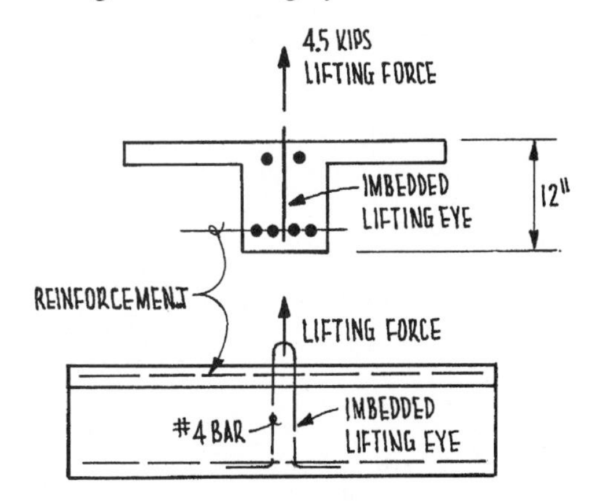

Solution: To develop full strength of the embedded No. 4 bar, a development length of 12 in. is required for a straight bar or 7 in. for a hooked bar. Since there is again not enough room for the straight bar, it must be hooked as shown. The capacity is then $2f_yA_s = 2(40{,}000)(0.2)$ = 16 kips.

In Example 20-10 it should be recognized that the solution did not include the actual load on the lifting eye. The bar is simply imbedded to develop its full capacity. Nor do the tables include any provision for loads other than full capacity. A further discussion of this omission is presented toward the end of this chapter.

Example 20-11

Determination of development lengths of hooked bars in tension.

Given: Rectangular beam, 16 in. wide, f'_c = 4000 psi, Grade 50 steel. Four - No. 6 bars in tension, classed as "other than top" bars. Required A_s = 1.01 in.^{2}, bars are to be hooked. Clear cover 2.5 in. both vertical and horizontal, exterior exposure.

To Find: Required development length of hooked bars in tension.

Solution: Compare cover requirements to cover actually provided:

Code minimum cover for No. 6 bars, exterior exposure, must be ≥ 2.0 in.

Required cover if modifier is allowed must be ≥ 2.50 in.

Cover actually provided = 2.50 in. ≥ 2.50 in.

Conclude: cover meets minimum requirements,
cover sufficient for modifier to be used.

Compare spacing requirements to actual spacing:
Code minimum spacing ≥ $1d_b$ but not less than 1 in.
Clear spacing actually provided:

$$\text{Spacing} = \frac{b - 2(\text{clear cover}) - \text{No. bars}(d_b)}{\text{No. bars} - 1}$$

$$= \frac{16 - 2(2.50) - 4(0.75)}{4 - 1} = 2.67 \text{ in.} \geq 3d_b.$$

Conclude: spacing meets Code minimums.
No multipliers are required.

Compare required steel area to area actually provided:
Required steel area = 1.01 in.^{2}
Area of steel provided = 1.77 in.^{2}
Conclude: development lengths may be reduced due to excess steel area.

Calculation of required length of imbedment:
From Table C-12, ℓ_d = 12 in.
No multipliers required due to insufficient spacing.
Apply modifier of 0.7 for excess cover:
ℓ_d= 12(0.7) = 8.4 in.

Apply modifier for excess steel area:
ℓ_d= 8.4(1.01/1.77) = 5.0 in.

Absolute minimum for No. 6 hooked bars, ℓ_d ≥ 8db, but not less than 6 in.
Use ℓ_d = 6 in.

20.7 Criteria for Cutoff Points

When determination of tensile reinforcement was made (Chapter 18), the amount of reinforcement was determined on the basis of maximum moment on the section. At some distance away from this maximum moment, the moment may become reduced or may even become zero. At such points, it is possible to cut off a part of the tensile reinforcement, retaining only that amount of reinforcement required for the reduced moment in that particular area. Code places strict limits, however, on the minimum amount of reinforcement that must be retained.

A typical moment envelope for a flexural member is shown in Figure 20-5b. The moment envelope is defined as the outermost moment diagram at any point resulting from any one of the possible load cases; any other load case will produce a lesser value of moment at that point. (Moment envelopes are discussed more fully in Chapter 17.) Note that the inflection point can shift a significant distance laterally under different loadings.

The point at which the bar must attain its full yield strength is called the *critical section.* The critical section is defined by Code (12.10.2) as the point of maximum stress, or the point within the span where adjacent reinforcement terminates or is bent. The development length must, of course, lie entirely outside this point. For example, the critical section for bars *MK c* in Figure 20-5 is at midspan, and for bars *MK d* is at the face of support.

Typical cutoff points for flexural reinforcement are shown in Figure 20-5b. In most cases, these cutoff lengths can be determined graphically simply by scaling the moment diagram. A higher degree of accuracy is difficult to defend in view of the empirical nature of the design.

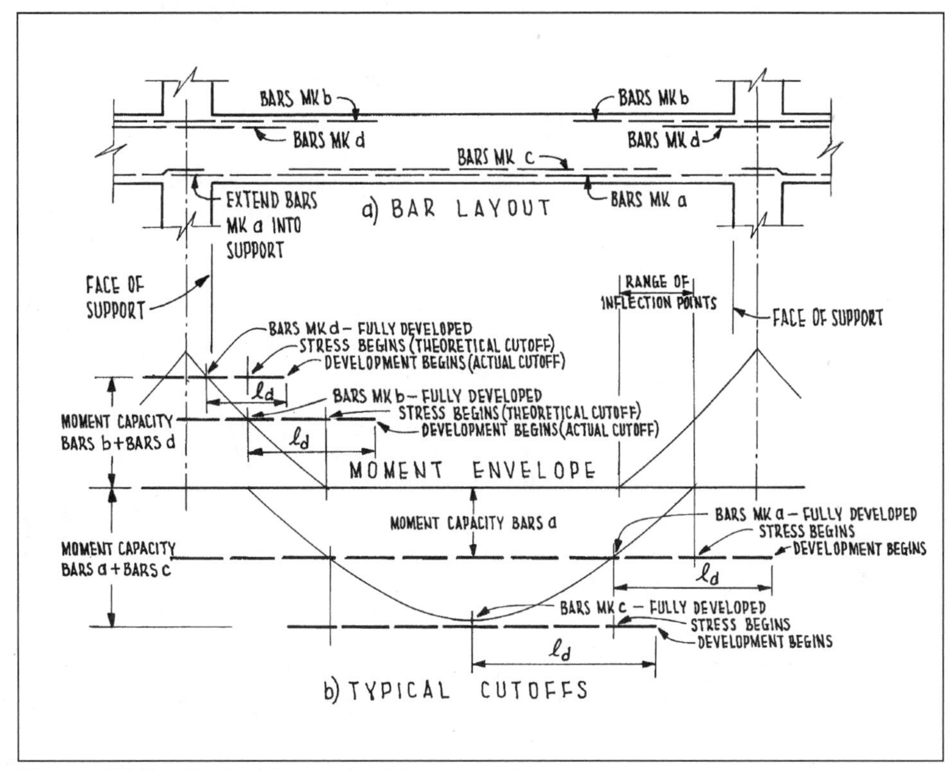

Figure 20-5 Typical flexural reinforcement.

It is required by Code that the reinforcement that is to be cut must be extended past its theoretical cutoff point (the point where it is theoretically no longer needed) by a distance not less than d nor less than $12d_b$. By this means, most of the strength of the bar is available where it is first needed and the remaining strength will be available further along the bar. At these theoretical cutoff points, however, the bars that have not been cut must carry the full moment and must be fully developed at such points.

It should be recognized that all cutoff points are measured from the theoretical point where the bar is needed, not from the actual cutoff points of adjacent bars. Such a case is shown for bars *MK a* in Figure 20-5b, where the cutoff length is measured from the theoretical point of cutoff of bars *MK c*, not their actual point of cutoff. It should also be recognized that more than one criterion may apply; the cutoff point for bars *MK b* must satisfy the requirement of extending at least a distance d or $12d_b$ beyond the point of inflection as well as extending at least their full development length beyond the theoretical point of cutoff of bars *MK d*. The development lengths are, of course, those of Table C-13 in the Technical Manual, as discussed earlier.

20.8 Abbreviated Criteria for Cutoff Points

Code has a long detailed list of requirements for cutoff points of all flexural reinforcement which includes a variety of exceptions. The list of requirements may be worth learning if one is deeply involved in detailing concrete every working day. Otherwise, a simplified approach is needed that can quickly be relearned whenever needed. One very practical simplification is to make steel cutoffs of up to one-half of the positive area of steel at one time, or all of the negative area of steel at one time. The list of requirements then reduces to the following rules.

1. In regions of negative moment:
   (a) Continue the entire area of flexural steel past the point of inflection by a distance d, $12d_b$, or span/16, whichever is farthest.
   (b) At integral columns, provide full development for all flexural steel at the face of support by providing full development length in or through the column, hooking as necessary, and keeping reinforcement diameters small enough that full development is achieved.
2. In regions of positive moment:
   (a) At interior supports, extend at least one-fourth of the area of flexural steel past the center of supports by a distance not less than 6 in., or past the face of support by a hook; extend the remaining flexural steel past the point of inflection by a distance not less than d nor less than $12d_b$, whichever is greater.
   (b) At end columns or simple supports, extend all tension reinforcement past the center of the support by a distance not less than ℓ_d or by a standard hook.

The foregoing abbreviated rules are summarized in Figure 20-6. Such an abbreviated set of rules is obviously conservative and will require more steel than if the full set of criteria were applied. In small projects, however, the savings in steel is generally offset by the additional labor hours required to fabricate and place the extra mark numbers. In larger projects, the savings would be significant and the more refined criteria could become worthwhile.

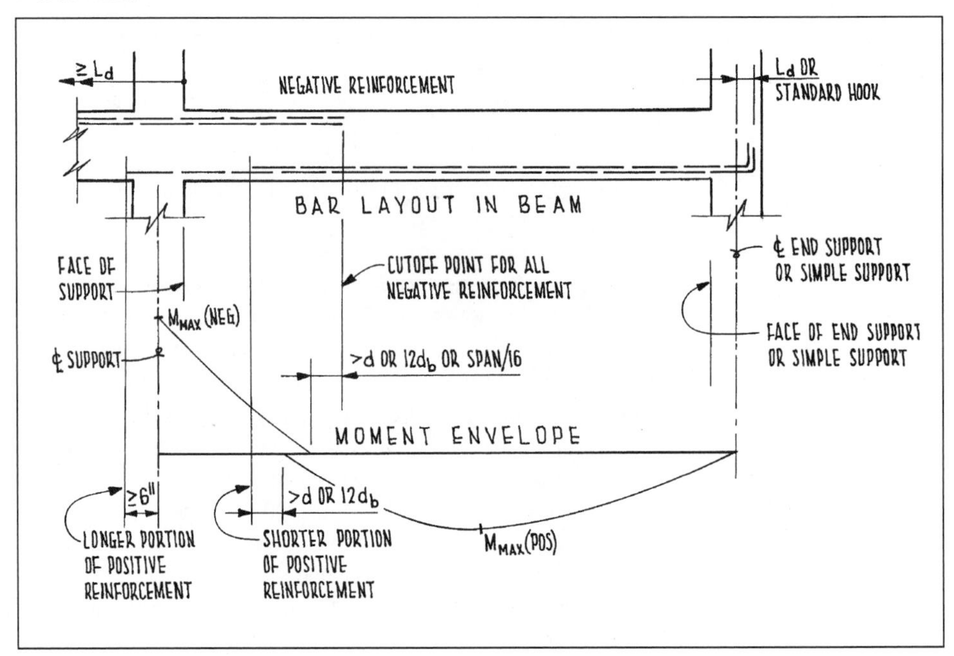

Figure 20-6 Potential cutoff points.

As an example in the application of the foregoing criteria, the beam of Example 19-2 is used. The final reinforcement sizes and stirrup sizes have already been determined, but no attempt has been made to check the development of the reinforcement. For the example, the various distances on the moment diagram have been computed; in practice, they would probably be scaled.

Example 20-12

Reinforcement cutoff points.

Given: Beam and conditions of Example 19-2.

To Find: Determine the cutoff points of the flexural reinforcement. The beam and the moment diagram are shown below.

Steel is Grade 60, f'_c = 3000 psi.

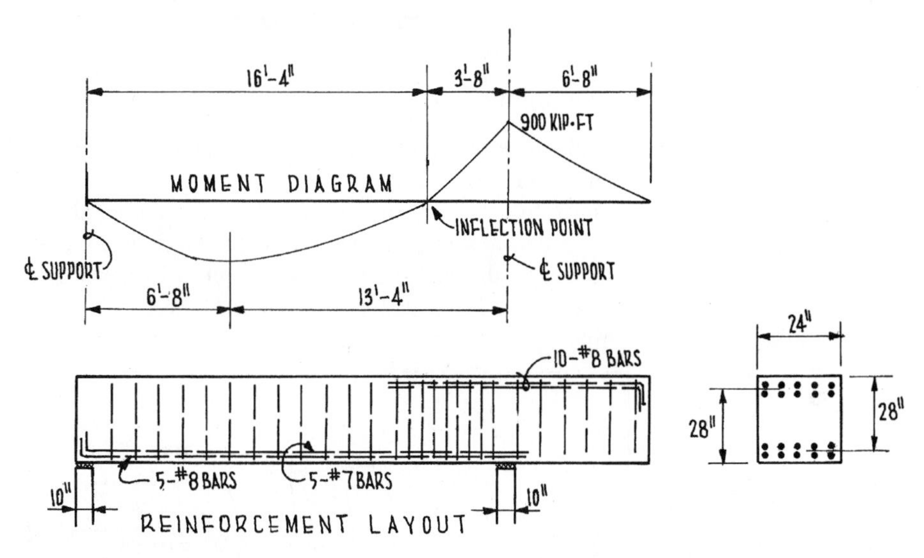

Solution: Determine the development lengths from Table C-13:

For No. 8 bars: ℓ_d = 34 in. or 48 in. for top bars.

For No. 7 bars: ℓ_d = 26 in.

For negative reinforcement at the right support, extend the bars to the end of the beam and provide standard hooks (see the foregoing sketch).

For negative reinforcement to the left of the right support:

Cutoff point: $\geq$ d (or 28 in.) past inflection point.

$\geq 12d_b$ (or 12 in.) past inflection point.

$\geq \frac{\text{Span}}{16}$ (or 15 in.) past inflection.

Use a cutoff point 28 in. past the inflection point, or 6ft.0 in. from the centerline of the support (see the following sketch).

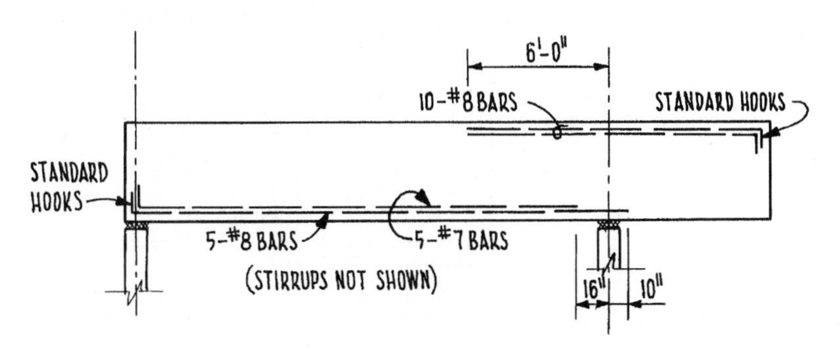

For positive reinforcement at the left support, extend all bars past the centerline of the support and provide standard hooks (see the foregoing sketch). At the right support, extend the bottom layer of bars 6 in. past the centerline of the support. For the remainder of positive bars at the right support,

Cutoff point: $\geq$ d (or 28 in.) past the inflection point.
$\geq 12d_b$ (or $10^1/_2$ in.) past inflection point.

Use a cutoff point 28 in. past the inflection point or 16 in. from the centerline of the support.

20.9 Development of Stirrups and Ties

Development lengths for stirrups and ties are, of course, comparable to those of flexural reinforcement. The problem is complicated, however, by the fact that the space available to provide anchorage for stirrups is severely limited.

A typical stirrup arrangement is shown in Figure 20-7, with a general case of loading. The load in the stirrup occurs as a result of diagonal cracking starting at the tension side of the beam. The actual size of the crack need be only a hairline, but once such a crack forms, regardless of how thin, the stirrups bridging the crack are fully loaded.

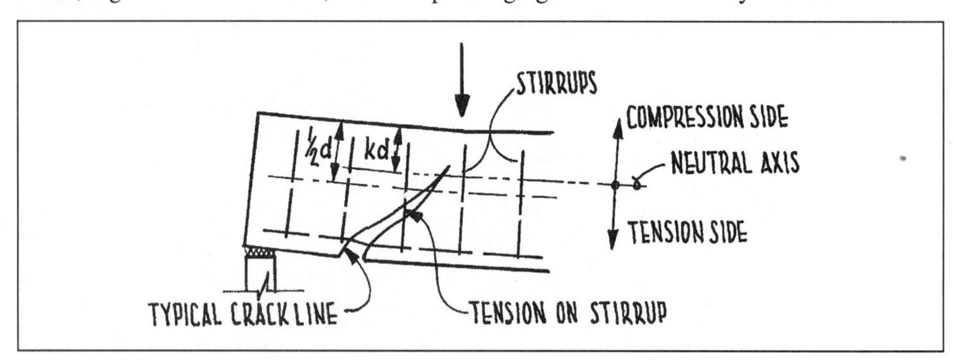

Figure 20-7 Loading on stirrups.

The close spacing used in the design of stirrups inherently limits any large buildup of forces in a single stirrup, which in turn serves to keep the size of stirrups within the smaller bar sizes (No. 5 bars and smaller). For these smaller bar sizes, anchorage is much simplified. Code (7.2.1, 7.2.2) establishes separate anchorage criteria for these smaller stirrup bars, to include both hook criteria and bend radii.

Requirements for standard hooks in stirrups and ties are shown in Figure 20-8 for bar sizes No. 5 and smaller. For the smaller bar sizes used for stirrups, Code (7.2.2) also permits a sharper bend radius, also indicated in Figure 20-8.

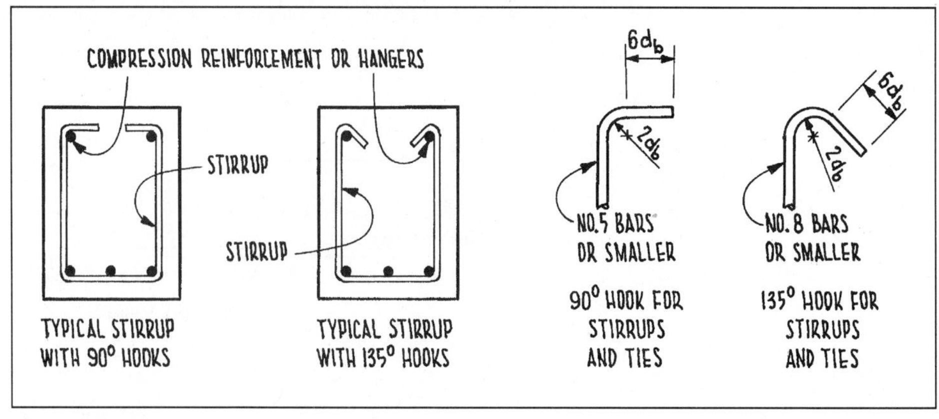

Figure 20-8 Typical stirrup and tie bends.

Code (12.13.2.1) requires that the ends of single leg, simply *U* or multiple *U* stirrups must be anchored by providing a standard hook around longitudinal bars. Such anchorage is shown in the sections of Figure 20-8. Where there is no longitudinal reinforcement to hook the stirrups over, it is necessary to provide additional No. 4 bars longitudinally on which to hang the stirrups. Called *hangers*, these additional bars are, in fact, a part of the shear reinforcement rather than the flexural reinforcement. Or, if conditions are suitable, two of the flexural reinforcing bars are sometimes extended across the span to provide hangers; such an alternative is quite commonly used.

At ultimate load, the diagonal cracking shown in Figure 20-7 can penetrate quite far into the compression side of the beam. To assure that the anchorage at the top of the stirrups remains always in the compression zone, Code (12.13.1) requires that the anchorage for the stirrup be held as close as possible (with proper cover) to the compression face of the member. Some common anchorage arrangements permitted in the 1982 Code were dropped in the 1989 Code; two such arrangements that are no longer permitted are pointed out in Figure 20-9.

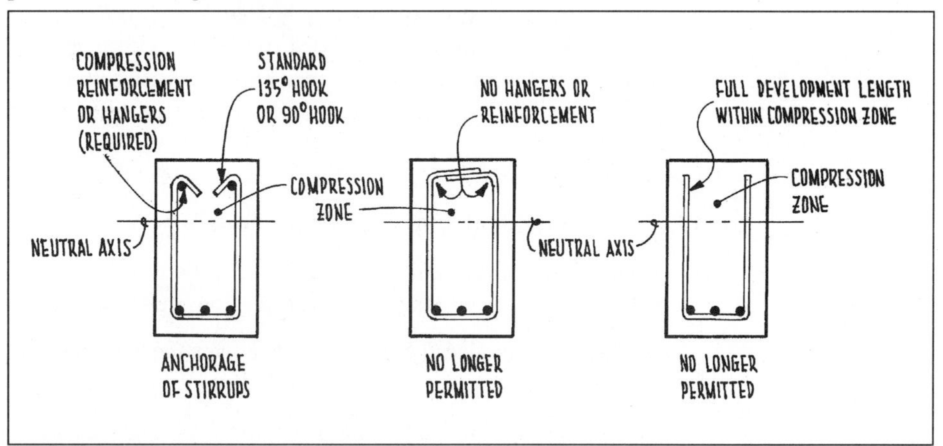

Figure 20-9 Stirrup anchorage in the compression zone.

From the foregoing requirements, it is seen that there are no choices to be made when anchoring web reinforcement. One simply hooks the ends of the stirrups or ties over the longitudinal steel. If there is no longitudinal reinforcement to hook the ends over, additional longitudinal hangers are provided on which to hang the stirrups or ties. Anchorage of stirrups and ties has thus been reduced to a detailing practice rather than a design problem.

20.10 Lap Splicing of Straight Bars

Reinforcing bars may be spliced simply by lapping them a specified length within a concrete member as shown in Figure 20-10. The efficiency of a lap splice is 100%; full strength is transferred. Code (12.14.2.1) does not permit bars larger than No. 11 to be lap spliced except in exceptional circumstances.

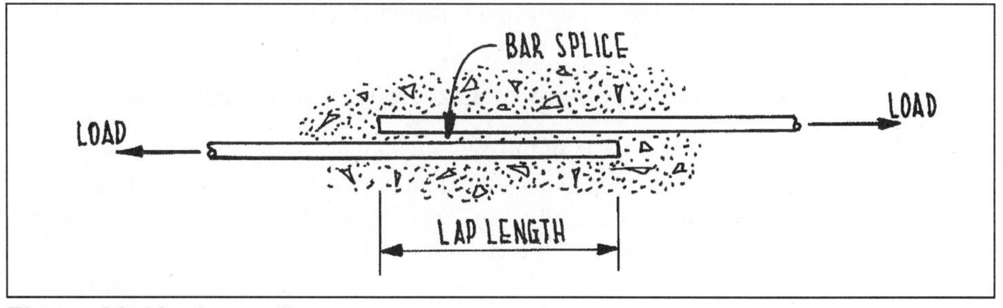

Figure 20-10 Lap splice.

Reinforcing bars need not contact each other in a lap splice. For an example, jump ahead to the sketch in Chapter 21, Figure 21-3. The No. 4 bars at the back of the cantilevered retaining wall are not at the same spacing as the No. 5 dowels projecting from the footing, nor are the two sets of bars the same size, yet a full transfer of load occurs. In this particular splice, 100% of the bars are spliced at the construction joint, although in other arrangements a splice may only involve 50% of the bars or even less.

For noncontact lap splices such as those of Figure 21-3, Code (12.14.2.3) specifies that:

> The transverse spacing of flexural reinforcing bars spliced by noncontact lap splices shall be not farther apart than one-fifth the required lap splice length nor farther apart than 6 inches.

Individual bars within a bundled set of bars may also be lap spliced. In such splices, only one bar may be spliced at a time, and no part of successive splices may overlap. Further, the entire bundle may not be spliced at a single location. Also, the computed splice length for bundled bars must be increased 20% for a three-bar bundle and 33% for a four-bar bundle, as discussed earlier.

Code (12.14.3) permits welded splices in reinforcement. Code (12.14.3) also permits mechanical (patented) splice connections to be used. In both cases, the splice is required to develop 125% of the yield strength of the bar (rather than the full ultimate strength of the bar).

20.11 Development of Lap Splices in Tension

Code separates lap splices in tension into two classes, *Class A* and *Class B*. Class A splices of deformed straight bars in tension are those in which:

a) (A_s provided)/(A_s required) ≥ 2 over the required lap length;
b) Less than one-half the A_s is spliced within the required lap length.

Splices not meeting the requirements for Class A splices are classified by default as Class B splices.

Required length of lap for the two classes of splices are prescribed by Code (12.15.1):

Class A: lap length = $1.0\,\ell_d$ (20-10a)
Class B: lap length = $1.3\,\ell_d$ (20-10b)
Class A and B: minimum lap = 12 inches (20-10c)

where ℓ_d is the development length for deformed bars in tension (see Table 20-1). When computing ℓ_d, however, the modification factor for excess A_s may not be used but multipliers for top bars, epoxy coating and lightweight concrete must be applied. The absolute minimum lap length after all multipliers have been applied is 12 inches.

The required length of lap splices in tension is specified in Table C-13 in the Technical Manual, including extensions for top bars. It is well to observe in Table C-13 that splice lengths of 8 feet or more can occur in larger bar sizes. The cost of making a lap splice 8 feet long can sometimes make the use of welded splices or mechanical connectors an economical alternative.

20.12 Development of Lap Splices in Compression

The criteria of this section applies to bars that are always in compression. If during a load reversal the bars should go into tension, no matter how slightly, the criteria of this section no longer apply. For those cases where tension may sometimes occur, the criteria of the next section apply.

There are no *Class A* or *Class B* categories for lap splices that are always in compression. For steels Grade 60 and below, with concrete strengths 3000 psi and above, the lap length is prescribed by Code:

$$\text{Lap length} = 0.0005 f_y d_b \quad (20\text{-}11a)$$
$$\text{Minimum lap} = 12 \text{ inches.} \quad (20\text{-}11b)$$

When bars of different sizes are lap spliced in compression, the lap length shall be the larger of the development length ℓ_d for the larger bar size or the splice length given by Eq.(20-11) for the smaller bar size.

The required length of lap splices for deformed bars in compression is included in Table C-13 in the Technical Manual. Note that there is no classification of "top bars" for bars in compression.

Welded splices and mechanical connectors are permitted by Code for lap splices in compression. The criteria given earlier for such welds and connections remain applicable.

Example 20-13

Determination of splice lengths.

Given: Beam section as shown, under negative moment. Grade 50 steel, $f'_c = 4000$ psi.

To Find: Required splice lengths for both tensile and compressive reinforcement.

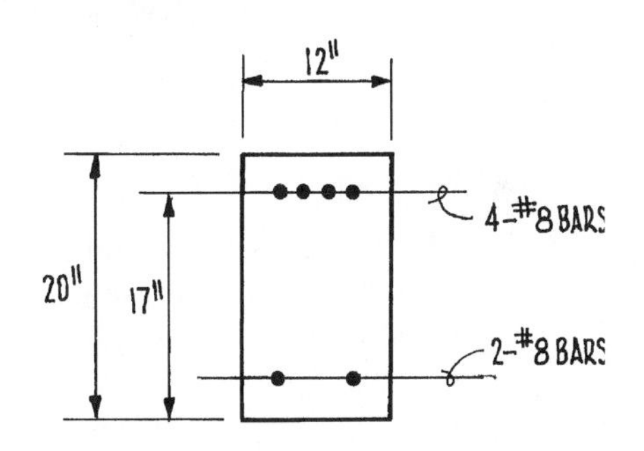

Solution: Tensile reinforcement is classified as top bars. Assume A_s provided = A_s required, so Class B splice is required. For No. 8 bars in tension, Class B splice for top bars is 42 in. long.

For No. 8 bars in compression, splice length is 25 in. long.

Example 20-14

Determination of splice lengths.

Given: Retaining wall of Chapter 21, Figure 21-3
Grade 60 steel, $f'_c = 3000$ psi.

To Find: Required splice length of No. 5 dowels to No. 4 vertical bars at back face of wall.

Solution: Code requires that spacing shall not be less than 6 in. nor less than 20% of the splice length. These conditions seem to be met by the two sets of bars.

100% of the bars are spliced at the same level; a *Class A* splice may not therefore be used.

Splice length for No. 5 bars in a Class B splice is 27 in.

Minimum transverse spacing is therefore 27/5 = 5.2 in. > 5 in. provided.

Required splice length is therefore 27 in., which is the length indicated.

Example 20-15

Determination of splice length.

Given: 4 - No. 6 top bars, bundled, in tension. $f'_c = 4000$, Grade 50 steel. Fewer than 25% of the bars are spliced at any location.

To Find: Required splice length.

Solution: With less than 25% of the bars spliced at any location, the total A_s is never doubled over the splice length, so the splice is a *Class B* splice.

From Table C-13, $\ell_d = 30$ in. for top bars.

Apply multiplier 1.33 for a 4-bar bundle, $\ell_d = 1.33(30) = 40$ in.

Use 40 in. splice length.

Review Questions

1. What is meant by the "development length" of a reinforcing bar?
2. What is the "bond strength" of concrete, and what are some of the factors that can affect it adversely?
3. How does the bond of concrete to smooth reinforcing bars compare to its bond to deformed bars?
4. In view of the answer to Question 3, about what percentage of the total load on a deformed bar might be attributed to the mechanical bearing of its deformations against the adjacent concrete?
5. How have development lengths of reinforcing bars been determined in recent years?
6. What is the primary advantage in using hooks?
7. What is the primary point of caution in using hooks?
8. When only a part of the required development length of a bar can be embedded in concrete, how can its allowable working load be computed using the strength method? Using the working stress method?
9. On flexural reinforcement in a simple span, where can bond stresses be expected to be highest? Lowest?
10. Why is it necessary to provide hooks for anchoring stirrups?
11. What particular advantages does the 135° hook provide when one is detailing ties and stirrups?
12. Where in the cross section of the beam does the development of stirrups occur?
13. What is "bundling" of reinforcement?
14. When mechanical anchorages or welding are used, how much of the strength of the reinforcement must be developed?

CHAPTER

21

APPLICATIONS IN CONCRETE STRUCTURES

All of the discussions of concrete to this point have been fundamental, but they have deliberately been centered around isolated details in isolated circumstances. It is the purpose of this chapter to broaden and generalize the scope of study significantly, to include broad concepts in the general design of concrete structures. The types of structures considered in this chapter include elevated simply supported slabs, continuous slabs, simply supported tee and ell beams, continuous tee and ell beams and the more common types of concrete foundations.

The topics treated in this chapter utilize only the basic theoretical concepts already introduced in earlier chapters, to include flexure, shear and anchorage. Since there is no development of any new theory in this chapter, this chapter might therefore be viewed as a "how-to" chapter on the overall design of concrete members. The study starts with a broad overview of design practices.

21.1 Design Practices

A structural member must be sized and reinforced to carry computed loads; the methods commonly used to accomplish this are called *design practices.* Once the sizes of the members are chosen, the members must be connected with reinforcement, notched for equipment mounts and penetrated by ducts; the methods used to accomplish these and hundreds of other such details are called *detailing practices.*

General design practices suited to small projects are learned largely by exposure over a long period of time. Every designer soon develops a preferred set of practices and will adapt this consistent set of practices to each project. Even so, there are basic practices common to the industry that are used by most designers with but little variation.

Some of these basic practices are presented in the following sections. Some rules of thumb are presented and several construction practices are discussed. Foundation settlements and thermal stresses are introduced and discussed. All these topics have a bearing on design and detailing practices; their effects are illustrated in later discussions.

A major factor influencing both design and detailing practices is that of deciding whether a member is to be precast or cast in place. Significant differences apply to the two designs, to include the minimum sizes and reinforcement that must be used. The use of precast components, even those cast on the job site, is so commonplace that the following criteria include both precast and cast-in-place construction whenever appropriate.

21.2 Estimated Nominal Loads

Loading on concrete buildings varies considerably for any number of reasons. Nonetheless, it is frequently necessary to estimate the total load (dead plus live) on a beam or a column or a slab. For common spans and routine design, the following values offer a first guess:

Floor load:	150 psf, dead plus live load.
Roof load:	125 psf, dead plus live load.
Column load:	30 tons per story, total load.

For routine concrete buildings, the dead load should be expected to be about 60% of the total load and live load to be about 40% of the total load.

For members at the perimeter of a concrete buildings, the loads should be expected to be only slightly less (about 15% less) than the loads at the interior. The fenestration and exterior walls commonly used in concrete buildings are so heavy that little difference should be expected.

21.3 Rules of Thumb

Rules of thumb can be useful, particularly when one is trying to make an initial estimate for a beam size or a slab thickness. They can also be useful when one is keeping a running check on a calculation and wishes to know if the results obtained are at least reasonable. The following rules and generalities may be useful as a first guess.

The optimum column module for concrete structures can be expected to be 18 to 20 ft. This module can be extended with little penalty in cost up to 25 ft for joist systems, with many advantages in utilization of space. Spans in reinforced concrete greater than 28 ft are uncommon, although the two-way joist systems (discussed further in later sections) work reasonably well with spans up to 32 ft or even more.

As a means to distinguish between girders and beams, it is assumed that girders are supported by vertical members and beams are supported by horizontal members. (Bearing walls are considered to be horizontal members.) The overall depth of a girder in reinforced concrete can be expected to be about $L/10$ and the overall depth of a beam can be expected to be about $L/12$, where L is the span. For spans greater than about 20 ft, the depths of the members increase rapidly.

Tee beams are a commonly used shape in concete construction; a typical tee beam arrangement is shown in Figure 21-1. Optimum spacing of the stems of tee beams is generally controlled by the floor slab they support. A floor slab 4 in. thick will span about 8 ft, a floor slab 6 in. thick will span about 12 ft and a floor slab 7 in. thick will span about 16 ft. All of these examples apply to the usual range of floor live loads and all examples observe the common 4-ft module for building materials.

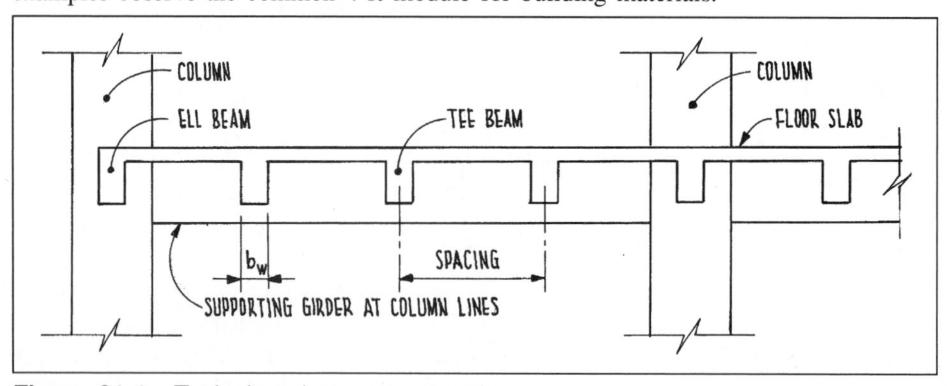

Figure 21-1 Typical tee beam construction.

The stem of a tee beam is designed to take all the shear on the tee beam. Proportions for width and depth have been found to work well for such shear when the width of the stem b_w is taken at roughly half the effective depth d; the dimensions d and b_w are shown in Figure 21-1.

Rectangular sections occur when a tee beam is placed in negative moment or when a rectangular frame is designed to receive precast floor planks. The proportions for such rectangular sections have been found to be economical when the width b_w is roughly two-thirds of the effective depth d.

For continuous tee beams subject to both positive and negative bending, the width of the stem should be somewhere between half and two-thirds of the effective depth d.

Concrete joist systems are special tee beam floor systems that utilize narrow joists spaced closely together, supporting a thin concrete floor slab; a typical cross section of a joist system is shown in Figure 21-2. The closely spaced tee joists are significantly shallower than a regular tee-beam floor with its widely spaced tees. The overall depth h of a joist system can be estimated at about two-thirds of the depth of a regular tee-beam- and-slab system.

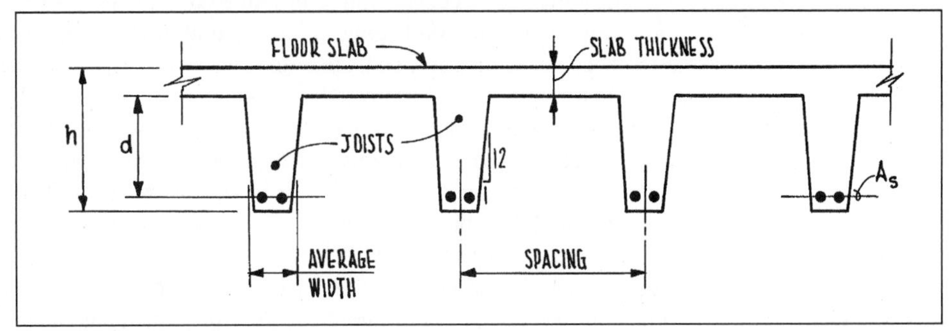

Figure 21-2 Typical joist system.

Concrete columns subject to bending (as part of a rigid frame) can vary widely in size depending on the magnitude of the moment. As a first guess the size of a column subject only to axial load may be estimated as 12 in. on a side plus an addition 1 in. for each story above the one being considered. Thus the columns in the third story of a five-story building can be expected to be about 12 in. on a side plus 1 in. times two stories above, for a total of 14-in. square. A rectangular column for this case would have only slightly more cross-sectional area than the square column, say 10 by 20 in.

Cantilevered retaining walls are usually tapered, being considerably thicker at the base than at the top as indicated in Figure 21-3. The thickness at the top can be expected to be about 8 in. for a wall 10 ft high and as much as 12 in. for a wall 20 ft high. The thickness at the base can be expected to be about one-ninth of the height, with a minimum thickness of 12 in.

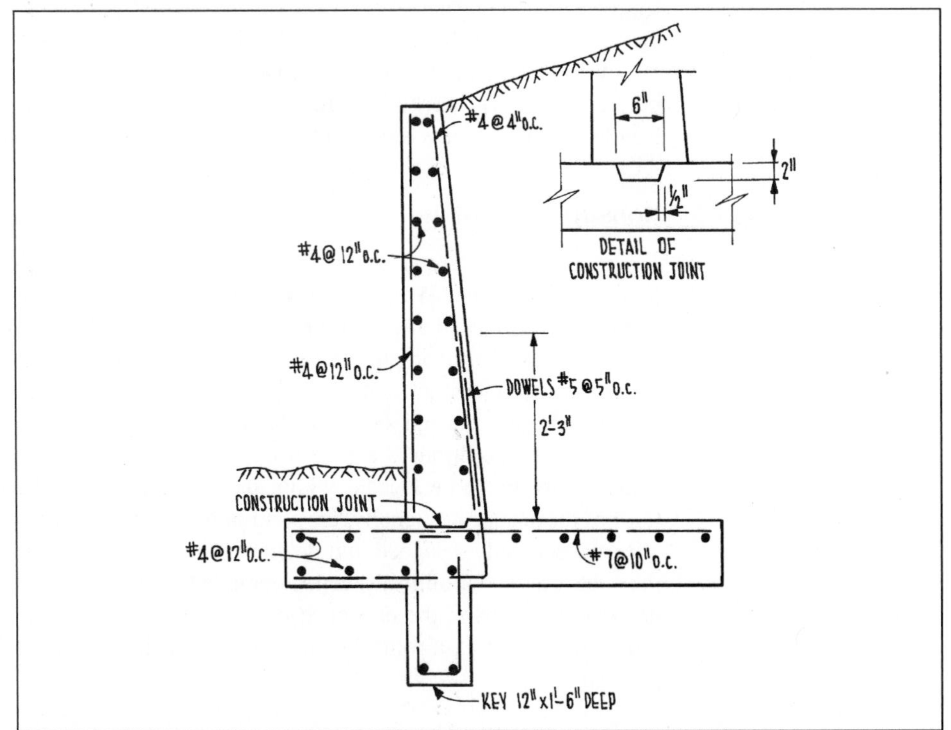

Figure 21-3 Typical cantilevered retaining wall.

21.4 Temperature and Shrinkage Joints

Due to the phenomenon of shrinkage in concrete, problems of contraction and expansion of structures in concrete become somewhat more severe than in structures of other materials. The contraction due to shinkage has been likened to that due to a temperature drop of 40°F. With such an addition to overall contraction, contraction joints in concrete structures should be expected to be at closer intervals than in structures of other materials.

Code does not give a maximum distance at which a full separation joint (expansion-contraction joint) is required since such a requirement is necessarily dependent on local temperatures. As a general guide in temperate climates, when routine continuous structures are more than 100 ft long, a full separation joint starts to become desirable. At 150 ft it becomes a pressing consideration and at 200 ft it becomes essential.

Slabs on grade are protected from temperature extremes by the huge heat sink of the soil that supports them. Nonetheless, slabs exposed to direct sunshine are subject to considerably higher temperatures than slabs located under shade. A common spcification allows slabs located in shaded areas to be cast up to 400 ft^2 in area with a maximum dimension of 25 ft between joints or, for exposed locations, up to 250 ft^2 with a maximum dimension of 20 ft between joints. A detail of the control joints used to meet these requirements is shown in Figure 21-4. The control joint produces a stress concentration; cracking will likely occur along the control joint rather than in some visible area.

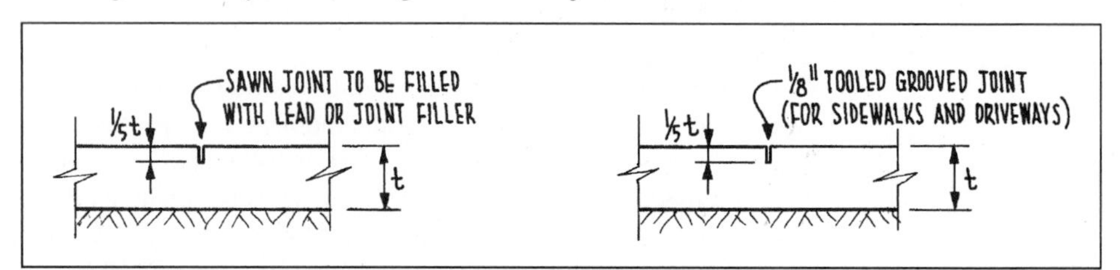

Figure 21-4 Typical control joints.

Temperature and shrinkage deformations occur in all concrete structures. There can be hundreds of combinations and variations of these deformations that might occur even in small structures, but it is not common practice to perform calculations for such stresses. Rather, the building is conscientiously designed and detailed to prevent such stresses from occurring; no special analysis is then required. Any accidental effects due to random thermal stress is then relegated to the factor of safety.

Where thermal stresses are allowed to occur, however, they should be expected to be significant. The associated forces are quite large and can be extremely difficult to handle. Such problems are far beyond the scope of this book.

21.5 Construction Joints

Construction joints are used to interrupt a casting; the casting can then be resumed at that joint at a later time. With few exceptions, Code permits construction joints in vertical members to be placed anywhere in the member, to include points of maximum shear and moment. A typical example may be seen at the base of a retaining wall (Figure 21-3); the construction joint in a retaining wall is almost always located at the base of the stem, where both moment and shear on the stem are highest.

Notable exceptions are drawn by Code (6.4.4) for joints in horizontal members. When joints are to be located within the span, they must be located within the middle third of the span. Additionally, the stem of a tee must be cast monolithically with the slab unless specifically designed and detailed otherwise. Similarly, haunches and drop panels must be cast monolithically unless detailed otherwise. It may be concluded that for horizontal members, the existence or absence of high flexural stress has no significant effect when placing a joint, but placing a joint in an area of high shear stress is to be avoided.

21.6 Differential Settlements

Uniform settlement of a structure may have highly deleterious effects on sewer, water, and power connections to a building, but it has no effect on the structure. Only the *differential* settlement between adjacent footings or supports will affect the stress levels in the structure. The structural analysis is therefore concerned only with differential settlements between supports, not with total settlements.

If, however, the largest settlement at any footing in a group of footings is limited to 1 in., the differential settlement between any two footings in the group can be expected to be somewhat less than 1 in., say a maximum of $^3/_4$ in. It is this approach that is commonly used in practice for the design of shallow footings — that the largest settlements will be limited to about 1 in. and that differential settlements, if any occur, can then be expected to be less than about $^3/_4$ in.

There are hundreds of combinations of differential settlements that might occur in a routine structure. If, however, the differential settlements are less than about $^3/_4$ in., the change in total stress due to any reasonable combination can be expected to be less than about 15% of the total. For this amount, a separate analysis for potential differential settlements is not usually considered to be necessary and is rarely performed in practice. Where circumstances are unusual, however, or where a key foundation is known to be subject to large settlements, a thorough study of the effects of differential settlements is necessary. For the sake of the foregoing discussion, a "routine" structure is one in which the largest column load is no more than four times the smallest column load and the shallow spread footings are between 3 ft and 8 ft on a side.

In some circumstances, a foundation system may be composed of a mixture of isolated spread footings at columns and continuous strip footings at bearing walls. Where both the spread footings and the strip footings have the same contact pressure on the soil, the strip footings can be expected to settle more than the spread footings, up to about 50% more. The use of a lesser allowable pressure under the strip footings will help equalize the settlements.

21.7 Elevated Floor and Roof Slabs

Elevated concrete floor slabs and roof slabs are so common in today's industry that it would be difficult to imagine modern construction without them. There is another type of concrete floor slab, the slab on grade, which is supported directly by the underlying soil; slabs on grade are discussed later in this chapter along with foundations.

Elevated slabs act as wide flat beams. They are analyzed and designed as rectangular beams one foot wide. Steel is selected for this typical one foot strip and is then used at regular spacing throughout the width of the slab, as shown in Figure 21-5.

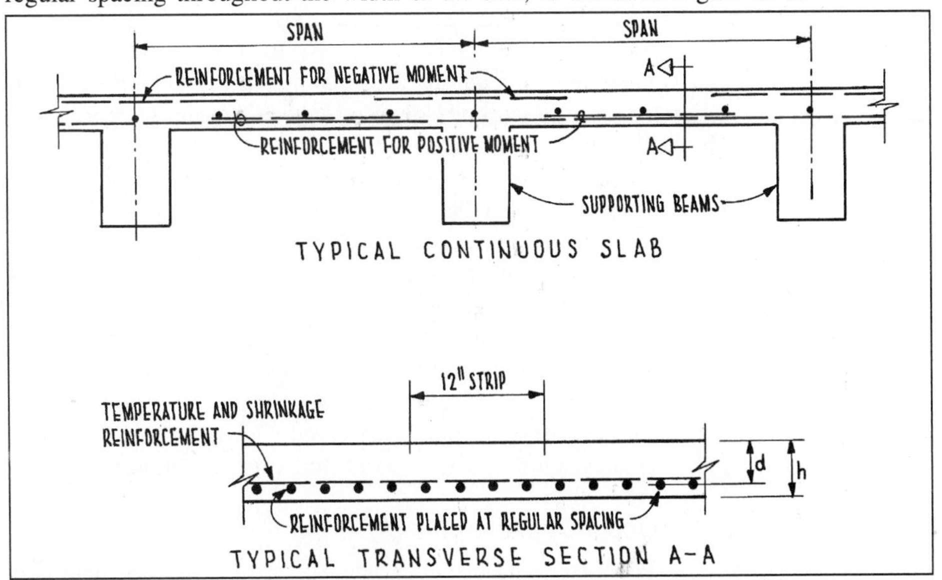

Figure 21-5 Typical structural slab.

Where negative moments occur over supports (producing tension on top), the reinforcement is placed at the top of the slab. At midspan, where moments are positive (producing tension on bottom), the reinforcement is placed at the bottom of the slab. A typical longitudinal section is included in Figure 21-5, showing typical locations for the positive and negative reinforcement.

Reinforcing bars are placed at a fixed spacing across the width of the slab. For the most commonly used spacings and bar sizes, steel areas per foot of width are tabulated in Table C-2. Bars may be no closer together than one bar diameter (clear distance), no farther apart than three times the slab thickness *h*, with an absolute minimum clear distance of 1 in. and an absolute maximum spacing of 18 in.

In American practice, slab thicknesses are varied in $^1/_2$ in. increments. Forms, screeds and accessories are manufactured in these dimensions and the tradition is so strong that change seems unlikely. In SI units, increments of 10 mm are common; reinforcement cannot reasonably be placed to closer tolerances than 10 mm.

Because the thickness of slabs is small, the reinforcement in slabs is similarly limited to smaller sizes. Bar sizes larger than No. 6 are not generally used in slabs; No. 4 is probably the most commonly used size, with No. 6 a close second. Bar sizes less than No. 4 are not used as structural reinforcement but may be used as temperature steel.

Slabs are almost never reinforced for compression. If a slab is made so thin that compressive reinforcement becomes necessary, the problems with deflections become almost insurmountable. It is far easier, cheaper, and more practical to add $^1/_2$ in. to the depth.

Where the shape of a slab is square, or nearly so, considerable savings in both concrete and steel can be effected by designing the slab for flexure in two directions. In such "two-way" slabs, part of the load is assumed to be carried in one direction, the remaining part in the other direction. The ACI Code contains a special section on the design of two-way slabs.

Very often, the area of steel in a slab is governed by minimum requirements for temperature and shrinkage reinforcement. Such minimum steel requirements are presented in Chapter 17; they are presented again in tabular form in Table 21-1 for immediate reference.

Table 21-1 Minimum Steel Ratios in Slabs for Temperature and Shrinkage Reinforcement.

Steel Grade	ρ
40	0.0020
50	0.0020
60	0.0018

In addition to requiring that minimum areas of reinforcement be provided in the primary direction of stress, Code also requires that the same minimum area of reinforcement be provided transverse to the primary direction; such reinforcement is required for temperature/shrinkage stresses regardless whether any flexural stress exists. The minimum steel ratios given in Table 21-1 are therefore applicable both in the primary direction and in the transverse direction.

The following sections present the design of elevated slabs under simple support conditions. Except for very short spans, the thickness of elevated slabs will be governed by deflections rather than by strength; the minimum thicknesses given in Chapter 17, Table 17-1 will govern in such cases. Whenever the thickness of a slab is governed by deflections, the compressive stress in the concrete is invariably low and the balanced stress condition cannot be achieved. For such slabs, one simply accepts the inefficiencies inherent in designing to meet limits on deflections.

21.8 One Way Slabs, Simply Supported

When an elevated slab has simple supports on two edges only, as shown in Figure 21-6, the slab undergoes bending in only one direction and is called a one-way slab. Since every foot of width is identical to every other foot, the slab may be designed for a one-foot width between supports, then the design may be extended laterally as far as support conditions remain unchanged.

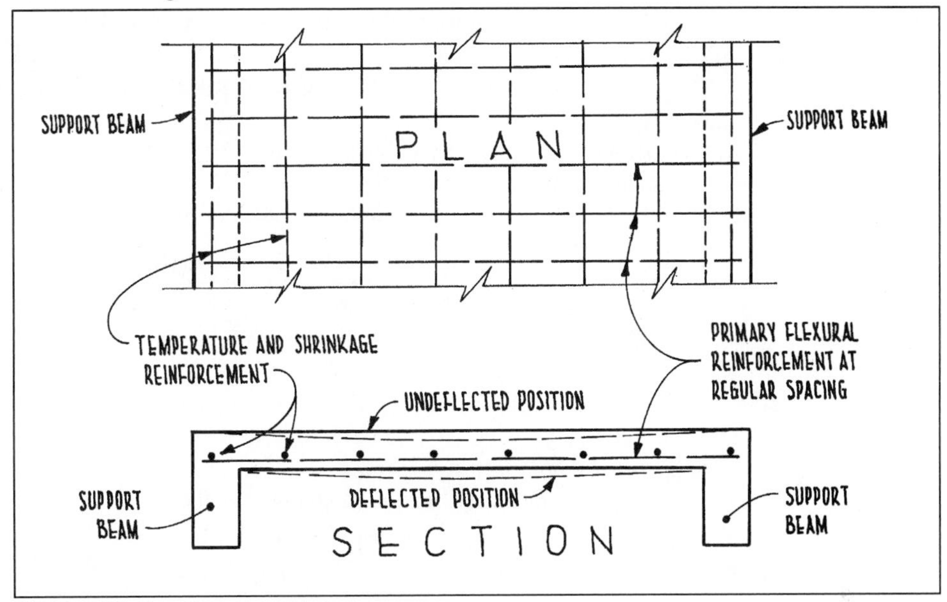

Figure 21-6 One-way slab.

An example will illustrate the design of such a simply supported slab.

Example 21-1

Design of a concrete floor slab. Simple supports, exposed to weather.

Given: Slab as shown, live load 100 psf over entire slab. Grade 60 steel, f'_c = 4000 psi. Normal weight concrete, exterior exposure.

To Find: Suitable section to sustain the load.

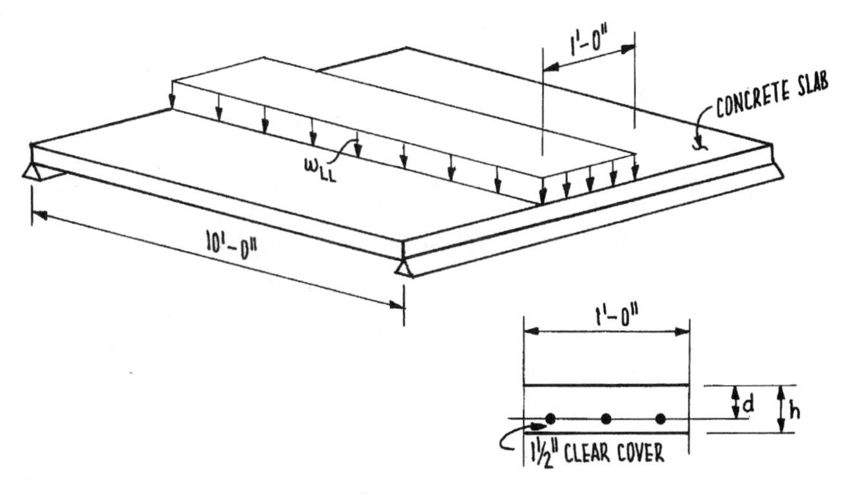

Solution: Calculate the live-load moment. For a 1-ft strip, the uniform live load becomes a distributed load of 100 plf, and:

$$M_{LL} = \frac{w_{LL}L^2}{8} = \frac{(100)(10)(10)}{8} = 1250 \text{ lb} - \text{ft} / \text{ft}$$

For control of deflections, overall slab thickness is limited (see Table 17-1). For this slab, overall thickness is limited to L/20 or 6 in.

Estimate thickness: h = 6 in. ±, d = 4 in. ±.

Determine the dead load of slab per foot of width:

Dead load = (150 pcf)(6/12) = 75 psf.

Find the estimated dead load moment:

$$M_{DL} = \frac{w_{DL}L^2}{8} = \frac{(75)(10)(10)}{8} = 938 \text{ lb} - \text{ft} / \text{ft}\cdot$$

Determine the moment at ultimate load:

$$M_n = (1.4M_{DL} + 1.7M_{LL})/\phi = [(1.4)(938) + (1.7)(1250)]/0.9$$
$$= 3820 \text{ lb-ft} = 45.8 \text{ kip-in.}$$

Solve for the magnitude of the required plastic section modulus:

$$Z_c = \frac{M_n}{0.85f_c'} = \frac{45{,}800}{(0.85)(4000)} = 13.50$$

Select the service stress f_c and design constants for balanced stress conditions:

From Table C-8, with no compressive reinforcement:

$$\rho = 0.0089,\ f_c = 2000,\ Z_c = 0.140bd^2.$$

Solve for required depth, where b = 12 in.:

$$Z_c = 13.50 = 0.140(12)(d^2);\ d = 2.83 \text{ in.}$$

The value of *d* is much less than the 4 in. estimated earlier, indicating that deflection conditions rather than stress conditions will control this design. Obviously, a balanced stress condition will not be possible so a new steel ratio will be selected.

For slabs it can be assumed that, as a general rule, the design condition will be imbalanced and the methods of Example 18-9 can be used to determine the steel area. For such a case, the solution for the section modulus becomes, for b = 12 in. and d = 4 in.:

$$\frac{M_n}{0.85f_c'} = Z_c = \text{coeff.}\,(bd^2);\ \frac{45{,}800}{(0.85)(4000)} = \text{coeff.}\,(12)(4^2)$$

coeff. = 0.0702

For this coefficient of Z_c, the steel ratio is found by interpolation in Table C-6 to be $\rho = 0.0042$. For this value of ρ:

$$\rho = 0.0042,\ f_c = 1352 \text{ psi},\ Z_c = 0.071bd^2,\ f_s/f_c = 27.29.$$

Verify the ultimate moment M_n for this section:

$$M_n = 0.85f_c'Z_c = 0.85(4000)(0.071)(12)(4^2)$$
$$= 46{,}300 > 45{,}800 \text{ lb-in. (O.K.).}$$

Select reinforcement:

Steel $A_s = \rho bd = 0.0042(12)(4) = 0.202$ in.^{2}/ft.

From Table C-2, use No. 4 bars @ 10 in. o.c.

Minimum steel ratio for temperature and shrinkage reinforcement is found from Table 21-1:

Min $\rho = 0.0018bh = 0.0018(12)(6.0) = 0.13$ in.^{2}/ft.

The primary reinforcement provides 0.42 in.^{2}/ft so no additional reinforcement will be necessary in the primary direction. In the transverse direction where there is no primary reinforcement, add No. 4 bars @ 18 in. o.c., to be placed directly on top of the other reinforcement.

Use h = 6 in., d = 4 in., A_s = No. 4 bars @ 10 in. o.c.
Use No. 4 bars @ 18 in. o.c. in the transverse direction, placed on top of the primary reinforcement.

For this slab, the concrete is working at very low stress levels, about 40% of idealized yield, indicating poor efficiency in materials. The design is controlled by deflections, however, and in such cases the reduced efficiency in stresses is simply accepted.

The investigation of a known section to find an allowable load is the reverse of the design procedure. The following example will illustrate.

Example 21-2

Investigation of a section to determine the allowable live load on the given slab. Simple supports, no exposure to weather.

Given: Slab as shown.
Grade 50 steel.
$f'_c = 3000$ psi.
Simple span, 12 ft.

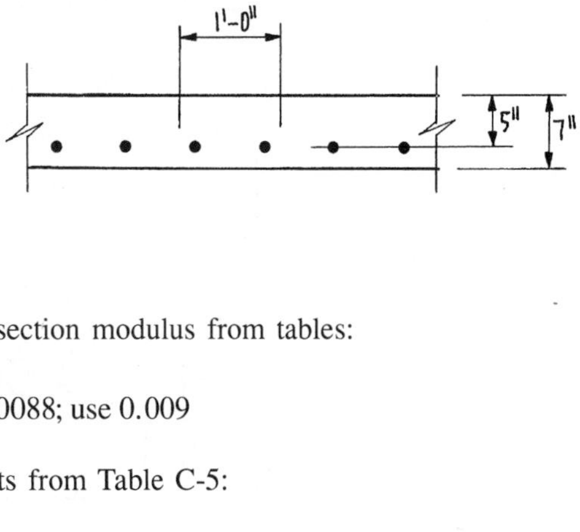

1'-0"
5"
7"

To Find: Allowable uniform live load W_{LL}.

Solution: Calculate ρ and find the section modulus from tables:

$$\rho = \frac{A_s}{bd} = \frac{0.53}{12(5)} = 0.0088;\ \text{use } 0.009$$

Select the design constants from Table C-5:

$$f_c = 1627 \text{ psi},\ Z_c = 0.161bd^2$$

Determine the ultimate moment the section can sustain:

$$Mn = 0.85 f'_c = 0.85(3000)(0.161)(12)(5^2);$$

$$M_n = 123 \text{ kip·in.} = 10.3 \text{ kip·ft.}$$

Determine the dead load and the dead load moment for a simple span:

$$w_{DL} = 150\ \text{pcf}(7/12) = 87.5\ \text{psf}$$

$$M_{DL} = \frac{w_{DL}L^2}{8} = \frac{87.5(12^2)}{8} = 1575\ \text{lb·ft.}$$

Solve for the live load moment:

$$M_n = (1.4M_{DL} + 1.7M_{LL})/\phi$$

$$10300 = [(1.4)(1575) + (1.7)(M_{LL})/0.9$$

$$M_{LL} = \frac{0.9(10{,}300) - 1.4(1575)}{1.7} = 4160\ \text{lb·ft.}$$

Solve for the uniform live load:

$$M_{LL} = \frac{w_{LL}L^2}{8};\quad 4160 = \frac{w_{LL}(12^2)}{8}$$

$$w_{LL} = 230\ \text{lb/ft}^2.$$

Other investigations are similar to those already discussed with the rectangular sections.

21.9 One-Way Slabs Continuous over Several Supports

In many, if not most, cases in modern construction, an elevated concrete slab will be continuous over three or more supports, as shown in Figure 21-7. Such slabs may be designed as continuous beams, with the design shears and moments being computed from the ACI coefficients presented in Chapter 17. Where negative moments occur at the supports, producing tension on the top face of the slab, the tensile reinforcement is placed at the top face as shown in Figure 21-7. Similarly, toward the center of the span where the moments are positive, tension occurs at the bottom face of the slab and the reinforcement is placed at the bottom face.

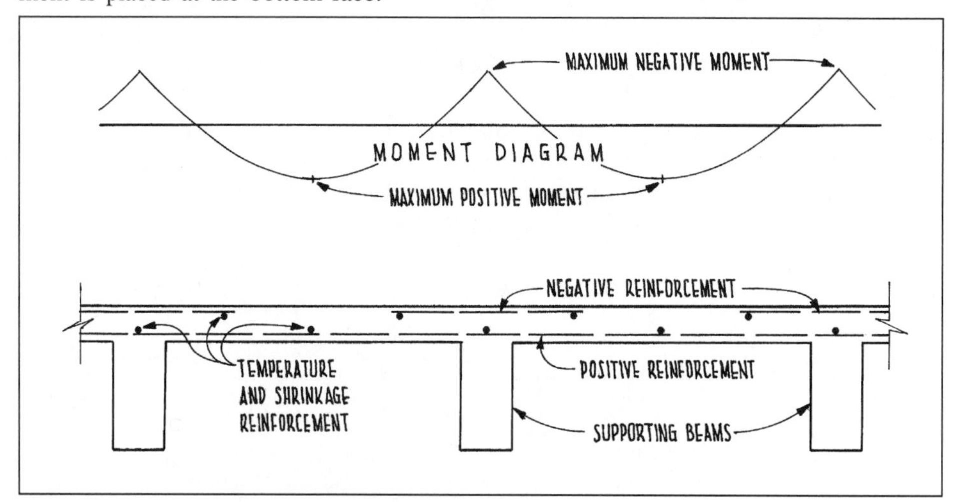

Figure 21-7 Continuous one-way slab.

An example will illustrate the design of a continuous one-way slab.

Example 21-3

Design of a continuous slab.

Given: Continuous slab as shown. Grade 60 steel, f'_c = 4000 psi; normal weight concrete, exterior exposure; live load 100 psf, clear span 15'-0".

To Find: Suitable section in reinforced concrete.

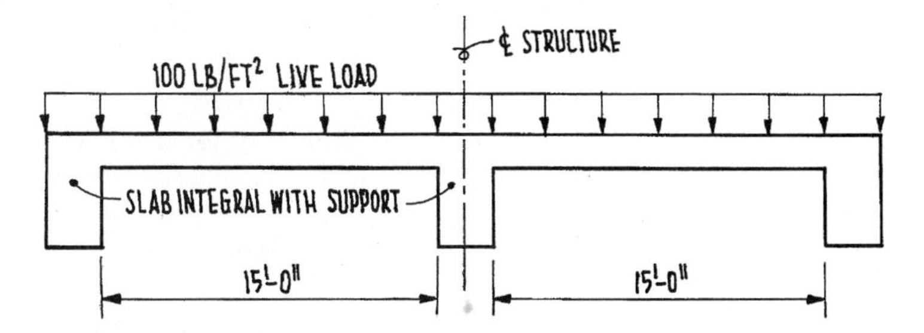

Solution: The slab reinforcement will obviously be symmetrical about the centerline. The design can therefore be limited to only one side and repeated for the other side. The coefficients for the design shears and moments are found from the ACI coefficients given in Chapter 17 and are shown in the following sketch. As a matter of interest, the envelopes and the inflection points are shown in the following sketches.

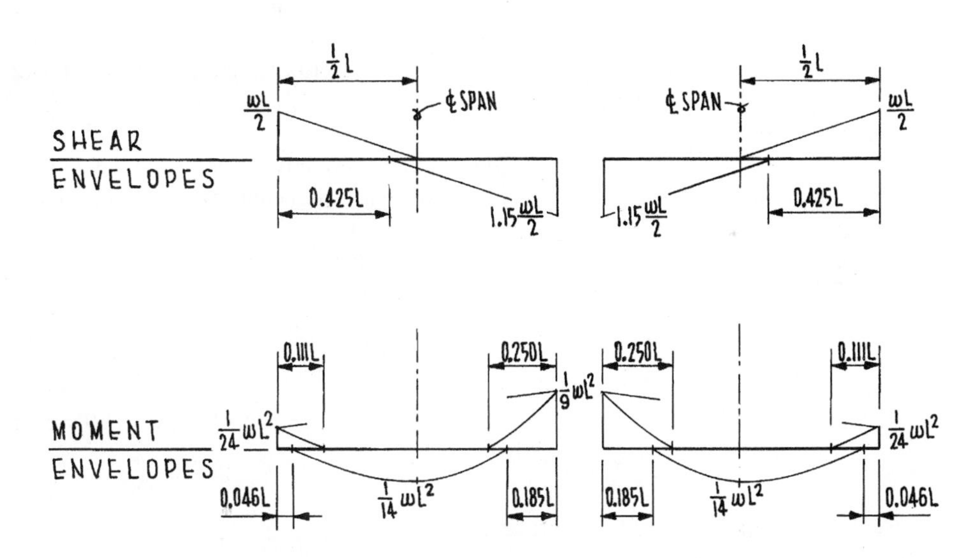

In order to establish the dead load of the slab, a trial thickness of the slab is obtained from the rules of thumb. A trial thickness of about 7 in. is estimated.

A check is also made for the minimum thickness required to control deflections. From Table 17-1 the minimum thickness is found to be $L/28$ where L is the length of span of a one-way slab. For a span of 15'-0", the minimum thickness is then $7^1/_2$ in.

From the foregoing estimates, an initial trial thickness of $^7/_{12}$ in. is adopted, for which the dead load is $(^{7.5}/_{12})(145 \text{ lb/ft}^3)$ or 90.7 lb/ft². The effective depth d is taken to be 5.5 in.

The maximum design moments are then:

For dead load on a 1-ft strip:

At exterior support, $M_{DL} = {}^1/_{24}wL^2 = {}^1/_{24}(90.7)(15^2)$
$= 0.85$ k·ft.

At midspan, $M_{DL} = {}^1/_{14}wL^2 = {}^1/_{14}(90.7)(15^2)$
$= 1.46$ k·ft.

At interior support, $M_{DL} = {}^1/_{9}wL^2 = {}^1/_{9}(90.7)(15^2)$
$= 2.27$ k·ft.

Similarly for live load on a 1-ft strip:

At exterior support, $M_{DL} = {}^1/_{24}wL^2 = {}^1/_{24}(90.7)(15^2)$
$= 0.94$ k·ft.

At midspan, $M_{DL} = {}^1/_{14}wL^2 = {}^1/_{14}(90.7)(15^2)$
$= 1.61$ k·ft.

At interior support, $M_{DL} = {}^1/_{9}wL^2 = {}^1/_{9}(90.7)(15^2)$
$= 2.50$ k·ft.

The nominal ultimate moments are computed from Eq.(3-1a):

$M_n = (1.4M_{DL} + 1.7M_{LL})/\phi$, for which:

At exterior support, $M_n = [(1.4)(0.85)+(1.7)(0.94)]/0.9$
$= 3.09$ k·ft.

At midspan, $M_n = [(1.4)(1.46)+(1.7)(1.61)]/0.9$
$= 5.31$ k·ft.

At interior support, $M_n = [(1.4)(2.27)+(1.7)(2.50)]/0.9$
$= 8.25$ k·ft.

Since both the effective depth *d* and the width *b* have been established (or estimated), the coefficient of Z_c can be found:

At the exterior support:

$$Z_c = \frac{M_n}{0.85f'_c} = \frac{3090(12)}{0.85(4000)} = 10.90$$

$$Z_c = \text{coeff.}(bd^2) = 10.90 = \text{coeff.}(12)(5.5^2)$$

$$\text{coeff.} = 0.030$$

From Table C-6, $\rho = 0.0017$.
$A_s = 0.0016\ A_s = 0.0017(12)(5.5) = 0.112$ in²/ft.

At midspan:

$$Z_c = \frac{M_n}{0.85f'_c} = \frac{5310(12)}{0.85(4000)} = 18.74$$

$$Z_c = \text{coeff.}(bd^2) = 18.74 = \text{coeff.}(12)(5.5^2)$$

$$\text{coeff.} = 0.0516$$

From Table C-6, $\rho = 0.0030$.
$A_s = \rho bd = 0.0030(12)(5.5) = 0.198$ in²/ft.

At the interior support:

$$Z_c = \frac{M_n}{0.85f'_c} = \frac{8250(12)}{0.85(4000)} = 29.12 \text{ in.}^3$$

$$Z_c = \text{coeff.}(bd^2) = 29.12 = \text{coeff.}(12)(5.5^2)$$

$$\text{coeff.} = 0.0802$$

From Table C-6, $\rho = 0.00475$.

$$A_s = \rho bd = 0.00475(12)(5.5) = 0.313 \text{ in}^2\text{/ft.}$$

Check minimum area requirements for temperature and shrinkage reinforcement:

$$\text{Min } A_s = 0.0018 \text{ bh} = 0.0018(12)(7.5) = 0.162 \text{ in.}^2\text{/ft.}$$

This minimum A_s is compared to the values of A_s just computed for strength. It is noted that the value of A_s = 0.112in.²/ft. at the exterior support does not meet these minimum requirements. That value of A_s is therefore revised upward to 0.14 in.²/ft.

Transverse reinforcement is set at its minimum value of 0.14 in.²/ft.

The final results are then from Table C-2:

At exterior support, A_s = 0.140 in.²/ft,
use No. 4 @ 16 in. o.c.
At midspan, A_s = 0.198 in.²/ft,
use No. 4 @ 12 in. o.c.
At interior support, A_s = 0.313 in.²/ft,
use No. 4 @ 7½ in. o.c.

Verify that the thickness is adequate for shear. Maximum shear force occurs at the interior support, for which V = 115wL/2:

$$V_{DL} = 1.15(90.7)(15/2) = 782 \text{ lb/ft.}$$
$$V_{LL} = 1.15(100)(15/2) = 863 \text{ lb/ft.}$$
$$V_n = (1.4V_{DL} + 1.7V_{LL})/\phi = [(1.4)(782) + (1.7)(863)]/0.85 = 3.01 \text{ k·ft.}$$

The capacity of the section in shear is, with no shear reinforcement:

$$V_n = V_c = 2\sqrt{f'_c}bd = 2\sqrt{4000}(12)(5.5)$$
$$= 8.4 \text{ k/ft} > 3.01 \text{ k/ft load}$$

It is concluded that the section is adequate in shear.

A great deal of latitude may be exercised in selecting and arranging the reinforcement. One solution is given in the following sketch (temperature and shrinkage reinforcement are not shown):

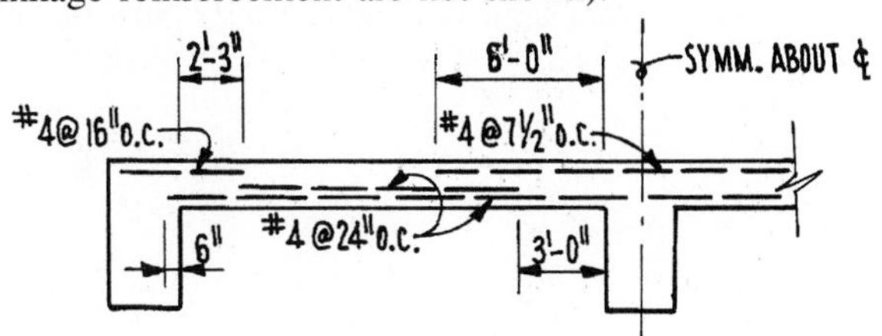

The cutoff points for the reinforcement in Example 21-3 are governed by anchorage requirements. One of those anchorage requirements is that at least 1/4 of the positive reinforcement shall extend into the supports by a distance not less than 6 in.; the remaining positive reinforcement shall extend past the point of inflection by 6 in. or by a distance of 12 bar diameters. Another anchorage requirement is that the negative reinforcement shall extend beyond the point of inflection by a distance d, 12 bar diameters, or span/16, whichever is larger. These requirements for cutoff points are met in the layout shown in the sketch.

21.10 Slab Supports Other Than Simple Supports

To this point, only simply supported slabs have been considered. Such slabs are distinctive in that the deformed surface is curved in only one direction, as indicated in Figure 21-8a. If additional supports are added at the other two sides, as indicated in Figure 21-8b, the surface of single curvature becomes distorted into some undefined surface of double curvature. The problem immediately becomes highly statically indeterminate and correspondingly quite complex.

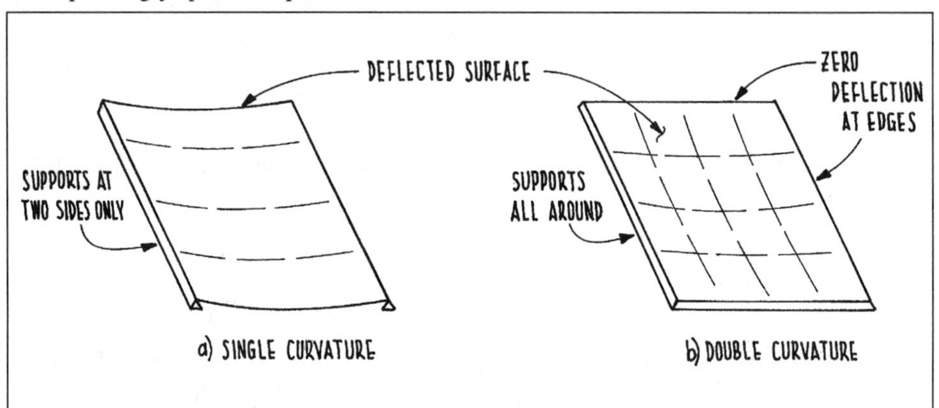

Figure 21-8 Deflection surfaces of slat slabs.

The support conditions need not be symmetrical as shown in Figure 21-8. A slab may also be supported only on 3 sides as shown schematically in Figure 21-9. Or, a slab may be simply supported in one direction and continuous in the other direction. Or, a slab may be continuous in all directions, with a corresponding increase in indeterminacy and complexity.

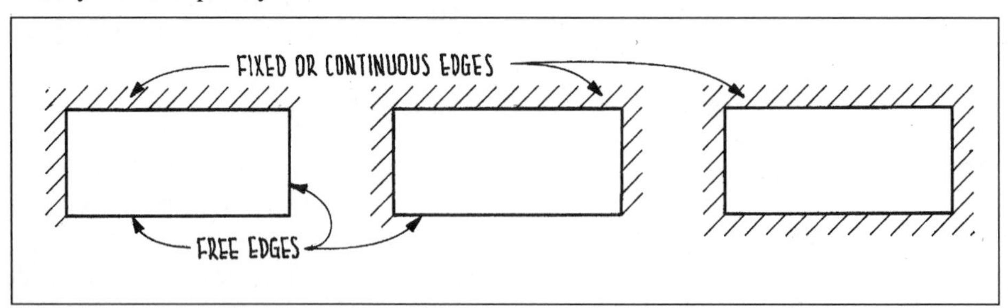

Figure 21-9 Support conditions for slabs.

The bending moment diagrams at the supports for a slab continuous in both directions are shown in Figure 21-10. Note that at the corners, the moment becomes negative. Along with negative moment, the reactions at these corners are also negative; the slab is trying to "kick up" at the corners.

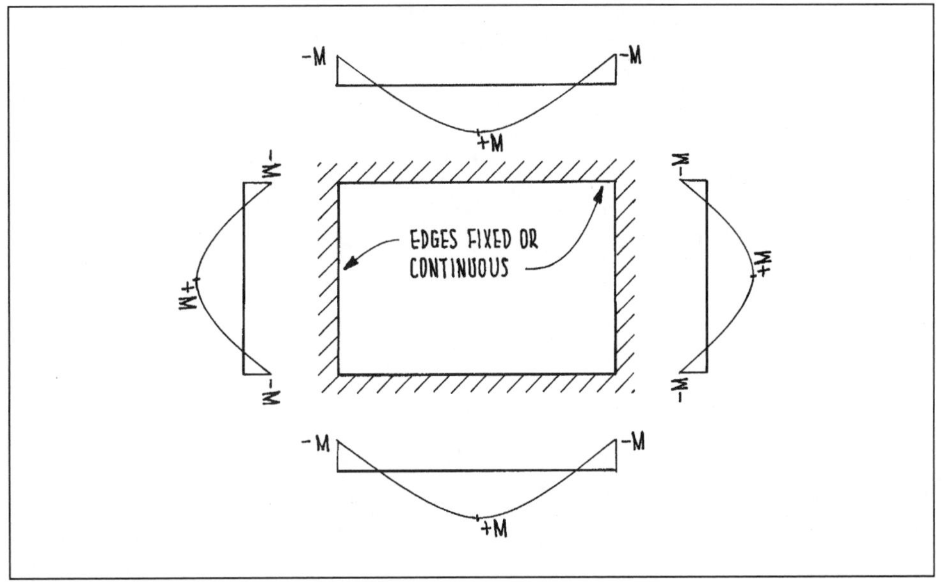

Figure 21-10 Moments at supports in a two-way slab.

It should be apparent that the design of slabs can become quite complex whenever the slabs are anything other than simple one-way slabs. Within the industry, however, the use of continuous slabs is a highly desirable feature, both in design and in construction. Long ago, ACI recognized the need for a simplified method to design such slabs and accordingly developed a simplified method for the design of continuous slabs. The use of these slabs is so common that the simplified design method has been included in and made a part of the Code.

Probably the most widely accepted form of this simplified design procedure was the "coefficient method" as it was developed for the 1963 Code. From that time to now, the coefficient method of the 1963 Code has been used successfully throughout the world both by highly qualified and minimally qualified practitioners. It is still in use by a large part of the practice even though ACI has, in the 1983 Code, added the "direct design method", a more sophisticated but less general method of designing such slabs.

The design of these highly indeterminate two-way slabs is beyond the scope of this book. Those interested in pursuing the design of such slabs can find numerous publications written specifically on this subject. The author prefers the relative simplicity of the coefficient method for the design of slabs and recommends it over the more recent direct design method; the success of the coefficient method over some 30 years of use is a strong argument in favor of such a preference.

21.11 Tee Beams

Tee beams are one of the more important features that may be used in concrete construction, important enough that a lengthy discussion devoted to their design is justified. The advantage of having a concrete deck working monolithically with its concrete beams offers a significant increase in efficiency of materials. For comparison, designing a steel deck to be stressed monolithically with its steel supporting member would rarely be feasible outside aircraft or ship design.

A typical concrete tee beam is shown in Figure 21-11. A certain width of the concrete floor slab becomes the compression flange whenever the beam is in positive moment (tension on bottom). This compressive width, designated b' in Figure 21-11, is the effective width for flexure only; the width of the web, b_w, is still the effective width for shear.

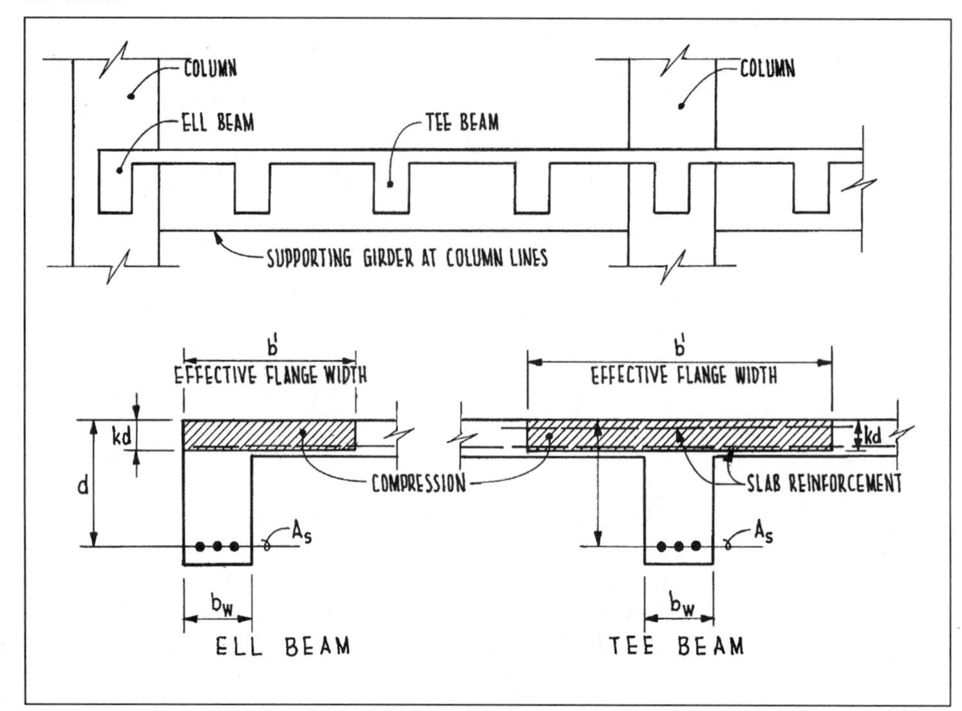

Figure 21-11 Typical tee beams and ell beams.

A system of repetitive tee beams might well be considered a thick slab that has had its reinforcement lumped together at regular intervals and, in addition, has had the concrete in the unreinforced areas removed to save weight. Since all concrete in the tension zone ceases to exist, insofar as the flexural analysis is concerned, it does not really matter whether these dead areas are solid or void. The tee beam is thus equivalent to a thick slab with its dead weight considerably reduced.

Although the removal of the recessed areas makes little difference in the capacity to resist flexure, it causes a serious reduction in the capacity to resist shear. Tee beams are quite weak in shear compared to slabs and usually require shear reinforcement. The spacing of repetitive tee beams should therefore be set with due regard to the shear capacity of each tee beam.

21.12 Tee Beams Subject to Negative Moment

Design for flexure and design for shear were developed independently of each other in earlier chapters. Both may now be combined in the design of a typical tee-beam stem subject to a large shear and a small negative moment. Such cases occur commonly where spans are short and loads are heavy.

Under negative moment, the compressive area of a tee beam is at the bottom of the stem, as shown in Figure 21-12. The top of the section is in tension and therefore disappears as far as the flexural analysis is concerned. The section responds to load exactly like an upside-down rectangular section.

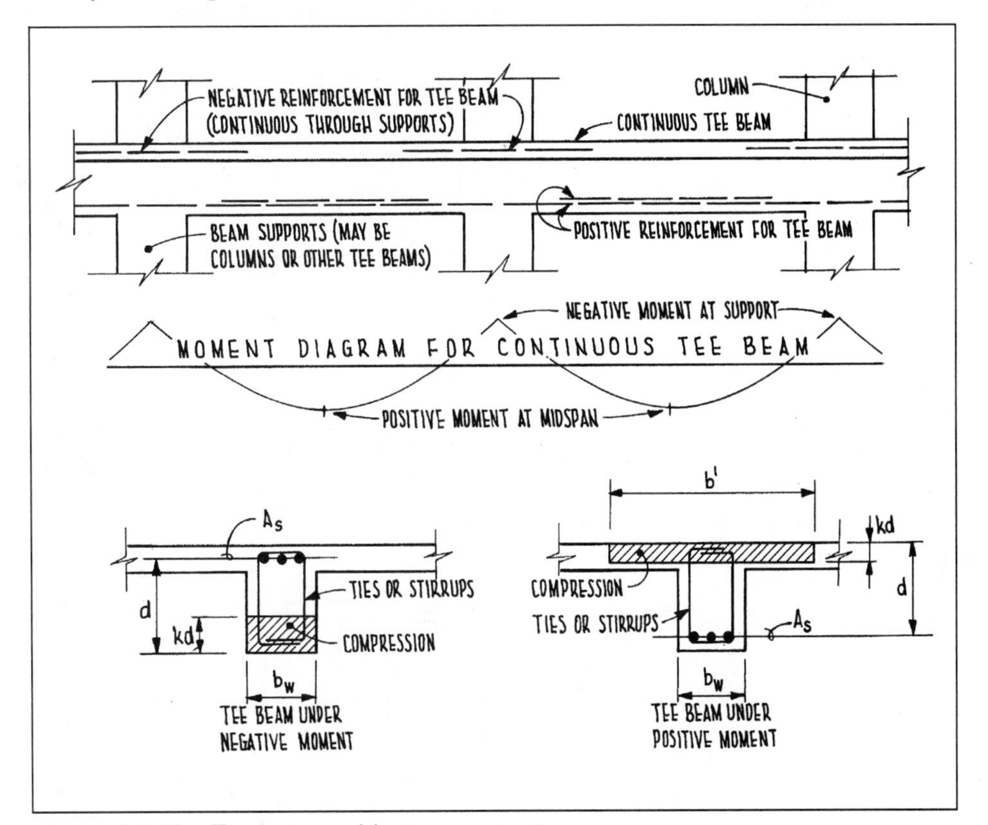

Figure 21-12 Tee beam subject to moments.

For continuous rectangular beams, the negative moment and the high shears at the supports can be expected to be larger than the positive moment and low shears at midspan; conditions at the supports will therefore usually govern the design. For continuous tee beams, where the compressive area is so much smaller at the support than at midspan, the conditions at the supports will almost always govern the size of the tee beam stem.

The size of the section is usually determined first for flexural considerations; in this solution the section modulus is found and solved for b_w and d. Then, from the shear criteria, a separate and independent solution for b_w and d can be found, where b_w and d are deliberately kept large enough that stirrups are not needed, or at best, a spacing closer than $d/2$ is not required. These two solutions for b_w and d are then compared and the final choice is made.

An example will illustrate the procedure.

Example 21-4

Selection of size of a tee-beam stem. Stem subject to shear and to negative moment.

Given: Beam as shown. Grade 60 steel. f'_c = 3000 psi. Values of shear and moment are those at ultimate load.

To Find: Required size of stem.

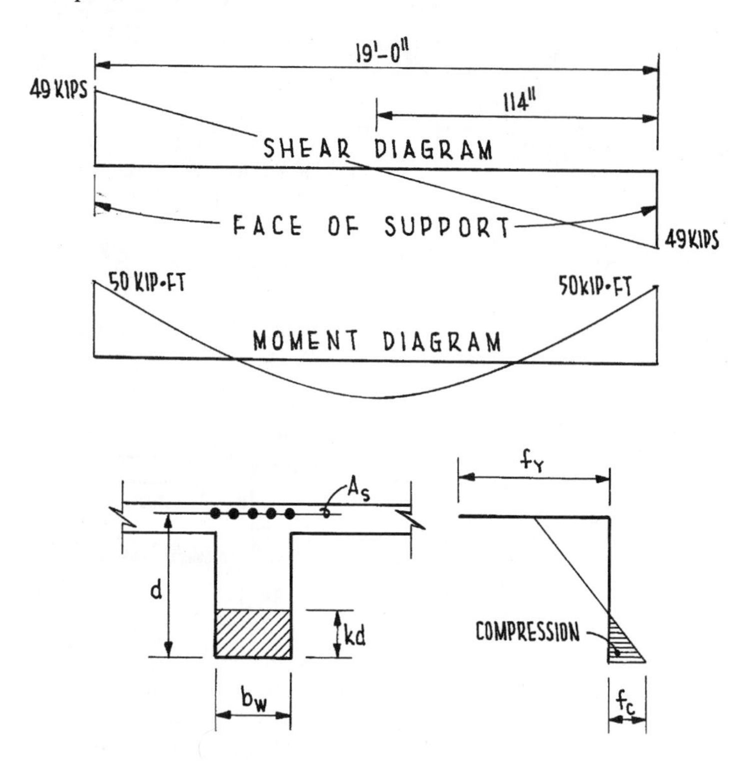

Solution: Sizes are first determined for flexural load, M_n:

At the face of the support, M_n = 50 kip·ft.

From Table C-8 for the balanced stress condition:

$$\rho = 0.0060,\ Z_c = 0.132bd^2$$

$$\frac{M_n}{0.85f'_c} = Z_c,\quad \frac{50,000(12)}{0.85(3000)} = 0.132bd^2$$

Use b = 0.5d, solve for d = 15.3 in.

For flexure, use b = 8 in., d = 15.5 in.

Second, determine sizes for the end shear, V_n = 49 kips

At a distance d from face of support, with d = 15.5 in. as a first approximation for d:

$$V_{cr} = \frac{114 - 15.5}{114}(49) = 42.3 \text{ kips}$$

Determine the required size for shear, with stirrups at d/2 and $b_w = 0.5d$:

$$V_{cr} = v_n b_w d; \quad 42{,}300 = 3(2\sqrt{3000})(0.5d)(d)$$
$$d = 16.0$$

For shear, use b = 8 in., d = 16.0 in.

The solution for shear is compared to the solution for flexure. The larger size is chosen for the final design.

For shear requirements:

Use b = 8 in., d = 16 in., stirrups at ½d.

Using these dimensions, solve for the final value of ρ. In this particular case, the flexural solution does not change, so:

Use b = 8 in., d = 16 in., ρ = 0.0060, stirrups @ ½d

It is again emphasized that the first calculation for the required size of the stem is made for flexure. The second calculation is made for shear. It was noted earlier that for continuous beams, such as this example, the negative moment can be expected to be larger than the positive moment and will therefore govern the size of the stem. The shears are then reviewed to see that shear reinforcement is acceptable.

21.13 Code Requirements for Tee and Ell Shapes

When the moment on a tee beam becomes positive, the tee section suddenly gains a great deal more compressive material, as shown in Figure 21-13. When the neutral axis falls within the top slab, or flange, as indicated in Figure 21-13b, the beam still responds to load as does any other rectangular section, but as one having a compressive width of b'. All the design procedures discussed previously are still valid; the section simply happens to be wide and shallow.

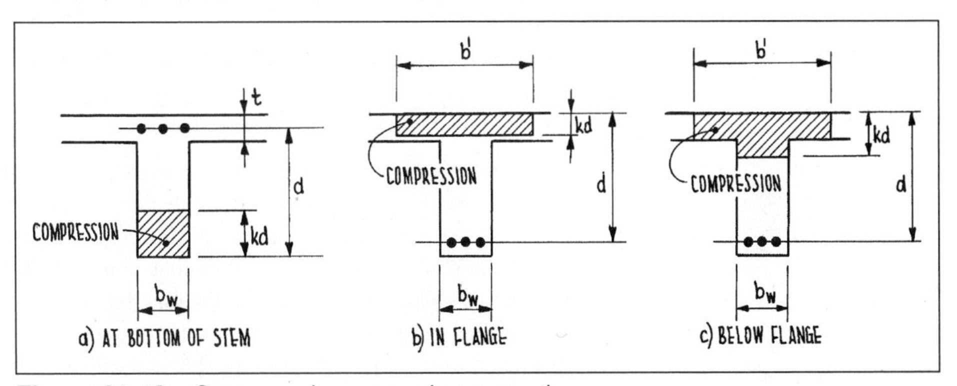

Figure 21-13 Compression zones in tee sections.

A complication arises when the neutral axis falls below the soffit of the slab, as shown in Figure 21-13c. For this case the compressive area is no longer rectangular. The amount of error between this case and the truly rectangular case will be seen later to be quite small at service levels.

Before beginning the design of a tee section subject to positive moment, it is first necessary to define the effective dimensions of a tee beam. Typical sections of the two most common types of tee beams are shown in Figure 21-14. One of these types is commonly called an ell beam but it functions like a tee beam. At midspan the moment is positive and the floor slab is in compression; the floor slab is seen to be the compression flange of the tee beams.

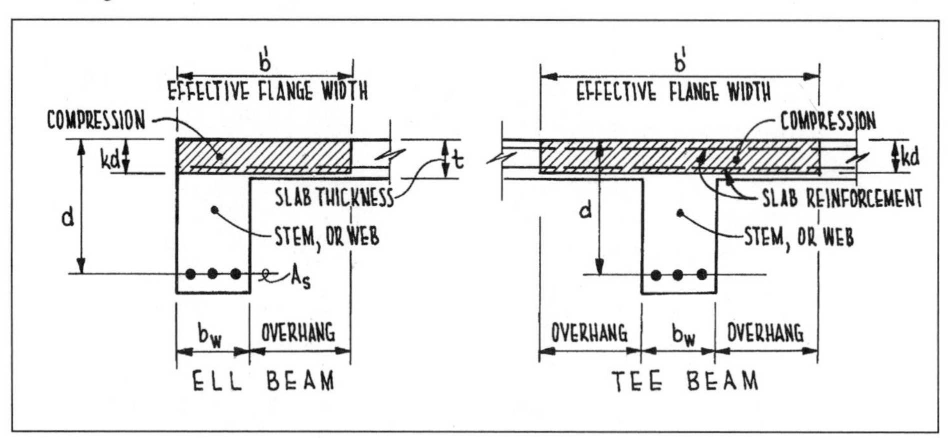

Figure 21-14 Effective flange widths.

As shown in Figure 21-14, not all of the slab will be effective as a compression flange. Code (8.10.2) prescribes the width of the slab that may be considered to be effective in compression; these limits and requirements are based on extensive performance tests. Test results indicate that the effective flange will not extend halfway to the next stem unless the stems are spaced fairly close together.

Code (8.10) limitations concerning the effective compression area are given in the following requirements.

1. The total width of slab effective as a tee beam flange or as an ell beam flange (dimension b' in Figure 21-14) shall not exceed one-fourth the span length of the beam.
2. The effective overhanging flange width on each side of the web (or stem) shall not exceed eight times the slab thickness nor one-half the clear distance to the next web.
3. For beams having a slab on one side only (ell beams), the effective overhanging flange width shall not exceed one-twelfth the span length of the beam nor six times the slab thickness nor one-half the clear distance to the next web.

The foregoing requirements are obviously somewhat arbitrary, since there can be no sharp break between the stress in the effective flange and the stress in the immediately adjacent parts of the slab. The rather rough approximation does not matter, however, since the total area of concrete is so high that concrete stresses at service levels are invariably quite low. The service stress in the concrete is rarely even checked in practice, but will be checked here as a matter of academic interest.

Occasionally, compressive reinforcement is used in a tee beam. Compressive reinforcement can be effective in reducing deflections. Tee beams, often being comparatively shallow, invite problems with deflections.

One additional point of the Code deserves repeating. The minimum steel ratio ρ is given by Code (10.5.1):

$$\text{minimum allowable } \rho \geq \frac{200}{f_y} \qquad (18\text{-}29)$$

In checking for the minimum steel ratio in tee beams, the width of the stem is used (see Figure 21-14):

$$\text{minimum usable } \rho_{min} = \frac{A_s}{b_w d} \geq \frac{200}{f_y}$$

This artificial steel ratio rmin, based on b_w, must be applied to tee sections. The real steel ratio, when based on the compressive width b' (see Figure 21-14), may be considerably smaller than this artificial value. The point will be illustrated later in examples 21-5 and 21-6 when the steel ratio based on b' must be used when selecting a tee section.

21.14 Tee Beams Subject to Positive Moment

Two common cases of loading on tee beams will be considered for tee-beam design. These cases are shown schematically in Figure 21-15.

1. *Continuous tee beam with negative moment at supports.* The tee beam is subject to negative moment at its ends and to positive moment at midspan.
2. *Simple span.* The tee beam is never subject to negative moment.

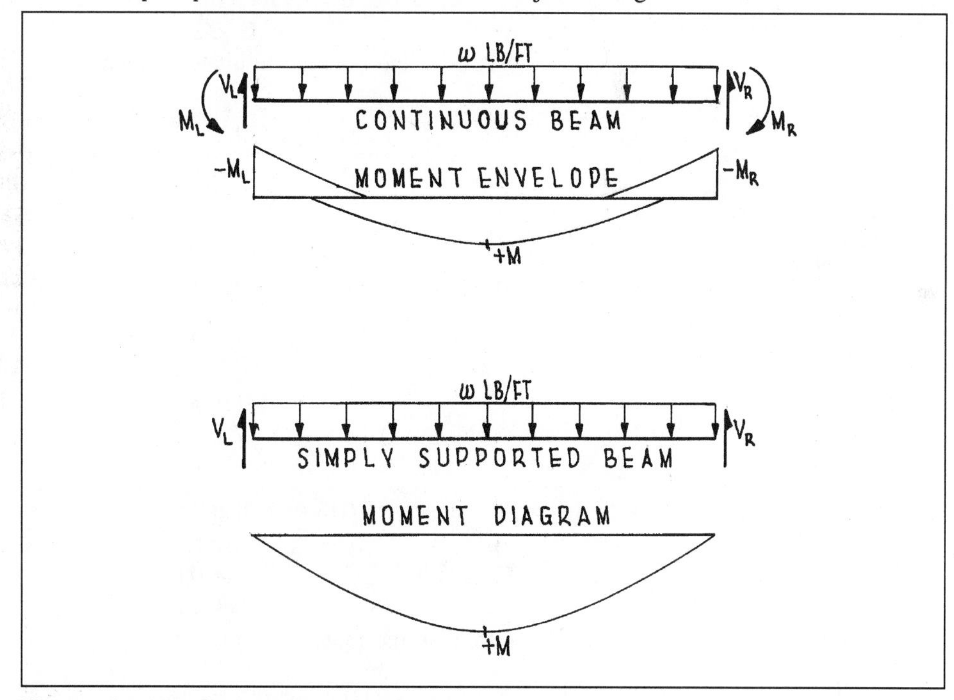

Figure 21-15 Common tee beam load systems.

For Case 1, the size of the stem is invariably set by shear and moment considerations at the support; such a calculation was presented in Example 21-4. At midspan, since the size of the stem is fixed, the only remaining calculation is for the area of reinforcement to take the positive moment. This calculation was first demonstrated in Example 18-9 where both b_w and d were fixed, but will be repeated in the next example to show the effects of the wider compression area. Tee beams in positive moment can rarely be designed for the balanced stress condition.

Example 21-5

Design of a tee beam subject to positive moment. Size of stem fixed by conditions at supports.

Given: Tee section as shown.
M_{DL} = 57 kip·ft.
M_{LL} = 61 kip·ft.
Grade 60 steel.
f'_c = 3000 psi.
Span = 23 ft 0 in.
Tees at 10 ft 0 in. o.c.

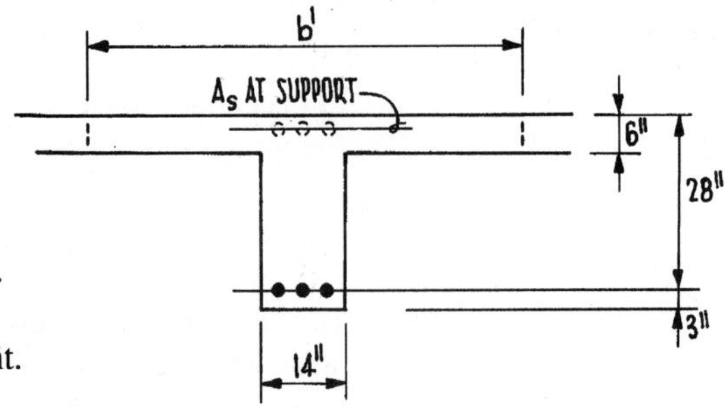

To Find: Required reinforcement.

Solution: Determine the effective width of the flange (in inches):

$$b' < \frac{\text{span}}{4}; \qquad b' < \frac{23(12)}{4} \text{ or 69 in.}$$

$b' < 8(\text{flange})(2) + b_w$; $b' < 8(6)(2) + 14$ or 110 in.

$b' <$ tee spacing; $b' < 10(12)$ or 120 in.

Use b' = 69 in.

Calculate the nominal ultimate moment:

$$M_n = \frac{1.4M_{DL} + 1.7M_{LL}}{\phi} = \frac{[(1.4)(57) + (1.7)(61)]}{0.9}$$

$$= 204 \text{ kip·ft.}$$

Since both b' and d are known, solve for the coefficient of Z_c:

$$\frac{M_n}{0.85f'_c} = Z_c; \quad \frac{204{,}000(12)}{0.85(3000)} = \text{coeff.}(b'd^2)$$

$$= \text{coeff.}(69)(28)(28)$$

coeff. = 0.018 (note that this is not a balanced stress condition).

From Table C-5, select $Z_c = 0.018b'd^2$ at $\rho = 0.00075$ (interpolated).

Calculate the required steel area:

$$A_s = \rho b'd = 0.00075(69)(28) = 1.45 \text{ in.}^2$$

From Table C-3, select 2 No. 8 bars, A_s furnished = 1.57 in.^{2}

Check: $\rho_{min} = 200/f_y = 0.00333$;
ρ furnished = 1.57/[(14)(28)] = 0.0040 > 0.0033 (O.K.)

Use d = 28 in., b' = 69 in., b_w = 14 in., 2 No. 8 bars.

Example 21-5 is quite direct. It demonstrates that the minimum steel requirement given by Code, $\rho_{min} = 200/f_y \leq A_s/b_w d$, must always be computed using the stem width b_w rather than the actual compressive width b'. The actual design, however, is still based on the actual compressive width b'.

The second case to be considered where tee beams are subject to positive moment is the case where the beam is simply supported and is therefore subject to positive moment throughout the span. For this case the size of the stem has not been set by moment conditions at the support as it was in the first case. However, the shear at the support must still be considered in selecting the size of the stem.

Other considerations must also enter the selection. Depending on the magnitude of loads and length of span, the shear conditions might not be serious and may not therefore require a very large section. consequently, a small shallow section might suffice if the end shear were to be the only consideration.

Unusually shallow tee sections, however, can introduce problems in deflections and may require excessive amounts of flexural reinforcement; they should be used with caution. To satisfy most of the routine requirements, the overall depth of a tee section should be about four to five times the thickness of the slab it supports. For shear requirements, the depth should be roughly equal to one-tenth to one-twelfth the span length. For deflection control, the minimum depths given in Table 17-1 will apply. Obviously, such rules must vary considerably with span length, intensity of load, and spacing of tee stems.

Such considerations are not usually a formal part of the calculations. All such limitations are usually juggled mentally as the designer makes the final choice. The following example, however, includes these items as formal considerations for the sake of demonstration.

Example 21-6

Design of a tee beam subject to positive moment. Simply supported span, slab thickness fixed.

Given: Grade 60 steel. f'_c = 4000 psi. Concrete weight, 145 pcf. ϕ = 0.90 for flexure and 0.85 for shear.

To Find: Suitable section to sustain the load.

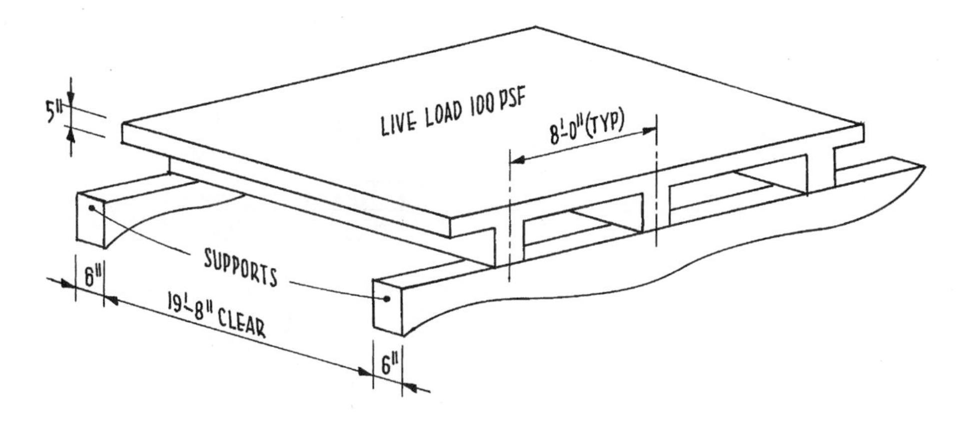

Solution: Estimate the stem size (for dead-load calculations):

$$\text{Approximate h} = \frac{\text{Span}}{10} \text{ to } \frac{\text{Span}}{12}; \quad \text{h} = 20 \text{ to } 24 \text{ in.}$$

$$\text{Approximate h} = 5(\text{slab thickness}); \quad \text{h} = 20 \text{ to } 25 \text{ in.}$$

$$\text{Minimum h} = \frac{\text{Span}}{16} \text{ (Table 17-1)}; \quad \text{h} = 15 \text{ in.}$$

Try h = 22 in., d = 19 in., b = 10 in.

Weight per foot = b(h - t) $\left({}^{145}\!/\!{}_{144}\right)$ = 171 plf.

Determine the dead load and live load for the shear and moment diagrams:

Uniform live load = 150 psf(8) = 1200 plf

Uniform dead load = $({}^{5}/_{12})(145)(8)$ = 483 plf

Uniform stem load = 171 plf

Total w_{DL} = 654 plf

For the shear and moment diagrams, compute the ultimate shear and moment:

$$M_{LL} = \frac{w_{LL}(L^2)}{8} = \frac{1200(19.67^2)}{8} = 58 \text{ kip·ft.}$$

$$M_{DL} = \frac{w_{DL}(L^2)}{8} = \frac{654(19.67^2)}{8} = 32 \text{ kip·ft.}$$

$$M_n = \frac{[(1.4)(32) + (1.7)(58)]}{0.9} = 159 \text{ kip·ft.}$$

$$V_{LL} = \frac{w_{LL}(L)}{2} = \frac{1200(19.67)}{2} = 12 \text{ kips}$$

$$V_{DL} = \frac{w_{DL}(L)}{2} = \frac{654(19.67)}{2} = 6.5 \text{ kips}$$

$$V_n = \frac{[(1.4)(6.5) + (1.7)(12)]}{0.85} = 35 \text{ kips}$$

Draw the shear and moment diagrams from the calculated values:

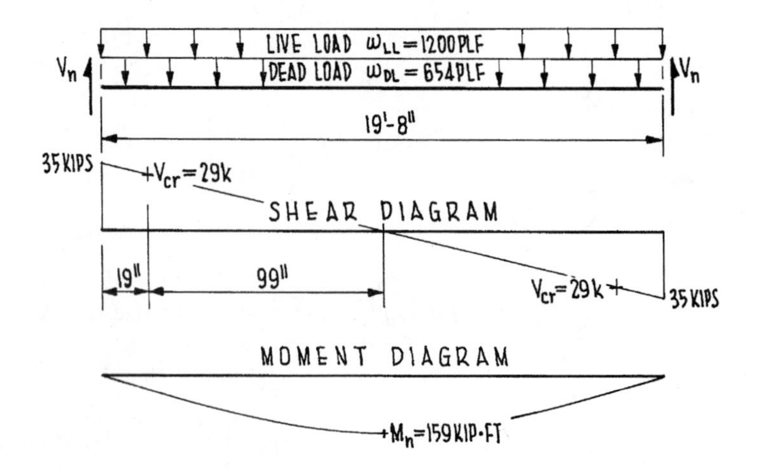

With no negative moment, the stem size is not controlled by flexure; stem size is therefore set to suit shear requirements. The dimensions *b* and *d* are computed first for the case where no stirrups are needed and second for the case where stirrups are placed at $^1/_2 d$; the two results are then compared.

With no stirrups: $v_n = 2\sqrt{f'_c} = 126$ psi

$V_n = v_n b_w d$; $29{,}000 = 126(0.5d)(d)$

Solve for d: d = 21 in., b = $10^1/_2$ in.

With stirrups at d/2: $v_n = 6\sqrt{f'_c} = 380$ psi

$V_n = v_n b_w d$; $29{,}000 = 380(0.5d)(d)$

Solve for d: d = 12.4 in., b = 6.2 in.

For the final choice between the two cases, it is elected to use the section that does not require stirrups. Critical shear is now corrected for d = 21 in. and the increase in dead load is added. Hence use h = 24 in., d = 21 in., b = 12 in. (The increase in the dead load above the initial estimate was found to be negligible.) Determine the effective width of the compression flange.

$b' < \frac{\text{Span}}{4}$; $\quad b' < \frac{242}{4} = 61$ in.

$b' < (8)(t)(2) + \text{stem}$; $\quad b' < (8)(5)(2) + 12 = 92$ in.

$b' <$ tee spacing; $\quad b' < 96$ in.

Use b' = 61 in.

Select reinforcement by find the required section modulus:

$$Z_c = \frac{M_n}{0.85 f'_c};\ \text{coeff.}(b'd^2) = \frac{M_n}{0.85 f'_c}$$

$$\text{coeff.}(61)(21)(21) = \frac{159{,}000(12)}{0.85(4000)}$$

Solve for coeff.: coeff. = 0.021

From Table C-6, $\rho = 0.0012$, $k_n\beta_1 = 0.021$ (not at the balanced stress condition).

Select steel; $A_s = \rho b'd = 0.0012(61)(21) = 1.54$ in.^{2}

Use 2 No. 7 and 2 No. 4 bars, no stirrups, A_s furnished = 1.60 in.^{2}

Check: $\rho_{min} = 200/f_y = 0.0033$;

Actual $\rho = 1.6/[(12)(24)] = 0.0056 > 0.0033$ (O.K.)

In Example 21-6 there were no limitations imposed on the overall height of the beam. Had such a limitation existed, a shallower section might have been required. A shallower section would, in turn, require shear reinforcement, probably stirrups at a spacing of *d*/2.

21.15 Approximate Analysis of Tee Beams

Many responsible designers use an approximate method for selecting the steel area for positive moment in all tee beams. They simply recognize that the stress in the concrete in such tee beams is always quite low, and that the approximate solution is adequate for all cases. For such a practice, the center of the compressive force *C* is taken at midheight of the slab as shown in Figure 21-16.

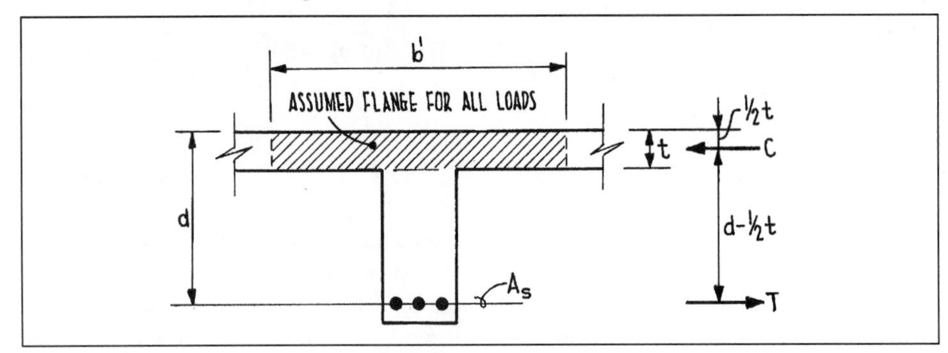

Figure 21-16 Assumed couple on a tee beam slab.

From the geometry of Figure 21-16:

$$M_n = T(d - {}^1\!/\!_2 t) = f_y A_s (d - {}^1\!/\!_2 t) \qquad (21\text{-}1)$$

Solve for required A_s to find:

$$A_s = \frac{M_n}{f_y (d - \frac{1}{2}t)} \qquad (21\text{-}2)$$

Equation (21-2) is then used for all cases, without regard for the location of the neutral axis. The result is almost always conservative, however, and will produce slightly higher values for the required steel area A_s than would be obtained using more exact methods.

An example will illustrate the method of designing tee beams, using both the exact and the approximate methods of design.

Example 21-7

Selection of tee beam reinforcement.
Simply supported span.
Size of stem fixed by conditions at supports.

Given: Tee section as shown.
M_{DL} = 88 kip·ft.
M_{LL} = 68 kip·ft.
Grade 60 steel.
f'_c = 4000 psi.
Span = 24'-0".
Tees @ 12'-0" o.c.

b' | t_f | 5" | 24" | b_w | 12" | 2½"

To Find: Tensile reinforcement for positive moment.

Solution: Exact solution:

Determine the effective flange width:

$$b' < \frac{\text{Span}}{4}, \qquad b' < \frac{(24)(12)}{4} \text{ or } 72 \text{ in.}$$

$$b' < 8t_f(2) + b_w, \qquad b' < (8)(5(2) + 12 \text{ or } 92 \text{ in.}$$

$$b' < \text{tee spacing}, \qquad b' < 12'\text{-}0'' \text{ or } 144 \text{ in.}$$

Use b' = 72 in.

Calculate the nominal ultimate moment:

$$M_n = \frac{1.4M_{DL} + 1.7M_{LL}}{\phi} = \frac{[(1.4)(88) + (1.7)(68)]}{0.9}$$
$$= 265 \text{ kip·ft.}$$

Determine the required magnitude of the plastic section modulus Z_c:

$$Z_c = \frac{M_n}{0.85f'_c} = \frac{265{,}000(12)}{0.85(4000)} = 935 \text{ in.}^3$$

With both *b'* and *d* known, calculate the required coefficient of the plastic section modulus Z_c:

$$Z_c = \text{coeff.}(b'd^2);\ 935 = \text{coeff.}(72)(24)(24)$$

coeff. = 0.023

Enter Table C-6; select a section:

$$\rho = 0.0013,\ Z_c = 0.023$$

Determine the required steel area:

$$A_s = \rho b'd = 0.0013(72)(24) = 2.25 \text{ in.}^2$$

From Tables C-3 and C-4:

Use 4 No. 7 bars, A_s furnished = 2.41 in.^{2}

Approximate solution:

Calculate the nominal ultimate moment as before:

$$M_n = 265 \text{ kip·ft.}$$

Using Eq.(21-2) solve for A_s,

$$A_s = \frac{M_n}{f_y(d - \frac{1}{2}t)};\ A_s = \frac{265{,}000(12)}{60{,}000(24 - 2.5)}$$

$$A_s = 2.47 \text{ in.}^2$$

From Tables C-3 and C-4, select reinforcement:

Use 2 No. 9 and 2 No. 6 bars,
A_s furnished = 2.88 in.^{2}

For the two solutions, it is seen that the required area of steel varies but little; either of the two solutions is acceptable.

21.16 Foundations and Slabs on Grade

Probably the single most common application of concrete in buildings is its use in foundations and slabs on grade. Regardless of whether a building is constructed of concrete, masonry, timber, or steel, its foundations will almost certainly be constructed of concrete. Any textbook concerning design in concrete must therefore include at least an introduction to the design of simple foundations.

The following discussions are limited to simple shallow foundations. Shallow foundations are defined herein as those founded within about 6 ft of the finished floor. They are by far the most common type of foundations.

21.17 Types of Shallow Foundations

Three distinct types of shallow foundations shown in Figure 21-17 are considered in the following discussions:

1. Spread footings under individual columns.
2. Strip footings under bearing walls.
3. Grade beams under repetitive columns.

All three types of foundations perform their function by distributing a concentrated load over a larger bearing area.

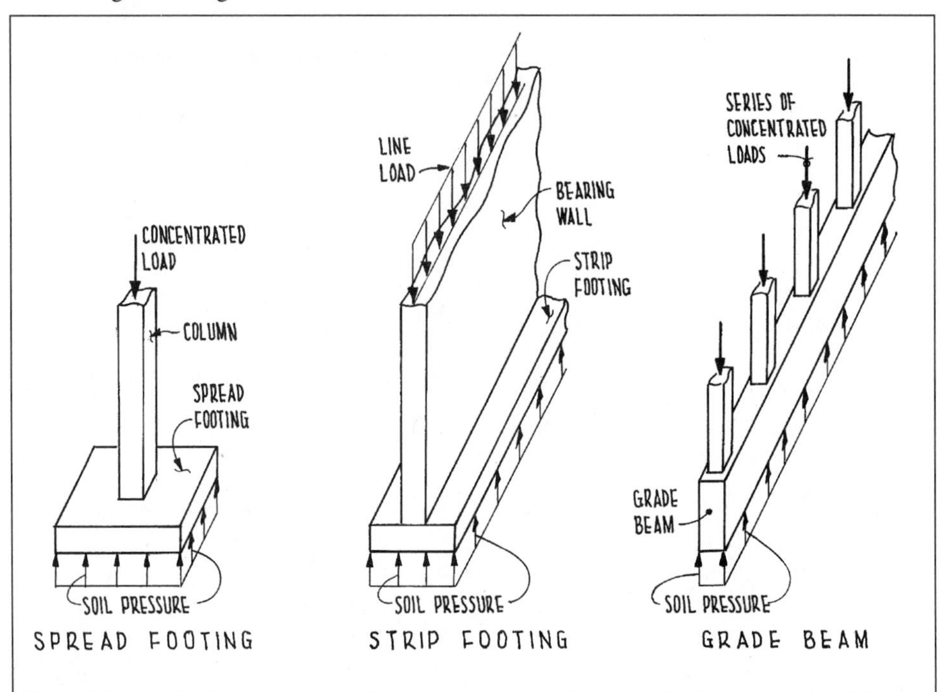

Figure 21-17 Types of foundations.

Spread footings, as shown in Figure 21-17, are subject to flexure as a cantilever in two directions. The column location is kept concentric; any eccentricities will result in a nonuniform distribution of soil pressure under the footing. Where space is restricted at one side, the spread footing may be made rectangular rather than square, but the column is still centered.

Strip footings, as shown in Figure 21-17, are subject to flexure only in the outstanding legs; flexural reinforcement is required only in the short direction. There is no stress in the footing in the direction of the wall. The wall itself must be designed to take any variations in loads or settlements along its length.

Grade beams, as shown in Figure 21-17, are continuous beams subject to flexure longitudinally along the line of columns they support. They are loaded on the bottom face by the distributed soil pressure. The loading system of the grade beam of Figure 21-17 may look more familiar if the sketch is viewed upside down.

Footings are rarely reinforced for shear. Since forming costs are minimal, the sections are simply made large enough to take the shear without reinforcement. Although Code permits shear reinforcement in footings, that case is not included in subsequent discussions.

21.18 Foundation Loading and Failure Modes

Allowable soil pressure under a footing may be limited by one of two considerations: either by the differential settlement between adjacent footings or by the bearing strength of soil. By far the more common limitation is settlement. Even in sandy soils, the progressive crushing or inelastic deformation of friable sands within the first year after construction usually produces the limiting case for footing pressures.

Whether the size of the contact area is limited by settlements or by soil strength, all soil criteria are specified at working levels. Ultimate soil pressure is not used. The working dead and live loads must therefore be carried forward in the calculations to be used in establishing the size of the contact area of the foundation.

21.19 Allowable Soil Pressures

The allowable soil pressure is the increase in soil pressure that may be applied to a soil at a certain stratum. The soil will safely accept this increase in pressure in addition to its regular overburden pressures. Usually, if the overburden is permanently removed (e.g., basements), the allowable soil pressure may be increased proportionately.

Settlements in soil are time dependent, usually taking place over several months or several years. As discussed earlier, when establishing the size of the contact area that will limit settlements, only those loads may be considered that will exist long enough to produce long-term settlements. Certainly, the dead load of the structure meets this requirement but only about half the live load (furnishings, carpets, files, books, etc.) may be considered to be long-term. The remaining live load comes and goes, causing only elastic deformations in the soil; long-term inelastic settlements have no time to develop.

When establishing the contact area that will limit settlements, it is common practice to use dead load plus about 50% live load for buildings that serve routine architectural functions. The long-term live load in buildings such as libraries may be much higher, as much as 80% of maximum live load, while in auditoriums the long-term live load may contain only 20% of the maximum live load. For simplicity in the subsequent examples, a value of dead load plus 50% live load will be used.

The allowable soil pressure corresponding to this long-term load is specified as a result of the soils investigation (or by Code). This pressure is commonly termed the "reduced allowable soil pressure" and is used to compute the required size of the contact area.

Once the size of the contact area is established, there is no further need for the reduced allowable soil pressure. When the higher peak loads are applied to the building, a higher soil pressure will obviously result. This higher soil pressure, called the peak pressure, is used for all subsequent calculations for stress; the steel and concrete must, of course, sustain the peak pressure, even if only for a short time.

When settlements control the design, the peak soil pressure is not limited to a maximum value. At the time the allowable soil pressure is being determined, all conditions of load, strength and settlement are considered. When the reduced allowable soil pressure is finally established, it may thereafter be assumed that the strength has been found adequate for all peak-load conditions; the soil pressure is limited only by settlements.

For the other case of loading (i.e., when the strength of the soil rather than settlement governs the design), the peak load is the only load ever considered. Combinations of loads that produce peak conditions are discussed with the load factors of Chapter 17. In the subsequent examples, the peak loading will be taken as dead load plus 100% live load.

21.20 Spread Footings

Spread footings are rarely, if ever, reinforced for shear. Like slabs, it is far more practical to increase the depth of the footing slightly to increase its shear capacity rather than place numerous stirrups. Since footings are cast directly on soil, formwork is minimal and the extra cost is only that of bulk concrete.

Since shear reinforcement is not used, spread footings can be expected to be quite thick in order to sustain the shear loads. Spans (or overhangs) are comparatively short, so flexure is not usually large enough to require a deeper section than that required for shear. As a general guide, the overall thickness of a spread footing can be expected to be about one-sixth of the maximum dimension, or less, with a minimum thickness of about 12 in. being commonly observed.

When concrete is cast against soil, the minimum cover over the reinforcement is specified by Code (7.7.1) at 3 inches. The consequences of foundation failure are so serious, however, that this limit is usually observed as the barest minimum. In subsequent examples, the concrete cover is taken as 4 in. from the centerline of flexural reinforcement, which provides somewhat more than the minimum 3 in. clear cover.

Spread footings are assumed to act as cantilevered beams in two directions. The critical section for bending in a spread footing that supports a concrete column is at the face of the column. For a footing that supports a steel column, the critical section for bending is taken halfway between the face of the steel column and the edge of the base plate. Critical sections are shown in Figure 21-18.

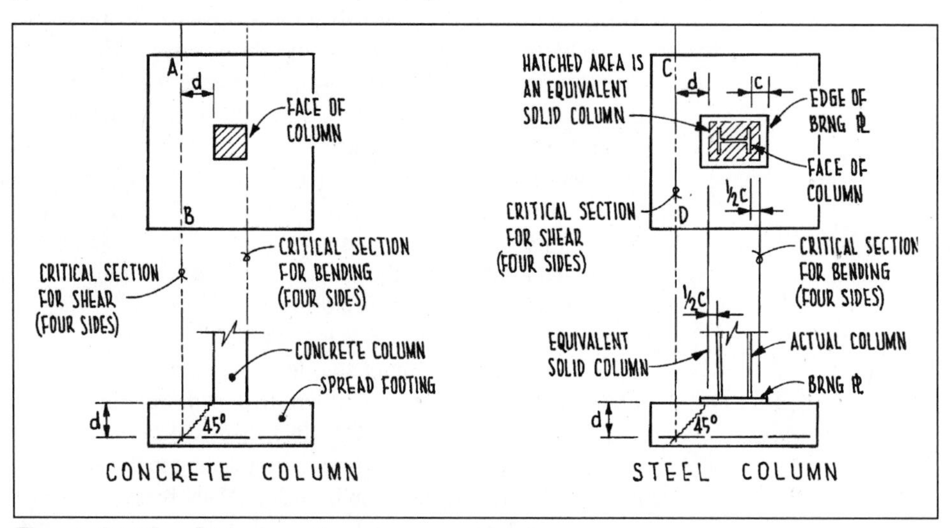

Figure 21-18 Critical sections in spread footings.

It should be noted that the bending of the footing is assumed to occur uniformly along the full width of the footing as shown in Figure 21-18, as if the column were actually a wall extending all the way across the footing. Although this assumption is admittedly a drastic simplification, its success over the years justifies its continued use. For rectangular footings, the procedure is repeated in the other direction to obtain the reinforcement in that direction.

The same simplifying assumption concerning bend lines applies also when designing the spread footing for beam shear. As for other types of beams, the critical section for beam shear is taken at a distance d from the face of the column, shown as lines AB and CD in Figure 21-18. The ultimate shear stress on the concrete at the critical section is, as usual in beams:

$$v_n = 2\sqrt{f'_c}\,. \tag{19-4a}$$

With no shear reinforcement, the ultimate shear force at the critical section may not be greater than V_c, where:

$$V_c = v_n b_w d \tag{19-3}$$

and b_w is the total width of the footing at the critical section.

In addition to the foregoing design criteria for beam shear and flexure, Code imposes an additional limitation due to "punching shear." Punching shear produces the pyramidal punch-out shown in Figure 21-19. Whereas critical beam shear is taken at a distance d from face of support, critical punching shear is taken at a distance $d/2$ from face of support, shown as line $ABCD$ in Figure 21-19.

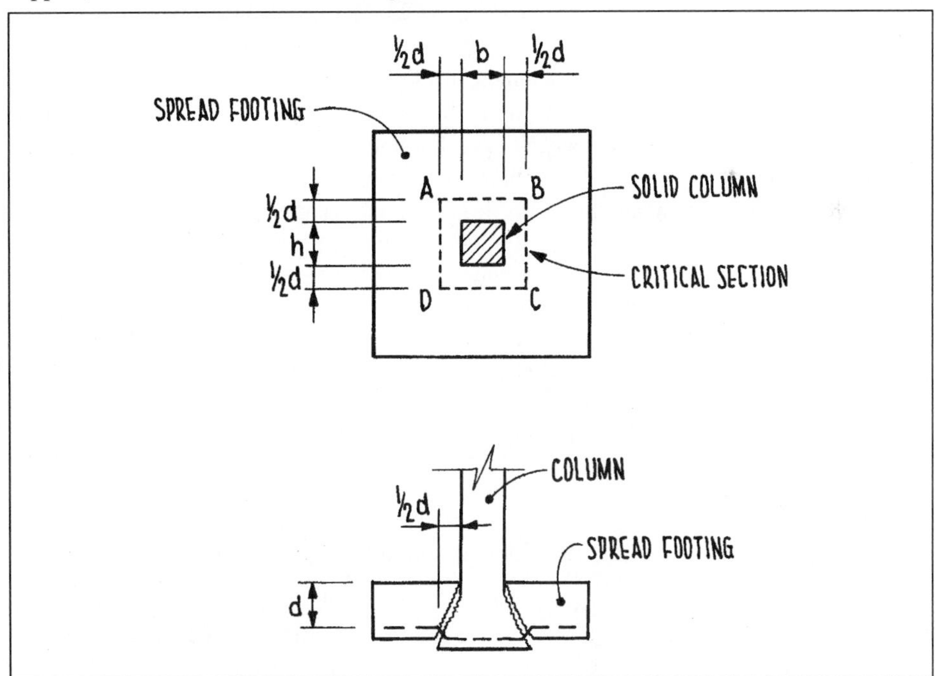

Figure 21-19 Punching shear.

The ultimate shear stress for punching shear in concrete without shear reinforcement is specified by Code (11.11.2.1):

$$v_n = \left(1 + \frac{2}{\beta_c}\right) 2\sqrt{f'_c} \tag{21-3}$$

but, as a maximum:

$$v_n \leq 4\sqrt{f'_c} \tag{21-4}$$

where β_c is the ratio of the long side to the short side *(t/b)* of the contact area between the column and the footing ($\beta_c = 1$ for square columns and $\beta_c = \infty$ for continuous walls). The ultimate punch-out load to be taken by the critical section is, then:

$$V_c = v_n b_0 d \tag{21-5}$$

where b_0 is the perimeter of the critical punch-out shown in Figure 21-19. For the line *ABCD* in Figure 21-19:

$$b_0 = 2(b + d) + 2(h + d) \tag{21-6}$$

In addition to flexure, beam shear, and punching shear, the footing must sustain the bearing load presented by the column or wall above. The bearing load on the footing is limited by Code (10.15):

$$P_n = 0.85 f'_c A_g \tag{21-7}$$

where all symbols are as used earlier and the undercapacity factor ϕ is 0.7 for bearing.

The allowable bearing load given by Eq.(21-7) may be increased by multiplying by the factor $\sqrt{A_2 / A_1}$, but not by more than 2, where A_2 is the area of the top of the footing concentric with the loaded area A_1. For footings, the factor $\sqrt{A_2 / A_1}$ will be much greater than 2, with the final result that bearing load will almost always be double that of Eq.(21-7).

For the design of footings, there are thus four conditions to be met: bearing load on top face, punching shear, beam shear, and beam flexure. There are special design tables and graphs for use in designing spread footings; they are useful if one is frequently engaged in such designs. For infrequent use, it is far faster simply to guess the depth of footing and check the four conditions to see if the guess is adequate. That procedure is illustrated in the following examples, first, for a square footing, and second, for a rectangular footing.

Example 21-8

Design of a square spread footing. Footing subject only to axial load (no moments). Settlements govern.

Given: P_{DL} = 115 kips. P_{LL} = 95 kips. Reduced soil p_a = 2300 psf. Column size 16 x 16 in. f'_c = 3000 psi. Grade 40 steel.

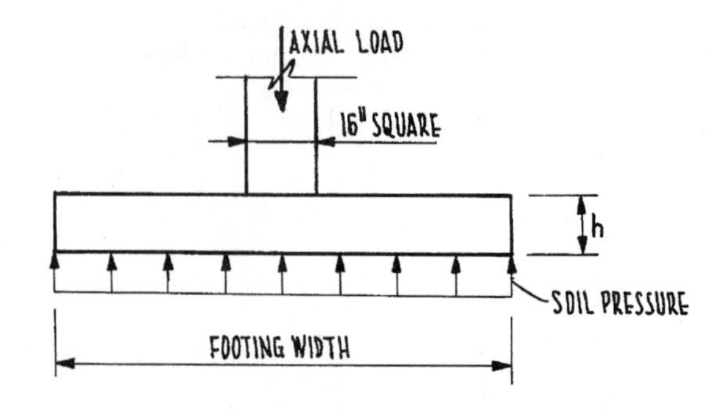

To Find: Suitable size for a square spread footing.

Solution: In foundation design, the difference in weight between concrete (145 pcf) and the displaced overburden (115 pcf) is commonly ignored. In subsequent calculations here, it is ignored.

The required contact area of the footing is the total load, $P_{DL} + P_{LL}$, divided by the reduced allowable soil pressure, 2300 psf:

$$\text{Area} = \frac{P_{DL} + 0.50P_{LL}}{p_a} = \frac{115 + 47.5}{2300} = 71\ \text{ft}^2$$

Use square footing, 8'-6" or 102 in. The soil pressure under maximum loading for this footing size is:

$$p_{DL} = \frac{P_{DL}}{\text{Area}} = \frac{115}{(8.5)(8.5)} = 1.6\ \text{ksf}$$

$$p_{LL} = \frac{P_{LL}}{\text{Area}} = \frac{95}{(8.5)(8.5)} = 1.3\ \text{ksf}$$

The first check is for bearing load on top of the footing. The total load P_n delivered to the top of the footing is, where $\phi = 0.7$ for bearing:

$$P_n = \frac{1.4P_{DL} + 1.7P_{LL}}{\phi} = \frac{[(1.4)(115) + (1.7)(95)]}{0.7} = 461\ \text{kips}$$

The allowable bearing load on the footing is:

$$P_n = 0.85 f_c' A_g = 0.85(3000)(16)(16) = 653\ \text{kips}$$

This allowable load is multiplied by $\sqrt{A_2 / A_1}$:

$$\sqrt{A_2 / A_1} = \sqrt{[(102)(192) / (16)(16)} = 6.38\ \text{but} < 2$$

Hence:

$$Pn = 2(653) = 1306\ \text{kips} > 461\ \text{kips}$$

The bearing capacity of the footing is more than adequate to carry the column load. It remains now to select the thickness of the footing.

A trial thickness *h* of about one-sixth of the footing width is assumed, or about 18 in. The effective depth *d* is then taken at 14 in. This trial thickness of 14 in. is first checked for punching shear. The average ultimate punching shear stress occurs at a distance *d/2* from the face of the column on all four sides of the column, as shown in the following sketch.

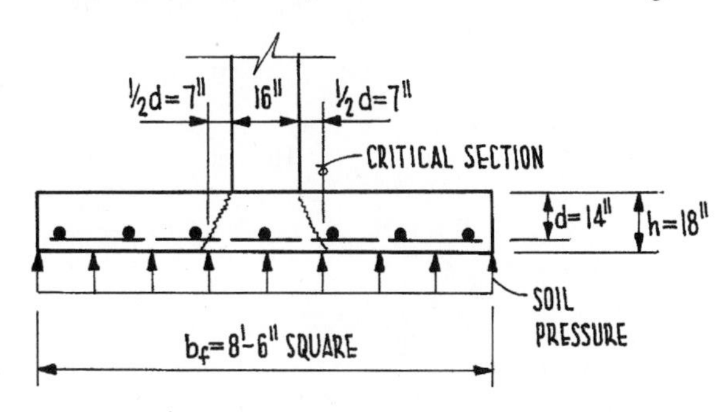

The total punching shear force acting on the section is found by statics:

$$P_{DL} = p_{DL}[b^2 - (t + d)^2] = 1.6(8.5^2 - 2.5^2) = 106 \text{ kips}$$

$$P_{LL} = p_{LL}[b^2 - (t + d)^2] = 1.3(8.5^2 - 2.5^2) = 86 \text{ kips}$$

Hence:

$$P_n = \frac{1.4P_{DL} + 1.7P_{LL}}{\phi} = \frac{[(1.4)(106) + (1.7)(86)]}{0.85} = 347 \text{ kips.}$$

The average punching shear stress at ultimate load is given by Code, where $\beta_c = 1$:

$$v_n = 2\sqrt{f'_c}\left(1 + \frac{2}{\beta_c}\right) = 6\sqrt{f'_c}$$

but v_n must not exceed $4\sqrt{f'_c}$. Hence:

$$v_n = 4\sqrt{f'_c} = 220 \text{ psi.}$$

The capacity of the footing to carry punching shear is, where $b_0 = 4(h + d) = 120$ in.:

$$V_c = v_n b_0 d = 220(120)(14) = 370 \ \rho \ 347 \text{ kips}$$

This trial depth of 14 in. is thus seen to be adequaate to take the punching shear.

Next the trial depth of 14 in. is checked for its capacity in beam shear. The critical shear force is found at a distance *d* from the face of the column, as shown in the following sketch.

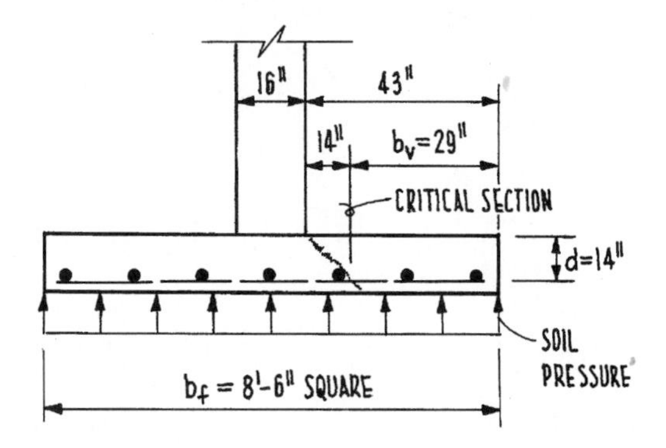

The shear acting on the footing beyond the line of the critical section is:

$$V_{DL} = p_{DL}(bw)(b_f) = 1.6(^{29}/_{12})(8.5) = 33 \text{ kips}$$

$$V_{LL} = p_{LL}(b_w)(b_f) = 1.3(^{29}/_{12})(8.5) = 27 \text{ kips}$$

Hence:

$$V_n = \frac{1.4V_{DL} + 1.7V_{LL}}{\phi} = \frac{[(1.4)(33) + (1.7)(27)]}{0.85} = 108 \text{ kips}$$

The capacity of the concrete in beam shear is:

$$V_{cr} = v_n b_w d = 2\sqrt{f'_c}\,(102)(14) = 156 \geq 108 \text{ kips}$$

The trial depth of 14 in. is thus seen to be adequate to carry the beam shear on the section.

The trial depth of 14 in. is now checked for beam flexure, where $M = wL_c^2/2$ on the cantilever length L_c, as shown in the following sketch.

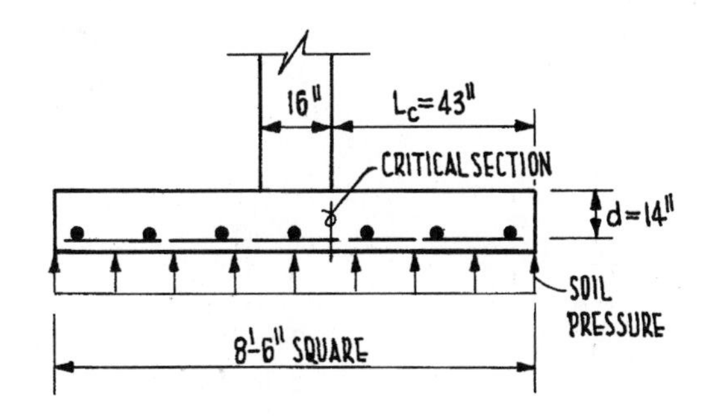

The moment acting on the critical section is:

$$M_{DL} = \frac{w_{DL}L_c^2}{2} = \frac{1.6\left[(8.5)(43/12)^2\right]}{2} = 87 \text{ kip·ft.}$$

$$M_{LL} = \frac{w_{LL}L_c^2}{2} = \frac{1.3\left[(8.5)(43/12)^2\right]}{2} = 71 \text{ kip·ft.}$$

Hence:

$$M_n = \frac{1.4M_{DL} + 1.7M_{LL}}{\phi} = \frac{[(1.4)(87) + (1.7)(71)]}{0.9}$$

$$= 269 \text{ kip·ft.}$$

The section modulus Z_c is found by the usual means:

$$\frac{M_n}{0.85f'_c} = Z_c; \qquad \frac{269{,}000(12)}{0.85(3000)} = \text{coeff.}(102)(14)(14)$$

$$\text{coeff.} = 0.063$$

From Table C-5, select $\rho = 0.005$ (ρ_{min} for Grade 40).

Solve for A_s, $A_s = \rho_{bd} = 0.005(102)(14) = 7.14 \text{ in.}^2$

Use 12 No. 7 bars each way, evenly spaced
(A_s provided = 7.22 in.^{2}). The trial depth of 14 in. is thus seen to be adequate for flexure, beam shear, punching shear, and bearing; it is selected as the final depth of the footing.

The following sketch shows the final design, to include dowels from the footing to the column above.

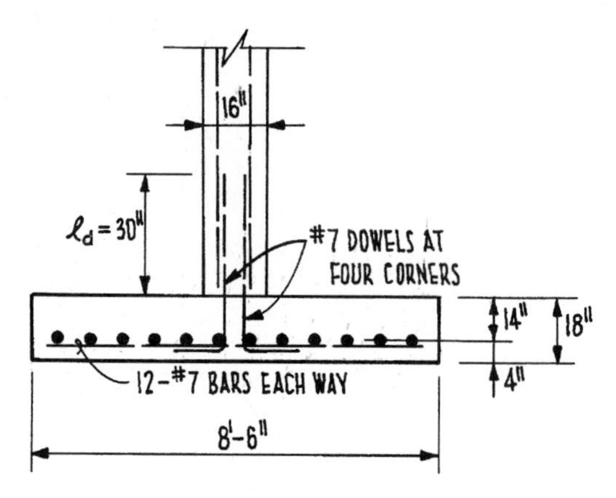

The dowels are chosen rather arbitrarily in this case. Had the applied column load been higher than the allowable bearing capacity of the footing, the excess load would have to be transferred by dowels; the size of the dowels and their embedment would then be designed to carry this excess load. In this footing, however, the footing is adequate to carry the entire load in bearing so theoretically the dowels are not needed. For such cases, the practice is to design the dowels to carry about 10% of the flexural capacity of the column to account for any accidental moments on the footing. This moment is, where $Z_c = bh^2/6$ (approximately):

$$M_n = (0.85f'_c Z_c)(0.10) = \left(\frac{(0.85)(3000)(16)(16^2)}{6}\right)(0.10)$$

$$= 174 \text{ kip·in.} = 14.5 \text{ kip·ft.}$$

For dowels at the four corners, $\rho' = \rho$ and:

$$\frac{M_n}{0.85f'_c} = Z_c; \quad \frac{174{,}000}{0.85(3000)} = \text{coeff.}(16)(16^2)$$

$$\text{coeff.} = 0.0167$$

From Table C-5, use minimum ρ; hence:

$$A_s = \rho_{min} b_w d = 0.005(16)(14) = 1.12 \text{ in.}^2$$

Use No. 7 bars at the four corners.

As a point of interest, the difference between the dead load of the concrete and the weight of the displaced soil in Example 21-8 can now be checked to see how much error is involved in ignoring this difference. At a total depth of 18 in., the additional weight is for a concrete weight of 145 pcf and a soil weight of 115 pcf:

$$\text{Weight/m}^2 = (145 - 115)(^{18}/_{12}) = 45 \text{ psf (error)}$$

Of the total maximum pressure of 2900 psf, this error is less than 2%, and is considered to be negligible.

21.21 Strip Footings

A strip footing is assumed to act as a cantilevered slab projecting from under the wall it supports. For strip footings supporting a concrete wall, the critical section for bending is at the face of the wall. If the wall is masonry, an equivalent concrete wall is used which is half the thickness of the masonry wall. The critical section for bending is then at the face of the equivalent concrete wall, as shown in Figure 21-20.

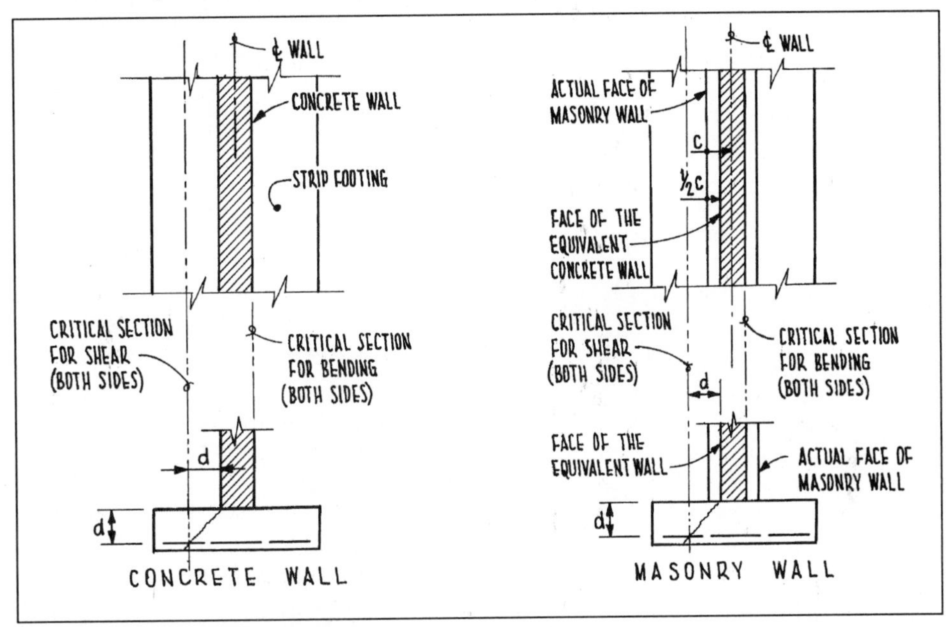

Figure 21-20 Critical sections in strip footings.

Although Code (15.5.2) permits the critical section for beam shear to be measured from the actual face of the masonry wall, it is common practice to measure the critical shear from the face of the equivalent wall. In such an approach, the entire design of the foundation is thus performed for an equivalent wall, affording a consistent treatment of the design. The ultimate strength of the equivalent wall in this approach is taken at twice the ultimate strength of the masonry, f'_m.

As with spread footings, shear reinforcement is rarely if ever used in strip footings. The strip footing is simply made thicker to take any excess shear. The thickness of strip footings may be expected to be somewhat less than the thickness of spread footings, but a thickness less than 12 in. is rarely seen.

There is no punching shear on a strip footing. A strip footing is designed only for beam shear and beam moment on the outstanding legs. There are no other special considerations in the design of a strip footing. It is simply a double cantilevered beam. A brief example will illustrate the procedure.

Example 21-9

Design of strip footing for a masonry wall. Footing subject only to axial load (no moment). Settlements govern the design.

Given: P_{DL} = 8 kips/ft.
P_{LL} = 5.5 kips/ft.
Reduced pressure
p_a = 1600 psf.
Wall thickness 12 in.
f'_m = 1350 psi.
f'_c = 3000 psi.
Grade 60 steel.

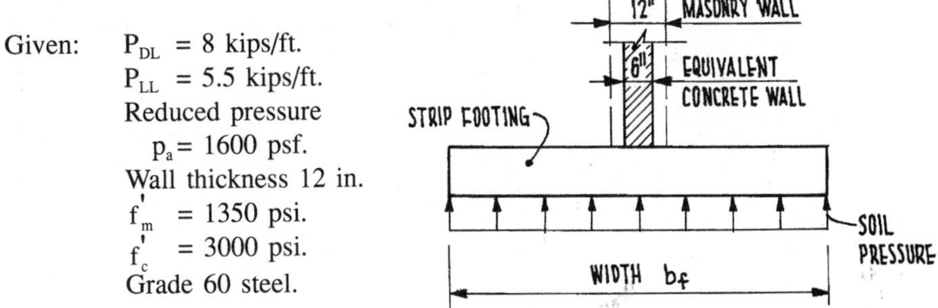

To Find: Suitable size for a strip footing.

Solution: The footing will be designed for an equivalent concrete wall 6 in. thick, with $f'_c = 2f'_m = 2700$ psi. The relative dimensions are shown in the sketch above. Determine the required contact area:

$$\text{Area} = \frac{P_{DL} + 0.5P_{LL}}{p_a} = \frac{8 + 2.75}{1600} = 6.72 \text{ ft.}$$

Use a footing width of 7 ft.

Determine the peak soil pressures:

$$p_{DL} = \frac{P_{DL}}{b_f} = \frac{8}{7} = 1.14 \text{ kips/ft.}$$

$$p_{LL} = \frac{P_{LL}}{b_f} = \frac{5.5}{7} = 0.79 \text{ kips/ft.}$$

Although not usually necessary for walls, the bearing load on the top of the footing will now be checked. The load delivered to the top of the footing is

$$P_n = \frac{1.4P_{DL} + 1.7P_{LL}}{\phi} = \frac{(1.4)(8) + (1.7)(5.5)}{0.7} = 29.4 \text{ kips/ft.}$$

The allowable bearing load on the footing is:

$$P_n = 0.85 f'_c A_g = 0.85(3000)(12)(6) = 184 \text{ kips/ft.}$$

The allowable load is multiplied by the factor $\sqrt{A_2 / A_1} = \sqrt{(7)(1) / (0.5)(1)}$ = 4; use 2.

$$P_n = 2(184) = 368 > 29.4 \text{ kips/ft. (O.K.)}$$

The width of 7 ft is thus seen to be more than adequate for bearing capacity.

A trial thickness is now assumed for the footing. As for spread footings, a thickness of one-sixth to one-eighth of the total width in flexure is usually a good start. For a total width of 7'-0", the estimated overall thickness h is then:

$$h = \frac{\text{Width}}{6} = \frac{7(12)}{6} = 14 \text{ in.}$$

The effective depth d is taken at 10 in. This trial depth of 10 in. for d is used to check the beam shear at a distance d from the face of the equivalent wall. The dimensions are shown in the following sketch.

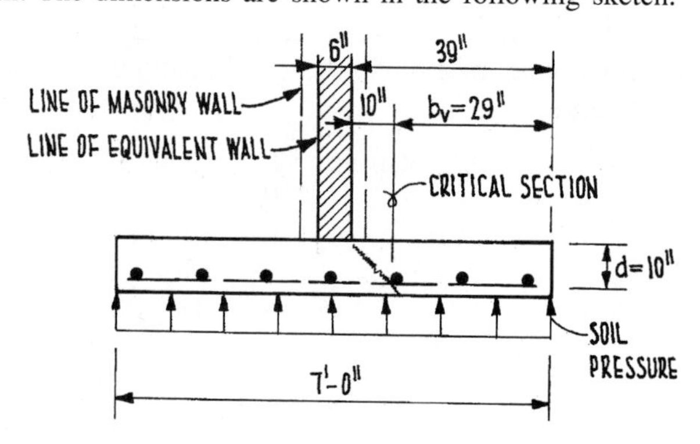

The shear on the section is, per foot of length:

$$V_{DL} = p_{DL}b_vL = 1.14(^{29}/_{12})1 = 2.76 \text{ kips/ft.}$$

$$V_{LL} = p_{LL}b_vL = 0.79(^{29}/_{12})1 = 1.91 \text{ kips/ft.}$$

Hence:

$$V_n = \frac{1.4V_{DL} + 1.7V_{LL}}{\phi} = \frac{(1.4)(2.76) + (1.7)(1.91)}{0.85}$$

$$= 8.37 \text{ kips/ft.}$$

The capacity of the section is, per foot of length:

$$V_{cr} = v_nb_wd = 2\sqrt{3000}(12)(10) = 13 > 8.37 \text{ kips/ft.}$$

The trial depth of 10 in. is thus seen to be adequate to take the beam shear.

The trial depth of 10 in. for d is now used for the design of the member in flexure. The critical section for flexure is at the face of the equivalent wall, as shown in the following sketch.

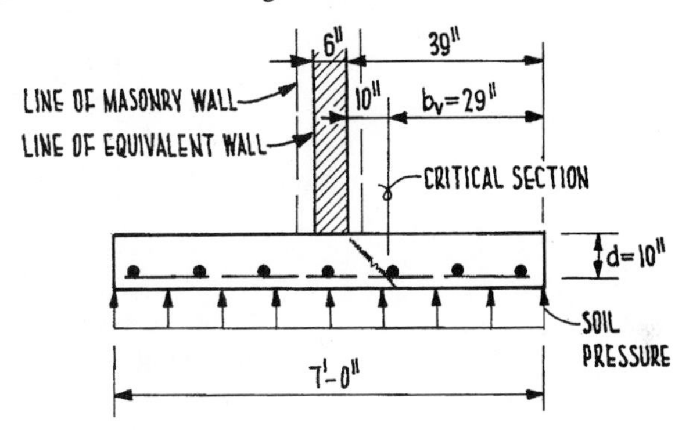

The moment acting on the critical section is:

$$M_{DL} = \frac{p_{DL}L_c^2}{2} = \frac{1.14(^{39}/_{12})^2}{2} = 6.02 \text{ kip·ft/ft.}$$

$$M_{LL} = \frac{p_{LL}L_c^2}{2} = \frac{0.79(^{39}/_{12})^2}{2} = 4.17 \text{ kip·ft/ft.}$$

Hence:

$$M_n = \frac{1.4M_{DL} + 1.7M_{LL}}{\phi} = \frac{(1.4)(6.02) + (1.7)(4.17)}{0.9}$$

$$= 17.2 \text{ kip·ft/ft.}$$

The section modulus Z_c is found by the usual means:

$$\frac{M_n}{0.85f'_c} = Z_c; \quad \frac{17{,}200(12)}{0.85(3000)} = \text{coeff.}(12)(10^2)$$

$$\text{coeff.} = 0.0675$$

From Table C-5, select $\rho = 0.0035$ (minimum).

Solve for $A_s = \rho bd = 0.0035(12)(10) = 0.420$ in.^{2}/ft.

Use No. 6 bars at 12 in. o.c.

In the longitudinal direction, there is no computable load on the footing. The only requirement for steel is that for temperature and shrinkage, which in this case is 0.0018bh. The required area of steel in the cross section is:

$$A_s = 0.0018bh = 0.0018(84)(14) = 2.12 \text{ in.}^2$$

Use 7 No. 5 bars, evenly spaced.

A sketch of the final design is shown below. The actual masonry wall is shown rather than the equivalent wall used throughout the foregoing calculations.

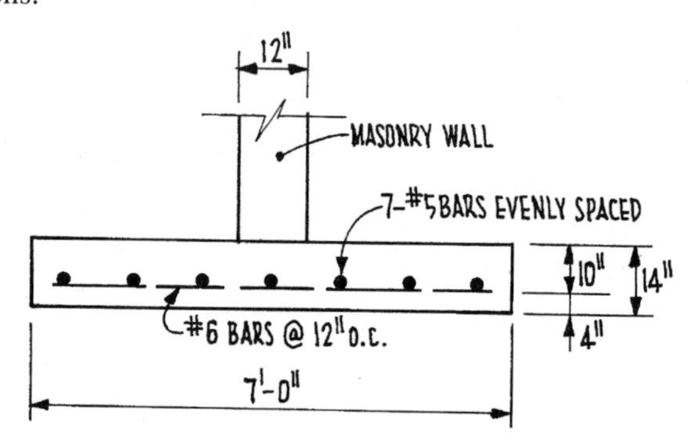

The dowels connecting the wall to its footing are as arbitrarily chosen for strip footings as they are for spread footings. If the wall is reinforced, it is common practice simply to match the wall reinforcement for size and location of dowels. If the wall is unreinforced, dowels may also be omitted.

21.22 Grade Beams

Grade beams are one of the more economical foundations in common use for light buildings. They are used quite often for the foundations of lightweight prefabricated steel buildings as well as for one- or two-story concrete frames. They are not usually suited for heavy loads, however, and are rarely feasible for buildings having more than two stories.

A grade beam may be designed the same way as any other continuous rectangular beam. Code (8.3) lists approximate coefficients for computing such moments. As noted earlier in this chapter, a grade beam is like any other continuous beam except that loads are upside down.

It may be argued (successfully) that a grade beam is an elastic beam on an elastic foundation. Consequently, when the beam at midspan deflects upward due to soil pressure, the soil pressure decreases somewhat. Approximately, a sinusoidal soil pressure distribution is eventually produced, as shown in Figure 21-21. The proposed use of a uniform pressure distribution and the ACI coefficients can therefore be seen to be in error by an undetermined amount.

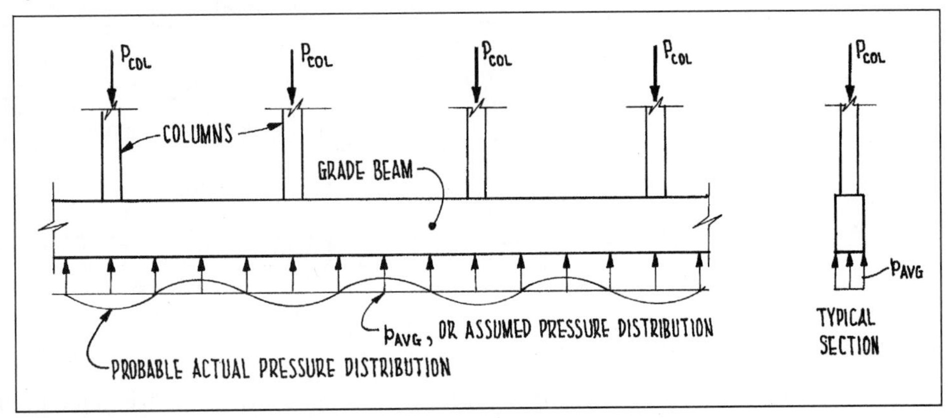

Figure 21-21 Soil pressures on a grade beam.

Although the foregoing argument is true, the magnitude of error is not prohibitively high. In comparing the sinusoidal pressure distribution of Figure 21-21 with the uniform distribution, it is seen that in all cases the load decreases at midspan and increases at the column points. Thus the moments both at midspan and at the column points decrease while the shears at the column points remain almost constant.

It is evident that the ACI coefficients will yield a conservative value of moment and a reasonable value for shear. Considering the inaccuracies in both the soils analysis and the concrete analysis, the additional error is not considered prohibitive, particularly since it is always on the safe side.

In the example following this discussion, the ACI coefficients are used with averaged distributed soil pressures. The soil-structure interaction that would produce the sinusoidal pressure distribution is left to more advanced study.

As with other types of footings, shear reinforcement is rarely used in grade beams. Since falsework and shoring are minimal, it is far more practical to increase the size of the beam slightly rather than to fabricate and place a large number of stirrups. As a consequence, the size of a grade beam is usually much deeper than that of other concrete beams having a similar span.

In addition, usually no effort is made to cut off the longitudinal reinforcement in a grade beam. The maximum required area of flexural steel, both top and bottom, is simply made continuous throughout the length of the grade beam. For such a design, only the highest numerical values of positive and negative moments are therefore needed when flexural reinforcement is selected.

Very often, the required width of the grade beam is so narrow that the column is wider than this width; the column would have to overhang the grade beam if it were to be centered on the grade beam. A simple solution is to make the grade beam as wide as the column; the column would then be properly seated on the grade beam. In such cases, the resulting soil pressure may be considerably less than the allowable pressure, but the overall suitability of the design justifies the configuration. The design used in the following example includes such circumstances.

Example 21-10

Design of a grade beam foundation. Repetitive column loads at uniform spacing. Settlements govern the design.

Given: Grade beam and loads as shown in the sketch.
Load on the end column is roughly half the load on an interior column.
Column size 12 in. x 12 in. for all columns.
P_{DL} = 30 kips and P_{LL} = 24 kips (each column).
Reduced soil pressure p_a = 2300 psf.
f'_c = 3000 psi, Grade 60 steel.

To Find: Suitable size for a grade beam.

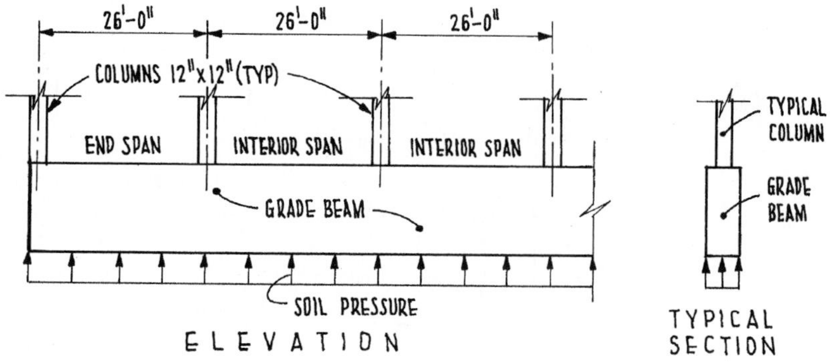

Solution: The required contact area under the grade beam is computed by simple statics, assuming that the grade beam has a bearing area 26 ft long:

$$\text{Area} = \frac{P_{DL} + 0.5P_{LL}}{p_a} = \frac{30 + 12}{2300} = 18.3 \text{ ft}^2 \text{ per bay.}$$

$$\text{Width} = \frac{\text{Area}}{\text{Length}} = \frac{18.3}{26} = 0.70 \text{ft} = 8^1/_2 \text{ in.}$$

If the footing width were to be made $8^1/_2$ in. as indicated in the foregoing calculations, the column with its width at 12 in. would be eccentric on the grade beam. To keep the column load concentric on the grade beam, the grade beam is simply made 12 in. wide, recognizing that the soil pressure will be somewhat less than the allowable:

$$p_{DL} = \frac{P_{DL}}{\text{Area}} = \frac{30}{(1)(26)} = 1.15 \text{ kips/ft}^2.$$

$$p_{LL} = \frac{P_{LL}}{\text{Area}} = \frac{24}{(1)(26)} = 0.92 \text{ kips/ft}^2.$$

The grade beam will now be checked for beam shear, using the ACI coefficients for maximum shear. At an end span:

$$V_{DL} = 1.15p_{DL}L_n = \frac{(1.15)(1.15)(25)}{2} = 16.5 \text{ kips}$$

$$V_{LL} = 1.15p_{LL}L_n = \frac{(1.15)(0.92)(25)}{2} = 13.2 \text{ kips}$$

Hence:

$$V_n = \frac{1.4V_{DL} + 1.7V_{LL}}{\phi} = \frac{(1.4)(16.5) + (1.7)(13.2)}{0.85}$$

$$= 53.6 \text{ kips}$$

A trial depth of about L/12 or 26 in. is adopted for the grade beam, with a corresponding value of 22 in. for the effective depth *d*. This tall slender section of 12 x 26 in. is now reviewed for its adequacy in shear. The critical section for shear is shown on the following partial shear diagram.

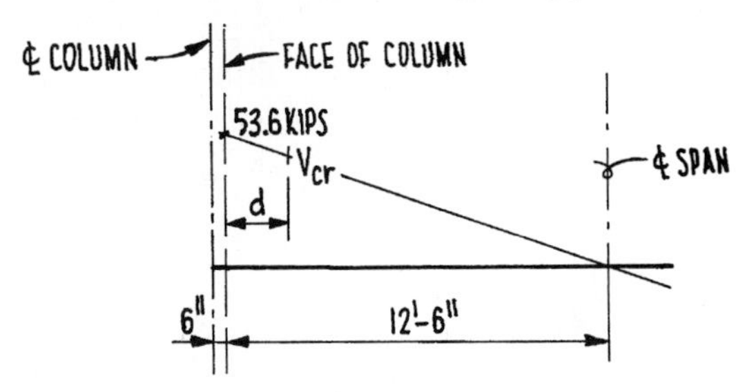

Critical shear on the section is found by ratios:

$$V_{cr} = \frac{150 - 22}{150} 53.6 = 45.7 \text{ kips}$$

The capacity of the section in shear is:

$$V_c = v_n b_w d = 2\sqrt{3000}(12)(22) = 29 \text{ kips} < 45.7 \text{ kips}$$

This section is not adequate for critical shear. A larger section, 38 in. deep, will be tried, effective depth d = 34 in. The critical shear on the new section is again computed by ratios:

$$V_{cr} = \frac{150 - 34}{150} 53.6 = 41.5 \text{ kips}$$

The capacity of this deeper section in shear is:

$$V_c = v_n b_w d = 2\sqrt{3000}(12)(34) = 44.7 \text{ kips} > 41.5 \text{ kips}$$

The trial effective depth of 34 in. is seen to be adequate for beam shear.

This trial depth of 34 in. is now reviewed for flexure. The maximum negative moment acting on the section is taken from the ACI coefficients:

$$M_{DL} = \frac{w_{DL} L_n^2}{10} = \frac{(1.15)(1)(25^2)}{10} = 71.9 \text{ kip·ft.}$$

$$M_{LL} = \frac{w_{LL} L_n^2}{10} = \frac{(0.92)(1)(25^2)}{10} = 57.5 \text{ kip·ft.}$$

Hence:

$$M_n = \frac{1.4 M_{DL} + 1.7 M_{LL}}{\phi} = \frac{(1.4)(71.9) + (1.7)(57.5)}{0.9}$$

$$= 220 \text{ kip·ft.}$$

The section modulus Z_c is found by the usual means:

$$\frac{M_n}{0.85 f_c'} = Z_c; \quad \frac{220{,}000(12)}{0.85(3000)} = \text{coeff.}(12)(34^2)$$

$$\text{coeff.} = 0.075$$

From Table C-5, select $\rho = 0.0035$.

Compute $A_s = \rho bd = 0.0035(12)(34) = 1.428 \text{ in.}^2$

Since the maximum positive moment is less than the maximum negative moment, the minimum value of ρ will be required both for positive and negative steel. Use 2 No. 8 bars top and bottom continuous. Since the distance along the side of the beam between positive and negative reinforcement is more than 18 in., use extra No. 8 bars at middepth. The final design of the grade beam is shown in the following sketch.

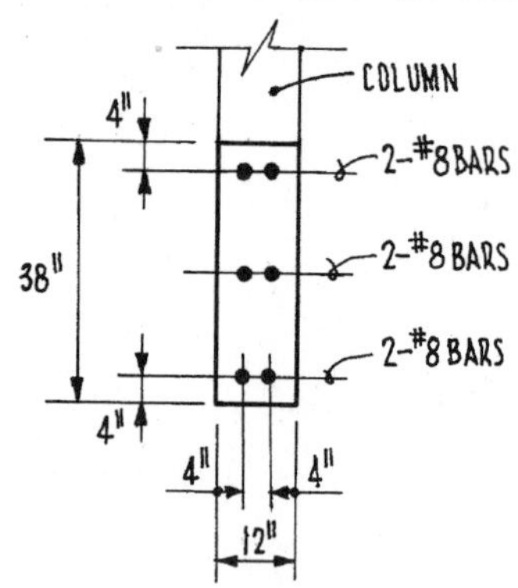

21.23 Slabs on Grade

The design of concrete slabs on grade is prescribed in ACI 302, *Recommended Practice for Concrete Floor and Slab Construction* (American Concrete Institute, 1980). The design method for the slab thickness is again empirical, based on wheel load, tire pressure, and concrete strength. A summary of some typical results is presented in Table 21-2.

Table 21-2 Minimum Slab Thicknesses[1*]

Light foot traffic: residential use or tile covered	4 in. minimum
Foot traffic:	
Office, churches, schools, hospitals	4 in. minimum (5 in. preferred)
Sidewalks in residential areas	5 in. minimum
Automobile wheels: automobile driveways, garages	5 in. minimum
Forklift and light truck loads: light industrial, commercial	5 in. minimum
Forklift and medium truck loads: abrasive wear, industrial/commercial	6 in. minimum

In addition to presenting a method of design of slabs on grade, ACI 302 also presents criteria for isolation joints, construction joints, and control joints. Typical isolation joints are shown in Figure 21-22. Isolation joints are used to isolate structural walls and columns from the floor slab such that "hard points" of lateral restraint are not created at the floor line.

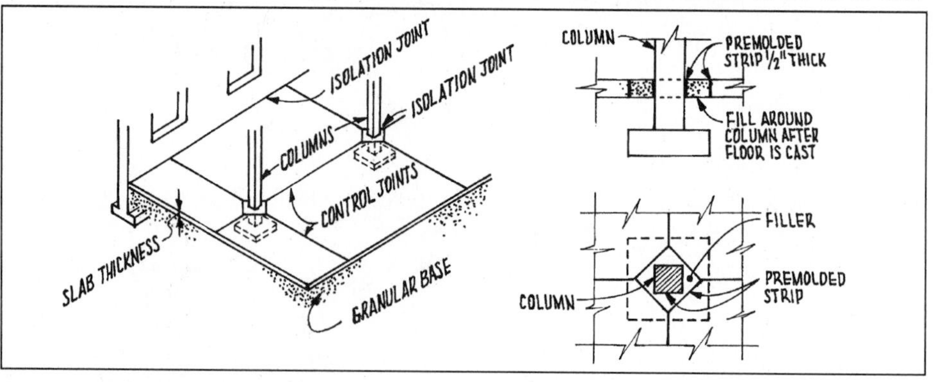

Figure 21-22 Isolation joints.

* If trucks are to pass over isolation joints that have no provision for load transfer, such as doorways, the slab should be thickened approximately 50% and tapered to the required thickness at a slope not more than 1 in 10.

Construction joints are placed in the floor slab to permit the casting to be interrupted and to be continued at a later time. When the interruption lasts long enough for the concrete to set, one of the construction joints of Figure 211-23 may be used. The joints shown in Figure 21-23 are taken from ACI 302; there are others in common use.

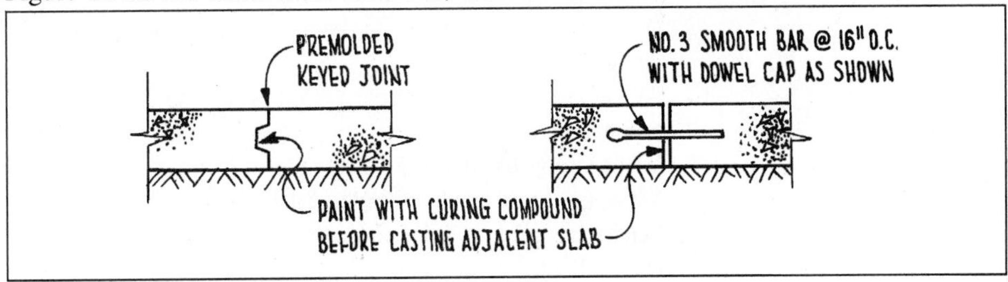

Figure 21-23 Construction joints.

Control joints create stress raisers that serve to control the location of shrinkage and thermal cracking. Cracking still occurs, but it is much more likely to occur along a control joint than elsewhere. Typical control joints were shown earlier in Figure 21-4. Some common practices in using control joints to control temperature and shrinkage cracking are given there.

Vapor barriers are also discussed in ACI 302. A vapor barrier is a plastic membrane placed under the floor slab, usually specified as polyethylene film. Rather elaborate precautions are required to protect the film from being punctured while the concrete is being cast.

As long as the vapor barrier is intact, it will presumably prevent "vapors" (whatever those are) from percolating upward through the slab. Assuming that it works, it will also prevent "vapors" (whatever those are) from percolating downward. ACI 302 suggests an alternative: a coarse granular fill about 4 in. thick will provide an effective barrier against capillary rise of water under a slab.

Slabs on grade are one of the more common features of construction in the industry and are used in all types of buildings. Details such as placement of joints, embedment of pipes, isolation of ducts, reinforcement of edges, prevention of undercutting, minimization of snow and ice hazards, and a wealth of other details are presented in ACI 302. A thorough knowledge of the accepted practices in ACI 302 is recommended to anyone working with slabs on grade.

Review Questions

1. About how much load can be expected on a footing that supports an interior column in a three-story building?
2. About how many pounds of structural material are required to carry 2 pounds of live load in an average concrete building?
3. A continuous floor slab is to be supported by beams spaced at 8 feet on center. What thickness of slab can be expected?
4. What size can be expected for a concrete column at the bottom floor of a five-story building?
5. A rectangular concrete beam is to be built to span 24 feet. About what depth can be expected for such a beam?
6. At what length of continuous structure does a full expansion/contraction joint become a consideration?
7. Why isn't a thermal analysis commonly made for routine concrete structures?
8. About how far can a floor slab on grade be cast before a joint is required? Why is the joint required?
9. A particular structural member spans between two columns. Is it classified as a beam or a girder?
10. A particular structural member spans between a girder and a bearing wall. Is it a beam or a girder?

11. An elevated floor slab is to be 4 inches thick. About what spacing should be used for the supporting tee beam stems?
12. A cantilevered retaining wall must retain a backfill height of 9 feet. What thickness might be expected at the top and bottom of the wall?
13. Why aren't differential settlements commonly included as a load case in building design?
14. At equal contact pressures, which would settle more, a square footing supporting a column or a strip footing supporting a masonry wall?
15. What strengths of reinforcing steel are most commonly used in American practice? What are their grade numbers? (See Chapter 16.)
16. What strengths of concrete are commonly used to cast concrete columns? Beams? (See Chapter 16.)
17. Why are shear and moment envelopes so necessary in the design of reinforced concrete but are so rarely used to design steel or timber members? (See Chapter 17.)
18. For what types of load are the ACI coefficients valid?
19. In using the ACI coefficients to determine positive moment, what is the length L_n? (See Chapter 17.)
20. What is the steel ratio ρ provided by No. 6 bars placed at 6 inches on center in a concrete slab 7 inches thick, where the center of the bars are placed $1^1/_2$ inches from the top of the slab?
21. Why are concrete slabs so rarely reinforced in compression?
22. How much Grade 60 temperature and shrinkage reinforcement is required in a slab 4 inches thick?
23. What is the maximum spacing that can be used for temperature and shrinkage reinforcement?
24. What is a "one way" slab?
25. Explain why elevated slabs usually serve at low levels of service stress.
26. State the anchorage requirements for positive reinforcement in an elevated concrete slab.
27. State the anchorage requirements for negative reinforcement in an elevated concrete slab.
28. Why is the design of a two way slab so much more complex than a one way slab?
29. For simple spans, how is the size of the tee-beam stem usually determined?
30. For continuous beams, how is the size of the tee-beam usually determined?
31. Tee beams are commonly spaced at about one-fourth of the span length. Why?
32. What width of beam is used to compute the minimum allowable steel ratio ρ ? How is it used in regions of positive moment?
33. Visualizing the "internal couple" concept for approximate analysis of tee beams, what is the approximate length of the moment arm *jd*?
34. Why is it so essential to keep a column concentric on its foundation?
35. Define "allowable soil pressure."
36. Why is the size of the contact area determined at service levels rather than at ultimate load?
37. Compare the design of a foundation where strength limits the allowable soil pressure to the design where settlements limit the allowable pressure.
38. For buildings having ordinary architectural functions and occupancies, how much of the live load can be expected to be in place long enough to produce foundation settlements?
39. What is the minimum cover over the reinforcement for concrete foundations cast directly against the soil? For concrete foundations cast against forms?
40. In a spread footing carrying a column load, where is the critical section for beam shear? For punching shear? For moment?
41. On a spread footing supporting a column, what is the limiting load that can be delivered to the footing by direct bearing of the column?
42. How is a strip footing designed to support a masonry wall?

43. Where is the critical section for punching shear on a strip footing supporting a masonry wall?
44. Under what types and configurations of buildings are grade beams usually a feasible foundation?
45. Why does the soil pressure under a grade beam become sinusoidal?
46. How thick should a concrete slab be made when it is used as a parking hard stand for an ordinary passenger car?
47. Why are isolation joints sometimes necessary where columns penetrate a floor slab?
48. How may capillarity be interrupted under a floor slab?

CHAPTER

22

INTERMEDIATE LENGTH COLUMNS

The study of reinforced concrete columns is a complex subject, so complex that only the rudiments of column design can be presented in an introductory-level textbook such as this. And, while this introductory study is adequate for small structures braced against sidesway, a great deal more study of columns is recommended before one ventures into more complex structures where lateral loads are taken by column bending.

22.1 Definitions and Concepts

The terms "braced against sidesway" or "sidesway prevented" mean that all lateral loads are taken by a diaphragm-and-shearwall system such as the one shown in Figure 22-1. In such a system, the columns are subject only to gravity loads, plus possibly some small eccentric moments. The other type of structural system, also shown in Figure 22-1, is the rigid frame, in which all of the lateral load is taken by bending in the columns; column moments in a rigid frame can be quite high.

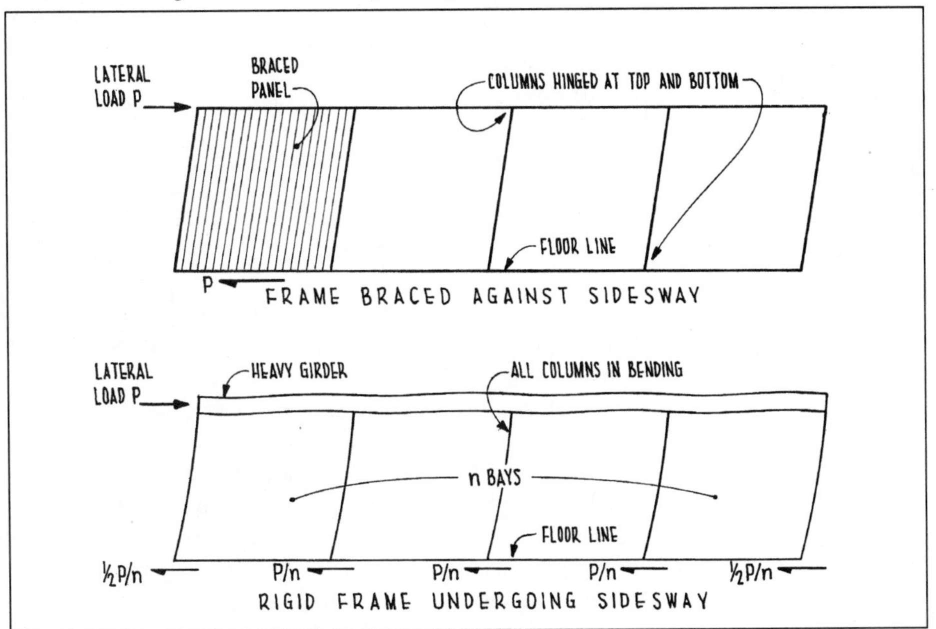

Figure 22-1 Braced frame and rigid frame.

The only type of structural system considered in this textbook is the braced frame. The limitation is not severe; the braced frame is used primarily in low structures, about six stories or less, which constitute probably 85% of the buildings in the world. The ACI coefficients given in Chapter 17 are specifically intended for this type of construction.

Code (B.6.1) requires that all reinforced concrete columns be designed to sustain the factored ultimate loads. There are no provisions in the Code for designing columns at service levels of stress. Further, there are no requirements (nor are there any restrictions) concerning the control of stresses at day-to-day service levels of load. A column design may therefore include whatever requirements at service levels that the designer considers appropriate, as long as the column section finally selected is capable of sustaining the factored ultimate load.

22.2 Configurations and Practices

Many shapes may be used for columns, such as square, rectangular, hollow, circular, Y-shaped, L-shaped, and so on. By far the most common shape is the rectangular shape, as shown in Figure 22-2, which includes the square as a special case. Only the rectangular shape is treated in the succeeding sections; other shapes may be treated similarly.

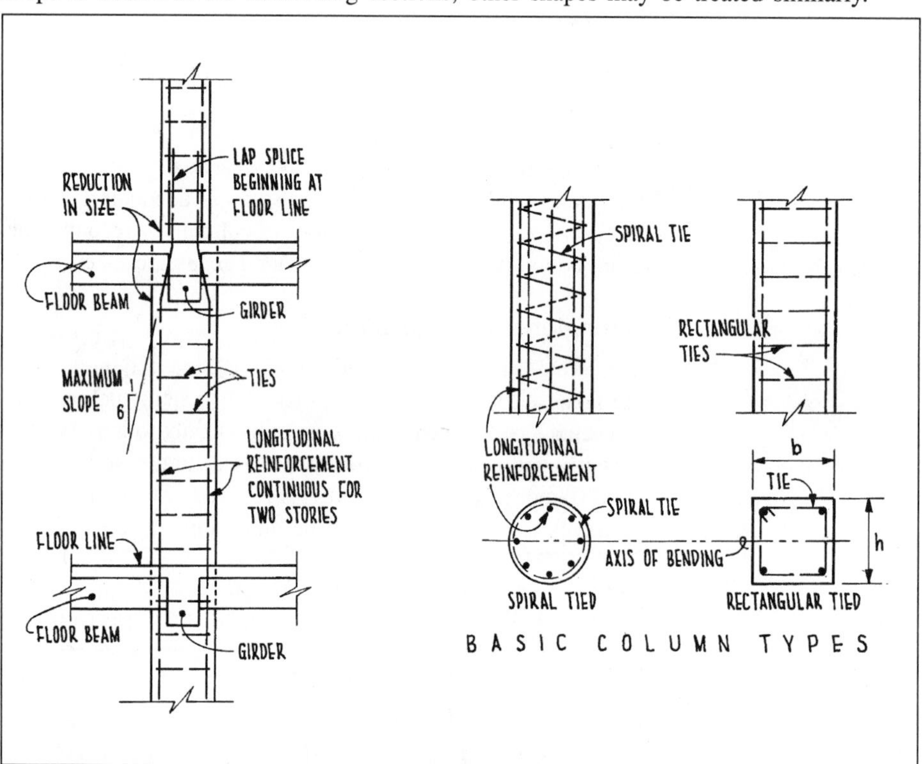

Figure 22-2 Column details.

In designing a column, it is always necessary to make an initial selection for the gross dimensions of the column section, b and h, as shown in Figure 22-2. The reinforcement is then determined for this particular gross size. If the amount of reinforcement required for this gross size is considered to be unacceptable, a new gross size must be selected and the process repeated until an acceptable design is found.

In making the first guess at the size of a column, the rules of thumb given in Chapter 21 can be helpful. Quite often, though, when a group of columns are being designed, the gross size of the column carrying the heaviest load is established first, and all other columns are made the same size. Then only the reinforcement of the other columns need be varied to suit the actual loads.

The rule of thumb for the size of a square column is repeated from Chapter 21:

Column width = 12 in. plus 1 in. per story above.

Where the column is to be rectangular, it should have roughly the same gross area as this square column, or slightly more. Where significant moments are present, the accuracy of this rule of thumb becomes even worse than usual.

A low concrete building (six stories or less) having a column module of 18 to 20 ft and concrete floors and roof can be expected to have a column loading of 30 to 40 tons per floor. This load is the actual load, not the ultimate load. A nominal column load for small buildings will be seen to be a useful index when guessing sizes of columns.

Older codes specified a minimum dimension of 10 in. for columns, but more recent codes have discontinued this minimum limit. The column size is now controlled by the designer and may be set to match the masonry or concrete walls used elsewhere in the design. Such an arrangement is shown in the wall section of Figure 22-3. While the minimum size is 10 in., the difficulty in casting columns 10 in. square (or less) severely discouraages the use of such small columns. A minimum dimension of 12 in. is commonly observed.

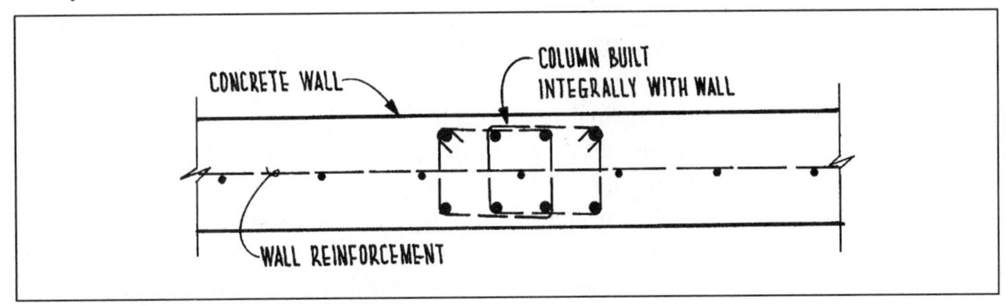

Figure 22-3 Integral column and wall.

For one- and two-story buildings, the loads are so low that a minimum-sized column with minimum longitudinal steel is the usual design. Even these sizes usually provide a capacity much larger than needed. Example 22-5, presented later in this chapter, lists the capacities of minimum-sized columns for various grades of steel and strengths of concrete.

In a typical concrete building, the strength of the concrete specified for columns is usually higher than for the beams and slabs. The primary benefit in using higher strength concrete is in its reduced susceptibility to creep under the high sustained loads. Similarly, the longitudinal reinforcement is almost always the higher-strength steels whever they are available.

In general, the longitudinal reinforcement in columns is spliced each two stories. Such frequent splicing requires large amounts of additional steel, but the reinforcing bars will not cantilever out of the forms far enough to permit going more than two stories. The splice is almost always placed just above floor level, as indicated earlier in Figure 22-2. The practice of splicing all bars at the same level effectively precludes the use of Class A lap splices in column bars at such locations, since 100% splicing of bars is not permitted with Class A splices.

Although Code (10.9.1) allows the steel areas in columns to be as high as 8% of the gross concrete area *bh*, the congestion in such heavily reinforced columns severely limits their use. The congestion is particularly severe where the vertical column bars must pass by the horizontal bars in the two intersecting girders that an interior column usually supports. As a practical matter, the steel areas are generally kept less than 3% of the gross concrete area *bh*; steel areas above 4% are rare.

To decrease congestion, it is common practice to use the larger bar sizes for longitudinal reinforcement in columns. A larger steel area is thus provided by fewer bars. The use of the larger bar sizes in columns usually does not create problems with bond since the shear in columns can be expected to be quite low.

Two of the more common arrangements of longitudinal reinforcement are shown in Figure 22-4 and repeated in tables C-9 through C-11 in the Technical Manual. Where moments are low, the longitudinal steel is usually distributed uniformly around the column. As the magnitude of the moment increases, it obviously becomes more efficient to concentrate the steel at the flexure faces.

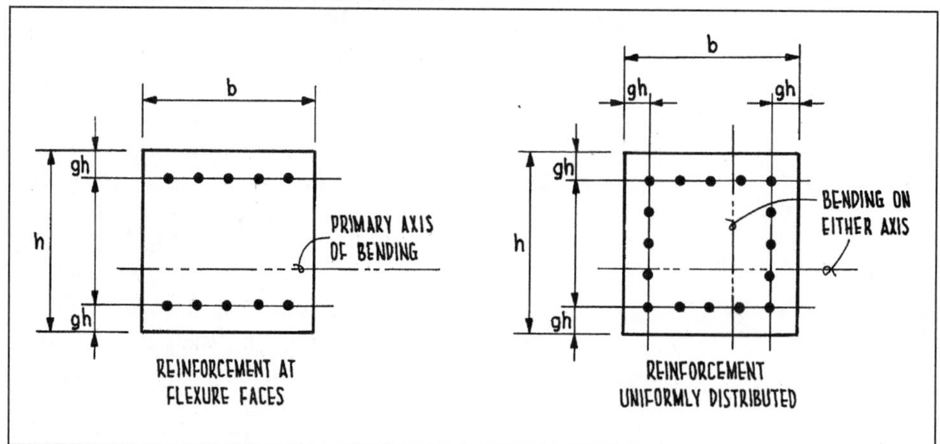

Figure 22-4 Common steel arrangements in columns.

Longitudinal reinforcement is almost always arranged symmetrically about the axes of bending. Even where lateral loads are not being resisted by the columns and load reversals do not exist, the column reinforcement is still arranged symmetrically. There is thus no chance that the column can be constructed backwards.

Code (7.10.5) requires that the longitudinal bars be tied laterally to prevent their buckling outward under load. Design requirements for the ties themselves are also given by Code:

1. Ties shall be at least No. 3 for longitudinal bar sizes No. 10 or smaller and at least No. 4 for larger bars and bundled bars.
2. Vertical spacing shall not exceed 16 longitudinal bar diameters or 48 tie-bar diameters or the least dimensions of the column.
3. Ties shall be arranged such that every corner bar and alternate longitudinal bars shall have lateral support provided by the corner of a tie having an included angle of not more than 135°; no bar shall be farther than 6 in. clear on each side along the tie from such a laterally supported bar.

Typical tie arrangements are shown in Figure 22-5 for some of the more common configurations.

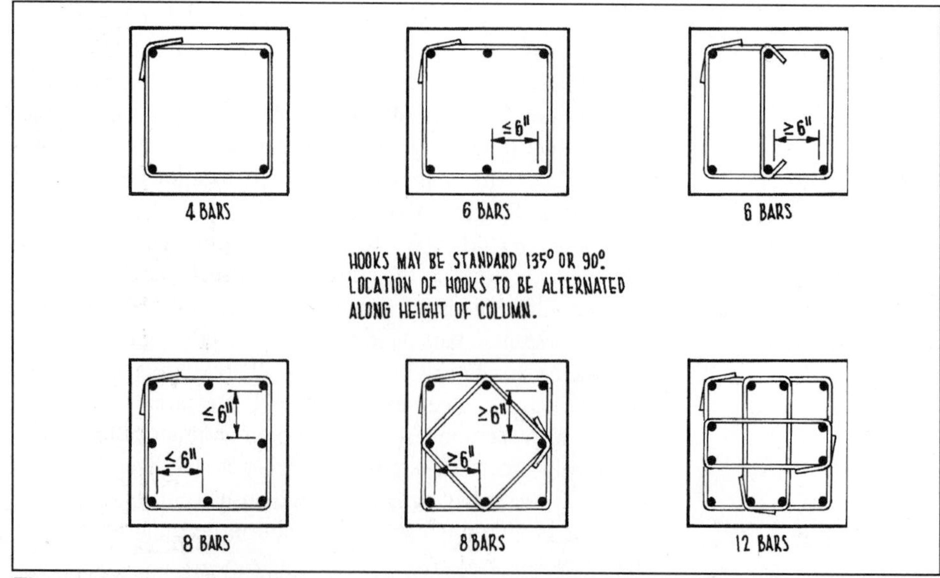

Figure 22-5 Column ties.

While seemingly an appendage to the design, the ties used in column design make a critical contribution to the overall strength of the column. Under heavy load, the longitudinal reinforcement has a strong tendency to buckle outward, bursting out of the concrete encasement and destroying the integrity of the column. Column ties are spaced and arranged to prevent such a failure; they force the steel to remain straight and to work monolithically with the concrete in carrying the load. Buckling of the longitudinal reinforcement, however, remains one of the more serious failure modes to be considered in the design of reinforced concrete columns.

Though not presented in this textbook, longitudinal column reinforcement may also be arranged in a circular pattern. The column itself is usually circular in cross section, but it may be square, simply encasing the circular arrangement of reinforcement in a square cross section. The ties for a circular arrangement of reinforcement are a continuous spiral, wound around the outside of the set of longitudinal bars. Circular columns with spiral ties are useful primarily as extremely heavily loaded columns subject to heavy bending in all directions; such an application is outside the scope of this textbook.

22.3 Behavior under Load

Columns can fail structurally by either of two separate modes: buckling or crushing. Long columns fail by buckling and short columns fail by crushing. However, many concrete columns are neither long nor short, but are somewhere in an intermediate range. For such columns, failure occurs through an indistinct mixture of the two modes.

The "critical" buckling stress of long columns is given by the well-known Euler column formula (see chapter 10):

$$\frac{P_c}{A} = \frac{\pi^2 E}{(L / r)^2} \tag{22-1}$$

where P_c/A = stress just as buckling impends.
E = modulus of elasticity.
L = column length.
r = radius of gyration, $\sqrt{I / A}$

The physical conditions (boundary conditions) assumed for the derivation of the Euler column formula are shown in Figure 22-6. Under axial load, the column fails by lateral displacement, but it will return to its original straight configuration when the load is removed. Note that the length L is measured between the hinge points and that the moment of inertia I is oriented about the axis of bending. Note also that the end conditions are hinges (or points of zero moment, such as inflection points).

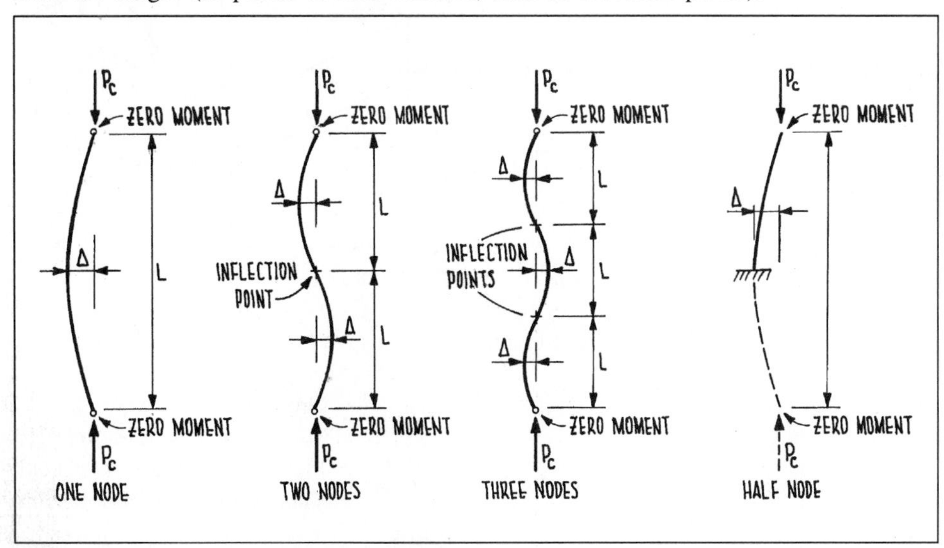

Figure 22-6 Euler column conditions.

It is important to be aware that the end moments are zero in the derivation of the Euler equation. The existence of end moments, even small ones, can seriously reduce the critical load P_c. The formula is valid, however, between any two consecutive points of zero moment.

Equally important in the derivation, it is assumed that the column is perfectly straight; there can be no accidental offset in its alignment that would produce an initial moment. It is also assumed that the load is always concentric on the section; there can be no moments introduced due to eccentric loading. It is further assumed that the moment of inertia I is constant throughout the length of the column; there can be no variations in the dimensions, nor can there be irregularities in reinforcement or in splices.

By this point in the presentation, it should be obvious that very few concrete columns could meet all the conditions required by the Euler formula. Even so, the basic parameters appearing in the Euler formula remain valid indicators for all column performance. The way in which these parameters enter into the semiempirical design of concrete columns is discussed in succeeding sections.

One such parameter that will appear later is the ratio L/r, which has a special significance in column design. Called the *slenderness ratio,* it affords an indication of the susceptibility of a column to buckling. The higher the slenderness ratio is, the higher the susceptibility to buckling becomes and the lower the buckling load is.

At the other extreme from long columns are short concrete pedestals. When the ratio of height to least lateral dimension is three or less, the member is not subject to Code criteria for columns. The design is performed by direct $P/A + Mc/I$ design procedures.

22.4 ACI Column Formula

For the vast majority of columns that are not long enough to be subject to design by the Euler formula nor short enough to be designed as a pedestal, ACI has developed a simple approach. For rectangular columns such as that shown in Figure 22-7, Code (10.3.5.2) requires that the nominal eccentric load P_n shall not exceed 80% of the concentric load at full plasticity, P_0, where:

$$P_0 = 0.85f'_c(A_g - A_{st}) + f_yA_{st} \quad (22\text{-}2)$$

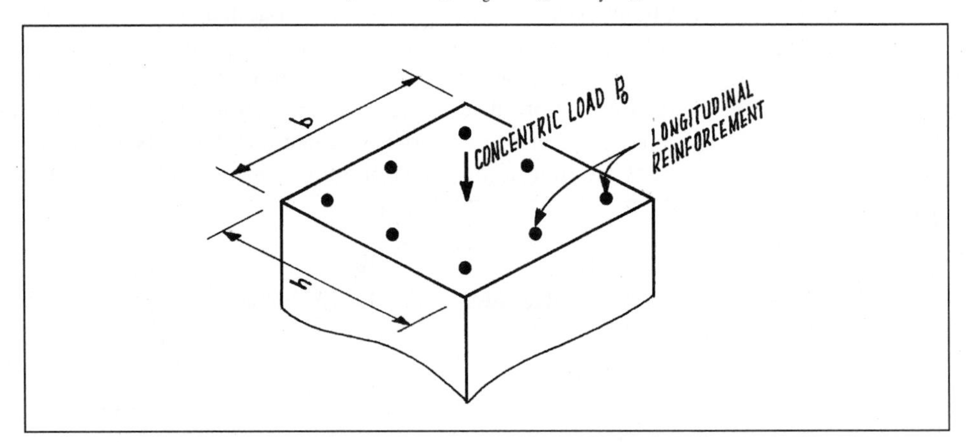

Figure 22-7 ACI basic column.

In the ACI column formula given by Eq.(22-2) with dimensions shown in Figure 22-7:

A_g = Gross area of concrete, *bh*.
A_{st} = Total area of longitudinal reinforcement.
$0.85f'_c$ = Idealized yield stress of concrete.
f_y = Yield stress of reinforcement.

It is emphasized that the load P_0 given by Eq.(22-2) is a concentric load. Also, it is the absolute maximum load that the cross section could sustain when it is in a fully plastic state of deformation. There is no extra capacity for moment.

When the nominal axial load P_n is equal to or less than 80% of this peak axial load P_0, there is some excess capacity available to take moment. This moment, M_n is viewed by Code (10.3.6) as the "maximum moment that can accompany the axial load." The section is thus designed first for axial load; moment can then be added to take up the excess capacity, if any exists.

The nominal ultimate axial load P_n and the nominal ultimate moment M_n are computed as always:

$$P_n = \frac{P_u}{\phi} \quad \text{and} \quad M_n = \frac{M_u}{\phi}$$

where P_u and M_u are the factored ultimate loads and ϕ is the strength reduction factor defined and used previously. For columns, $\phi = 0.7$ for both axial load and moment, but the strength reduction factor ϕ may be varied where P_n is less than $0.10f'_c bh/\phi$. The following relationship applies:

$$\phi = \frac{0.9}{1 + 0.2\left(P_n / 0.10 f'_c bh\right)}. \qquad (22\text{-}3)$$

This allowable increase in ϕ applies only where axial load is very small and moment is very large; under such circumstances, the member begins to act as a beam subject to axial load rather than a column subject to flexure.

It is important to recognize that the ACI column formula given by Eq.(22-2) has no provisions for length, radius of gyration, or buckling. Buckling criteria and effects of length are treated by separate limits and requirements, imposed and computed independently from the column formula. The column formula provides only the maximum capacity of a section under concentric load, without regard to any other limitations.

22.5 Buckling Criteria

The parameter used by Code (10.11.4) to classify buckling criteria in columns is the slenderness ratio, taken from the Euler column formula:

$$\text{Slenderness ratio} = \frac{KL_u}{r}$$

where K = numerical factor dependent on end conditions of the column and on the type of overall lateral-load-carrying system.

L_u = unsupported length of the column, taken as the clear distance between attached or supporting members at top and bottom.

r = radius of gyration of the column section, taken as 0.3 times the least dimension for rectangular sections.

The value of K is given by Code (10.11.2.1) as 1.0 for all buildings or structures braced against sidesway; these are the only structures considered in this text. Although the value of K is known to be 1.0 herein, the symbol K will still be shown wherever the slenderness ratio is referenced. Its inclusion will indicate where the effects of end conditions and sidesway must be considered.

For columns braced against sidesway, Code (10.11.4.1) permits the effects of slenderness to be neglected when:

$$\frac{KL_u}{r} < 34 - 12\frac{M_1}{M_2} \tag{22-4}$$

where M_1 and M_2 are the factored end moments from the analysis for vertical loads only (no lateral loads included), and where

M_1 = smaller moment, having a positive sign if the column is bending in single curvature and a negative sign if in double curvature.

M_2 = larger moment, always having a positive sign.

A sketch of the end moments used in Eq.(22-4) is shown in Figure 22-8.

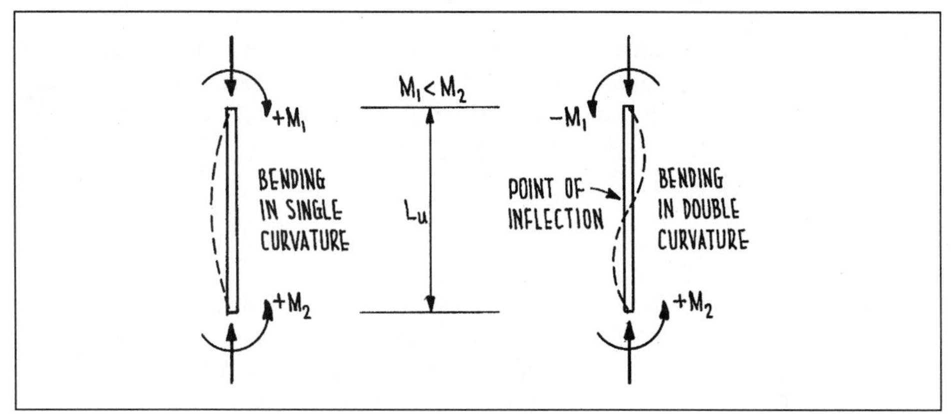

Figure 22-8 End moments on a column.

The least value of the slenderness ratio computed by Eq.(22-4) is seen to occur when $M_1 = M_2$, for which case the slenderness ratio is 22.

All columns considered in this book fall within this intermediate category, where slenderness effects may be neglected. For the other category, where slenderness effects must be considered, Code (10.11.5) prescribes a means to magnify the design moments. The result of such moment magnification is to cause an overdesign of an intermediate column such that it will carry a lighter load (the actual design load) under the more severe conditions.

A final point concerns the length L_u. The Euler formula, from which the slenderness ratio is drawn, uses the length between hinge points as its buckling length, while the ACI criteria specifies that L_u is the "unsupported" length without regard to end conditions. A typical determination of the length L_u is shown in Figure 22-9. The ACI has thus chosen a simple but conservative value for length, in recognition of the myriads of combinations of loads, inflection points and end rotations that could affect the buckling length of a structural column.

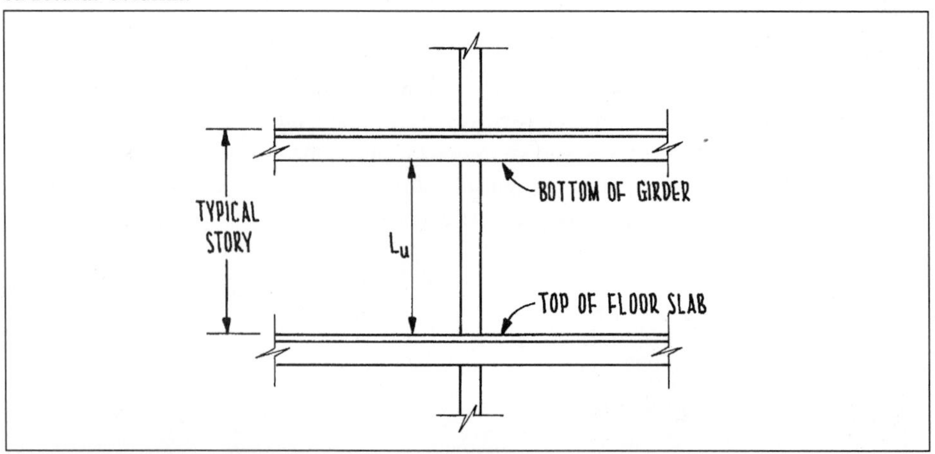

Figure 22-9 ACI column length in a building.

It is again emphasized that the bending in the columns under discussion is developed entirely by vertical loads. There is no bending on these columns due to wind and earthquake; such bending of columns does not occur in braced frames.

22.6 Ultimate Strength Analysis

In column analysis, a very useful dimension is the eccentricity of load, e_n, where:

$$e_n = \frac{M_n}{P_n} \tag{22-5}$$

This eccentricity of the load P_n is shown in Figure 22-10 and is used frequently throughout the subsequent discussions and analyses. Note particularly that the eccentricity is measured from the centerline of the section, not from the neutral axis.

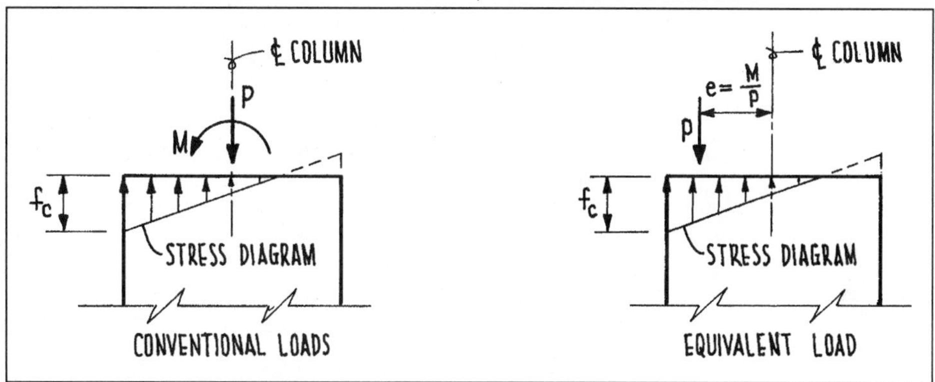

Figure 22-10 Eccentricity of load.

In applying the ACI column formula to the analysis of columns, there are other conditions prescribed by ACI that must be met:

1. Longitudinal reinforcement may not be less than 1% nor more than 8% of the gross cross-sectional area of concrete, A_g.
2. Columns shall be designed for the maximum moment M_n that can accompany the axial load P_n. (Where moment varies along the length of the column, the largest value of moment is used.)
3. Strains shall be assumed to vary linearly across the section.
4. Maximum strain in the concrete shall be assumed to be 0.003.
5. When steel is in the elastic range, the tensile stress shall be taken as the modulus E_s times the strain; when in the plastic range, the stress shall be taken at the specified yield stress.
6. Tensile strength of concrete shall be taken as zero.
7. Stress variation in concrete may be assumed to be any shape that provides results in substantial agreement with tests.
8. When P_n is less than the axial load at balanced strain conditions, P_b, or less than $0.10 f'_c A_g / \phi$, the ratio of reinforcement ρ provided shall not exceed 75% of the balanced ratio ρ_b that would be required for flexure only.
9. Where there is no computed moment on a column, the column may be designed for an accidental eccentricity not less than $0.1h$ for the column load P_n (not a Code requirement but a recommended practice).

All the foregoing conditions are included in the subsequent analyses. Condition 2, concerning the design for moments, recognizes that the allowable moment on a column is interrelated with the axial force; as axial load is decreased, moment can increase (up to a point). Condition 9 was a Code requirement prior to 1971; it recognizes that there cannot be such a thing as a perfectly concentric load or a perfectly straight column.

It is noted here that when P_n is at its maximum allowable value of $0.8P_0$, there remains a small extra capacity for moment. The magnitude of this small amount of moment is commonly taken to be $P_n(0.1h)$ as suggested in Condition 9. Accordingly, given the computed value for the load P_n when $M_n = 0$ (or M_n is negligible), one may design a column for either of the following cases and achieve essentially the same end result:

Case 1. Design for the fully plastic load $P_0 = P_n/0.8 = 1.25P_n$ with $M_n = 0$.
Case 2. Design for the computed load P_n plus a moment $M_n = P_n(0.1h)$.

In this text, Case 2 is used exclusively whenever the computed moment M_n is zero or is less than $P_n(0.1h)$ (see Condition 9).

A typical column section is shown in Figure 22-11. The total area of steel is designated as A_{st} and its steel ratio as ρ. That part of the steel distributed to the flanges is A_s' and its steel ratio is ρ'. That part of the steel distributed to the web is A_s'' and its steel ratio is ρ''.

In the equivalent section of Figure 22-11, the web steel A_s'' is replaced by an equivalent imaginary strip of steel having a finite width, as shown. All other symbols are the same as used previously.

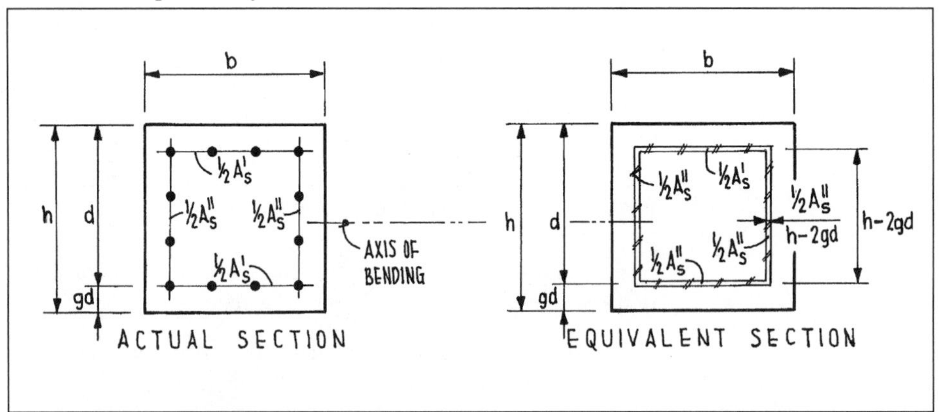

Figure 22-11 Column section.

A full definitive analysis for the ultimate loads on a column section is quite long and tedious. For those who are interested, a brief summary of such an analysis is presented in the author's more complete work, *Reinforced Concrete Technology,* Delmar, 1994. Study of these detailed derivations is not essential to the design procedure; one may skip these derivations and proceed to the next section with no loss in continuity.

22.7 Parametric Design Tables

The equations resulting from the detailed analysis are unwieldly and complicated. Fortunately, the computer solves complicated expressions as readily as simple ones, with the end result of the computer output being the parametric column design tables, Tables C-9 through C-11, given with the design tables in the Technical Manual. The following discussions refer to those tables, Tables C-9, C-10 and C-11.

The ratio R_n defined in the design tables is something of an artificial quantity. It is simply a convenient parameter suggested by the 1971 ACI design manual. It is dimensionless, so the values given in the design tables in the Technical Manual are valid either for imperial (English) units or for SI units.

It should be observed that the lowest value of e_n/h in the design tables is 0.1. As stated earlier, the assumption of a minimum eccentricity of $0.1h$ is considered to be good practice. In addition, the use of this minimum e_n/h produces the same end result as limiting P_n to $0.80P_0$ when moment is zero. Eccentricities in the tables therefore begin at $e_n/h = 0.1$.

22.8 Examples in the Strength Method

The following examples illustrate the use of the column design tables in the Technical Manual, Tables C-9 through C-11. In these first few examples, the stress at service levels is not considered; stresses at service levels are treated in a later discussions. Comments are included within the examples to clarify assumptions or identify arbitrary choices. The first example is the design of a simple column to take only axial load, without moment.

Example 22-1

Strength method, no consideration of service stress. Design of a column subject only to axial load. No limitations on dimensions or reinforcement.

Given: Apartment building, 5 floors.
At a first-floor column, L_u = 9'-0"
P_{DL} = 229 kips, P_{LL} = 201 kips.
Grade 60 steel, f_c' = 4000 psi.

To Find: Suitable column section.

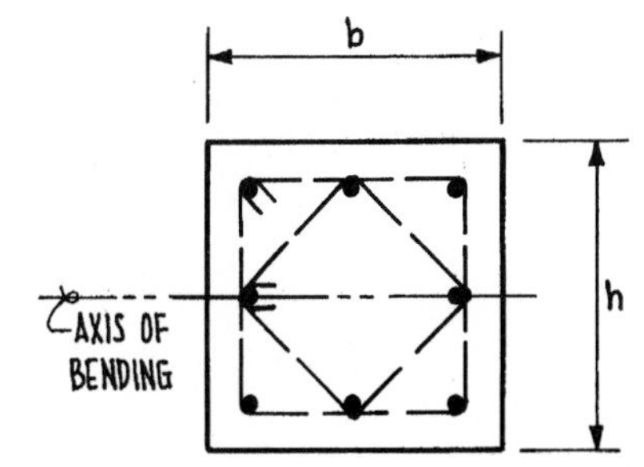

Solution: Calculate the nominal ultimate load P_n:

$$P_n = \frac{1.4P_{DL} + 1.7P_{LL}}{\phi} = \frac{(1.4)(229) + (1.7)(201)}{0.7} = 946 \text{ kips}$$

Choose an overall size and gross area (square column). Use the rule of thumb:

b = h = 12 in. + 1 in. x stories above = 12 in. + 1 in.(4).
Try h = 16 in., b = 16 in.

Check the buckling criteria:

$$\frac{KL_u}{r} < 34 - 12\frac{M_1}{M_2}; \quad \frac{(1)(9)(12)}{(0.3)(16)} = 22.5 < 34 \text{ (O.K.)}$$

Determine R_n and e_n/h:

$$R_n = \frac{P_n / bh}{0.85f_c'} = \frac{946{,}000 / (16)(16)}{0.85(4000)} = 1.09$$

$$\frac{e_n}{h} = \text{minimum} = 0.1$$

From Table C-10, with steel uniformly distributed;
use A_s = 2.4% = 0.024(16)(16) = 6.14 in.^{2}

From Table C-3, select 8 No. 8 bars.

Select the ties: for No. 8 bars, use tie size No. 3.

Spacing:	< 16 bar diameters or	< 16 in.
	< 48 tie diameters or	< 18 in.
	< least dimension or	< 16 in.

Use a column 16 in. x 16 in.; 8 No. 8 longitudinal bars, No. 3 ties at 16 in. o.c. Such a section is shown in the sketch at the beginning of this example.

Example 22-2

Strength method, no consideration of service stress. Design of a column subject only to axial load. One dimension restricted.

Given: Same conditions as in Example 22-1. Height h across axis of bending limited to 12 in.

To Find: Suitable column section.

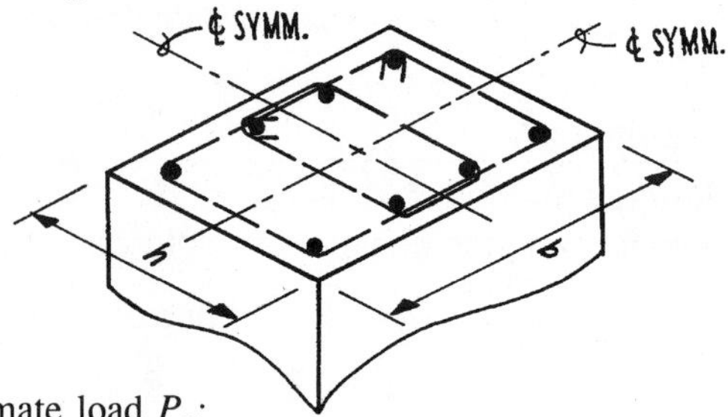

Solution: Calculate the nominal ultimate load P_n:

$$P_n = 946 \text{ kips (same as Example 22-1).}$$

Choose an overall size and gross area. Use the rule of thumb: if a square column section is 16 in. x 16 in. in size, a rectangular section should have the same area.

$$\text{Gross area} = (16)(16) = 256 \text{ in.}^2$$

With one size 12 in., try 12 in. x 22 in., $A_g = 264$ in.^{2} (O.K. - near enough to 256 in.)

Check the buckling criteria:

$$\frac{KL_u}{r} < 34 - 12\frac{M_1}{M_2}; \quad \frac{(1)(9)(12)}{(0.3)(12)} = 30 < 34 \text{ (O.K.)}$$

Determine R_n and e_n/h:

$$R_n = \frac{P_n / bh}{0.85f'_c} = \frac{946{,}000/(12)(22)}{0.85(4000)} = 1.054$$

$$\frac{e_n}{h} = \text{minimum} = 0.1$$

From Table C-10, steel on two faces only; use 2% steel:

$$A_s = 0.02(12)(22) = 5.28 \text{ in.}^2$$

From Table C-3, select 4 No. 8 and 4 No. 7 bars.

Select the ties: for No. 8 bars, use tie size No. 3.

Spacing:			
<	16 bar diameters or	<	14 in. (for No. 7 bars)
<	48 tie diameters or	<	18 in.
<	least dimension or	<	12 in.

Use 12 in. x 22 in. column, 4 No. 8 and 4 No. 7 bars, No. 3 ties at 12 in. o.c., with No. 8 bars placed at the four corners. The chosen section is similar to that shown at the beginning of this example.

Example 22-3

Strength method, no consideration of service stress. Design of a column that is subject to flexure. Configuration limited to square sections.

Given: Same criteria as Example 22-1.

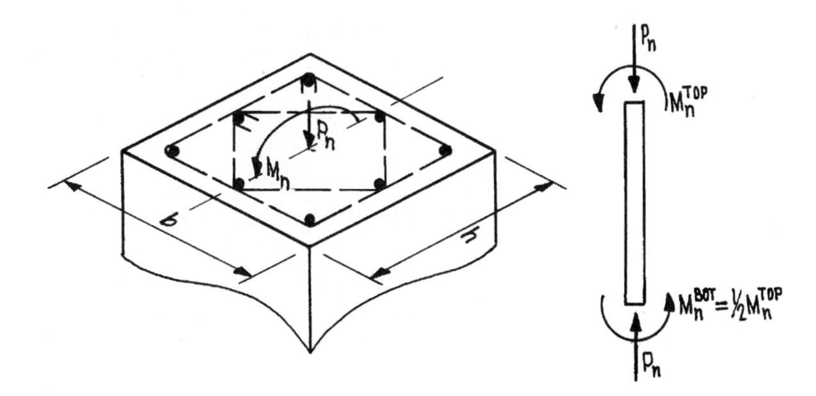

At top of column, add M_{DL} = 65 kip·ft.
M_{LL} = 48 kip·ft.
At bottom of column, M_{DL} = 33 kip·ft.
M_{LL} = 24 kip·ft.

To Find: Suitable column section.

Solution: Calculate the nominal ultimate loads M_n and P_n:

P_n = 946 kips (from Example 22-1).

$$\text{At top: } M_n = \frac{1.4M_{DL} + 1.7M_{LL}}{\phi} = \frac{(1.4)(65) + (1.7)(48)}{\phi(?)}$$

= 247 kip·ft.

At bottom: M_n = 124 kip·ft.

For a first trial, choose an overall size: b = h = 16 in. (same as Example 22-1). Check the buckling criteria:

$$\frac{KL_u}{r} < 34 - 12\frac{M_1}{M_2};\quad \frac{(1)(9)(12)}{(0.3)(16)} < 34 - 12\frac{-124}{247}$$

= 22.5 < 40 (O.K.)

Determine R_n and e_n/h:

$$R_n = \frac{P_n / bh}{0.85f_c'} = \frac{946{,}000/(16)(16)}{0.85(4000)} = 1.09$$

$$\frac{e_n}{h} = \frac{M_n / P_n}{h} = \frac{247{,}000(12/946{,}000)}{16} = 0.196$$

From Table C-10, with steel uniformly distributed, find 4.8% steel (too high).

Since this column section is considered to be unacceptable, the trial size must be increased and the entire procedure repeated for this new trial size. An increment of 4 in. will be added, producing a trial section of 20 in. square. For the new gross size, recalculate R_n and e_n/h:

$$R_n = \frac{P_n / bh}{0.85f'_c} = \frac{946{,}000 / (20)(20)}{0.85(4000)} = 0.70$$

$$\frac{e_n}{h} = \frac{M_n / P_n}{h} = \frac{247{,}000(12 / 946{,}000)}{20} = 0.16$$

From Table C-10, select $\rho < 1\%$ steel (too low).

Again the trial size is unacceptable. For the next trial, select 18 in. square, halfway between the first and second trial sizes. For the new gross size, recalculate R_n and e_n/h:

$$R_n = \frac{P_n / bh}{0.85f'_c} = \frac{946{,}000 / (18)(18)}{0.85(4000)} = 0.86$$

$$\frac{e_n}{h} = \frac{M_n / P_n}{h} = \frac{247{,}000(12 / 946{,}000)}{18} = 0.174$$

From Table C-10, find $\rho = 2.0\ \%$ (O.K. - use 2%).

$$A_s = 0.02(18)(18) = 6.58 \text{ in.}^2$$

From Table C-3, select 4 No. 9 and 4 No. 8 longitudinal bars.

Select the ties: for No. 9 longitudinal bars, use tie size No. 3.

Spacing: < 16 bar diameters or < 16 in. (smallest bar size)
< 48 tie diameters or < 18 in.
< least dimension or < 18 in.

Use a column 18 in. x 18 in., 4 No. 9 and 4 No. 8 longitudinal bars with the No. 9 bars at the four corners, No. 3 ties at 16 in. o.c.

The final column section is similar to that shown at the beginning of the example.

Example 22-4

Strength method, no consideration of service stress. Design of a column that is subject to flexure. Depth of section limited on the axis of bending to a maximum of 11 in.

Given: Same criteria as Example 22-1.

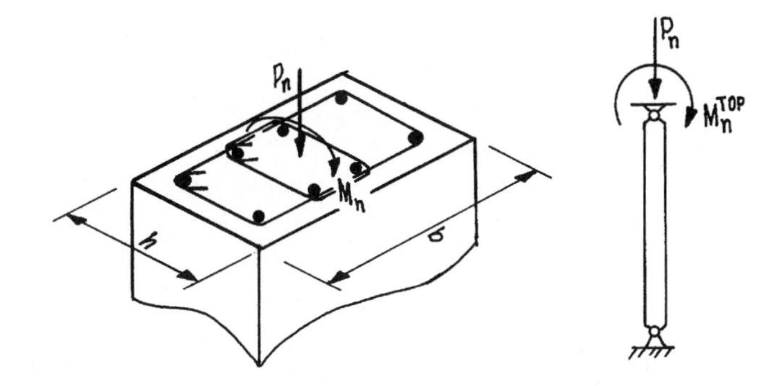

At top of column, add $M_{DL} = 50$ kip·ft.
$M_{LL} = 30$ kip·ft.
At bottom, add hinge, $M_{DL} = 0$
$M_{LL} = 0$

To Find: Suitable column section.

Solution: Calculate the nominal ultimate loads M_n and P_n:

$P_n = 946$ kips (from Example 22-1).

$$M_n = \frac{1.4M_{DL} + 1.7M_{LL}}{\phi} = \frac{(1.4)(50) + (1.7)(30)}{0.7} = 173 \text{ kip·ft.}$$

Choose an overall size and gross area for a square column. From the rule of thumb, try an area roughly equal to a square section 16 in. x 16 in., having $A_g = 256$ in.^{2}

Check the buckling criteria:

$$\frac{KL_u}{r} < 34 - 12\frac{M_1}{M_2}; \quad \frac{(1)(108)}{(0.3)(11)} < 34 - 12\frac{0}{173}$$

$= 33 < 34$ (O.K.)

Compute R_n and e_n/h:

$$R_n = \frac{P_n / bh}{0.85f'_c} = \frac{946{,}000 / (11)(24)}{0.85(4000)} = 1.054$$

$$\frac{e_n}{h} = \frac{M_n / P_n}{h} = \frac{173{,}000(12 / 946{,}000)}{11} = 0.20$$

From Table C-10, steel on two faces, find ρ of almost 4%. (Too high - try a larger section with lower ρ).

Try a section 11 in. x 30 in. For the new trial size, recompute R_n and e_n/h:

$$R_n = \frac{P_n / bh}{0.85f'_c} = \frac{946{,}000 / (11)(30)}{0.85(4000)} = 0.84.$$

$$\frac{e_n}{h} = \frac{M_n / P_n}{h} = \frac{173{,}000(12 / 946{,}000)}{11} = 0.20$$

From Table C-10, with steel at two faces, read ρ of 2% (O.K. - use).

Determine the steel area:

$$A_s = \rho bd = 0.02(11)(30) = 6.60 \text{ in.}^2$$

From Table C-3, select 4 No. 9 and 4 No. 8 bars.

Select the ties: for No. 9 longitudinal bars, use tie size No. 3.

Spacing: < 16 bar diameters or < 16 in. (for No. 8 bars).
< 48 tie diameters or < 18 in.
< least dimension or < 11 in.

Use a column 11 in. x 30 in., 4 No. 9 and 4 No. 8 bars, No. 3 ties at 11 in. o.c.

The final section is shown in the sketch at the beginning of the example.

A summary of the first four examples follows.

Example	P_n (kips)	M_n (kip-ft)	b (in.)	h (in.)	e/h	A_s (in.^{2})
22-1	946	0	16	16	0.10	6.14
22-2	946	0	22	12	0.10	5.28
22-3	946	247	18	18	0.17	6.48
22-4	946	173	30	11	0.20	6.60

In these four examples, the axial load was taken at the same value each time and other factors were then varied. When Example 22-3 is compared to Example 22-1, it is noted that adding a significant amount of moment had only a small effect on the size of the column and its reinforcement. When Example 22-2 is compared to Example 22-4, it is seen that rather drastic changes in one dimension do not change the total area $(b)(h)$ by a large amount, and even adding a large moment in the shallow direction changes the area of steel only 20%. It is concluded that for braced frames, the axial load dominates to such an extent that other influences become relatively minor.

When axial loads become small, as in one- or two-story buildings, very often the minimum-sized column sections must be used. The next example lists the allowable loads on minimum-sized columns.

Example 22-5

Strength method, no consideration of service stresses. Design of columns subject only to axial load. Minimum dimensions and minimum reinforcement.

Determine the nominal axial load P_n for column sections fabricated using f'_c of 3000, 4000 and 5000 psi, and for grades 40, 50 and 60 steels. Tabulate the results for $e_n/h = 0.1$ for minimum or no moment. Use A_s of 1%, steel uniformly distributed. Read R_n from the Technical Manual tables and compute $P_n = 0.85 f'_c bhR_n$.

f_y (ksi)	f'_c (psi)	R_n	P_n (kips) 10 in. x 10 in. A_g = 100 in.^{2}	P_n (kips) 12 in. x 12 in. A_g = 144 in.^{2}
40	3000	0.91	232	334
40	4000	0.87	296	426
40	5000	0.85	361	520
50	3000	0.93	237	341
50	4000	0.89	393	436
50	5000	0,87	370	532
60	3000	0.96	245	353
60	4000	0,91	309	446
60	5000	0.89	378	545

Without incurring load reductions due to length, where $KL_u/r \leq 34$ and r = 0.3h:

Maximum length of a 10 in. column: 102 in. = 8 ft. 6 in.
Maximum length of a 12 in. column: 122 in. = 10 ft. 2 in.

Typical loads per story can be expected to be:

Actual P per story = 30 tons or 60 kips

The nominal ultimate load P_n can be expected to be between $1.4/\phi$ and $1.7/\phi$ times the actual load:

P_n per story = $60(1.4/\phi)$ to $60(1.7/\phi)$ = 120 kips to 146 kips

From an examination of the tabulation, it is seen that the allowable load on a minimum-sized column should be adequate for a two- or three-story building, even where nominal moments are present. For lengths longer than the indicated maximum lengths, Code requires significant reductions in the allowable loads.

22.9 Investigation of a Column Section

The reverse of the design problem can occur occasionally, that is, the size of the column and its reinforcement are known and it is one of the loads that is to be determined. Since the loads M_n and P_n are interrelated, one of the loads must be known, else there are an infinite number of combinations that could be solutions. In most cases it is the axial load P_n that is known and it is desired to find how much moment M_n the section can take in addition to the axial load; the next example is such a case.

Example 22-6

Strength method. Investigation of a section to find the service moment, given the axial load.

Given: Section as shown.
P_{DL} = 86 kips.
P_{LL} = 70 kips.
Grade 60 steel.
f'_c = 4000 psi.

To Find: Service moment M_{sv}.

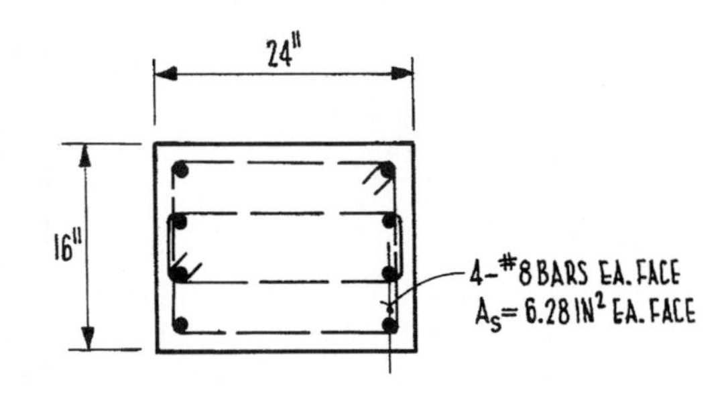

Solution: Calculate the nominal ultimate load P_n:

$$P_n = \frac{1.4P_{DL} + 1.7P_{LL}}{\phi} = \frac{(1.4)(86) + (1.7)(70)}{0.7} = 342 \text{ kips}$$

Determine R_n and the steel ratio ρ:

$$R_n = \frac{P_n / bh}{0.85f'_c} = \frac{342{,}000 / (16)(21)}{0.85(4000)} = 0.30$$

$$\rho = \frac{P_n bh}{0.85f'_c} = \frac{6.28}{16(21)} = 0.019$$

From Table C-11, read $e_n/h = 0.78$.

Solve for M_n from the e_n/h ratio:

$$\frac{e_n}{h} = \frac{M_n / P_n}{h}; \quad 0.78 = \frac{M_n / 342{,}000}{21}$$

Solve for M_n: M_n = 5602 kip·in. = 467 kip·ft.

Use a factor of 1.7 to obtain M_{sv}:

$$\text{Service moment } M_{sv} = \frac{467 \text{ kip}\cdot\text{ft}}{1.7} = 275 \text{ kip·ft.}$$

22.10 Elastic Analysis

In the elastic range, the analysis of a column section is much like that of a beam section except that an axial force has been added and there may be additional reinforcement in the middle of the section. A typical column section is shown in Figure 22-12, with the load components P_e and M_e representing the axial force and moment at working levels. As with the strength method, the web steel is replaced by an imaginary strip of steel having a finite width as shown.

A discontinuity is introduced when the value of k is equal to $1+g$. For higher values of k, all concrete is effective; for lower values of k, the concrete in tension is assumed to be cracked and ineffective. Two sets of equations are therefore required to bridge the discontinuity.

For k greater than $1+g$, the stress diagrams of Figure 22-12 are valid. The sum of forces yields an equation for the ratio R_e:

$$R_e = \frac{P_e / bh}{f_c} = \frac{2k - 1 - g}{2k(1+g)}\left[1 + g + (2n-1)(\rho' + \rho'')\right] \quad (22\text{-}6)$$

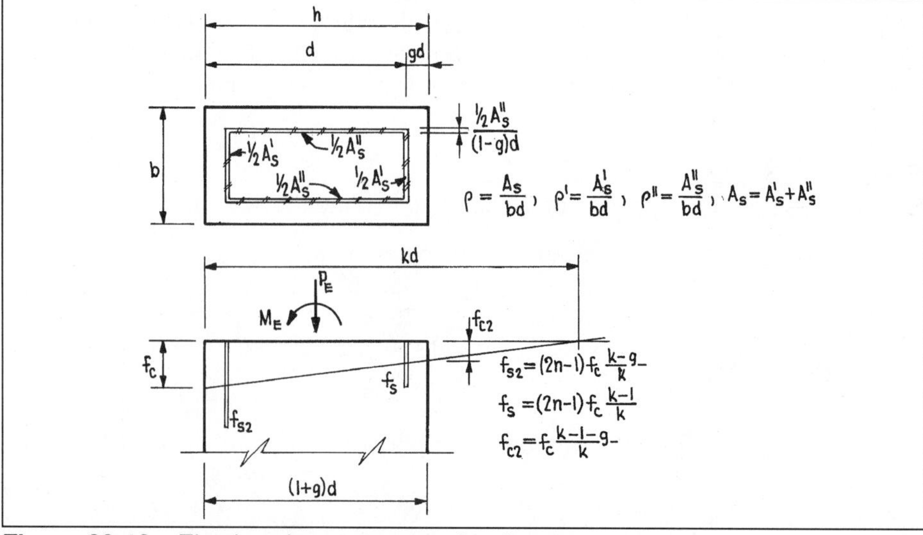

Figure 22-12 Elastic column stresses, k ≥ (1+g).

The sum of moments about the centerline yields a similar equation in moments:

$$R_m = \frac{M_e / bh^2}{f_c} = \frac{1}{2k}\left[1 + g + (2n-1)(3\rho' + \rho'')\frac{(1-g)^2}{(1+g)^2}\right] \tag{22-7}$$

Dividing Eq.(22-7) by Eq.(22-6) yields a solution for the eccentricity ratio:

$$\frac{e_e}{h} = \frac{R_m}{R_e} \tag{22-8}$$

For k less than *(1+g)*, the state of stress in Figure 22-13. For those stresses, the sum of horizontal forces yields the solution for R_e:

$$R_e = \frac{P_e / bh}{f_c} = \frac{1}{2k(1+g)}[k^2 + (2n-1)\rho'(k-g) + (2n-1)\rho''\frac{(k-g)^2}{1-g} - n\rho''\frac{(1-k)^2}{1-g} - n\rho'(1-k)] \tag{22-9}$$

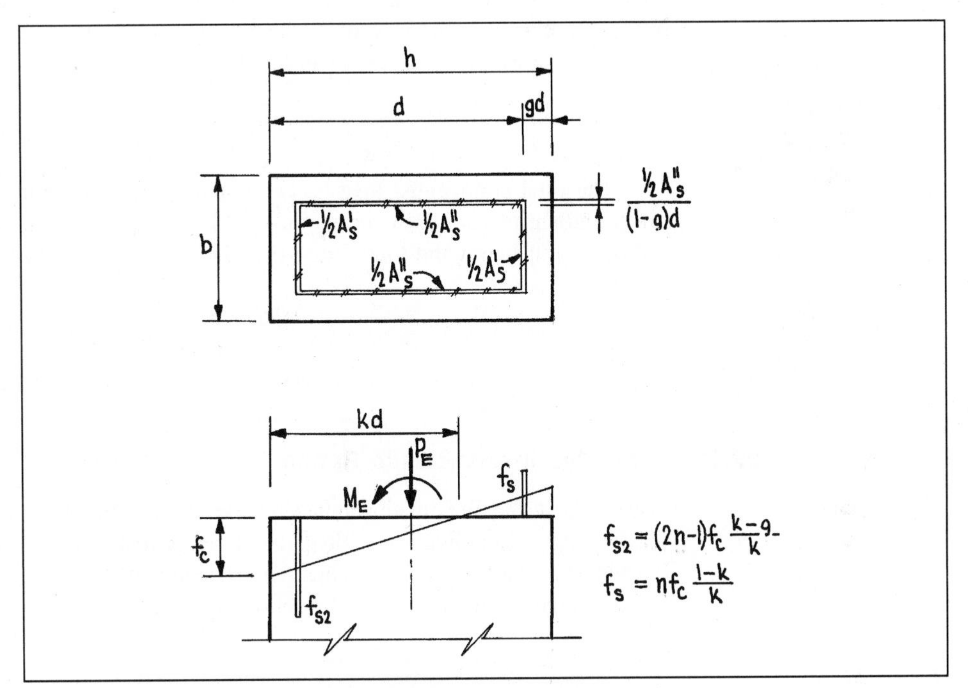

Figure 22-13 Elastic column stresses, k ≤ (1+g).

The sum of moments about centerline yields a similar equation in moments:

$$R_m = \frac{M_e / bh^2}{f_c} = \frac{1}{4k(1+g)^2}[\frac{k^2}{3}(3+3g-2k) + n\rho'(1-k)(1-g) + (2n-1)\rho'(k-g)(1-g) + (2n-1)\rho''\frac{(k-g)^2}{3(1-g)}(3-g-2k) + n\rho''\frac{(1-k)^2}{3(1-g)}(1-3g+2k)] \tag{22-10}$$

For this range of k, the eccentricity ratio is again given by

$$\frac{e_e}{h} = \frac{R_m}{R_e} \tag{22-11}$$

The actual numerical values of the stress ratio R_e are tabulated in the column tables in the Technical Manual, Tables C-9 through C-11, at the lower portion of each table. In developing the tables, the value of k was varied to produce the desired value of e_e/h [Eq.(22-8) or (22-11)]; then the value of R_e corresponding to that e_e/h was listed [Eq.(22-6) or (22-9)]. Since all stresses are in the elastic range, the tabulation is seen to be independent of f_y, the yield stress of steel.

The tables are set up in terms of two parameters, e_e/h and R_e. The stress ratio R_e is analogous to the stress ratio R_n introduced earlier in the strength method; R_e, of course, uses elastic load and elastic stress, whereas R_n uses nominal ultimate load and yield stress. For easy reference, both R_n and R_e are defined at the top left corner of each table.

The stress ratio R_e affords a means to determine the compressive stress in the concrete during service conditions. The stress f_c is the maximum working stress in the concrete and includes both axial compression plus flexure. When R_e, P_e and the overall dimensions b and h are known, the service stress can be computed.

When investigating the elastic stresses as it affects brittle finishes or coverings, it should be borne in mind that creep and shrinkage in concrete affect strain but not stress. When the elastic stress is known, the related elastic strain is found simply by dividing elastic stress by the modulus of elasticity:

$$\text{Elastic } e_c = \frac{f_c}{E_c} \qquad (22\text{-}12)$$

The total strain must then be computed to include both elastic strain and inelastic creep and shrinkage. As stated in Chapter 16, the inelastic strain may be as much as the elastic strain; hence the total strain may be as much as twice the elastic strain:

$$\text{Total } e_c \le 2\frac{f_c}{E_c} \qquad (22\text{-}12)$$

The additional strain can have severe effects on finishes and coatings.

22.11 Examples in the Elastic Range

The tables in the Technical Manual include provisions for the analysis of columns in the elastic range. An indication of the general performance of a column during its day-to-day working life can therefore be obtained. The procedure is directly parallel to that for the plastic range, as illustrated in the following examples.

Example 22-7

Elastic analysis of columns. Investigation of service stress.
Column subject to axial load only.

Given: Column of Example 22-1.
$P_{DL} = 229$ kips.
$P_{LL} = 201$ kips.
Grade 60 steel.
$f'_c = 4000$ psi.

To Find: Service stress in the concrete.

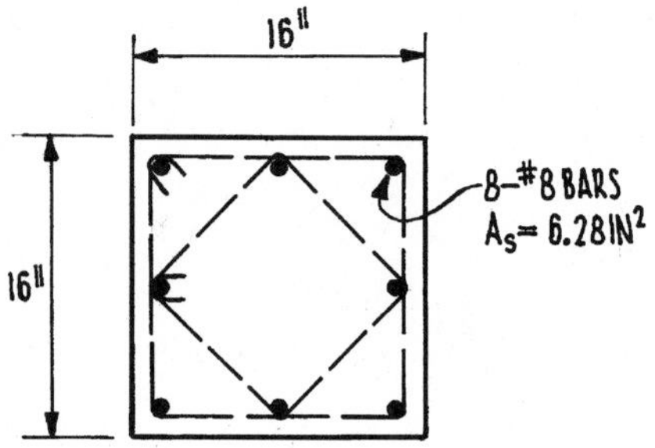

Solution: Calculate the service load P_{sv}:

$$\left(\tfrac{1.4}{1.7}P_{DL} + P_{LL}\right)/\,\phi = 557 \text{ kips}$$

Determine the steel ratio ρ:

$$\rho = \frac{A_s}{bh} = \frac{6.28}{(16)(16)} = 0.025.$$

From Table C-10, using $e_e/h = 0.1$ to account for any accidental eccentricities, read $R_e = 0.89$.

Determine the elastic stress:

$$R_e = \frac{P_{sv}/bh}{f_c}; \quad 0.89 = \frac{557{,}000/(16)(16)}{f_c}$$

Solve for f_c:

$$f_c = 2445 \text{ psi.}$$

The elastic stress in concrete is 2445 psi, or 61% of f'_c or 72% of idealized yield.

Example 22-8

Elastic analysis of columns. Investigation of service stress.
Column subject to axial load plus flexure.

Given: Column of Example 22-3.
P_{DL} = 229 kips.
P_{LL} = 201 kips.
M_{DL} = 65 kip·ft.
M_{LL} = 48 kip·ft.
Grade 60 steel.
f'_c = 4000 psi.

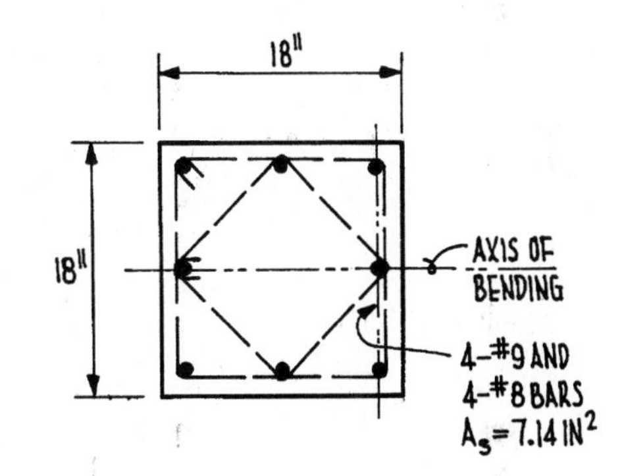

To Find: Service stress f_{sv}.

Solution: Calculate the service loads M_{sv} and P_{sv}:

$$M_{sv} = \frac{{}^{1.4}\!/_{1.7}M_{DL} + M_{LL}}{\phi} = \frac{{}^{1.4}\!/_{1.7}(65) + 48}{0.7} = 145 \text{ kip·ft.}$$

$$P_{sv} = \frac{{}^{1.4}\!/_{1.7}P_{DL} + P_{LL}}{\phi} = \frac{{}^{1.4}\!/_{1.7}(229) + 201}{0.7} = 557 \text{ kips}$$

Determine the steel ratio ρ:

$$\rho = \frac{A_s}{bh} = \frac{7.14}{(18)(18)} = 0.022$$

Calculate the eccentricity ratio e_e/h:

$$\frac{e_e}{h} = \frac{M_{sv}/P_{sv}}{h} = \frac{145{,}000(12/557{,}000)}{18} = 0.174$$

From Table C-10 read $R_e = 0.66$.

Determine the elastic stress:

$$R_e = \frac{P_{sv}/bh}{f_c}; \quad 0.66 = \frac{557{,}000/(18)(18)}{f_c}$$

Solve for f_c:

$$f_c = 2605 \text{ psi}$$

The elastic stress in concrete is 2605 psi, or 65% of f'_c or 76% of idealized yield.

It should be recognized that the computed stress f_c in examples 22-7 and 22-8 includes the effects of long-term creep and shrinkage. Until the long-term effects actually happen, the computed value may be considerably in error.

Investigation of elastic stresses can serve a very practical purpose, as demonstrated in the next example.

Example 22-9

Elastic analysis of columns. Investigation of elastic stresses.
Column subject to axial load plus flexure.

The column shown below is to be clad with sculptured marble; the marble is to be rigidly attached to the concrete. The modulus of elasticity of the marble is $(6)(10^6)$ psi.

Given: Section as shown.
$P_{DL} = 230$ kips.
$P_{LL} = 200$ kips.
$M_{DL} = 66$ kips.
$M_{LL} = 47$ kip·ft.
Grade 60 steel.
$f'_c = 4000$ psi.
$E_c = 57{,}000^4 = 3{,}600{,}000$ psi.

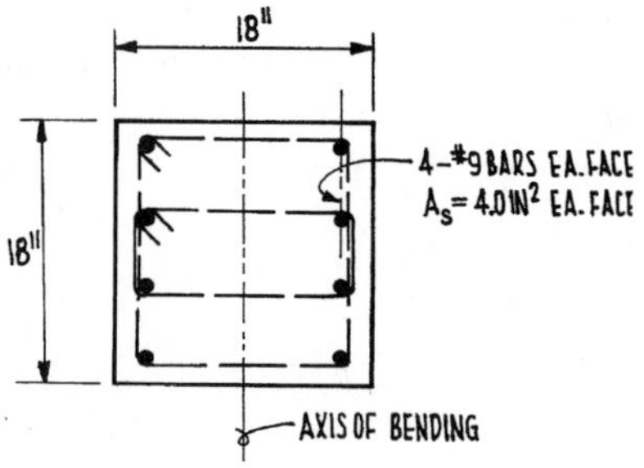

18"
18"
4-#9 BARS EA. FACE
A_s= 4.0 IN² EA. FACE
AXIS OF BENDING

To Find: Maximum elastic stress that can occur in the marble (DL + 100% LL).

Solution: Calculate the elastic loads P_e and M_e:

$$P_e = P_{DL} + P_{LL} = 230 + 200 = 430 \text{ kips}$$
$$M_e = M_{DL} + M_{LL} = 66 + 47 = 113 \text{ kip·ft.}$$

Determine ρ and e_e/h:

$$\rho = \frac{A_s}{bh} = \frac{8.00}{(18)(18)} = 0.0247, \text{ say } 2.5\%$$

$$\frac{e_e}{h} = \frac{M_e / P_e}{h} = \frac{113{,}000(12/430{,}000)}{18} = 0.18, \text{ say } 0.2\%.$$

From Table C-10 read $R_e = 0.69$.

Determine the elastic stress:

$$R_e = \frac{P_e / bh}{f_c}; \quad 0.69 = \frac{430{,}000/(18)(18)}{f_c}$$

Solve for f_c:

$$f_c = 1923 \text{ psi (maximum)}.$$

Determine the elastic strain in the concrete:

$$e_c = \frac{f_c}{E_c} = \frac{1923}{(3.6)(10^6)} = 0.000534 \text{ in./in.}$$

The column tables in the Technical Manual include the effects of creep and shrinkage in the concrete. The computed elastic strain of 0.000534 in./in. cannot occur, therefore, until an additional inelastic strain of 0.000534 in./in. has also occurred. The total strain at the surface of the concrete is thus the sum of the two:

$$e_c = 0.000534 + 0.000534 = 0.00107 \text{ in./in.}$$

The stress in the marble can now be computed from this total strain. Since the marble is rigidly attached to the concrete, the total strain in the marble e_m will be equal to the total strain in the concrete; the stress can therefore be found from Hooke's law:

$$e_m = e_c = 0.00107 \text{ in./in.}$$
$$f_m = E_m e_m = (6)(10^6)(0.00107) = 6420 \text{ psi}$$

The maximum stress that can occur in the marble is 6420 psi.

It should be recognized that the computed stress in the marble in Example 22-9 is quite high, probably approaching the ultimate strength of the marble. Not all of it is likely to occur, however, since a large part of the inelastic strain in the concrete will have occurred during construction. As construction progresses, the dead load increases and much of the creep that is going to occur will occur progressively during that time. Attaching the marble would, of course, be one of the last items on the construction schedule.

Nonetheless, the elastic strain by itself induces a stress in the marble of 3210 psi (half the total), which is still a significant stress. A great deal of attention will have to be paid to the attachments, or the marble may separate from its concrete backing. Such failures do occur.

Review Questions

1. In the strength method for design of columns, how is the axial service load P_{sv} obtained?
2. Why should the factor of safety be higher for columns than for beams?
3. What purpose do lateral ties serve in a reinforced concrete column?
4. What is the minimum required steel area for longitudinal reinforcement in a column?
5. What is the maximum allowable steel area for longitudinal reinforcement in a column?
6. Why is the steel area in columns usually held to less than 4% of gross concrete area *bh*?
7. What is the radius of gyration, and how is it computed?
8. What is the slenderness ratio, and how is it used?
9. Describe the state of stress in a column section when it is loaded by the load P_0 as defined by the ACI column formula. What is the magnitude of the strain in the concrete under this load?
10. In the strength method, at what axial load does a member change from a column carrying a dominant flexural load to a beam carrying a small axial load?
11. How are end moments on a column accounted for when using the ACI column formula?
12. How is the effect of slenderness of a column accounted for when using the ACI column formula?
13. The ACI column formula is expressed only in terms of axial load. How is moment accommodated?

CHAPTER

23

MASONRY CONSTRUCTION

The term *masonry* encompasses a great many products. Included in the term are various sizes and shapes of concrete blocks, many sizes and shapes of fired clay bricks, unfired dried adobe bricks, terra cotta tile and so on. All of these products are commonly available and all of them can be used structurally.

As a means to control the volume of these discussions, the consideration of masonry construction is limited to the two most common structural masonry products: concrete masonry units (CMU) and fired clay bricks. Other masonry products respond to load in much the same way as these two products do. There are differences, of course, in allowable stress levels and construction details among the other products. Nonetheless, a person who is familiar with the procedures for designing CMU and fired brick can readily adapt to the other types of masonry.

23.1 The Empirical Design Method

In recent years, structural masonry has been extended far past the empirical designs that have been used for centuries. Masonry is now commonly reinforced for flexural stresses as well as for compressive stresses. Reinforced structural masonry is now universally accepted by modern building codes both in zones of high earthquake risk and of high hurricane incidence.

Even with the advances, however, the empirical designs of past centuries remain completely valid. Consequently, the empirical methods of masonry design remain the methods used in much of today's construction industry worldwide. These empirical methods carry a reassuring advantage: they have withstood the test of time; they are known to work.

There are limitations, however, beyond which empirical masonry construction is simply not suited. One of those limitations is in the design for high lateral load (wind and earthquake) and another is in the design of high-rise buildings. It is in these areas of contemporary analysis and design that the new developments in reinforced masonry must be brought into use.

The method presented in this chapter is termed the "empirical" method of design. The empirical method is prescribed in the publication TMS 402-92 *Building Code Requirements for Masonry Structures* and its companion publication TMS 602-92 *Specifications for Masonry Structures*. These publications are published by the Masonry Standard Joint Committee, formed by the American Concrete Institute (ACI 530-92 and 530.1-92), the American Society of Civil Engineers (ASCE 5-92 and 6-92) and The Masonry

Society (TMS). All references to the Code in this chapter will mean this code. The Code includes both reinforced masonry for the higher loadings and empirically designed masonry for lesser loadings, but only the empirical methods are presented here.

A second publication recommended to anyone involved in the design of structural masonry is the *Masonry Designers' Guide*, published by the Masonry Standards Joint Committee under the auspices of ACI Committee 530. The guide is carefully keyed to the provisions of the *Building Code Requirements for Masonry Structures* (TMS 402) and contains numerous examples of "real-world" applications of masonry in determinate systems.

23.2 Limitations in the Empirical Design Method

TMS 402-92 contains requirements for the design of unreinforced masonry, reinforced masonry and empirically designed masonry. In spite of these names, however, almost all masonry in modern construction is reinforced in some fashion, particularly if the structure is subject to earthquake loads.

The empirical methods of design may be used in all structural masonry within the following limitations:

- Empirical design methods may be used for the design or construction of masonry for buildings, parts of buildings, or other structures in all earthquake risk zones lower than Zone 3. (Earthquake risk zones are defined in Chapter 13.)
- Empirical design methods may be used for the design or construction of masonry for buildings, parts of buildings, or other structures where the wind stagnation pressure at 30 feet above ground does not exceed 25 psf (100 mph). (Wind stagnation pressures are defined in Chapter 13.)
- Empirical design methods may be used for the design or construction of masonry elements of the lateral load resisting system in buildings, parts of buildings or other structures where the height of the building or structure is 35 feet or less.
- Empirical design methods may be used for the design or construction of masonry for foundation walls for buildings, parts of buildings or other structures where all of the following limits are met:
  1. Height of unbalanced fill above inside grade does not exceed 8 feet.
  2. Equivalent fluid weight of the unbalanced fill does not exceed 30 psf.
  3. Height of wall between lateral supports does not exceed 8 feet.
- Where lateral loads occur other than those described in the foregoing list, the empirical design methods may not be used.

The foregoing limitations are absolute. When these limitations cannot be met, design requirements for higher strength reinforced masonry must be used. The overwhelming majority of masonry structures will, however, fall within the limits of the empirical method.

The empirical design method can best be characterized as a "cookbook" approach to masonry construction. The method was developed for routine smaller buildings having masonry exterior walls; the masonry walls commonly serve both as bearing walls for the gravity loads and as shear walls for the lateral loads. Interior supports may be masonry bearing walls, wood stud walls, wood columns or concrete columns. Floor and roof will invariably serve as the diaphragms for the lateral load carrying system; floors and roof may be built of wood, concrete or steel.

In the empirical design method, masonry elements may be subject only to direct stress. Bending or torsion on the masonry section is not permitted. The masonry elements may be subject only to in-plane direct compressive stress or to in-plane direct shear stress.

23.3 Mortar for Structural Masonry

In masonry construction, the masonry units are positioned and held together in a cementing matrix called *mortar*. Very often, the mortar is the "weak link" in the construction, since both brick and concrete units are frequently stronger than the mortar. One may, in fact, think of masonry construction as a hand-laid form of concrete, with each piece of aggregate — the masonry unit — being hand placed in its cementing matrix of sand-cement mortar.

In earlier times, before the development of portland cement, masonry mortar was made from lime. Lime mortar has one major disadvantage: lime morter will not harden unless it has a supply of air, or more specifically, a supply of carbon dioxide. As a consequence, lime mortar cannot be used under water.

The lime used to make masonry mortar is *quicklime*, CaO. Quicklime is made by heating limestone, $CaCO_3$, to drive off one molecule of carbon dioxide gas:

$$CaCO_3 + Heat = CaO + CO_2.$$

Quicklime has an extremely high affinity for water, with which it hydrates to form *slaked lime*, $Ca(OH)_2$. During slaking, the quicklime gives off large amounts of heat, large enough to boil the slaking water. If the slaking of the quicklime is done during the manufacturing process, the end product is called *hydrated lime*, otherwise it is called slaked lime.

Slaked lime is made into mortar by adding enough excess water to form a thick slurry called *lime putty*. The lime putty is usually aged overnight, then sand is added to give bulk and stiffness. The resultant mortar is then ready for use in masonry construction.

Lime mortar "sets" into a solid in a few hours. It continues to harden with time, returning eventually to its limestone origin by combining with the carbon dioxide that occurs naturally in the air:

$$Ca(OH)_2 + CO_2 = CaCO_3 + H_2O$$

Lime mortar has been used with success since antiquity. There are many masonry and stone structures in use today that were built centuries ago with lime mortar. In such structures, the slaked lime mortar will have transformed itself almost entirely back into limestone.

Traditional lime mortar is rarely used in modern construction. Lime mortar must have air to harden, and even with an adequate air supply, its strength gain, though steady, is quite slow. A faster setting and stronger hydraulic mortar can be made simply by adding portland cement.

The portland cement used to make mortar for unit masonry may be Type I, II or III. Type I portland cement is most commonly used but Type II may be used where the masonry will be in contact with sulphurous soils. In extremely sulphurous enrivonments (such as sewers), one may wish to forego the portland cement entirely and simply use lime mortar as in centuries past.

Portland cement mortar for masonry units may be mixed to specified proportions on site, using hydrated lime and sand. As an alternative field mix, a factory prepared "masonry cement" (containing lime) may be purchased in bag form and used in lieu of the hydrated lime. In most cases, the project specifications will simply specify the strength to be attained; the choice of using hydrated lime or the factory-prepared mix is left to the contractor. Project specifications may specify either the mix proportions or the strength, but not both.

Types of mortar are specified by ASTM C270. The four most common types are those listed in Table M-1 in the Technical Manual, reproduced here for immediate reference. A general description of these types of mortar is given in the following list.

- Type M mortar is the highest grade and strongest mortar. It may be used for load-bearing masonry in all exposures, interior or exterior, to include severe conditions of freeze-thaw and in direct contact with earth.
- Type S mortar has most of the qualities of Type M mortar but is less expensive. It may be used for load-bearing masonry in moderate freeze-thaw exposures and in direct contact with earth.

- Type N mortar may be used for load-bearing masonry in severe freeze-thaw exposures above grade; it may not be used in direct contact with earth.
- Type O mortar may be used in non-load-bearing masonry in interior locations; it may not be exposed to freeze-thaw nor to direct contact with earth.

Table M-1 Mortar Proportions by Volume*

Mortar Type	Minimum Compressive Strength at 28 days (psi)	Portland Cement	Hydrated Limes or Lime Putty		Masonry Cements	Damp Loose Aggregate
			Minimum	Maximum		
M	2500	1	—	$1/4$	—	Not less than $2\frac{1}{4}$ and not more than 3 times the sum of the volumes of the cement and lime used
		1	—	—	1	
S	1800	1	$1/4$	$1/2$	—	
		$1/2$	—	—	1	
N	750	1	$1/2$	$1/4$	—	
		—	—	—	1	
O	350	1	$1\frac{1}{4}$	$2\frac{1}{2}$	—	

* Source: ASTM C270 Property Specification Requirements.

(For a definition of "severe" and "moderate" weathering, jump ahead to the discussions surrounding Figure 23-1, where effects of weathering on fired clay brick are discussed.)

Two possible mixes for each type of mortar are given in Table M-1. The first mix is that using hydrated lime, the second for factory-prepared mix. For either mix, the strength is essentially the same.

The allowable compressive strengths listed in Table M-1 are the strengths specified by ASTM C270 for laboratory test specimens. In general, masonry cement mixes are not sampled and tested in the same way that concrete being placed in a concrete casting is sampled and tested. Since masonry cement mixes are made up in numerous small batches throughout the working day, a rigorous field program of sampling and testing is simply not practical. Rather, a laboratory mix is designed and tested using the actual specified materials and the approved mix is then prescribed for use on the project.

One may wonder why lime is used at all in a masonry mortar since the sand-cement paste will provide the necessary strength. It has been found over the years that the lime improves the texture and workability of the mortar and at the same time improves its water retention and adhesion properties. It should be noted that all of the mixes prescribed in Table M-1 require the addition of hydrated lime in some form.

The mix proportions of Table M-1 are unusual in that the proportions are specified by volume rather than by weight. It is one of the few places in modern construction where such latitude is permitted in making a key structural component of the load-carrying system. One presumes that the margins for error have been adequately incorporated.

A second material which has minimal control over its quality is *grout*. Void areas in masonry cells as well as separations between adjacent walls are sometimes filled with a weak portland cement concrete termed grout. Grout proportions are given in Table M-2, again in terms of volume rather than by weight. The minimum (nominal) specified strength of grout in all applications is 2000 psi at 28 days.

23.4 Masonry of Fired Clay Brick

The primary ingredient used in making brick is clay, but there are numerous types of clay used to make brick. As a result, brick can vary widely in strength and quality, even brick made from similar clay sources. Largely due to such variability, the design of structural brick masonry has been divided into several broad brackets of strength and quality.

The manufacture of fired clay brick is treated in detail in coursework on construction materials and is not repeated here. In brief summary, however, fired clay brick is manufactured in the following steps:

1. Quarried clay is blended with coloring agents (and sometimes sawdust) and water to a consistency suitable for forming and holding its shape as a brick.
2. The clay mud is formed into bricks either in separate molds, by an extrusion process or by high-pressure forms, corresponding to the water content of the mud.
3. The bricks are stacked on mobile rail carts, leaving an air space around all bricks in order that each brick can dry properly.
4. The stacks are moved into a kiln for some 72 hours and heated gradually to about 450°. Dehydration occurs, leaving the brick dry and hard but not fired (or *vitrified*).
5. The stacks are moved into a hotter part of the kiln and fired at high temperature (up to 1650°F) over a period of some 72 hours. Essentially all of the hydrated water in the clay $[Al_2SiO_3 \cdot (H_2O)_2]$ is driven off, leaving a hard vitrified clay mass. Some shrinkage occurs during vitrification.
6. The fired clay bricks are cooled over a period of some 48 hours. They are then tested, sorted, graded and packaged, then stored to await shipment.

The quality of the finished brick in structural applications is judged by its strength, durability and hardness, but these qualities of strength, durability and hardness are very difficult to predict. One of the most reliable general indicators of these qualities has been found to be the resistance of the brick to weathering. As a consequence, the quality of brick is commonly classified by its durability under three broad levels of weathering:

- SW, severe weathering, for use above or below grade.
- MW, moderate weathering, for use above grade only.
- NW, negligible weathering, for use above grade only.

The regions of the United States in which these levels of weathering occur are shown in the map of Figure 23-1. The map reflects cycles of freeze-thaw, where it is the larger number of cycles of freeze-thaw that produces the more severe environment, rather than just cold temperatures.

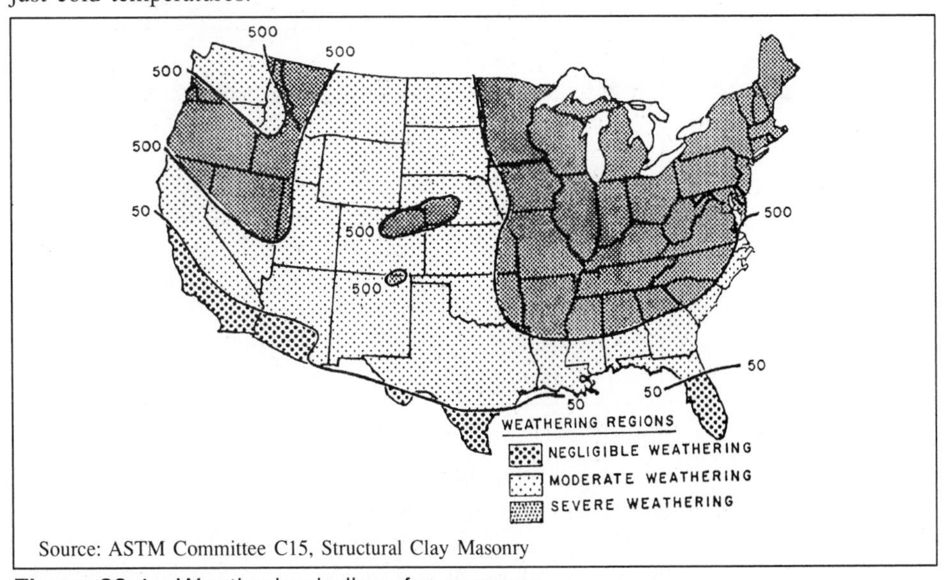

Source: ASTM Committee C15, Structural Clay Masonry

Figure 23-1 Weathering indices for masonry.

When selecting the quality of brick to be used in a particular application, whether SW, MW or NW, one must also match the quality of mortar to the quality of the brick. The quality of mortar for masonry units was discussed in the preceding section and is summarized there in Table M-1.

Bricks are laid up in patterns; a layup pattern is called *bond*. There are many bonds in common use and more are being developed by designers every year. Some of the more widely used bonds are shown in Figure 23-2. The horizontal joints are called *bed joints*; the vertical joints are *head joints*.

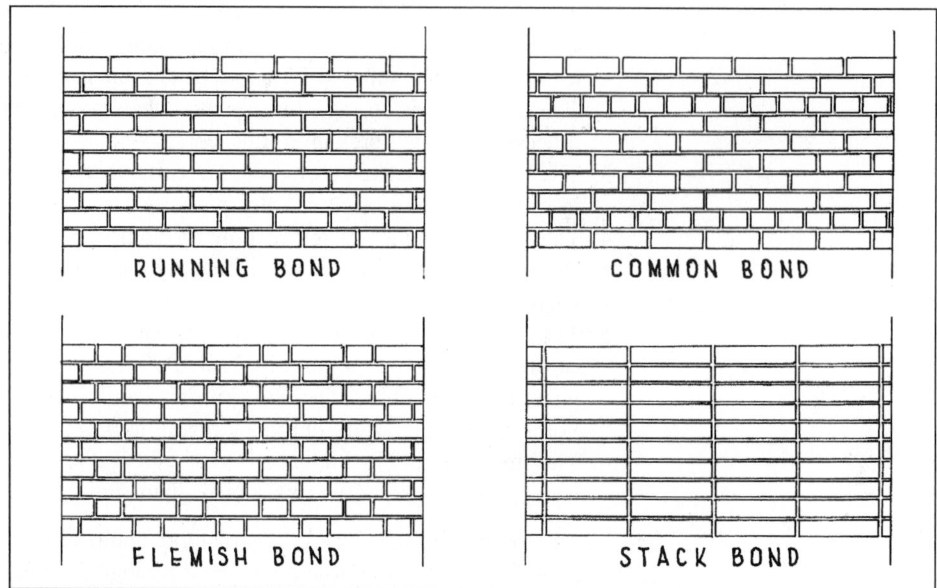

Figure 23-2 Commonly used brick bonds.

The empirical method of design presumes a running bond or a common bond for structural applications. Under that presumption, all other bonds, including short-lapped bonds such as flemish bond, are classed as stack bonds. Such stack bonds may still be used in structures designed by the empirical design method, but they must be suitably reinforced horizontally along the length of the wall.

Individual bricks may be placed in the bond in one of the four positions shown in Figure 23-3. As indicated, a brick placed with its long dimension parallel to the axis of the wall is called a *stretcher*. A brick placed with its long axis perpendicular to the axis of the wall is a *header* if placed flat and a *rowlock* if placed on edge. A brick placed with its long dimension upright is called a *soldier*.

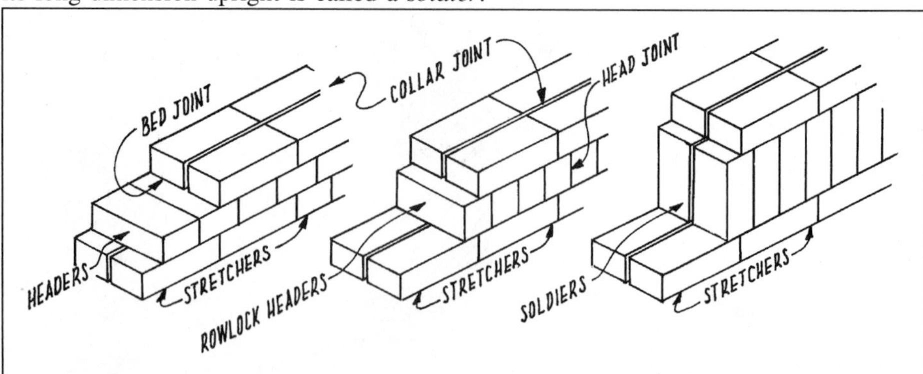

Figure 23-3 Positions of brick in a bond.

The length of bricks may be cut to accommodate openings or corners. Bricks cut in half are called *batts*. If cut at lengths longer than half, the longer piece is called a *three-quarter* brick and the shorter piece is called a *closer*. There are numerous other specialty names for bricks cut at angles or cut to half width or cut to half height.

Bricks may be laid up in adjacent walls as shown in Figure 23-3, in which case the masonry wall is called a *solid* wall. The individual sides are called *wythes*. The joint between wythes is called a *collar joint*. Alternatively, the walls may be separated slightly, forming a *cavity* or a *hollow* between the two wythes (rather than a collar joint). Three such *hollow walls* are shown in Figure 23-4.

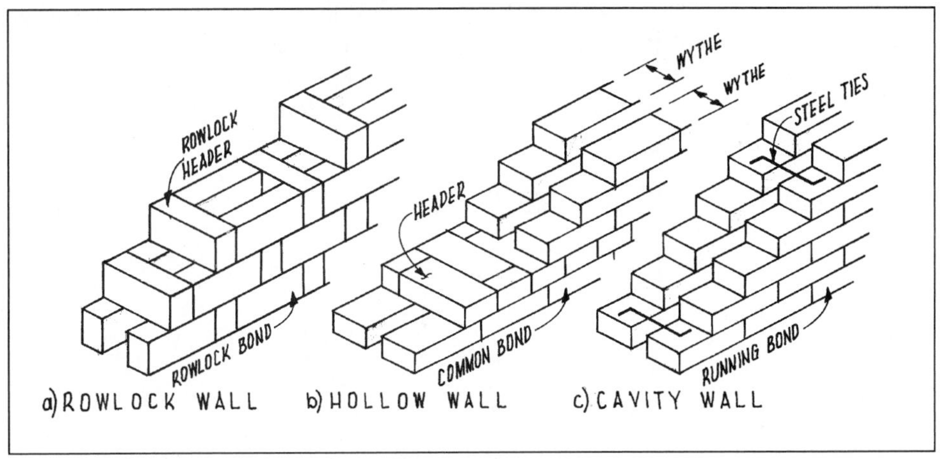

Figure 23-4 Hollow walls of brick masonry.

When bricks are placed on their edges, as shown in Figure 23-4A, the stretchers are called *bull stretchers* and the associated headers are called *bull headers*. The bond shown in the hollow wall of Figure 23-4b, with each sixth course a header course, is called common bond, or *American bond*. Alternatively, rather than using a header course to tie the two wythes together, they may be tied with steel wire *wall ties* placed in the mortar joints as shown in Figure 23-4c.

The cavity walls of Figure 23-4 are generally laid up using "standard" brick of 4 in. x $2^2/_3$ in. x 8 in. nominal dimensions. For walls having only two wythes, the rowlock wall will be nominally 8 inches thick, the hollow wall will be nominally 10 inches thick and the cavity wall will be nominally 10 inches thick.

Hollow wall or cavity wall masonry is readily reinforced by placing the reinforcement in the cavity. The cavity is then grouted full around the reinforcement as the wall is built, forming a wall with both vertical and horizontal reinforcement at its center. The wythes are tied together by headers (as in a rowlock wall) or by wire wall ties placed in the bed joints. Such reinforcement is shown in the sketches of Figure 23-4 and Figure 23-5.

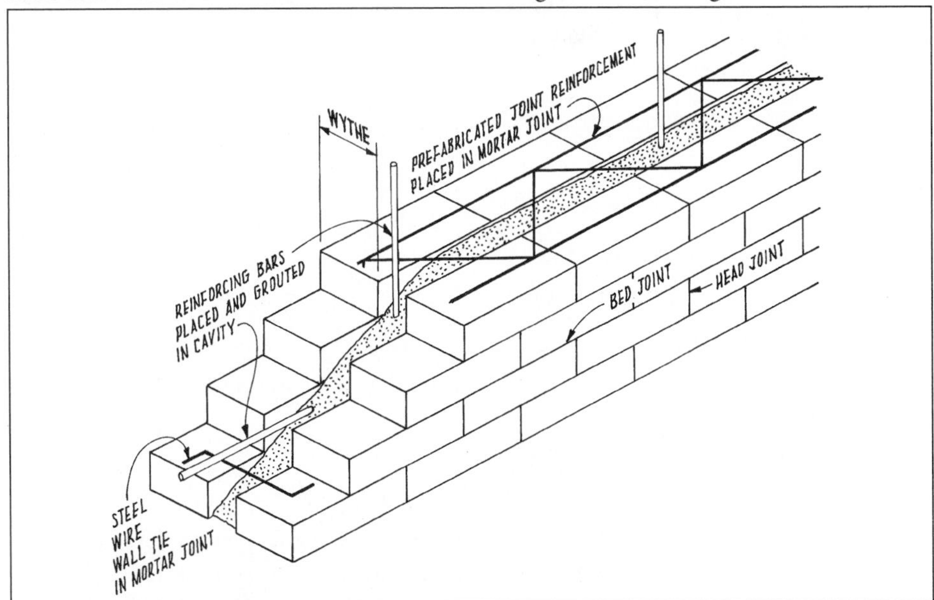

Figure 23-5 Elements of masonry construction.

Alternatively, manufactured wire trusses are available which may be placed in the bed joints as shown in Figure 23-4. These trusses, manufactured under a variety of brand names, are used frequently in "unreinforced" masonry as a means to control cracking and improve longitudinal stability. In such applications, they function not only as longitudinal reinforcement but also as very effective wall ties.

Fired clay bricks are made in a variety of sizes and types. The most common are the *standard* bricks, shown in Figure 23-6. In addition to fired clay bricks, bricks of standard size are also made from concrete. One advantage of concrete brick is that they do not have holes and can therefore be laid up in rowlock cavity walls.

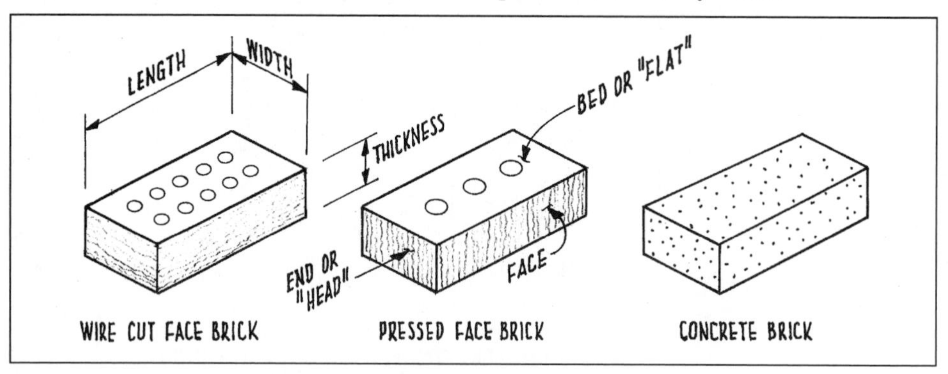

Figure 23-6 Standard brick, nominal 4 inches wide.

With a standard mortar joint, a standard brick is nominally 4 inches wide, $2^2/_3$ inches thick and 8 inches long. Its actual dimensions, as shown in Table 23-1, is $3^5/_8$ x $2^1/_4$ x $7^5/_8$. Including its mortar joint, the brick will form a module of 3 stretcher courses vertically in 8 inches, 2 header courses horizontally in 8 inches and 1 stretcher each 8 inches. The 8 inch module in all directions is the "standard" module for most fired clay brick.

The foregoing sizes of bricks are only approximate. During production and firing, the clay bricks will shrink somewhere between 5 to 15%, depending on water content, the kiln temperature and the clay itself. Specifications allow generous tolerances in size to account for such variations.

Table 23-1 Brick Types and Sizes

Brick Type	Dimensions in Inches		
	Actual	Nominal	Module
Standard	$3^5/_8$ x $2^1/_4$ x $7^5/_8$	4 x $2^2/_3$ x 8	8 x 8 x 8
3 in.	3 x $2^1/_4$ x $7^5/_8$	$3^1/_3$ x $2^2/_3$ x 8	10 x 8 x 8
Norman	$3^5/_8$ x $2^1/_4$ x $11^5/_8$	4 x $2^2/_3$ x 12	8 x 8 x 12
	$5^5/_8$ x $2^1/_4$ x $11^5/_8$	6 x $2^2/_3$ x 12	6 x 8 x 12
	$7^5/_8$ x $2^1/_4$ x $11^5/_8$	8 x $2^2/_3$ x 12	8 x 8 x 12
Roman	$3^5/_8$ x $1^5/_8$ x $7^5/_8$	4 x 2 x 8	8 x 8 x 8
	$3^5/_8$ x $1^5/_8$ x $11^5/_8$	4 x 2 x 12	8 x 8 x 12
Saxon	$3^5/_8$ x $3^5/_8$ x $11^5/_8$	4 x 4 x 12	8 x 8 x 12
Monarch	3 x $3^5/_8$ x $15^5/_8$	$3^1/_3$ x 4 x 16	10 x 8 x 16
	$3^5/_8$ x $3^5/_8$ x $15^5/_8$	4 x 4 x 16	8 x 8 x 16
Giant	$3^5/_8$ x $3^5/_8$ x $15^5/_8$	4 x 4 x 16	8 x 8 x 16
	$5^5/_8$ x $3^5/_8$ x $15^5/_8$	6 x 4 x 16	6 x 8 x 16
	$7^5/_8$ x $3^5/_8$ x $15^5/_8$	8 x 4 x 16	8 x 8 x 16

The "standard" joint in masonry unit construction is usually taken to be $^3/_8$ in. If the joint thickness were to be made smaller, problems in accommodating the variations in size of the brick could arise. If the joint thickness were to be made larger, the masons could have problems in keeping the bricks from settling too low in the soft mortar. In general, a joint of about $^3/_8$ in. has been found workable.

One of the more valuable properties of brick masonry is its ability to insulate against sound. Quite often, in fact, one of the major reasons for using brick masonry is to provide sound insulation. Such applications include the brick veneer over wood frame structures or the party wall between row house apartments.

The reduction of sound across a wall may be accomplished by any one or all of the following ways:

1. *Sound absorption.* The molecular wave energy of sound is absorbed by the wall material and is converted to molecular motion (heat) in the material. The common acoustical materials provide sound reduction in this way.
2. *Sound Reflectance.* A sound wave is reflected by a solid masonry surface in much the same way as light is reflected by a shiny surface. Such reflection causes the echos and reverberations that are so common in gymnasiums. On masonry walls, interior or exterior, such reflection can provide a significant reduction in sound from one side of the wall to the other.
3. *Diaphragm action.* A sound wave impinging on one side of a wall sets up lateral vibrations in the wall. The vibrations of the wall in turn sets up similar vibrations in the air on the other side of the wall, thus transmitting the sound across the wall (diaphragm). Flexible lightweight diaphragms transmit sound in this way with little loss; rigid massive walls reduce the amplitude of the vibration so much that very little sound is transmitted.

Sound is measured by its energy, expressed in decibels (dB). Typical sound levels and their related decibel values are given in Table 23-2 for various sources.

Table 23-2 Decibel Levels of Common Sounds

Description of Sound Level	Typical Sources	Decibel Level
Deafening	Artillery fire	115
	Elevated train	110
	Boiler factory	105
	Nosiy factory	100
Very loud	Loud street noise	95
	Unmuffled truck	90
	Police siren	85
	Noisy office	80
Loud	Average street noise	75
	Average radio	70
	Average factory	65
	Noisy home	60
Moderate	Average office	55
	Average conversation	50
	Quiet radio	45
	Quiet home	40
Faint	Private office	35
	Average auditorium	30
	Quiet conversation	25
	Rustle of leaves	20
Very faint	Whisper	15
	Soundproofed room	10
	Threshold of audibility	5
	Vacuum	0

Brick masonry produces sound reduction both by reflectance and by diaphragm action (or lack thereof). Even relatively small thicknesses of brick masonry produce significant levels of sound reduction. Some typical values of sound reduction across masonry walls are given in Table 23-3.

Table 23-3 Sound Reduction Across Brick Masonry Walls

Masonry wall thickness plus 1/2 in. cement plaster on both sides	Average reduction dB	Average Weight lb/ft^2
2 1/2 in. Brick	49	32
3 5/8 in. Brick	53	49
7 5/8 in. Brick	57	87

A comparison of the reduction values given in Table 23-3 to the decibel values of Table 23-2 indicates that brick masonry is indeed effective in producing sound reduction. A brick masonry wall of nominal 8 inch thickness can effectively reduce loud street noise on one side of the wall (95dB) to the noise level of a quiet home (38dB) on the other. A problem arises, of course, when the integrity of the masonry wall must be compromised for such things as door and window openings.

Another valuable property of brick masonry is its resistance to heat transmission. While much less resistant than commercial insulation, the resistance provided by the masonry wall can permit significant reductions to be made in the amount of commercial insulation to be used. Some typical values of heat transmission values (U values) and resistance values (R values) are given in Table 23-4.

Table 23-4 Coefficients of Heat Transmission *U* and Resistances *R* for Typical Brick Masonry Walls

Normal wall type and thickness	U	R
6-in. Solid brick	0.72	1.38
8-in. Solid brick	0.55	1.82
12-in. Solid brick	0.43	2.34
10-in. Brick cavity wall	0.36	2.77

The coefficients of Table 23-4 have the following units, where R = 1/U:

Heat transmission coefficient U:

Btu/Hr/°F difference across wall/ft^2 of surface area

Heat resistance coefficient R:

°F across wall to cause heat flow of 1 Btu/Hr/ft^2 of surface area

A property related to heat resistance is the fire resistance of the masonry. Fire codes require that a building or structure must stand for a certain length of time even though the building is burning. The requirement allows the human occupants to be evacuated before the building collapses.

In a fire, the length of time for the structural integrity to be maintained depends on such things as the size of the building, its height, its occupancy (or usage) and its importance in an emergency situation. An auditorium or a hospital, for example, would take much longer to evacuate in an emergency than a single-level office building and will therefore need a longer fire rating. The "fire rating" of structural elements for buildings is commonly given in hours, as indicated in the typical fire ratings of Table 23-5.

Table 23-5 Minimum Thickness of Brick Walls for Fire Ratings

	Minimum Thickness in Inches for Fire-Resistance Rating of:			
Wall Construction	**1/2 hour**	**1 hour**	**2 hours**	**4 hours**
Solid brick units, 80% solid and over: actual overall thickness	2.5	3.5	5	7
Cored brick units, less than 80% solid: equivalent solid thickness*	2	2.8	4	5.6

*Equivalent solid thickness is the "percent solid" times the overall thickness, divided by 100.

The final engineering property of fired clay brick to be considered here is its strength. The test strength, or rupture strength, of individual fired clay bricks varies both with the type of clay and the manufacturing process. Brick is available in a wide range of ultimate compressive test strengths, ranging from about 1500 psi to about 15,000 psi.

The "specified" compressive strength of masonry construction, denoted f'_m, is taken somewhat below the actual compressive test strength of the individual masonry units. The compressive test strength of the individual units is, in turn, taken as an average value from a number of test results. The specified compression strength f'_m to be used in design calculations is generally taken somewhere between 60% to 80% of the average compressive test strength of the individual units.

Typical values of f'_m are given in Table M-3 in the Technical Manual. As indicated there, the values of f'_m depend not only on the strength of the masonry units but also on the strength of the mortar. In all subsequent discussions, terms containing the word "strength" such as "compressive strength" or "ultimate strength", will mean this design stress f'_m, not the test strength of the individual units. (The adjective "allowable" is used only to describe stress, never to describe strength).

In setting the compressive strength f'_m in masonry construction, it must be remembered that the masonry units may have holes or voids left in them from the manufacturing process. (Such holes are shown earlier in Figure 23-6). This reduction in the cross sectional area of a brick is reflected in the values given in Table M-3. The compressive strengths of Table M-3 are computed using the actual net cross sectional area of the brick with the voids deducted; the percent of voids in the actual brick must therefore be known (or estimated).

23.5 Masonry of Concrete Masonry Units

Concrete masonry units, abbreviated as CMU but better known as *concrete blocks*, have been in wide use for only about two generations. Nonetheless, they are now so widely used that it is difficult to imagine modern construction without them. And as their usage continues to grow, even more configurations and uses are being developed, both in architectural applications and in structural applications.

Early concrete masonry units were made from normal weight concrete weighing 125 lb/ft^3 or more and having a maximum aggregate size of 3/8 in. These units were so heavy and hard to handle that lighter blocks were soon developed from concrete weighing as little as 105 lb/ft^3. Further reductions came as lighter aggregates came into wide use, and concrete blocks are now made from concrete weighing as little as 90 lb/ft^3. Remarkably, there is no loss in strength between the earlier heavy concrete blocks and the more recent lightweight blocks.

Concrete blocks are manufactured in a wide variety of sizes and shapes. Only the more common sizes and shapes are included here. A complete listing of the concrete blocks available in a specific locale can be obtained from the manufacturers serving that locale.

The most common sizes of concrete blocks are shown in Figure 23-7. All of the blocks shown there are building blocks, nominally 8 inches high and 16 inches long, including their 3/8 in. mortar joint. Widths of 8 inches and 12 inches are by far the most common widths used in structural applications, with 4 inch and 6 inch widths being used for fillers and for interior partitions.

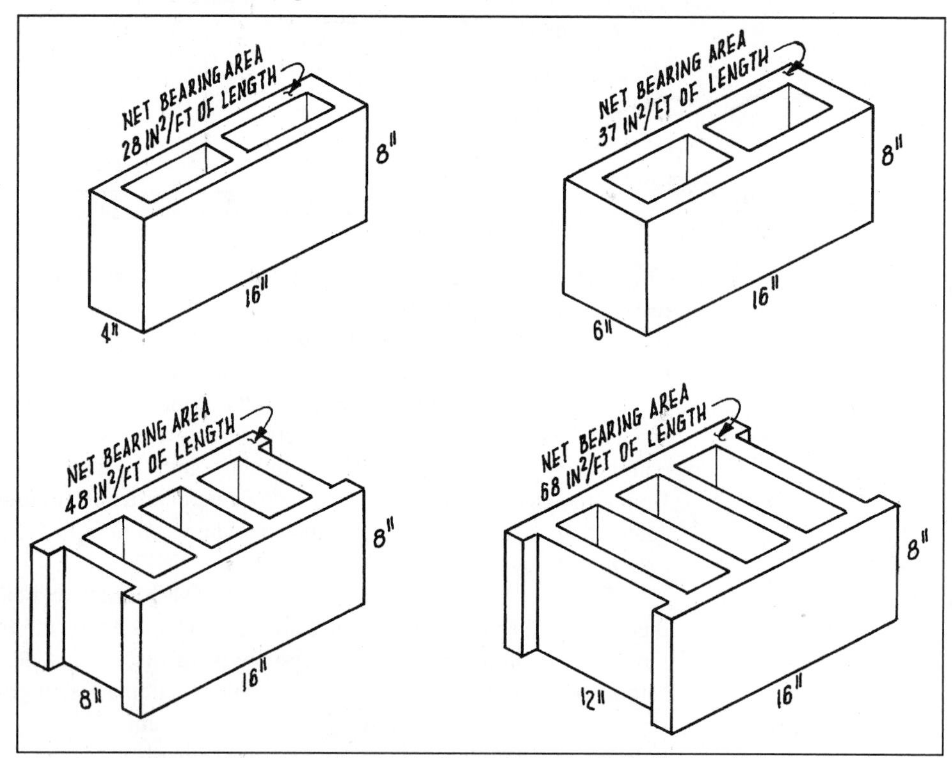

Figure 23-7 Commonly used concrete masonry units.

All of the block sizes shown in Figure 23-7 are also manufactured in half-lengths for use at jambs and wall ends. They are also manufactured with one end solid for the same purpose. The module remains the same, however, 8 inches high by 16 inches long.

Concrete blocks are manufactured in one of five types:

- Hollow load-bearing block
- Solid load-bearing block
- Hollow non-load-bearing block
- Concrete brick
- Special-purpose block

A concrete block is said to be hollow if its cross sectional bearing area is less than 75 percent of the gross area and solid if more than 75 percent. A variety of solid masonry units are manufactured, most of which are manufactured on a 4 inch module. Concrete brick are manufactured both in a 4 inch module and in the same standard size as fired clay brick, that is, three courses in 8 inches.

Specifications require that the wall thickness of concrete blocks meet minimum standards, depending on the size of the block. As a practical matter, however, the walls are tapered to permit easier removal of the forms during manufacturing. Some average dimensions of the walls are shown in Figure 23-8.

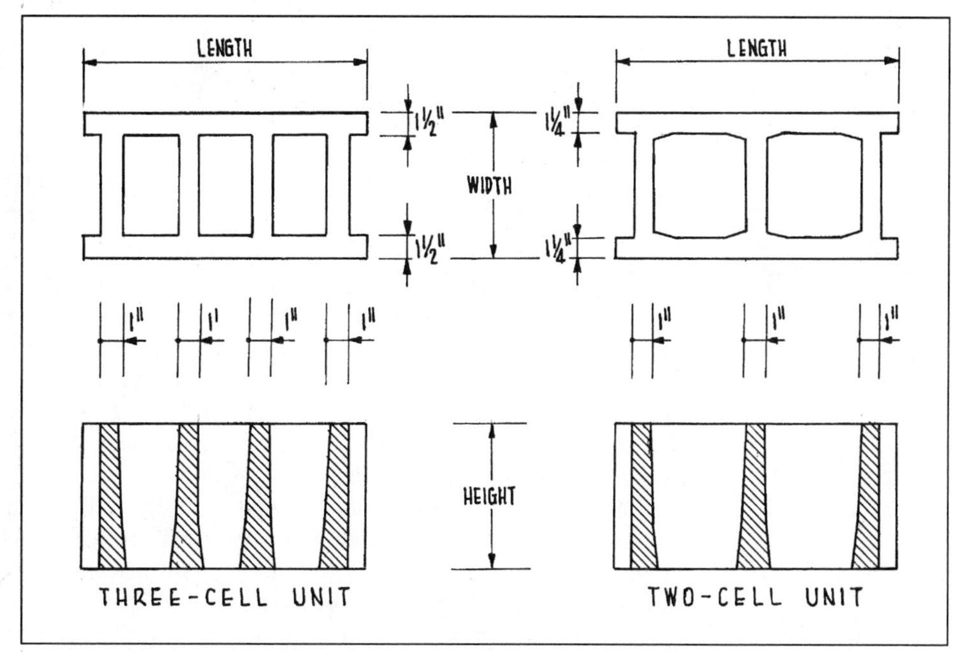

Figure 23-8 Cross sections of concrete masonry units.

When concrete masonry units are laid up in running bond, the open cells are aligned vertically. In three-cell blocks, the inside ties are also aligned, permitting the entire bearing area to be used to transmit load from one course to the next. For bearing to occur over the full bearing area, however, the mortar bedding must also cover the full bearing area, as shown in Figure 23-9.

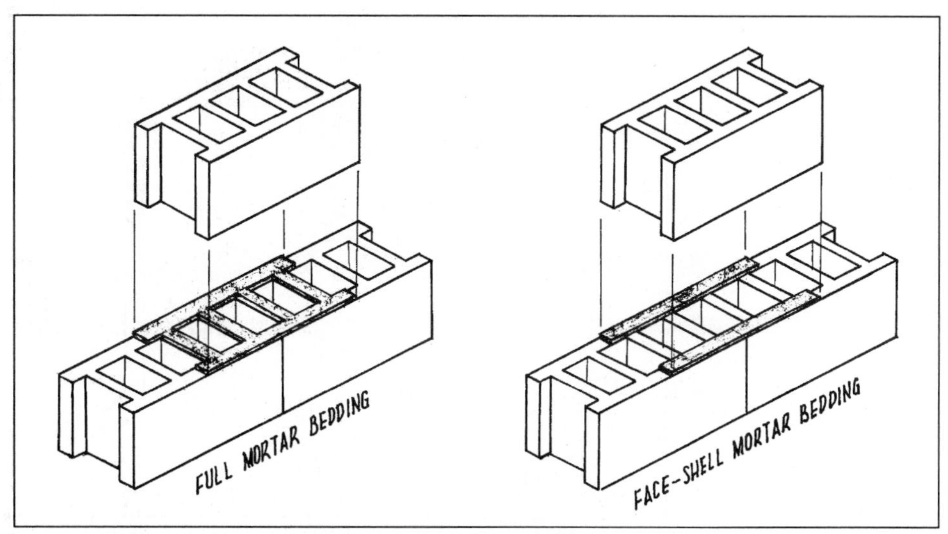

Figure 23-9 Mortar bedding on bearing areas.

In general, full mortar bedding is not used; face shell bedding is the norm for CMU construction. With bedding only along the two faces, the contact area for load transmission in bearing diminishes somewhat. Table 23-6 gives the bearing areas for common block sizes laid up in running bond.

Table 23-6 Cross Sectional Properties of Hollow Block Construction

Wall Thick-ness in.	Net Area ini.²/ft. of wall length	Gross Area in.²/ft. of wall length	Wall Weight per ft² of Wall Surface				Contact Bearing Areas Type of Bedding			
			Concrete weight, psf				Face shell		Full bed	
			90	105	125	145	A in.²	% of gross	A in.²	% of gross
4	28	48	20	23	28	32	24	50	28	58
6	37	72	30	35	42	48	32	44	37	51
8	48	96	36	42	49	51	41	43	48	50
12	68	144	50	58	70	81	49	34	68	47

One of the more attractive features of CMU construction is the ease with which it can be reinforced. For crack control, the wall can be reinforced about each third horizontal joint with the same commercial wire trusses discussed earlier for the reinforcement of fired clay masonry. Additionally, vertical reinforcement, usually 1/2 in. diameter or 5/8 in. diameter bars, can be placed in the cells at regular intervals (usually 24 in. or 32 in.) after the wall is built; these cells are then grouted full. Even with these small amounts of horizontal and vertical reinforcement, the wall is much stronger and is much less likely to develop any unsightly cracks.

Horizontal reinforcing bars can also be easily installed, but special blocks are required in order to provide room for any horizontal reinforcement. Bond-beam blocks and lintel blocks are manufactured for this purpose and are available in all the standard widths. Sketches of these blocks are shown in Figure 23-10.

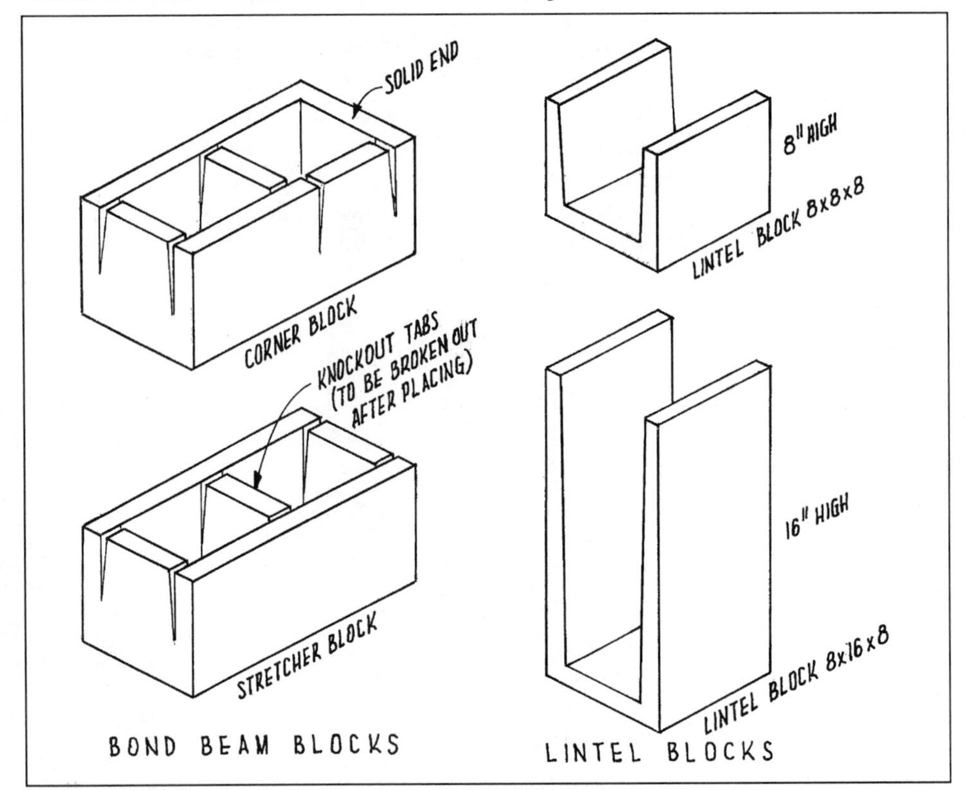

Figure 23-10 Bond-beam blocks and lintel blocks.

Bond-beam blocks are commonly used at about each sixth course to provide a void in which horizontal reinforcement can be placed and grouted. The tabs that are broken out are dropped into the bottom of the cells to prevent the grout from falling into the courses beneath. The end result is a small concrete tie beam that is cast using the sides of the bond beam as the form.

A typical reinforced concrete block wall is shown in Figure 23-11. Masonry walls are invariably placed on a "cutoff" wall or a grade beam foundation such as that of Figure

23-11. A facing of brick masonry may or may not be used; if used, it will likely serve only as a veneer (for weather and appearance) and not as a structural component.

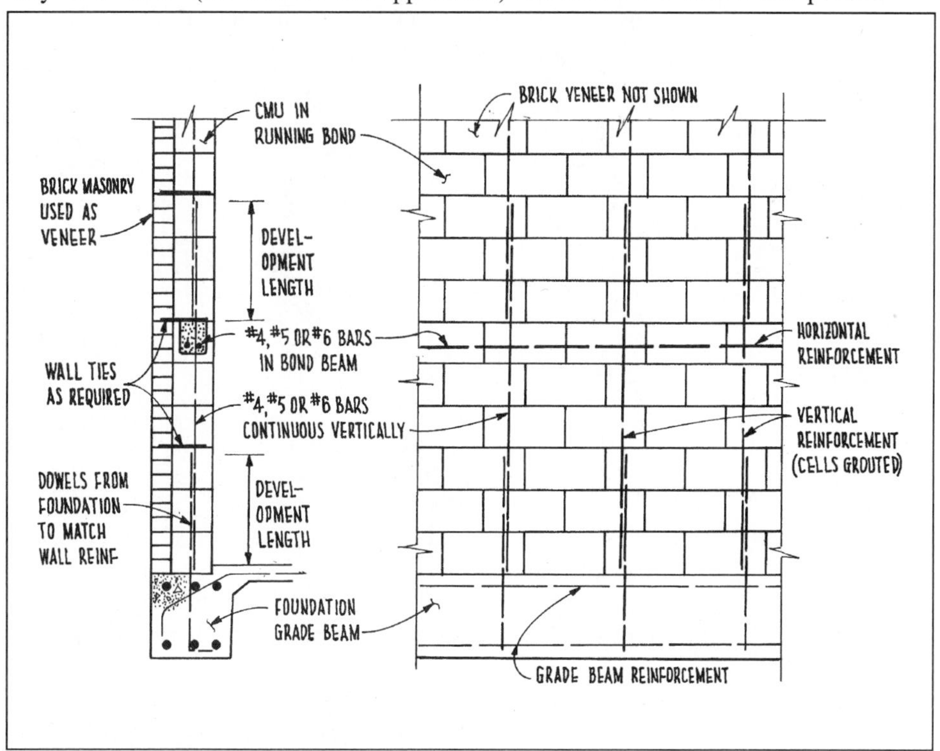

Figure 23-11 Typical reinforced CMU wall.

In building the CMU wall of Figure 23-11, the masons must lift the blocks up and over the dowels for the first few courses. The wall is then built on up to the bond beam. The vertical bars are then placed to match the dowels and the horizontal bars are placed in the bond beam. The bond beam and the vertical cells containing the vertical bars are then grouted full. The entire cycle is then repeated up to the next bond beam.

Bond beams may be cast within a single course or extended upward over two courses. These two possibilities are shown in Figure 23-12. The use of the deeper bond beam may sometimes be necessary over wide doorways or large windows.

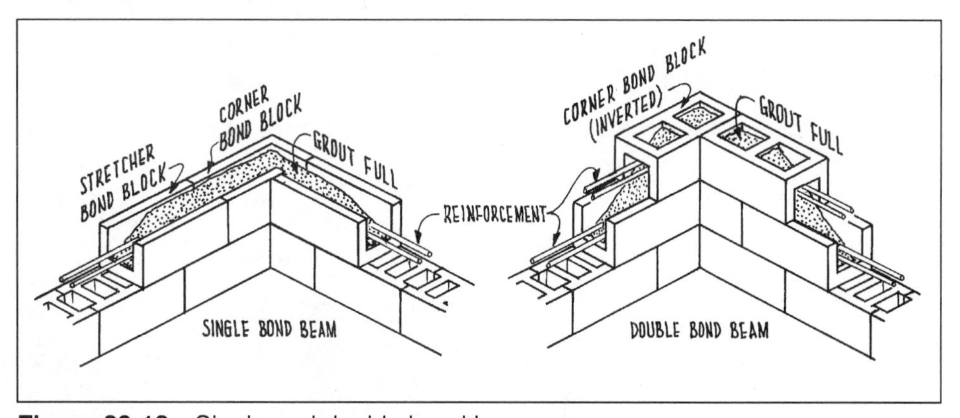

Figure 23-12 Single and double bond beams.

The bond beams in Figure 23-12 are shown at a corner. In such a case, a corner bond-beam block is required, in which the breakout tab is located at the side of the block rather than at the end (see Figure 23-10). For the double course bond beam, reinforcement may be placed at one or both levels, as shown.

All openings more than 12 in. wide must have a lintel spanning the opening. The lintel beam may be made using specially manufactured lintel blocks. Unlike bond-beam blocks, lintel blocks are made with a smooth lower face; a sketch of such lintel blocks was included earlier in Figure 23-10. Lintel blocks are typically 8 inches long and in appearance are comparable to a soldier course in brick masonry. A sketch of a lintel made with lintel blocks is shown in Figure 23-13.

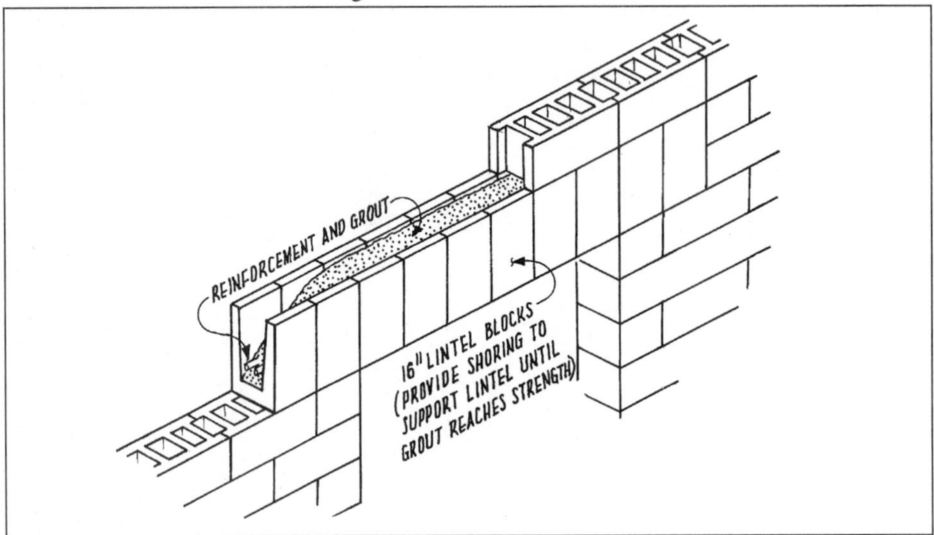

Figure 23-13 Typical lintel made from lintel blocks.

For openings in which a door or window is to be placed, a special lintel block is manufactured. The lintel block is formed to include the jamb into which the door or window frame will later be fitted. Except for its slightly different cross section, such lintels are built in the same way as the lintel shown in Figure 23-13.

As an alternative to lintel blocks, precast concrete lintel beams are also manufactured in various lengths, in sizes that match the concrete block. They are simply lifted into place over the opening and become a part of the masonry. The larger and heavier ones, however, can be difficult to handle manually; a cherry picker or other lifting device may be required. Steel angles and tees are also commonly used as lintel beams but are used primarily in brick masonry rather than CMU masonry.

Structural concrete columns called *pilasters* can also be cast into CMU walls. Two typical types of pilasters are shown in Figure 23-14. The *pilaster* performs either or both of two functions: it can provide a column for concentrated beam or girder loads; it can provide lateral stability in long CMU walls.

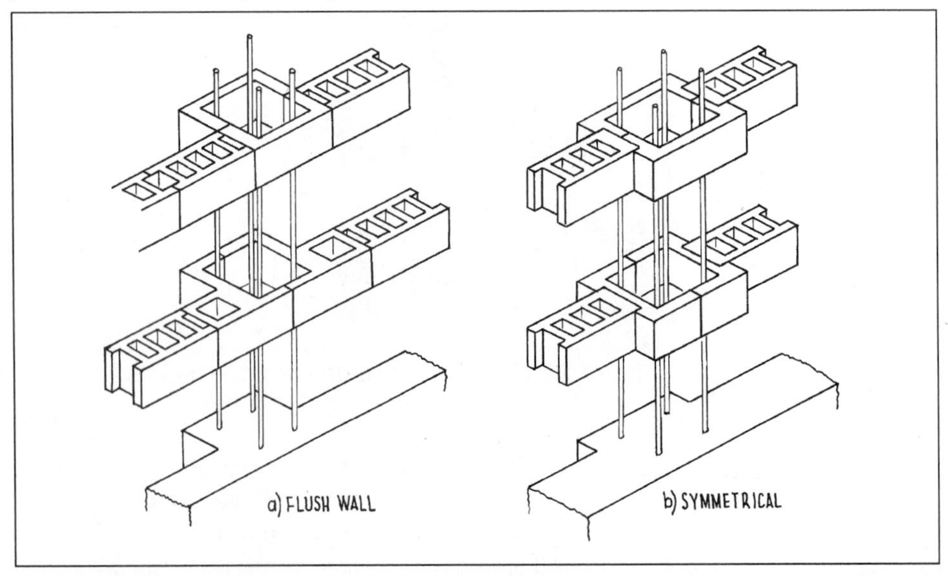

Figure 23-14 Typical pilasters in CMU walls.

The advantage of the type of pilaster shown in Figure 23-14a is that it provides a smooth face at one side of the pilaster. Both types of pilasters are built over dowels coming out of the matching foundation. At periodic intervals, such as at horizontal bond beams, reinforcement matching the dowels is placed in the pilaster and the pilaster is grouted full. The result is a concrete column cast integrally with the wall.

Like reinforced concrete construction, CMU construction is susceptible to cracking due to temperature changes. Such cracking becomes more pronounced when one face of the wall is subject to interior heating while the other face is subject to exterior winter weather. In such cases, a thermal gradient of 80°F or even more can occur across the thickness of the wall.

In addition, ambient temperature between winter and summer in a temperate climate can often exceed 100°F. The linear change over the length of a 50-foot long CMU wall subject to a temperature change of -100°F is about $^3/_8$ inch. A crack of such size would seriously jeopardize the weathering integrity of the wall and could conceivably weaken the wall structurally.

The usual means to provide for such movements is by the use of expansion-contraction joints. Some typical expansion-contraction joints are shown in Figure 23-15. Such joints are also used routinely in CMU construction as a means to force any random cracking to occur along a predetermined "weak" line; such joints are called *control joints*.

Code does not prescribe placement of control joints or expansion-contraction joints in CMU masonry. The location and frequency of all such joints are left to the designer. These joints necessarily produce a loss of longitudinal structural continuity in the wall; their existence must be considered in the overall structural design.

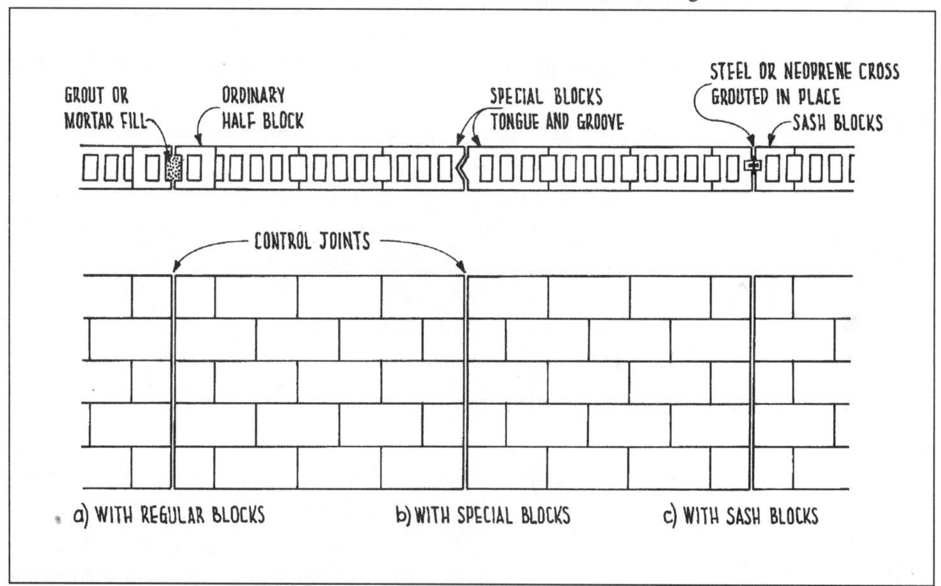

Figure 23-15 Common expansion-contraction joints.

It should be evident that the primary function of the joints shown in Figure 23-15 is to interrupt the wall longitudinally along a single vertical line. Correspondingly, wherever an expansion-contraction joint occurs in a wall, it is also necessary to interrupt the bond beams or joint reinforcement at that same vertical line. The end result is a line at which the lateral integrity of the wall is preserved but the longitudinal continuity (and longitudinal structural integrity) of the wall is interrupted.

The placement of expansion-contraction joints in CMU construction is not a matter to be taken lightly. The structural discontinuity introduced at all such joints must be included in all design calculations involving the structure as a whole.

Sound attenuation in CMU construction closely parallels that of fired clay brick masonry. One exception is notable, however, in that special masonry blocks are manufactured that specifically enhance the sound attenuation properties of a CMU wall. Such units are indeed effective but are not universally available; their primary application to date is in controlling noise in industrial plants.

Typical reductions in sound across ordinary CMU walls is given in Table 23-7 for standard wall thickness. One can improve these values markedly, however, by grouting all cells with concrete or by adding sound-absorbing insulation material to one or both sides. A comparison of the reductions for CMU construction to those given in Table 23-3 for fired clay brick indicates that the two types of construction are roughly comparable in their sound reduction properties.

Table 23-7 Sound Reduction Across CMU Walls

CMU wall thickness plus total 1 in. plaster, either one or both sides	Average Reduction dB	Approximate Weight lb/ft²
3⁵/₈ in. lightweight	43	30
5⁵/₈ in. lightweight	49	35
7⁵/₈ in. lightweight	50	40
11⁵/₈ in. lightweight	54	50

The resistance of CMU walls to the transmission of heat is generally better than that of fired clay brick, that is, less heat is transmitted by CMU walls than by fired brick walls. Some typical transmission values are given in Table 23-8 for 8 inch and 12 inch bare CMU walls. As indicated, the transmission values can be varied widely by filling the cells with insulating material.

Table 23-8 Coefficients of Heat Transmission U[a] and Resistance R[b] for CMU Construction

Nominal wall thickness: cells open or cells filled with thermal insulation	U	R
8 in. lightweight, cells open	0.37	2.70
8 in. lightweight, cells open	0.20	5.00
8 in. lightweight, cells open	0.35	2.86
8 in. lightweight, cells open	0.20	5.00

[a]U in Btu/Hr/°F of difference across wall/ft² of surface area.
[b]R in °F across wall to cause flow of 1 Btu/Hr/ft²

As a general property, the fire resistance or "fire rating" of CMU construction is quite good. The actual numerical rating, however, varies with the type of aggregate used to manufacture the blocks and with the amount of void space. To account for the void space in CMU construction, fire ratings are based on an "equivalent solid thickness" for the CMU blocks.

The equivalent solid thickness of hollow masonry blocks is taken as the thickness of an imaginary solid masonry unit having the same total volume of solid material as the hollow block. It is computed as the "percent solid" times the gross thickness of the CMU block, divided by 100. Some typical equivalent thicknesses are shown in Table 23-9.

Table 23-9 Typical Equivalent Thickness for Estimating Fire Ratings of CMU

Nominal Thickness in.	Actual Thickness in.	Net Area* in.²	Gross Area in.²	Percent Solid	Equivalent Solid Thickness in.
4	3.625	28	48	58	2.10
6	5.625	37	72	51	2.87
8	7.625	48	96	50	3.81
12	11.625	68	144	47	5.46

*Net areas are determined as prescribed by ASTM C140.

The computed value of equivalent solid thickness is used to establish the fire rating of CMU construction. The fire ratings for some common types of aggregate are given in Table 23-10. The term *calcareous* used in Table 23-10 indicates a material derived from a limestone origin; the term siliceous indicates a silica origin.

Table 23-10 Estimated Fire Rating of CMU Blocks

	Minimum Equivalent Solid Thickness in Inches For Indicated Fire Rating		
Aggregate Type	**1.0 HR**	**2.0 HR**	**4.0 HR**
Pumice	1.8	3.0	4.7
Expanded Slag	2.2	3.3	5.0
Expanded Shale or Clay	2.5	3.7	5.5
Limestone or unexpanded slag	2.7	4.0	5.9
Calcareous Gravel	2.8	4.2	6.2
Siliceous Gravel	3.0	4.5	6.7

An examination of Table 23-10 indicates that the lighter the weight of the CMU, the higher its effectiveness in fire protection. For example, a thickness of 3.0 in. of heavy siliceous gravel is required to provide 1 hour protection, while only 1.8 in. of lightweight pumice will provide the same protection.

The strength and other physical properties of concrete blocks are also dependent on the type of aggregate used to manufacture it. For comparison, some typical values of rupture stress for various aggregates are given in Table 23-11. Note that the rupture stress is given as an "average" stress adjusted over the gross area; the percent void is thus eliminated from further consideration.

Table 23-11 Typical Ranges of Test Strengths of Concrete Masonry Units, psi

Type of Aggregate	Range of Density of Aggregate lb/ft^3	Nominal Density of Concrete lb/ft^3	Typical Weight of One Block 8 x 8 x 16	Rupture Stress on Gross Area lb/in^2	Thermal Coeff. of Expansion in./in./°F
Siliceous sand and gravel	130–145	135	40	1200–1800	0.0000050
Limestone	120–140	135	40	1100–1800	0.0000050
Blast furnace slag	100–125	120	35	1100–1500	0.0000046
Expanded clay, shale, or slag	75–90	85	25	1000–1500	0.0000045
Expanded blast furnace slag	80–105	95	28	700–1200	0.0000040
Cinders (coal ash)	80–105	95	28	700–1000	0.0000025
Pumice (volcanic ash)	60–85	75	22	700–900	0.0000040
Scoria (volcanic ash)	75–100	95	28	700–1200	0.0000040

The values of rupture stress listed in Figure 23-11 are those for the individual concrete blocks, not for a wall made of these blocks. For a CMU wall, both the type of mortar and the strength of the mortar must be included. In the empirical method of design, presented in following sections, the allowable stresses are specified by code for various combinations of masonry units, to include the masonry mortar.

Similarly, the modulus of elasticity E_m of a CMU wall must include the effects of the mortar. Since the material is so variable, the modulus of elasticity is empirically (experimentally) derived. Typical values of E_m for both clay masonry and concrete masonry as specified by Code are given in Table M-5 in the Technical Manual. In all cases, the shear modulus E_v is taken at $0.4E_m$.

The "specified" compressive strength of concrete blocks in a CMU wall, denoted f_m', is taken somewhat below the actual compressive test strength of the individual concrete blocks. The compressive test strength of the individual blocks is, in turn, taken as an average value from a number of test results. The specified compression strength f_m' to be used in further calculations is generally taken somewhere between 60% to 80% of the average compressive test strength of the individual blocks.

Typical values of f_m' to be used in subsequent calculations are given in Table M-3 in the Technical Manual. As indicated there, the values of f_m' of the masonry units depend also on the strength of the mortar and the amount of voids. In all subsequent discussions, terms containing the word "strength", such as "compressive strength" or "ultimate strength," will mean this design stress f_m', not the test strength of the individual units. (The term "allowable" is used only to define stress, never to define strength).

For solid or grouted units, the values of f_m' given in Table M-3 are based on the net solid area of the cross section to include grout where appropriate. For ungrouted blocks, the net areas with voids deducted are used in computing the specified compressive stress f_m'. Net areas for some of the more commonly used blocks are given earlier in Table 23-6.

23.6 Allowable Stresses in the Empirical Design Method

Masonry that is designed by the empirical method of design is classified as unreinforced masonry. In spite of the classification, the method does occasionally require nominal levels of reinforcement in foundation walls and in earthquake shearwalls. In such applications, neither the size nor the spacing of the reinforcement is computed; both are stipulated by Code. In the design calculations, the existence of any such reinforcement is ignored; it is regarded simply as a construction feature that is required by Code.

The requirements for the empirical design of masonry are given in Chapter 9 (the last chapter) of the Code. In some areas of loads and stresses, however, there are no specified requirements. For those areas not specifically addressed in Chapter 9, the appropriate requirements for unreinforced masonry stipulated elsewhere in the Code are presumed here to remain applicable.

The general limitations of the empirical design method are discussed earlier in this chapter. They are condensed here as:

- The method may not be used in earthquake risk zones 3 and 4.
- The method may not be used where wind velocities exceed 100 mph.
- The method may not be used for foundation walls unless all of the following conditions are met:
  1. Height of unbalanced fill above inside grade is not more than 8 ft.
  2. Equivalent fluid weight of the unbalanced fill is not more than 30 psf.
  3. Lateral supports are provided at vertical spans not greater than 8 ft.
- The method may not be used to design a masonry element that is subject to any lateral loads other than those listed above.

The allowable compressive stresses on masonry in the empirical design method are specified in Chapter 9 of the Code. These allowable stresses are reproduced in Table M-4 in the Technical Manual.

A curiosity occurs in Chapter 9 concerning the allowable compressive stresses. Elsewhere in the Code, the rupture strength of masonry units is based on the net area of the unit in the plane of rupture. For determination of the allowable compressive stresses in the empirical design method, the strength of masonry units is based on the gross area.

To convert strength based on net area to strength based on gross area, the strength based on net area must be multiplied by A_{GROSS}/A_{NET}. Values of A_{GROSS} and A_{NET} are given earlier in Table 23-6 for the more common masonry units. Where appropriate, the areas of grouted cells should be included in the value of A_{NET}.

The allowable bearing stress at concentrated loads on a masonry bearing wall is specified as:

$$F_p \leq 0.25 f'_m \tag{23-1}$$

Bearing plates may be used to distribute concentrated loads over a larger area. The dispersion of bearing loads into a masonry wall in running bond may be taken at a 45° angle from the horizontal, beginning at the ends of the area that is subject to direct bearing.

In the empirical design method prescribed by Chapter 9 the Code, the allowable shear stress on masonry is not specified, even though other requirements for structural shear walls are specifically addressed. Consequently, it is assumed here that the allowable shear stresses specified in Chapter 6 for unreinforced masonry remain valid for the empirical design method as well.

Masonry walls or panels can fail in shear in one of three modes, as indicated in Figure 23-16. In walls where the masonry units are significantly stronger than the mortar, the failure mode of Figure 23-16a will likely occur. Where the mortar is stronger than the masonry units, the failure mode of Figure 23-16b is more likely to occur. Where adhesion of the mortar to the masonry units is weak, the failure mode of Figure 23-16c is more likely to occur.

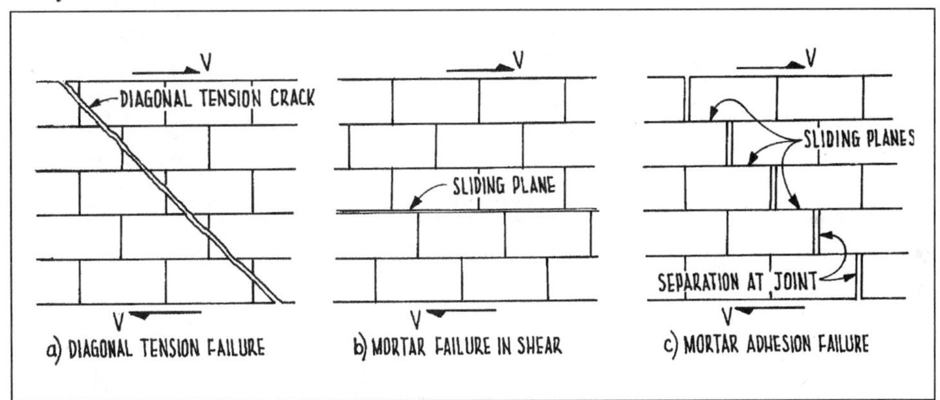

Figure 23-16 Modes of shear failure in masonry walls.

Susceptibility to the failure modes of Figure 23-16a and c can be improved by the addition of reinforcement (prefabricated wire trusses) in the horizontal joints. Such joint reinforcement is commonly used in walls to prevent cracking, regardless whether or not the wall is subject to computed in-plane shears. The maximum allowable spacing of joint reinforcement is 48 in.; a spacing of 24 in. is more commonly used.

The shear stress in masonry walls is computed using the full shear flow equation, presented and defined earlier in Chapter 9:

$$f_v = \frac{VQ}{Ib} \tag{9-39}$$

For rectangular sections, $Q = bh^2/8$, $I = bh^3/12$, and the maximum shear stress on a section given by Eq.(9-39) degenerates to:

$$\text{Maximum } f_v = \frac{3V}{2A} \tag{23-2}$$

In all calculations of shear in the empirical design method, the maximum values of shear stress given by Equations (9-39) and (23-2) are to be used. For masonry, the use of an average shear stress V/A (as permittted in some codes) is frowned upon.

Allowable shear stresses in unreinforced masonry are given in Table M-6 in the Technical Manual. Examination of Table M-6 indicates that the allowable shear stresses in masonry approach those for portland cement concrete. It should therefore be apparent that wherever masonry shear walls are permitted, they will be quite competitive with concrete.

Structural loadings other than compression, bearing and shear are not specifically included in the requirements for the empirical design methods. Consequently, structural masonry elements subject to such loads are not included in this textbook. While their design may in fact be permitted elsewhere in the Code, their design must be made using methods other than the empirical method and are thus excluded from consideration here. Those interested in pursuing other such design methods are referred to Chapter 6 of the Code.

23.7 Configuration Requirements for Walls and Foundations

The code imposes numerous limitations on size, thickness, spacing and lateral support on structural masonry that is designed by the empirical design method. Remember that there is no analysis of the structural elements in the empirical method. A wall that satisfies the Code requirements may be used to sustain certain levels of load with no further investigative analysis required.

Code requirements for lateral support of masonry walls are listed in Table M-7 in the Technical Manual. Lateral support of masonry walls is required both longitudinally, as determined by the horizontal length/thickness ratio (*l*/t ratio) of the wall, and vertically, as determined by the vertical height/thickness ratio (h/t ratio) of the wall. Lateral support along the length of the wall may be provided by cross walls, pilasters, buttresses, or structural frame members; for this case, the wall spans the clear horizontal distance between these lines of support. Lateral support along the height of the wall may be provided by floor or roof diaphragms or by structural frame members; for this case, the wall spans the clear vertical distance between these lines of support.

In addition to requirements for lateral supports, shear walls must also meet requirements for their spacing. As a practical matter, shear walls are commonly built with openings for doors and windows, rendering the shear wall a series of intermittent segments. A typical example is shown in Figure 23-17.

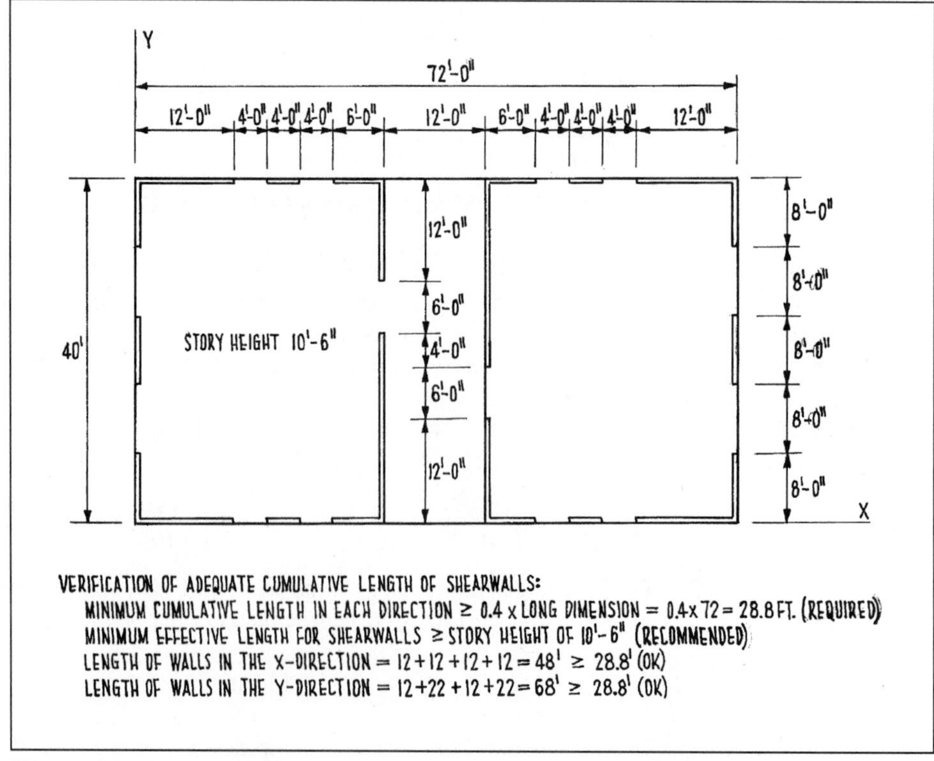

Figure 23-17 Intermittent and cumulative lengths of a shear wall.

As in other materials, only the masonry walls parallel to the lateral load are effective in resisting the load. In each direction, the minimum cumulative length of the various segments of the shear wall cannot be less than 40% of the length of the structure in the long direction. The *total cumulative* length of a pair of shear walls is simply the sum of all intermittent segment lengths in the two shear walls lying parallel to the load. Though one shear wall in a pair of shear walls may be markedly longer than the other, the shorter one should be at least half the minimum cumulative length.

It should be noted that the requirement for 40% of the length of the structure applies to all structural shearwalls regardless of the earthquake risk zone or building height. Though not a requirement, Code recommends that only those segments having a horizontal length at least as long as the story height be counted as effective segments in resisting shear.

The maximum allowable spacing between pairs of shear walls depends on the rigidity and continuity of the structural diaphragms. Maximum spacing between pairs of shearwalls are given in Table M-8 in the Technical Manual.

Requirements for the minimum thickness of masonry walls are given in Table M-10 in the Technical Manual. The minimum thickness required at the lower floor must be maintained throughout the height of the floor; reductions may be made only at floor (diaphragm) lines. Where thickness is reduced by a step in thickness, the top course of the thicker wall must be solid masonry in order to receive and transmit the loads wythe-to-wythe from the upper wall to the lower wall.

Mortar for foundation walls must be M or S. Minimum thicknesses listed in Table M-10 apply only to walls having unbalanced fill extending not more than 8 feet in height above the inside grade, having lateral supports spaced not more than 8 feet apart (no cantilever walls), and where the equivalent fluid weight of the soil is not more than 30 lb/ft^3.

The term *bonding* when used in masonry construction does not refer to bond between reinforcement and grout. It refers to the bonding together transversely of the various elements and wythes of masonry. Transverse bonding may be accomplished using masonry header courses, wire wall ties or prefabricated joint reinforcement (wire trusses).

When masonry headers are used to bond a masonry wall together transversely, the header courses are placed at regular intervals as shown in Figure 23-18. As indicated, the surface area devoted to header courses may not be less than 4% of the total surface area. In reality, the surface area devoted to headers is usually 15% or more.

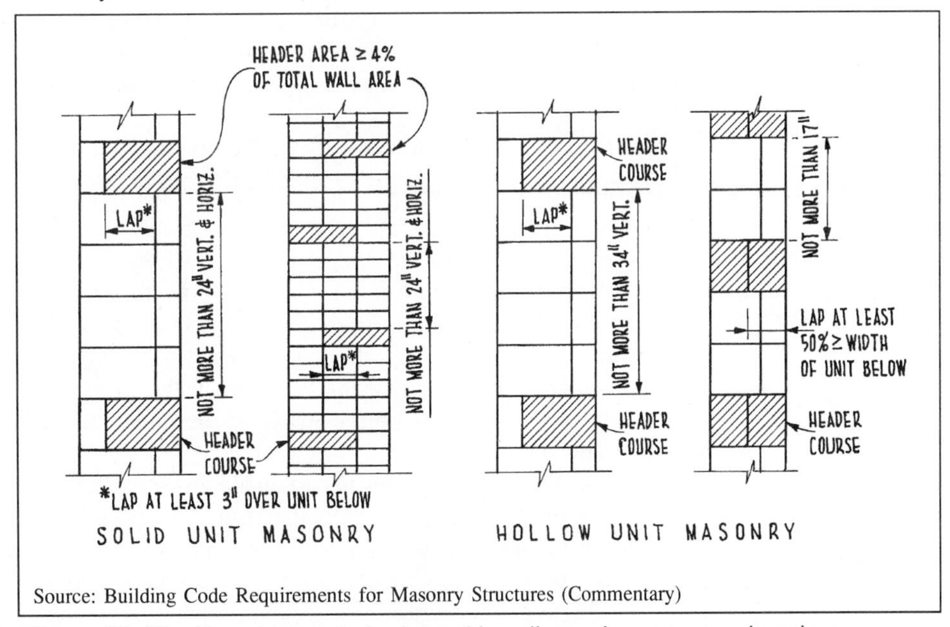

Source: Building Code Requirements for Masonry Structures (Commentary)

Figure 23-18 Requirements for lateral bonding using masonry headers.

When steel wall ties are used to tie a masonry wall together transversely, both the wire size and the layout are rigidly prescribed by the Code. Requirements have been extracted from the Code and are summarized in Table M-11 in the Technical Manual. A listing of wire sizes is included with Table M-11 for immediate reference.

When prefabricated joint reinforcement is used to tie a masonry wall together transversely, Code permits a smaller wire size to be used for the cross ties but such ties must be provided at a closer spacing. The minimum requirements are shown in Table M-12 in the Technical Manual. Refer back to Table M-11 for wire sizes.

Wood or steel ledgers are frequently used to attach floor diaphragms to a masonry shear panel. Typical examples of such ledgers are shown in Figure 23-19. Depending on the detail, a ledger may be used to transfer either vertical shears or horizontal shears or both from the floor to the masonry shear panel.

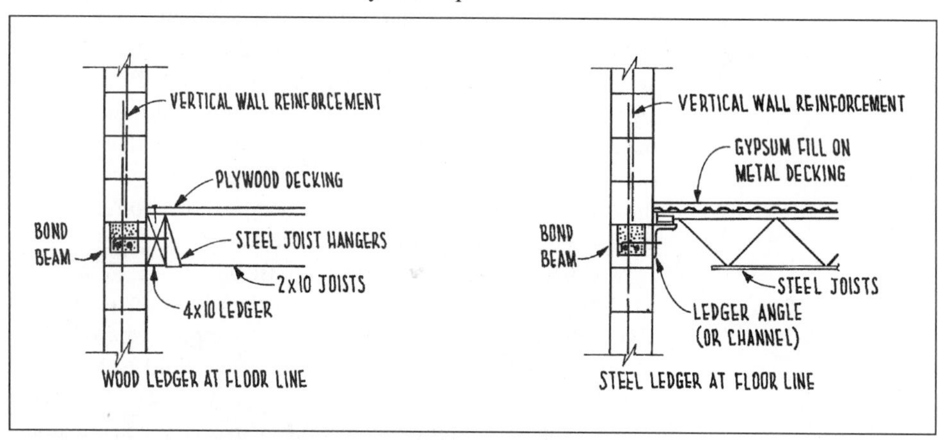

Figure 23-19 Typical ledgers on a masonry wall.

Where a ledger is used to transfer sizeable shear loads to masonry walls, the anchor bolts are usually placed in a bond beam; the bond beam serves to distribute the load and prevent unwanted load concentrations in the masonry. The anchor bolts are commonly placed in the head joints, extending out far enough to secure the ledger as shown in Figure 23-19.

Allowable shear loads on anchor bolts imbedded in masonry walls are given in Table M-13 in the Technical Manual. The anchor bolts may be imbedded in a horizontal bond beam as shown in Figure 23-19, or the vertically aligned cells in which they are located may be grouted full. Either way, the values given in Table M-13 for grouted masonry will apply.

23.8 Earthquake Requirements in the Empirical Method

In earthquake risk Zones 0 and 1, Code does not require any special provisions in the empirical method of design. In areas of such low earthquake intensities, wind loading will invariably govern the design.

In earthquake risk Zone 2, Code requires all structural masonry to be reinforced, both horizontally and vertically. Further, the masonry must be securely anchored or dowelled to the adjoining structural elements at all junctures. Also, reinforcement is required around all openings in walls and at the ends or corners of masonry walls.

In earthquake risk Zones 3 and 4, the empirical method of design of masonry structures may not be used.

Additional requirements in earthquake risk Zone 2 have been extracted from Appendix A of the Code and are summarized in Table M-14 in the Technical Manual. References in Table M-14 to "computed" loads are understood to mean loads computed by the methods presented in Chapters 13 and 14 of this textbook.

The term "anchorage" as used in Table M-14 refers to a positive structural tie between masonry elements. The anchorage may be a header course, steel ties between wythes, anchor bolts tying a ledger to a wall, prefabricated joint reinforcement extending through the juncture of two elements, or a suitably reinforced continuous bond beam. In designing for earthquake shaking of a structure, it is essential that every structural element be securely attached (anchored) to all adjoining elements; the foregoing requirements for anchorage reflect that concern.

23.9 Applications of the Empirical Design Method

Some examples in using the empirical design requirements are presented in this section. Discussions pertaining to Code requirements are included as appropriate in the body of the example. In addition, design practices and detailing practices are presented and discussed whenever they affect the load paths.

There is an expression that "... the devil is in the details." That expression applies fully to masonry design. It is relatively fast and easy to select and proportion masonry walls, but it is tedious and time-consuming to provide the details at the connections and bearings. Many years of experience are required for one to become a proficient masonry detailer.

Example 23-1

Design of masonry walls for a two story structure.

Given: Floor plan and sections of a two story commercial office building. Seismic Zone 2, wind velocity 90 mph.

To Find: Suitable design of the CMU masonry walls, used both for bearing and for shear.

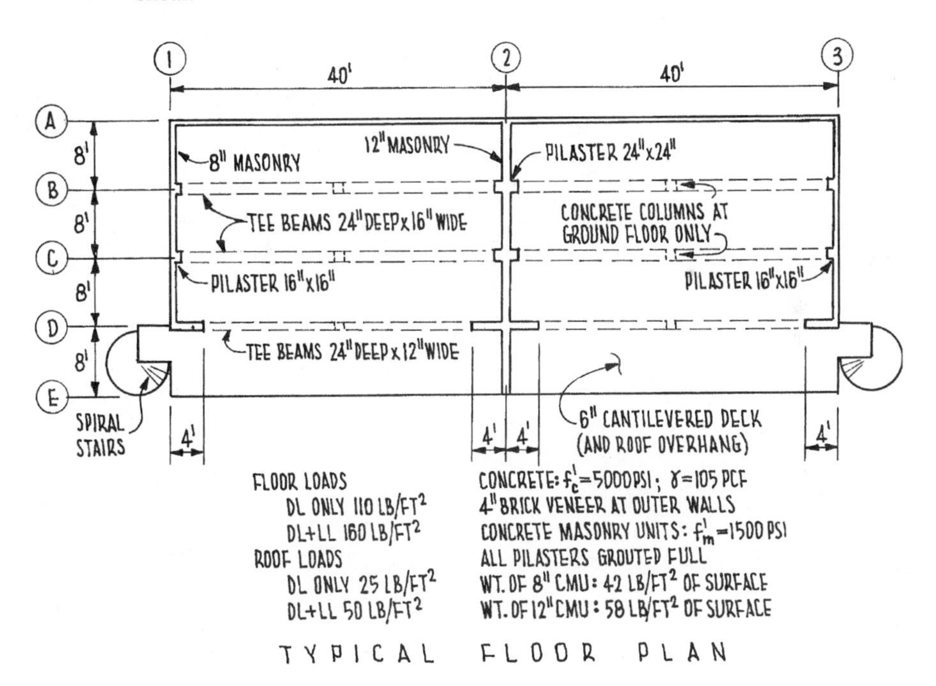

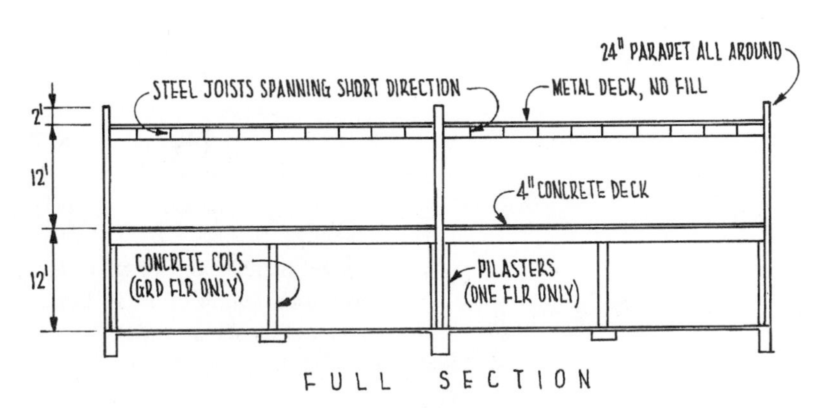

Solution: Check for applicability of the empirical design code:

- Earthquake zone less than Zone 3 (O.K.)
- Wind load less than 25 psf (or 100 mph) (O.K.)
- Height of building less than 35 feet (O.K.)
- No lateral loads other than wind or earthquake (O.K.)

(Empirical method may be used)

Selection of shearwall/bearing wall along Lines A and D:

Try 8 in. exterior CMU walls with 4 in. brick veneer (Table M-10).

Try 12 in. interior CMU party wall along Line 2.

- Minimum wall thicknesses:

  Either horizontally between intersecting wall lines (see Table M-7)

  $L = 18t - 18 \times 8 = 144$ in. $<$ 480 in. furnished (No Good)

  or vertically between story supports (see Table M-7)

  $h = 18t = 18 \times 8 = 144$ in. $>$ 120 in. furnished (O.K.)

  (Note: Floor and roof diaphragms must be designed to provide lateral support for walls.)

  Parapet wall (see Table M-7):

  Minimum $t = 8$ in. $= 8$ in. Furnished (O.K.)

  Maximum height $= 3t = 24$ in. $=$ actual 24 in. (O.K.)

- Minimum wall lengths at lower floor (see Table M-8):

  Distance between walls at lines A and D is 24'-0".

  Minimum length of walls $= {}^{24}/_{5} = 4.8$ ft $<$ 8 ft at Line D (O.K.)

  Minimum length of shearwall = story height = 12 ft (No Good).

  (Length of wall at Line D must be increased).

- Minimum wall lengths at upper floor (see Table M-8).

  Minimum length of walls $= {}^{24}/_{2} = 12.0$ ft (No Good)

  (Wall length at Line D is too short).

  Minimum length of shear walls = story height = 12 ft.

  (Wall length at line D must be at least 12 ft.)

(Note: Increase the length of the 8 ft. wall along Line D at the partywall to a total length of 12 ft. Leave end walls 4'-0", but they may not be counted as shear walls).

- Minimum cumulative length must be ≥ 0.4 x long dimension.

  Minimum cumulative length > 0.4 x 80 = 32 ft.
  Cumulative length furnished = 80 + 12 = 92 ft
  > 32 ft (O.K.)

Check selected wall thickness for compressive stress.

- Compressive stress along Line A,

  Allowable F_a = 115 psi (see Table M-4).

  Load per foot of wall at base of wall (see Table 13-1):

  Roof load = 50 lb/ft² x 4 ft = 200
  Floor load = 160 lb/ft² x 4 ft = 640
  Wall weight = 26' x 42 lb/ft² = 1092
  Total = 1932 lb/ft

$$f_a = \frac{1932}{7.63x12} = 21 \text{ psi} < 115 \text{ psi (O.K.)}$$

- Compressive stress alone Line D:

  Allowable F_a = 115 psi (see Table M-4)
  Assume total load at Line D is distributed uniformly along the total length of the wall segments (see Table 23-6 for dead load of wall).

  Roof load = 50(4 + 8)80 = 48000 lb
  Floor load = 160(4 + 8)80 = 153600 lb
  Wall Weight = 26 x 42 x 20 = 21800 lb
  Total = 223400 lb.
  Load/ft 223,400/20 = 11,170 lb/ft

$$f_a = \frac{11,170}{7.63x12} = 122 \text{ psi} > 115 \text{ psi allowed (No Good)}$$

(Note: Wall at Line D is inadequate for the compressive stress. Increase wall thickness to 12 in. to match the width of the 12 in. concrete lintel beam above.)

Roof load = 48000 lb
Floor load = 153600 lb
Wall weight = 26 x 58 x 20 = 30200 lb
Total = 231800 lb
Load/ft = 231,800/20 = 11,600 lb/ft

$$f_a = \frac{11,600}{11.63x12} = 83 \text{ psi} \le 115 \text{ psi}$$

(Note: Alternatively the wall segments at the ends of the wall could have been increased to 6 ft. For this building, it was elected to increase the wall thickness to match the lintel over the openings).

Selection of shear wall/bearing walls at lines 1, 2 and 3:

- A minimum wall thickness of 8 inches was found earlier to be adequate (Lines 1 and 3 are 8 in., Line 2 is 12 in.)

- Minimum wall lengths at lower floor (see Table M-8). Distance between walls at Lines 1 and 2 is 40'-0".

Minimum length of walls = $^{40}/_{5}$ = 8 ft < 24 ft (O.K.)
Minimum length of shearwall = story height = 12 ft (O.K.)

- Minimum wall lengths at upper floor (see Table M-8).
  Minimum length of walls = $^{40}/_{2}$ = 20 ft < 24 ft (O.K.)
  Minimum length of shearwalls = story height = 12 ft (O.K.)

- Minimum cumulative length must be (0.4 x 80 = 32 ft.
  Cumulative length furnished = 24 + 24 + 224 = 72 > 32 (O.K.)

Check selected wall thicknesses for compressive stress.

(Note: The design of pilasters in the empirical design method is not specifically prescribed by the Code. For this building, it is assumed that the grouted pilasters will have to carry the end reactions of the tee beams. It is then assumed that the walls will carry only the roof and their own dead weight.)

- Tee beam reactions at Lines 1 and 3:
  R = 160 x 8 x 20 = 25,600 lbs

- Tee beam reactions at Line 2:
  R = 160 x 8 x 40 = 51,200 lbs

- Stress in pilasters at base of walls:
  At Lines 1 and 2, including dead load of 24 ft of CMU plus 10 ft of grout.

(Note: To compute the weight of the grout per foot of height, the open area of the pilaster by the weight of the grout, 145 lb/ft^3. See Table 23-6 for solid and void areas).

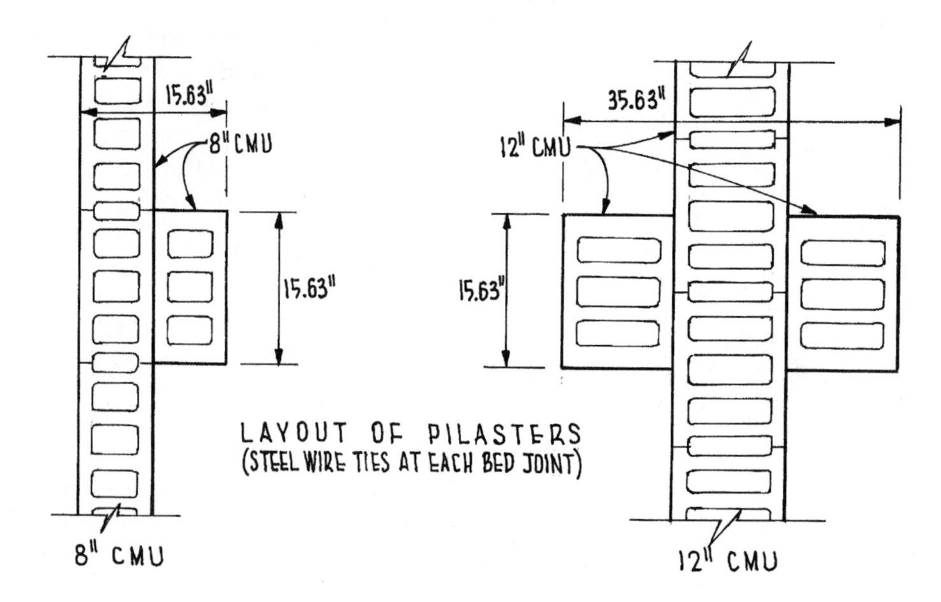

Weight of 16" x 16" pilaster at base of wall (pilaster height = 10 ft):
Wt. of CMU = 1 x 42 x 24 + 1 x 42 x 10= 1430 lb
Wt. of grout = [(96 - 48)/144]145 x 10 = 483 lb
Total = 1910 lb

Weight of 16" x 36" pilaster at base of wall (pilaster height = 10 ft):
Wt. of CMU = 1 x 58 x 24 + 2 x 58 x 10 = 2550 lb
Wt. of grout = [(144 - 68)/144]145 x 3 x 10 = 2300 lb
Total = 4850 lb

Stress in 16" x 16" pilaster at base of wall:

$$f_a = \frac{25,600 + 1910}{15.63x15.63} = 113 \text{ psi} < 115 \text{ psi allowed (O.K.)}$$

Stress in remainder of 8 in. walls at Lines 1 and 3:

$$f_a = \frac{42x26}{7.63x12} = 11.93 \text{ psi} < 115 \text{ psi allowed (O.K.)}$$

Stress in 16" x 36" pilaster at base of wall:

$$f_a = \frac{51,200 + 4850}{35.63x15.63} = 101 \text{ psi} < 115 \text{ psi allowed (O.K.)}$$

Stress in remainder of 12 in. wall at Line 2:

$$f_a = \frac{58x26}{11.63x12} = 10.81 \text{ psi} < 115 \text{ psi allowed (O.K.)}$$

The selected final sizes and dimensions are shown in the floor plan below:

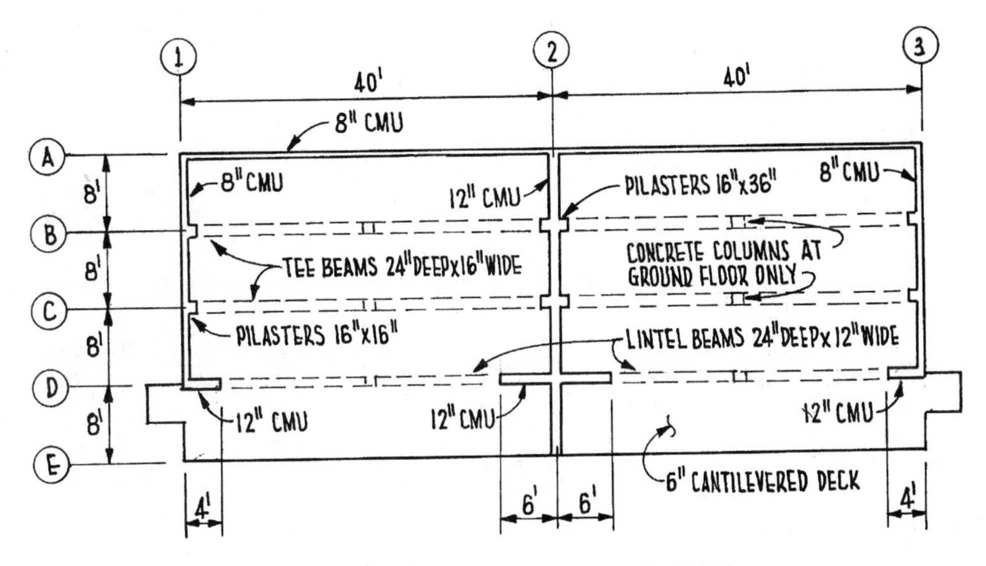

FINAL PLAN DIMENSIONS

Typical details that might be used to provide lateral support to the walls at the floor and roof levels are shown in the following sketches.

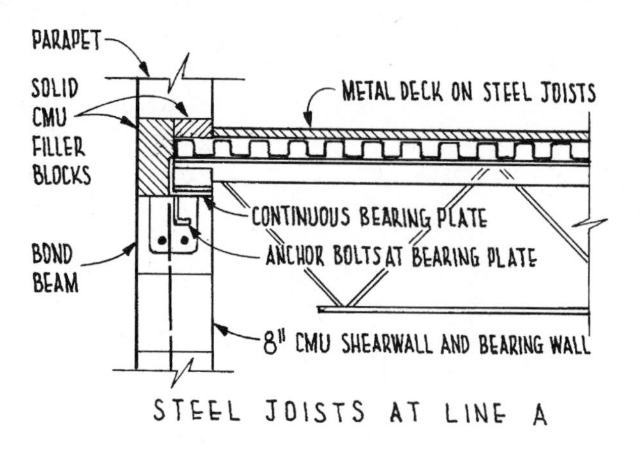

STEEL JOISTS AT LINE A

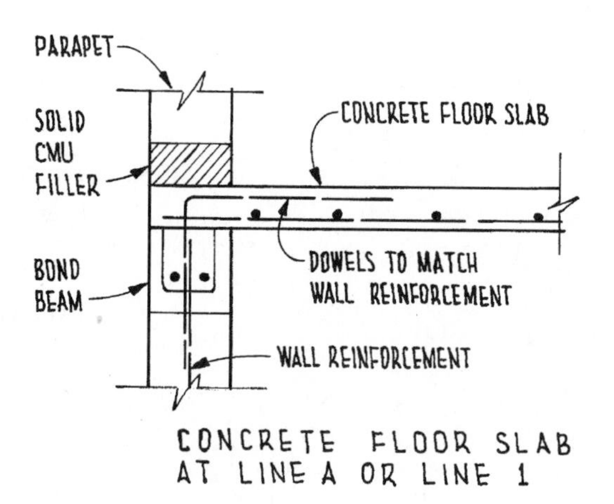

CONCRETE FLOOR SLAB
AT LINE A OR LINE 1

Detailing requirements for earthquake Zone 2 are given in Table M-14 in the Technical Manual. Requirements that would affect the example building are given in the following list.

- Steel joists must be seated on bond beams (as indicated in the foregoing sketches)
- Anchorages of joists must be capable of transmitting (or receiving) a load not less than 200 lb/ft.
- Spacing of steel joists may not exceed 4 ft.
- Anchors for steel joists may not be less than 3/8 in. diameter.
- Vertical bars placed in grouted cells must be used at all corners, wall openings and wall ends. Dowels to foundation must match this wall reinforcement.
- There must be continuous horizontal bars at top and bottom of wall openings. (The lintel beams satisfy this requirement).

Example 23-2

Design of masonry basement walls.

Given: Basement configurations as shown. Equivalent fluid weight of soil is 28 lb/ft^3 f'_m = 1500 psi, f'_c = 4000 psi. Type S mortar.

To Find: Suitable masonry for the basement walls.

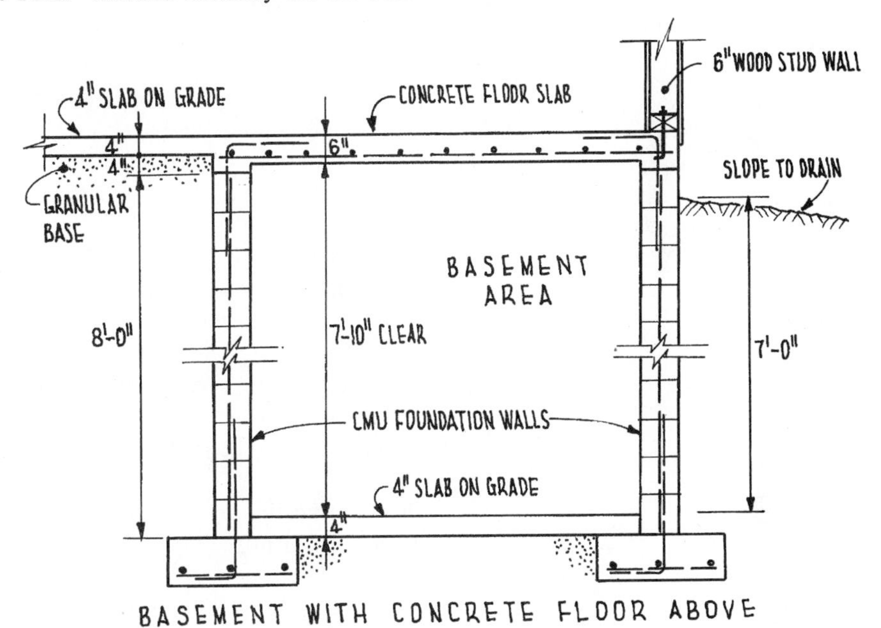

BASEMENT WITH CONCRETE FLOOR ABOVE

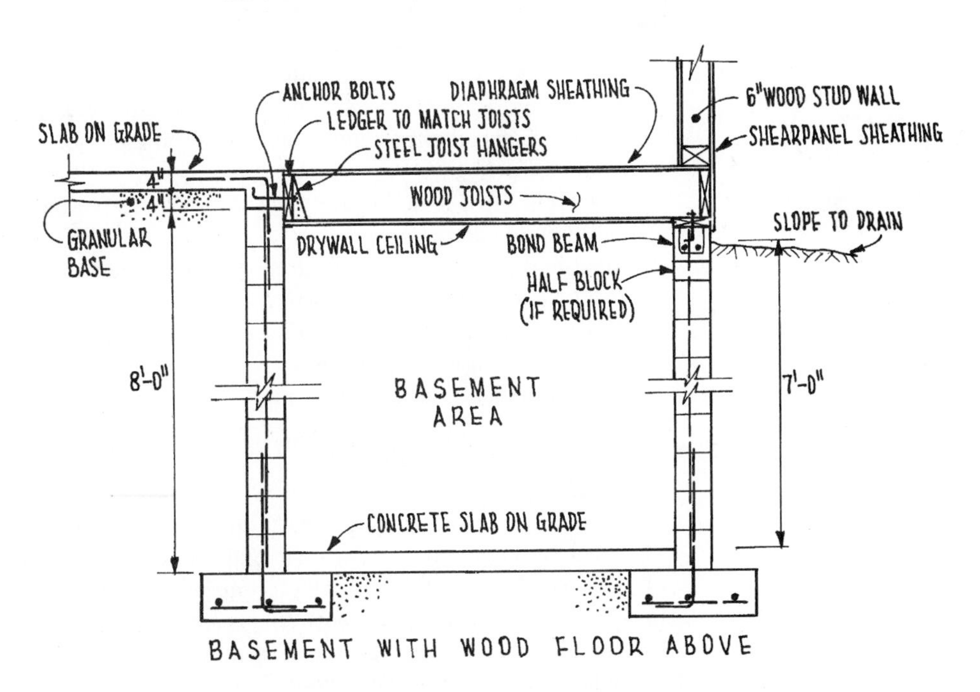

BASEMENT WITH WOOD FLOOR ABOVE

Solution: Check for applicability of the empirical design code. All of the following conditions must be met with either wood or concrete floor over the basement:

- Height of unbalanced fill above inside grade cannot be more than 8 ft.
  At exterior wall, unbalanced fill ≤ 8'-0" (O.K.)
  At interior wall, unbalanced fill ≤ 8'-0" (O.K.)

- Equivalent fluid weight of the soil cannot be greater than 30 pcf.
  Actual equivalent fluid weight = 28 pcf < 30 pcf maximum
  (O.K.)
- Lateral supports must be provided not farther apart than 8'-0".

It is concluded that the given configurations may be designed using the empirical design method.

Select wall thicknesses (see Table M-7):

For the exterior walls, it is found from Table M-7 that the walls may be 12 in. grouted units, unreinforced, or, the exterior walls may be 8 in. reinforced units. For the example configurations, it is elected to use 8 in. reinforced units, #4 bars vertical @ 24" o.c. in grouted cells.

For the interior walls, it is found that the only option for backfill 8'-0" high is to use solid units, either 10 in. or 12 in. wide. It is elected to use 12 in. solid units.

Summary for the given configurations:

Exterior walls 8 in. CMU, #4 bars @ 24 in. o.c., grouted.
Interior walls 12 in. Solid units.

Final verification requires a check for bearing and shear stresses (if any) as performed in Example 23-1.

Review Questions

1. Where does one find the details of the *empirical design method*?
2. Is the empirical design method based on elastic stresses or ultimate loads?
3. Condense and list the limitations where the empirical design methods may not be used.
4. Is masonry that is designed by the empirical design method classified as reinforced or unreinforced masonry?
5. How is lime mortar different from portland cement mortar?
6. Why can't lime mortar be used underwater?
7. What is the end compound produced by the aging of lime mortar?
8. Why is lime used in portland cement mortar?
9. List the four primary types of mortar and their applications.
10. Why does Code permit mortar to be batched by the volume of the components rather than by their weights?
11. What is grout?
12. Where is grout commonly used in masonry construction?
13. What is the nominal ultimate strength of standard grout?
14. List the steps used in the manufacture of fired clay brick.
15. How is brick classified for its quality?
16. How is moarter classified for its quality?
17. What is meant by running bond?
18. What is a head joint? A bed joint? A collar joint?
19. How is a hollow wall different from a cavity wall?
20. How can walls of brick masonry be reinforced?
21. How can walls of concrete masonry units be reinforced?
22. What is the nominal module for the length of brick masonry?
23. What is the nominal module for the width of brick masonry?
24. What is the nominal module for the height of brick masonry?

25. What is the standard joint size for brick masonry?
26. How is sound transmitted across a barrier wall?
27. By what mechanism does brick masonry reduce sound transmission?
28. What minimum thickness of solid brick units is necessary to obtain a 2-hour fire rating?
29. It is proposed to use brick encasement of solid brick units around some steel columns to obtain a 4-hour fire rating for the steel column. What is the required thickness of the encasement?
30. What is the difference between "specified" compressive strength of masonry and the "ultimate" strength?
31. What are the four most commonly used sizes of CMU?
32. What is meant by face-shell mortar bedding for CMU?
33. What is a lintel block?
34. What is accomplished by the use of a *bond beam*?
35. What is a pilaster?
36. Where would a pilaster be commonly used?
37. About how long can a masonry wall be used before temperature effects become serious?
38. How is the elastic modulus of CMU masonry determined?
39. How is the shear modulus of CMU masonry determined?
40. What is the maximum required cumulative length of shearwall in the short direction for a rectangular building, 60 ft x 100 ft?
41. Under what conditions may the empirical design method be used in earthquake Risk Zone 3?
42. What is the absolute maximum unsupported length that may be used in a masonry foundation wall when the empirical design method is used?
43. The longitudinal axes of a pair of shearwalls are to be spaced 36 ft apart. The diaphragm to be supported is metal deck with concrete fill. What is the minimum length of each shearwall?
44. A masonry shearwall is to span 32 ft horizontally and 16 ft vertically between lateral supports. What is the required thickness of the CMU wall?
45. What is the allowable compressive stress in a CMU wall with units having a compressive strength of 2500 psi and Type M mortar?
46. For brick masonry units having a minimum net area compressive strength of 4500 psi, what is the allowable compressive stress?
47. In earthquake Zone 2, how is the strength of brick veneer over a CMU wall taken into account when the total strength of the wall is computed?
48. What is the capacity in shear for a 1/2 in. diameter anchor bolt imbedded 6 in. in a bond beam?

PART

5

ENGINEERING OF STEEL STRUCTURES

CHAPTER

24

STEEL AS AN ENGINEERING MATERIAL

The topics in this chapter do not include any design procedures, but they are necessarily directed toward the design procedures to be presented in succeeding chapters. The design procedures presented later are based on elastic response to load, called in the industry the "allowable stress design" (ASD) method. The other major design method, the "load and resistance factor design" (LRFD) method, is dependent on inelastic deformations (yield) in the steel to equalize the margins of strength at ultimate load. While the LRFD method is gaining slowly in popularity, the ASD method is still by far the most widely used method in American practice and is the method presented in these chapters.

24.1 Steel in Modern Construction

Probably no construction material in history has impacted civil engineering as much as steel. From its first use in the Firth of Forth bridge in Scotland, completed in 1890, steel has quickly come to be the most universal material ever to be developed in the long history of civil construction. From the fasteners used in timber construction, to the reinforcement used in concrete construction, to the frames of bridges and buildings, steel is the one major ingredient for which there is no substitute in modern construction.

Such prominence in the industry is well deserved. As a construction material, steel is incredibly strong, remarkably rigid and universally available. Such desirable properties do not come without drawbacks, however. Steel requires huge amounts of energy to manufacture, it is expensive in comparison to other construction materials, and it requires expensive protection against corrosion and fire. In its performance over a hundred years, however, steel has gained the position in today's industry as the ideal construction material against which all other construction materials are compared.

In its performance under load, steel exhibits an extremely desirable feature: it is forgiving. When overloaded, steel may indeed deform excessively, so much, in fact, that the structure may have to be torn down and replaced, but in undergoing such excessive deformations, the steel has given adequate warning of distress; it did not collapse suddenly in a brittle heap. In structures under catastrophic loadings such as earthquake, this forgiving nature of steel is of immense, if not paramount, value.

The ability of steel to yield, or to undergo "plastic" deformations without failure, is exploited throughout all of steel design. Even at elastic levels of stress under service levels of load, the design of steel structures depends heavily on the plasticity of steel to distribute load in connections, to equalize stress concentrations after welding and to compensate for misalignments in fabrication and construction. So, while we may call allowable stress design an elastic method, the success of the method depends in large part on the ability of steel to undergo localized plastic yield.

24.2 Manufacturing and Production of Steel

Steel is an alloy of iron and carbon. Common structural steels have carbon contents ranging from about 0.15% to 0.5% by weight. These extremely small quantities of carbon produce a remarkable change of crystalline iron into crystalline steel, with a striking improvement in engineering properties.

Iron, the elemental metal, does not occur naturally in nature (except for very small quantities in meteorites). Iron is extracted from iron-rich rock called *iron ore*, where it occurs primarily as one of the oxides of iron, FeO_2 or Fe_2O_3. The higher the concentration of iron in the ore, the higher the "grade" of the ore and the more economical the extraction.

There is no shortage of iron ore in the world, but many of the small but very "high grade" deposits are now exhausted and production has had to shift to lower grade deposits (which are huge). Even so, modern technology has improved to the extent that the extraction of iron from low grade deposits can successfully compete with that of higher grade deposits, provided energy sources are plentiful and cheap.

Iron is extracted from its ore by heating the ore to a fully liquid state in a container called a blast furnace. The iron component of the molten mass weighs some three times as much as the mineral components. The liquid iron sinks quickly to the bottom of the liquid mass, leaving the mineral residue floating on top. The liquid iron is tapped and drained off, leaving the inert mineral residue as waste material, called *slag*. The disposal of the resulting small mountains of waste slag can sometimes be quite troublesome to the steel mill operators.

While simple to describe, the process is not so simple to execute. A major problem is that there are very few fuels within economic reach that will burn hot enough to melt rock; temperatures in excess of 3000°F are required (paper burns at 451°F, wood at 800°F, natural gas at 2400°F). One of the few fuels that will burn hot enough to melt rock is coke, or *pyrolized* coal (heated without oxygen until the volatiles are driven off.) The preparation of coke is a major expense in the production of iron.

A much simplified schematic of a blast furnace is shown in Figure 24-1. The blast furnace is loaded in lifts of coke, ore, limestone and dolomite (a high-grade limestone). Heated air is blasted upward through the mass, igniting the coke and providing oxygen for its burning. The limestone acts as a "flux," coagulating the mineral residue and holding it as a scum, floating on top of the liquid iron.

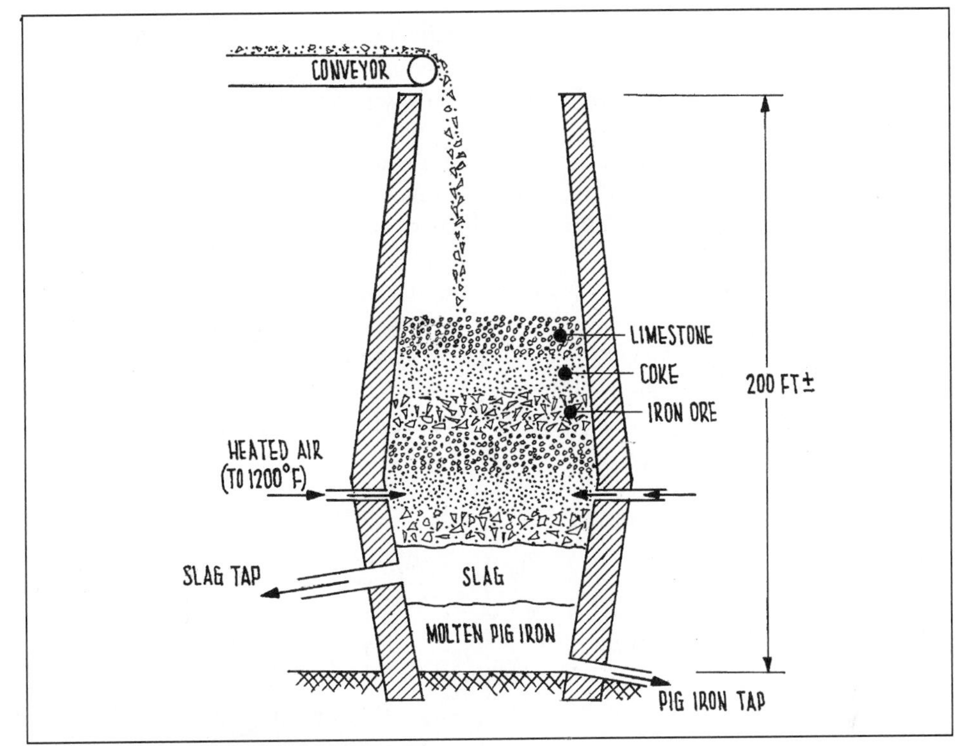

Figure 24-1 Schematic of blast furnace.

The liquid iron is tapped off into troughs (about 3 ft x 4 ft x 10 ft) placed along the base of the blast furnace. The appearance of the troughs receiving the white-hot iron at the side of the furnace was noted by early iron makers to resemble a litter of pigs suckling a sow. The name *pig iron* was used to identify the product; the name is now the accepted technical term in the industry for this product.

Pig iron is highly impure. It retains unacceptably large amounts of the mineral ore and limestone, as well as high amounts of unburned carbon. A further refining stage is necessary to convert the pig iron into a purified form and subsequently into steel. This next stage is performed in a more refined and more sophisticated form of the blast furnace which is called a *converter*.

An early converter, no longer used, was the Bessemer converter. It resembled a huge bucket, with an opening at the top. Like a blast furnace, it was loaded with coke, dolomite and pig iron. Also like a blast furnace, it was charged with heated air which produced a spray of sparks, color and flames spewing out of the top as the final impurities (and coke) were separated from the pig iron. The final product was judged to be "right" when the spray coming out of the converter reached a certain color and hue; at that point the conversion was stopped and the finished steel was poured out of the bucket into molds to form *ingots*.

In today's industry, the converter will more likely be an *electric hearth* furnace. The electric hearth furnace is again a container, but the heat source is electricity, passed through the iron by huge carbon electrodes, sometimes 18 inches in diameter and several feet long. The *melt* is started in a *puddle* deliberately left (or reintroduced) from a preceding melt. The ingot (or scrap iron, or both) is placed in the puddle along with dolomite (and sometimes coke as a source of carbon for alloying).

A huge electric current at relatively low voltage is passed through the mass; resistive heat in the mass causes it to melt. Control of the electric current permits very close and unhurried control to be exercised over the *melt*, to include immediate and on-going control of the carbon as well as other alloying materials. The output of the electric hearth furnace is a high quality steel *ingot*, with its chemistry controlled to a precision that cannot be matched by older fuel-fed converters.

The relationship between iron and carbon is indicated in Figure 24-2. The name *steel* is applied to iron-carbon alloys containing less than 2% carbon. High-carbon alloys containing more than 2% carbon are called *cast iron*, though products made from these alloys need not be cast. The high-carbon alloys were originally used to make castings, and even though the limitation has long since been lost, the name is still applied. (In today's industry, high quality castings are also made from steel, with less than 1% carbon).

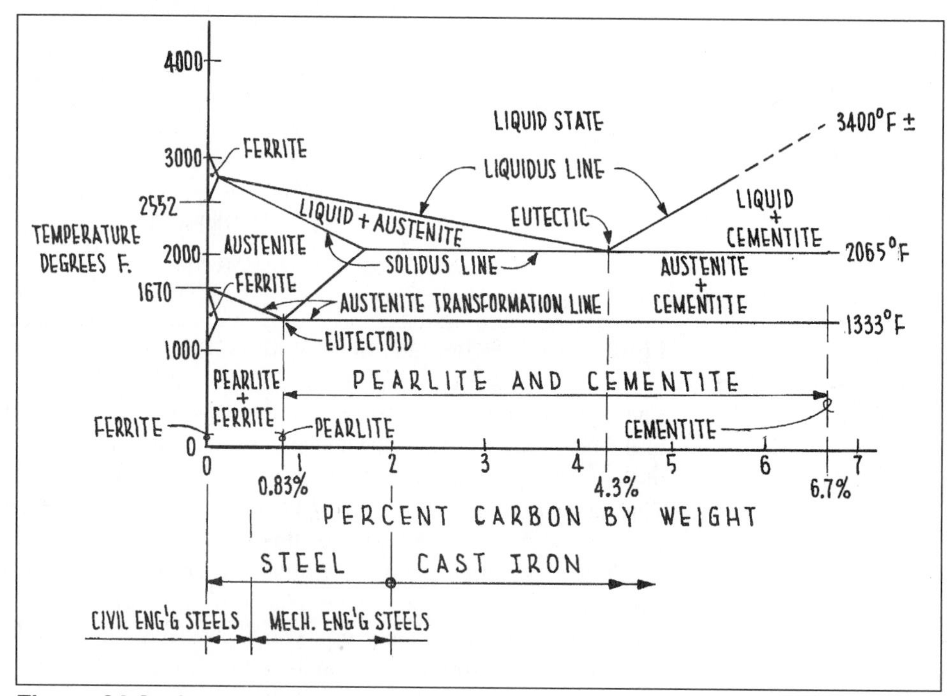

Figure 24-2 Iron-carbide phase diagram.

Also indicated in Figure 24-2 are the general ranges of carbon contents for mild steel (civil engineering steels) and high-carbon steel (mechanical engineering steels). The distinction is quite general; civil engineering also uses a few high carbon steels and mechanical engineering also uses a few low carbon steels. As a general rule, however, the distinction is appropriate.

The temperatures shown in Figure 24-2 reveal several interesting points. Pure iron becomes liquid at about 2800°F. Iron containing 4.3% carbon (called eutectic iron) becomes liquid at 2065°F. The melting point of steel is therefore dependent on its carbon content; a considerable variation in melting temperatures is seen to occur.

Iron and carbon form several *allotropic* crystals. Allotropic forms of a material are forms that assume different crystalline structures even though they are composed of identically the same material. (Probably the best-known of all such allotropic forms are carbon, graphite and diamonds, all of which are allotropic forms of carbon.)

The allotropic crystals of iron and carbon that are of interest here are *ferrite* (less than 0.025%C), the *eutectoid pearlite* (0.83%C), *cementite* (6.67%C) and *austenite* (at temperatures greater than 1333°F). These allotropic forms of steel are indicated in the schematic of Figure 24-2. Unless the iron is heavily alloyed, austenite does not exist at temperatures lower than 1333°F, which is called the austenite transformation temperature.

Steel can be hardened and strengthened by *heat-treatment*. If medium carbon or high carbon steel is heated above the austenite transformation temperature, then its temperature quickly reduced to room temperature (*quenched*), the steel crystals will collect into a hard, brittle form called *martensite*. With time, some of the martensite will decay, but the heat-treated steel that remains will have markedly improved properties of hardness and strength. As suggested by Figure 24-3, such heat-treatment does not provide much improvement in the low carbon steels commonly used in civil construction, but can offer considerable improvement in the medium and high carbon steels commonly used in mechanical engineering in machine design.

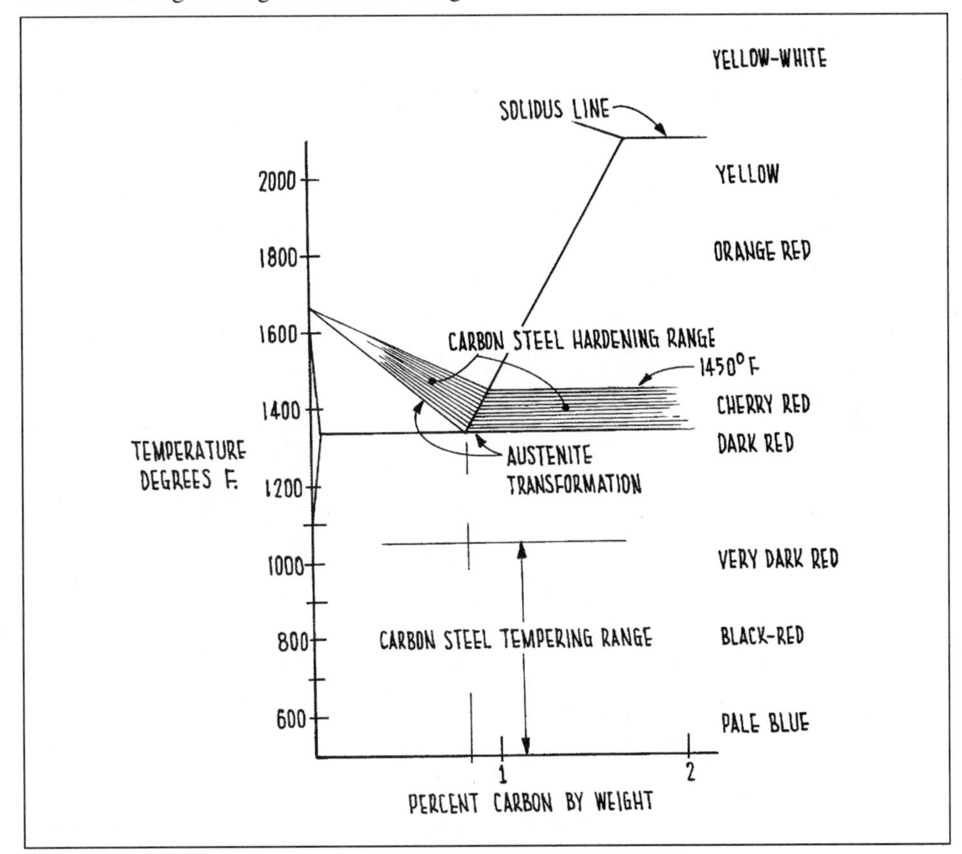

Figure 24-3 Tempering and heat treatment ranges.

The heat treatment can be removed and the steel restored to its original state by *annealing* it. To anneal the material, it is again heated to temperatures above the austenite transformation line into heat treatment ranges, but it is then allowed to cool to room temperatures very slowly (over night, in a controlled oven). In its annealed state, the steel can be worked, drilled, or fabricated, after which its hardened state can be restored simply by heat treating it again.

A heat treated steel can also be *tempered*. Tempering will accelerate the decay of that part of the martensite that is going to decay, causing the steel to "age," or to stabilize into its final crystalline structure much sooner. As indicated in Figure 14-3, tempering consists of heating the steel up to about 900°F to 1000°F, holding it at this temperature for several hours, then allowing it to cool slowly to room temperatures. Both hardness and brittleness will be reduced and some of the toughness restored by tempering the heat treated steel.

Tempering is also useful in stress-relieving a material after it has been welded. The melting of steel in small spots or strips during the welding process creates a very confused stress pattern in the material as it cools down. Tempering the steel produces a release of the worst of those residual stresses.

Similarly, both heat treatment and built-in stresses (due to fabrication, shaping, bending or forming) can be largely removed by *normalizing*, a variation of annealing. A steel is normalized by heating it above the austenite transformation line and then allowing it to cool in still air (an hour or so). Some residual stress or hardness may remain, but the worst part will be removed.

A metallurgist reading the foregoing descriptions of phase changes, heat treatment, tempering and stress relieving would probably object to the oversimplifications. The metallurgy of steel is acknowledged to be an extremely complicated subject, a subject which can easily be extended into a lifetime of study. The foregoing topics are included here, however simplified and generalized, only in order that references can be made to them in later discussions.

Another very complex topic in steel manufacturing is alloying; its presentation here also requires similar simplification. *Alloying agents* other than carbon are often added to steel in the final melt (usually electric hearth) to impart specific properties to the finished steel. A short list of alloying agents is given in Table 24-1, along with the specific improvements they can give to the steel.

Table 24-1 Alloying Agents in Steel.

Alloying Agent	Effects on Steel
Aluminum	Deoxidizer, improves grain structure.
Carbon	Improves strength and hardness at the expense of ductility and toughness. Called low-carbon up to 0.3%, medium-carbon 0.3% to 0.5% and high-carbon 0.5% to 2%.
Chromium	Improves strength, hardness, corrosion resistance and retention of strength at high temperatures.
Niobium	Improves strength dramatically. Also used with nickel to improve corrosion resistance (formerly called Columbium).
Manganese	Widely used to offset detrimental effects of sulphur. Improves capability to be rolled. Decreases ductility. Improves capability to receive heat treatment.
Molybdenum	Improves strength at high temperatures, corrosion resistance and resistance to creep.
Nickel	With chromium, used to make stainless steel. Improves toughness and impact strength.
Phosphorus	Improves strength and machinability, reduces ductility.
Silicon	Used in relatively large mounts (up to 25%) as oxidizing agent to improve ability of steel to harden.
Sulphur	Improves machinability, decreases ductility and ability to be rolled.
Vanadium	Improves grain structure and strength at high temperatures. Improves capability to receives heat treatment.

In the manufacturing process, impurities such as oxygen and sulphur commonly are left in the melt; large amounts of oxygen and sulphur can have detrimental effects on the finished steel (oxygen embrittles it, sulphur reduces its strength at elevated temperatures). Rather than remove these impurities, it is common practice to add alloying agents to tie them up chemically. Aluminum and manganese are two such agents; aluminum deoxidizes steel and manganese neutralizes the effects of sulphur.

One particular alloy, stainless steel, deserves special mention. Stainless steel has gained wide acceptance in many areas of technology but due primarily to its high cost, it has not been used extensively in general construction. Times are changing; stainless steel is now starting to make significant inroads into structural applications (such as the Gateway Arch in St. Louis).

Stainless steel is an alloy of steel with chromium and nickel. Corrosion of stainless steel does not produce the familiar "rust" stains that are ordinarily associated with corrosion. Alloys used in construction can contain as little as 11% chromium, with nickel being added in various amounts to improve ductility.

As a rule, stainless steel is softer (and weaker) than carbon steel. Stainless steel can be made harder and stronger, however, by proper alloying and heat treatment.

Another alloy that was created especially for use in civil engineering is *weathering* steel. Weathering steel forms a dense deep red to black oxide coating when exposed to air. The dense coating (called *patina*) acts much like paint, protecting the iron inside from further corrosion.

Unfortunately, the coating produced by weathering steel is brittle and tends to crack under deformation or vibration. It immediately "heals" itself after cracking by forming a new protective coating over the newly exposed material. The natural protective coating reduces maintenance costs considerably, a valuable feature for structures located in remote areas (such as bridges).

Weathering steel seems to work best in moderate climates. In very wet or very dry environments, particularly where large deformations or vibrations are present, the coating continues to crack and reform, allowing the corrosion to penetrate ever deeper and deeper into the steel. In view of their advantages in maintenance costs, it seems likely that weathering steels will be improved and that applications will be expanded into other areas in the coming years.

One final iron product, wrought iron, warrants attention. Wrought iron is a form of pig iron containing large amounts of impurities (*silica*) but containing very little if any carbon. The high amount of impurities in the pig iron reduces the affinity of the iron for oxygen; wrought iron has a very low tendency toward oxidation (rust). Wrought iron is soft, weak and malleable. While rarely used in structural applications today, it is the material that was used to build the Eiffel Tower in 1889.

One may occasionally hear the terms "weldable" and "nonweldable" applied to certain steels. A welding steel is one in which the chemistry has been deliberately controlled during manufacturing such that the steel can be successfully welded. A nonweldable steel has no such deliberate control over its chemistry; while it may in fact be welded, there is no assurance that the resulting weld will meet the high standards of a structural weld.

All heat treated steels should be considered nonweldable since welding will normalize the steel immediately adjoining the weld. AISC does include specifications for welding and heat treating some structural steels, but such ventures should be considered only where no alternative is available.

24.3 Engineering Properties of Steel

Probably the most significant indicator of the engineering properties of steel is the stress-strain curve. A typical stress-strain curve for mild steel is shown in Figure 24-4.

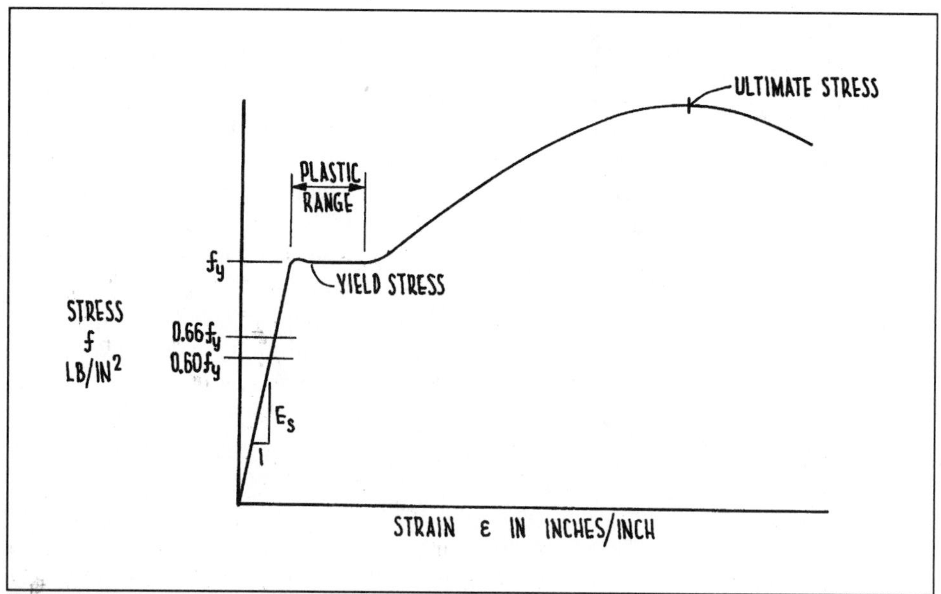

Figure 24-4 Stress-strain curve for mild steel.

The stress-strain curve of Figure 24-4 is introduced and discussed fully in Strength of Materials, Chapter 8. Related topics in fatigue, relaxation and strain hardening are presented in Chapter 12. Insofar as mild structural steel is concerned, the engineering properties have been presented elsewhere and are not repeated here.

It is appropriate here, however, to examine the effects of added carbon and heat treatment to the stress-strain curves of steel. One way to examine those effects is to compare the stress-strain curves of the high strength steels against that of mild steel. Such a comparison is shown in Figure 24-5 for several high strength steels.

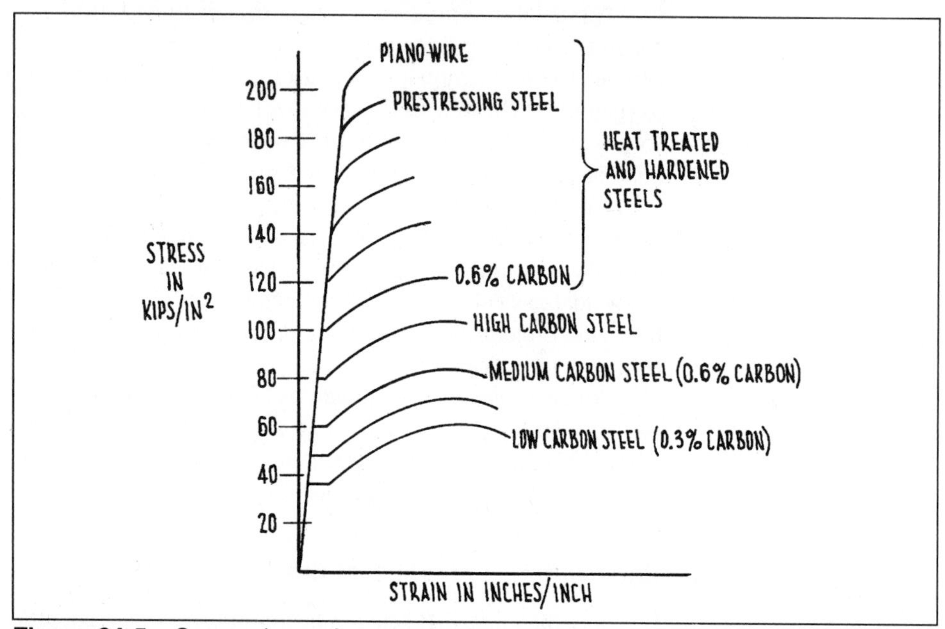

Figure 24-5 Comparison of stress-strain curves.

As a first observation, the curves of Figure 24-5 illustrate quite clearly that the modulus of elasticity of steel is a constant for all steels, regardless of strength. In all cases, the slope of the stress-strain curve, up to the elastic limit of each steel, is a constant. Neither added carbon nor heat treatment have any effect on the modulus of elasticity.

The curves of Figure 24-5 also illustrate that high strength steels lose the distinctive yield strength and plastic range that characterize mild steel. The most serious consequence of that loss is that high strength steels become brittle and lose their forgiving qualities. High strength steels can, in fact, fail by brittle rupture with little warning that they are in distress.

The effects of heat treatment and of higher carbon content is readily apparent from the curves of Figure 24-5. Consider for example the steel having 0.6% carbon with a yield stress of 60,000 lb/in.^{2} Following heat treatment, that same steel has a yield strength of 100,000 lb/in.^{2}; it is shown again higher up on the set of curves. Such a gain in strength occurs for other heat treated steels as well, though they are not shown on the sketch in order to reduce clutter.

A machine part made from a heat-treated steel would likely be too hard to mill or to saw or to work. Such a steel would have to be annealed, after which it could be reworked. Following rework, the part would then be heat treated to restore its previous hardness and strength. Such annealing and heat treatment processes are routine in machine manufacturing, but they would rarely be used in civil engineering.

An additional property of steel is revealed in Figure 24-5. The remarkably high strength of steel is quite vividly apparent in the rupture strength of 215,000 psi for piano wire, the strongest steel shown in the figure. One might dismiss this point, however, with the observation that the volume of piano wire used in the world is quite small and that such a specialty is unimportant. But the next steel down the scale is prestressing steel, which is manufactured in large quantities worldwide for use in making prestressed concrete. With its yield strength of 185,000 psi, prestressing steel is indeed a remarkable product to be manufactured in bulk in modern steel manufacturing.

24.4 Structural Steels in Common Use

The position in today's industry of the American Society of Testing and Materials (ASTM) is discussed in Chapter 10. ASTM specifications cover essentially all of the structural steels commonly used in civil engineering construction. In manufacturing, the American Iron and Steel Institute (AISI) and the Society of Automotive Engineers (SAE) also have commonly used steel specifications, but such steels are rarely used in civil engineering construction.

A summary of the steels commonly used in construction is presented in Table 24-2. Steel designation ASTM A36 shown in the table was introduced earlier, but the others were not. Table 24-2 is adapted from data given in Part I of the *Steel Handbook.*

Some terms are used in Table 2-2 which warrant definition. ASTM A36 is commonly termed a *carbon steel.* The term means that the principal alloying agent is carbon. Carbon steels are those having less than about 0.30% carbon as an alloying agent.

Another term used in Table 24-2 is *high strength* steel. The term indicates that the carbon content is above 0.30% which, with other alloying agents such as vanadium, chromium, silicon and copper, produces a steel having a significantly higher strength.

Table 24-2 Common Structural Steels.[a]

ASTM Designation	Type of Steel	Yield Stress F_y ksi	Ultimate Stress F_u ksi	Applicability
A36	Carbon	36	58	All shapes and plates
A53 Gr. B	Carbon	35	60	Round pipe
A307	Carbon	—	60	Bolts to 4 in. diameter
A325	Carbon	92	120	Bolts to 1 in. diameter
		81	105	Bolts to 1 1/2 in. diameter
A490	Carbon	—	150	Bolts to 1 1/2 in. diameter
A500 Gr. B	Carbon	42	58	Round pipe, structural tube
A501	Carbon	36	58	Round pipe
A529	Carbon	42	60	Shapes, plates to 1/2 inch
A441	High-strength, low alloy	46	67	Shapes, plates 3/4 in. to 1 1/2 in.
		50	70	Shapes, plates to 3/4 in.
A572 Gr. 50	High-strength, low alloy	50	65	Shapes, plates to 4 in.
A242	Corrosion-resistant, high-strength, low alloy	46	67	Shapes, plates 3/4 to 1 1/2 in.
		50	70	Shapes, plates to 3/4 in.
A588	Corrosion-resistant, high strength, low alloy	50	70	Shapes, plates to 4 in.

[a]Source: AISC Manual of Steel Construction, reprinted by permission of AISC.

Another term used in Table 24-2 is *low alloy* steel. The term indicates that the total amount of alloying material is low. Exactly what constitutes a "low" amount of alloying materials is vague, but it is taken here to be less than 5%.

The term *corrosion resistant* in Table 24-2 refers to weathering steels. There are rather strict rules to be observed when designing, detailing, fabricating and erecting these steels. Such rules are necessary in order to protect the brittle patina that in turn protects the steel. The term corrosion resistant refers only to atmospheric corrosion, not to chemical corrosion from road salts, stack exhaust or chemical fumes.

The column on "applicability" shows the most notable uses for the particular steel. It should not be assumed that these are the only uses for the steel; other applications are often likely.

24.5 Rolled Steel Shapes

Preceding discussions concerning the manufacturing of steel were stopped with the production of ingots. Ingots are the end product of the converter or of the electric hearth furnace. Ingots are simply huge blobs of steel, weighing almost 30 tons, whose chemistry has been tightly controlled to conform to a particular type of steel.

While awaiting further processing, ingots are held in *soaking pits*. Eventually, the ingots are taken out of the soaking pits and passed through huge rolls which form the ingots into huge, thick rectangular *slabs*. The slabs are then further rolled into thinner and longer rectangular *blooms*, then into thinner and longer *billets*. Billets may be as small as 8 inches square in cross section, cut into lengths up to 100 ft or more.

Billets are the bulk steel that are used to make the familiar shapes of everyday steel construction. To make these shapes, the billets are reheated to about 2200°F (usually by natural gas) and then passed through an incremental series of rollers (up to about 16 sets) until the desired final shape is gradually formed. The end product is called a *rolled steel shape*, one of the more recognizable steel products that we see in routine construction.

Essentially all of the steel used in civil engineering construction is in the form of these rolled steel shapes. Rolled steel shapes include round bars, rectangular bars, plates, "I" beams, tees, channels, angles, tube and pipe. A few of these shapes are introduced and discussed in strength of materials in conjunction with the flexure formula and shear formula. A more detailed look at these shapes is presented in this section.

A comparison of bars and plates is shown in Figure 24-6. The dividing line between bars and plates is a width of 8 inches. Bars are 8 in. or less in width. Plates are more than 8 in. in width.

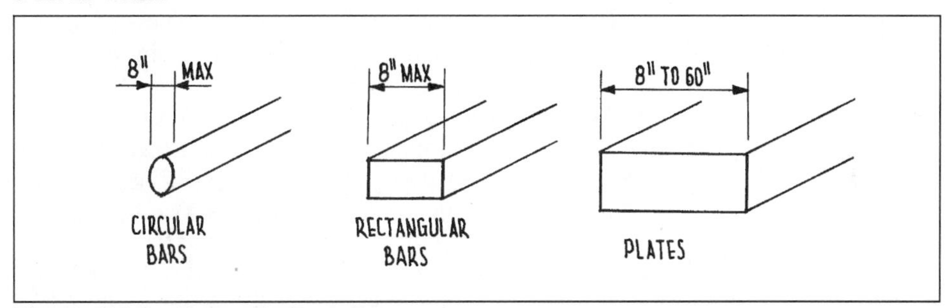

Figure 24-6 Bar and plate sizes.

Bars are available in $^1/_{16}$ inch increments of thickness or diameter. The preferred practice, however, is to specify widths in $^1/_4$ inch increments, to specify thickness in $^1/_8$ inch increments and to specify diameter in $^1/_8$ inch increments.

Plates are available in $^1/_{32}$ inch increments up to $^1/_2$ inch thick, then $^1/_{16}$ inch increments up to 1 inch thick, then $^1/_8$ inch increments to 3 inches thick, then $^1/_4$ inch thicknesses thereafter. Widths of rolled plates are generally available to 60 inches wide.

Typical *American Standard* rolled shapes are shown in Figure 24-7. Selected sizes available in the various shapes are given in Tables S-2, S-3, S-4 and S-6 in the Technical Manual.

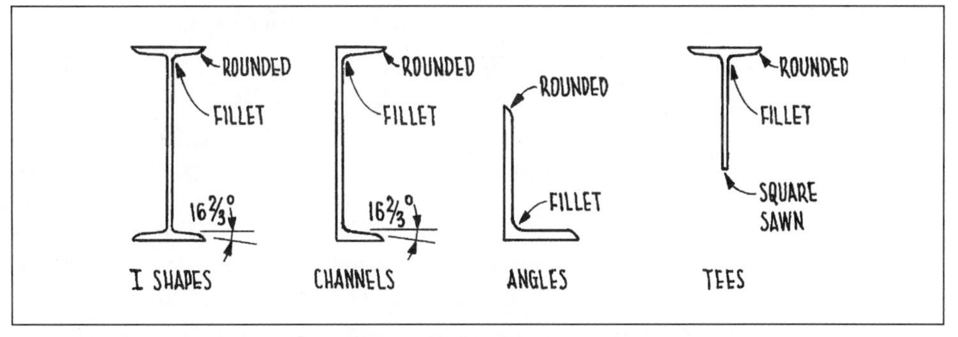

Figure 24-7 American Standard rolled shapes.

In the tables in the Technical Manual, American Standard I shapes are listed as S shapes, channels as C shapes, angles as L shapes and tees as ST shapes. ST shapes are simply S shapes that have been cut in half.

The size of American Standard shapes is increased by opening up the rolls as shown in Figure 24-8. The tables list 2 or 3 sizes for each beam depth; those variations were obtained as shown in Figure 24-8.

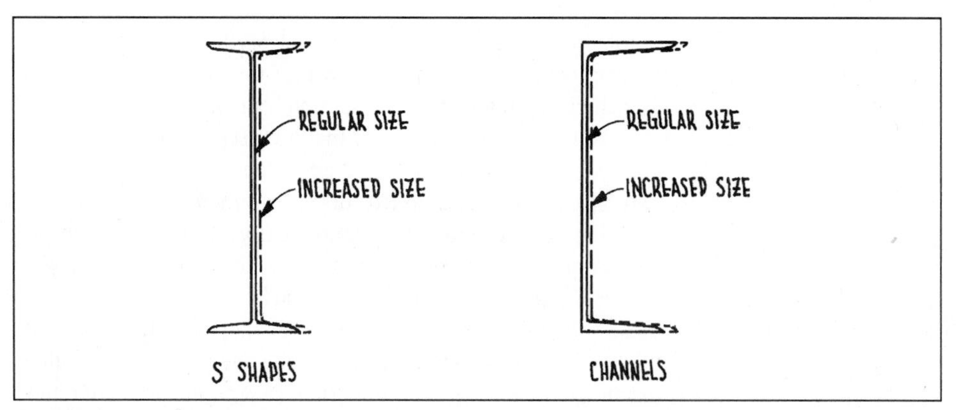

Figure 24-8 Increasing the size of American Standard shapes.

Increasing the capacity of an S shape or a C shape in moment is quite inefficient. As indicated in Figure 24-8, the only way to increase the size of the flange (and thereby the moment capacity) is to increase also the thickness of the web. A large increase in area and weight is thus necessary in order to obtain a small increase in flange area and corresponding moment capacity.

In comparison, a typical wide flange rolled shape is shown in Figure 24-9. As indicated, the control dimension T for wide flange shapes is the straight portion of the web (between fillets). A partial listing of the sizes available in wide flange shapes is given in Tables S-1 through S-5 in the Technical Manual.

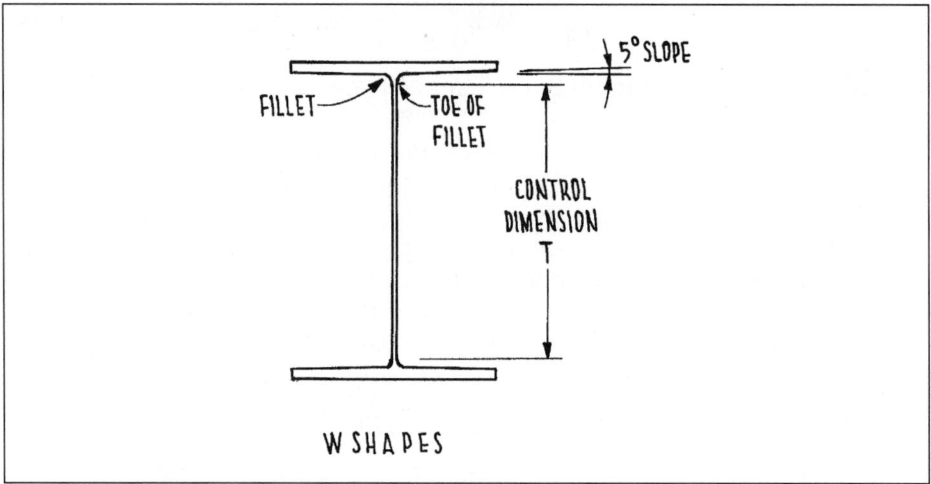

Figure 24-9 Wide flange shapes.

In the tables in the Technical Manual, wide flange I shapes are listed as W shapes and tees as WT shapes. Tees are simply W shapes that have been cut in half.

A great deal more latitude is available in varying the size of wide flange sections than in American Standard sections. Both the flange thickness and the web thickness can be varied independently, as indicated in Figure 14-10. In wide flange beam sections, the dimension T is held constant for a given group of beams.

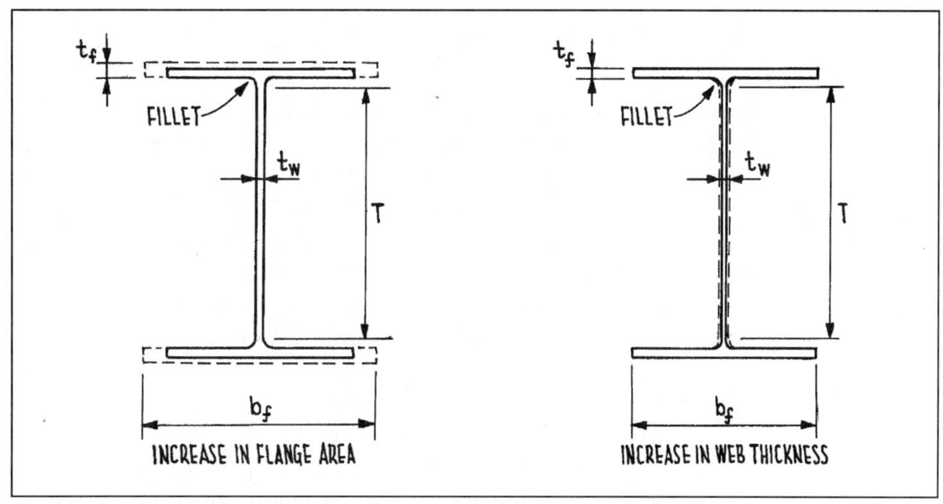

Figure 24-10 Increasing the size of wide flange shapes.

In addition to American Standard shapes and wide flange shapes, there are a group of shapes that do not fit into either category. Tall slender lightweight sections are available from some manufacturers that are very efficient in their moment-carrying capacities. Called "miscellaneous" sections, these shapes are rolled in both I and channel shapes. Miscellaneous shapes are not included in this textbook due to their lack of general availability.

Also available from some rolling mills are a wide variety of piling shapes. The most widely available of these are the HP shapes, similar in appearance to wide flange shapes. Foundations (and piling) are not treated in this textbook.

In recent years, pipe and tube have seen an increase in popularity, possibly because they have the same properties in all directions. There is no "weak" axis in a pipe or in a square tube. Typical examples of pipe and square tube are shown in Figure 24-11.

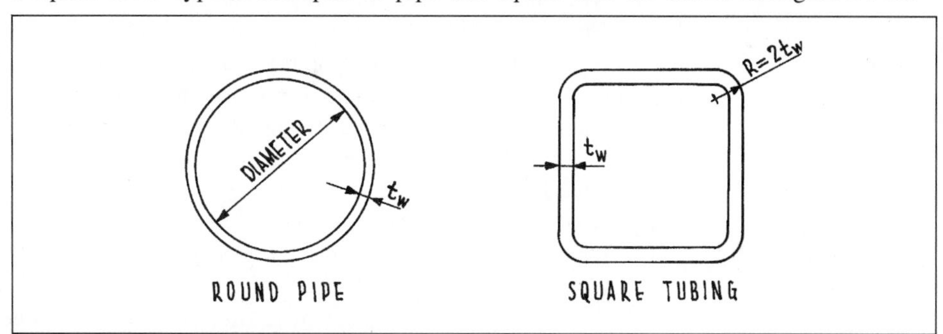

Figure 24-11 Round pipe and square tube.

Round pipe is manufactured in three wall thicknesses for each diameter. The resulting pipe is called *standard, extra strong*, and *double extra strong*. Dimensions and properties of round pipe are given in Table S-8 in the Technical Manual.

Tubing is manufactured in rectangular shapes as well as square shapes. Only square shapes are included in the tables in the Technical Manual. Dimensions and properties of square structural tubing are given in Table S-9.

24.6 Codes and Practices

The Allowable Stress Design (ASD) method for the design of structural steel was developed over a period of many years by the American Institute of Steel Construction. The ASD method is given in Part 5, Specifications and Codes, of the *Manual of Steel Construction,* AISC, ninth edition, dated June 1, 1989. The standard symbols used in the ASD method are included in the Design Tables in the Technical Manual.

References in this chapter and in subsequent chapters to the ASD Specifications will mean these AISC design specifications. Such references will include the paragraph number. A reference to ASD (B5.1), for example, will be understood to mean Chapter B, Section 5, Subsection 1 of the ASD specification. Similarly, a reference to an ASD equation such as ASD EQ(F1-2) will be understood to be Equation (F1-2) given in Chapter F, Section 1 of the ASD Specification. And similarly, a reference to ASD Table J3.2 will be understood to be Table J3.2 of chapter J, Section 3 of the ASD Specification.

The ASD Specification is quite detailed. The topics presented in this introductory text amount to only a small fraction of the topics presented in the ASD Specification. Anyone involved in the design or detailing of steel on a long-term basis should keep a personal marked-up copy of the entire ASD Specification on hand for continuing reference. When the meaning of a particular provision in the ASD Specification becomes clear only after repeated study, a marginal note will save time several weeks or months hence when the provision is encountered again.

Review Questions

1. What is the difference between the ASD method of steel design and the LRFD method?
2. How long has structural steel been used?
3. In its manufacture, would steel be classified as energy-intensive, technology-intensive or labor-intensive?
4. What makes steel a "forgiving" material?
5. What is the difference between iron and steel?
6. What materials are loaded into a blast furnace to make iron?
7. Why is coke used to make iron rather than other fuels?
8. What purpose does the limestone serve in the blast furnace?
9. What impurities can be expected in pig iron?
10. What is a converter?
11. What is the advantage of electric hearth furnaces over fuel-fed converters?
12. What is the name of the end product of a converter?
13. What is the eutectoid of steel?
14. What is the carbon content of ferrite? pearlite? cementite?
15. What is the austenite transformation temperature and what happens to steel at that temperature?
16. How is heat treatment accomplished?
17. How is heat treatment removed?
18. In what kinds of steel is heat treatment most effective?
19. How is tempering accomplished?
20. What purpose does tempering serve?
21. What is the difference between annealing and normalizing?
22. What effect does active oxygen have in the finished steel?
23. What effect does active sulfur have in the finished steel?
24. How is stainless steel made?
25. What is weathering steel?
26. How are the detrimental effect of oxygen or sulfur counteracted?
27. What is wrought iron?
28. What is meant by the classification "weldable" as applied to steel?

29. What would happen to the modulus of elasticity of steel if its strength were to be doubled by alloying and heat treatment?
30. How can heat treated steel parts be reworked?
31. What are the yield stress and ultimate stress in A36 steel?
32. What does ASTM stand for?
33. What is the most distinctie property of A242 steel?
34. What is the dividing line between steel plates and steel bars?
35. Name three of the American Standard shapes.
36. Compare and contrast methods of varying the size of wide flange shapes against varying the size of American Standard shapes.
37. What advantages do pipe and tube have over W and S shapes?
38. What is the wall thickness of 8 in. standard pipe? Of 8 in. double extra strong pipe?
39. Where does the ASD method come from?
40. Where could one find a complete copy of the ASD method?

CHAPTER

25

STEEL TENSION MEMBERS AND THEIR CONNECTIONS

One of the major applications of steel as a construction material is in tension members. The most numerous of such members are probably in trusses, where steel has gained wide acceptance. From major river bridge trusses to lightweight bar joist trusses, steel tension members are a common application of steel in today's construction.

With its extremely high strength, steel makes very efficient tension members. Even very small steel members (or bars) can sustain very high loads in tension. Quite often, however, there can be difficulties in delivering such large loads into such small members; the design of connections to tension members can sometimes be quite intricate.

In the design of steel structures, there is a very heavy concentration of attention on the design of connections. The reason for such concentration is that some 70% of all failures in structural steel originate at a connection. Rarely does a steel beam fail in flexure or a steel column fail in compression. Much more likely, the connection between the two will fail, causing a propagation of failures to adjacent connections and members. Due to its importance, the detailing of steel connections is the primary topic of this chapter.

25.1 Load Capacity of Bolted and Welded Tension Members

A typical bolted tension member is shown in Figure 25-1. There are two levels of stress in the member, one in the shank of the member and another in the vicinity of the holes, where some of the material has been removed. The stressed cross-sectional area in the shank, indicated as Section *a-a*, is called the gross *area* of the member. The stressed cross-section area with the holes deducted, indicated as Section *b-b*, is called the *net area* of the member.

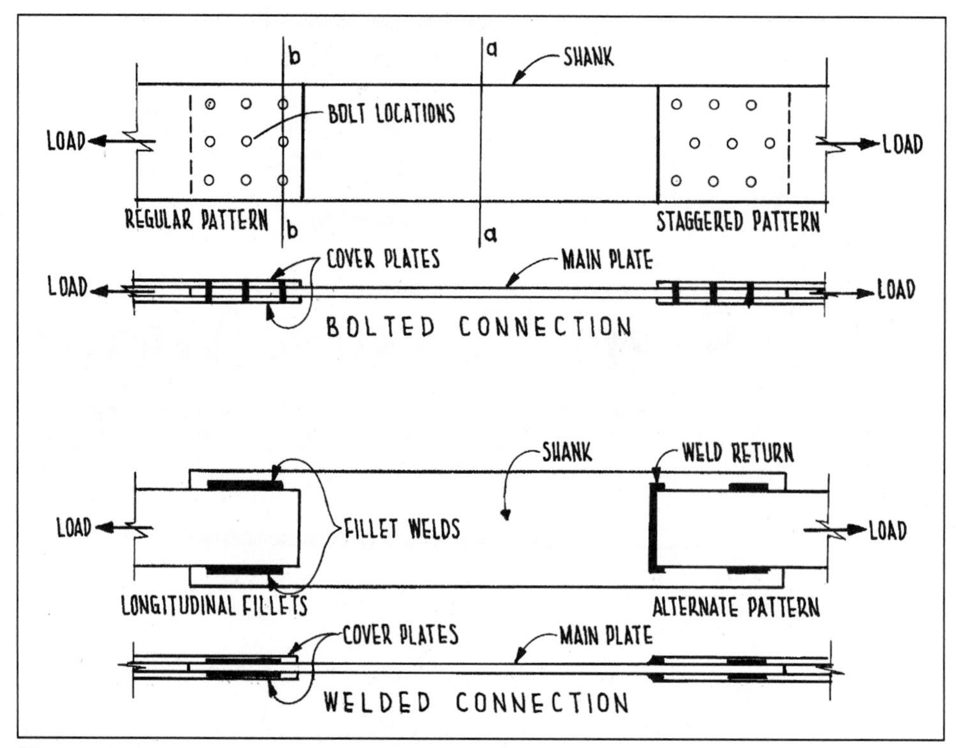

Figure 25-1 Typical bolted and welded tension member.

The outer plates in Figure 25-1 are called *cover plates* or *splice plates*. The inner plate is called the *main plate* or the *shank*. The connection may be either welded or bolted; a welded connection has the advantage that no material need be removed to accommodate the connection.

The computed tensile stress f_t in the shank of a tension member is found very simply as the direct stress:

$$f_t = P/A_g \tag{25-1}$$

where A_g is the gross cross sectional area. The basic assumption in such a calculation is, of course, that the tensile stress is distributed uniformly across the section. Regardless whether the load is delivered to the shank by a welded connection or a bolted connection, the allowable stress F_t on the shank of a tension member is given by ASD(D1) as:

$$F_t = 0.60F_y \tag{25-2}$$

The selection of a tension member is thus reduced to selecting a member having a large enough cross sectional area that the direct stress is less than the allowable tensile stress given by Eq.(25-2).

There is another part of the member, however, that has a different area but which must also sustain the same applied load. On the net area along the bolt holes, some of the material has been removed to provide the bolt holes. As a general rule, the diameter of the bolt hole is $^1/_{16}$ in. larger than the diameter of the bolt; the area removed is thus slightly larger than the area of the bolt.

A further consideration arises in the design of bolted connections. It is not likely that all the bolts in a line will be loaded exactly equally. Due to slight hole misalignments, some bolts will be loaded higher than other bolts. The load transferred to the plates will therefore be slightly higher at those bolts.

Further, there will be some level of stress concentration around the holes due simply to the discontinuity in the stressed area. There may also be some further stress concentrations due to the fact that the bolt size is not exactly equal to the hole size. The existence of the larger hole sizes, the uncertain stress concentrations and the load inequalities suggests that the allowable load be reduced somewhat to compensate for the potential overstress.

The design specification ASD(B-3) provides such a compensation by requiring a reduction in the net area:

$$A_e = UA_n \tag{25-3}$$

where A_e is the effective net area
U is the reduction coefficient at a line of fasteners (rivets, bolts or pins)
A_n is the net area

The net area A_n indicated in Eq(25-3) can lie along a straight line or it may lie along a zigzag line, as shown in the two layouts of Figure 25-2. The net area is computed as the gross area of the member with all holes, indentations and recesses deducted.

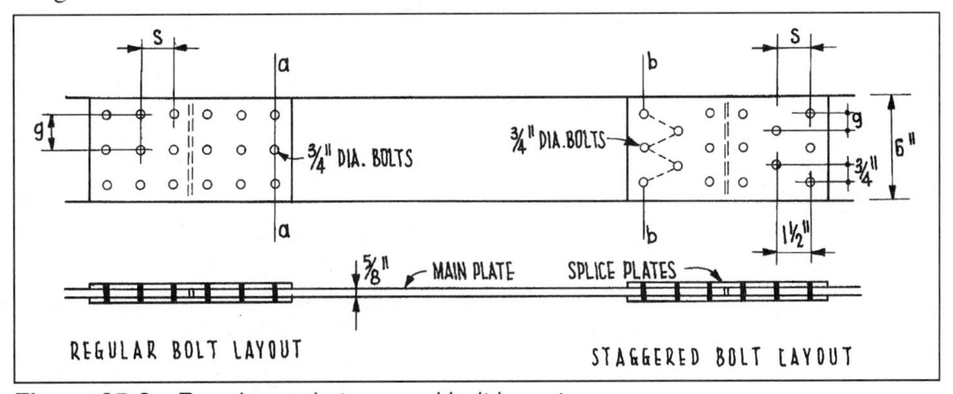

Figure 25-2 Regular and staggered bolt layouts.

In the two layouts shown in Figure 25-2, the main plate could fail along the straight line *aa* in the regular layout or it could fall along the zigzag line *bb* in the staggered layout. In either case, the main plate could actually separate along these lines without shearing any bolts. In the regular layout, the net area is the gross area A_g less the 3 bolt holes:

$$\begin{aligned} A_n &= (6 \times \tfrac{5}{8}) - 3(\tfrac{3}{4} + \tfrac{1}{16})(\tfrac{5}{8}) \\ &= 2.23 \text{ in.}^2 \end{aligned}$$

In the staggered layout, ASD(B2) requires that the full width of all 5 holes be deducted from the gross width, then the length $s^2/4_g$ must be added back for each inclined portion of the zigzag line:

$$\begin{aligned} A_n &= (6 \times \tfrac{5}{8}) - 5(\tfrac{3}{4} + \tfrac{1}{16})(\tfrac{5}{8}) + 4(1\tfrac{1}{2})^2 / (4 \times \tfrac{3}{4})(\tfrac{5}{8}) \\ &= 2.34 \text{ in.}^2 \end{aligned}$$

In the particular bolt layout shown in Figure 25-2, the net area along the straight line is thus found to be less than that along the zigzag line. Failure in the main plate, if it should occur, would therefore occur on the smaller area along the line *aa*.

For welded connections, similar stress concentrations arise where very large loads are being transferred from member to member in very short distances. Stress concentrations inevitably occur in such cases, becoming more severe as the weld lengths become shorter.

For welded connections, the design specification ASD(B3) provides a similar reduction coefficient for computing A_e:

$$A_e = UAg$$

where A_e is the effective stressed area
U is the reduction coefficient at a welded connection
A_g is the gross area of the stressed member

The conditions where the reduction coefficient U is to be applied are given in Table S-19 in the Technical Manual, along with the specific values of U for particular configurations. Table S-19 is referenced frequently in subsequent examples.

The allowable stress in the effective net area A_e is given by ASD(D.1):

$$F_t = 0.50\ F_u \tag{25-5}$$

where, as before, F_u is the ultimate stress of the steel.

Accordingly, the allowable load on a tension member in the vicinity of a connection is given as:

$$\text{Allowable } P_t = 0.50\ F_u A_e \tag{25-6}$$

where the area A_e is the effective area undergoing the direct stress, whether straight or zigzag.

For any tension member of A36 steel, the allowable capacity of the member itself thus becomes the lesser of two values:

a) $P_t(\text{kips}) \leq 0.60 F_y A_g = 22 A_g$ in the shank of the beam (25-7a)
b) $P_t(\text{kips}) \leq 0.50 F_u A_e = 29 A_e$ at the end connections (25-7b)

From Eqs.(25-7), the capacity of the member at a connection is found to be governed by a higher allowable stress but a lower effective area than it is in the shank. It is rarely worthwhile to try to predict which of these two cases will govern. Both cases are simply computed and the lesser value chosen as the limiting load.

Some examples will illustrate the application of Eqs.(25-7).

Example 25-1

Determination of allowable load on a tension member.

Given: Single angle 5 x 3 x 1/4 used as tension member (Table S-4b). Two 5/8 in. bolts connect angle to plate. All steel is ASTM A36.

To Find: Capacity of the angle in tension.

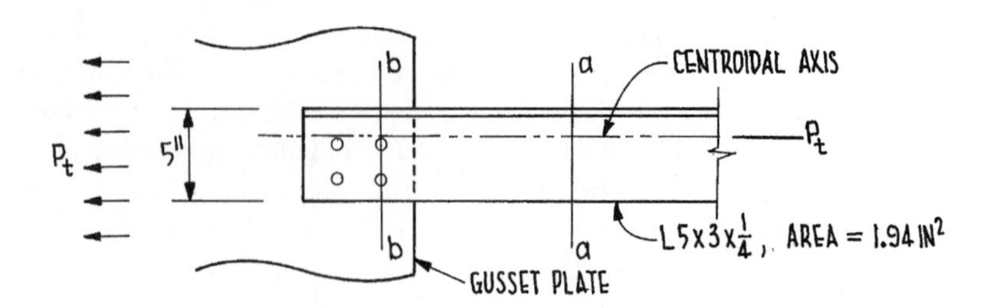

Solution: Capacity is the lesser of two cases, section *aa* or *bb*.

Section *aa*:

$P_t \leq 0.60F_yA_g = 22 \times 1.94$

≤ 42.68 kips

Section *bb*:

$P_t \leq 0.50\ F_uA_e = 29 \times A_e,\ U = 0.75$ (from Table S-19)

$A_e = UA_n = U(A_g - \text{holes})$

$A_e = 0.75\left[1.94 - 2(5/8 + 1/16)(1/4)\right] = 1.20\ \text{in.}^2$

$\leq 29 \times 1.20 = 34.71$ kips

For this case, the lesser value is at the connection.
Allowable $P_t = 34.71$ kips

Example 25-2

Determination of allowable load in a tension member.

Given: WT 4 x 12 used as a tension member (Table S-5f).
Six 1/2 in. bolts connect tee to plate. All steel is ASTM A-36.

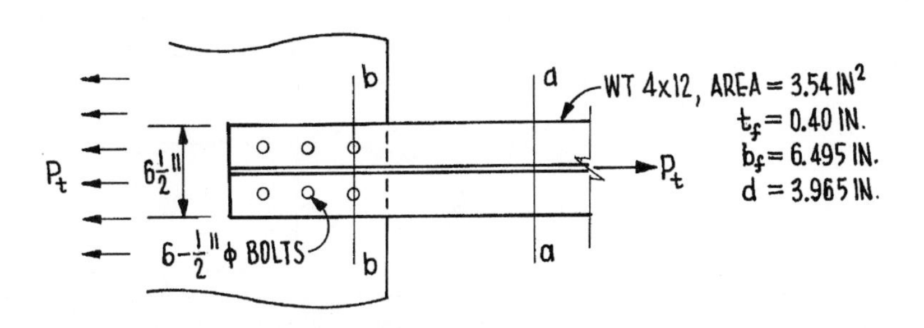

To Find: Capacity of the tee as a tension member.

Solution: Capacity is the lesser of two cases, aa or bb:

Section *aa*:

$P_t \leq 0.60F_yA_g = 22 \times 3.54$

≤ 77.88 kips

Section *bb*:

$P_t \leq 0.50\ F_uA_e = 29 \times A_e,\ U = 0.90$ (from Table S-19)

$A_e = UA_n = U(A_g - \text{holes})$

$0.90\left[3.54 - 2(1/2 + 1/16)(0.40)\right]$

$= 2.78\ \text{in.}^2$

$\leq 29 \times 2.78 = 80.65$ kips

For this case, the lesser value is in the shank.
Allowable $P_t = 77.88$ kips

In bolt groups on plates, it is frequently necessary to visualize the actual failure of the tension member should complete separation occur. Consider, for example, the splice connection of Figure 25-2. In order to determine the capacity of the main member in tension, it becomes necessary to identify the lines at which the member will actually tear apart.

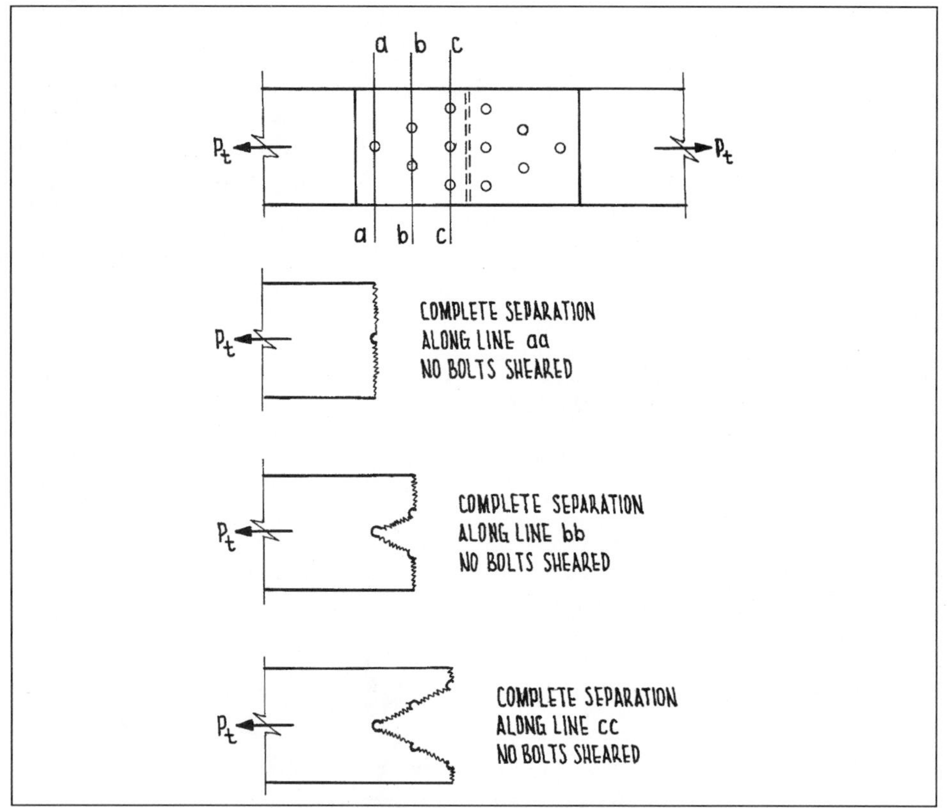

Figure 25-3 Lines at which full separation can occur.

The capacity P_t of each of the cases shown in Figure 25-3 must be determined just as tearing impends; the least value is then the limiting capacity.

The concept of visualizing a full separation is applied in the following examples.

Example 25-3

Determination of allowable load in a tension member.

Given: Bolt layout in splice plates as shown. Bolts 3/4 in. diameter, A36 steel.

To Find: Capacity of the main plate in tension.

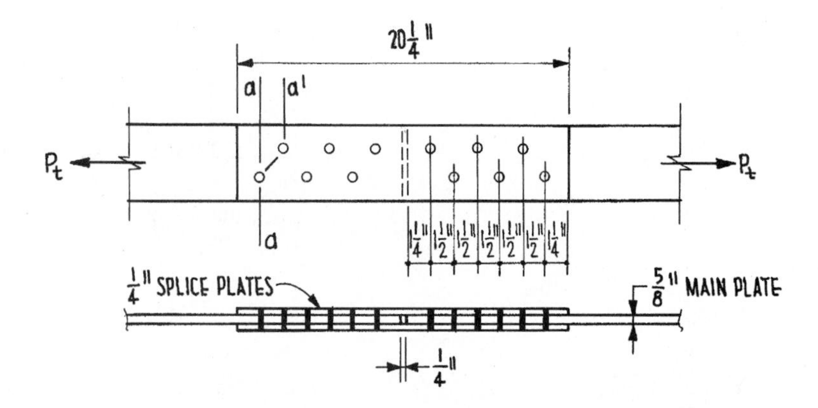

Solution: The capacity will be the lesser of two cases, either at the shank or at the connection.

At the shank:

$P_t \leq 0.60\ F_yA_g = 0.60 \times 36 \times 4 \times 0.625$

≤ 54 kips

When failure impends, the main plate could tear apart and separate either along line *aa'* or along line *aa*. The capacity at elastic levels will be computed for both cases.

Along line *aa'*:

$P_t \leq 0.50\ F_uA_e,\ U = 0.85$ (from Table S-19)

$A_e = UA_n = U[A_g - \text{holes} + \Sigma(s^2/4g)t]$

$= 0.85 \times \frac{5}{8}\left[4 - 2\left(\frac{3}{4} + \frac{1}{16}\right) + \left(1\frac{1}{2}\right)^2 / \left(4 \times 1\frac{1}{2}\right)\right]$

$= 1.46\ \text{in.}^2$

$\leq 0.50 \times 58 \times 1.46 = 42.37$ kips

Along line *aa*:

$P_t \leq 0.50\ F_uA_e,\ U = 0.85$ (from Table S-19)

$A_e = UA_n = U[A_g - \text{hole}]$

$= 0.85 \times \frac{5}{8}\left[4 - (1)\left(\frac{3}{4} + \frac{1}{16}\right)\right] = 1.99\ \text{in.}^2$

$\leq 0.50 \times 58 \times 1.99 = 57.71$ kips

Capacity is therefore limited by the capacity along line *aa'*.

$P_t = 42.37$ kips

It is noted in Example 25-3 that the total thickness of the two splice plates is less than the thickness of the main plate. Such a feature is poor design; it means that the capacity of the splice plates will be less than the capacity of the main plate. A better design would provide slightly more total thickness in the splice plates than in the main plate in order to assure that the "weak point" will not lie in the splice plates.

For a very short distance, at the gap between the main plates, the splice plates become the sole load-carrying tension members in the connection of Figure 25-3. The capacity of the splice plates is computed similarly to that of the main plate, but the full separation would occur at a different line. An example will illustrate the calculation of failure in the splice plates.

Example 25-4

Determination of allowable load in a tension member.

Given: Splice of Example 25-3.

To Find: Capacity of the splice plates.

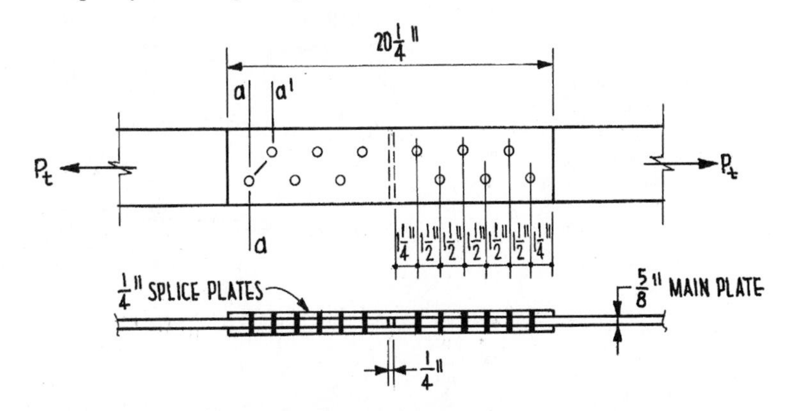

Solution: The capacity of the splice plate will be the lesser of two cases, either at the shank or at the connection.

The shank of the splice plates is limited to the 1/4 in. gap between the main plates. To tear apart at that point, both splice plates would have to fail. The basic capacity for that potential failure mode is calculated as:

$$P_t \leq 0.60\ F_yA_g = 0.60 \text{ x } 36 \text{ x } 4 \text{ x } 2 \text{ x } 1/4$$
$$\leq 43.20 \text{ kips}$$

The splice plates might also tear apart at line *bb'* or at line *bb*. In either case, both splice plates would have to fail. The elastic capacity for these failure modes is readily calculated.

Along line *bb'*:

$$P_t \leq 0.50\ F_uA_{e,}$$
$$U = 0.85 \text{ (from Table S-19)}$$
$$A_e = UA_n = U(A_g - \text{holes} + \Sigma s^2/4g)$$
$$= 0.85 \text{ x } 2 \text{ x } \tfrac{1}{4}\left[4 - 2(\tfrac{3}{4} + \tfrac{1}{16}) + (1\tfrac{1}{2})^2 / (4 \text{ x } 1\tfrac{1}{2})\right]$$
$$= 1.17 \text{ in.}^2$$
$$\leq 0.50 \text{ x } 58 \text{ x } 1.17 = 33.9 \text{ kips}$$

Along line *bb*:

$$P_t \leq 0.50\ F_uA_{e,}$$
$$U = 0.85 \text{ (from Table S-19)}$$
$$A_e = UA_n = U(A_g - \text{holes })$$
$$= 0.85 \text{ x } 2 \text{ x } \tfrac{1}{4}\left[4 - 1(\tfrac{3}{4} + \tfrac{1}{16})\right]$$
$$= 1.35 \text{ in.}^2$$
$$\leq 0.50 \text{ x } 58 \text{ x } 1.35 = 39.3 \text{ kips}$$

The limiting load is seen to be on the zigzag line *bb'*.
Least P_t = 33.9 kips

Example 25-5

Determination of allowable load in a tension member.

Given: Plate 1/2 in. x 4 in. welded to gusset as shown.

To Find: Capacity of plate as a tension member.

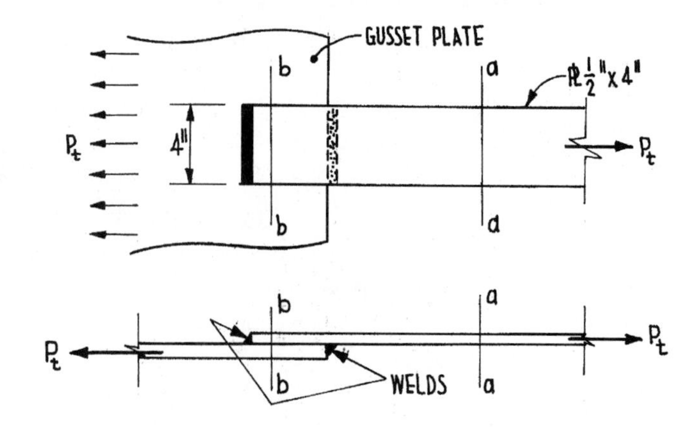

Solution: Capacity is the lesser of two cases.

Section *aa*:

$P_t \leq 0.60\ F_yA_g = 22 \times (1/2 \times 4)$
≤ 44 kips

Section *bb*:

$P_t \leq 0.50\ F_uA_e = 29A_e,\ U = 1.00$
$\leq 29 \times 1.00 \times 1/2 \times 4 = 58$ kips

For this case, the lesser value is in the shank.

Allowable $P_t = 44$ kips

Example 25-6

Determination of allowable load in a tension member.

Given: Transfer of tensile load from angle to plate as shown.

To Find: Capacity of connection.

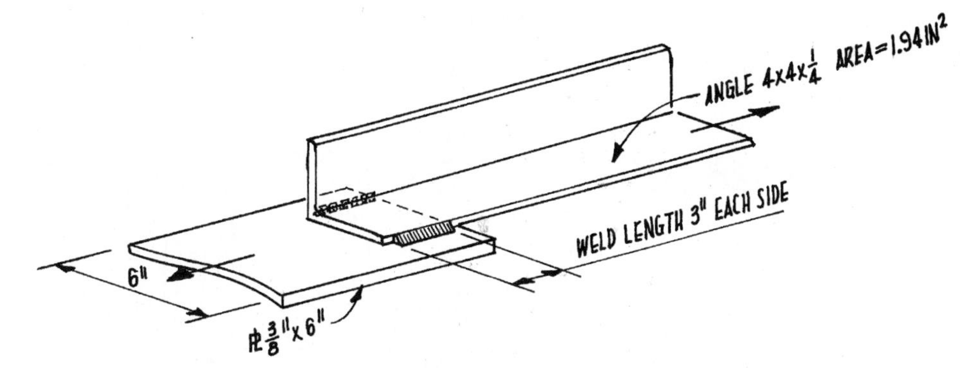

Solution: There are four possibilities to be investigated:

1. Capacity of the angle at some distance from the connection.
2. Capacity of the angle in the vicinity of the connection.
3. Capacity of the plate at some distance from the connection.
4. Capacity of the plate in the vicinity of the connection.

Capacity of the shank of the angle:

$P_t \leq 0.60\ F_yA_g = 22 \times 1.94$
≤ 42.68 kips

Capacity of the angle in the vicinity of the connection:
ASD(B3) is vague on this case; it is not clear whether the reduction factor applies to both members or only to the plate. In such cases, a "judgement call" becomes necessary. For this case, it is chosen to apply the reduction coefficient both to the plate and to the angle.

$P_t \leq 0.50\ F_uA_e = 29\ A_e,\ U = 0.75$ (from Table S-19)
$\leq 29 \times 0.75 \times 1.94 = 42.20$ in.^{2}

Capacity of the shank of the plate:

$P_t \leq 0.60\ F_yA_g = 22 \times 3/8 \times 6$
≤ 49.50 kips

Capacity of the plate in the vicinity of the connection:

$P_t \leq 0.50\ F_u A_e = 29\ A_e$, U = 0.75 (from Table S-19)

$\leq 29 \times 0.75 \times 3/8 \times 6 = 48.94$ kips

From the four possible limitations, it is found that the load is limited to 42.20 kips by the angle in the vicinity of the connection.

Use Pt ≤ 42.20 kips

25.2 Load Capacity of Threaded Tension Members

Placing any threaded region of a bolt under a tensile load is generally frowned upon, even though it is commonly done. The attitude extends into other threaded tension members as well. Typically, such threaded tension members may range from the cross bracing in a prefabricated steel building to the hangars supporting a mezzanine floor in a bank. In all cases, it is much preferred to design all connections such that no threaded member is loaded in tension at the threads.

The reason for such an attitude lies in the existence of the stress concentrations that inevitably occur at the roots of threads. A sketch of a typical threaded member is shown in Figure 25-4. The sharp reentrant corner at each thread can easily produce stress concentration factors as high as two or even higher. Coupled with vibrations or with cyclical loading, such stress concentrations are an eminent point of concern in the design of the member.

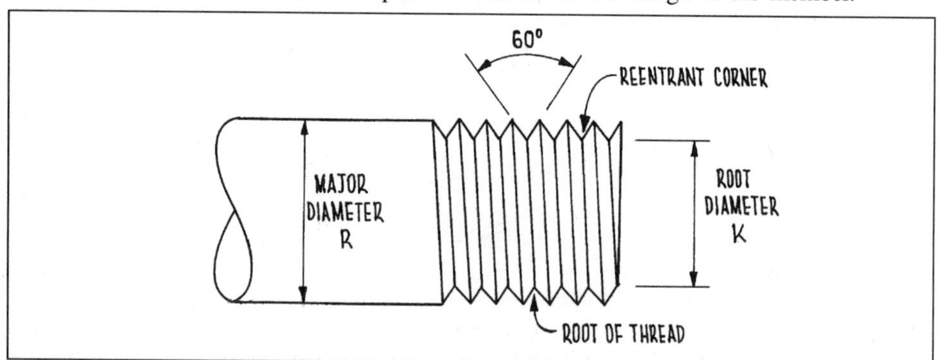

Figure 25-4 Typical threaded tension member.

A very common use of threaded bars in tension is in the diagonal cross-bracing in prefabricated steel buildings. A sketch of such a structure is shown in Figure 25-5. For loads acting against the length of the building, the structure is the three hinged arches formed by the building frames. For loads acting against the ends of the building, the structure is the trussed bays at the ends of the building, where the counterdiagonals (usually made of threaded rods) form a truss between the two end frames.

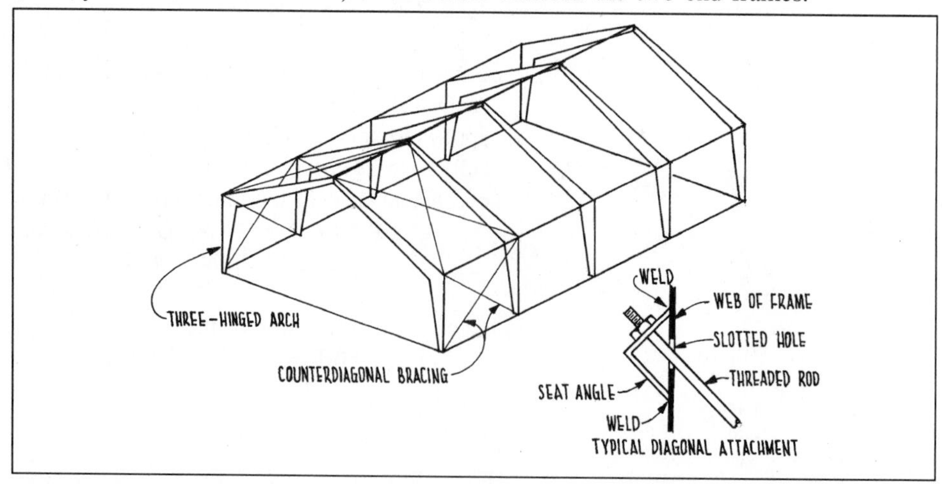

Figure 25-5 Typical prefabricated building.

In applications such as that shown in Figure 25-5, the use of threaded bars is quite inefficient. The reduction in cross sectional area at the threaded ends can be significant. The end result is that a large diameter bar must be provided over many feet of unthreaded length in order that the cross-sectional area will be large enough at the few inches of threaded length.

To counter such inefficiency, it is the practice to mechanically compress the ends of the bar longitudinally to produce an *upset* end through plastic deformation. The upset portion is then threaded. Such a threaded upset bar is shown in Figure 25-6.

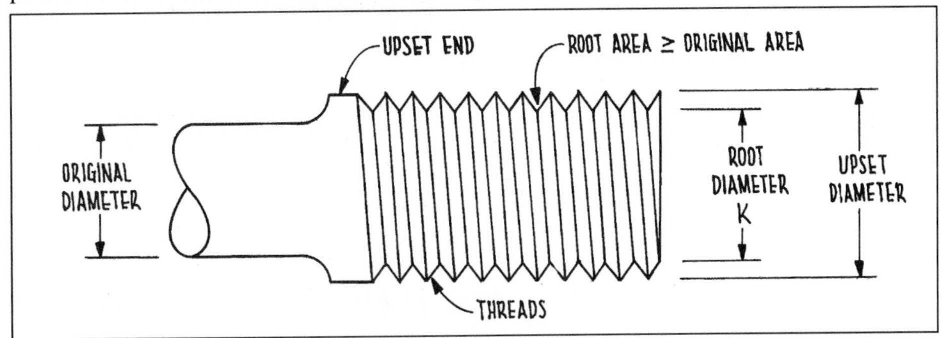

Figure 25-6 Typical threaded upset bar.

In upset bars such as that of Figure 25-6, the bar is deliberately fabricated such that the allowable load on the root area of the threads will be larger than the allowable load on the gross area of the shank. In that way, no efficiency is lost due to threading.

Dimensions of standard threads are given in Table S-20 in the Technical Manual. Allowable tensile stresses on fasteners and other threaded parts are given in Table S-21; particular attention is directed to footnote *c* of Table S-21. With such data, the allowable load on threaded parts is readily calculated.

Some examples will illustrate the computation of allowable load on threaded tension members.

Example 25-7

Determination of allowable load on tension members.

Given: One inch diameter bar, threaded ends, A36 steel.

To Find: Comparison of allowable tensile load between shank and ends.

Solution: Allowable tensile load on shank:

$$P_t = 0.60F_yA_g = 0.60 \times 36 \times (1)^2\pi/4$$
$$= 16.96 \text{ kips}$$

Allowable load on threaded ends:

From Table 20, tensile stress area at threads = 0.606 in.^{2}

From Table 21, the allowable stress is $0.33F_u$.

The allowable tensile load at the threads is:

$$P_t = 0.33F_u \times A = 0.33 \times 58 \times 0.606 = 11.60 \text{ kips}$$

The allowable load at the threads is thus reduced to 68% of that on the shank.

Example 25-8

Determination of allowable load on tension members.

Given: One inch diameter bar with upset threaded ends, A36 steel.

To Find: Allowable tensile load on bar and required upset diameter.

Solution: Allowable load as governed by the shank:

From Table S-20, tensile stress area = area of shank
= 0.785 in.^{2}

From Table S-21, see footnote *c*, allowable stress on shank = 0.60 F_y = 21,600 psi

Allowable load on shank = $0.60F_y$ x area of shank
= 21,600 x 0.785 = 19,600 lb.

Required area of upset end to provide capacity at least as large as shank load:

From Table S-21, allowable stress on upset threaded area
= $0.33F_u$ = 19,000 psi

Required upset threaded area = load/stress:
A = P/f_s = 19,600/19,000
= 1.03 in.^{2} tensile stress area

From Table S-20, required diameter to obtain at least 1.03 in.^{2} tensile area: diameter = 1$^3/_8$ in.

It is concluded that the end of the bar must be upset to 1$^3/_8$ in. diameter before threading if it is to be stronger than the shank.

25.3 Types of Connections

Load is transferred from one member to another member at a *connection*. The connection itself may be made by bolting or by welding. Typical examples of welded and bolted connections are shown in Figure 25-7.

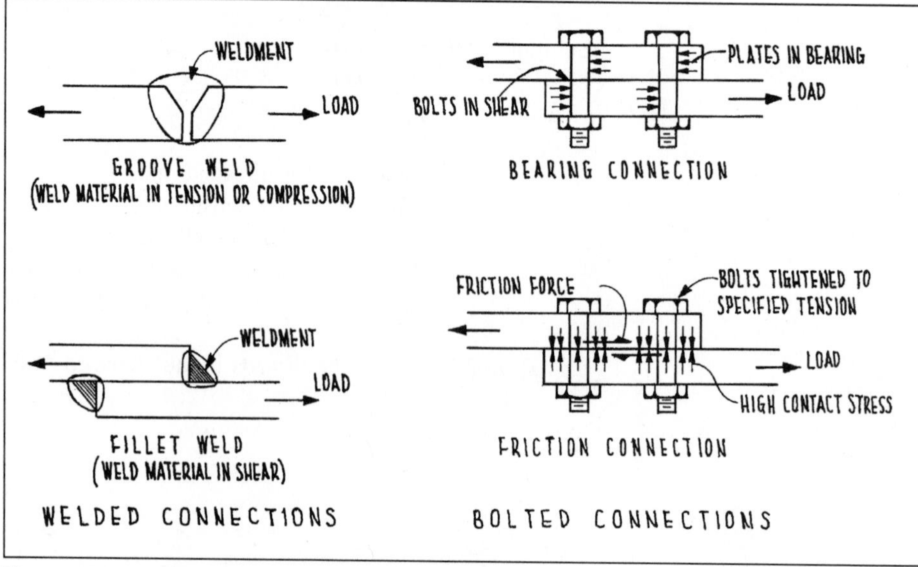

Figure 25-7 Typical structural connections.

The two basic systems of connections in current use are those shown in Figure 25-7.

I **Bolted Connections** — Members are joined by being bolted together. Bolted connections are made in two types:

1. Bearing connections, in which some slight slippage occurs between the members. Load is transferred by bearing of the plates against the bolts, then by shear in the bolts.
2. Friction connections, in which high tensile strength bolts are used to clamp the two members so tightly together that the entire load is transferred directly from plate to plate by friction.

II **Welded Connections** — Members are joined by fusion welding, either by electric arc or by gas heat. Welded connections are made in two types:

1. Groove (or butt) welds, in which the weld material is loaded in direct tension or compression.
2. Fillet welds, in which the weld material is loaded in shear.

The load path in a bolted bearing connection must always be kept in mind: the applied load is transferred by bearing from one structural member to the bolts. The bolts in turn transfer the load to a second structural member, but for a very short distance in the load path, the bolts become the primary load carrying member. In friction type connections, however, as opposed to bearing type connections, the bolts do not transfer any of the applied load; the bolts simply clamp the structural members together so tightly that the applied load is transferred member-to-member entirely by friction.

Akin to bolted bearing connections, all welded connections transfer the load from a structural member to an intermediate weld material, then transfer the load onward from the weld material to a second structural member. Over this short distance, the weld material becomes the primary load carrying member. There is no welded connection that transfers load directly from member to member as does the bolted friction connection.

In the following sections, the transfer of load from member-to- connector-to-member is carefully traced. It will be seen that the major uncertainty does not lie in the load carrying members or even in the connectors. Rather, the problem lies in the *transfer* of load from one member to a connector, and then in the *transfer* of the load onward from that connector to the next member.

25.4 Load Capacity of Bolts in Bearing Connections

The capacity of bolts in shear is readily determined. The capacity is simply the allowable shear stress times the sheared area. Some typical cases of bolts in shear are shown in Figure 25-8.

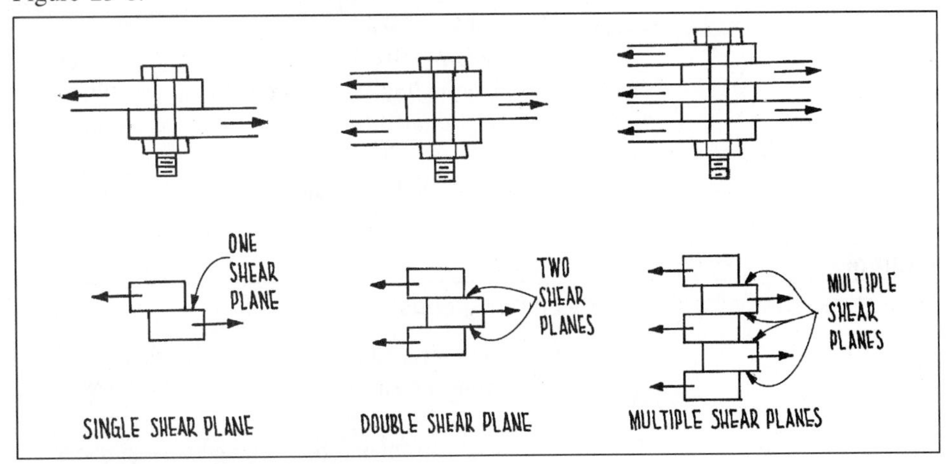

Figure 25-8 Bolts in shear.

The capacity of the load cases shown in Figure 25-8 is seen to be a direct shear calculation:

$$\text{Allowable load} = \text{allowable shear stress x sheared area} \qquad (25\text{-}8)$$

In the direct shear calculation given in Eq.(25-8), the allowable shear stress is that given in Table S-21 in the Technical Manual. The last column on the right gives the values of allowable shear stress for rivets, ASTM A307 bolts, A325 bolts and A490 bolts, in bearing type connections. (Bolts made of A325 steel or A490 bolts are high tensile strength bolts which may also be used to make friction type connections.)

One additional consideration is included in Table S-21, that of having the threaded portion of the bolt in a shear plane. Two possible configurations are shown in Figure 25-9, one with threads deliberately excluded from all shear planes and the second with threads not deliberately excluded from the shear planes.

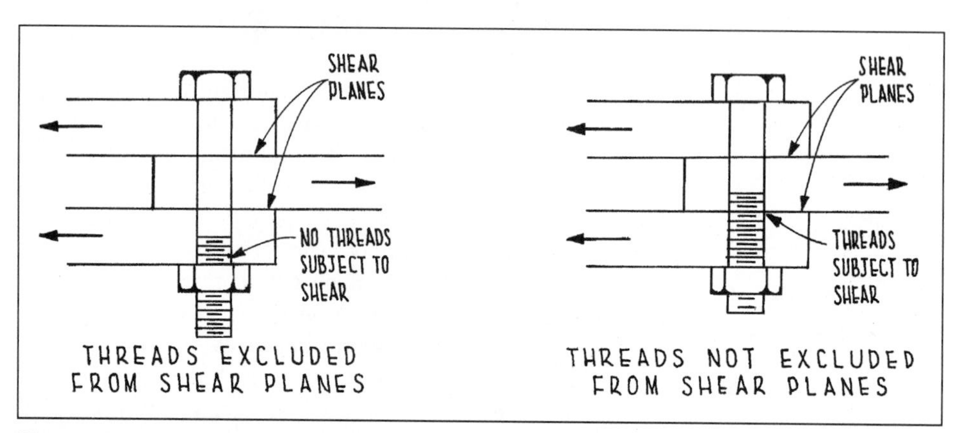

Figure 25-9 Threads in shear planes.

When threads of A325 bolts are excluded from the shear planes, the allowable shear stress on the bolt is given in Table S-21 as 30 ksi. When threads are not excluded from the shear planes, the allowable shear stress on *all* shear planes is reduced to 21 ksi, or 70% of that with threads excluded. Note that when the values of Table S-21 are used, it is not necessary to find or to use the actual root area; the reduced allowable shear stress is applied to the unthreaded gross area A_g of the bolt.

It is recalled from the previous section that the allowable force in tension on a threaded member is computed as the unreduced stress $0.60F_y$ times a reduced area A_e. In calculations for shear, however, the shear force on a threaded fastener is computed as a reduced stress times the unreduced bolt area A_g. It is important to remember the distinction between the two cases.

Sizes of standard bolts and their shear areas are given in Table S-26 in the Technical Manual. Also given in Table S-26 are the load capacities, or *bolt values*, for the several possibilities. Also included for general reference are the shank areas of the bolts to four decimal places.

Some examples will illustrate the calculation of capacity of bolt groups in shear.

Example 25-9

Determination of allowable loads on bolt groups.

Given: Bolt arrangement shown in the sketch, A325 bolts, threads not excluded from the shear plane.

To Find: Capacity of the bolt arrangement in shear.

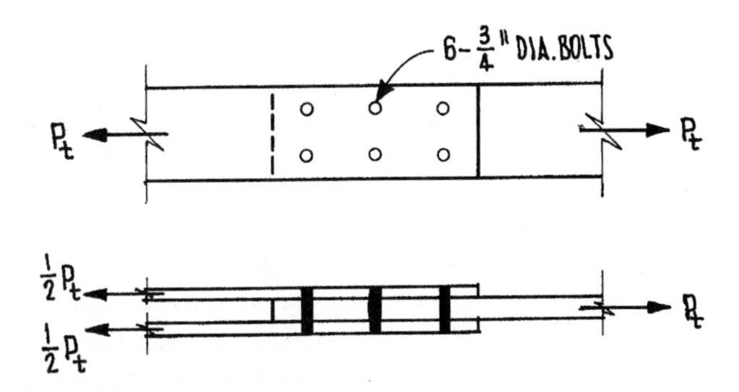

Solution: The given arrangement places six bolts 3/4 in. diameter in double shear. The total sheared area is then:

$$A_v = 2 \times 6 \times \pi/4 (0.75)^2 = 5.30 \text{ in.}^2$$

The allowable shear stress on A325 bolts where threads are not excluded from the shear plane is found from Table S-21 to be 21.0 ksi.

The allowable load is then:

$$P_t = F_v A_v = 21 \times 5.30 = 111.3 \text{ kips}$$

Alternatively, the allowable load might be computed from Table S-26 by finding the allowable load on one 3/4 in. A325 bolt in double shear and multiplying by 6:

$$P_t = 6 \times 18.6 = 111.6 \text{ kips}$$

The final result is of course the same, within ordinary roundoff variation.

Example 25-10

Determination of allowable load on bolt groups.

Given: Bolt arrangement as shown in the sketch, A307 bolts, threads not excluded from the shear planes.

To Find: Capacity of the bolt arrangement in shear.

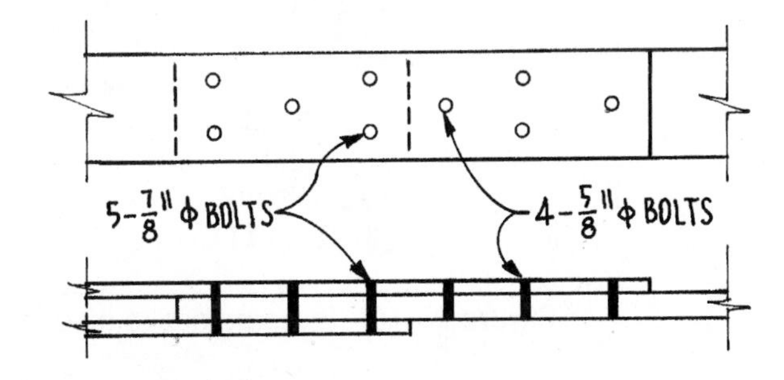

Solution: The given arrangement places four 5/8 in. bolts in single shear and five 7/8 in. bolts in double shear. The total sheared area is then:

$$A_v = 4 \times 1 \times \pi/4 (0.625)^2 + 5 \times 2 \times \pi/4 (0.875)^2 = 7.24 \text{ in.}^2$$

The allowable shear stress on A307N bolts is found from Table S-21 to be 10.0 ksi.

The allowable load is then:

$$P_t = F_v A_v = 10 \times 7.24 = 72.4 \text{ kips}$$

Alternatively, the allowable load might be computed from Table S-26 by finding the allowable load on one $^7/_8$ in. diameter bolt in double shear and multiplying by 5. To this is added the allowable load on one $^5/_8$ in. diameter bolt in single shear multiplied by 4:

$$P_t = 12 \times 5 + 3.1 \times 4 = 72.4 \text{ kips}$$

The final result is of course the same.

25.5 Load Capacity of Plates in Bearing Against Bolts

In earlier sections, methods of finding the load capacity of tension members were developed to include potential limitations at both the shank and the connections; the tear line at a connection included straight lines of holes as well as zigzag lines of holes. Methods of finding the load capacity of bolt groups where the fasteners resisted the load through shear were then developed. In this section, methods are introduced for completing the load path, that is, finding the load capacity for transferring load from the plate to the bolt groups and from the bolt groups onward to the next plate.

Load is transferred from plate-to-plate or bolt-to-plate through bearing between the two elements. Two cases of failure can occur:

1. Small bolt - thick plate: the bolt will shear without causing any damage or yield in the plate.
2. Large bolt - thin plate: the plate will wrinkle in bearing at the contact area and the hole will elongate, both without causing any damage to the bolt.

A sketch showing these two extremes is given in Figure 25-10. It should be apparent that the preferred design for a connection will keep the failure in Case 1, where the bolt shears before the holes start to elongate.

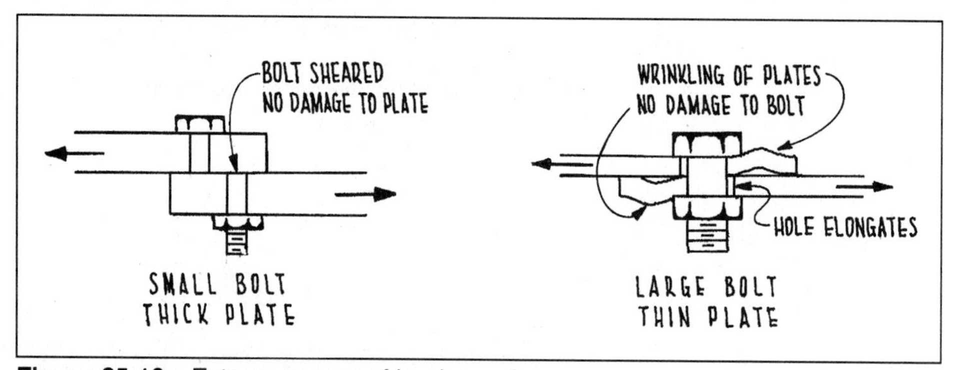

Figure 25-10 Extreme cases of load transfer.

In a bearing connection, the bearing stress to be allowed between the plate and the bolts depends heavily on the bolt layout. In turn, the layout of the bolts depends heavily on the bearing stresses to be allowed. The interrelationship between layout requirements and stress requirements thus creates a rather intricate design procedure.

The dimensions used in the bolt layout are shown in Figure 25-11. The gage distance *g* shown in Figure 25-11 can sometimes be confusing. It is usually taken to be the transverse distance between bolts along a straight line as shown in Figure 25-11. However, in computing plate tearing along a zigzag line (as shown earlier in Figure 25-2), it is taken to be the transverse distance between bolts along the zigzag line. In succeeding calculations, it will be necessary to observe the distinction between the two cases.

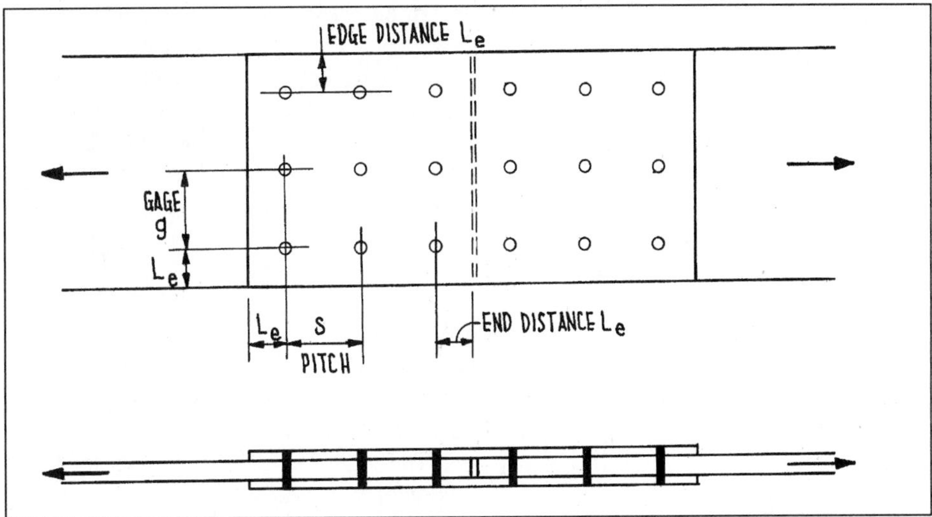

Figure 25-11 Bolt layout dimensions.

In the dimensions of Figure 25-11, note that the symbol L_e is used to denote both end distance and edge distance. Note also that the gage distance g is measured transverse to the load, and the pitch distance s is measured parallel to the load. Similarly, *edge distance* is measured transverse to load, and *end distance* is measured parallel to load.

The layout dimensions and stress requirements for bearing connections are prescribed in ASD(J3). They have been summarized in Table S-24 in the Technical Manual. One point in Table S-24 is immediately questionable: the *allowable* bearing stress F_p given in Requirement 3 is seen to be 20% to 50% greater than the *ultimate* stress F_u of the plate. Though seemingly impossible, there is no error or misprint; the values are correct. They yield an equivalent solution to a very complex stress problem. Over the years, this equivalent solution has been found to produce results consistently in agreement with full scale tests.

The following examples will demonstrate the calculation of load capacity using the values of Table S-24.

Example 25-11

Determination of load capacity in bearing.

Given: Trial bolt layout for a splice as shown in the sketch. Applied load = 130 kips; ASTM A36 steel; sheared edges. Bolts 3/4 in. diameter, A325N; no wrinkling of the plate is permitted.

To Find: Whether the layout will sustain the load in bearing on the main plate.

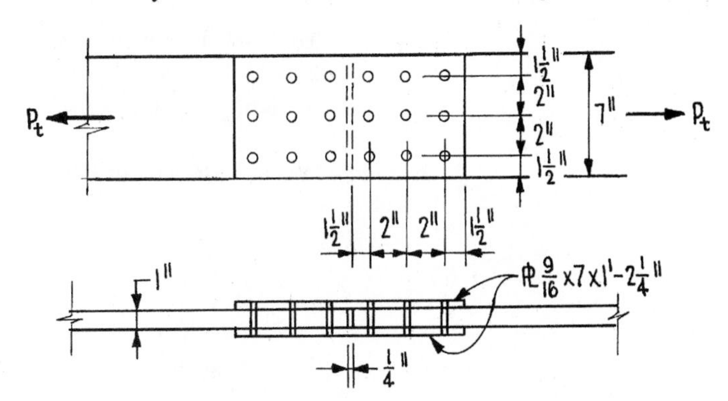

Solution: Values of s, g and L_e are determined:

In all cases, L_e is $1^1/_2$ in. or 2d

In all cases, s is 2 in. or 2.67 d

In all cases, g is 2 in. or 2.67 d

From these results, it is seen that the conditions do not satisfy Requirement 3 of Table S-24. The allowable stress is therefore given by Requirement 4:

$F_p = L_e F_u / 2d = (1.5)(58)/(2)(0.75)$

$= 58$ ksi but $1^3/_8$ in. $\leq 1.2F_u$

Use $F_p = 58$ ksi

For $F_p = 58$ ksi, the gage g of 2.67 in. is seen to satisfy Requirement 5.

For $F_p = 58$ ksi, the pitch s must also satisfy the computed limit given in Requirement 5:

$$S \geq 2P / F_u t + d/2 = 2(130/9) / (58 \text{ x } 1) + (3/4)(1/2) = 0.87 \text{ in.}$$

The pitch s of 2.67 in. is seen to satisfy all conditions in Requirement 5.

For $F_p = 58$ ksi, end distance and edge distance must also satisfy the computed limit given in Requirement 6:

$$L_e \geq 2P / F_u t = 2(130/9) / (58 \text{ x } 1) = 0.50$$

The end and edge distances of $1^1/_2$ in. are seen to satisfy Requirement 6.

The allowable load in bearing of the main plate against the group of 9 bolts is therefore found to be:

$P_t = 9 \text{ x } 58 \text{ x } 1 \text{ x } 3/4 = 392\text{k} > 130$ kips (O.K.)

It is noted that the allowable load of 392 kips in bearing is much greater than the design load of 130 kips. Such a high capacity in bearing is not unusual; it is when bolts are large and plates are thin that bearing becomes a limitation.

It should be noted that an allowable stress of $1.2F_u$ could, in some circumstances, be obtained from Requirement 4. In such a case, even though the numerical value of F_p turns out to be the same as that of Requirement 3, all subsequent calculations are those used when F_p is found from Requirement 4.

Another example will illustrate the calculation of load capacity in bearing when s, g and L_e are unusual.

Example 25-12

Determination of load capacity in bearing.

Given: Trial bolt layout for a splice as shown in the sketch. Applied load = 60 kips; ASTM A36 steel; sheared edges; bolts 1 in. diameter; A325N; no wrinkling of plate permitted.

To Find: Whether the layout will sustain the load in bearing on the main plate.

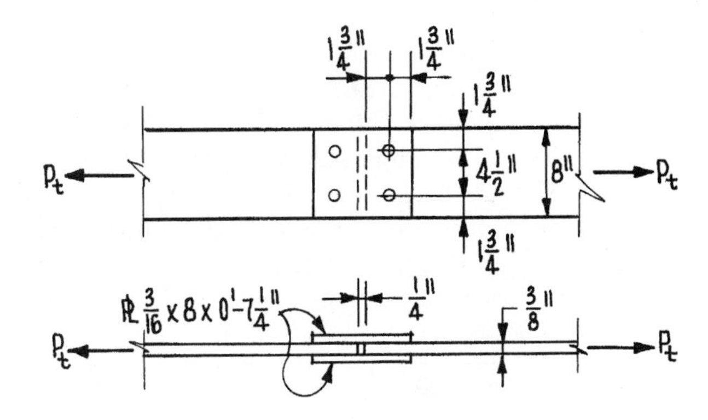

Solution: Values of s, g and L_e are determined.

In all cases, $L_e = 1^3/_4$ in. or 1.75 d

$s = 0$ (only one bolt in the line of load)

$g = 4^1/_2$ in. or 4.5 d

It is seen that these values do not satisfy Requirement 3 of Table S-24. The allowable stress is therefore that of Requirement 4.

$F_p = L_eF_u/2d = (1.75)(58)/(2)(1) = 51 \text{ ksi} \leq 1.2F_u$

Use $F_p = 51$ ksi.

For $F_p = 51$ ksi, the gage g is seen to satisfy Requirement 5.

For $F_p = 51$ ksi, the pitch s does not apply; a single line of bolts in the direction of load is permitted.

For $F_p = 51$ ksi, the end distance must satisfy the computed limit given in Requirement 6:

$$L_e \geq 2P / F_u t = 2(^{60}/_2) / (58)(^3/_8)$$
$$= 2.75\text{in.} \geq 1.75 \text{ in. (No Good)}$$

It is found that the end distance is inadequate. But, if the end distance in the main plate were to be extended 1 in., the layout would then be adequate for the main plate. Note, however, that the end distance of the splice plates would also have to be extended by the same amount (verification is left to the reader). The total length of the splice plates would therefore have to be increased to $11^1/_4$ in.

Assuming the end distance is, in fact, increased to this minimum required distance, the allowable load in bearing on the two bolts would then be:

$P_t = 2 \times F_u \times$ projected area

$= 2 \times 51 \times 1 \times 0.375 = 38 \text{ kips} \leq 60 \text{ kips}$ (No Good)

It is concluded that the design is also inadequate in bearing. It will probably be necessary to use a larger number of smaller bolts. A completely new trial design is obviously in order.

25.6 Load Capacity in Block Tearout of Bearing Connections

In relatively recent years, a type of failure that involves both tension and shear has been included in the AISC design specification. The failure is called *block tearout* and is most likely to be found where a small tension member is connected to a much larger member. In such a case, the loaded area on the large member is relatively small, almost in the realm of being a point load.

Two typical cases of such loading is shown in Figure 25-12, where truss members are bolted to a relatively large gusset plate. The potential failure mode is shown also, where the tensile load on the truss members tears out a small block of the gusset plate. For such a failure to occur (i.e., "as failure impends"), the block would have to fail in tension along its interior end and in shear along its sides. Note that no bolts have been sheared.

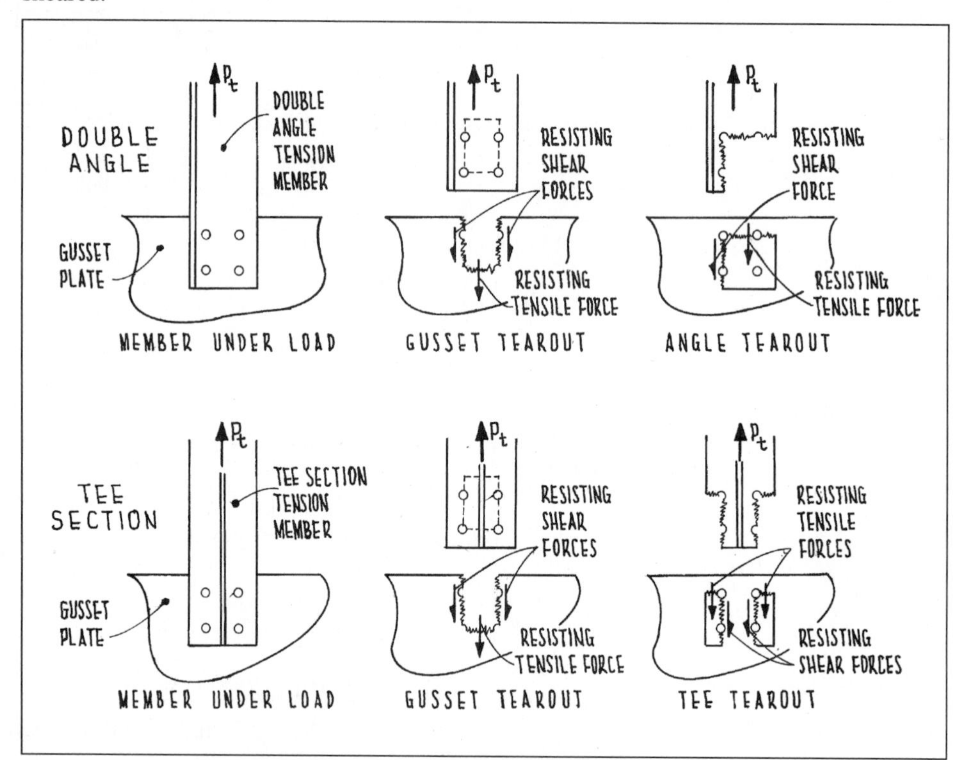

Figure 25-12 Block tearout at a gusset plate.

Also shown in Figure 25-12 is the potential for block tearout in the double angles and the structural tee. For either member, there is no way to predict whether the limiting capacity will be in the truss member or in the gusset plate. The capacities are simply computed for both cases and the lesser capacity taken as the limiting capacity.

The allowable load for block tearout is readily computed. In the block of Figure 25-12, the allowable load is simply the sum of the resisting forces:

$$\begin{aligned}\text{Allowable load} &= \text{allowable tension stress x area undergoing tensile stress} \\ &\quad + \text{allowable shear stress x area undergoing shear stress} \qquad (25\text{-}9)\end{aligned}$$

The allowable shear stress F_v and the allowable tensile stress F_t in block tearout are given in ASD(J4):

$$F_v = 0.30\ F_u \qquad (25\text{-}10)$$

$$F_t = 0.50\ F_u \qquad (25\text{-}11)$$

The areas undergoing the shear and tension stresses are computed as net areas, that is, with bolt holes deducted.

An example will illustrate the calculation of block tearout.

Example 25-13

Determination of load capacity in block tearout.

Given: Double angle strut connected to a gusset plate as shown in the sketch. A325X bolts, ASTM A36 steel. Standard hole sizes. Standard gage spaces (see Technical Manual Table S-22). Bolts $^5/_8$ in. diameter.

To Find: Allowable load capacity in block tearout.

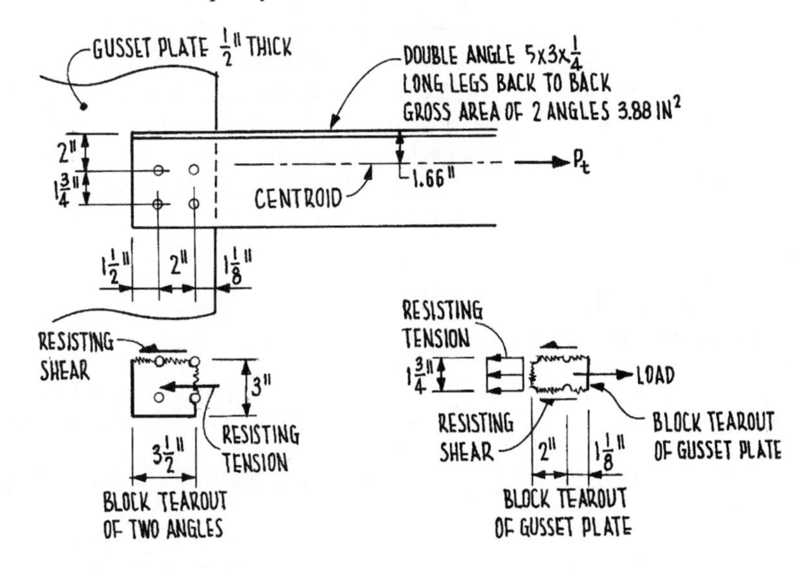

Solution: Allowable stresses are given by Eq.(30-10) and Eq.(30-11).

$$F_t = 0.50\ F_u = 29\ \text{ksi}$$
$$F_v = 0.30F_u = 17.4\ \text{ksi}$$

Stressed areas are computed as net areas.

(In computing the net areas, the bolt holes are deducted as full diameters on the sides and as half diameters at the two inside corners).

For the tension area in the gusset plate:

$$A_t = \tfrac{1}{2}\left[1\tfrac{3}{4} - (\tfrac{5}{8} + \tfrac{1}{16})(\tfrac{1}{2})(2)\right] = 0.53\ \text{in.}^2$$

For the shear area in the gusset plate:

$$A_v = (2)(\tfrac{1}{2})\left[(2 + 1\tfrac{1}{8}) - (\tfrac{5}{8} + \tfrac{1}{16})(1\tfrac{1}{2})\right] = 2.09\ \text{in.}^2$$

The total allowable resisting force on the gussett plate is then:

$$P_t = F_tA_t + F_vA_v = 29 \text{x} 0.53 + 17.4 \text{x} 2.09 = 52\ \text{kips}$$

For the tension area of the two angles:

$$A_t = (2)(\tfrac{1}{4})\left[3 - (\tfrac{5}{8} + \tfrac{1}{16})(1\tfrac{1}{2})\right] = 0.98\ \text{in.}^2$$

For the sheared area of the two angles:

$$A_v = (2)(\tfrac{1}{4})\left[3.5 - (\tfrac{5}{8} + \tfrac{1}{16})(1\tfrac{1}{2})\right] = 1.23\ \text{in.}^2$$

The total allowable resisting force on the two angles is then:

$$P_t = F_t A_t + F_v A_v = 29 \times 0.98 + 17.4 \times 1.23 = 49.82 \text{ kips}$$

The limiting case of block tearout is thus found to be in the two angles.

Allowable capacity = 49.8 kips

As a matter of interest, the allowable load in the double angle was computed in an outside calculation and was found to be 69 kips at the connection. The capacity of the four A325X bolts in double shear was found to be 74 kips. The capacity of the connection in bearing was found to be adequate. The "weak" part of this connection is found to be in the block tearout, with its capacity of 49.8 kips.

Another example will illustrate the calculation of the capacity of a tension connection in block tearout.

Example 25-14

Determination of load capacity in block tearout.

Given: Tension hanger attached by splice plates to a structural tee as shown. A325N bolts, ASTM A36 steel. Standard hole sizes.

To Find: Allowable load capacity on the WT 8 x 25 in block tearout.

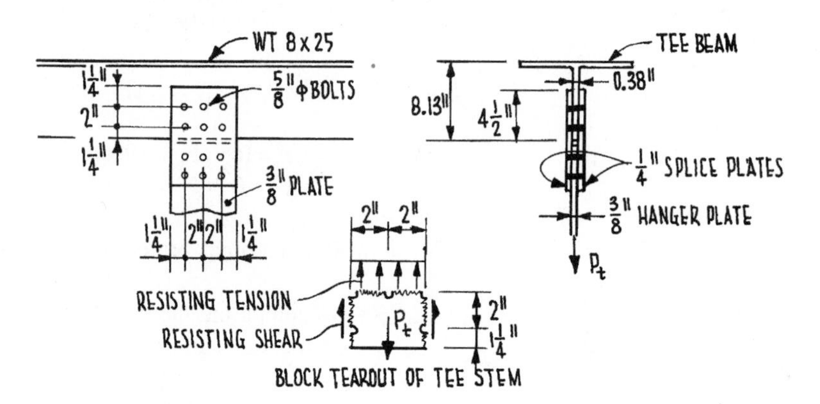

Solution: Allowable stresses are given to be Eq.(30-10) and Eq.(30-1):

$$F_t = 0.50F_u = 29 \text{ ksi}$$
$$F_v = 0.30F_u + 17.4 \text{ ksi}$$

In computing the net areas, the bolt holes are deducted as full diameters on the sides and as half diameters at the two inside corners.

For the net area of the web undergoing tension:

$$A_t = 0.38\left[4 - (5/8 + 1/16)(2)\right] = 1.00 \text{ in.}^2$$

For the net area of the web undergoing shear:

$$A_v = 2(0.38\left[(2 + 1\tfrac{1}{4}) - (5/8 + 1/16)(1\tfrac{1}{2})\right] = 1.69 \text{ in.}^2$$

The total allowable resisting force is then:

$$P_t = F_t A_t + F_v A_v = 29 x 1.00 + 17.4 x 1.69 = 58.41 \text{ kips}$$

It is noted that the two splice plates will be subject to block tearout in a pattern identical to that or the tee. Their combined thickness, however, is greater than that of the tee, so the tee is the critical member.

The capacity of the 3/8 in. hanger plate was calculated aside and found to be 36.2 kips. The capacity of six 5/8 in. bolts in double shear was also calculated aside and found to be 77.4 kips. With a block tearout capacity of 58.4 kips, the three capacities are seen to be badly imbalanced.

A better strategy might be to change the bolt layout to a single line of three 5/8 in. diameter bolts placed 2 in. from the bottom edge of the tee. Such an arrangement should provide better balance in load capacity. Verification of this revised layout is assigned as an outside problem.

25.7 Design of Bolted Bearing Connections in Tension

Choosing plate thicknesses and bolt layouts for a bolted connection is called the *design* of the connection. It is largely a trial and error procedure in which a complete trial layout is made, which includes all sizes, spacings, thicknesses and dimensions. The trial layout is then analyzed in detail to find its weakest failure mode; the load capacity of this weakest failure mode is the limiting load capacity for that particular load.

In preceding sections, methods of finding the load capacity of various layouts have been investigated for the following failure modes:

1. Load capacity of a tension member at its shank.
   (Tensile failure of plate, in direct stress).
   $P_t = F_t A_g$ $F_t = 0.60F_y$
   A_g = gross cross sectional area.

2. Load capacity of a tension member at its end connections.
   (Tensile failure of plate, with no bolts sheared).
   $P_t = F_t A_e$ $F_t = 0.50F_u$
   $A_e = UA_n$
   A_n = net area, less holes, straight or zigzag.

3. Load capacity of A325 bolt groups in shear.
   (Shear failure of bolts in direct shear).
   $P_t = F_v A_v$ F_t = 21 ksi, threads not excluded.
   F_t = 30 ksi, threads excluded
   $A_v = A_g$ = Area of bolt at shank.

4. Load capacity in bearing from plate-to-bolts-to-plate.
   (Bearing failure of plate due to excessive yielding).
   $P_t = F_p A_p$ $F_p = 1.2F_u$ if wrinkling is not permitted.
   $F_p = 1.5F_u$ if wrinkling is permitted.
   $F_p = L_e F_u / 2d$ if layout has deficiencies.
   $A_p = dt$ = projected bearing area of bolt.

5. Load capacity of a plate in block tearout.
   (Tearout of a segment of plate through shear and tension with no bolts sheared).
   $P_t = F_v A_v + F_t A_t$ $F_v = 0.30F_u$
   $F_t = 0.50F_u$
   A_v = Net area in shear, less holes.
   A_t = Net area in tension, less holes.

The methods presented earlier to find the foregoing load capacities are valid only where the bolt layout conforms to certain dimensional requirements or conditions. A summary of these layout requirements and the corresponding allowable stresses is given earlier in Table S-24.

When it becomes necessary to design a bearing connection, usually the only information available is the magnitude of the load and the types of members to be connected (plate to angle, plate to plate, angle to angle, etc.). Quite often, the design must even include determination of the final size of one or more of the members being connected. When completed, the design is expected not only to be adequate for the given load, but that it will be reasonably well balanced, that is, roughly the same load in most if not all modes of failure (tension, shear, bearing, block tearout, etc.)

Step 1 in the design procedure: establish the type of connection and establish shank size where possible. A good beginning point in a design is to decide whether the fasteners will be in single shear or double shear. Quite often, there is no choice on this point; the type of connection may be set by outside conditions which cannot be changed. Where there is a choice, however, placing fasteners in a symmetrical configuration relative to the load is much preferred. A typical layout comparing an eccentric lapped layout to a symmetrical layout is shown in Figure 25-13.

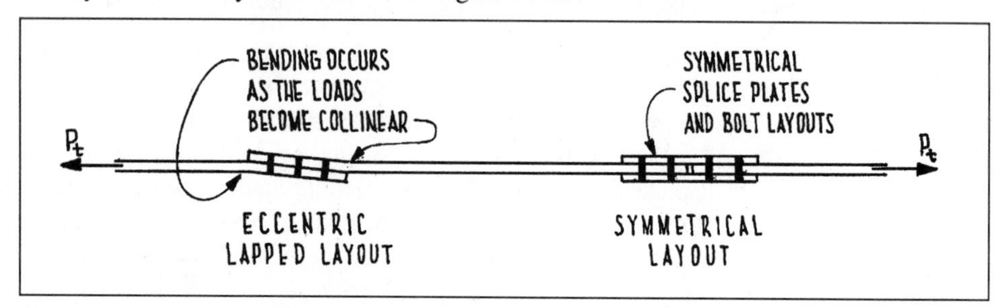

Figure 25-13 Single shear and multiple shear connections.

Though symmetrical layouts are preferred, eccentric lapped layouts are quite common. All of the calculations developed in preceding sections are valid for either a symmetrical or eccentric layout, but it is easy to visualize some complications in the eccentric layout.

If it happens that the size of the connected tension member has not yet been set, the required area of the shank can be computed simply as the applied load P_t divided by the allowable stress $0.60F_y$. A section having at least this much area is then selected from the appropriate table (angle, tee W, S, plate, etc.). Since this selected area will always be somewhat larger than the computed area, it is well at this point (if possible) to compute the *capacity* of the chosen section for future reference.

Step 2 in the design procedure: select number and size of bolts; set allowable bearing stress F_p. Since the decision has now been made whether to use single or double shear, the number and size of the bolts can now be selected to match the capacity of the connected tension member. It is again noted that for a very short distance, the bolts become the primary load-carrying member in the load path. The bolts, therefore, should have roughly the same (or more) capacity than the shank of the tension member.

Following this logic, the number of bolts is calculated as the capacity of the shank divided by the capacity per bolt. The capacity per bolt for various bolt sizes is found from Table S-26 in the Technical Manual, to include effects of threads in the shear plane. It is emphasized that the capacity of the bolts is being matched to the *capacity* of the shank; the actual external loading is not considered in making this match.

In choosing the number and size of bolts from Table S-26, there will be two or three alternatives, where one may choose a large number of small bolts or a small number of larger bolts. The final selection is one of personal preference. As a guide, the most widely used bolts are 5/8, 3/4 and 7/8 in. diameter.

Once the number and size of the bolts has been tentatively selected, one may wonder whether the plate thickness and bolt size so chosen are suitable in plate-to-bolt bearing. A quick check of such suitability can be made from Table S-25, in the Technical Manual.

If the selected plate thickness is at least as large as that listed in Table S-25, there will be no problems with bearing capacity (large-bolt/thin-plate problems).

In making this check on bearing capacities, it will be necessary at this time to set the maximum level of bearing stress F_p for the connection, whether $1.2F_u$ or $1.5\ F_u$. It is this maximum value of F_p that must be used later in setting pitch, gage, edge and end distances.

Step 3 in the design procedure: verify the load capacities of all connected members at the connection. With the trial values thus determined for member thickness, bolt sizes and bearing stress, the next step is to verify that the connected member will still have adequate capacity at the proposed connection (when the bolt holes are deducted). It is not necessary to determine the pitch and gage settings in order to make this verification; it is enough simply to visualize the connection. The correct number of holes can then be deducted from the gross area A_g to obtain the effective area A_e. The capacity of the tension member at the connection is then found as before, where $P_t = 0.50F_uA_e$. (Remember that the reduction coefficient U must be applied.)

Step 4 in the design procedure: make a detailed trial layout of the connection. With the overall capacity of the connected members and the bolt group thus verified, the final trial layout can be made. The layout dimensions for g, s and L_e in the final trial layout are found from the limits given earlier in Table S-24. (The previous choice of allowable bearing stress F_p selected from Table S-24 and used subsequently in Table S-25 must now be used throughout the remainder of the design).

Step 5 in the design procedure: verify the capacity of the connection in all failure modes. With a complete trial layout thus determined, the capacity of this complete trial connection is now verified by detailed calculations.

- Determine the load capacity at the shank in all connected members, to include sets of splice plates.
- Determine the load capacity at the connection in all connected members, to include sets of splice plates, whether the effective area is straight or zigzag.
- Determine the load capacity of the bolt group in shear.
- Determine the load capacity of main plate and splice plates in bearing.
- Determine the load capacity of all members in block tearout.

Step 6 in the design procedure: revise and correct the design as required. The load capacity of the trial layout is taken as the least value thus obtained. At this point, it is well to incorporate any desired refinements. Also, one might choose to improve the balance between the various loads, if such improvements are warranted. Once such modifications are complete, the trial layout may then be adopted as the final design.

Some examples will demonstrate the design procedure.

Example 25-15

Design of a bolted bearing connection.

Given: Tension load of 40 kips on a single angle truss member. Member is to be connected to the stem of a WT 8 x 25. A325N connection, ASTM A36 steel. Angle is gas cut at ends, tee stem is sawn.

To Find: Suitable bolted bearing connection.

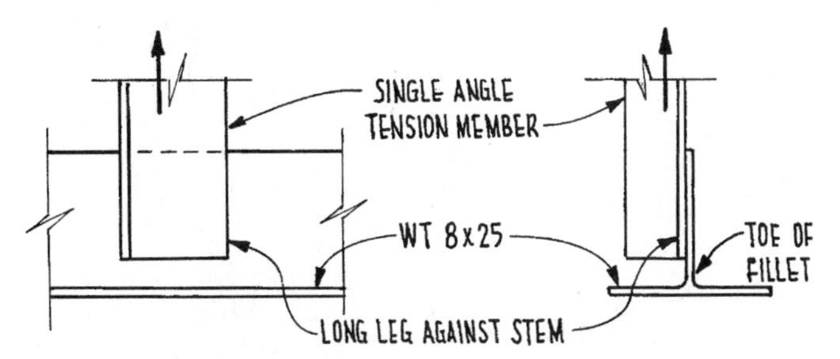

Solution: Stem thickness is found from Table S-5b to be 0.380 in. Use stem thickness 3/8 in. For calculations:

1) Establish type of connection and shank size:
Bolts are in single shear: try 4 bolts. Set angle thickness at 3/8 in. to match stem. Required shank area = $40/0.60F_y$ = 1.85 in.^{2}

2) Select number and size of bolts and set bearing stress F_p.
Required bolt capacity in single shear = 40/4 = 10 kips.
From Table S-26, choose 7/8 in. diameter bolts, capacity 12.6 kips/bolt. From Table S-25, $F_p = \leq 1.2F_u$, find that 3/8 in. plate is adequate.

3) Determine the effective area of the shank and its capacity for the angle; the leg next to the tee must have adequate length for two 7/8 in. bolts. From Table S-22, minimum leg length for 7/8 in. bolts is 6 in.

Try angle 6 x 3$^1/_2$ x 3/8, A = 3.42 in.^{2}

Verify capacity of tension member at connection:

$$P_t = F_t A_e,\ U = 0.75 \text{ for two bolts}$$
$$A_e = UA_n = U[A_g - 2 \text{ holes}]$$
$$= 0.75[3.42 - 2(7/8 + 1/16)(0.375)]$$
$$= 2.04 \text{ in.}^2$$

$$P_t = 0.5F_u A_e = 29 \times 2.04 = 59.09 \text{ kips} \geq 40 \text{ kips (O.K.)}$$

4) Make a detailed trial layout.
From Table S-24, select s ≥ 3d = 3 in.
g ≥ 2$^2/_3$d for angle gage of 2$^1/_2$ in.
L_e = 1$^1/_8$ in. at edge of tee
L_e = 1$^1/_8$ in. at end of angle

Requirement No. 3 is satisfied for $F_p = \leq 1.2F_y$. Trial layout is shown in the sketch.

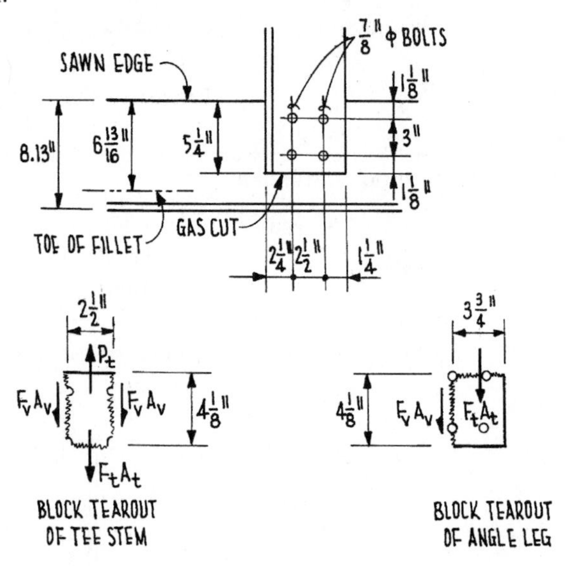

(The distance 6$^{13}/_{16}$ in. from edge of stem to toe of fillet is found from Table S-5b. For a W16 x 50, the wide flange beam from which this tee is cut, the toe-to-toe dimension *T* is given there as 13$^5/_8$ in.)

5) Verify all capacities:

Capacity at shank of angle 6 x $3^2/_3$ x $^3/_8$, A = 3.42 in.^{2}

$P_t = 0.60F_yA_g = 73.9$ kips $\geq$ 40 kips (O.K.)

Capacity at connection of angle, 2 bolts deducted, U = 0.75:

$P_t = 0.50F_uA_e = 29[0.75[3.42 - 2(^7/_8 + ^1/_{16})(0.375)]]$
$= 59.09$ kips $\geq$ 40 kips (O.K.)

Capacity of four $^7/_8$ in. bolts in shear at 12.6 kips/bolt:

$P_t = 4(12.6) = 50.40$ kips $\geq$ 40 kips (O.K.)

Capacity of $^3/_8$ in. plate in bearing against $^7/_8$ in. bolts:

$P_t = F_pA_p = 1.2F_udt = (1.2)(58)(0.875)(0.375)$
$= 22.84$ kips each bolt
$= 91.36$ kips $\geq$ 40 kips (O.K.)

Capacity of tee in block tearout:

$P_t = 2F_vA_v + F_tA_t = 0.30F_u[2t[4.125 - (^7/_8 + ^1/_{16})(1^1/_2)]$
$+ 0.50\ F_ut[2^1/_2 - (^7/_8 + ^1/_{16})(^1/_2)(2)]$
$= 35.5 + 17.0$
$= 52.5$ kips $\geq$ 40 kips (O.K.)

Capacity of angle in block tearout:

$P_t = F_vA_v + F_tA_t = 0.30F_ut[4^1/_8 - (^7/_8 + ^1/_{16})(1^1/_2)]$
$+ 0.50\ F_ut[3^3/_4 - (^7/_8 + ^1/_{16})(1^1/_2)]$
$= 17.7 + 25.5$
$= 43.2$ kips

6) Revise and refine as required:

Tension in shank of angle	$P_t = 73.9$ kips
Tension at connection of angle	$P_t = 59.1$ kips
Four $^7/_8$ in. bolts in shear	$P_t = 50.4$ kips
Bearing of angle (or stem) against bolts	$P_t = 91.4$ kips
Block tearout of stem of tee	$P_t = 52.5$ kips
Block tearout of angle	$P_t = 43.2$ kips

The least value is in block tearout of the angle, 43.2 kips. While adequate, the load capacities are seen to be highly imbalanced. One possible remedy would be to increase the thickness of the angle to $^7/_{16}$ in. The block tearout would then increase proportional to the thicknesses,

$$P_t = 43.2\frac{7/16}{3/8} = 50 \text{ (O.K.)}$$

A second remedy would be to increase the end distance of the angle from $1^1/_8$ in. to $2^1/_2$ in. The capacity of the angle in block tearout would then be:

$P_t = F_vA_v + F_tA_t = 0.30F_ut[3 + 2^1/_2 - (^7/_8 + ^1/_{16})(1^1/_2)]$
$+ 0.50\ F_ut[3^3/_4 - (^7/_8 + ^1/_{16})(1^1/_2)]$
$= 26.7 + 25.5 = 52.2$ kips

As a check, the total length of the angle in contact with the tee would now be $6^3/_8$ in.; it would not encroach onto the fillet.

Use layout as shown in Step 4, but with end distance of $2^1/_2$ in. for the angle.

Capacity = 50.4 kips (4 bolts in shear)

Note that there is consistent excess capacity (at least 25%) in all of the 6 failure modes, but there is no readily apparent way to get a consistent reduction. One must choose at this point whether it is better to have a consistently high excess capacity or to have inconsistent capacities with the lowest capacity closer to the applied load of 40 kips.

Example 25-16

Design of a bolted bearing connection.

Given: Continuous plate $^1/_4$ in. thick to be lapped spliced to an adjoining continuous plate. ASTM A36 steel, A325 bolts, all edges gas cut. Bolt pattern as shown. No wrinkling permitted.

To Find: Bolt size and spacing for maximum efficiency. Efficiency $e\%$ of the connection is given by:

$$e\% = \frac{\text{Capacity of connected plates}}{\text{Capacity of undisturbed plate}} \text{ x } 100$$

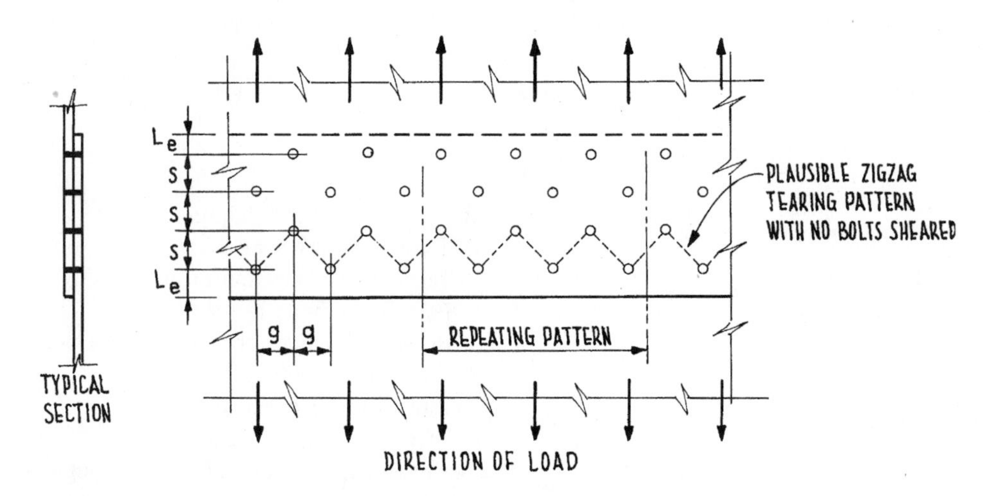

Solution: A repeating pattern is removed for analysis:

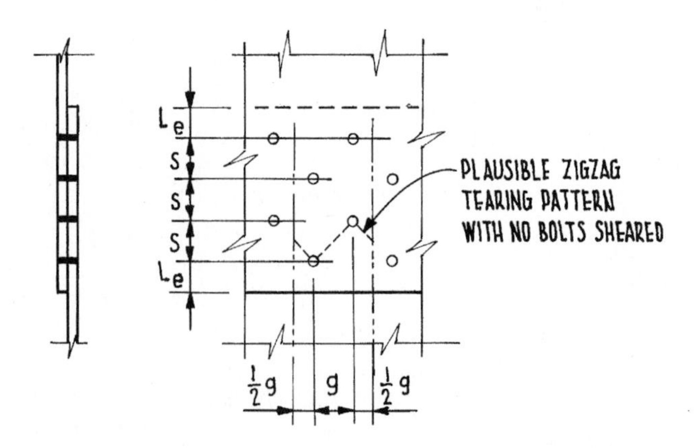

1. Establish type of connection and shank size:
   Bolt pattern is given, bolts in single shear.
   Plate thickness $^1/_4$ in.
   Shank width of repeating section cannot yet be established.

2. Set number and size of bolts and set bearing stress F_p:
   Bolt pattern already set.
   From Table S-25, set $F_p = 1.2\ F_u$.
   From Table S-25 choose $^7/_8$ in. bolts to match the $^1/_4$ in. plate.

3. Determine effective area of the shank and its capacity:
   Width of repeating section is still unknown. Shank capacity at the connection cannot be determined yet.

4. Make a detailed trial layout:

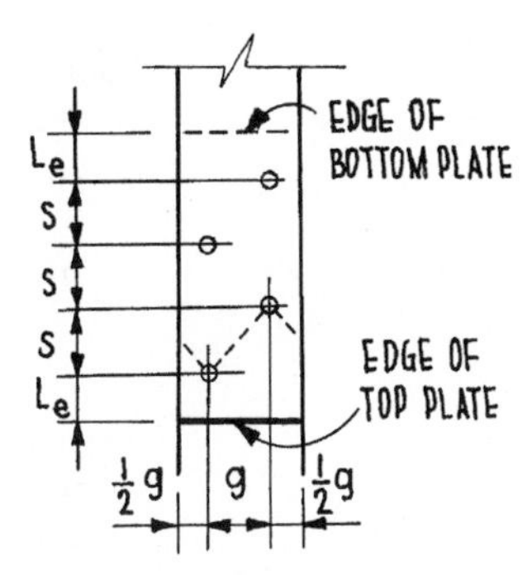

Applicability of Requirement 3 in Table S-24 is uncertain. Use Requirement 4. Use $F_p \leq 1.2\ F_u$:

$$F_p \leq L_e F_u/2d,\ L_e \geq \frac{2dF_p}{F_u}$$

$$\text{Set } L_e \geq \frac{(2d)1.2F_u}{F_u} = 2.4d \text{ to keep } F_p \leq 1.2\ F_u$$

Set $L_e \geq 2^1/_8$ in.
Set $g \geq 2^2/_3 d = 2^1/_2$ in.
Set $s \geq 2^2/_3 d = 2^1/_2$ in.

(The computed minimum value of $s \leq 2_P/F_u t + d/2$ cannot be calculated yet since the value of P is unknown. This will have to be verified later after P can be determined.)

Trial layout of a repeating section is shown in the following sketch:

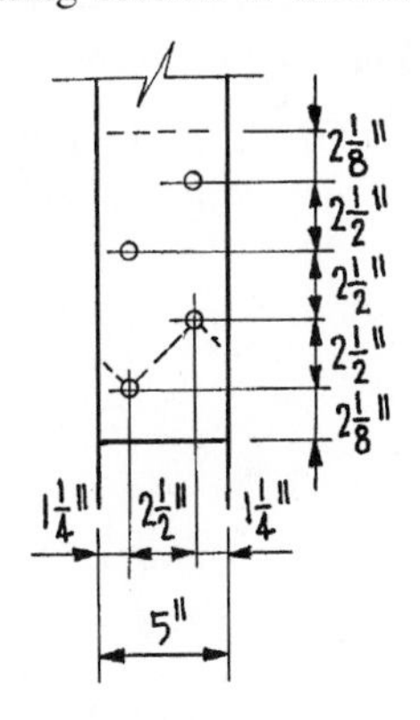

5. Verify all capacities:

Capacity of plate at some distance from connection:
$P_t = 0.60F_Ybt = 21600 \times 5 \times {}^1/_4 = 27.0$ kips

Capacity of plate at the connection line (zigzag):
$P_t = 0.5F_uA_e$ $U = 0.85$ for 3 lines of bolts
$A_e = UA_n = U[A_g - 2\text{ holes} + 2(s^2/4g)t]$
$= 0.85[(5)(0.25) - 2({}^7/_8 + {}^1/_{16})(0.25)$
$+ 2(0.625)(0.25)] = 0.93$ in.^{2}

$P_t = 29 \times 0.93 = 27.0$ kips

Capacity of 2 bolts in single shear at 12.6k/bolt:
$P_t = 2(12.6) = 25.2$ kips

Capacity of ${}^1/_4$ in. plate in bearing against ${}^7/_8$ in. bolts:
$P_t = F_PA_P$, $F_P \leq L_eF_u/2d = 70$, ksi $\leq 1.2F_u$ (O.K.)
$A_P = dt = ({}^7/_8)(0.25) = 0.218$ in.^{2}

$P_t = 70 \times 0.218 = 15.26$ kips/bolt
$= 30.52$ kips for 2 bolts (O.K.)

Capacity of plate in block tearout:
Block tearout does not occur in continuous plates.

6. Select limiting case:

Capacity of connected plate is ${}^{25.2}/_5 \times 12 = 60.5$ kips/ft
Recall that pitch *s* must be verified (from Step 4):
Load per bolt = P = ${}^{25.2}/_2 = 12.6$kips/bolt

$$s \geq 2P/F_ut + d/2 = \frac{(2)(12.6)}{(58)(0.25)} + \left(\frac{1}{2}\right)\left(\frac{7}{8}\right)$$

$= 2.175$ in. $\leq 2^1/_2$ in. selected (O.K.)

7. Compute efficiency:

$$e\% = \frac{\text{Capacity of connected plates}}{\text{Capacity of undisturbed plate}} \times 100 = \frac{25.2}{27} \times 100$$

$= 93\%$ efficiency

Example 25-17

Design of a bolted bearing splice connection.

Given: Two main plates 9" x ${}^1/_2$" as shown. ASTM A36 steel, A325 bolts, edges rolled, ends gas cut, 6 bolts in two patterns as shown. No wrinkling permitted under bearing stress.

To Find: 1) Capacity of the connected plates at the left side of the splice.
2) Efficiency e% of the connection as given by:

$$e\% = \frac{\text{Capacity of connected plates}}{\text{Capacity of undisturbed plate}} \times 100$$

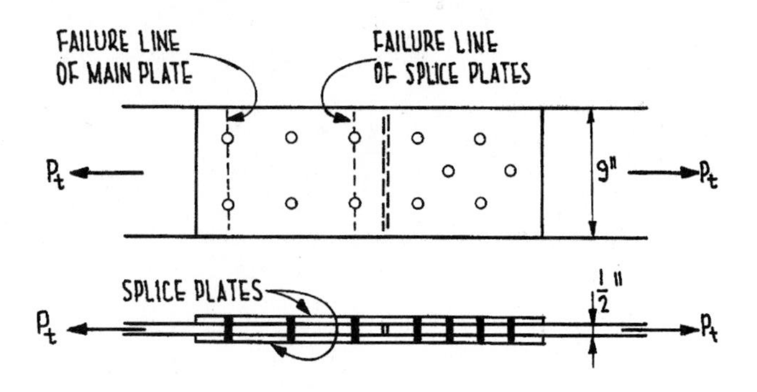

Solution: 1) Establish the type of connection and shank size.
Bolts are in double shear.
Splice plates are set at 9 x $^1/_4$ to match the main plate.
Capacity of main plate is 0.60 F_y x 9 x $^1/_2$ = 97.2 kips.
2) Select number and size of bolts and set bearing stress F_p:
Required capacity of one bolt in double shear
= 97.4/6 = 16.2 k
From Table S-26, choose $^3/_4$ in. diameter bolts.
From Table S-25 set $F_p \leq 1.2\ F_u$.
From Table S-25, check minimum plate size to be
$^3/_8 \leq {}^1/_2$ (O.K.)
3) Determine effective area of shank and its capacity:
Capacity $P_t = F_tA_e$, U = 0.85[4.5 - 2($^3/_4$ + $^1/_{16}$)$^1/_2$]
= 3.13 in.^{2}
$P_t = 0.5F_uA_e$ = 29 x 3.13 = 90.9 kips

4) Make a detailed trial layout:
From Table S-24 for Fp ≤ 1.2 Fu,
Set g ≥ 3d ≥ 4 in.
s ≥ 3d ≥ 3 in.
$L_e \geq 1^1/_2d \geq 1^1/_2$ in.

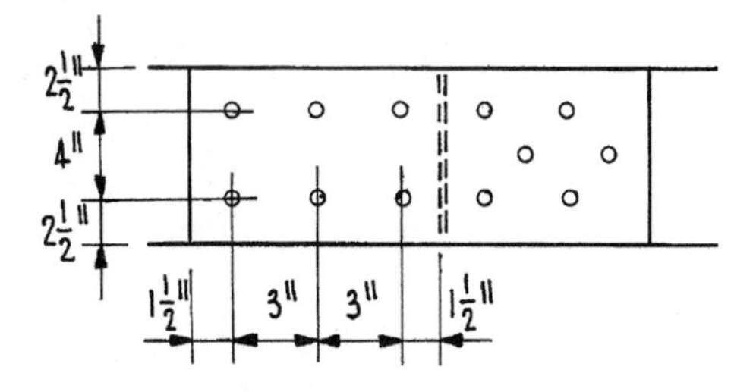

5) Verify all capacities:
Capacity of main plate at the shank (no change).
P_t = 97.2 kips.

Capacity of main plate at the connection (no change).
P_t = 90.9 kips.

Capacity of 6 bolts in double shear @ 18.6 kips/bolt:
$P_t = 6 \times 18.6 = 111.6$ kips.

Capacity of 1/2 in. plate in bearing against 3/4 in. bolts:
$P_t = F_pA_p = 1.2F_udt = 26.1$ kips per bolt = 157 kips for 6 bolts.

Capacity in block tearout (main plate or splice plates)

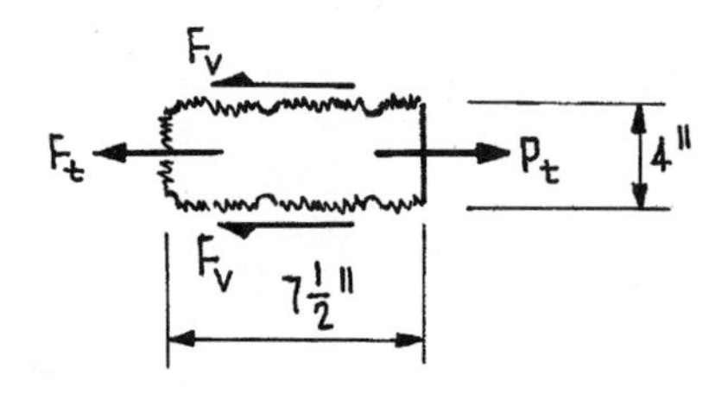

$$P_t = F_vA_v + F_tA_t = 0.50F_u \times t[4 - (3/4 + 1/16)(1/2)(2)] + 0.30F_u \times 2t\,(7.5 - (3/4 + 1/16)(2\,1/2)] = 46 + 95 = 141 \text{ kips}$$

6) Select limiting case:
Least load is 90.9 in main plate at the connection.

$$\text{Efficiency} = \frac{90.9}{97.2} \times 100 = 93.5\%$$

Example 25-18

Design of a bolted bearing splice connection.

Given: Two main plates 9 x 1/2 as shown. ASTM A36 steel, A325 bolts, edges rolled, ends gas cut, 6 bolts in two patterns as shown. No wrinkling permitted under bearing stress.

To Find: 1) Capacity of the connected plates at the right side of the splice.
2) Efficiency e% of the connection as given by:

$$e\% = \frac{\text{Capacity of connected plates}}{\text{Capacity of undisturbed plate}} \times 100$$

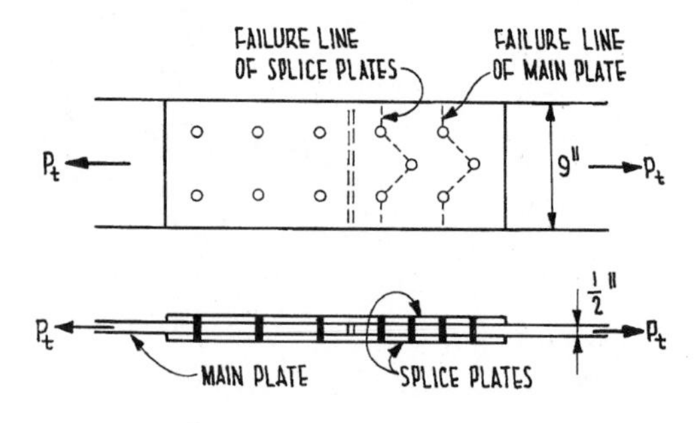

Solution: 1) Establish the type of connection and shank size.
Bolts are in double shear.
Splice plates are set at 9 x 1/4 to match the main plate.
Capacity of main plate is $0.60\ F_y\ A_g = 97.2$ kips.

2) Select number and size of bolts and set bearing stress F_p:
   Required capacity per bolt in double shear
   = 97.2/6 = 16.2 kips
   From Table S-26, choose ³/₄ in. diameter bolts.
   From Table S-25 set $F_p \le 1.2\ F_u$.
   From Table S-25, check minimum plate size to be
   $3/8 \le 1/2$ (O.K.)
3) Determine effective area of shank and its capacity:
   Capacity $P_t = F_t A_e$, U = 0.85 for plate with 4 lines of bolts
   $A_e = UA_n = U[A_g - 3 \text{ holes} + 2(S^2/4g)t]$
   Capacity of main plate cannot be verified until *s* and *g* are set.

4) Make a detailed trial layout:
   From Table S-24 for $F_p = 1.2\ F_u \le L_e F_u/2d$,
   Set $g \le 2^2/_3 d = 2$ in.
   $s \le 2^2/_3 d = 2$ in.

$$L_e \geq \frac{1.2F_u(2d)}{F_u} = 2.4d = 2 \text{ in.}$$

$$s \geq \frac{2P}{F_u t} + \frac{d}{2} = \frac{2\left(\frac{97.2}{6}\right)}{(58)(0.75)} + \frac{0.75}{2} = 1.2 < 2 (\text{O.K.})$$

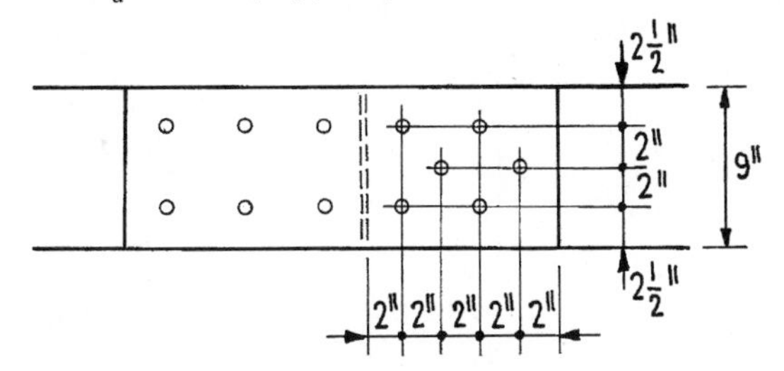

5) Verify all capacities:
   Capacity of main plate at the shank (no change).
   $P_t = 97.2$ kips

   Capacity of main plate at the connection.
   $P_t = F_t A_e$, U = 0.85 for plate with 4 lines of holes
   $A_e = 0.85[Ag - 3 \text{ holes} + 2(s^2/4g)t]$
   $= 0.85[4.5 - 3(3/4 + 1/16)(0.5)$
   $+ 2(0.50)(0.5)] = 3.78 \text{ in.}^2$

   $P_t = 0.5F_u A_e = (29)(3.78) = 109.7$ kips

   Capacity of 6 bolts in double shear @ 18.6 kips/bolt:
   $P_t = 6 \times 18.6 = 111.6$ kips

   Capacity of ¹/₂ in. plate in bearing against ³/₄ in. bolts:
   $P_t = F_p A_p = 1.2 F_u dt = 26.1$ kips per bolt = 157 kips for 6 bolts

   Capacity in block tearout:
   No feasible block tearout pattern is evident without shearing at least one bolt.

6) Select limiting case:
   Least load is shank load of 97.2 kips.

   Efficiency is 100%.

25.8 Bolted Slip-Critical Connections in Tension

In an earlier section, it was stated that bolted connections may be made in either of two types:

1. Bearing connections, in which load is transferred by bearing of the tension member against the bolts, then by shear in the bolts.
2. Friction connections, in which bolts clamp the members together so tightly that the entire load is transferred by friction.

Bearing connections were presented in the preceding sections. Friction connections are the topic of this section. It will be seen that friction connections, also called *slip-critical connections*, are simpler to design but more expensive to use than are bearing connections.

A typical slip-critical connection is shown in Figure 25-14. The area of the plates immediately surrounding the tightened bolts is under extremely high contact stress. As a consequence the connection can sustain a high lateral load due to friction between these matching surfaces, or *faying surfaces*.

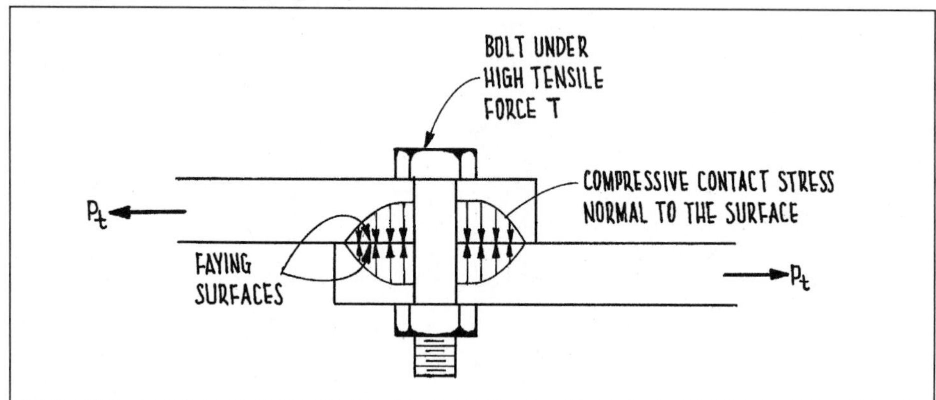

Figure 25-14 Slip-critical connection.

The amount of friction force V that can be developed between faying surfaces is the coefficient of friction μ times the normal contact force N:

$$V = \mu N = \mu T \tag{25-12}$$

where the contact force N between the plates is equal to the tensile force T in the bolt. As the tensile force T increases, the allowable shear force V per bolt increases correspondingly.

When a bolt clamps a stack of several plates together, it will produce the same contact force N between plates at each level. As a consequence, the lateral shear force μN occurs at each shear plane. The force on each plate is then the sum of friction forces top and bottom, as indicated in Figure 25-15.

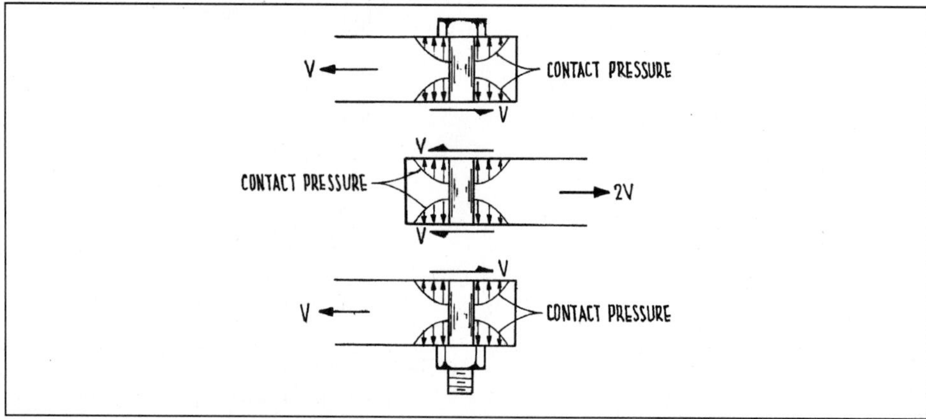

Figure 25-15 Multiple slip-critical shear planes.

It is probably more proper to use the term "single shear plane" or "double shear plane" when referring to the connections in Figures 25-14 and 25-15. It is the practice, however, to refer to them as having bolts in single shear or bolts in double shear, as if they were in a bearing connection. In truth, there is no shearing force at all on the bolts; the only force in the bolt is the tensile force T.

There are obviously both economical and practical limits on the bolt force T. The design specification ASD(J4) prescribes a lower limit for the tensile force which, in turn, will assure a consistent and reliable shear load capacity for the connection. Values of these minimum tension forces are given in Table S-27 in the Technical Manual for various bolt sizes, along with the corresponding allowable shear load.

The coefficient of friction μ relating the forces in Table S-27 is readily computed simply as N/V. Values of μ in the table vary slightly, ranging from 0.26 to 0.30. Since no shear stress occurs in the bolts, there is no concern whether there are threads in the shear plane.

The required minimum tension forces given in Table S-27 are computed for stress levels at 70% of the tensile strength of the bolts. Tensile yield is specified as 92 ksi for A325 bolts up to and including 1 inch diameter and as 81 ksi for larger bolts. Tensile "proof" strength for A490 bolts ranges from 112 ksi for bolts $^5/_8$ in. diameter up to 120 ksi for bolts $1^1/_2$ in. diameter.

When the bolts are installed and tightened in the actual connection, achieving the specified tensile force is critical to the integrity of the connection. If the installed tensile force is too low the connection will slip, placing the bolts in a combined state of stress having very high tensile stress plus an added shear stress. If it is too high, the bolt will forever be overstressed in tension.

Quality control in slip-critical connections can sometimes be difficult to achieve under field conditions. Inspection is continuous (and expensive) when slip-critical connections are being made. And, while several techniques have been developed to achieve proper tension in the bolts, the variation in the final results can still be significant.

The analysis and design of slip-critical connections is somewhat simpler than for bearing connections. Bearing stresses no longer occur and the bolts do not undergo shear. The design considerations are thus reduced to providing adequate load capacity in only three potential failure modes.

1. Load capacity of shanks of connected members.
2. Load capacity of connected members in tearing at the connection.
3. Load capacity of all members in block tearout.

Methods of finding the load capacity of friction connections are the same as those developed earlier for bearing connections. Layout requirements for bolts are also the same, presented earlier in summary form in Table S-24. Plate tearing and block tearout are also the same; they are considered to be unaffected by the highly localized compression zones.

The design specification ASD(J3.2) introduces a somewhat confusing "equivalent" shear stress for bolts that can be used to design slip-critical connections. Table S- 21 in the Technical Manual lists values of the allowable shear stress on cross-sectional bolt areas in a slip-critical connection. Such a shear stress in the bolts does not actually exist in a slip-critical connection, but it allows the design procedure to more closely resemble that of bearing connections.

It is observed in Table S-21 that the equivalent shear stresses for bolts in a slip-critical connection are significantly smaller than those for a bearing connection. For a given load, therefore, a slip-critical connection will require either more bolts or bigger bolts than a bearing connection. Since slip-critical connections cost more, require bigger connections (or bigger bolts) and create problems in field quality control, one must wonder where the advantage lies in using slip-critical connections.

Design specification ASD(J1.12) *requires* that slip-critical (or welded) connections be used in column splices in tall slender structures, in connections subject to fatigue loading or frequent stress reversals, and in connections subject to vibrations (from rotating machinery, overhead cranes, etc.). Obviously, AISC has found that slip-critical connections are less likely to loosen under vibration or load reversals, and are less likely to slip under static loads. The advantage in slip-critical connections thus lies in their much-reduced danger of slippage, either under static loads or dynamic loads.

Some examples will demonstrate the design of slip-critical connections. In general the design procedure is identical to that for bearing connections, except that finding the capacity in bearing is of course deleted and that the bolt values for lateral load are those due to friction between plates (Table S-27) rather than those due to shearing of a bolt (Table S-26).

Example 25-19

Design of a bolted slip-critical connection of 40 kips.

Given: Tension load of 40 kips on a single angle truss member. Member is to be connected to the stem of a WT8 x 25, A325 bolts, ASTMA36 steel. Angle is gas cut at ends, tee stem is sawn.

To Find: Suitable bolted slip-critical connection.

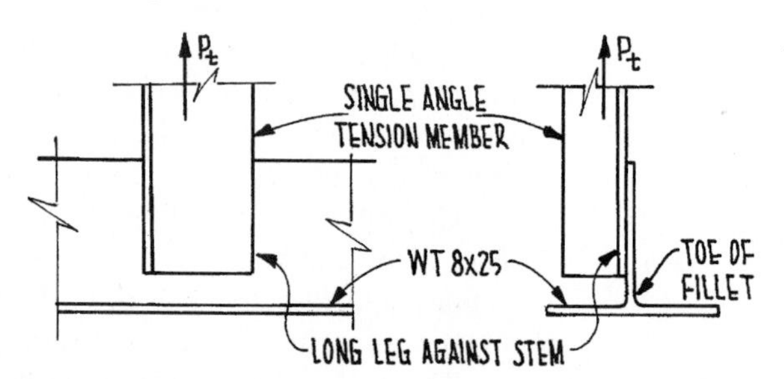

Solution: Stem thickness of tee is found from Table S-5b to be 0.380 in.

1) Establish type of connection and shank size:

Bolts have a single shear plane: try 4 bolts, 2 bolts/line.
Required shank area = $40/0.60F_y = 1.85$ in.^{2}
Size of the angle cannot yet be established.

2) Select size of bolts:

Required bolt capacity for single plane
= 40/4 = 10 kips/bolt
From Table A-27, choose $^7/_8$ in. bolts,
capacity 10.2 kips/bolt

3) Determine the angle size and capacity:

For the angle, the leg next to the tee must have adequate length for two $^7/_8$ in. bolts. From Table S-22, minimum leg length is 6 inches.

Try angle 6 x $3^1/_2$ x $^5/_{16}$, A = 2.87 in.^{2}

Verify capacity of angle at connection:

$P_t = F_t A_e$, U = 0.75 for only 2 bolts in a line.

$$A_e = UA_n$$
$$= 0.75[2.87 - 2(^7/_8 + ^1/_{16})(0.3125)]$$
$$= 1.713 \text{ in.}^2$$

$$P_t = 0.5F_u A_e = 29 \times 1.713$$
$$= 49.7 \text{ kips} > 40 \text{ kips (O.K.)}$$

4) Make a detailed trial layout:
   From Table S-24, select s ≥ 3d = 3 in.
   g ≥ 2²/₃ d for gage distance of 2¹/₂ in.
   L_e ≥ 1¹/₈ in. at edge of tee
   L_e ≥ 1¹/₈ in. at edge of angle

Trial layout is shown in the sketch.

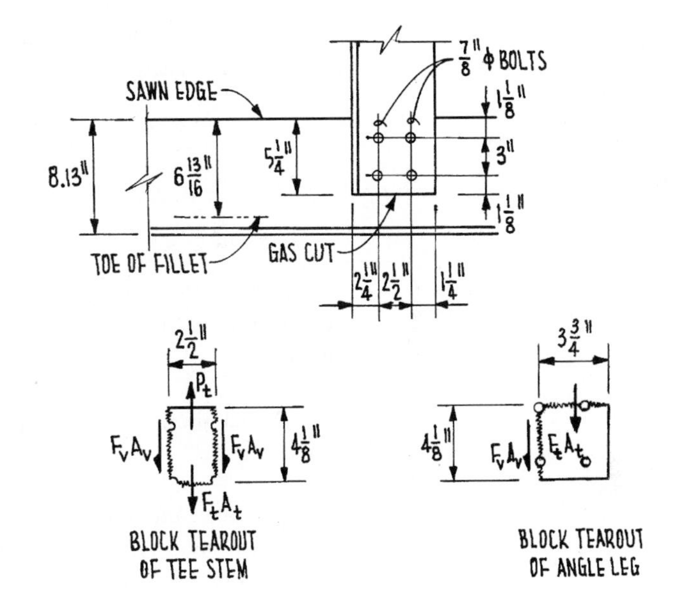

5) Verify all capacities:
   Capacity at shank of angle 6 x 3¹/₂ x ⁵/₁₆, A = 2.89 in.²
   $P_t = 0.60F_yA_g$ = 62 kips > 40 kips (O.K.)

   Capacity of angle with 2 bolts deducted, U = 0.75:

$$P_t = 0.50F_U A_e$$

$$= 29\left[0.75\left[2.87 - 2\left(\tfrac{7}{8} + \tfrac{1}{16}\right)(0.3125)\right]\right]$$

$$= 49.7 \text{ kips} > 40 \text{ kips (O.K.)}$$

   Capacity of four ⁷/₈ in. bolts in slip-critical connection:
   V = 4(10.2) = 40.8 kips > 40 kips (O.K.)

   Capacity of tee in block tearout, t = 0.38 in.

$$P_t = 2F_vA_v + F_tA_t$$

$$= 0.30F_u\left[2t\left[41.25 - \left(\tfrac{7}{8} + \tfrac{1}{16}\right)\left(1\tfrac{1}{2}\right)\right]\right]$$

$$+ 0.50F_ut\left[2\tfrac{1}{2} - \left(\tfrac{7}{8} + \tfrac{1}{16}\right)\left(\tfrac{1}{2}\right)(2)\right]$$

$$= 36.0 + 17.2 = 53.2 \text{ kips} > 40 \text{ kips (O.K.)}$$

Capacity of angle in block tearout:

$$P_t = F_vA_v + F_tA_t = 0.30F_ut\left[4\tfrac{1}{8} - \left(\tfrac{7}{8} + \tfrac{1}{16}\right)\left(1\tfrac{1}{2}\right)\right]$$

$$+ 0.50F_ut\left[3\tfrac{3}{4} - \left(\tfrac{7}{8} + \tfrac{1}{16}\right)\left(1\tfrac{1}{2}\right)\right]$$

$$= 14.78 + 21.24$$

$$= 36.0 \text{ kips} < 40 \text{ kips (No good)}$$

6) Revise and refine as required:

Tension in shank of angle	$P_t = 62$ kips
Tension at connection of angle	$P_t = 49.7$ kips
Shear on four 7/8 in. slip-critical bolts	$P_t = 40.8$ kips
Block tearout on stem of tee	$P_t = 53.2$ kips
Block tearout on angle	$P_t = 36.0$ kips

The load capacity in block tearout on the angle can be increased by increasing the end distance from 1 1/8 in. to 2 inches. The capacity of the angle would then be:

$$P_t = F_v A_v + F_t A_t = 0.30F_u t\left[(3+2) - \left(\tfrac{7}{8} + \tfrac{1}{16}\right)\left(1\tfrac{1}{2}\right)\right]$$
$$+ 0.50F_u t\left[3\tfrac{3}{4} - \left(\tfrac{7}{8} + \tfrac{1}{16}\right)\left(1\tfrac{1}{2}\right)\right]$$
$$= 19.54 + 21.24 = 40.8 \text{ kips}$$

As a check, the total length of the angle in contact with the tee would now be 6 1/8 in.; it would still be well clear of the fillet.

Use layout shown in Step 4, but with end distance of 2 in. for the angle.

Example 25-19 is the same problem as Example 25-15; one is a bearing connection, the other a slip-critical connection. The solution to the slip-critical connection of Example 25-19 has a minimal capacity of 40.8 kips in a poorly balanced design. This minimal capacity of 40.8 kips compares to 25% excess capacity at 50.4 kips in the well balanced bearing design of Example 25-15. Either design is valid; the final choice is the prerogative of the individual designer.

Example 25-20

Design of a bolted slip-critical connection.

Given: Tension splice of Example 25-18, 9 in. x 1/2 in. main plate, ASTM A36 steel, A325 bolts, 6 bolts in the patterns shown.

To Find: 1) Capacity for a slip-critical connection at the right side of the connection.
2) Efficiency e% of the connection as given by:

$$e\% = \frac{\text{Capacity of connected plates}}{\text{Capacity of undisturbed plate}}$$

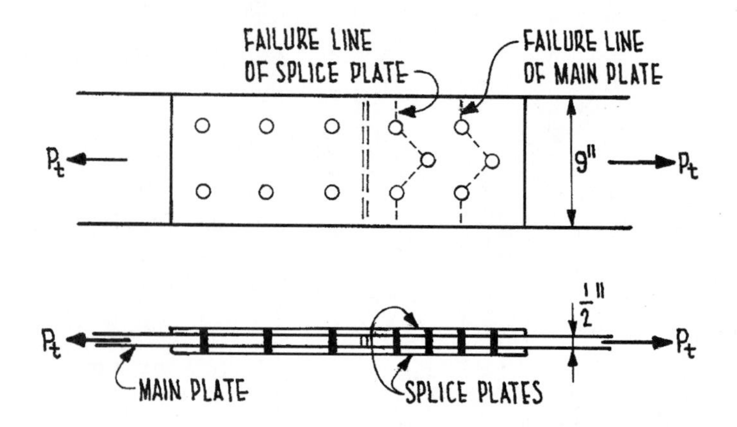

Solution: 1) Establish the type of connection and shank size:
Slip-critical connection.
Bolts in double shear planes.
Splice plates selected at 9 in. x $^1/_4$ in. to match main plate.
Capacity of main plate:

$$P_t = 0.60\ F_y\ A_g = 97.2 \text{ kips}$$

2) Select the number and size of bolts:
Required capacity of bolts with two shear planes:
Capacity = 97.2/6 = 16.20 kips
From Table S-27, choose $^7/_8$ in. diameter bolts.

3) Determine capacity of main plate at the connection:
$P_t = F_t A_e$, U = 0.85 for a plate with 4 lines of holes
$A_e = U[A_g - 3 \text{ holes} + 2(s^2/4g)t]$

Capacity of main plate at the connection cannot be verified until *s* and *g* are set.

4) Make a detailed trial layout from Table S-24:
Set $g \geq 2^2/_3 d = 2^1/_2$ in.
$s \geq 2^2/_3 d = 2^1/_2$ in.
$L_e \geq 1^1/_8$ in.

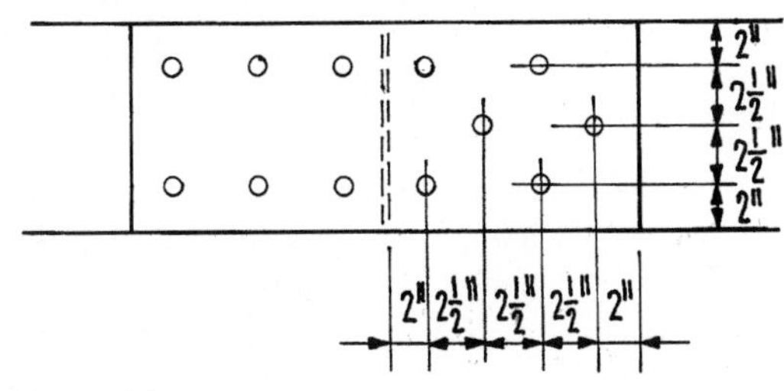

5) Verify all capacities:
Capacity of the main plate at the shank (no change):
Pt = 97.2 kips

Capacity of the main plate at the connection:

$$P_t = 0.5F_uA_e, A_e = U\left[A_g - 3\text{ holes} + 2\left(s^2/4g\right)t\right]$$

$$A_e = 0.85\left[4.5 - 3\left(\tfrac{7}{8} + \tfrac{1}{16}\right)\tfrac{1}{2} + 2(0.625)\left(\tfrac{1}{2}\right)\right]$$

$P_t = 29 \times 3.72 = 107.8$ kips

Capacity of 6 bolts in a slip-critical connection:
$P_t = 6(20.4) = 122.4$ kips

Capacity in block tearout:
No feasible block tearout pattern is evident. (All patterns return to that of Step 3.)

6) Select limiting case:
Lease load is shank load of 97.2 kips.

Efficiency is 100%.

25.9 Welded Connections in Tension

Bolted connections for tension members are presented in earlier sections of this chapter. In this section, welded connections are presented, to include brief discussions on the two major types of welded connections, groove welded and fillet welded.

Welded beam connections are presented in Chapter 32 with beam design. Similarly, welded column connections are presented in Chapter 31 with column design. This section is devoted to welded tension connections. Perhaps the best place to start such a discussion is in describing the interdependence of bolted and welded connections in modern construction methods.

Before being sent to the construction site for final assembly into a structure, steel structural members go through a process of *fabrication*. In the fabrication shop, a steel beam, for example, will be cut to length, ends will be shaped as required, holes will be punched or drilled in all required locations and attachments will be fixed where prescribed by the project drawings. Each member will be tagged with a permanent ID number, coded to the erection drawings. All beams, girders, columns, struts, ties and major members will be thus fabricated and labeled before being shipped to the field. The job of the field erection crew is then to assemble all these large prepared members into the final structure as if it were a huge erector set; ideally, the only loose items or small items would be the assembly bolts.

As a general rule, the most practical way to achieve such a stated end result is to fabricate the members by welding them under shop conditions and assembling them in the field by bolting. The process is, in fact, so common that the term *shop weld field bolt* is recognized throughout the entire construction industry. The process does introduce the idea, however, that one end of every connection will be welded to a major load-carrying member in the shop; the other end will be bolted to another major load-carrying member in the field.

A typical shop-weld field-bolt connection is shown in Figure 25-16. Double angle connector angles are shop-welded to the web of the beam. The connector angles and the column are shop drilled to identical layouts. The beam is shipped to the site and field-bolted to the column in the final assembly.

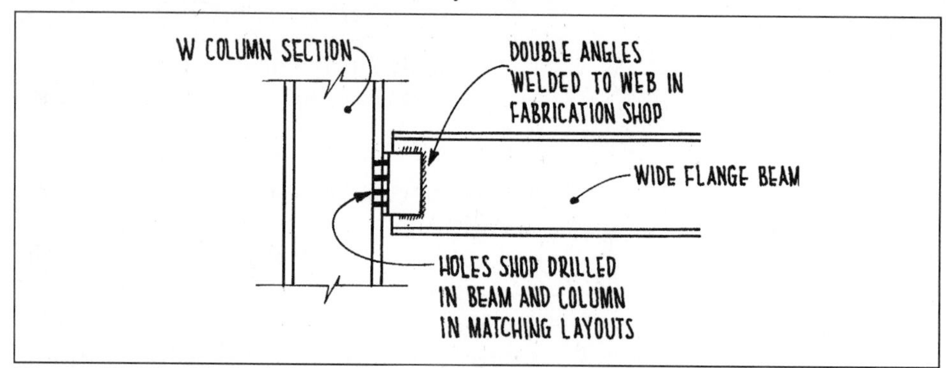

Figure 25-16 Typical shop-weld, field-bolt connection.

Properly designing and detailing these shop-welded field-bolted connections is a critical item in today's construction. Due to their importance, a great many design aids and tables have been developed to assure that such a mix of load transfers in these connections will be achieved successfully. It must be remembered that these connections involve a sequence of load transfers starting at one structural member, then transferring the entire load to a weldment, then to a connection device, then to bolts, then to a second structural member. With such a multiplicity of load transfers at every connection, it should not be surprising that some 70% of all failures in structural steel originate at a connection.

There are three major methods of welding in common use for fabricating structural steel:

1) Gas welding (oxyacetylene)
2) Electric arc welding, to include automatic machines
3) Electric resistance welding (spot welding)

A weld is accomplished by joining two members together, then agitating the molecules at their juncture (usually by heat) until they fuse together. When the source of agitation is removed, the members are permanently jointed. The agitation may be sound, a laser beam, friction, heat or any of a number of other things; in succeeding discussions only heat will be considered.

Of the modern welding techniques, gas welding is probably the oldest method that is still in common use. There are few practical heat sources, however, that can attain the 3000°F temperatures required to melt steel. Acetylene gas burned in pure oxygen (oxyacetylene) is one of these, reaching temperatures of about 6000°F.

In gas welding, a filler rod is used to supply additional material to the weld. As the two edges being joined melt and run together, the filler rod supplies any makeup material required to obtain a full smooth joint. In many cases, no filler rod is needed.

Acetylene gas, C_2H_2, cannot be used with metals that would react either with the carbon or the hydrogen. Steel does not react, titanium does. Oxyacetylene welding, therefore, should not be considered a universal method.

While oxyacetylene works well on steel, it is a very slow method of welding. It has a further disadvantage that a wide band of material adjacent to the weld is also heated to very high temperatures, which can cause distortion when the material cools. The method is quite simple, however, and requires a minimum of equipment and capital investment.

Oxyacetylene is also used for brazing. Brazing is used whenever it is necessary to join two dissimilar metals. The two members are placed in close proximity and heated. A filler material is deposited to join them, adhering to both. The filler rod can be of several compositions, but is usually made of some combination of copper, silver, aluminum, tin or lead. Unlike welding, no fusion takes place in a brazed joint.

One of the widest uses for acetylene is in cutting steel into various lengths and shapes. A special nozzle is used for cutting, which places a fine stream of pure oxygen onto the preheated steel. The steel oxidizes, literally burns, producing a "torch cut" groove in the steel.

In production work, oxyacetylene welding is too slow to compete with electric arc welding. Electric arc welding has another advantage in that its heat is highly localized, which sharply reduces the problem of distortion heating. Further, electric arc welding is hotter than oxyacetylene welding and the point of heating is much easier to control.

Electric arc welding of two members is accomplished by placing the two members in close proximity, both of them in contact with an electrical conductor. A low-voltage, high current arc is struck with an electrode to complete the electrical circuit at the joint. The distance between the electrode and the work is controlled such that the electric arc is sustained, creating temperatures high enough to melt the members at the joint. The electrode is gradually consumed in the process, supplying additional metal to the joint as it melts.

Both alternating current and direct current are used in arc welding. In either case, the electrode is deposited in the work and becomes an integral part of the weld. It is essential, therefore, that the material in the electrode be of comparable strength and composition to the material being welded.

There are many types and configurations of welds. Only the most common welds are considered here. Some of the types of welds used frequently in steel structures are shown in Figure 25-17. Not all of the welds are structural, that is, not all are able to carry predictable levels of load.

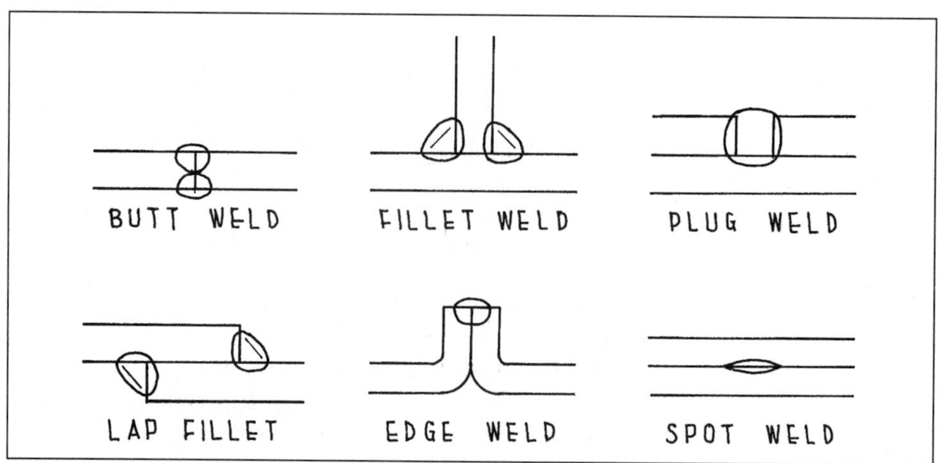

Figure 15-17 Types of welds.

The *butt weld* shown in Figure 25-17 is a type of groove weld made with an initial gap between the plates. For plates $^1/_4$ in. to $^5/_8$ in. thick, the gap is half the plate thickness. For plates less than $^1/_4$ in., no gap is required. For plates thicker than $^5/_8$ in., the edge must be shaped before it can be welded.

The *fillet weld* shown in Figure 25-17 is made with equal legs. The thinnest section is then at the throat of the weld, at 45° from the legs. The governing stress in fillet welds is shear on the throat of the weld.

The *plug* weld shown in Figure 25-17 provides a means to connect two overlapping plates without having any weldment along the edges. The hole can be elongated to provide additional weld length, in which case the weld is called a *slot* weld.

The *lap fillet* weld shown in Figure 25-17 is more of a weld arrangement than it is a type of weld. The two welds shown are ordinary fillet welds. The maximum size of the fillet weld is typically $^1/_{16}$ in. less than the edge thickness of the plate.

The *edge* weld shown in Figure 25-17 is used primarily to join very thin strips. It is a joining weld rather than a structural weld. It is commonly used on standing seams as shown when the sheet metal is so thin that a butt weld or a lap weld would likely burn holes in it.

The *spot* weld shown in fig. 25-17 provides another means of joining thin sheets. A spot weld is made in a small press having the two electrodes mounted one directly above the other with a gap between. The plates are placed in the gap on top of one electrode. The other electrode is lowered, pressing the two plates together briefly at a small spot. Power is switched on, and even though the plates are in contact there is enough electrical resistance at the juncture that high heat is generated, causing fusion of the two sheets at the small spot.

For plates thicker than $^5/_8$ in., the butt weld of Figure 25-17 requires edge preparation. Depending on thickness, the shape at the joined edges may be a bevel, vee, *J* or *U* shape. Some typical edge preparations for groove welds are shown in Figure 25-18.

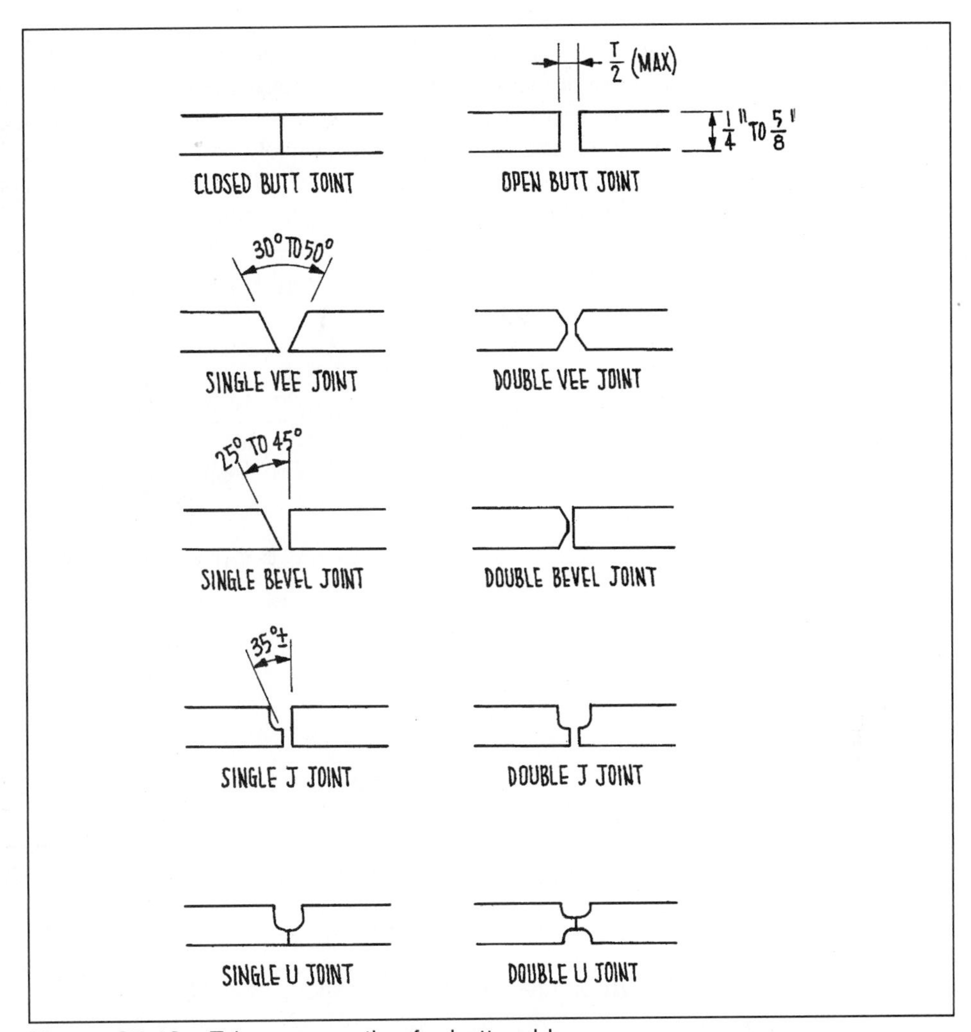

Figure 25-18 Edge preparation for butt welds.

The difference between the bevel shape and the vee shape in edge preparations is that the bevel is made only on one plate; the vee is made on both plates. Similarly, a J shape is made only on one plate and requires a root gap; a U shape is made on both plates with no root gap.

AISC has developed a set of standard symbols for calling out all types of welds on the project drawings. A complete set is presented in the *Steel Handbook;* some of the more common symbols have been extracted and are shown in Figure 25-19.

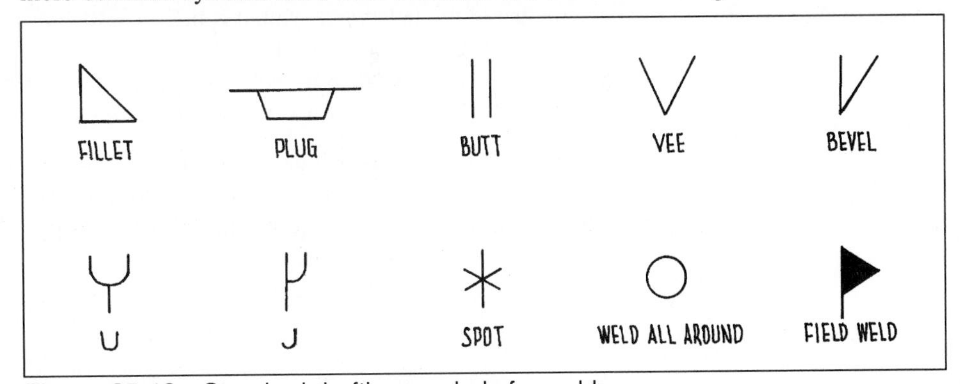

Figure 25-19 Standard drafting symbols for welds.

The standard symbols shown in Figure 25-19 are placed on arrows that indicate the location of the weld. If a symbol appears on the bottom of the horizontal reference line, as shown in Figure 25-20, the weld is to be made on the near side (the arrowhead side) at the indicated juncture. If the symbol appears on the top of the line, the weld is to be made on the far side of the juncture. If symbols appear both on top and on bottom, the weld is to be made both near and far side.

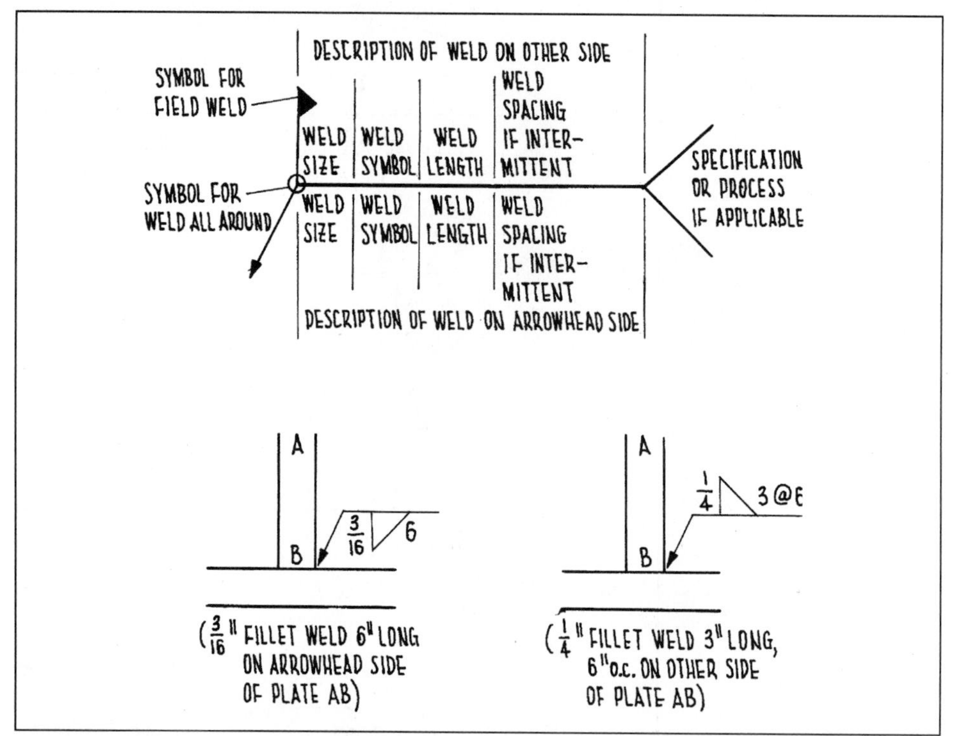

Figure 25-20 Arrow designations of weld types.

The rules for entering further information concerning sizes, symbols, lengths, and other relevant information on the horizontal reference line are given by AISC.

1. The size, the weld symbol, the length and the spacing must appear in that order.
2. The perpendicular leg of the weld symbol always appears at the left side of the symbol.
3. For all welds, the size of the weld may be entered on one side and the other side may be assumed to be the same size. For fillet welds, length and spacing must be entered at both near and far side.
4. The flag of the field weld symbol is placed at the juncture of the two lines, above and at right angles to the reference line.
5. The symbol for the type of weld is understood to apply between abrupt changes in direction of the weld unless the *all around* symbol is used.

Some examples of weld callouts are given in Figure 25-21, along with their descriptions. The size of the groove welds (butt, vee and bevel welds) sometimes may not be specified; if not, it is understood to be full thickness of the plates.

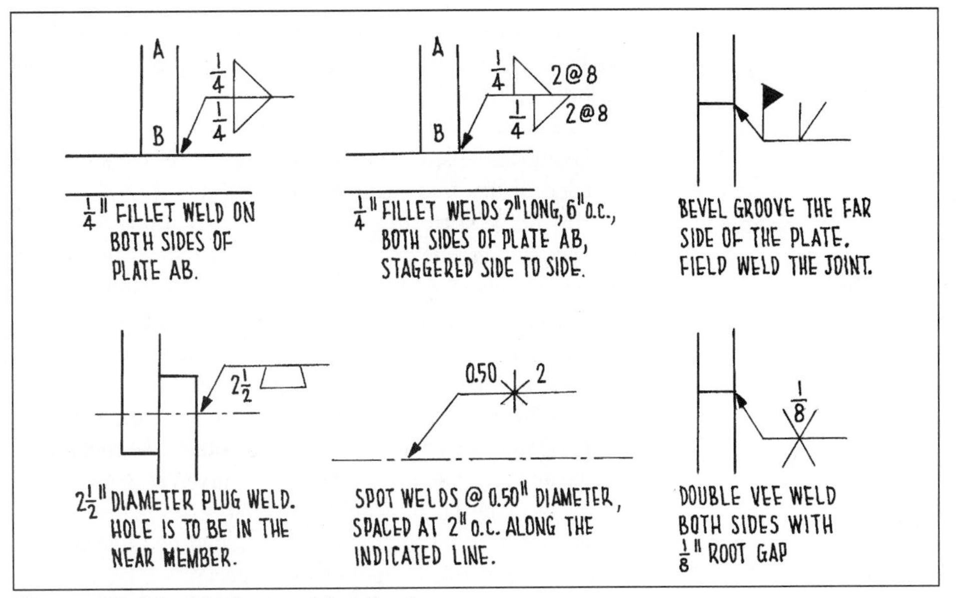

Figure 25-21 Typical weld callouts.

In manufacturing, automatic-feed welding machines are becoming increasingly common. These machines use a bare wire electrode which is consumed as filler material. The machine deposits a granular flux material just ahead of the arc which shields and protects the molten metal during and after the pass. Where the process can be applied, the penetration and quality are excellent. The process is called Submerged Arc Welding (SAW).

Other automated processes include Metal Inert Gas (MIG) and Tungsten Inert Gas (TIG), in which an inert gas is used to protect and shield the molten weld. Either a special bare wire metallic electrode or a bare wire tungsten electrode is used. As in other processes, the electrode is consumed as a filler material.

Of all welding processes, however, the familiar manual method of arc welding is by far the most common. In manual methods also, the electrode is consumed and becomes a filler material in the weldment. It is obviously essential in all processes, therefore, that the electrodes be compatible with, and as strong as, the material being welded.

In earlier years, bare carbon wire was used as the electrode in arc welding. In more recent years, the electrodes used in manual methods have a tightly controlled chemistry and are coated with a flux material. The flux melts as the electrode is consumed, providing a protective gas covering and a slag coating over the molten weld. The slag coating absorbs impurities from the molten weld material and prevents the weld material from absorbing atmospheric gases. This type of welding using a protective flux is called Shielded Metal Arc Welding (SMAW).

The electrodes used in manual arc welding are identified by the letter E followed by a four digit number, such as E6018. The first two numbers indicate the strength of the deposited material in ksi. The third digit will be either 1 or 2. A third digit of 1 indicates the rod "freezes" quickly and is therefore suitable for flat, vertical or overhead welding; a third digit of 2 indicates that the rod "freezes" more slowly and is suitable only for flat welding.

The fourth digit in the identification number is coded to indicate a set of conditions. A number 8, for example, indicates that the electode is formulated for use in alternating current welders, it has a low-hydrogen flux coating, it is suited for a medium arc, it develops medium penetration into the materials being welded and there is 30% to 50% iron in the coating. A complete listing of the types of electrodes can be found in the specifications of the American Welding Society (AWS).

In following discussions, electrodes are designated E60*xx* or E70*xx*, the 60 or 70 indicating strength and the *xx* indicating the other numbers not related to strength.

Electrodes are manufactured in grades E45*xx*, E60*xx*, E70*xx*, E80*xx* and even higher strengths. In structural welding, the grades E60*xx*, E70*xx* and E80*xx* are the most common. Since A36 steel has an ultimate strength of 58 ksi, the E60*xx* electrode best matches it and is commonly used for welding it.

The allowable stress in various types of welds is given in ASD Table J2.5. The table is included in the Technical Manual as Table S-28.

It should be noted in the third column of Table S-28 that the strength of the welding rod is specified as one "matching" the strength of the material being welded. An E60*xx* electrode "matches" A36 steel, with E70*xx* being one strength level above (see footnote c). A "matching" strength electrode is a requirement only when the weld is in direct tension normal to the effective area. In all other cases, a lower strength could be tolerated.

The allowable stress in the weld material is given in the second, or middle column of Table S-28. Except for partial penetration welds, the allowable tension and compression stress is consistently given as that of the base metal (the material being welded). In shear, the allowable stress is consistently given as 30% of the specified minimum strength of the weld material (either 60, 70 or 80 ksi).

The partial penetration weld is included in Table S-28 are groove welds that do not extend through the full depth of the material being welded. The *throat* of these welds is the penetration thickness actually achieved. Partial penetration welds are not included in succeeding discussions.

From the allowable stresses specified in Table S-28, it is concluded that a full penetration groove weld is at least as strong as the base material. The allowable stresses in tension and compression remain the same. The allowable stress in shear is $0.30\ F_u =$ 18,000 psi for E60xx electrodes, which compares to $0.40F_Y = 14{,}400$ psi for the A36 steel base material. A properly made, full penetration weld in A36 steel is therefore 100% efficient.

In spite of their efficiency, groove welds are not the most common structural weld; fillet welds are used far more than groove welds. The reason for such a preference lies in the fitting tolerances required to make a groove weld. As shown in Figure 25-22, the member lengths must be fitted exactly to include even the required root gap. It is far simpler to lap the material with a splice plate and a fillet weld, and to take up any dimensional inaccuracies by increasing or decreasing the lap length, as indicated in Figure 25-22.

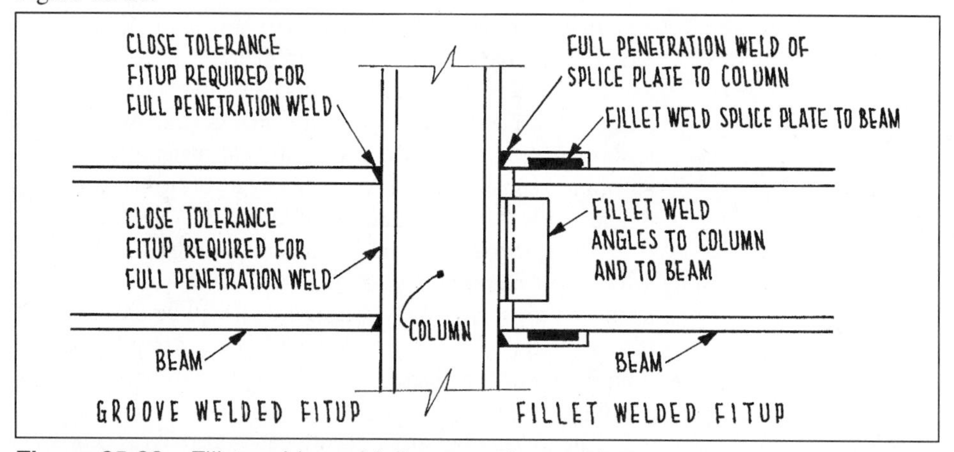

Figure 25-22 Fillet welds and full penetration welds.

Since groove welds in A36 steel are 100% efficient, there is no stress analysis to be made. One simply accepts that properly made groove welds are at least as strong as the base material; the member is then treated as if there were no weld at all.

An introduction to the stress analysis of fillet welds is usually included in the study of direct shear stress in strength of materials. That study, however, is limited to the direct shear stresses in the weldment. There are several additional factors that will be examined here, directly comparable to those considered for bolted connections.

1. Capacity of the connected members at their shanks.
2. Capacity of the connected members at the welds, to include the ASD area (and strength) reduction coefficients (Table S-19).
3. Capacity of the weld material in direct shear.
4. Conformance of weld size and layout to ASD requirements.
5. Capacity in block tearout.

Each of the foregoing items will be examined in sequence.

The capacity of the connected members at their shanks was discussed earlier in this chapter. The procedure was found to be the same for both bolted and welded members. The procedure need not be repeated here.

Similarly, the capacity of the connected members at a fillet welded connection was presented earlier in this chapter. It is recalled that ASD(B3) requires that a capacity reduction factor U must be applied to the gross area A_g to obtain the effective stressed area A_e. Examples 25-5 and 25-6 demonstrate this calculation; the procedure need not be repeated here.

The capacity of the weld material in direct shear is presented in somewhat limited detail in Chapter 8. The procedure is expanded here to include additional configurations and load cases.

Typical fillet welds in direct shear are shown in Figure 25-23. In the fillet weld aligned parallel to the load, the shear stress occurs along the throat of the fillet parallel to the load. In the fillet weld aligned transverse to the load, the shear stress occurs at 45° to the load, acting transverse to the axis of the fillet.

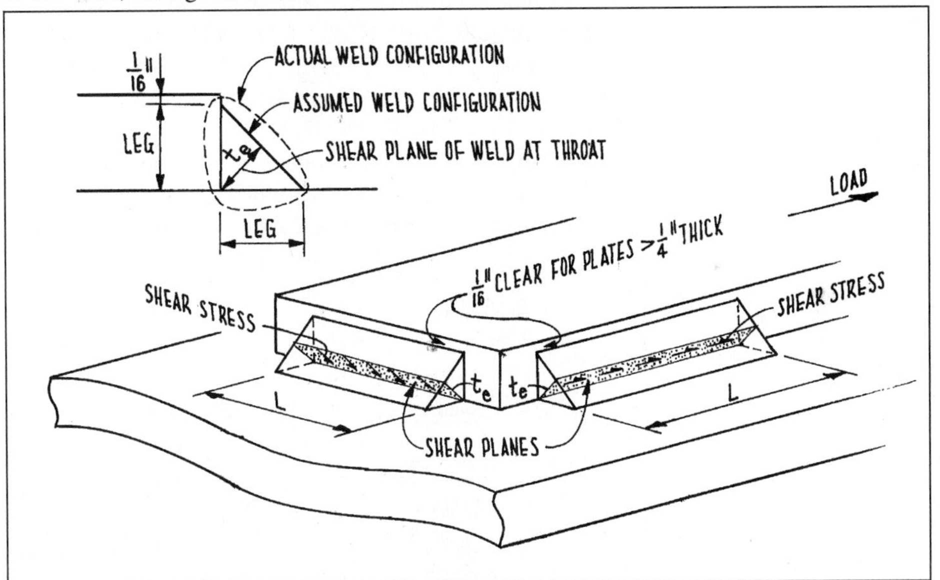

Figure 25-23 Shear planes in fillet welds.

The allowable shear stress on a fillet weld is given in ASD Table J2.5. When the fillet sizes and layout conform to ASD(J2), the allowable shear stress is given as

$$F_V = 0.30 \times \text{nominal tensile strength of the weld material} \quad (25\text{-}13)$$

The allowable stress is thus the same for both Submerged Arc Welds (SAW) and for Shielded Metal Arc Welds (SMAW). It is noted that for E60*xx* electrodes, the allowable shear stress in the weld material is 18 ksi, greater than the allowable shear stress of 14 ksi in A36 steel.

Fillet welds must conform to requirements for sizes and layout as specified by ASD(J2). The requirements are summarized in Table S-32 in the Technical Manual. Fillet welds must conform to these requirements if the connection is to have a predictable response to load.

It is noted in Table S-32 that the effective thread thickness t_e for machine-made SAW welds is larger than it is for the manually made SMAW welds. This allowable increase in thickness t_e (and effective area A_e) is due to the much better penetration and consistently higher quality obtained in machine welding.

The effective length given in Table S-32 includes "returns." Where appropriate, it is common practice in making fillet welds to follow the edge of a member around a corner for a short distance as shown in Figure 25-24. Those short extensions are called *returns*.

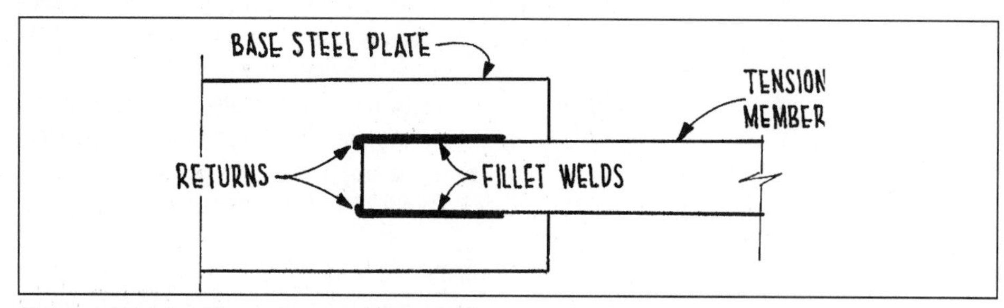

Figure 25-24 Returns on a fillet weld.

The use of returns is a sign of good welding practices. The return helps to reduce the stress concentrations when stress abruptly starts and stops at the ends of a highly loaded fillet. The length of a return is nominally twice the leg size of the weld, but few designers would include the return as a part of the weld length.

In finding the capacity of a fillet weld, it is useful to have the capacity of welds in allowable load per inch of length. A table of such values is given in Table S-31 in the Technical Manual, reprinted here for immediate reference. The values in Table S-31 are computed simply as $0.707t_e \times F_v$.

The final item to be examined in a system of fillet welds is its capacity in block tearout. Block tearout occurs in welded connections in much the same way it occurs in bolted connections. Some typical cases of block tearout are shown in Figure 25-25.

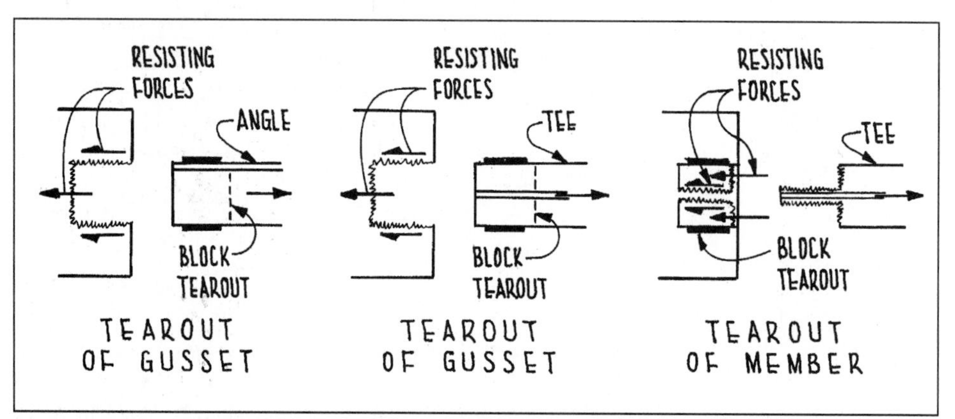

Figure 25-25 Block tearout in fillet welded connections.

Some examples will illustrate the analysis of fillet welded connections. The analysis follows the format stated earlier:

1. Determine the capacity of the connected members at their shanks.
2. Determine the capacity of the connected members at the connection.
3. Determine the capacity of the weld material in direct shear.
4. Verify that the weld conforms to requirements of ASD(J2), otherwise the performance of the connection under load is not predictable and the analysis is not valid.
5. Determine the capacity of all connected members in block tearout.

Example 25-21

Analysis of a fillet welded connection in tension.

Given: Structural tee truss member welded to a gusset plate. A36 steel, E60*xx* electrodes.

To Find: Capacity of the connection.

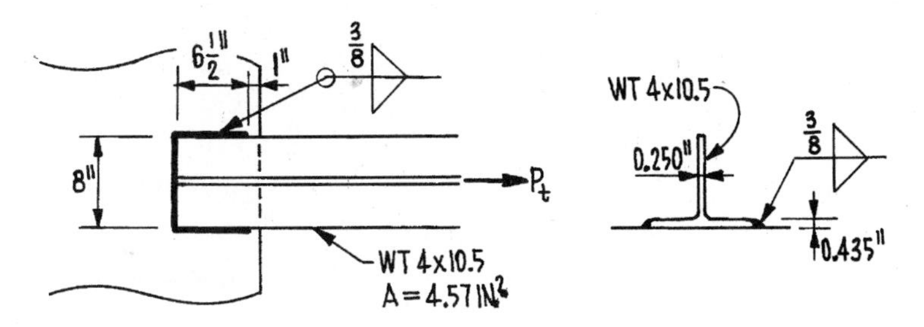

Solution: Capacity of tee section at its shank.

$P_t = 0.60F_yA_g = (0.60)(36)(4.57) = 98.7$ kips

Capacity of tee section at the connection.

The total length of weld: 21 in. > 2 x width

From Table S-19, U = 1.0

$P_t = 0.60F_uA_e = (0.60)(58)(1.0) = 132.5$ kips

Capacity of weld material in direct shear. For symmetrical load:

$P_t = [0.30(60)t_eL_{eft}]2$

$= 0.30(60)(0.707)(^3/_8)(21) = 100.2$ kips

Alternatively, with allowable load

= 4.8 kips/in. from Table S-31,

P_t = load/in. x length = 4.8 x 21 = 100.1 kips

Verify conformance to ASD(J2) as given in Table S-32:

Minimum left ≥ 4 x leg size = $1^1/_2$ in < 21 in. (O.K.)

Minimum leg size 0.435 - $^1/_{16}$ in. = 0.372 ≅ $^3/_8$ in. (O.K.)

Capacity of plate and tee in block tearout:

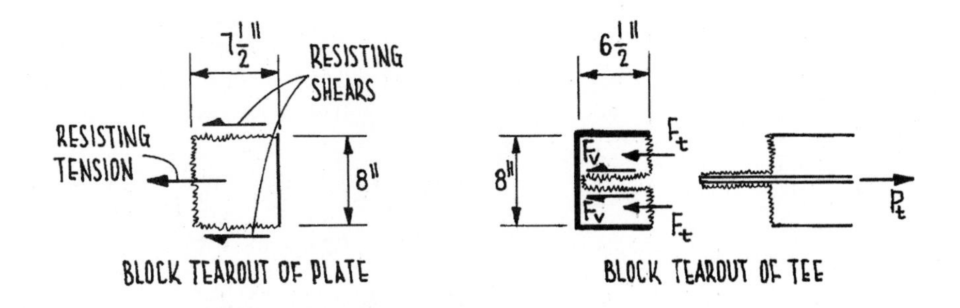

Block tearout in plate, $^1/_2$ in. thick

$P_t = F_tA_t + F_vA_v$

$= 0.50F_u \times 0.5 \times 8 + 0.30F_u \times 0.5 \times 7^1/_2 \times 2$

$= 116 + 130.5 = 247$ kips

Least capacity is in the shank of the tee.

$P_t = 98.7$ kips

Efficiency = 100%

Example 25-22

Analysis of a fillet welded connection in tension.

Given: Eccentric load on a weld plate as shown. ASTM A36 steel, E60xx electrodes.

To Find: Whether the connection is adequate.

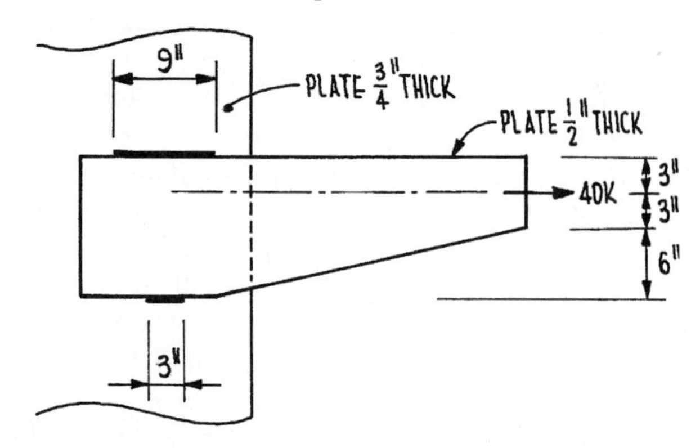

Solution: The welds are unsymmetrically loaded. The load per weld is found in the same way that reactions are found. Loads are shown in the following sketch.

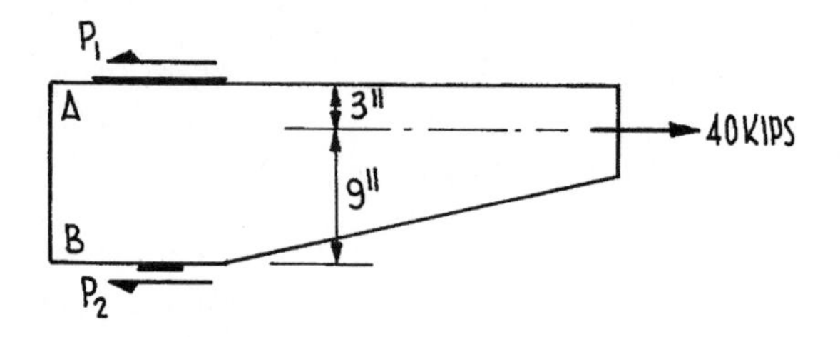

To find P_2, sum moments about A:

$-40 \times 3 + P_2 \times 12 = 0;$ $P_2 = 10.0$ k

To find P_1, sum moments about B:

$40 \times 9 - P_1 \times 12 = 0;$ $P_1 = 30.00$ k

Capacity of tension member at shank:

$P_t = 0.60F_yA_g,$ use least area as gross area:

$= 0.60 \times 36 \times 4 \times 1/2 = 43.20$ kips > 40 kips (O.K.)

Capacity of tension member at connection:

$P_t = 0.50F_uA_e$, $A_e = UA_g$, $U = 0.75$ from Table 19-1:

$= 0.50 \times 58 \times 12 \times 1/2 = 174$ kips > 40 kips (O.K.)

Capacity of weld material in direct shear:

Capacity of top fillet in shear:

P_t = Allowable load/in. x length

$= 4 \times 9 = 36$ kips > 31 (O.K.)

Capacity of bottom fillet in shear:
P_t = Allowable load/in. x length
= 4 x 3 = 12 kips > 10 (O.K.)

Verify that the connection conforms to ASD(J2) as given in Table S-32:
All lengths ≥ 4 x leg size = 1¼ in. (O.K.)
Minimum size of fillet = 3/16 in. < 5/16 used (O.K.)
Maximum size of fillet = 1/2 - 1/16 = 7/16 > 5/16 used (O.K.)

Capacity of weld plate in block tearout:
Tearout is assumed to occur at the two welds:

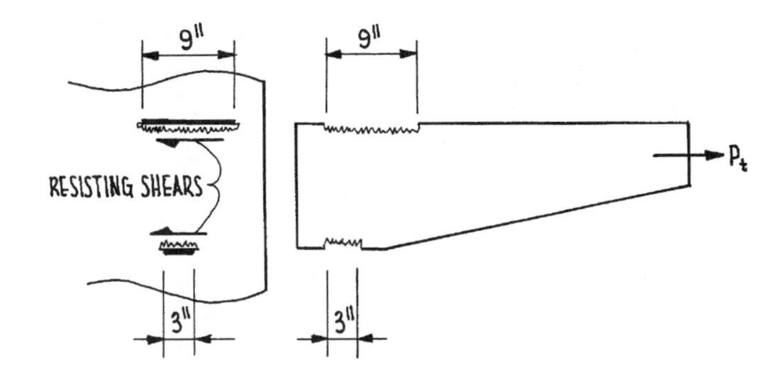

$P_t = F_tA_t + F_vA_v$, no tension failure occurs, shear failure only:
= $0.30F_u$ x 0.5[9+3] = 104 kips > 40 kips (O.K.)

All capacities > 40 kips. Connection is adequate.

The design of welded connections follows the same general procedure as for bolted connections:

1. Establish type of connection and trial sizes for all members.
2. Select size of fillets and establish their required lengths.
3. Make a detailed trial layout for the connection with all sizes and dimensions established.
4. Verify the capacity of the connection in all potential failure modes.
5. Revise and correct the design as necessary.

Some examples will illustrate the design procedure.

Example 25-23

Design of a fillet welded connection.

Given: Tensile load of 84 kips on a single angle truss member. Gusset plate is 5/8 in. thick. ASTM A36 steel; E60*xx* electrodes.

To Find: Suitable angle and its connection.

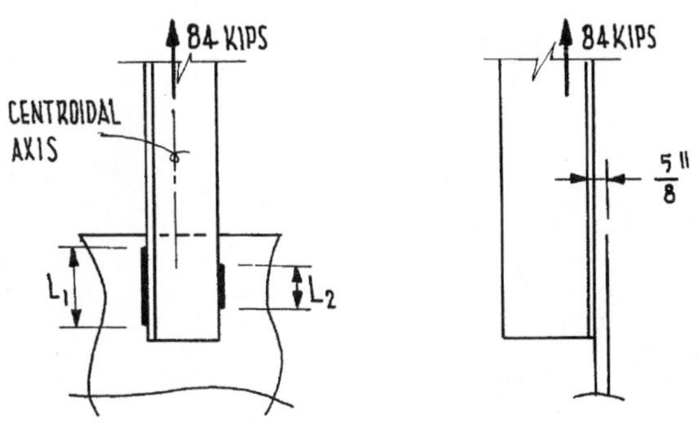

Solution: 1) Establish type of connection and a trial size for the angle.

It is elected to try fillet welds on the two sides of the angle as shown in the sketch.

The required cross-section area of the angle is found readily:

$$A_g = \frac{P}{0.60F_y} = \frac{84}{0.60(36)} = 3.89 \text{ in.}$$

Looking ahead, it will be desirable to have a reasonably thick angle in order to keep the weld size large; a larger weld size will permit a shorter weld length.

From Table S-4b, try L 4 x 3 x 5/8, A = 3.98 in.^{2} Place 3 in. leg next to the gusset. Centroid is shown in the following sketch.

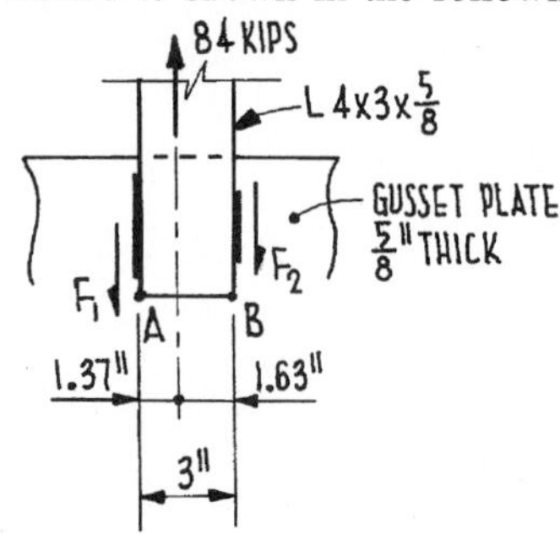

2) Select size of fillets and establish their required lengths.

For a 5/8 inch angle, the maximum allowable weld size is 9/16 in., for which the allowable load is found from Table S-31 to be 7.2 kips per inch.

Since the load is eccentric between the welds, the force at each weld line must be determined. The calculation is similar to that for computing reactions.

Summing moments about A yields the force F_2:

$-84 \times 1.37 + F_2 \times 3 = 0;$ $\quad F_2 = 38.4$ kips.

Summing moments about B yields the force F_1:

$84 \times 1.63 - F_1 \times 3 = 0;$ $\quad F_1 = 45.6$ kips.

Weld lengths are now established for a weld capacity of 7.2 kips/inch:

For L_1, $F_1 = 7.2L_1 = 45.6$ kips; $\quad L_1 = 6.33$ in.

For L_2, $F_2 = 7.2L_2 = 38.4$ kips; $\quad L_2 = 5.33$ in.

Try $L_1 = 6^1/_2$ in.; $\quad L_2 = 5^1/_2$ in.

3) Make a detailed trial layout with all sizes given. The trial layout is shown in the sketch.

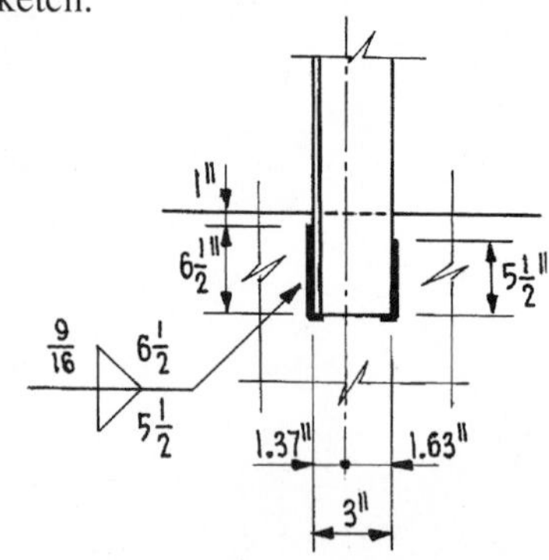

4) Verify the capacity of the connection in all failure modes:

Capacity of shank in tension:

$P_t = 0.60F_yA_g = 0.60 \times 36 \times 3.98 = 86$ kips

Capacity of the shank at the connection:

$P_t = 0.50F_uA_e = 0.50F_uUA_g$, from Table S-19, with $l > 2w$. $U = 1.00$

$= 0.50 \times 58 \times 1 \times 3.98 = 115$ kips

Capacity of the fillets in direct shear:

For the $6^1/_2$ in. fillet, at 7.2 kips/in.:

$P_t = 7.2 \times 6^1/_2$

$= 46.80$ kips > 45.6 k load (O.K.)

For the $5^1/_2$ in. fillet, at 7.2 kips/in.:

$P_t = 7.2 \times 5^1/_2$

$= 39.60$ kips > 38.4 k load (O.K.)

Verify conformance to Table S-32.

All sizes and lengths were deliberately selected to conform to ASD; no further verification needed.

Capacity in block tearout:

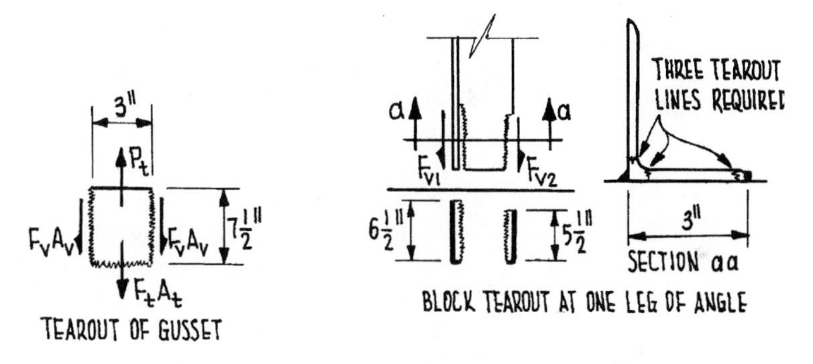

For gusset plate:

$P_t = F_tA_t + F_{v1}A_{v1} + F_{v2}A_{v2}$

$= 0.50F_u(^5/_8)(7^1/_2) + 0.30F_u(^5/_8)(7^1/_2)(2)$

$= 136 + 163 = 299$ kips

For angle:

$P_t = (F_{v1}A_{v1})2 + F_{v2}A_{v2}$

$= 0.30F_u(^5/_8)(6^1/_2) + 0.30F_u(^5/_8)(5^1/_2)$

$= 201$ kips

The least failure load is observed to be 86 kips at the shank.

The connection is adequate for the load of 84 kips.

Review Questions

1. Why is there such a concentration on connections in the study of steel structures?
2. Where is the *shank* of a tension member?
3. What is meant by the *gross area* of a tension member?
4. What is meant by the *net area* of a tension member?
5. How big would the holes be in a tension member if it is to be connected with $^{7}/_{8}$ in. diameter bolts?
6. Why does AISC require a further reduction to be applied to the net area of bolted tension members, even byond the deduction of bolt holes?
7. What is the gage in a hole pattern?
8. What is the pitch in a hole pattern?
9. Where is the edge distance in a hole pattern?
10. Where is the end distance in a hole pattern?
11. Why does AISC require a reduction in the gross area of welded tension members when there are no holes or other physical reductions?
12. What is the allowable tensile stress on a tension member at its shank? To what area does this stress apply?
13. What is the allowable tensile stress on a tension member at its connections?
14. Describe the potential failure lines in a bolt pattern consisting of staggered bolt locations.
15. How is the effective length established for a zigzag line of bolt holes?
16. Why should the combined thickness of splice plates be equal to or greater than the thickness of the plate being spliced?
17. At what point do the splice plates become the sole load carrying members in a structural connection?
18. What criteria is used to determine the amount of upset in upset threaded tension members?
19. Why is it preferred to use fasteners in shear rather than in tension?
20. Name the two types of bolted connections in common use and describe the means by which they transfer load from a tension member to another member.
21. Name the two types of welded connections in common use and describe the means by which they transfer load from a tension member to another member.
22. What is meant by *double shear* in a bolt?
23. Why should a designer be concerned about the location of the bolt threads in a bolted bearing connection?
24. Why should a designer be concerned about the location of the bolt threads in a bolted slip-critical connection?
25. In comparison, will a bolted bearing connection use more or fewer bolts for a given load than a bolted slip-critical connection?
26. How does a connection fail in bearing?
27. What is the allowable bearing stress of an A36 steel plate against an A325 bolt?
28. How can an allowable stress be higher than the ultimate strength of the material?
29. How is block tearout different from other modes of tensile failure in the main member?
30. What is the allowable stress in shear for block tearout?
31. What is the allowable stress in tension for block tearout?
32. What is the primary difference between the analysis and the design of structural connections?
33. What are *faying* surfaces?
34. How can slip-critical connections be designed for an allowable shear stress in the bolts when the bolts never undergo shear?
35. How is the friction force obtained in a slip-critical connection?
36. How is the analysis of bolted slip-critical connections different from that of bolted bearing connections?

37. What is the advantage of a bolted slip-critical connection over a bolted bearing connection?
38. What is meant by *shop weld, field bolt* in construction practice?
39. List the load transfers of a shop weld field bolt connection as the load is passed from one primary member to another.
40. Why isn't gas welding used very much in production welding?
41. What is the chemical formula for acetylene gas?
42. Under what circumstance would acetylene gas be prohibited as a welding method?
43. How is brazing different from welding?
44. How is steel torch cut with an acetylene torch?
45. What happens to the electrode in electric arc welding?
46. Can alternating current be used in welding?
47. Why are fillet welds preferred over groove welds, even when tension members are to be connected?
48. When does edge preparation of plates become mandatory?
49. What is meant by SAW, SMAW, MIG and TIG welds?
50. Of the methods listed in Question 49, which of the methods use bare wire electrodes and which use coated wire electrodes?
51. What is the tensile strength of an E6011 electrode? An E8013 electrode?
52. What is the allowable shear stress on weld material?
53. What electrode strength best matches A36 steel?
54. What is a *return* in a fillet weld?
55. What is the *throat* of a fillet weld?
56. Why is the throat of a fillet weld made by SAW techniques higher than one made by SMAW techniques?
57. How does the allowable shear stress on SAW welds compare to the allowable shear stress on SMAW welds?
58. How is the design of welded connections different from the analysis of welded connections?

CHAPTER

26

STEEL COLUMNS AND THEIR CONNECTIONS

Under the ASD specification, all compression members are designed under the same criteria as structural columns. Other compression members might include such things as bracing, truss members and struts. For the sake of simplicity, all compression members are included here within the generic term *columns*.

The discussions in this chapter are limited to rolled sections, to include tube and pipe sections. Built-up sections are not included, not because of any particular difficulty but because of the intricate controls over their design. The same basic principles apply to built-up sections as to rolled sections; the details are simply more numerous and more intricate.

The discussions in this chapter are limited to statically determinate structures of the type presented in Chapters 13, 14 and 15. In steel, this type of structure is called a *braced frame*, though its response to load is the same as that of any other diaphragm-shearwall structure. The important point to be recognized here is that in a steel braced frame, columns are not subject to bending; columns are subject only to axial load.

26.1 Buckling in Long Columns

The basic equation for buckling of long slender columns was developed by the Swiss mathematician Leonhard Euler in 1757. The "Euler column" is assumed to be straight, prismatic, of uniform cross-section, with pinned ends. Further, the Euler column is assumed to be concentrically loaded on its longitudinal axis, as shown in Figure 26-1.

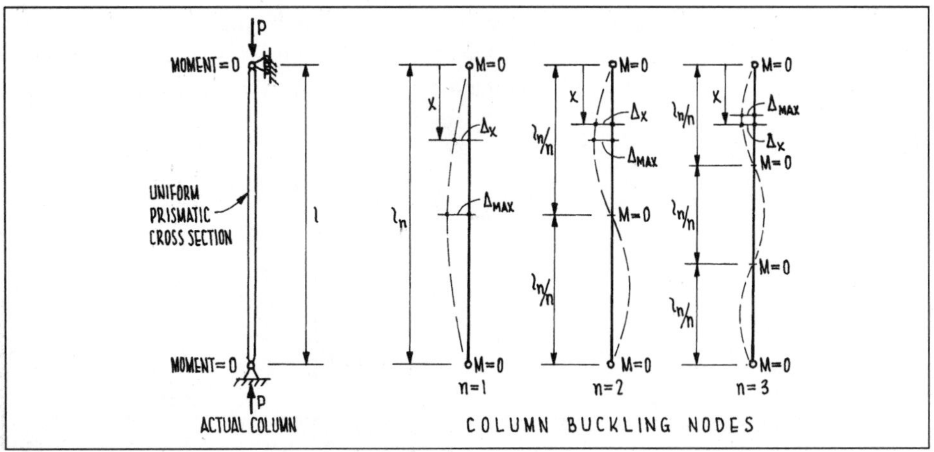

Figure 26-1 Euler column and buckling modes.

The load at which column buckling impends is given by the Euler formula:

$$P_{cr} = \frac{n^2\pi^2 EI}{l^2} \tag{26-1}$$

where P_{cr} is the critical load as buckling impends,
E is the modulus of elasticity,
I is the least moment of inertia of the cross section,
l is the length between hingepoints,
n is an integer denoting the number of buckling segments.

The elastic curve of the deflection shape is also given by the Euler solution:

$$\Delta_x = \Delta_{MAX} \sin\left(n\pi\frac{x}{l}\right) \tag{26-2}$$

where Δ_x is the deflection at any point x along the elastic curve,
Δ_{MAX} is the maximum deflection between hinge points, or, between any two consecutive points of zero moment,
l is the length between hinge points.

It is noted that buckling occurs in a sine curve, having n segments and $n+1$ "node points," or points of zero moment. The least load P_{cr} will be that when $n = 1$, for which case:

$$\text{Least } P_{cr} = \frac{\pi^2 EI}{l^2} \tag{26-3}$$

An alternate way of interpreting the buckling mode is to take $K = 1/n$, then Kl becomes the distance between any two consecutive points of zero moment. For this case, where nodal length $l/n = Kl$:

$$P_{cr} = \frac{\pi^2 EI}{(Kl)^2} \tag{26-4}$$

Quite often, it is the stress at failure f_{cr} that is wanted, not the load at failure P_{cr}. The stress is obtained by dividing both sides of Eq.(25-4) by the cross-section area A, and noting that $I = Ar^2$ where r is the radius of gyration:

$$\text{For any length } Kl, \quad f_{cr} = \frac{\pi^2 E}{\left(\frac{Kl}{r}\right)^2} \tag{26-5}$$

where f_{cr} is the critical cross-sectional stress at which buckling impends,
and Kl is the buckling length between any two consecutive points of zero moment.

In the form given in Eq.(14-4) or (25-5) the Euler formula can be applied to columns having a variety of end conditions. Some of these alternative end conditions are shown in Figure 25-2. The "factored" length Kl is shown as the buckled length between any two consecutive points of zero moment; the unfactored length l remains the actual distance between end supports.

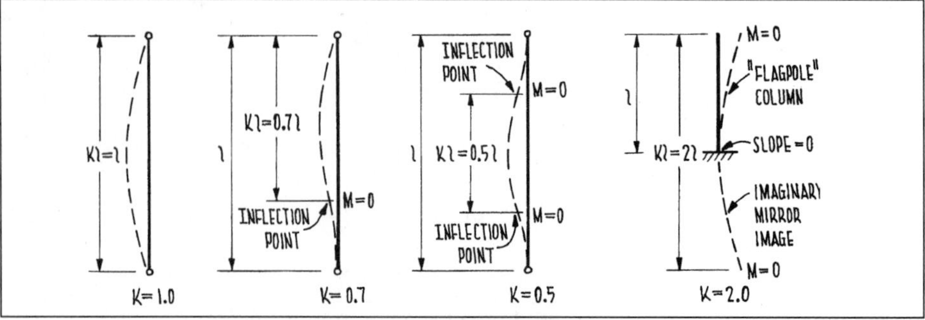

Figure 26-2 Alternative column buckling lengths.

The term "as buckling impends" has been used repeatedly in the foregoing discussions. The failure load is the highest load attained just before the column buckles, or just "as buckling impends." Once buckling starts, the column will continue to deflect laterally unless the load is released. If the load is immediately released, however, the column will return to its straight configuration with no damage or any other indication that it has failed under load.

In summary, buckling of a long column is an elastic phenomenon. If the load is immediately released, there will never be any yield and there will be no damage to the material. When the load is released, the return of the column to its straight configuration is also elastic.

The failure mode for buckling is, however, a failure in bending. Since steel members are invariably weaker in bending on one axis than on the other, failure will occur on the weaker of the two axes. The weaker axis is, of course, the axis having the lesser moment of inertia I.

This weak axis-strong axis concept is readily demonstrated just by pressing on the end of a yardstick, making it an axially loaded column. It will always fail in the weak direction, bending about the least moment of inertia.

If, however, the column can be braced on its weak axis, the stress as buckling impends can be markedly increased. Such a braced column is shown in Figure 26-3, where a steel column is braced at midpoint on its weak axis only. In this example, the bracing does not provide lateral support on the other axis.

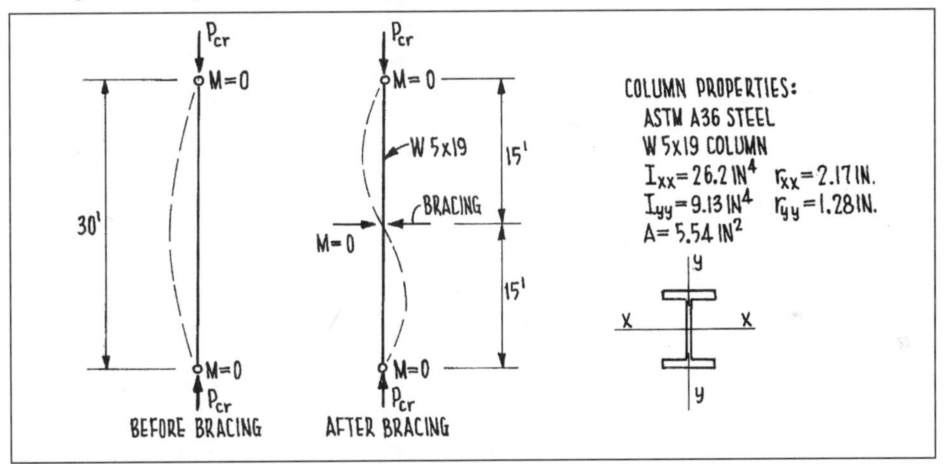

Figure 26-3 Bracing on weak axis of bending.

Without midpoint bracing, the critical buckling loads (on both axes) for the steel column of Figure 26-3 is computed from the Euler formula, Eq. (26-4):

$$\text{On the weak } yy \text{ axis } P_{cr} = \frac{\pi^2 EI}{(Kl)^2} = \frac{\pi^2(29)(10^6)(9.13)}{(30x12)^2} = 20.1 \text{ kips}$$

$$\text{On the strong } xx \text{ axis, } P_{cr} = \frac{\pi^2 EI}{(Kl)^2} = \frac{\pi^2(29)(10^6)(26.2)}{(30x12)^2} = 57.9 \text{ kips}$$

With no lateral bracing, the column is thus found to be some three times as strong on its strong xx axis as it is on its weak yy axis.

The column is now braced on its weak axis at its midpoint. The buckling length between points of zero moment has thus been reduced to 15 feet on the weak axis, but remains 30 feet on the strong axis.

$$\text{On the weak } yy \text{ axis: } P_{cr} = \frac{\pi^2 EI}{(Kl)^2} = \frac{\pi^2(29)(10^6)(9.13)}{(15x12)^2} = 80.7 \text{ kips}$$

$$\text{On the strong } xx\text{axis: } P_{cr} = \frac{\pi^2 EI}{(Kl)^2} = \frac{\pi^2(29)(10^6)(26.2)}{(30x12)^2} = 57.9 \text{ kips}$$

The braced column is now stronger in its weak *yy* direction than in its strong *xx* direction. Such increases in allowable column loads can often be achieved by providing bracing (where physically possible).

As a matter of interest, the maximum direct stress in the column as buckling impends is found readily:

$$f_A = \frac{P}{A} = \frac{80,700}{5.54} = 14,600 \text{ lb / in.}^2$$

This stress is well below the yield stress of 36,000 lb/in.²; the column will therefore fail in buckling long before it reaches yield stress.

It is important to note that all of the loads just calculated are the failure loads, not the allowable loads. The allowable loads are calculated as usual, by dividing the failure load by a factor of safety. For long columns, ADS(E2) sets the factor of safety at 23/12. In terms of allowable direct stress F_a, the Euler formula for long steel columns thus becomes, from Eq.(26-6):

$$F_a = \frac{f_{cr}}{FS} = \frac{12}{23} f_{cr} = \frac{12\pi^2 E}{23\left(\frac{Kl}{r}\right)^2} \qquad (26\text{-}6)$$

The multiplier 12/23 amounts to 0.52 x critical failure stress. It is recalled that in tension members, the usual multiplier was 0.60 x failure stress, where the failure stress was taken to be F_y. The distinct reduction in allowable stress in columns is due to the finality of buckling failure in long columns, since there is no "forgiving" yield in long columns to warn of impending collapse.

Some examples will illustrate the calculation of buckling loads and buckling stresses in long columns.

Example 26-1

Determination of failure load on a column.

Given: Pipe column fixed at both ends. ASTM A53 steel is equivalent to A36.

To Find: 1) Critical buckling load.
2) Stress as buckling impends.
3) Allowable buckling load (ASD specifications).

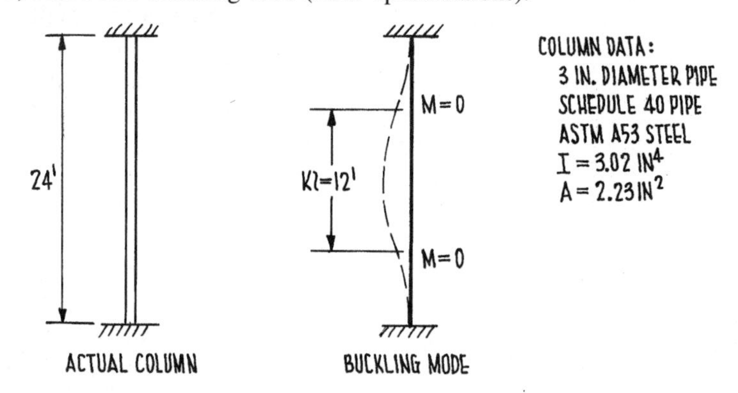

Solution: Critical buckling load is given by the Euler formula:

$$P_{cr} = \frac{\pi^2 EI}{(Kl)^2} = \frac{\pi^2(29)(10^6)(3.02)}{(12 \times 12)^2} = 41.7 \text{ kips}$$

Stress as buckling impends:

$$f_{cr} = \frac{P_{cr}}{A} = \frac{41,700}{2.23} = 18.7 \text{ ksi} < 36 \text{ ksi}$$

(column buckles before it yields.)

Allowable buckling load:

With FS = 23/12 on the critical load,

$$P_a = \frac{P_{cr}}{23/12} = \frac{12P_{cr}}{23} = \frac{12(41.7)}{23} = 21.8 \text{ kips}$$

This result may be verified by finding the allowable column load on a 3 in. diameter schedule 40 pipe in Table S-12 in the Technical Manual. The allowable load is given there for Kl = 12 feet is 22 kips, verifying the foregoing calculation.

Example: 26-2

Determination of failure load on a column.

Given: Structural tee WT4x7.5 with end conditions as shown. ASTM A36 steel, ASD specifications.

To Find: 1) Critical buckling load on both axes.
2) Allowable buckling load on both axes.

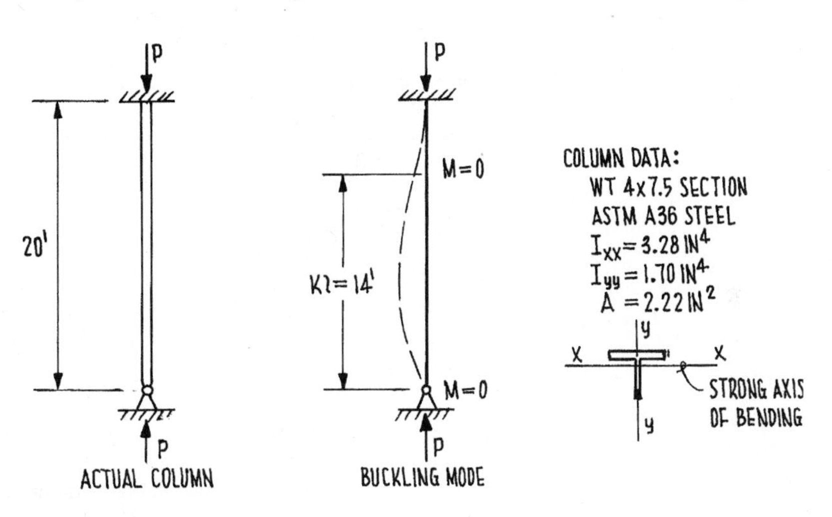

Solution: Critical buckling load is given by the Euler formula:

On the strong axis, $P_{cr} = \frac{\pi^2 EI}{(Kl)^2} = \frac{\pi^2(29)(10^6)(3.28)}{(14 \, x \, 12)^2}$

$= 33.3 \; kips$

On the weak axis, $P_{cr} = \frac{\pi^2 EI}{(Kl)^2} = \frac{\pi^2(29)(10^6)(1.70)}{(14 \, x \, 12)^2}$

$= 17.2 \; kips$

Allowable buckling load, with FS = 23/12:

$$\text{On the strong axis, } P_a = \frac{P_{cr}}{FS} = \frac{12}{23}(33.3) = 17.4 \text{ kips}$$

$$\text{On the weak axis, } P_a = \frac{P_{cr}}{FS} = \frac{12}{23}(17.2) = 9.0 \text{ kips}$$

As in the previous example, the results of Example 26-2 may be verified by finding the allowable column load on a WT4x7.5 in Table S-11b. The allowable loads given there for Kl = 14 feet is 17 kips on the *xx* axis and 9 kips on the *yy* axis, verifying the calculations.

Example: 26-3

Determination of failure load on a column.

Given: Double angle strut used as a truss member as shown. A36 steel.

To Find: 1) Allowable load on the strut.
2) Stress in the angles at critical buckling load.

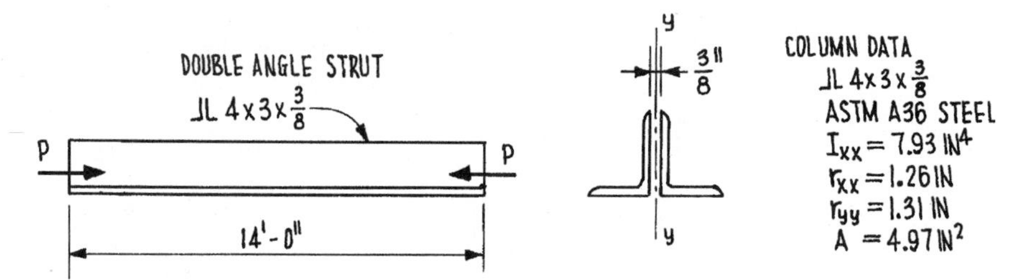

Solution: The moment of inertia could be computed, but numerical errors are far less likely to be made if the values are found in Table S-7b in the Technical Manual. It is observed, however, that the table provides only the radius of gyration on the *yy* axis. It will be necessary, therefore to compute I_{yy}, where I_{yy} = Ar^2:

$$I_{yy} = Ar^2_{yy} = 4.97 \text{ x } 1.312 = 8.53 \text{ in.}^4$$

The moments of inertia are compared to find that the least *I* occurs on the *xx* axis. The least load will therefore be on the *xx* axis:

$$P_a = \frac{12\pi^2 EI}{23(Kl)^2} = \frac{12(\pi^2)(29)(10^6)(7.93)}{23(14 \text{ x } 12)^2}$$

$$= 42 \text{ kips allowable load}$$

The critical buckling load is the allowable load times the factor of safety:

$$P_{cr} = \frac{23}{12}P_a = \frac{23}{12}42 = 80.4 \text{ kips}$$

The stress at critical load is then:

$$f_{cr} = \frac{P_{cr}}{A} = \frac{80,400}{4.97} = 16.2 \text{ ksi} < 36 \text{ ksi}$$

Alternatively, f_{cr} can be computed directly from Eq.(26-5):

$$f_{cr} = \frac{\pi^2 E}{\left(\frac{Kl}{r}\right)^2} = \frac{\pi^2 (29)(10^6)}{\left(\frac{(14)(12)}{1.26}\right)^2} = 16.1 \text{ ksi} < 36 \text{ ksi}$$

Conclusion: This strut will buckle long before it reaches the yield stress of 36 ksi.

At times a column may be exceptionally weak on one axis, in which case bracing the weak axis at midpoint will help strengthen it, but not enough. In such cases, it is entirely possible to brace the column at its 1/3 points, or even 1/4 points, if necessary. An example will demonstrate the calculations.

Example 26-4

Determination of failure load on a column.

Given: W6x16 column, hinged ends, A36 steel, ASD specifications.

To Find:
1) Buckling load on both axes with no bracing.
2) Buckling load with bracing on weak axis only at midpoint.
3) Buckling load with bracing on weak axis only at 1/3 points.
4) Stress at buckling load with bracing at 1/3 points.

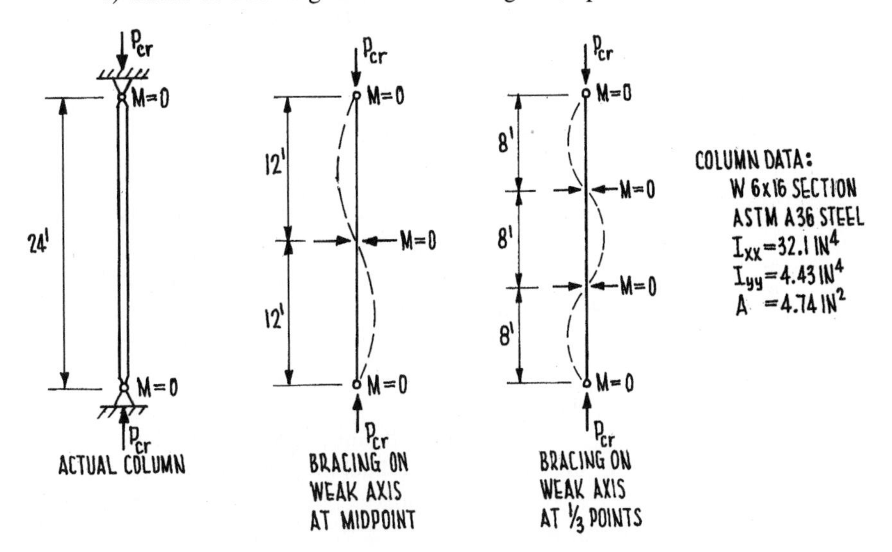

Solution: Critical load is given by the Euler formula Eq.(26-4):

On the strong axis, with no interior bracing:

$$P_{cr} = \frac{\pi^2 EI}{(Kl)^2} = \frac{\pi^2 (29)(10^6)(32.1)}{(24 \times 12)^2} = 111 \text{ kips}$$

On the weak axis, with no interior bracing:

$$P_{cr} = \frac{\pi^2 EI}{(Kl)^2} = \frac{\pi^2 (29)(10^6)(4.43)}{(24 \times 12)^2} = 15.3 \text{ kips}$$

(very low)

On the weak axis, with bracing at midpoint:

$$P_{cr} = \frac{\pi^2 EI}{(Kl)^2} = \frac{\pi^2 (29)(10^6)(4.43)}{(12 \times 12)^2} = 61.1 \text{ kips}$$

(still low)

On the weak axis, with bracing at 1/3 points:

$$P_{cr} = \frac{\pi^2 EI}{(Kl)^2} = \frac{\pi^2 (29)(10^6)(4.43)}{(8 \times 12)^2}$$

$$= 137.6 \text{ kips} > 111 \text{ kips (O.K.)}$$

Stress at buckling load with bracing at 1/3 points:

$$f_{cr} = \frac{P_{cr}}{A} = \frac{111{,}000}{4.74} = 23.4 \text{ ksi} < 36 \text{ ksi (O.K.)}$$

Conclude: With buckling at 1/3 points this column will buckle on its *xx* axis at 111 kips. At failure, the column is still elastic; buckling will occur long before yield stress is reached.

All of the columns in the foregoing examples were deliberately chosen to be *long* columns or *Euler* columns. Long columns are those that buckle before yield stress is reached. If the column is too short, the steel reaches yield stress before it reaches buckling load. In such cases the Euler formula is no longer valid and other criteria must be used.

26.2 Allowable Stresses in Columns

In routine building construction, most columns are not long columns. Rather, they are of some intermediate length and they fail in some mixture of buckling and yielding. Such a failure by a mixture of buckling and yielding is presented in this section.

The allowable stress in intermediate-length columns is prescribed in ASD(E2). The allowable stress given there is based on extensive full scale testing of thousands of sections under various types of lateral support and various kinds of end conditions. This allowable stress requires that the section begins to yield before any buckling phenomena occur.

The buckling failures considered in the previous section are readily visualized. There are other modes of buckling that may occur, however, that are not so readily visualized. These alternate modes come about due to the slenderness of the thin projecting elements of a steel section.

Consider, for example, the wide flange section shown in Figure 26-4. The flanges of the section consist of thin projecting elements. Under high compressive stress these elements can undergo local buckling failure completely independently of the overall column failure.

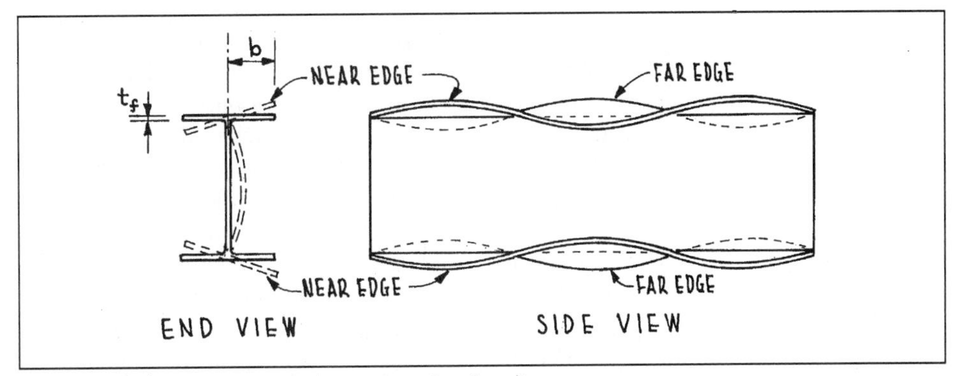

Figure 26-4 Buckling failure of projecting flange.

The type of failure shown in Figure 26-4 can happen in sections where the overhanging flange width b is long and the flange thickness t is small. The ratio b/t is the *indicator* that warns whether a particular steel section is susceptible to this type of local failure. If the values of b/t can be kept high enough, the material will yield before it can develop this type of buckling failure.

As a second example, consider the tee section shown in Figure 26-5. The stem of a tee is, in general, much thinner than the flanges. Under compressive load, the thin stem can buckle prematurely in the sine curve as shown, propagating a buckling failure much lower than that predicted by the Euler formula.

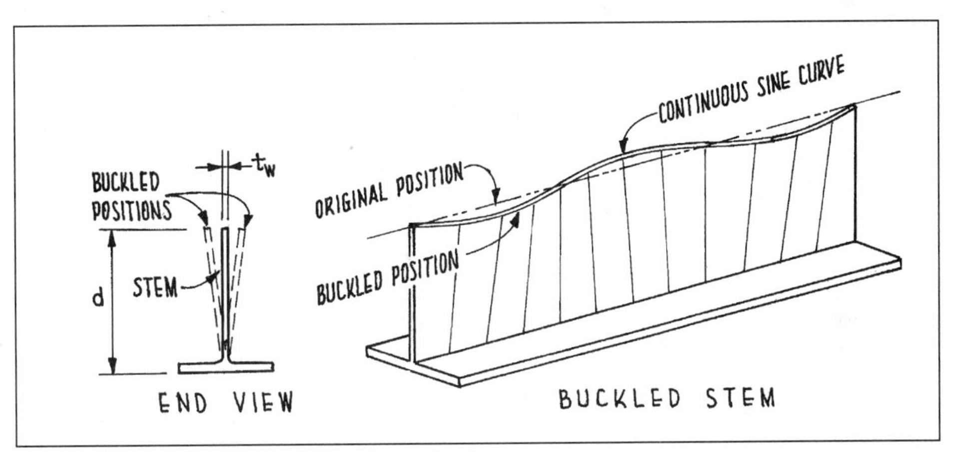

Figure 26-5 Buckling of the stem of a tee.

In the column of Figure 26-5, it should be noted that the load is properly applied at the centroid of the section. The failure is nonetheless premature, due to the independent buckling pattern (a non-Euler pattern) developed in the thin stem. The "indicator" of the susceptibility of a tee section to this type of failure is again the width-thickness ratio d/t of the stem. If the value of d/t can be kept high enough, the material will yield before it can develop this type of buckling failure.

Unwanted buckling patterns in the projecting elements can be avoided by keeping the projecting elements short and stocky. Such short, stocky elements will undergo yield before any of these erratic buckling patterns occur.

AISC has developed limiting values for the width-thickness ratios of projecting elements. Those steel sections having width-thickness ratios within these limits will fail in predictable patterns. Those having width-thickness ratios above these limits can still be used as columns, but the allowable stress must be reduced to a safe level.

The limiting values of the width-thickness ratio are given in ASD Table B5.1. The values for columns have been extracted and are shown in Table 26-1. Sections having *b/t* ratios within these limits are designed at one level of stress; sections having *b/t* ratios that exceed these limits are designed at a reduced level of stress.

The allowable stress for steel columns is a variable. Much higher stresses are allowed as the column becomes shorter, when buckling becomes less of a problem. The factor of safety for intermediate columns is also a variable; allowable stress is 0.60 x yield stress where length is zero, decreasing to 0.52 x buckling stress for Euler columns.

A graph of the AISC column formulas is shown in Figure 26-6. It should be noted immediately that the graph is made up of two equations, one for Euler columns that buckle before they yield, and one for intermediate columns that yield before they buckle. The parameter C_c is the value of kl/r that separates the two cases.

Table 26-1 Limiting Width-Thickness Ratios for Columns

Description of Element	Width-thickness Ratio	Limiting Ratio, λ_r	λ_r for A36 Steel
Flanges of W, S, channel and tee shapes	b/t	$95/\sqrt{F_y}$	15.8
Outstanding legs of double angle struts			
With inner legs in continuous contact	b/t	$95/\sqrt{F_y}$	15.8
With separators at inner legs	b/t	$76/\sqrt{F_y}$	12.7
Both legs of single angle struts	b/t	$76/\sqrt{F_y}$	12.7
Elements supported along one edge	b/t	$76/\sqrt{F_y}$	12.7
All elements supported on two edges	b/t	$253/\sqrt{F_y}$	42.2
	h_c/t_w	$253/\sqrt{F_y}$	42.2
Stems of tees	d/t	$127/\sqrt{F_y}$	21.2
Circular pipe sections	D/t	$3300/\sqrt{F_y}$	91.7

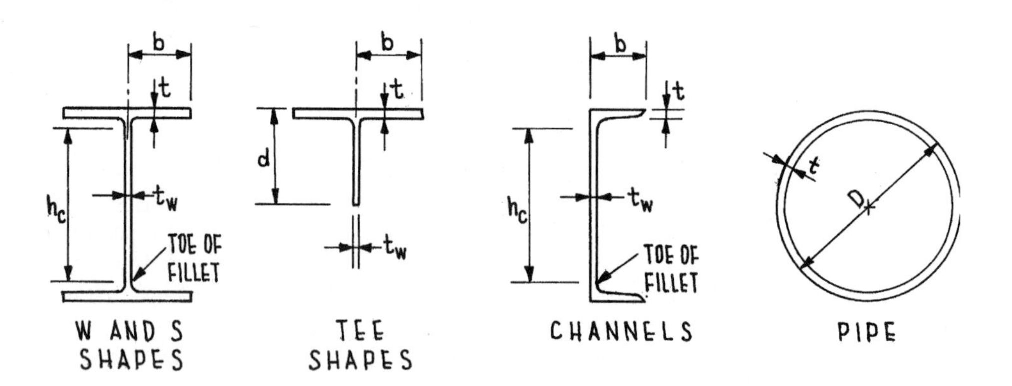

Source: AISC Manual of Steel Construction.
Reprinted by permission.

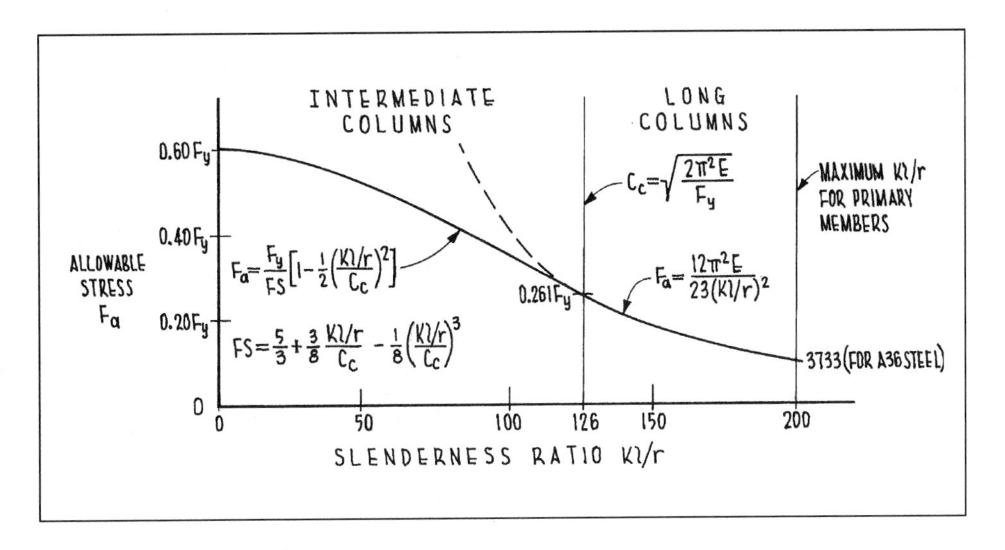

Figure 26-6 AISC column formula for A36 steel.

The AISC column equations given with Figure 26-6 are those to be used when the column section meets the limiting values of b/t given in Table 26-1. For sections that have values of b/t exceeding those limits, AISC prescribes a modified form of the equations. The modified form is presented later in this section.

For A36 steel, the allowable stress F_a can be tabulated for various values of Kl/r. Such a tabulation is presented in Table 26-2. The values given in Table 26-2 are nothing more than an evaluation of the AISC column equations for values of Kl/r from 0 to 200, with $C_c = 126.1$ for A36 steel. [ASD(B7) recommends that the value of Kl/r be limited to 200 for primary load-carrying columns.]

For $\dfrac{Kl/r}{C_c} > 1$ (long columns):

$$F_a = \left(\frac{12}{23}\right)\frac{\pi^2 E}{(Kl/r)^2} \tag{26-6}$$

$$\text{where } C_c = \sqrt{\frac{2\pi^2 E}{F_Y}}$$

For $\dfrac{Kl/r}{C_c} \leq 1$ (intermediate columns):

$$F_a = \frac{F_Y}{FS}\left[1 - \frac{1}{2}\left(\frac{Kl/r}{C_c}\right)^2\right] \tag{26-8}$$

$$\text{where } FS = \frac{5}{3} + \frac{3}{8}\left(\frac{Kl/r}{C_c}\right) - \frac{1}{8}\left(\frac{Kl/r}{C_c}\right)^3 \tag{26-9}$$

Table 26-2 Allowable Column Stress F_a in ksi for Sections Having No Slender Elements.

A36 STEEL

Kl/r	F_a	Kl/r	F_a	Kl/r	F_a	Kl/r	F_a	Kl/r	F_a
1	21.6	41	19.1	81	15.2	121	10.1	161	5.8
2	21.5	42	19.0	82	15.1	122	10.0	162	5.7
3	21.5	43	18.9	83	15.0	123	9.8	163	5.6
4	21.4	44	18.9	84	14.9	124	9.7	164	5.6
5	21.4	45	18.8	85	14.8	125	9.6	165	5.5
6	21.3	46	18.7	86	14.7	126	9.4	166	5.4
7	21.3	47	18.6	87	14.6	127	9.3	167	5.4
8	21.3	48	18.5	88	14.4	128	9.1	168	5.3
9	21.2	49	18.4	89	14.3	129	9.0	169	5.2
10	21.2	50	18.4	90	14.2	130	8.8	170	5.2
11	21.1	51	18.3	91	14.1	131	8.7	171	5.1
12	21.1	52	18.2	92	14.0	132	8.6	172	5.0
13	21.0	53	18.1	93	13.8	133	8.4	173	5.0
14	20.9	54	18.0	94	13.7	134	8.3	174	4.9
15	20.9	55	17.9	95	13.6	135	8.2	175	4.9
16	20.8	56	17.8	96	13.5	136	8.1	176	4.8
17	20.8	57	17.7	97	13.4	137	8.0	177	4.8
18	20.7	58	17.6	98	13.2	138	7.8	178	4.7
19	20.7	59	17.5	99	13.1	139	7.7	179	4.7
20	20.6	60	17.4	100	13.0	140	7.6	180	4.6
21	20.5	61	17.3	101	12.9	141	7.5	181	4.6
22	20.5	62	17.2	102	12.7	142	7.4	182	4.5
23	20.4	63	17.1	103	12.6	143	7.3	183	4.5
24	20.3	64	17.0	104	12.5	144	7.2	184	4.4
25	20.3	65	16.9	105	12.3	145	7.1	185	4.4
26	20.2	66	16.8	106	12.2	146	7.0	186	4.3
27	20.1	67	16.7	107	12.1	147	6.9	187	4.2
28	20.1	68	16.6	108	11.9	148	6.8	188	4.2
29	20.0	69	16.5	109	11.8	149	6.7	189	4.2
30	19.9	70	16.4	110	11.7	150	6.6	190	4.1
31	19.9	71	16.3	111	11.5	151	6.5	191	4.1
32	19.9	72	16.2	112	11.4	152	6.5	192	4.1
33	19.7	73	16.1	113	11.3	153	6.4	193	4.0
34	19.7	74	16.0	114	11.1	154	6.3	194	4.0
35	19.6	75	15.9	115	11.0	155	6.2	195	3.9
36	19.5	76	15.8	116	10.8	156	6.1	196	3.9
37	19.4	77	15.7	117	10.7	157	6.1	197	3.8
38	19.3	78	15.6	118	10.6	158	6.0	198	3.8
39	19.3	78	15.5	119	10.4	159	5.9	199	3.8
40	19.2	80	15.4	120	10.3	160	5.8	200	3.7

The allowable stresses given in Table 26-2 are valid for sections having no slender elements. Such a limitation is not severe. Except for some tees and some angles, none of the rolled sections in common use have any slender projecting elements.

In tees, however, the stem of the tee is sometimes so long and so thin that it is classed as a slender element. For such sections, ASD(A-B5) prescribes a reduction factor Q_s to be applied to the yield stress of the steel:

$$\text{When } \frac{127}{\sqrt{F_Y}} < \frac{b}{t} < \frac{176}{\sqrt{F_Y}}, \tag{26-10}$$

$$\text{then } Q_s = 1.908 - 0.00715\left(\frac{b}{t}\right)\sqrt{F_Y}$$

$$\text{When } \frac{b}{t} > 176\sqrt{F_y}, \tag{26-11}$$

$$\text{then } Q_s = \frac{20{,}000}{\left(\frac{b}{t}\right)^2 F_Y}$$

where b is the length of the projecting stem;
and t is the thickness of the stem.

Not all tees have stems that fall into the classification of slender elements. Those that do are easily identified. The AISC tables of dimensions and properties for tee sections, Tables S-5 and S-6 in the Technical Manual, list the values of Q_s for all tee sections that have a slender element. If no value of Q_s is listed, the value of Q_s is 1.00.

The reduction factor Q_s is applied to the yield stress of the steel in all calculations for allowable stress; F_y thus becomes Q_sF_Y. For tee sections, Eq.(26-6) is unchanged since it is not a function of F_y. Equations (26-6, 7, 8 and 9) for allowable stress then become, when F_Y becomes Q_sF_Y:

$$\text{For } \frac{Kl/r}{C_c'} > 1 \text{ (long columns)}$$

$$F_a = \left(\frac{12}{23}\right)\frac{\pi^2 E}{(Kl/r)^2} \tag{26-6}$$

$$\text{where } C_c' = \sqrt{\frac{2\pi^2 E}{Q_s F_Y}} \tag{26-12}$$

$$\text{For } \frac{Kl/r}{C_c'} \leq 1 \text{ (intermediate columns)}$$

$$F_a = \frac{Q_s F_Y}{FS}\left[1 - \frac{1}{2}\left(\frac{Kl/r}{C_c'}\right)^2\right] \tag{26-13}$$

$$\text{where FS} = \frac{5}{3} + \frac{3}{8}\left(\frac{Kl/r}{C_c'}\right) - \frac{1}{8}\left(\frac{Kl/r}{C_c'}\right)^3 \tag{26-14}$$

The net effect of applying the reduction factor Q_s in this way is to require that such tees be designed as if they were made of a lower strength steel. For that lower strength steel, with its yield stress of Q_sF_Y, the stem is no longer a slender element and Equations (26-6, 7, 8 and 9) remain valid.

For long columns, that is, for columns having $(Kl/r)/C_c' > 1$, the allowable stress is unaffected by the existence of slender elements; all stresses are elastic so slender elements remain elastic as well. For intermediate columns having slender elements, AISC has developed a table of coefficients for calculating the allowable stress. Shown here as Table 26-3, the table is entered with the ratio $(Kl/r)/C'_c$ and a coefficient C_a is obtained. The allowable stress is then calculated as $C_a Q_s F_Y$.

Alternatively, the values of Q_s can be included in the design aids, such as the column load tables in the Technical Manual. Table S-11, for example, lists the allowable column loads on two axes for both WT and ST shapes. The listed values include the modified yield stress $Q_s F_Y$ where appropriate.

The allowable column stresses for sections having no slender elements are thus given by Equations (26-6, 7, 8 and 9). The allowable column stresses for sections having slender elements are similarly given by Equations (26-6, 12, 13 and 14). Applications of these equations are presented in the next section.

Table 26-3 Coefficients for Allowable Column Stress F_a in ksi for Sections Having Slender Elements[a,b]

A36 STEEL

$\frac{Kl/r}{C'_c}$	C_a	$\frac{Kl/r}{C'_c}$	C_a	$\frac{Kl/r}{C'_c}$	C_a	$\frac{Kl/r}{C'_c}$	C_a	$\frac{Kl/r}{C'_c}$	C_a
0.01	0.599	0.21	0.562	0.41	0.506	0.61	0.436	0.81	0.353
0.02	0.597	0.22	0.558	0.42	0.502	0.62	0.432	0.82	0.348
0.03	0.596	0.23	0.556	0.43	0.499	0.63	0.428	0.83	0.344
0.04	0.594	0.24	0.553	0.44	0.486	0.64	0.424	0.84	0.339
0.05	0.593	0.25	0.551	0.45	0.493	0.65	0.420	0.85	0.335
0.06	0.591	0.26	0.548	0.46	0.489	0.66	0.416	0.86	0.330
0.07	0.589	0.27	0.546	0.47	0.486	0.67	0.412	0.87	0.325
0.08	0.588	0.28	0.543	0.48	0.483	0.68	0.408	0.88	0.321
0.09	0.586	0.29	0.540	0.49	0.479	0.69	0.404	0.89	0.316
0.10	0.584	0.30	0.538	0.50	0.476	0.70	0.400	0.90	0.311
0.11	0.582	0.31	0.535	0.51	0.472	0.71	0.396	0.91	0.306
0.12	0.580	0.32	0.532	0.52	0.469	0.72	0.392	0.92	0.301
0.13	0.578	0.33	0.529	0.53	0.465	0.73	0.388	0.93	0.296
0.14	0.576	0.34	0.527	0.54	0.462	0.74	0.384	0.94	0.291
0.15	0.574	0.35	0.524	0.55	0.458	0.75	0.379	0.95	0.286
0.16	0.572	0.36	0.521	0.56	0.455	0.76	0.375	0.96	0.281
0.17	0.570	0.37	0.518	0.57	0.451	0.77	0.371	0.97	0.276
0.18	0.568	0.38	0.515	0.58	0.447	0.78	0.366	0.98	0.271
0.19	0.565	0.39	0.512	0.59	0.444	0.79	0.362	0.99	0.266
0.20	0.563	0.40	0.509	0.60	0.440	0.80	0.357	1.00	0.261

[a] Source: AISC Manual of Steel Construction, reprinted by permission.
[b] $F_a = C_a \times Q_s \times F_y$, where Q_s is a stress reduction factor, given with the dimensions and properties of the section, Tables S-5 and 6.

26.3 Concentrically Loaded Columns

It is again emphasized that the only type of steel structures considered in this textbook are braced frames. In braced frames, columns do not undergo any bending due to lateral loads of wind and earthquake. In braced frames, columns are generally hinged at both ends, though occasionally they may be fixed to steel girders at top or bottom or both.

Further, it is assumed that the columns in a braced frame are detailed such that loads are applied concentrically, that is, the load is applied at the centroid of the cross section. Concentric loads do not produce moments in the column.

The wide flange sections most commonly used for columns are the 10, 12 and 14 inch sections. Other sections are used, however, some of which are not well suited for use as a column. Generally, a section can be said to be suited for use as a column when its allowable strength on its weak axis of buckling is at least half its allowable strength on its strong axis of buckling.

The capacity of a column is found from the equations (or table) developed in the preceding section. The procedure is quite straightforward.

1. Given the radius of gyration r for the section and the longest distance *Kl* between any two consecutive points of zero moment, compute the actual *Kl*/*r*.
2. Determine the *Kl*/*r* that separates long columns from intermediate columns for the particular steel being used. For A36 steel, that value of *Kl*/*r* is 126.1.
3. Determine whether the column is a long column or an intermediate column.
4. If the column is a long column, its allowable stress is found from Eq.(26-6). If it is an intermediate column, its allowable stress is found from Eq.(26-8) and Eq.(26-9).
5. Load capacity for a concentrically loaded column is then the allowable stress times the cross-sectional area.

Some examples will illustrate the calculation of load capacity for some typical columns.

Example 26-5

Determination of column capacity.

Given: W12x58 section loaded axially. End conditions as shown in the sketch. A36 steel.

To Find: Allowable load capacity.

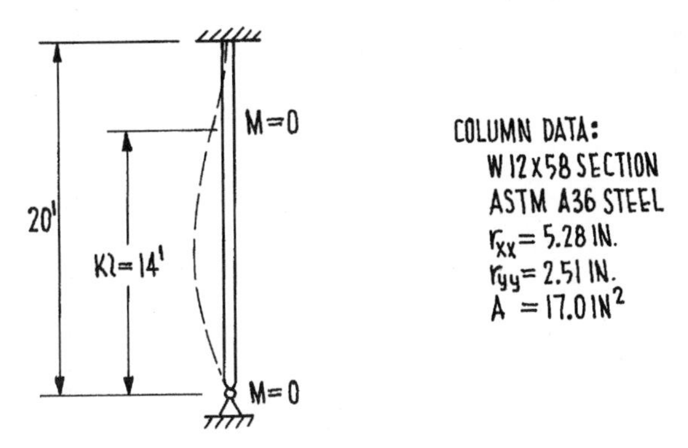

Solution: With no intermediate bracing, the column will fail on its weak axis, the *yy* axis.

Actual K*l*/r = (14 x 12)/2.51 = 66.9

Limiting *Kl*/*r* for long columns in A36 steel is 126.1. This column has its K*l*/r < 126.1; it will therefore yield before it buckles. Its capacity is determined as an intermediate column.

Equation (26-8) may be evaluated manually to find the allowable stress F_a, or its evaluation may be found in Table 26-2:

$$F_a = 16.7 \text{ ksi}$$

The capacity is the allowable stress times the area:

$$P = F_a A = 16.7 \times 17.0 = 284 \text{ kips}$$

Alternatively, the capacity of this section could be found in Table S-10a in the Technical Manual. For a length of 14 ft between points of zero moment, Table S-10a lists the capacity of a W12x58 as 337 kips on the *xx* axis and 285 kips on the *yy* axis. The limiting value of the section is of course 285 kips on the *yy* axis.

Note that the sections listed in Table S-10 are listed in order of descending weights. To find a column weighing 58 lbs/ft, simply follow the weights (in the first column) downward until a section weight of 58 is reached.

Example 26-6

Determination of column capacity.

Given: Tube column 5 x 5 with wall thickness 1/4 in. ASTM A500 steel, F_Y = 46 ksi.

To Find: Capacity of the column.

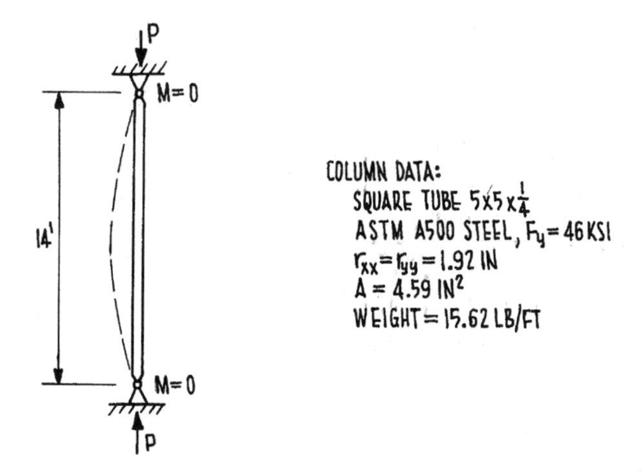

Solution: Determine the actual $Kl/r = (14 \times 12)/1.92 = 87.5$

Determine the limiting $Kl/r = \sqrt{\dfrac{2\pi^2 E}{F_Y}} = \sqrt{\dfrac{2\pi^2 x 29{,}000}{46}} = 111.6$

This column is seen to be an intermediate column. Its allowable stress is given by Eq.(26-6).

In this case, Table 26-2 cannot be used, since it is computed for a yield stress of 36 ksi. Eq.(26-8) will have to be evaluated manually for a yield stress of 46 ksi:

$$FS = \frac{5}{3} + \frac{3}{8}\left(\frac{Kl/r}{C_c}\right) - \frac{1}{8}\left(\frac{Kl/r}{C_c}\right)^3$$

$$= \frac{5}{3} + \frac{3}{8}\left(\frac{87.5}{111.6}\right) - \frac{1}{8}\left(\frac{87.5}{111.6}\right)^3 = 1.90$$

$$F_a = \frac{F_Y}{FS}\left[1 - \frac{1}{2}\left(\frac{Kl/r}{C_c}\right)^2\right] = \frac{46}{1.9}\left[1 - \frac{1}{2}\left(\frac{87.5}{111.6}\right)^2\right]$$

$$= 16.77 \text{ ksi}$$

The allowable column load is found as usual:

$$P = F_a A = 16.77 \times 4.59 = 77 \text{ kips.}$$

Alternatively, the load can be found in Table S-13 in the Technical Manual. For a 5 x 5 tube weighing 15.62 lb/ft with a length of 14 ft between points of zero moment, the allowable load is found to be 77 kips.

Example: 26-7

Determination of column capacity.

Given: Circular pipe section loaded concentrically as shown. ASTM steel, F_Y = 35 ksi.

To Find: Capacity of the pipe column.

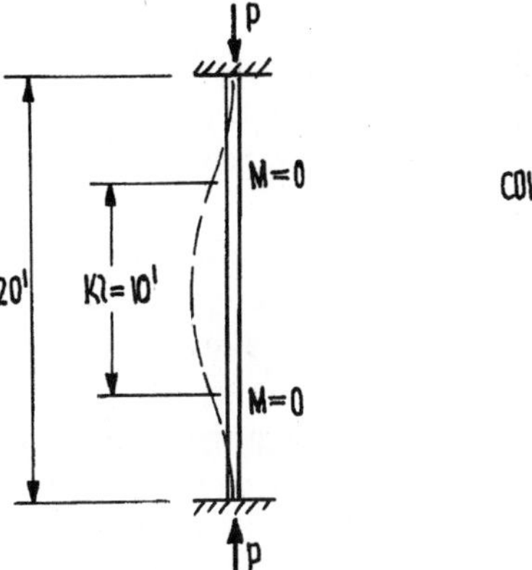

Solution: Though the yield stress of the ASTM A53 is not exactly 36 ksi, AISC permits the design tables for A36 steel to be used for pipe columns.

Actual $Kl/r = (10 \times 12)/1.51 = 79.5$

Limiting $Kl/r = C_c = 126.1$

The column is seen to be an intermediate column. The allowable stress is given by Eq.(26-8) or Table 26-2.

$F_a = 15.4$ ksi

The capacity of the column is the allowable stress times the area:

$$P = F_aA = 15.4 \times 3.17 = 48.8 \text{ kips}$$

Alternatively, the capacity of a circular pipe section may be found in Table S-12 in the Technical Manual. For a length of 10 ft between points of zero moment, the capacity listed in Table S-12 for a 4 in. diameter standard pipe is 49 kips.

Example: 26-8

Determination of column capacity.

Given: W8x28 column braced at its midpoint in the weak direction. A36 steel.

To Find: Allowable load capacity.

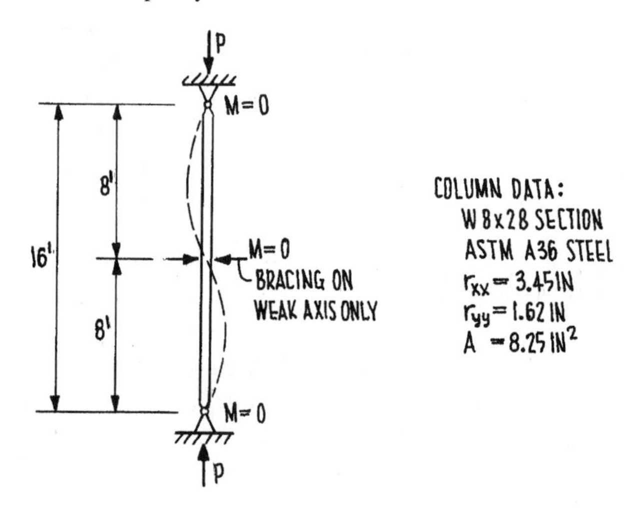

Solution: At this point it is not known whether the load will be limited by the allowable stress on the weak axis or on the strong axis. Both will be determined and the smaller one will be used as the limiting stress.

On the strong axis, actual $Kl/r = (16 \times 12)/3.45 = 55.7$. The column therefore is an intermediate length column in this direction.
From Table 26-2, $F_a = 17.8$ ksi.

On the weak axis, actual $Kl/r = (8 \times 12)/1.62 = 59.3$. The column is therefore an intermediate length column in this direction.
From Table 26-2, $F_a = 17.5$ ksi.

The allowable F_a is thus found to be limited on the weak axis of bending to 17.5 ksi.
$P = F_aA = 17.5 \times 8.25 = 144$ kips.

Alternatively, this capacity can be found in the column tables in the Technical Manual. In Table S-10b, the capacity of a W8x28 column on its strong *xx* axis for a buckling length of 16 ft is found to be 147 kips. The capacity of a W8x28 column on its weak *yy* axis for a buckling length of 8 ft is found to be 144 kips. The limiting load is thus 144 kips on the weak axis.

In the foregoing examples, the column section was always given; finding the capacity of the given section was then the problem. The other form of the column problem occurs when it is the load and the unsupported length that are known; a section must be found that will sustain that load over that length.

The selection of a column section to carry a known load can be a very clumsy procedure. It is, however, the usual form of problem encountered in column design. Some examples will illustrate a few of the methods used to reduce the labor.

Example 26-9

Selection of a column section to carry a known load.

Given: Column with end conditions and load as shown. A36 steel.

To Find: Suitable section to carry the load.

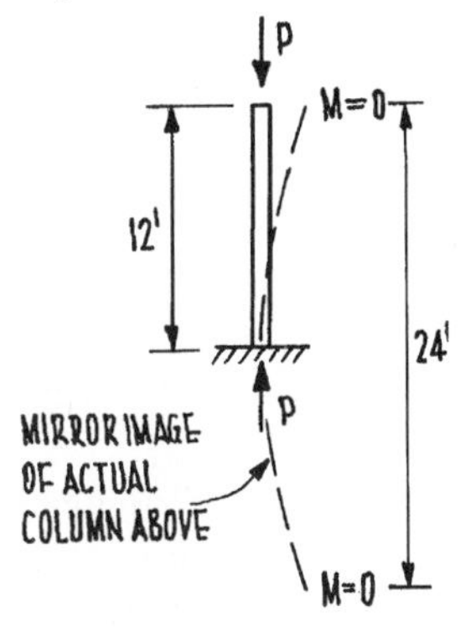

Solution: Since the column section has not yet been selected, it is not possible to calculate its Kl/r, since r is unknown.

To make a column selection, it is necessary to select a trial section, then with its value of r, and find whether it is adequate. If it is too weak, a heavier section is then tried and its capacity is determined. If it is too strong, a lighter section is chosen and its capacity is determined. This successive selection process is repeated as necessary to find the lightest (most economical) column section that will sustain the load over the given unsupported length.

Obviously a design aid is needed that will permit a comparative selection to be made without having to go through such a time-consuming procedure. There are many such aids in the design handbooks. One is given in Table S-10 in the Technical Manual.

Table S-10 lists the column sections in order of descending weights. Enter the table at the lower right-hand corner of Table S-10b, where the lightest sections are listed. With K of 24 ft, proceed upward until the first column section is reached that will sustain 32 kips on both axes. That section is the lightest section that will sustain the 32 kip load.

Where no entry is given in Table S-10, the Kl/r is greater than 200; for primary members, values of $Kl/r > 200$ are not recommended.

For a load of 32 kips with Kl = 24 ft, find W8x24 to be the lightest section that will sustain the load.

Example: 26-10

Selection of a column section to carry a known load.

Given: Conditions of Example 26-9.

To Find: Lightest steel section, whether *W*, *S*, *WT*, *ST*, pipe or tube, to sustain the load of 32 kips.

Solution: For wide flange *W* shapes, the section was found in Example 26-9 to be a W8x24.

For American standard *S* shapes, Table S-10b reveals that there is no section that can sustain a 32 kip load on both axes over a 24 ft length. The *Kl/r* on the *yy* axis is always in excess of 200.

For *WT* shapes, Table S-11b indicates that the lightest tee section that will sustain 32 kips over a length of 24 ft is a WT7x21.5.

For *ST* shapes, Table S-11b shows no *ST* shape that will sustain 32 kips on both axes over a 24 ft length. As with the *S* shapes, the *Kl/r* is always in excess of 200.

For pipe sections, Table S-12 indicates that a 6 in. diameter schedule 40 pipe at 18.97 lbs/ft is the lightest pipe section that will sustain 32 kips over a 24 ft unsupported length.

For square tube sections, Table S-13 shows that a 6 x 6 tube weighing 19.02 lbs/ft will sustain 32 kips over a 24 ft unsupported length.

The lightest section is found from the foregoing investigations to be the 6 in. diameter schedule 40 pipe at 18.97 lbs/ft.

Example: 26-11

Selection of a column section to carry a known load.

Given: Column load of 161 kips with hinged end supports. Unsupported length is 20 feet. A36 steel.

To Find: 1) Lightest wide flange section that will carry this load with no interior bracing.

2) Lightest wide flange section that will carry this load if bracing is provided at midpoint on the weak axis only.

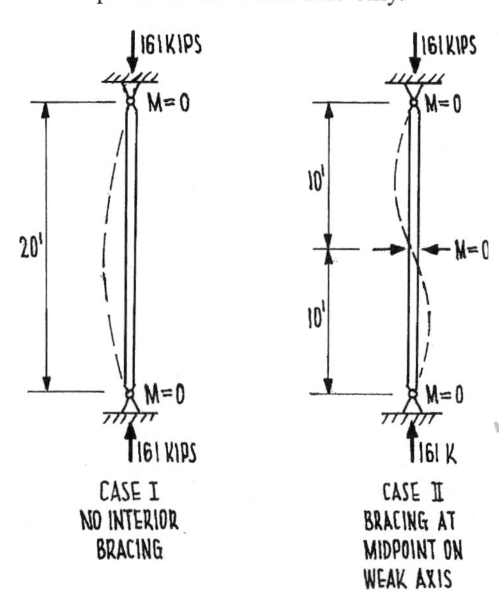

Solution: As before, the solution to this type of design problem is impractical without design aids of some kind.

Table S-10 in the Technical Manual lists the capacity of wide flange column sections over a range of lengths. Enter Table S-10b for an unsupported length of 20 ft and proceed upward until the first section is reached that will sustain a load of 161 kips on both axes.

1) With no interior bracing, select W10x49:
   Capacity = 258 kips on the *xx* axis.
   Capacity = 197 kips on the *yy* axis.

With interior bracing at midpoint on the weak axis only, enter Table S-10b under the *xx* axis on the 20 ft length and simultaneously enter under the *yy* axis on the 10 ft length. Proceed upward until the first section is reached that will sustain a load of 161 kips on both of these axes.

2) With interior bracing at midpoint, select W10x33:
   Capacity = 172 kips on the *xx* axis.
   Capacity = 167 kips on the *yy* axis.

Example: 26-12

Selection of a column section to carry a known load.

Given: Column load of 78 kips to be carried on a column with end conditions as shown. Interior bracing can be provided on the weak axis but at only one level. A36 steel.

To Find: 1) Location of interior bracing.
2) Suitable wide flange section for the column with the interior bracing.

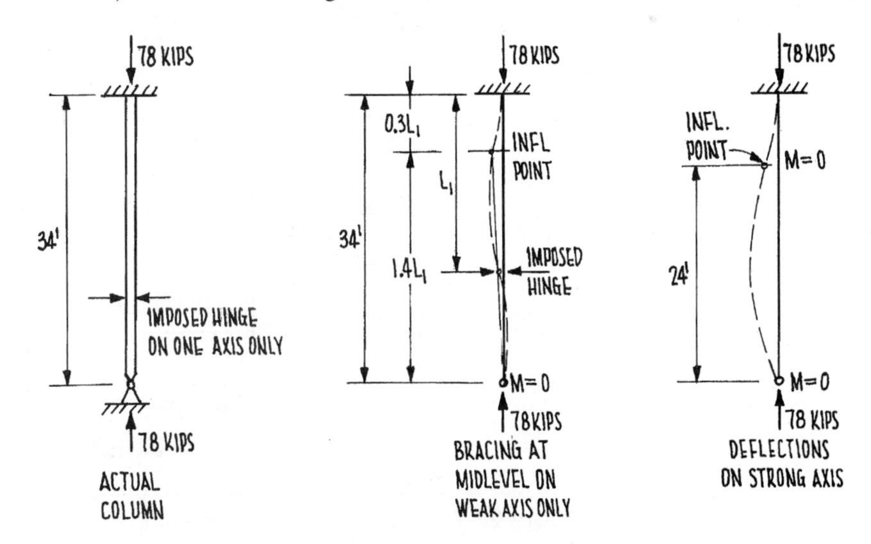

Solution: The point at which the midpoint bracing is to be located is shown in the sketch. From the geometry:

$L = 1.7L_1$, hence $L_1 = 34/1.7 = 20.0$ ft.

The distance *KL* between points of zero moment on the strong axis is 0.7L = 24 feet. The distance *KL* between points of zero moment on the weak axis is $0.7L_1 = 14.0$ ft.

Table S-10b is entered as before, under the *xx* axis for a 24 ft length and under the *yy* axis for a 14 ft length. Proceed upward until a section is reached that will sustain 78 kips on both axes.

The lightest section is found to be a W8x24:
Capacity on the *xx* axis is 105 kips.
Capacity on the *yy* axis is 88 kips.

26.4 Connections to Columns

The connections in a braced frame are classified by ASD(A2.2) as Type 2 "simple framing" connections. In braced frames under gravity loading, the ends of beams and girders are connected for shear only and are considered to be free to rotate. Some typical Type 2 connections are shown in Figure 26-7.

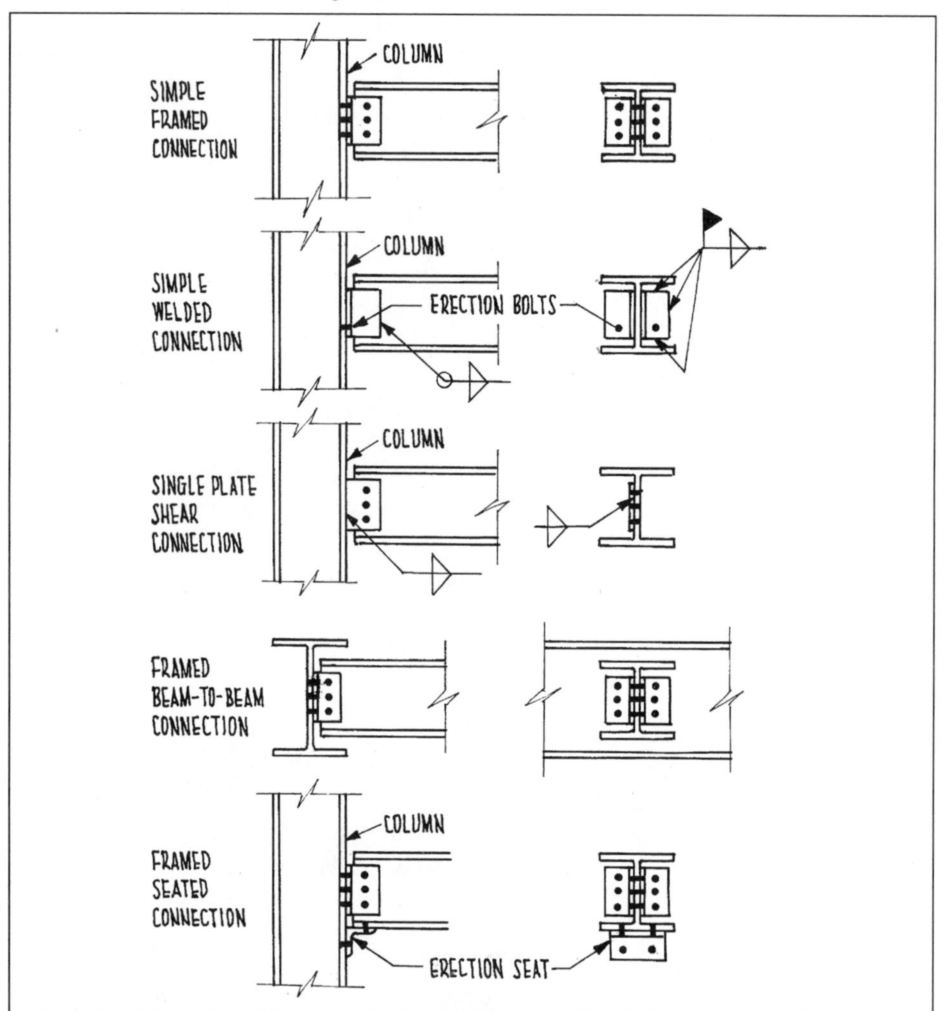

Figure 26-7 Typical Type 2 connections in a braced frame.

The analysis and design of Type 2 connections for beams is presented in the next chapter with beam design. It is well to note at this point, however, that a Type 2 connection to the flange of a column introduces an eccentric shear force at the outer face of the column flange. Such a load introduces unwanted moments into the column. The moments thus created occur on the strong axis of the column, however, where they are usually of lower consequence.

A better beam-to-column Type 2 connection is one where the beam is framed directly to the web of the column. The eccentricity of the shear force in such connections is only $^1/_2$ the web thickness. Moment due to such small eccentricities is usually ignored.

The only column connection presented in this section is the column-to-column connection, or column splice. When the sizes of wide flange columns are to be changed at a splice, it is the practice to stay within one size grouping. Certain groups of wide flange sections are rolled on the same roller size, producing sections having the same clear distance between the inside faces of the flanges. The groups of beams rolled from such a single roller size are listed in Tables S-1, a space separating one group from another.

As an example of W sections rolled in the same roller size, consider the group of sections listed in Table S-1e as W10x45, W10x39 and W10x33. These three sections are shown in Figure 26-8 along with their overall depth, flange thicknesses and clear distance between flanges.

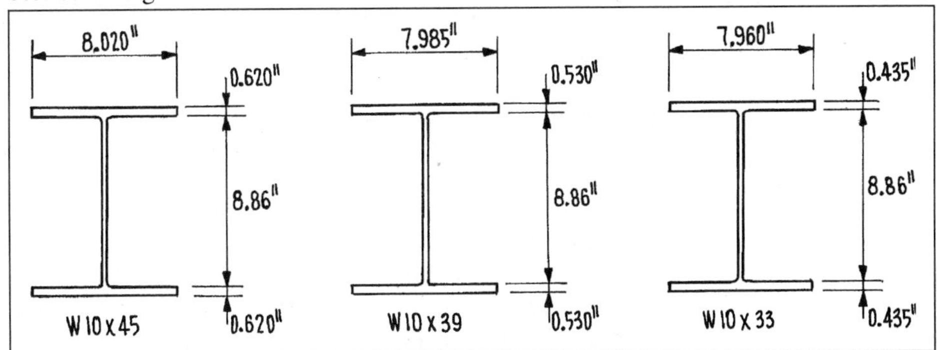

Figure 26-8 Clear distance between flanges.

As indicated in Figure 26-8, the clear distance between flanges in this group is a constant dimension of 8.86 inches. When a large variety of loads must be accommodated, columns from one of the larger groups should be considered. Typical of such large groups is the group of 10 inch sections in Table S-1e going from W10x49 to W10x112 or the group of 12 inch sections in Table S-1d going from W12x65 to W12x336. Within each group, the clear distance between flanges is a constant; for such sections, the bearing connections shown in Figure 26-9a or b can be developed.

Where the column sizes cannot be matched within a 2 in. nominal difference, a butt plate is welded to the lower column and the upper column is seated on the butt plateas shown in Figure 26-9C. As indicated, fillet welds are preferred to full penetration welds.

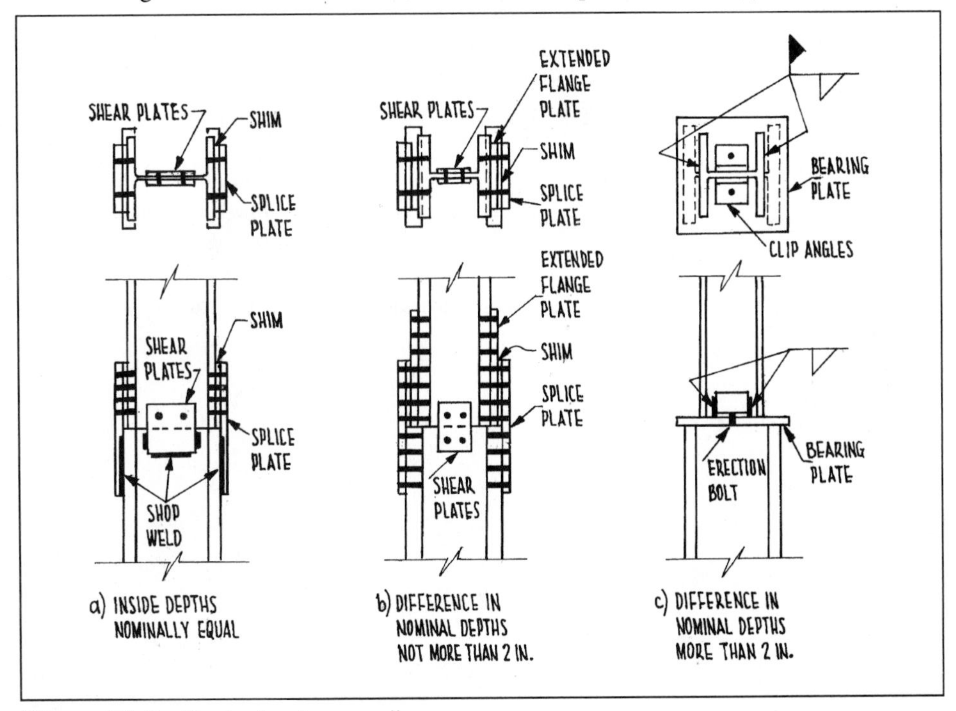

Figure 26-9 Typical column splices.

Column splices are expensive. It is rarely economical to splice columns at every floor. It is difficult, however, to extend columns for more than two stories and to hold them in proper alignment. The usual practice is to use the same column section for two stories, then splice the next two stories, then the next two, and so on. Column splices are generally made just above floor line, thus staying clear of the floor beams and further complicating their connections.

The transfer of the axial load from the upper column to the lower column in a column splice is accomplished by end bearing. The ends of the columns are milled to assure a full transfer of axial load by bearing. The transfer of moment is treated independently by adding flange splice plates. The transfer of shear is treated independently by adding web splice plates. All of the three loads — axial, flexure and shear — are treated without any consideration of the others.

The configurations, edge distances and end distances for column splices are the same as those given earlier for tension splices (Table S-24 and Table S-32). In most cases, column splices are shopwelded, field bolted, but field welded column splices are now common.

Design specification ASD(J1.12) requires that slip-critical bolted splices or welded splices be used in tall slender buildings (100 ft or higher). On lower structures, bolted bearing connections are permitted, but even in bearing connections, ASD(E4) requires that the bolts be tightened to the same tension as in slip-critical connections. Under such requirements, the use of slip-critical connections for all column splices is advisable.

The axial load in a column splice is transferred by bearing. The allowable bearing stress F_p on the contact area of milled surfaces is given by ASD(J8):

$$F_p = 0.90F_y \tag{26-15}$$

The moment in a column splice is transferred by the splice plates connecting the flanges. As indicated in Figure 26-9a and 9b, these splice plates may be bolted or welded. The load capacity of the splice plates in moment is specified in ASD(J1.4):

Splice capacity = computed moment on the section but not less than 50% of the moment capacity of the section. (26-16)

Similarly, the shear in a column splice is transferred by the splice plates connecting the webs. As indicated in Figure 26-9, these splice plates may be bolted or welded. The load capacity of the splice plates in shear is specified in ASD(J1.4):

Splice capacity = computed shear on the section but not less than 50% of the shear capacity of the section. (26-17)

An example will illustrate the procedure for designing a column splice for matching columns.

Example 26-13

Design of column splice in a braced frame.

Given: Column sections W10x33 and W10x45, A325 bolts, ASTM A36 steel. Column load is 110 kips. No computable moment on the column. No computable shear on the section.

To Find: Suitable spliced connection.

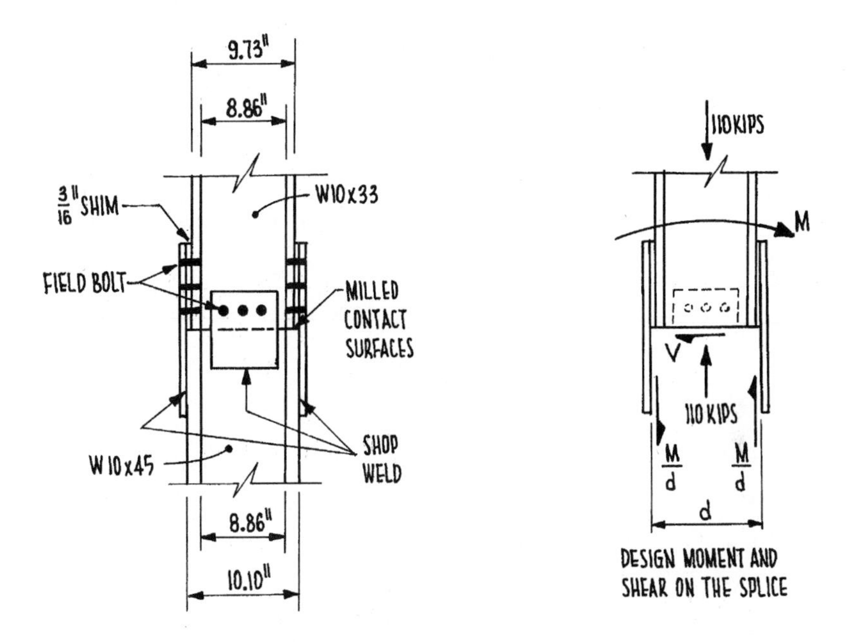

Solution: Proposed configuration is shown in the sketch.

The design moment for the splice is $^1/_2$ the moment capacity of the smaller section. From Table S-1e, the section modulus is found to be 35.0. The allowable flexure stress F_b is taken at 24 ksi (see Chapter 10, Strength of Materials). The flexure formula provides the design moment capacity:

$$\text{Required moment capacity} = {}^1/_2 \text{ x } F_b \text{ x } S$$
$$= {}^1/_2 \text{ x } 24 \text{ x } {}^{35}/_{12} = 35 \text{ kip·ft}$$

Similarly, the design shear force for the splice is $^1/_2$ the shear capacity of the smaller section. From Table S-1e, the web thickness is found to be 0.290 inches. The allowable average shear stress F_v is taken at 14.0 ksi (see Chapter 10, Strength of Materials). The shear force is then calculated as:

$$\text{Required shear capacity} = {}^1/_2 \text{ x } F_v \text{ x } A_{WEB}$$
$$= {}^1/_2 \text{ x } 14 \text{ x } 9.73 \text{ x } 0.290 = 20 \text{ kips}$$

The tensile force in the flange splice plates is the couple M/d:

$$p_t = \frac{M}{d} = \frac{35{,}000 \text{ x } 12}{10.10} = 41.6 \text{ kips}$$

Assume 4 - $^3/_4$ in. diameter bolts in a slip-critical connection; load per bolt in single shear is given in Table S-27 as 7.5 kips.

Use 6 - $^3/_4$ in. diameter bolts.
Capacity = 6 x 7.5 = 45 kips

Arrange bolts and welds as shown in the following sketch. See Table S-24 for minimum spacings and edge distances.

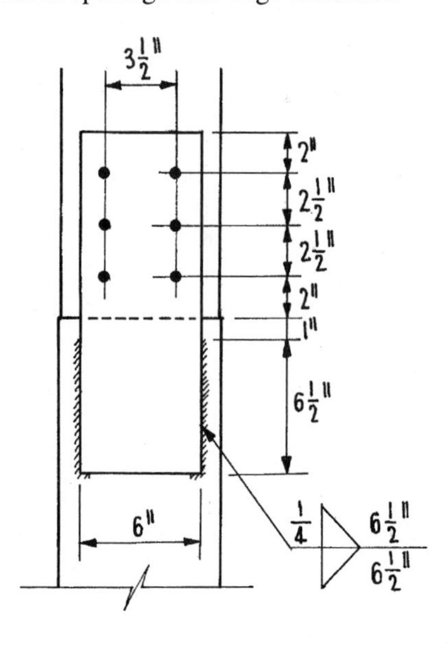

Selection of the flange splice plates is taken first for the bolted side of the connection, see Table S-19:

b_f = 8.02 inches, d = 9.73 inches

$$\frac{b_f}{d} = 0.824 > \frac{2}{3}; \text{ use } U = 0.90$$

$$A_e = UA_n = 0.90\left[(6.5)(t) - 2\left(\frac{3}{4} + \frac{1}{16}\right)t\right] = 4.3875t$$

Select t to sustain the tensile force of 41.6 kips:

$T = 0.60F_yA_g = 21.6 \times 6^1/_2 \times t = 41.6$ kips.
Minimum t = 0.296 inches

or $T = 0.50F_uA_e = 29 \times 4.3875 \times t = 41.6$ kips.
Minimum t = 0.327 inches

Try flange splice plates $6^1/_2$ in. x $^3/_8$ in.

For the welded side of the connection, see Table S-19 and Table S-32:

Maximum weld size = $^3/_8$ - $^1/_{16}$ = $^5/_{16}$ in.
Minimum weld size = $^1/_4$ in.

Minimum length of weld = $6^1/_2$ in.
For l = 2W, U = 1.00

Try $^1/_4$ in. weld $6^1/_2$ in. each side.

Capacity of fillet = 3.2 kips/in. (from Table S-31).

Load capacity = 3.2 kips/in. x 13 in.
= 41.6 kips > 40 kips (O.K.)

Use flange plate $^3/_8$ in. x 6$^1/_2$ in. x 1ft - 4$^1/_2$ in.

Final selection for two flange splice plates is shown in the following sketch:

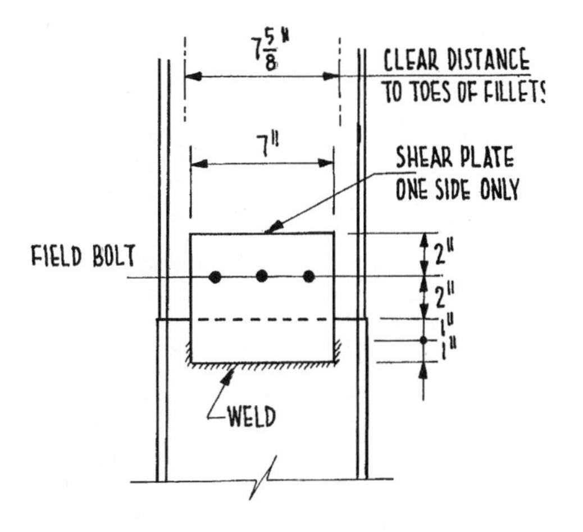

Selection of the web splice plate is taken next.
Design shear load = 20.0 kips; trial sizes as shown in the following sketch.

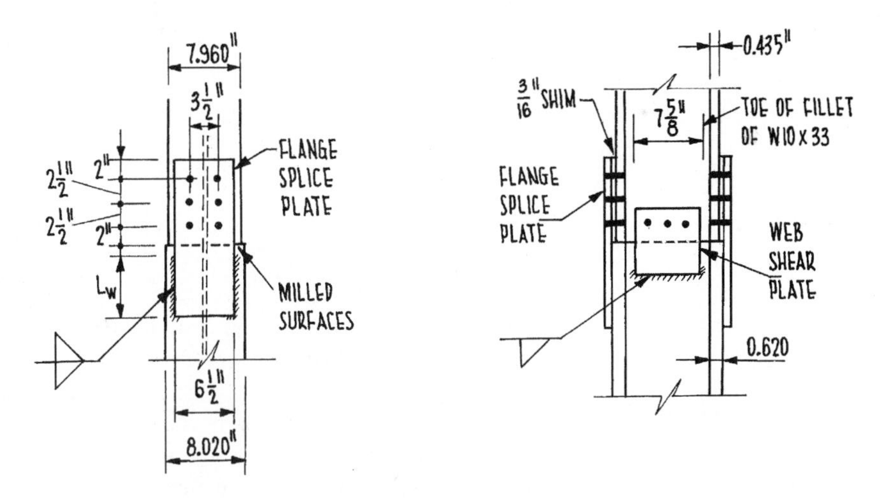

Use plate thickness $^1/_4$ in. to match web thickness 0.290 in.

For the bolted side of the connection, use 3 bolts in single shear in a slip critical connection. At 7.5 kips per bolt:

Capacity = 3 x 7.5 = 22.5 kips > 20 kips shear (O.K.)

Capacity of net area in shear (similar to block tearout).

$$\text{Capacity} = F_v A_n = 0.3F_u\left[7 - 3\left(\frac{3}{4} + \frac{1}{16}\right)\right]$$

$$= 79 \text{ kips} > 20 \text{ kips shear (O.K.)}$$

For the welded side of the connection, see Table S-19 and Table S-32:

Maximum size weld = $^1/_4$ in.
Minimum size weld = $^3/_{16}$ in.

Try $^3/_{16}$ in. weld $7^1/_2$ in. long with 1 in. returns.

Capacity of fillet weld = 2.4 kips/in.

Capacity of welded connection = $2.4(1 + 7^1/_2 + 1)$
= 22.8 kips > 20 kips shear (O.K.)

Final selection for one web splice plate is shown in the following sketch.

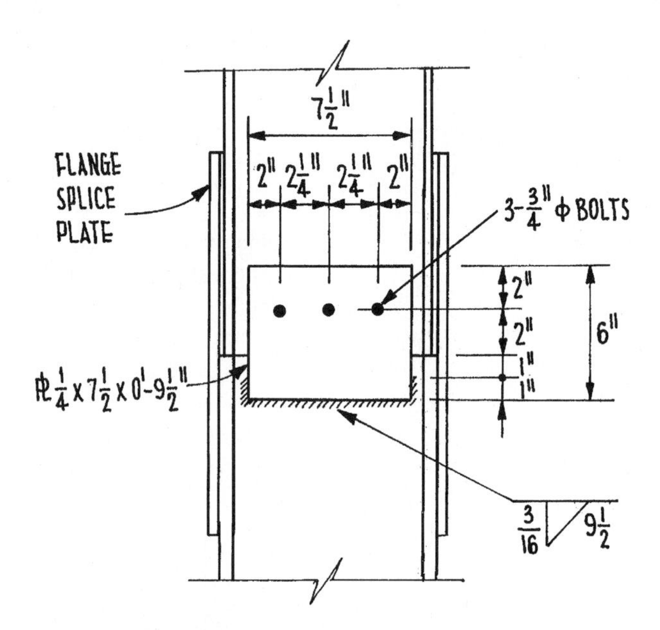

It should be noted that the column load of 110 kips never entered the calculations for the splices. The flange splice plates were designed for half the capacity of the W10x33. Similarly, the web shear plate was designed for half the capacity of the W10x33 in shear. The actual load of 110 kips was never considered.

It is important to observe that in a slip-critical column connection, there can never be any lateral movement between the upper column and the lower column along the milled surfaces.

The two columns in Example 26-13 were matched in size such that the upper column was in full bearing on the lower column. Some mismatch can be tolerated, however, as long as there is enough contact area to transmit the column load at a bearing stress less than $0.90F_y$.

When the mismatch becomes too large to permit a transfer of the column load in bearing, alternative methods must be used. Two such alternatives are shown in Figure 26-10. In these alternatives, it is assumed that the change in size is a nominal 2 inches, that is, going from a nominal 10 inch section to a nominal 12 inch section or from a nominal 12 inch section to a nominal 14 inch section.

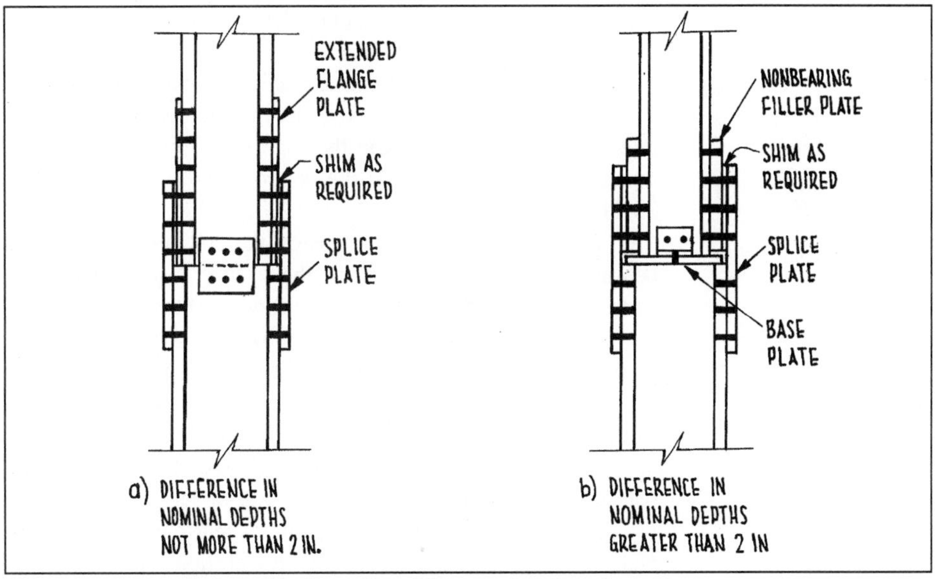

Figure 26-10 Column splices for different depths of sections.

In the splice of Figure 26-10a, the depth of the smaller section is built out by adding thick flange plates. These flange plates may be bolted or welded to the smaller section. The end of the smaller column is milled with these flange plates in place. The splice is designed using the same procedure as that in Example 26-13.

In the splice of Figure 26-10b, a butt plate is added to the upper column. The butt plate is made large enough to transmit the load in bearing to the lower column. The butt plate is finished on both sides to provide a smooth contact surface. Thick filler plates are added to make the depths of the two sections match; the filler plates are nonbearing. Clip angles are used to transmit the shear from one web to the other. The splice is designed using the procedures of Example 26-13.

It is well to recall again that column splices are slip critical. There is no relative motion between any of the plates, neither on the flanges nor on the webs.

26.5 Column Base Plates

Eventually, all column loads must be transferred to a foundation. The most common means to accomplish such a transfer is by the use of a *base plate*. A base plate that is commonly used for columns in a braced frame is shown in Figure 26-11.

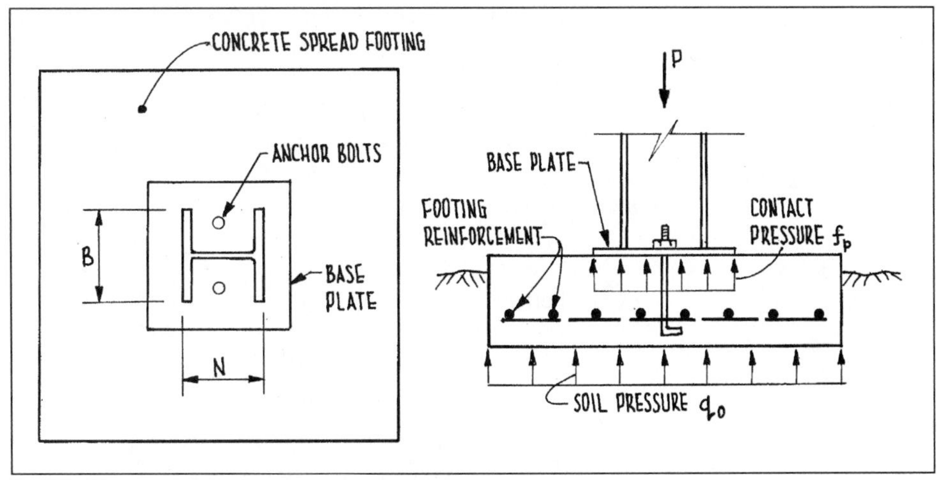

Figure 26-11 Typical base plate in a braced frame.

The type of column base shown in Figure 26-12 is considered to be a hinge. While it does offer some degree of resistance to large rotations, its resistance to the small rotations common to steel structures is considered to be negligible. Moment-resistant column bases are not used in braced frames.

Foundations for a braced frame are almost always concrete. Masonry rubble foundations are rarely used anymore. Even when steel pile foundations are used, a concrete pile cap is used to distribute the load to the piles. The structural columns of the superstructure are then seated on the concrete pile cap using base plates like those of Figure 26-11.

The allowable contact stress on the concrete is much lower than that for steel. The bearing plate serves to distribute the column load over a larger area, reducing the contact stress to an allowable level. The allowable bearing stress on concrete is given in Table C-1 in the Technical Manual. The allowable contact stress on concrete is denoted here as F_p; the computed (actual) contact stress is denoted as f_p.

The anchorage of the bearing plate serves to transmit any horizontal shear forces from the column to the foundation. The anchor bolts must therefore be of such size and number that they can sustain these horizontal forces. Table S-34 in the Technical Manual lists the load capacities of anchor bolts under lateral loads.

The design procedure for column bearing plates is prescribed by AISC. The base plate is designed as if the column were composed of a solid area 0.95d x 0.80b as shown in Figure 26-12. The projections of the bearing plate outside this solid area are considered to be cantilevers in bending; the thickness of the base plate must be adequate to sustain such bending.

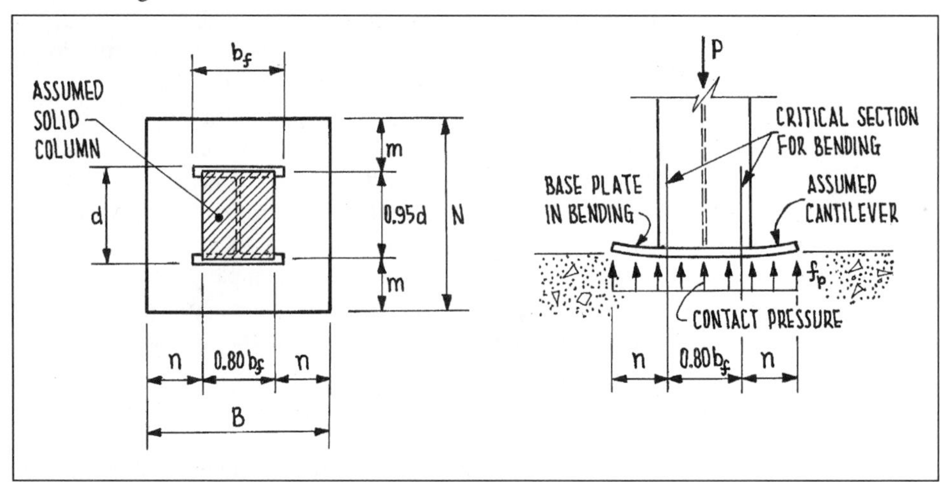

Figure 26-12 Column bearing plate loads.

The cantilevered projection shown in Figure 21-12 will be the distance m in one direction and n in the other direction. The plate dimensions are optimal when $m = n$. This optimum size is obtained when:

$$\text{Area BN} = \frac{P}{F_P} = (0.80b_f + 2n)(0.95d + 2m), \text{ where n = m}$$

Solving for m or n yields:

$$m = n = \frac{1}{4}\sqrt{(0.95d + 0.80b_f)^2 - 4\left(0.76db_f - \frac{P}{F_p}\right)} - \frac{1}{4}(0.95d + 0.80b_f) \tag{26-18}$$

The selection of a base plate consists of two requirements:

1. Select an area *BN* such that the actual bearing stress f_p on the concrete is less than the allowable bearing stress F_p, where F_p is given by Table C-1 in the Technical Manual.
2. Select a plate thickness t such that the actual bending stress in the plate f_b is less than the allowable bending stress F_b, where

$$F_b \leq 0.75\ F_Y \tag{26-19}$$

An example will illustrate the design procedure.

Example: 26-14

Selection of a column base plate.

Given: W10x33 column carrying an axial load of 185 kips. A36 steel. concrete footing is concrete, 7'-6" square. f'_c = 3000 psi.

To Find: Size and thickness of the base plate.

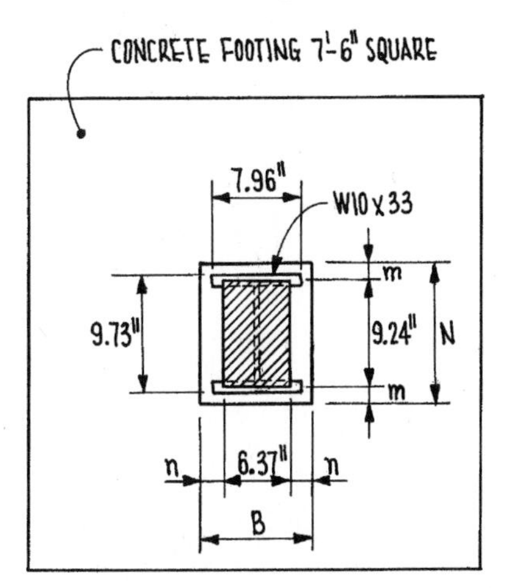

Solution: The allowable contact pressure is found from Table C-1. Since A_2 is much greater than A_1, the allowable bearing pressure is assumed to be its maximum value of $0.60f'_c$ = 1800 psi. This value will have to be verified later when *B* and *N* are known.

The distances *m* and *n* are found from Eq.(26-16). They could be estimated and verified, but it is usually faster to evaluate Eq.(26-16):

$$m = n = \frac{1}{4}\sqrt{(9.24+6.37)^2 - 4\left(0.76x9.73x7.96 - \frac{185{,}000}{1{,}800}\right)}$$

$$-\frac{1}{4}(9.24+6.37)$$

= 5.12 - 3.90 = 1.22 in.

With the value of m and n at 1.22 in., both B and N can be found.

B = 6.37 + 2(1.22) = 8.80 in., try B = 9 in.
N = 9.24 + 2(1.22) = 11.68 in., try N = 12 in.

$$\text{For Table C-1, } \sqrt{A_2/A_1} = \sqrt{90^2/(9x12)} = 8.66, \text{ use } 0.6\, f_c'$$

Actual contact pressure for this size of plate is:

$$f_p = \frac{P}{BN} = \frac{185{,}000}{(9)(12)} = 1710 \text{ psi} < 1800 \text{ psi (O.K.)}$$

Actual m = (12 - 9.24)/2 = 1.38 in., n = (9 - 6.37)/2 = 1.32 in.

m is thus the longer actual cantilever at 1.38 in.

The plate thickness is selected for the bending conditions:

Take a 1 inch wide strip of the plate:

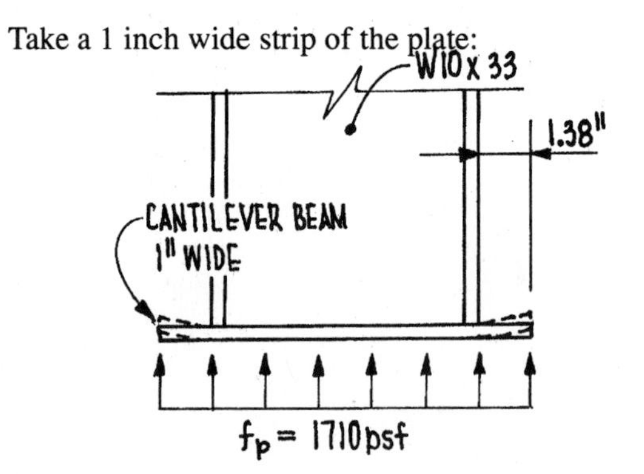

Moment on the cantilever is $f_p(m)\left(\frac{m}{2}\right)$

$$M = (1710)\left(\frac{1.38^2}{2}\right) = 1628 \text{ lb·in.}$$

Section modulus of the 1 in. strip is $\frac{bh^2}{6}$:

$$S = (1)\left(\frac{t^2}{6}\right)$$

Allowable stress $F_b = 0.75(F_y) = 27{,}000$ psi

Solve for thickness:

$$S = \frac{M}{F_b};\ (1)\left(\frac{t^2}{6}\right) = \frac{1628}{27{,}000}$$

$$t = 0.60 \text{ in.}$$

Required thickness 5/8 inch.

Select bearing plate 5/8 x 9" x 1'-0".

Review Questions

1. How is the design of truss members in compression different from the design of building columns?
2. What is distinctive about the loads on the columns in a braced frame?
3. State the Euler column formula and define each term.
4. What are the physical conditions assumed for the derivation of the Euler column formula?
5. What is the shape of the deflection curve in an Euler column?
6. What is the advantage of using the factored length Kl in applying the Euler column formula?
7. Is the critical load P_{CR} in the Euler column formula the load before deflections begin or after deflections begin?
8. In the Euler column formula, what does the integer n indicate? At what value of n is buckling load lowest?
9. Is column buckling a failure in axial stress, flexural stress or shear stress?
10. Given the Euler load in a column at failure, how can a safe working load be determined?
11. In the AISC column formula, what is the factor of safety for long columns?
12. What is the value of Kl/r for A36 steel that separates long columns from intermediate columns?
13. How is the failure mode different for intermediate columns than for long columns?
14. What dimensions in a cross sectional element indicate whether the element will be susceptible to local buckling before the Euler column load can be developed?
15. State the AISC column formula for intermediate columns and define each term.
16. How is the factor of safety determined for the AISC column formula for intermediate columns?
17. It is recognized that the stems of many structural tees are slender elements. How is it that these tees can be used as columns under the AISC column formula?
18. Why is the design procedure for selecting a column size so clumsy when no design aids are available?
19. In a column splice, how is the axial load transmitted?
20. In a column splice, how are the matching column ends prepared to assure a uniform load transfer?
21. How often are column splices usually made?
22. In a field bolted column splice, where does one find the requirements for bolt spacings, edge distances, end distances, etc.?
23. Why are slip-critical connections used almost exclusively for column splices?
24. For a steel column, what is the minimum moment and shear force used in the design of a splice?
25. What is the allowable column-to-column bearing stress in a column splice?
26. What is the funcion of a column base plate?
27. What is the block size of a wide flange column used in the design of the base plate for the column?
28. How does bending occur in a base plate in bearing?
29. Where does one find the allowable bearing stress on a reinforced concrete foundation?
30. What is the difference in allowable bearing stress on a built-up concrete pedestal as compared to a localized bearing stress in the center of a large square footing?

CHAPTER

27

Steel Beams and Their Connections

In the design of columns, sections were divided into two types, sections having slender elements and sections having no slender elements. In the design of beams, that same distinction is observed. A further distinction is drawn in beams, however, in that beam sections containing no slender elements are broken into two further subdivisions, compact sections and noncompact sections.

Compact sections are somewhat more stocky than noncompact sections. As a consequence, the projecting elements in their compression flanges are not so subject to local buckling under heavy flexural loadings. A higher stress level, 10% higher, is therefore permitted for compact sections than for noncompact sections.

The difference between compact sections and noncompact sections is not great. Except for one section, W6x15, all of the ASTM A36 wide flange sections listed in the Technical Manual qualify as compact sections. Similarly, all of the *S* shapes and channels qualify as compact sections. The one major group of beams that does not contain large numbers of compact sections are the *WT* and *ST* sections.

27.1 Buckling of the Compression Flange of Beams

Under flexure, the compression flange of a beam is loaded in axial compression, very much like a column. Unless the compression flange is braced laterally, the entire compression flange is free to buckle laterally, just as if it were a column buckling on its *yy* axis. Such a case of sinusoidal lateral buckling of a compression flange is shown in Figure 27-1.

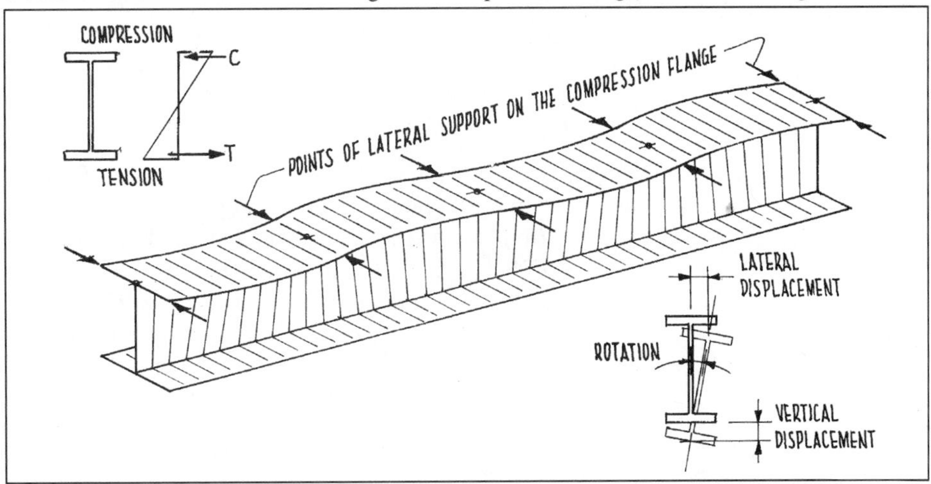

Figure 27-1 Flexure-torsion buckling in a beam.

It should be noted in Figure 27-1 that the tension flange is being pulled straighter under the flexural loading. While the entire beam may be subject to twist, or torsion buckling, the tension flange remains in its correct alignment.

The lateral support on the compression flange, as indicated in Figure 27-1, may be provided by flooring, by transverse floor beams, or by bridging. Typical examples of these three types of support are shown in Figure 27-2. In all three cases, the compression flange is securely braced against lateral deflections by other rigid members.

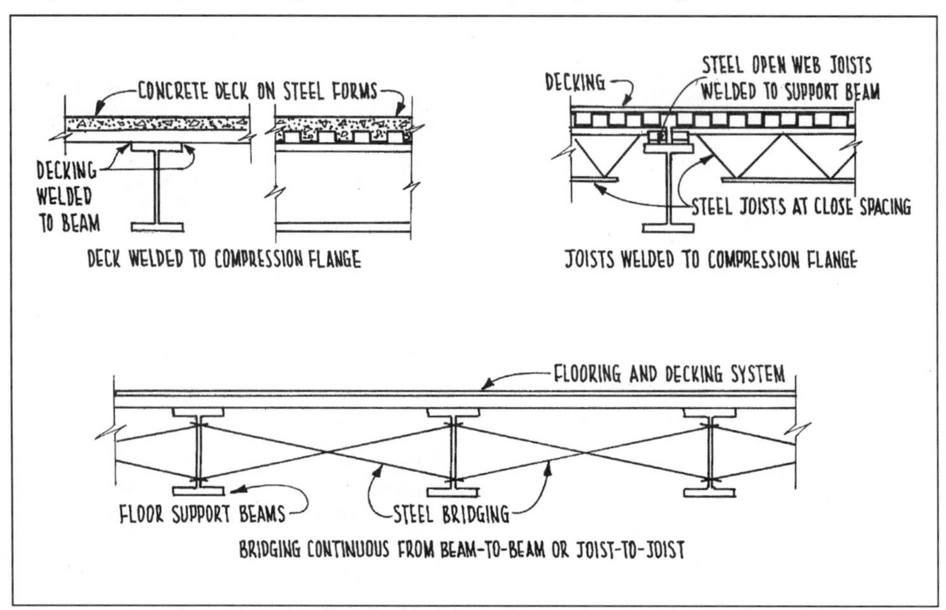

Figure 27-2 Systems providing acceptable lateral support.

In all of the systems shown in Figure 27-2, the compression flange is supported by steel members rigidly attached to the compression flange. Timber joists framed to steel support beams are not considered to offer adequate lateral support. The timber members, with their much lower modulus of elasticity, will permit excessive amounts of lateral movement in the steel beam.

Another type of local buckling was discussed earlier with column stresses. Buckling of the compression flange vertically in a sinusoidal deflection pattern was shown earlier in Figure 26-4. This type of localized buckling failure is not prevented by lateral supports; it is prevented by having the width-thickness ratio, b/t, small enough that the section enters yield before such elastic buckling can occur.

For the compression flange of beams, the limiting cases of buckling are thus defined by two sets of circumstances.

1. The b/t ratio of all projecting elements must be low enough that localized buckling of the projecting element will not occur.
2. Lateral supports must exist along the compression flange, placed closely enough together to prevent lateral "column" buckling of the entire compression flange.

Both of these limitations are prescribed by ASD specifications. The limiting b/t ratios are prescribed in ASD Table B5.1. The limiting values for ASTM A36 steel have been extracted from the ASD specification and are summarized in Table 27-1.

Table 27-1 defines the dividing lines between compact sections and noncompact sections, as well as the dividing line between sections having slender elements. As noted earlier, most steel sections (except tees) satisfy the requirements for compact sections. For rolled sections, it is rarely necessary to check the b/t ratio of a section, but when sections are being custom built, these b/t ratios must be strictly observed.

Table 27-1 Limiting Width-Thickness Ratios[a] for Beams
ASTM A36 Steel

Description of Element	Section classified as having no slender elements: Compact	Noncompact	Section classified as having slender elements
Flanges of W, S, channel and tee shapes	$b/t < 10.83$	$10.83 < b/t < 15.83$	$b/t > 15.83$
Flanges of rectangular box sections (or square box sections)	$b/t < 31.67$	$31.67 < b/t < 39.67$	$b/t > 39.67$
Flange cover plates (between lines of fasteners)	$b/t < 31.67$	$31.67 < b/t < 39.67$	$b/t > 39.67$
Webs in flexural compression	$d/t < 106.7$ —	— $h/t_w < 126.7$	$d/t > 106.7$ $h/t_w > 126.7$
Stems of tees	—	$d/t < 21.17$	$d/t > 21.17$
Circular pipe sections	$D/t < 550.0$	—	$D/t_w > 550$

a Source: AISC Manual of Steel Construction, reprinted by permission
b is the width of the compression element
t is the thickness of the compression element
d is the depth of a beam cross section
h is the clear distance between flanges
t_w is web thickness
D is the outside diameter of a circular pipe

27.2 Allowable Stresses in Beams

By itself, the classification of a beam as a compact section or a noncompact section does not indicate the allowable stress that may be used in designing the beam. The allowable stress depends also on a second factor, the unsupported length between points of lateral bracing along the compression flange. ASD(F1) prescribes the allowable stresses corresponding to various values of unsupported length; a summary of the allowable stresses for compact and noncompact sections is given in Table 27-2.

As indicated in Table 27-2, the allowable stress on steel beams depends on the distance between lateral supports. The allowable flexure stress on compact sections is given by:

$$F_b = 0.66\ F_Y \qquad (27\text{-}1)$$

where the unsupported length of the compression flange does not exceed either of the two following lengths (in inches):

$$L_b = \le \frac{76b_f}{\sqrt{F_y}} \text{ (or 12.67 } b_f \text{ for A36 steel)} \qquad (27\text{-}2)$$

$$L_b = \le \frac{20{,}000}{F_Y d / A_f} \text{ (or } \frac{555.6}{d/A_f} \text{ for A36 steel)} \qquad (27\text{-}3)$$

The smaller of the lengths given by Equations (27-2) and (27-3) is denoted L_c; the larger is denoted L_u.

If only one of the conditions given by Equations (27-2) and (27-3) can be met, the allowable flexure stress for both compact and noncompact sections is given by:

$$F_b = 0.60F_Y \qquad (27\text{-}4)$$

If neither of the conditions given by Equations (27-2) and (27-3) can be met, the allowable stress declines very sharply, as indicated by the formulas in the third column of Table 27-2. It is important to note that the allowable stress on a beam having excessively long lengths between lateral supports is different for every beam. Further, the allowable stress varies with each value of unsupported length.

Table 27-2 Allowable Flexure Stresses in ksi for Beams Having No Slender Elements[a] ASTM A36 Steel

Sections symmetrical about, and loaded in, the plane of their webs		
Compact sections only	**Both compact and noncompact**	**Both compact and noncompact**
Unsupported length[b] $l < 12.67b_f$ and $l < \frac{555.6}{(d/A_f)}$ then $F_b = 0.66 \times Fy$ (for tension or compression)	Unsupported length $l < 12.67\ b_f$ or $l < \frac{555.6}{(d/A_f)}$ then $F_b = 0.60 \times Fy$ (for tension or compression)	Unsupported length $l > 12.67\ b_f$ and $l > \frac{555.6}{(d/A_f)}$ then $F_b \le \frac{12000}{\frac{ld}{A_f}} \le 0.60\ Fy$ (for compression) $F_b \le 0.60 \times Fy$ (for tension in all cases) *Special Case I* (for compression) when $53.23 \le \frac{l}{r_T} \le 119.0$ then $F_b = 24 - 0.000847\left[\frac{l}{r_T}\right]^2$ but $F_b \le \frac{12000}{\frac{ld}{A_f}}$ and $F_b \le 0.60F_y$ *Special case II* (for compression) when $\frac{l}{r_t} > 119.0$ then $F_b = \frac{170000}{\left[\frac{l}{r_T}\right]^2}$ but $F_b \le \frac{12000}{\frac{ld}{A_f}}$ and $F_b \le 0.60F_y$

a Source: AISC Manual of Steel Construction reprinted by permission

b Unsupported length l is the distance, in inches, between cross sections braced against twist or lateral displacement of the compression flange.

b_f is the width of the compression flange, in inches

d is the depth of the beam cross section, in inches

A_f is the area of the compression flange, in inches^2

r_T is the radius of gyration, in inches, of a section comprising the compression flange plus $^1/_3$ of the compression web area, taken about an axis in the plane of the web

A typical graph of allowable flexure stress on a wide flange beam is shown in Figure 27-3. The graph is drawn for a W10x22, a widely used section in steel flooring systems.

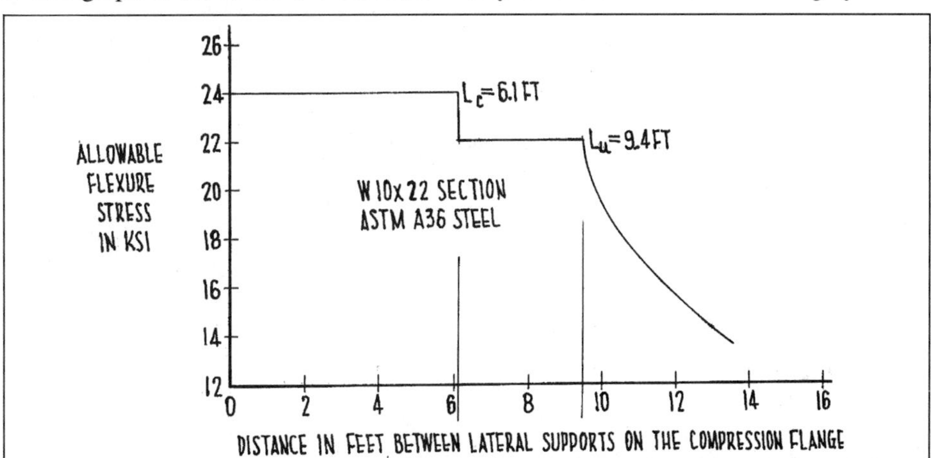

Figure 27-3 Allowable stress variation in a wide flange beam.

As indicated in Figure 27-3, when the unsupported length exceeds L_u the allowable stress drops so sharply that it is rarely practical to use such a design. It is far better to provide lateral supports along the compression flange at closer spacing in order to gain the higher allowable stresses. Alternatively, one may consider using a slightly shallower but more compact section that does not require such closely spaced lateral supports.

It should be immediately evident that the selection of steel beams would indeed be clumsy without some sort of design aid or design table. Since steel is purchased by the pound, the selected section should be the lightest available section that will sustain the given load. The design aid or design table should therefore allow such a selection to be made, based on the weight of the beam.

Table S-18 in the Technical Manual is one such design aid. The steel sections listed in Table S-18 are listed in order of descending weights. The lightest sections are those in the lower right-hand column; as one proceeds upward, the sections become heavier (and stronger) throughout the three columns.

Also listed in Table S-18 are the lengths L_c and L_u. For laterally unsupported lengths less than L_c, the corresponding allowable flexural stress is $0.66F_y$; for lengths greater than L_c but less than L_u, the corresponding allowable flexural stress is $0.60\ F_y$. For laterally unsupported lengths greater than L_u, Table S-18 cannot be used.

It is a design requirement that beams must be braced against lateral torsion ("roll") at points of support. It is the practice also to provide such bracing at the free ends of cantilevers and at all other points where concentrated loads are introduced.

Some examples will illustrate the selection of steel beam sections.

Example 27-1

Selection of a steel beam section.

Given: Shear and moment diagrams as shown for a floor beam. Lateral support provided at end reactions and at midspan. A36 steel.

To Find:
1) Lightest steel section to carry the load with an allowable stress of $0.60\ F_y$.
2) Lightest steel section to carry the load with an allowable stress of $0.66\ F_Y$.

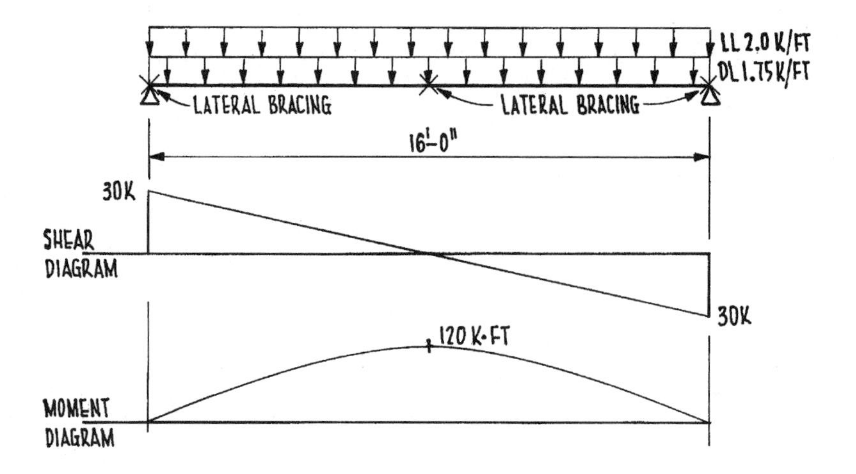

Solution: From the moment diagram, it is seen that the section must sustain a moment of 120 kip·ft.

For an allowable stress of 0.60 F_Y, or 22,000 psi, the corresponding unsupported length L_u cannot be greater than 8'-10". The required size of the section modulus S_{xx} is computed from the flexure formula:

$$\frac{I}{c} = S_{xx} = \frac{M}{F_a} = \frac{(120,000)(12)}{22,000} = 65.5\ in.^3$$

Enter Table S-18 at the lower right hand corner in the column indicated S_{xx}. Proceed upward through this column then upward through the center column until a section modulus at least 65.5 in.3 is reached with a value of L_u greater than 8'-0". The first (and lightest) such section is the W18x40 section, having a section modulus of 68.43 and an allowable unsupported length L_u of 8.2 feet.

1) For F_b = 22,000 psi, $L_u \geq$ 8'-0", use W18x40.

For an allowable stress of 0.66F_y, or 24,000 psi, the corresponding unsupported length is now L_c Rather than L_u. The required size of the section modulus is again computed from the flexure formula:

$$\frac{I}{c} = S_{xx} = \frac{M}{F_a} = \frac{(120,000)(12)}{24,000} = 60.0\ in.^3$$

Again enter Table S-18 at the lower right hand corner in the column indicated S_{xx}. Proceed upward until a section is that which has a value of S_{xx} greater than 60 in.^{3} and a value of L_c greater than 8'-0". The first such section encountered is the W14x43, which has a section modulus of 62.80 in.^{3} and an allowable unsupported length L_c of 8.4 feet.

2) For F_b = 24,000 psi, $L_c \geq$ 8'-0", use W14x43.

It should be noted in Example 27-1 that the restrictions on L_c are so stringent that the required section size at F_b = 24,000 psi is heavier than that for F_b = 22,000. The most economical section is therefore the W18x40 with its allowable stress of 22,000 psi. Such anomalies are common in the selection of steel beams; it is always advisable to check both sets of conditions before making a final selection.

Example 27-2

Selection of a steel beam section.

Given: Shear and moment diagrams as shown for a loaded span. Lateral supports provided at ends of overhangs, at supports and at 1/3 points within the span. A36 steel.

To Find: 1) Lightest steel section to carry the load with an allowable stress of $0.60F_Y$.

2) Lightest steel section to carry the load with an allowable stress of $0.66F_Y$.

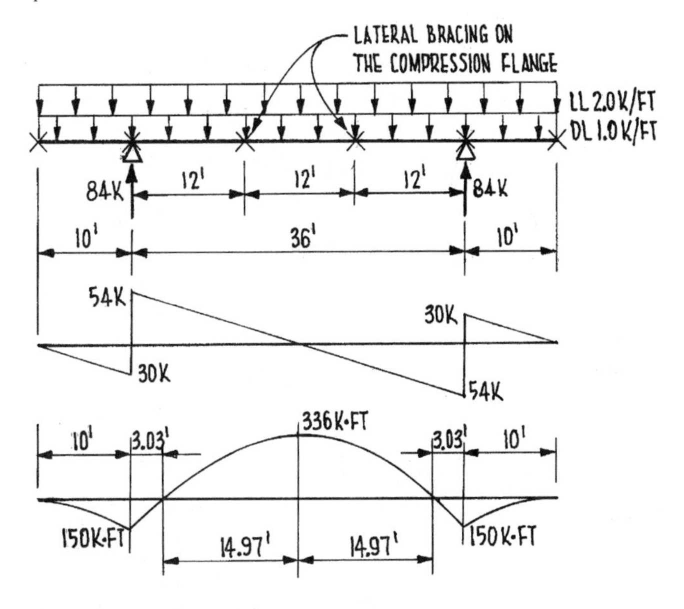

Solution: From the moment diagram, it is seen that the section must carry a moment of 336 kip·ft over a laterally unsupported length of 12'-0".

For an allowable stress of 22,000 psi, the corresponding unsupported length L_u is 12'-0". The required section modulus is computed from the flexure formula:

$$\frac{I}{c} = S_{xx} = \frac{M}{F_a} = \frac{(336{,}000)(12)}{22{,}000} = 183\ in.^3$$

Table S-18 is entered with this value of S_{xx} and a maximum value of L_u not less than 12'-0". The first section encountered that satisfies both requirements is the W24x84.

1) For $F_b = 22{,}000$, $L_u \geq$ 12'-0", use W24x84.

For an allowable stress of 24,000 psi, the corresponding unsupported length is now L_c rather than L_u. The required section modulus is computed from the flexure formula.

$$\frac{I}{c} = S_{xx} = \frac{M}{F_b} = \frac{(336{,}000)(12)}{24{,}000} = 168\ in.^3$$

Table S-18 is entered with this value of S_{xx} and a minimum value of L_c not less than 12'-0". The first section encountered that satisfies both requirements is the W14x109.

2) For $F_b = 24{,}000$ psi, $L_c \geq$ 12'0", use W14x109.

In Example 27-2, the penalty for trying to use the higher allowable stress of 24,000 psi is indeed severe. At 22,000 psi with L_u = 12 ft, the chosen section weighs 84 lbs/ft; at 24,000 psi with L_c = 12 ft, the chosen section weighs 109 lbs/ft. The limitations on L_c are often so stringent that it is better just to accept the lower stress level.

The application in which compact sections (and a stress level of 24,000 psi) are best suited are those where the compression flange is supported at very close intervals, as by flooring. Steel floor joists, for example, are commonly placed at 4'-0" on center along their supporting girders. With such closely spaced lateral supports along the compression flange of these girders, a stress of 24,000 psi is readily attainable.

Note also in Example 27-2 that the compression flange at the overhanging ends is on the bottom of the beam. The unsupported length of the compression flange at the overhangs is seen to be 10 ft. In this case, the governing case is the positive moment of 336 kip·ft with an unsupported length of 12 ft; nonetheless, one must always be alert to cases where the compression flange shifts from top to bottom.

27.3 Laterally Supported and Unsupported Beams

It has been found that the allowable stress in steel beams is intimately linked to the distance between lateral supports along the compression flange. In addition, the allowable stress is dependent upon the classification of the beam, whether compact, noncompact or having slender elements. Both of these conditions must be known before the allowable stress can be established.

One is again faced with the situation that the allowable stress cannot be established until the beam section is chosen, and the beam section cannot be chosen until the allowable stress is established. Obviously, some sort of design aid or design table is in order. There are many such design aids in the literature; Tables S-14 through S-17 in the Technical Manual are typical of such aids.

Tables S-14 through S-17 apply only to beams having no slender elements; they therefore apply only to beams classified as compact or noncompact. They do include laterally unsupported lengths of the compression flange greater than L_u, but only for sections classified as compact or noncompact.

This textbook does not include flexure in beams having slender elements. The topic is somewhat vague in the current ASD specification and is generally relegated to the LRFD specification where it is covered in more concise detail. In the design tables of this textbook, those sections having slender elements are simply omitted. The limitation is not severe; the only sections affected are tee sections, and only about half of the tee sections have such slender elements.

Tables S-14 through S-17 are all set up the same way. The sections are listed vertically in order of descending weights, with the laterally unsupported length along the compression flange increasing to the right. The table lists the allowable moment on the particular section for the particular unsupported length.

The positions of L_c and L_u are indicated in the tables by asterisks. Their inclusion provides only supporting information. The position of L_c is indicated by the first asterisk from the left, the position of L_u is indicated by the second. (Values of moment to the right of the second asterisk are computed from the formulas in the third column of Table 27-2).

Some examples will illustrate the use of the design aids.

Example 27-3

Selection of a steel beam section.

Given: Design moment (from the moment diagram) of 162 kip·ft, with a laterally unsupported length of 20 ft on the compression flange.

To Find: 1) Suitable wide flange beam to sustain this moment at the given unsupported length.
2) The actual stress in the chosen section under the given moment.

Solution: Table S-14 lists the allowable moment on wide flange sections for unsupported lengths from 0 to 34 feet.

Enter Table S-14C at the bottom of the column indicated 20 feet. Proceed upward into Table 5-14b until a section is reached that will sustain a moment of 162 kip·ft. The first (and lightest) section is found to be a W14x61, which will sustain a moment of 169 kip·ft.

Note that the second asterisk for this section (the value of L_u) lies between 20 and 21 feet. The allowable stress on this section is therefore 22,000 psi. As a matter of interest, the exact value of L_u can be found in Table S-18 as 21.5 feet. Similarly, the value of L_c is indicated in Table S-14b between 10 ft and 11 ft; its exact value can be found in Table S-18 as 10.6 ft.

The actual stress in the chosen section is found from the flexure formula. The section modulus S_{xx} of a W14x61 is given in Table S-1c as 92.2 in.^{3}:

$$f_b = \frac{Mc}{I} = \frac{M}{S_{xx}} = \frac{(162,000)(12)}{92.2} = 21,084\ psi$$

Example 27-4

Selection of a steel beam section.

Given: Design moment (from the moment diagram) of 42 kip·ft, with a laterally unsupported length of 15 feet along the compression flange.

To Find: 1) Suitable American Standard S section to sustain this moment at the given unsupported length.
2) The actual stress in the chosen section under the given moment.

Solution: Table S-15 lists the allowable moment on American Standard S sections for unsupported lengths from 0 to 34 feet.

Enter Table S-15 at the bottom of the page for an unsupported length of 15 feet. Proceed upward until a section is reached that will sustain a moment of 42 kip·ft. The first and lightest section is found to be an S12x31.8.

Note that this moment lies to the right of the second asterisk. The allowable stress will therefore be somewhat less than $0.60F_Y$.

The actual stress is found from the flexure formula. The section modulus S_{xx} is found from Table S-2 to be 36.4 in.^{3}:

$$f_b = \frac{Mc}{I} = \frac{M}{S_{xx}} = \frac{(42,000)(12)}{36.4} = 13,846\ psi$$

This stress is seen to be well below the 22,000 psi usually allowed, a severe penalty for exceeding the unsupported length L_u.

Example 27-5

Selection of a steel beam section.

Given: Design moment (from the moment diagram) of 20 kip·ft, with a laterally unsupported length of 4 feet along the compression flange.

To Find: Suitable American Standard channel section to sustain this moment at the given unsupported length.

Solution: Table S-16 lists the allowable moment on American Standard channel sections for unsupported lengths from 0 to 17 feet.

Enter Table S-16 at the bottom of the page for an unsupported length of 4 feet. Proceed upward until a section is reached that will sustain a moment of 20 kip·ft. The first such section is a C8x18.75.

It is observed that this moment lies between the two asterisks. The allowable stress is therefore $0.60F_Y$ or 22,000 psi.

Example 27-6

Selection of a steel beam section.

Given: W10x22 with an unsupported length of 18 feet on the compression flange.

To Find: 1) Allowable moment on this section.
2) Actual flexural stress under the given moment.

Solution: Enter Table S-14; find the section W10x22. The allowable moment is found to be 21 kip·ft.

The listed moment is well to the right of both asterisks in Table S-14. The section modulus is found from Table S-1e to be 23.2:

$$f_b = \frac{Mc}{I} = \frac{M}{S_{xx}} = \frac{(21{,}000)(12)}{23.2} = 10{,}862\ psi$$

This allowable stress is quite low again, indicating the severe penalty to be paid for using long unsupported lengths on the compression flange.

Bending in pipes and rectangular tubes is specified separately in ASD(F3). To qualify as a compact section, a pipe or rectangular section must meet the b/t or D/t requirements given earlier in Table 27-1. In addition, the depth d of the section may not be greater than six times the width b. Further, the thickness of the flanges may not be more than twice the thickness of the webs. All of the sections listed in Tables S-8 and S-9 in the Technical Manual meet these requirements.

For rectangular (or square) tubes meeting the requirements of a compact section, the unsupported length may not exceed the following limitation where there are no moments at the ends of the beam:

$$L_c \leq \frac{1950b}{F_Y} \qquad (27\text{-}5)$$

For sections meeting the requirements for a compact section the allowable bending stress is given by:

$$F_b = 0.66\ F_Y \qquad (27\text{-}6)$$

When the unsupported length of rectangular sections is greater than the length given by Eq.(27-1), the allowable bending stress is given by:

$$F_b = 0.60\ F_Y \qquad (27\text{-}7)$$

There are no further requirements other than Eq.(27-5) for unsupported length of rectangular sections, provided that the depth *d* of the section is less than 6 times the width *b*. There are no requirements at all for unsupported length of circular sections.

An example will illustrate the selection of a pipe or tube used as a beam.

Example 27-7

Selection of a pipe section used as a beam.

Given: Circular pipe on a simple span of 38 feet, carrying a load of 400 lbs/ft. $F_Y = 36$ ksi.

To Find: Required size of the beam.

Solution: The moment on the simple span is given by:

$$M = \frac{wL^2}{8} = \frac{(400)(38^2)}{8} = 72.2k'$$

As a first trial, it will be assumed that a compact section can be found. For such a case, the required section modulus is computed from the flexure formula:

$$S_{xx} = \frac{I}{c} = \frac{M}{F_b} = \frac{(72{,}200)(12)}{24{,}000} = 36.1\ in.^3$$

The lightest section listed in Table S-8 for a section having a section modulus at least 36.1 is a 12 in. diameter standard pipe. It must now be checked to see that it meets the requirements of Table 27-1 for a compact section, as assumed.

$$D/t = 12.75/0.375 = 34$$

This is much less than the allowable value of 550 given in Table 27-1. The 12 in. diameter standard pipe is therefore accepted.

Example 27-8

Selection of a tubular section used as a beam.

Given: Conditions of Example 27-7, except that $F_Y = 46$ ksi.

To Find: Square tube section to carry the load.

Solution: The moment is unchanged at 72.2 kip·ft. If a compact section can be found the allowable stress is given by:

$$F_b = 0.66\ F_Y = 30.4 \text{ ksi.}$$

The required section modulus is found from the flexure formula:

$$S_{xx} = \frac{I}{c} = \frac{M}{F_a} = \frac{(72{,}200)(12)}{30{,}400} = 28.5\ in.^3$$

From Table S-9, the lightest section having a section modulus greater than 28.5 in.^{3} is a 10 in. x 10 in. tube with a wall thickness of 0.25 in.

$$L_c \le \frac{1950b}{F_y} = \frac{(1950)(10)}{46} = 424 \text{ in.} = 35.3 \text{ ft. (no good)}$$

The next section having a larger width *b* is a 12 in.x12 in. section with a wall thickness of 0.25 in. For this section:

$$L_c \le \frac{1950b}{F_Y} = \frac{(1950)(12)}{46} = 509 \text{ in.} = 42.4 \text{ ft (O.K.)}$$

The 12x12 section will work. However, it is well also to examine a noncompact section with an allowable stress of 0.60 F_Y = 27.6 ksi, but which has no limitations on unsupported length:

$$S_{xx} = \frac{M}{F_b} = \frac{(72,200)(12)}{27,600} = 31.4 \text{ in.}$$

From Table S-9, it is seen that this alternative offers no further advantage. The 12 in. x 12 in. x 0.25 in. tube is chosen.

27.4 Beam Shear Stress

In the great majority of steel beams, the shear stress is not usually a concern. Steel is quite strong in shear. The allowable stress on the web of a steel beam is given by ASD(F4) for beam webs having a depth to thickness ratio $d/t_w \le 63.3$:

$$F_v = 0.40F_Y \tag{27-8}$$

For A36 steel, the allowable shear stress is taken as 14,000 psi. The limitation of $d/t_w \le$ 63.3 is not severe. For beams 18 in. or less in depth, it is rarely encountered.

Whenever flexure exists, beam shear exists. Whenever a beam is selected to sustain the maximum moment (taken from the moment diagram) the member so selected must also sustain the maximum shear (taken from the shear diagram).

The shear stress distribution for a wide flange beam is shown in Figure 27-4. To obtain the graph of the stress distribution, the shear stress was computed at short intervals along the height of the section using the shear stress formula:

$$f_v = \frac{VA'\bar{y}}{It} \tag{27-9}$$

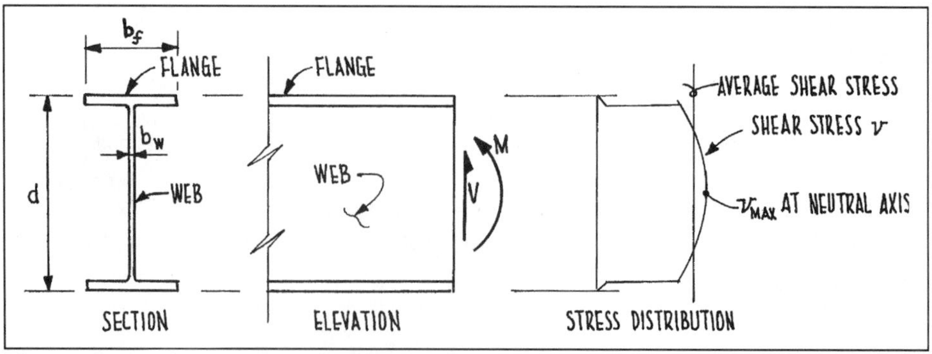

Figure 27-4 Shear stress distribution.

The use of Eq.(27-9) is discussed in detail in Chapter 10 and is not repeated here. An alternative method will be introduced in the following discussions. The jump in shear stress indicated in Figure 27-4 occurs when the dimension t jumps from the larger width of the flange to the very thin thickness of the web.

The computation of the shear stress at numerous levels along the height of the section is a somewhat tedious procedure. The value of $A'\bar{y}$ is of course different at each level, being maximum at the neutral axis. The calculation reveals, however, that the distribution of shear stress along the web of the section is relatively flat, varying but little from the average stress f_{AVG}, as indicated in Figure 27-4.

Over the years, it has been found that the average shear stress is an adequate indicator of shear stress in steel beams, and that it is not necessary to use Eq.(27-9) to find the actual maximum stress. The average stress on the section is found as the shear force V divided by the area of the web, where the web area is that shown in Figure 27-5.

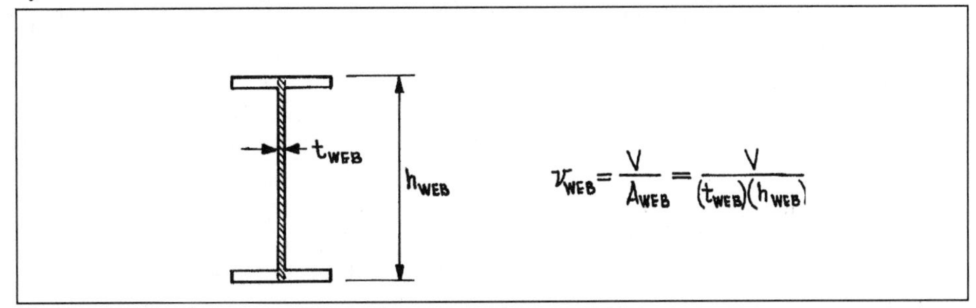

Figure 27-5 Average shear stress on a beam web.

Note that the area of the web is computed as the thickness of the web times the total depth of the beam, *not* the actual depth of the web.

Some examples will illustrate the computation of average shear stress on a beam web.

Example 27-9

Determination of average shear stress on beam webs.

Given: Conditions of Example 27-1.

To Find: Average shear stress on the web of the W18x40.

Solution: From Table S-1 the depth of the W18x40 is found to be 17.90 in., and the thickness of the web is found to be 0.315 in.

The maximum shear on the section is found from the shear diagram to be 30 kips. The average shear stress is computed by:

$$f_v = \frac{V}{A_{WEB}} = \frac{V}{dt_w} = \frac{30{,}000}{17.9x0.315} = 5321\ lb/in.^2$$

This value of shear stress is much less than the allowable stress of 14,000 lb/in.^{2}, so the section is adequate.

As a matter of curiosity, the allowable stress of 14,000 psi is allowable only if the value of d/t_w is less than 63.3. The value is readily computed:

$$\frac{\mathrm{d}}{\mathrm{t_w}} = \frac{17.90}{0.315} = 56.8 \le 63.3\,(\text{O.K.})$$

Example 27-10

Determination of average shear stress on beam webs.

Given: Conditions of Example 27-2.

To Find: Average shear stress on the web of the W24x84.

Solution: From Table S-1a, the depth of the W24x84 is found to be 24.10 in., and the web thickness is found to be 0.470 in.

The maximum shear on the section is found from the shear diagram to be 54 kips. The average shear stress is computed by:

$$f_v = \frac{V}{A_{WEB}} = \frac{V}{dt_w} = \frac{54{,}000}{(24.10)(0.470)} = 4767 \text{ lb / in.}^2$$

This value of shear stress is much less than the allowable stress of 14,000 lb/in.^{2} so the section is adequate.

Again, the limiting value of d/t_w will be checked to see that the allowable stress is indeed $0.4F_y$, or 14,000 psi:

$$\frac{d}{t_w} = \frac{24.10}{0.470} = 51.3 \leq 63.3 \text{ (O.K.)}$$

27.5 Control of Deflections

Control of deflections in steel beams is accomplished much like it is for concrete beams or timber beams. The allowable deflection in beams is set by the design specification (or building code). When a steel beam is being selected, it is checked to see that its actual deflection does not exceed the allowable deflection. If it does, a larger (deeper) section must be selected.

The allowable deflection Δ in beam is generally specified as three limiting cases, based on the span length L,

- For floor beams, maximum Δ = L/240 for dead load plus live load (27-10a)
- For roof beams, maximum Δ = L/180 for dead load plus live load (27-10b)
- In addition to the above, for any beam supporting brittle elements, maximum Δ = L/360 for live load only (27-10c)

The term "brittle elements" refers to materials being supported by the beam that might crack or be damaged by excessive deflections. Such brittle elements include plastered walls or ceilings, fixed glass panels or mirrors, ceramic tile floors or walls, glass brick and any other such architectural design features. If the length L in the equations is expressed in feet, the calculated deflection Δ will be in feet; if L is expressed in inches, Δ will be in inches.

The calculation of the actual deflection of beams is presented in Chapter 15 and is not repeated here. It is shown there that the maximum deflection of a simply supported beam will occur within the middle 15% of the span, and that the deflection at midspan will be within 97% of this absolute maximum deflection. An exaggerated comparison of these deflections is shown in Figure 27-6.

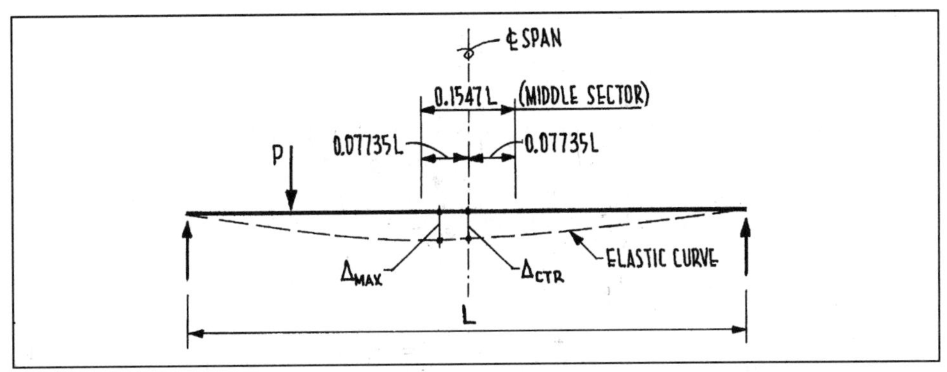

Figure 27-6 Typical beam deflections.

It is the practice in engineering not to find the absolute maximum deflection in a beam, but to find the deflection at midspan, a much simpler procedure. The result is within 97% of the absolute maximum and is simply accepted as close enough.

The deflection formulas given in Table 15-1 include the most common cases of load. At any given stress in the compression flange, the maximum deflection will occur under the full uniform load, indicated in Table 15-1 as Case III. For any rolled section except tees, with:

$$M = \frac{wL^2}{8}, \quad I_{xx} = S_{xx}\frac{d}{2}, \quad E = 29{,}000 \text{ ksi},$$

$$\Delta \text{ in inches}, \quad L \text{ in feet}, \quad f_b = \frac{M}{S_{xx}} \text{ in ksi},$$

The maximum deflection that can occur in a steel beam regardless how it is loaded is therefore given by Case III as:

$$\text{Upper Bound } \Delta = \frac{5wL^4}{384EI} = \frac{5}{48} M \frac{L^2}{E} \frac{2}{S_{xx}d} = 0.00103\, f_b \frac{L^2}{d} \tag{27-11}$$

The highest allowable stress that can occur in any steel beam is that for a compact section, $F_b = 0.66F_Y$, for which case:

$$\text{Upper Bound } \Delta = 0.02458 \frac{L^2}{d} \quad \text{for } F_b = 0.66F_Y, \text{ L in feet}, \Delta \text{ in inches} \tag{27-12a}$$

The next highest case is that for noncompact sections when $F_b = 0.60F_Y$, for which case:

$$\text{Upper Bound } \Delta = 0.02234 \frac{L^2}{d} \quad \text{for } F_b = 0.60F_Y, \text{ L in feet}, \Delta \text{ in inches} \tag{27-12b}$$

Equations (27-12) afford a means to obtain a fast check on the maximum deflection that a particular section can develop. It does not matter how the beam is loaded; at its maximum allowable stress, regardless how the beam is loaded, the maximum deflection that can occur is that given by Eqs.(27-12). Approximately, Eqs.(27-12) can be written as:

$$\text{Upper Bound } \Delta = \frac{L^2}{40d} \quad \text{for } F_b = 0.66F_Y, \text{ L in feet}, \Delta \text{ in inches} \tag{27-13a}$$

$$\text{Upper Bound } \Delta = \frac{L^2}{45d} \quad \text{for } F_b = 0.60F_Y, \text{ L in feet}, \Delta \text{ in inches} \tag{27-13b}$$

A useful correlation between depth *d* and span *L* can be developed by comparing Eqs.(27-13) to Eqs.(27-10). The result of such a correlation is given in Table 27-3.

Table 27-3 Limiting Depth of Steel Beams For Control of Deflections (Beam depth *d* and span length *L* in inches)

Load Cases	$F_b = 0.66F_Y$	$F_b = 0.60F_Y$
Floor beams supporting dead load plus live load	d > L/24	d > L/27
Roof beams supporting dead load plus live load	d > L/32	d > L/36
Any beam supporting brittle elements	$d > \left(\frac{LL}{DL + LL}\right) L/16$	$d > \left(\frac{LL}{DL + LL}\right) L/18$

It is well to note that for floors, the depth requirement for beams carrying brittle elements will not govern until the live load is more than twice the dead load. For roofs, however, the depth requirement for brittle elements will govern when the live load is equal to the dead load.

The limiting depths given in Table 27-3 are the only deflection controls for steel beams used in this textbook. They correspond to the limiting depths used earlier in controlling the deflections of concrete beams. In later chapters in the design of timber beams, a comparable table of limiting depths is developed for timber beams.

Some examples will demonstrate the procedure for checking deflections in steel beams.

Example 27-11

Verification of deflection limitations in steel beams.

Given: Design conditions of Example 27-1 with W18 x 40 beam.

To Find: Determine whether the W18 x 40 section is adequate.
1) When no brittle elements are to be supported.
2) When brittle elements are to be supported.

Solution: From Table 27-3, minimum required depth for *DL+LL* when the allowable stress is $0.60F_Y$ and no brittle elements are present:

1) Minimum d > L/27 = 16 x 12/27 = 7.11 in.

Since this depth is much less than the 18 in. beam provided, the section is adequate when no brittle elements are present.

For $F_b = 0.60F_Y$ and when brittle elements are present:

$$\text{2) Minimum } d > \left(\frac{LL}{DL + LL}\right) L / 18$$

$$= \left(\frac{2.0}{2.0 + 1.75}\right)(16x12) / 18 = 5.7 \text{ in.}$$

This depth is also seen to be much less than the 18 in. provided.

The beam is found to meet deflection requirements.

Example 27-12

Verification of deflection limitations in steel beams.

Given: Design conditions of Example 27-2.

To Find: Determine whether the W24 x 84 beam is adequate.
1) When no brittle elements are to be supported.
2) When brittle elements are to be supported.

Solution: From Table 27-3, the minimum required depth when no brittle elements are to be supported and the allowable flexure stress is 0.60 F_Y is given by:

1) Minimum d > L/27 = 36 x 12/27 = 16 in.

Since this depth is less than the 24 inch depth provided, the section is found to be adequate when no brittle elements are to be supported.

When brittle elements are to be supported:

$$2)\ \text{Minimum d} > \left(\frac{LL}{DL + LL}\right)L / 18$$

$$= \left(\frac{2}{1+2}\right)(36x12)/18 = 16 \text{ in.}$$

Since this depth is also less than the 24 in. depth provided, the section is also found to be adequate when brittle elements are to be supported.

The beam is found to meet deflection requirements.

27.6 Bending on Two Axes

Bending on two axes is introduced in Chapter 12, Strength of Materials. The discussions there, however, are limited to finding the combined stress at a point in the cross section. In this section, selecting a steel section to carry that combined state of stress is presented.

Combined states of stress are very common in structures. A typical example of such a case is shown in Figure 27-7, where a roof purlin is mounted on a sloping gable where it receives a vertical load from the roofing. The combined loading on the two axes is also shown in Figure 27-7.

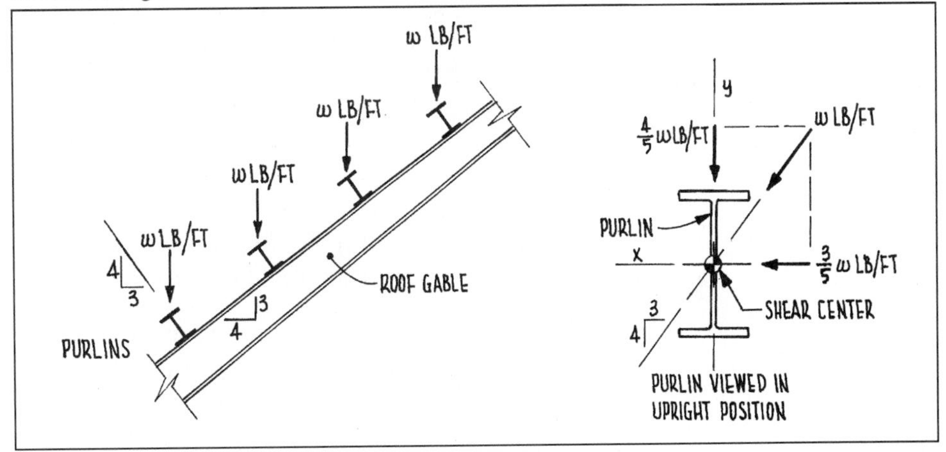

Figure 27-7 Beam loaded on two axes.

The beam of Figure 27-7 will have a moment on both its *xx* and *yy* axes. The two moments will produce stresses that will be directly additive. The vertical load, however, will produce compression at *B* and *C* along with tension at *A* and *D*. The horizontal load will similarly produce compressive stress at *C* and *D* along with tension at *A* and *B*. It is up to the designer to determine which points undergo maximum compression and which undergo maximum tension.

The flexural stress is computed by the flexure formula, where a positive sign indicates tension and a negative sign indicates compression:

$$\text{Stress at A: } f_A = +\frac{M_{xx}}{S_{xx}} + \frac{M_{yy}}{S_{yy}}$$

$$\text{Stress at B: } f_B = -\frac{M_{xx}}{S_{xx}} + \frac{M_{yy}}{S_{yy}}$$

$$\text{Stress at C: } f_C = -\frac{M_{xx}}{S_{xx}} - \frac{M_{yy}}{S_{yy}}$$

$$\text{Stress at D: } f_D = +\frac{M_{xx}}{S_{xx}} - \frac{M_{yy}}{S_{yy}}$$

The critical stress on the projecting flange elements will, as usual, be the highest compressive stress. For the loading shown in Figure 27-7, the highest compressive stress occurs at *C*, where both loads (and resultant bending) will produce compression. It is the compressive stress at *C* that must be limited to the maximum allowable value specified by ASD specifications.

ASD(F1) and (F2) specify different allowable stresses for the weak axis than for the strong axis. For bending about the strong (*xx*) axis, the allowable stresses have already been presented; they are listed in Table 27-2 for various values of unsupported length of the compression flange. Those allowable stresses remain the limiting stresses for bending about the *xx* axis, even though there is additional bending about the *yy* axis.

For bending about the weak (*yy*) axis, there are no additional lateral bracing requirements given by ASD(F2), provided the load passes through the shear center. Without bracing requirements, the allowable bending stresses become quite simple:

For doubly symmetrical compact sections, for all lengths:

$$F_b = 0.75\ F_Y \qquad (27\text{-}14)$$

For all other sections except pipes and tubes, for all lengths:

$$F_b = 0.60F_Y \qquad (27\text{-}15)$$

It is observed from Eq.(27-14) that ASD specifications give a different allowable compressive stress on one axis than they do on the other.

When loads occur on two axes at the same time, ASD(H1) requires that the sum of the two cases may not exceed the limiting case:

$$\frac{f_{bx}}{F_{bx}} + \frac{f_{by}}{F_{by}} \leq 1 \qquad (27\text{-}16)$$

where f_{bx} is the computed flexural stress about the *xx* axis computed by the flexure formula for M_{xx}.

F_{bx} is the allowable flexural stress about the *xx* axis as prescribed in Table 27-2.

f_{by} is the computed flexural stress about the *yy* axis computed by the flexure formula for M_{yy}.

F_{by} is the allowable flexural stress about the *yy* axis as prescribed by Equations (27-14) or (27-15).

Equation (27-16) warrants some reflection. The first term indicates the *proportion* of the allowable stress about the *xx* axis that is being used by the given load case. Similarly, the second term indicates the *proportion* of the allowable stress about the *yy* axis that is being used by the given load case. Their sum may not exceed 1.0 (or 100%).

Some examples will illustrate the selection of flexural members carrying moment about both axes.

Example 27-13

Selection of a steel beam loaded on both axes.

Given: Steel section loaded as shown. Simple span of 24'-0" on both axes. Laterally supported each 10 ft on weak axis only. Laterally supported on both axes at end supports. A36 steel.

To Find: Suitable section to support the load.

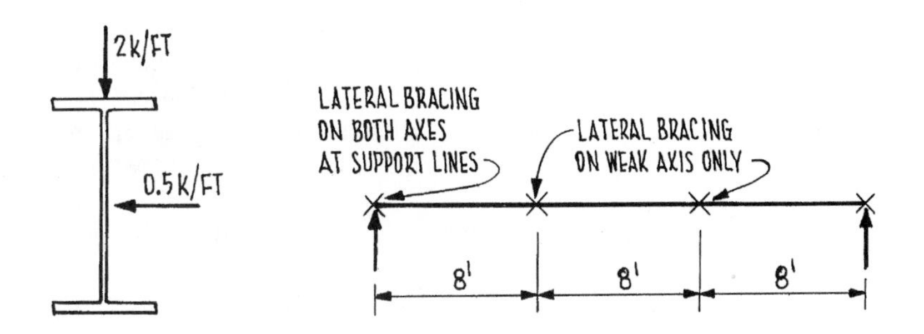

Solution: The design moments on the two axes are readily computed:

$$M_{xx} = \frac{wL^2}{8} = \frac{2x24^2}{8} = 144 \text{ kip·ft}$$

$$M_{yy} = \frac{wL^2}{8} = \frac{0.5x24^2}{8} = 36 \text{ kip·ft}$$

The old design quandary now returns. The allowable stresses cannot be established until the section is chosen and the section cannot be chosen until the allowable stress is established.

Some type of starting point must be established. One such starting point is to assume the beam will use about half its strength for bending about the *xx* axis and the other half for bending about the *yy* axis.

If the beam is to use about half its strength in each direction, then for a compact section, the stress f_b should be about $1/2 F_{bx}$ on the *xx* axis and about $1/2 F_{by}$ on the *yy* axis.

Trial values for S_{xx} and S_{yy} can be computed on this basis, assuming a compact section will be chosen:

$$S_{xx} = \frac{M_x}{\frac{1}{2}F_{bx}} = \frac{144{,}000 \text{x} 12}{12{,}000} = 144 \text{ in.}^3$$

$$S_{yy} = \frac{M_x}{\frac{1}{2}F_{by}} = \frac{36{,}000 \text{x} 12}{12{,}000} = 32 \text{ in.}^3$$

Enter Table S-1a with these values of S_{xx} and S_{yy}, remembering that they are only trial values.

The first beam encountered is in Table S-1d. A W12 x 96 satisfies these values. Proceeding into the 14 in. beams, however, it is found that a lighter W14 x 90 also satisfies these values. The lighter W14 x 90 section is chosen for a first trial.

Try W14 x 90, $S_{xx} = 143$, $S_{yy} = 44.9$:

$$f_{bx} = \frac{M_x}{S_{xx}} = \frac{144 \text{x} 12}{143} = 12.08 \text{ ksi}$$

$$f_{by} = \frac{M_y}{S_{yy}} = \frac{36 \text{x} 12}{49.9} = 8.66 \text{ ksi}$$

The next problem is to find the allowable stresses F_{bx} and F_{by}. Since it is only needed to know whether the section is compact or noncompact, the necessary information can be found in Table S-14a. Enter Table S-14a with an unsupported length of 8 ft, and find that 8 ft is to the left of the first asterisk for a W14 x 90; the section is therefore compact, for which:

$$F_{bx} = 0.66F_Y = 24 \text{ ksi}$$

$$F_{by} = 0.75F_Y = 27 \text{ ksi}$$

The section can now be checked for combined bending:

$$\frac{f_{bx}}{F_{bx}} + \frac{f_{by}}{F_{by}} \leq 1$$

$$\frac{12.08}{24} + \frac{8.66}{27} = 0.824 < 1 \quad (\text{O.K.})$$

This section is thus found to be adequate. Other sections were examined, but no lighter section could be found (though a W14 x 87 was close).

Example 27-14

Selection of a steel beam loaded on both axes.

Given: Conditions of Example 27-13, except that lateral supports exist only at the end supports. A36 steel.

To Find: Whether W14 x 90 is still adequate.

Solution: Moments remain the same:

$$M_{xx} = 144 \text{ kip·ft}; \; M_{yy} = 36 \text{ kip·ft}$$

For the W14 x 90:

$$S_{xx} = 143 \text{ in.}^3; \; S_{yy} = 49.9 \text{ in.}^3$$

At an unsupported length of 24 feet, it is found in Table S-14a that the allowable moment on the strong axis now lies between the two asterisks; the allowable stress on the strong axis has therefore dropped to 22 ksi.

Since the section is a doubly symmetrical compact section, and since for bending on the weak axis there are no limitations on unsupported length, the allowable stress on the weak axis remains 27 ksi.

The section is now checked for combined bending:

$$f_{bx} = \frac{M_{ss}}{S_{xx}} = \frac{144{,}000 \text{ x } 12}{143} = 12{,}080 \text{ psi}, \; F_{bx} = 22 \text{ ksi}$$

$$f_{by} = \frac{M_{yy}}{S_{yy}} = \frac{36{,}000 \text{ x } 12}{49.9} = 8660 \text{ psi}, \; F_{by} = 27 \text{ ksi}$$

$$\frac{12.08}{22} + \frac{8.66}{27} = 0.87 < 1 \text{ (O.K.)}$$

It is well to note at this point that the allowable stress F_{bx} for use in Eq.(27-16) can be found for any beam from Table S-14, simply by applying the flexure formula. For example, the allowable moment on a W21 x 62 with an unsupported length of 20 ft (far longer than L_u) is found in the table to be 136 kip·ft. The corresponding allowable stress Fbx is then found from the flexure formula, where S_{xx} for a W21 x 62 is found in Table S-1a to be 127:

$$F_{bx} = \frac{M_{xx}}{S_{xx}} = \frac{136{,}000 \text{x} 12}{127} = 12{,}850 \text{ psi}$$

27.7 Beams Having Small Axial Loads

On occasion, a steel beam may be subject to a small axial load in addition to its flexural loads. Design specifications treat this case differently than the case where axial compression is a significantly higher load. Columns with flexural loads are discussed in the next section.

A typical case of combined axial load and flexural load is shown in Figure 27-8. Though bending may or may not occur on both axes, the general case shown in Figure 27-8 includes both.

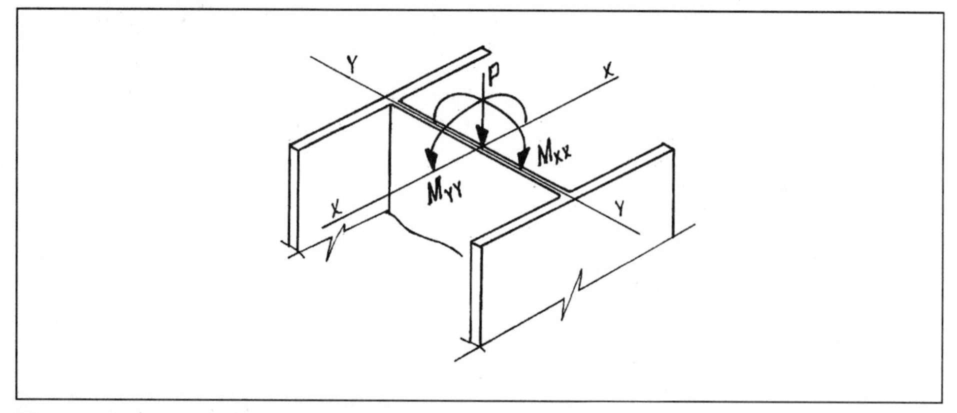

Figure 27-8 Combined loading on a beam section.

When the axial force P is in compression, ASD requires that stresses produced by the three loads shall not exceed the limiting case:

$$\frac{f_a}{F_a} + \frac{f_{bx}}{F_{bx}} + \frac{f_{by}}{F_{by}} \leq 1 \tag{27-17}$$

where $\frac{f_a}{F_a} \leq 0.15$

and where f_a is the computed axial direct stress, ksi.

F_a is the allowable column stress on the section if no flexure were to exist, ksi.

f_{bx} is the computed flexural stress about the xx axis, computed by the flexure formula, ksi.

F_{bx} is the allowable compressive flexural stress about the xx axis as prescribed in Table 27-2, ksi.

f_{by} is the computed flexural stress about the yy axis computed by the flexure formula, ksi.

F_{by} is the allowable compressive flexural stress about the yy axis as prescribed by Eq.(27-14) or Eq.(27-15), ksi.

The terms f_{bx}, F_{bx}, f_{by} and F_{by} are those introduced earlier with Eq.(27-16) but are included again here for immediate reference.

Equation (27-17) follows the same format as that used earlier. The first term is the proportion of the allowable stress used for axial load, the second term is the proportion of the allowable stress used for bending on the xx axis and the third term is the proportion of the allowable stress used for bending on the yy axis.

The procedure for selecting a member using Eq.(27-17) is similar to the procedure used earlier, compounded somewhat by the addition of the axial stress. An example will demonstrate one approach to the problem.

Example 27-15

Selection of a beam carrying a small axial load.

Given: Axial load P = 20 kips, bending moment M_{xx} = 50 kip·ft and bending moment M_{yy} = 10 kip·ft. A36 steel.

To Find: Steel section to carry this load.

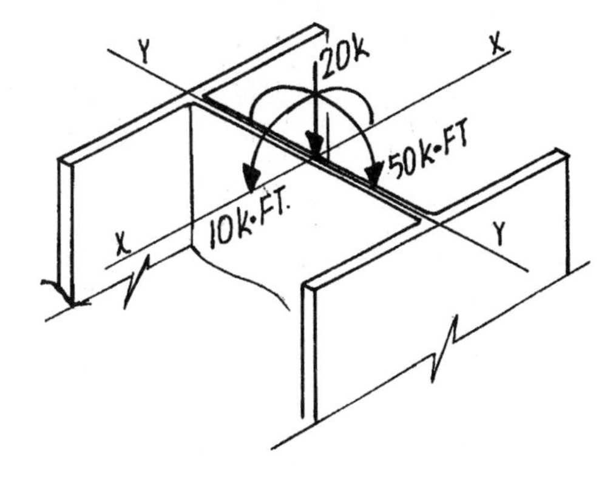

Solution: The rationale used earlier can be used again here.

It is assumed that the axial stress will use about 15% of the beam's capacity as a column. The allowable column stress F_a is estimated from Table 26-2 as 18 ksi:

$$\text{Required area} = \frac{P}{f_a} = \frac{20,000}{0.15 x 18,000} = 7.40 \text{ in.}^2$$

The remaining 85% of the beam's strength is assumed to be equally divided by bending about the *xx* axis and bending about the *yy* axis. Assume a compact section on the *xx* axis, with F_{bx} = 24 ksi:

Usable stress = $\frac{1}{2}$ x 0.85 x 24,000 = 10,000 psi

$$\text{Required } S_{xx} = \frac{M_{xx}}{F_{bx}} = \frac{50,000 x 12}{10,000} = 60 \text{ in.}^3$$

Similarly on the *yy* axis, with F_{by} = 27 ksi:

Usable stress = $\frac{1}{2}$ x 0.85 x 27,000 = 11,500 psi

$$\text{Required } S_{yy} = \frac{M_{yy}}{F_{by}} = \frac{10,000 x 12}{11,500} = 10 \text{ in.}^3$$

Table S-1 is entered with these values. It is desired to find a section having an area of about 7.4 in.^{2}, a section modulus S_{xx} of about 60 in.^{3} and a section modulus S_{yy} of about 10.

From Table S-1d, a W12 x 40 seems adequate. It will be reviewed using Eq.(27-17). The area is seen to be higher than the required area of 10 in.^{3}, but the value of S_{xx} compensates by being somewhat low:

A = 11.8 in.^{2}, S_{xx} = 51.9, S_{yy} = 11.0, r_{xx} = 5.13 in.,
f_{yy} = 1.93

Review for the limiting case:

$$\frac{f_a}{F_a} + \frac{f_{bx}}{F_{bx}} + \frac{f_{by}}{F_{by}} \leq 1$$

The computed stress f_a is found as a direct stress:

$$f_a = \frac{P}{A} = \frac{20{,}000}{11.8} = 1.7 \text{ ksi}$$

The allowable column stress F_a can be found from Table 26-2:

For kl/r = 8 x 12/1.93 = 50

F_a = 18.4 ksi from Table 26-2

Alternatively, the allowable column load on a W12 x 40 can be found from Table S-10b to be 217 kips. The allowable column stress F_a (if no flexure were to exist) is therefore:

$$F_a = \frac{P}{A} = \frac{217{,}000}{11.8} = 18.4 \text{ ksi}$$

The computed flexural stress on the *xx* axis is:

$$f_{bx} = \frac{M_{xx}}{S_{xx}} = \frac{50{,}000\text{x}12}{51.9} = 11.6 \text{ ksi}$$

The computed flexural stress on the *yy* axis is:

$$f_{by} = \frac{M_{yy}}{S_{yy}} = \frac{10{,}000\text{x}12}{11.0} = 10.9 \text{ ksi}$$

The allowable flexure stresses F_{bx} and F_{by} are found as before, from Table S-14b. For an unsupported length of 8 ft, the section is found to be a compact section, with

$F_{bx} = 0.66$; $F_y = 24$ ksi; $F_{by} = 0.75$; $F_y = 77$ ksi

(This same result could be deduced from Table S-18, where L_c is given as 8.4 ft.)

The foregoing values are substituted into Eq.(27-17):

$$\frac{1.7}{18.4} + \frac{11.6}{24.0} + \frac{10.9}{27.0} = 0.98 \leq 1 \text{ (O.K.)}$$

The first term is found to be $0.092 \leq 0.15$ maximum (O.K.)

The section W12 x 40 is adequate for this load case.

(Author's note: rarely will a beam selection turn out this nicely on the first trial. This is blind dumb luck.)

As a matter of interest, the same approach can be used when the axial load P is in tension rather than compression. When the axial load is in tension, however, ASD specifications do not set a limiting value on the proportion of the beam's strength that may be used for axial stress. The limiting case for combined tensile stress and flexural stress is given by ASD(H.2):

$$\frac{f_a}{F_t} + \frac{f_{bx}}{F_{bx}} + \frac{f_{by}}{F_{by}} \leq 1 \qquad (27\text{-}18)$$

where F_t is the allowable tensile stress on the member as given by Eq.(25-2) or Eq.(25-5), ksi.

F_{bx} is the allowable tensile stress in flexure about the *xx* axis as prescribed in Table 27-2, ksi.

F_{by} is the allowable tensile stress in flexure about the *yy* axis as prescribed by Eq.(27-14) or Eq.(27-15), ksi.

fa, f_{bx} and f_{by} are the computed tensile stresses due to axial load or flexural load as defined earlier.

The application of Eq.(27-18) for combined tensile stresses is identical to that presented earlier for combined compression stresses. In most cases, however, the allowable stresses F_t, F_{bx} and F_{by} are much easier to determine.

27.8 Framed Beam Connections

ASD(A2.2) lists three basic types of construction insofar as connections are concerned:

Type 1 construction is rigid frame construction, in which the members are rigidly fixed to each other. Moments are transferred from member to member essentially without slippage or loss. The 90° angle between beams and columns remains 90° under all conditions of lateral sway or drift.

Type 2 construction is braced frame construction, in which the gravity loads are carried by the system of beams and columns and the lateral loads are carried by an independent system of diaphragms and braced panels. Connections in the gravity load-carrying system transmit only shear. They are relatively free to rotate, thereby essentially eliminating moment resistance at the connections.

Type 3 construction is an intermediate or partially rigid framed construction. Connections are designed to provide a predictable and reliable resistance to moment at some fixed level between Type 1 and Type 3 connections.

ASD(A2.2) recognizes that beam and girder connections in Type 2 construction must provide simple supports for gravity loads. Further, ASD(A2.2) requires that under lateral loads, the connections in Type 2 construction must provide enough additional capacity in rotation to prevent overstress of fasteners or welds. It is the "slop" in these Type 2 connections that separates the gravity load-carrying system from the lateral load-carrying system.

Type 2 construction constitutes probably 75% of all construction in the world. The reason for its immense popularity is that it is economical, fast and reliable. One of the features of Type 2 construction that makes it economical, fast and reliable is the use of simple, proven and familiar connections.

Some typical simple connections are shown in Figure 27-9. One of the distinctive features of a simple beam connection is that the beam flanges are not attached to the receiving member. The beam-to-beam connections are always made web-to-web.

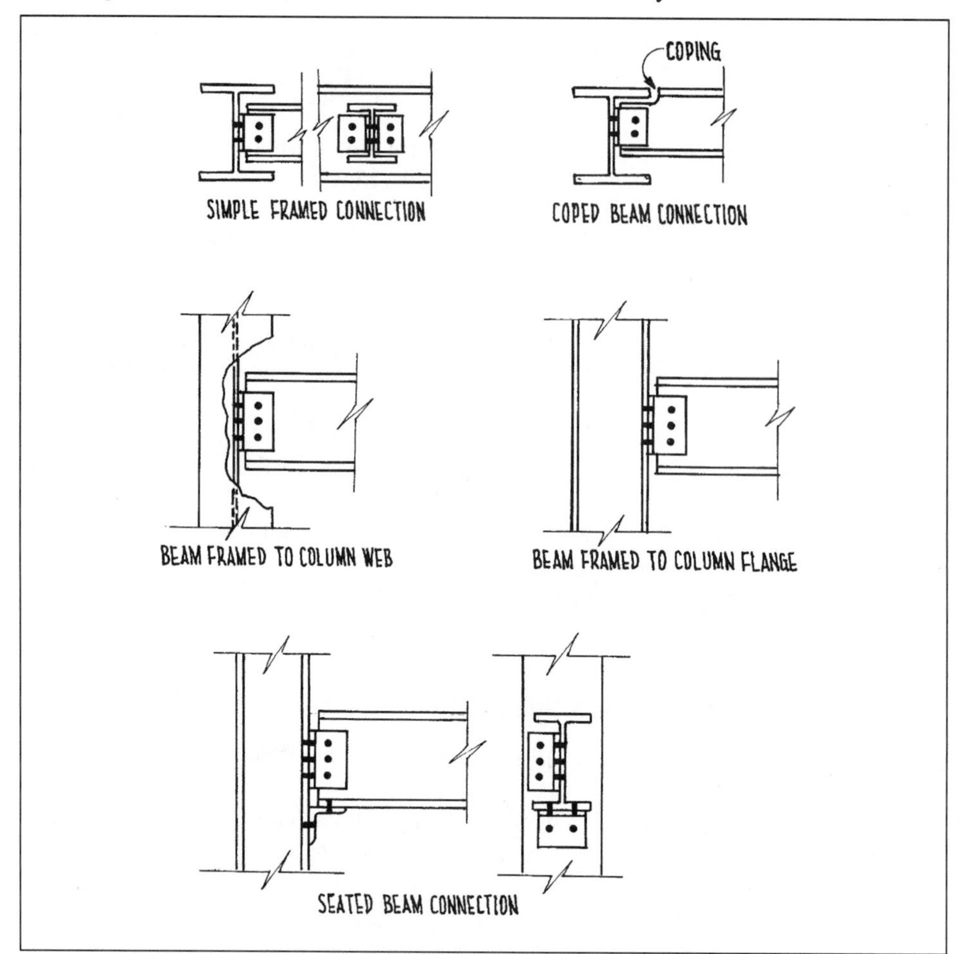

Figure 27-9 Typical simple connections.

The beam-to-column connections shown in Figure 27-9 may be made either to the column web or to the column flange, as indicated. Either way, no moment is transmitted to the column due to rotations at the end of the beam. When the beam is connected to the column flange, however, the load is significantly eccentric to the centroid of the column, thus creating a small moment on the column. Such small moments on column sections are treated in the next chapter.

A *seat angle* is sometimes used to facilitate erection. Usually, the web connection is designed to take the entire vertical shear. In simple connections, the seat angle is an erection feature that is not a part of the load carrying system.

Typically, a simple beam connection consists of two angles, attached to either side of the web of the beam as shown in Figure 27-10. In general, the angles are shop-connected to the web of the beam and are field connected to the supporting member. The connections to the web of the beam may be bolted or welded; the same size angles are used in either case.

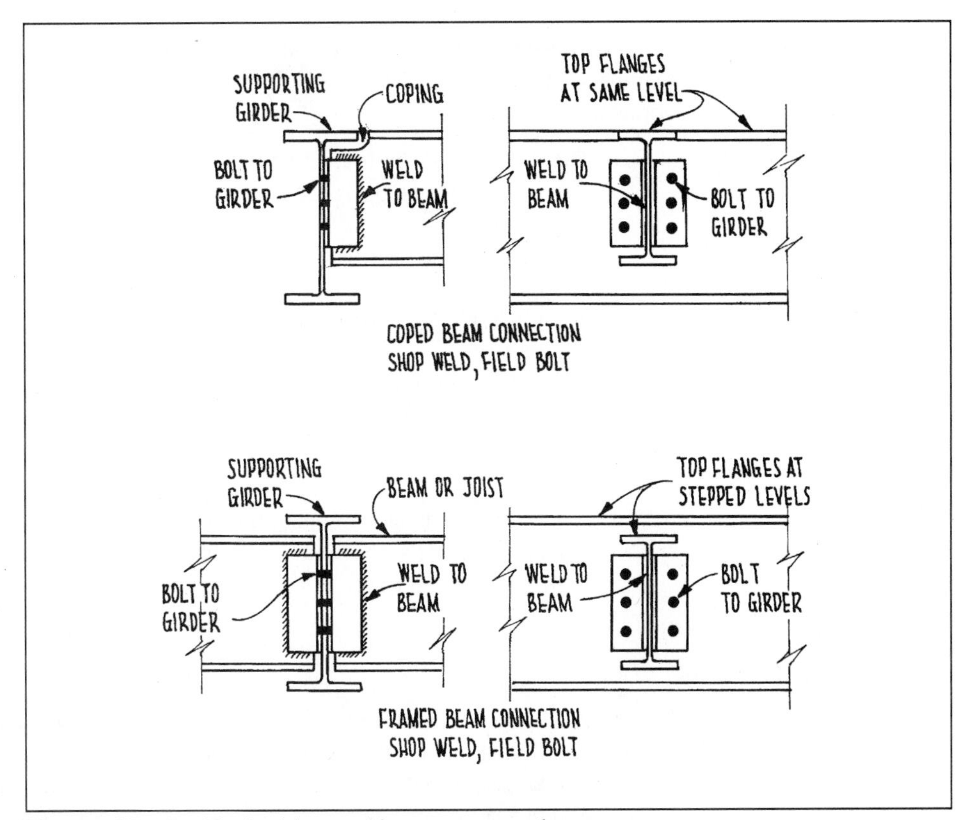

Figure 27-10 Typical framed beam connections.

Framed beam connections may be made such that the top flanges are held at the same elevation. In such cases, the top flange of the beam is *coped* as shown in Figure 27-10. Connections to coped beams are subject to block tearout due to the vertical shear.

Framed beam connections may be designed as bearing connections or as slip-critical connections. The procedure is identical to that introduced with tension connections. The only difference is that the load is introduced by shear rather than by tension.

As a rule, the angle thickness in framed beam connections is kept as thin as possible. Thick, rigid angles can offer a great deal more resistance to rotation than thinner, more flexible angles. As indicated in Figure 27-11, bending in the thin angles can serve to reduce moment buildup at the connection.

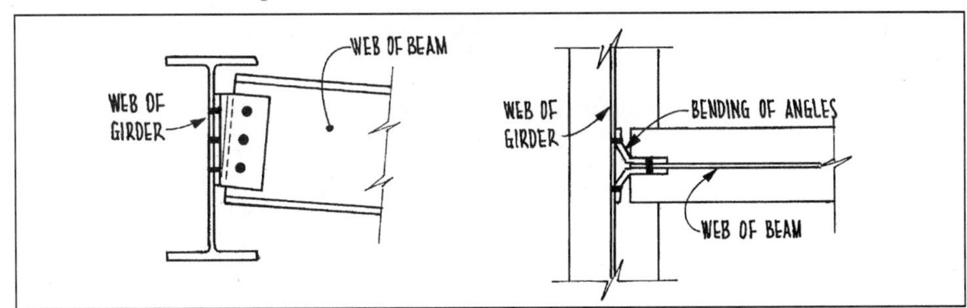

Figure 27-11 Bending in a framed beam connection.

In years past, wide angles having two lines of bolts were used in framed beam connections. In more recent years, narrower angles are used which can accommodate only one line of bolts. Again, the reason for such preference is to reduce any potential moment buildup at the connection.

The design of framed beam connections is much like that of connections to tension members, presented in Chapter 25. For bearing type connections, the design considerations are:

1. The design load for framed connections is the beam reaction. If the design load is not specified, the design load may not be less than half the capacity of the beam web in shear.
2. The number and size of bolts shall be adequate in single shear or double shear, as appropriate, to sustain the design load. Bolt values are those given earlier and listed in Table S-26. Inclusion or exclusion of threads in the shear planes remains a limitation.
3. The effective area of the beam web, with holes deducted, must be capable of sustaining the design load in shear. The allowable shear stress F_v on the beam web is:

$$F_v = 0.40F_y \qquad (27\text{-}19)$$

4. When the top flange is coped, the beam web must be capable of sustaining the design load in block tearout. The allowable shear stress F_v and the tension stress F_t in block tearout are:

$$F_v = 0.30F_u \qquad (27\text{-}20)$$

$$F_t = 0.50F_u \qquad (27\text{-}21)$$

5. The beam web must be capable of sustaining the design load of the bolts in bearing. The limitations in bearing are the same as those given earlier in Table S-24.
6. The angles or plates comprising the connection must be capable of sustaining the design load of the bolts in bearing. The limitations in bearing are the same as those given earlier in Table S-24.
7. End distances, edge distances and bolt spacings must conform to ASD requirements, as summarized earlier in Table S-24. Gage distances for angles must conform to ASD requirements given in Table S-22. For beam connections, the direction of load is that of the beam reaction.

For slip-critical connections, the design considerations remain those in the foregoing list, except that bearing requirements no longer exist. In addition, the bolt values are those for slip-critical connections given in Table S-27.

Some examples will illustrate the procedures for the analysis and design of bolted beam connections.

Example 27-16

Analysis of a bolted beam connection.

Given: Bolted bearing connection as shown. A36 steel. A325 bolts.

To Find: Whether the connection is adequate.

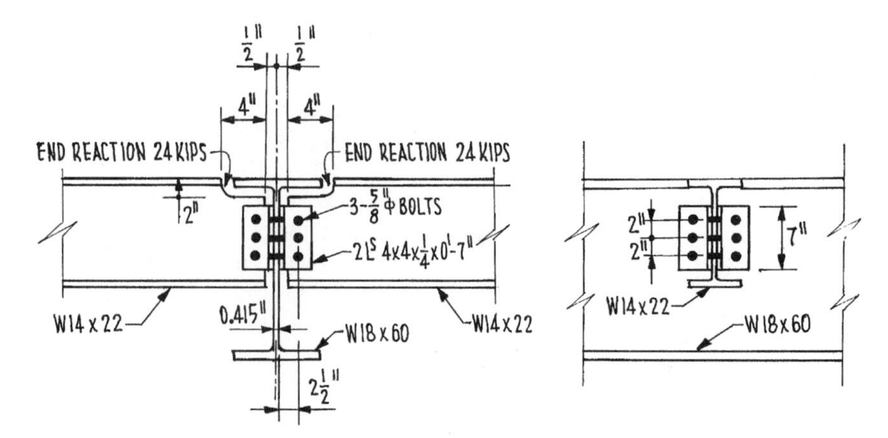

Solution: 1. Determine the design load for a W14 x 22; d = 13.74 in., t_w = 0.23 in.:

The design load has been computed; use V = 24 kips.

2. Determine the bolt capacity for 3 bolts in double shear from Table S-26, bolt value is 12.9 kips:

Capacity = 3 x 12.9 = 39 kips > actual load of 24 kips (O.K.)

3. Determine the capacity of the beam web in shear:

Effective area = (d - 2 in.) t_w - 3 holes
= (13.74 - 2)(0.23) - 3(0.23)($^5/_8$ + $^1/_{16}$)
= 1.766 in.^{2}

Capacity = $0.4F_v$ x A = $0.4F_y$ x 1.766 = 25.43 kips

4. Determine the capacity of the web in block tearout:

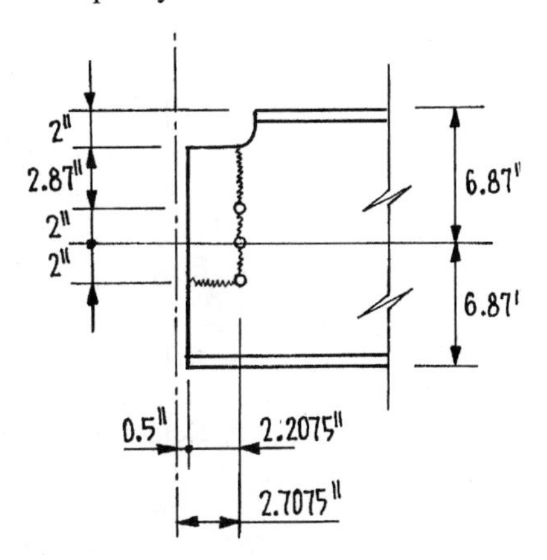

Capacity = $0.4F_uA_t + 0.3F_vA_v$
= $0.4F_u$[2.2075 - $^1/_2$($^5/_8$ + $^1/_{16}$)](0.23)
+ $0.3F_u$[6.87 - 2$^1/_2$($^5/_8$ + $^1/_{16}$)](0.23)
= 43.2 + 20.6 = 63.8 kips

5. Determine the capacity of the web in bearing from Table S-24 with no wrinkling permitted, all end and edge distances > 1$^1/_8$ in., bolt spacing > 3 bolt diameters:

$F_P = 1.2F_u$

Capacity of 3 bolts = 3($1.2F_u$)(0.23)($^5/_8$)
= 30.02 kips > 24 kips (O.K.)

6. Determine whether the angles are adequate:

Thickness of 2 angles = 0.5 in.
Thickness of web of W14 x 22 = 0.23 in.
Thickness of web of W18 x 60 = 0.415 in.

7. Determine whether end distances, edge distances and bolt spacings conform to ASD requirements:

   This item was examined in Step 5 and found adequate.

The analysis is only half complete at this point. The other half involves the capacity of the W18 x 60.

1. Determine the design load on the W18 x 60:

   Total load is 24 kips per side.
   $V_{TOTAL} = 48$ kips

2. Determine the bolt capacity of 6 bolts in double shear:

   Capacity = 6 x 12.9 = 77.4 kips > 48 kips (O.K.)

3. Determine the capacity of the beam web in shear:

   $\text{Capacity} = 0.4F_yA_{WEB} = 0.4F_y[(18.24) - 3(5/8 + 1/16)]0.415$
   $= 97$ kips

   Since actual shear on this beam is not known, this value is assumed to be adequate.

4. Determine the capacity of the web in block tearout:

   This item is not appropriate for the W18 x 60.

5. Determine the capacity of the web in bearing:

   From Table S-24, $F_P = 1.2F_u$

   $\text{Capacity of 6 bolts} = 6(1.2F_u)(0.415)(5/8)$
   $= 108$ kips > 48 kips (O.K.)

6. Determine whether the angles are adequate:

   This item examined earlier.

Conclusion: The capacity of the connection is 25.43 kips, as limited by the capacity of the web of the W14 x 22 in shear.

Example 27-17

Analysis of a shop weld field bolt connection.

Given: Bolted bearing connection of Example 27-16. The angles are to be welded to the web of the W14 x 22 rather than bolted. E60xx electrodes.

To Find: Whether the weld is adequate.

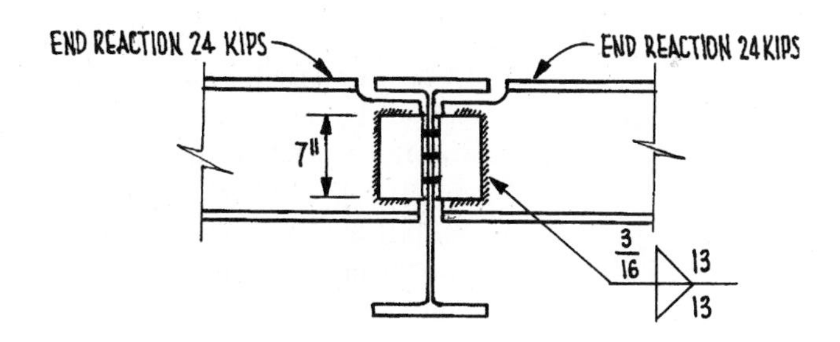

Solution: The capacity of a 3/16 in. weld is found from Table S-31 to be 2.4 kips per inch. Length of weld includes two returns of 3 in. each.

It is noted that the load is eccentric to the vertical weld. There will therefore be some torsion on the weld. The resistance of the connection is assumed to be developed as shown in the following sketch.

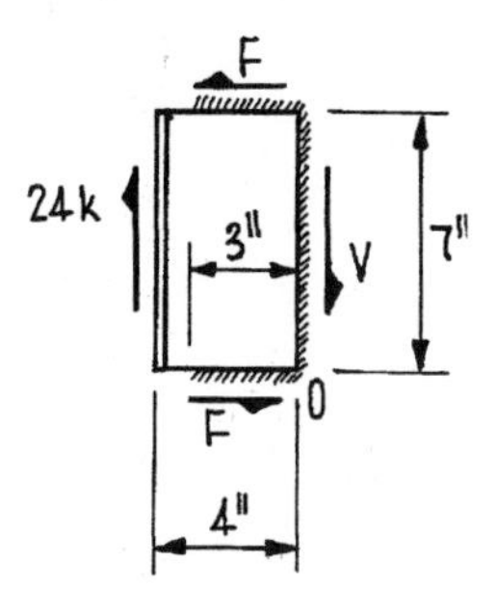

Summing moments about point *0* yields the force *F*:

$\Sigma M_0 = 0;\ 24 \times 4 - F \times 7 = 0$

$F = 13.7 \text{ kips} = 6.85 \text{ kips/side}$

Load on the 3 in. weld = 2.3 kips/in. < 2.4 kips/in. allowed

Summing forces vertically yields the force *V*:

$\Sigma F_v = 0;\ 24 - V = 0$

$V = 24 \text{ kips} = 12 \text{ kips/side}$

Load on the 7 in. weld = 1.7 kips/in. < 2.4 kips/in. allowed

Conclusion: The weld is adequate.

The design of framed beam connections is such a common problem that numerous design aids have been developed. Some of the most detailed design aids are those given in the older steel handbooks, those published before about 1980. There are many newer tables, however, many of them computer generated. Such proprietary design tables relieve the designer of this repetitious (and error-prone) calculation. Both the novice and the seasoned designer are referred to such prepared tables for the selection of framed beam connections.

27.9 Beam Bearings at Points of Loading

Quite often, steel beams are not supported by other steel members where a steel-to-steel connection can be made. Steel beams are frequently seated on concrete or masonry walls which are much weaker than the steel beam they support. Further, the load from the steel beam must be transferred to the concrete or masonry in a rather limited distance. Such transfer of loads produces bearing stresses that must be accommodated both in the steel beam and in the concrete or masonry wall.

A typical wall bearing is shown in Figure 27-12, where a beam is seated on a concrete wall. If the beam were to be placed directly on the wall, the large concentrated beam reaction could overstress the concrete in bearing, causing cracking or even failure. The addition of the thick *bearing plate* serves to distribute the load over a larger area, reducing the stress to a level within the capacity of the concrete. The capacity of concrete in bearing is given in Table C-1 and for masonry in Table M-1.

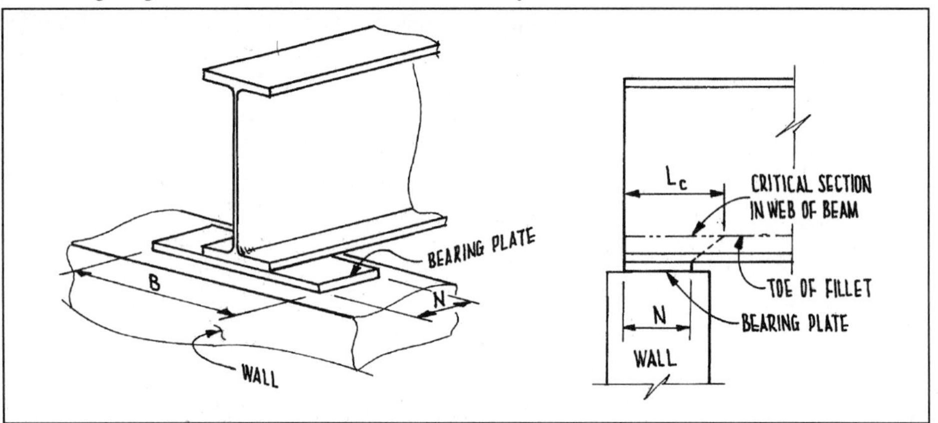

Figure 27-12 Typical beam bearing plate.

Note that the width N of the bearing plate is less than the width of the wall. If the bearing plate is made as wide as the wall, the slight "rocking" at the end of the beam as it is loaded and unloaded would cause chipping at the corners of the wall. It is preferable to make the bearing plates slightly narrower than the wall (1 inch or so at each side) in order to avoid such problems.

It is often possible that lightly loaded steel beams do not need a bearing plate. The bottom flange of the steel beam may be wide enough and thick enough to distribute the reaction by itself. Such a possibility should always be investigated.

When the width of the wall is small, the width N of the bearing plate can become so narrow that the beam web could be overstressed. As indicated in Figure 27-13, the load is delivered into the web in a very short distance. If the distance is too short, the compressive stress in the beam web can cause local yielding of the web. The critical section in the web is that at the toe of the fillet, as shown.

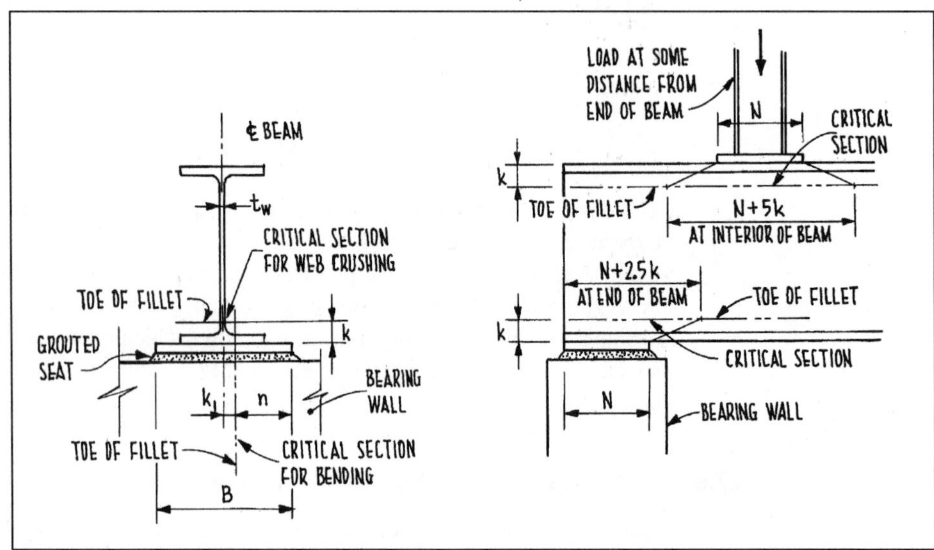

Figure 27-13 Critical section for web crippling.

The values of k and k_l shown in Figure 27-13 are those given in Table S-1 in the Technical Manual. As indicated in the sketches of Table S-1, the values of k and k_l define the position of the toe of the fillet.

A final condition must be included in the design of bearing plates. The bearing plate distributes the load laterally by bending in the plate. The thickness of the bearing plate must be adequate to sustain such bending. (If no bearing plate is used, the thickness of the beam flange must similarly be thick enough to sustain such bending.)

The design of bearing plates thus reduces to two cases:

1. No bearing plate may be required.
   a. The concrete or masonry must be adequate to support the load without overstress when the contact area is that of the width of the flange times the grout length N:

$$f_P = \frac{P}{b_f N}$$

   If this stress is less than the allowable stress F_P for the concrete or masonry given in Tables C-1 and M-1, then the wall will not be overstressed.

   b. The beam flange must be adequate to take the bending stress. A 1 inch strip of the beam flange is analyzed as a cantilever beam, with the critical section in bending being that at the toe of the fillet.

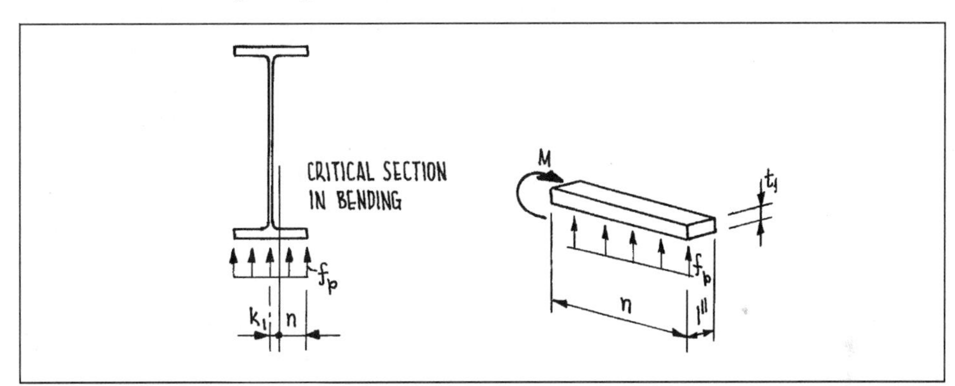

Figure 27-14 Bending on unit width of flange.

The moment at the critical section is computed as usual for a cantilever beam:

$$M = \tfrac{1}{2} f_P n^2$$

The stress is computed by the flexure formula:

$$f_b = \frac{M}{S}, \quad S = \frac{1xt^2}{6}$$

The allowable stress in bending on a flange is given by:

$$F_b = 0.75F_Y.$$

If the allowable stress is not exceeded, then the flange is adequate to distribute the load in bending.

   c. The beam web must not be overstressed locally. The stress at the critical section is given by:

$$f_w = \frac{P}{(N + 2.5k)t_w} \quad \text{for reaction at the end of the beam}$$

$$f_w = \frac{P}{(N + 5k)t_w} \text{ for reaction at an interior point in the beam}$$

The allowable stress in compressive yield in the web is given by:

$$F_b = 0.66F_Y$$

If the allowable stress is not exceeded, then the web is adequate to receive the concentrated load.

If any of the foregoing conditions are not met, a bearing plate will be required. The selection of a suitable bearing plate follows the chronology given above.

2. When a bearing plate is found to be necessary.
   a. Select a size such that the concrete or masonry will not be overstressed.

$$\text{Required area} = \frac{P}{F_P}\text{; select N and B}$$

where F_P is the allowable bearing stress given in Tables C-1 or M-1.

   b. Select a plate thickness adequate to take the bending stress. As before, a 1 in. strip of the plate is analyzed as a cantilever beam. The critical section remains that at the toe of the fillet. Only the bending in the plate is considered; the beam flange is ignored. The moment is:

$$M = \tfrac{1}{2} f_P n^2$$

The thickness is solved from the flexure formula for an allowable stress $F_b = 0.75F_Y$:

$$F_b = \frac{M}{S}, \quad S = \frac{1xt^2}{6}$$

$$0.75F_Y = \frac{\tfrac{1}{2} f_P n^2}{1xt^2/6}.$$

$$t = \sqrt{\frac{3f_P n^2}{0.75F_Y}}$$

Select a suitable plate size and thickness.

   c. Check the beam web for local yielding. The procedure is the same as that given earlier.

An example will illustrate the procedure for beam bearings.

Example 27-18

Selection of a beam bearing plate.

Given: W16 x 50 beam, end reaction 40 kips. Seated on a 8 in. concrete wall, f_c' = 4000 psi. A36 steel.

To Find: 1) Whether a bearing plate is needed.
2) If a bearing plate is needed, select a suitable size.

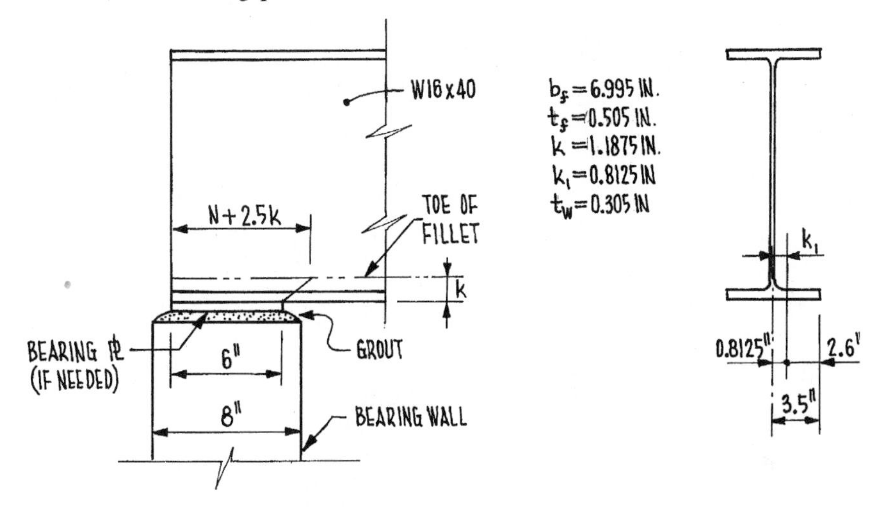

Solution: a. Check the contact stress on the concrete with no bearing plate:

$$f_P = \frac{P}{b_f N} = \frac{40{,}000}{6.995x6} = 953 \text{ psi}$$

The allowable stress on the concrete is found in Table C-1:

F_P = 1200 psi > 953 psi (O.K.)

The concrete will not be overstressed.

b. Check the bending stress in the beam flange:

$$M = \tfrac{1}{2} f_P n^2 = \tfrac{1}{2}(953)(2.685^2) = 3435 \text{ lb·in.}$$

$$f_b = \frac{M}{S} = \frac{6x3435}{0.505^2} = 81{,}000 \text{ psi} > 27{,}000 \text{ psi allowed.}$$

The beam flange is not adequate to distribute the load in bending.

Select a suitable bearing plate.

a. Select the required size:

$$\text{Required } A = \frac{P}{F_p} = \frac{40{,}000}{1200} = 33 \text{ in.}^2$$

Try PL 5 in. wide x 8 in. long.

$$\text{Actual } f_p = \frac{P}{A} = \frac{4000}{40} = 1000 \text{ psi.}$$

b. Select the thickness of the plate:

$$n = \tfrac{1}{2}x8 - k_1 = 3.1875 \text{ in.}$$

$$\text{Required } t = \sqrt{\frac{3f_p n^2}{0.75F_Y}} = \sqrt{\frac{3(1000)(3.1875^2)}{(0.75)(36{,}000)}} = 1.06 \text{ in.}$$

Try PL $1\tfrac{1}{8}$"x5"x0'–8"

c. Check for web yielding:

$$f_{WEB} = \frac{P}{(N + 2.5k)t_w} = \frac{40{,}000}{(7.5)(1.1875)(0.305)}$$

= 14,700 psi < 24,000 psi allowed.

Use PL $1\tfrac{1}{8}$"x5"x0'–8"

Review Questions

1. How is a compact section distinguished from a noncompact section?
2. How are compact and noncompact sections distinguished from slender element sections?
3. How are the allowable stresses established for a given steel beam?
4. What makes the selection of steel beams such a "guesswork" procedure when design aids are not used?
5. When a compact section is selected with its allowable stress of 0.66 F_Y, what is the purpose of redesigning the beam for an allowable stress of $0.60F_Y$?
6. Are circular pipes and square tubes always compact?
7. When a steel section is reviewed for its average shear stress, what steel area is used in the calculation?
8. What are the limiting deflections for floor beams?
9. What are the limiting deflections for roof beams?
10. What is the ASD formula for reviewing the stresses in a beam subject to bending on two axes? State the formula and define each symbol.
11. What is the ASD formula for reviewing the stresses in a beam subject to bending on two axes plus having a small axial compressive load? State the formula and define each symbol.
12. What is the ASD formula for reviewing the stresses in a beam subject to bending on two axes plus having a small axial tension load? State the formula and define each symbol.
13. In the ASD specifications, what is meant by "Type 2" construction?
14. Why is Type 2 construction so popular?
15. What is meant by a framed beam connection?
16. Under what conditions can the possibility of block tearout be introduced into a framed beam connection?
17. List the review points for reviewing the capacity of a framed beam connection.
18. How is a beam bearing plate similar to a column bearing plate? How is it different?
19. Where is the critical section in a beam web for local yielding due to a concentrated load?
20. In a beam seat, where is the critical section in a beam flange for flexural stress?
21. In a beam seat, what three conditions must be satisfied if no bearing plate is to be used?
22. In a beam seat, what three conditions must be satisfied in selecting a base plate when one is needed?

CHAPTER

28

Special Topics in Steel Structures

To this point, the design of steel structures has been focused on two conditions:

1. Type 2 construction with columns pinned top and bottom (no column bending).
2. The use of rolled sections with no added elements (no built-up sections).

Very early, a designer will find that wind loading on a structure is frequently resisted by bending in the columns and that crane runways must be stiffened by building up or reinforcing a rolled section. Because these exceptions to the foregoing general rules are so common, these exceptions are included here as special topics.

28.1 Columns Under Added Flexural Load

A typical column in a braced frame is shown in Figure 28-1. The column section is spliced at each story, carrying a total load on the lowest story of 251 kips on its 12-foot story height. The beam framing is Type 2. The column is supported in both directions at each story level. The buckling mode on the weak axis has a buckling length of 12 feet between points of zero moment. The wind load is 20 lbs/ft^2. Columns are spaced at 20 feet on center.

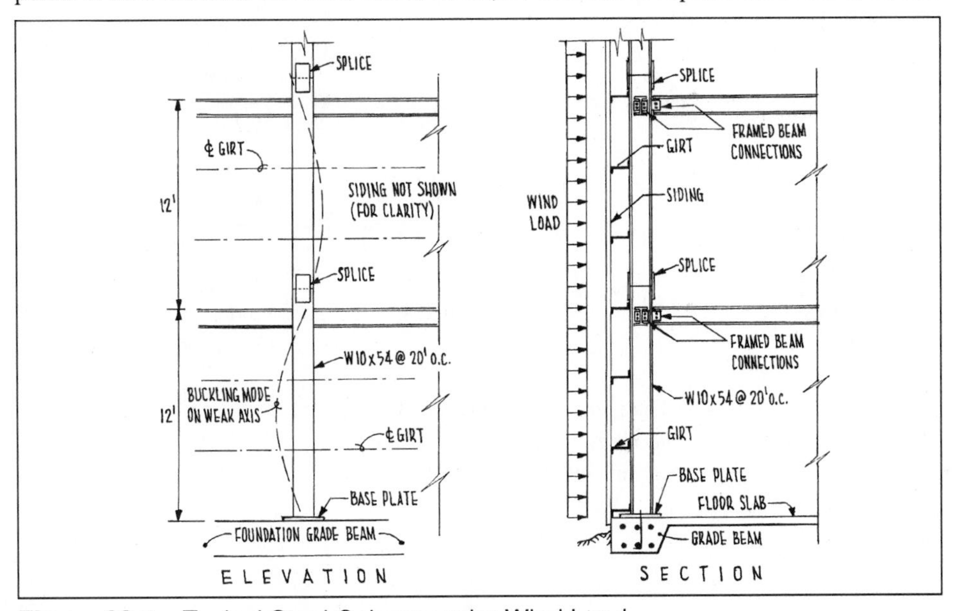

Figure 28-1 Typical Steel Column under Wind Load.

The column must sustain *DL+LL* loading regardless whether wind load exists. The capacity of the W10x54 is found from Table S-10a to be 281 kips on its weak axis for KL = 12 ft. The section is therefore adequate when there is no wind load.

Wind load places flexure on the column in addition to the axial load. The uniform wind load on the column at a 20-ft. spacing is 20x20 = 400 lb/ft. The moment at midheight is calculated as:

$$M = {}^1/_8 wL^2 = {}^1/_8 \text{ x } 400 \text{ x } 122 = 7200 \text{ lb-ft.}$$

The flexural stress produced by this moment is found from the flexure formula, for bending on the strong axis as shown:

$$f_{bx} = \frac{M}{S_x} = \frac{7200 \text{ x } 12}{60} = 1440 \text{ psi}$$

While seemingly a small stress due to moment, it must be remembered that the column is under high compressive stress and any flexural stress at all can drastically affect buckling load.

ASD Specification H1 gives two limiting conditions for columns subject to flexural load:

$$\frac{f_a}{F_a} + \frac{f_{bx}}{\left(1 - \frac{f_a}{F'_{ex}}\right)} + \frac{f_{by}}{\left(1 - \frac{f_a}{F'_{ey}}\right) F_{by}} \leq 1 \qquad \text{(28-1a)}$$

$$\frac{f_a}{0.60F_y} + \frac{f_{bx}}{F_{bx}} + \frac{f_{by}}{F_{by}} \leq 1 \qquad \text{(28-1b)}$$

where f_a is the computed axial stress in the section.
f_{bx} is the computed flexural stress about the *yy* axis.
f_{by} is the computed flexural stress about the *yy* axis.
F_a is the allowable concentric column stress on the section from the AISC column formula, Table 26-2.
F_{bx} is the allowable flexural stress about the *xx* axis.
F_{by} is the allowable flexural stress about the *yy* axis.
F'_{ex} is the Euler stress for buckling about the *xx* axis, with its usual factor of safety:

$$F'_{ex} = \left(\frac{12}{23}\right)\left[\frac{\pi^2 E}{(Kl/r)^2_{xx}}\right]$$

F'_{ey} is the Euler stress for buckling about the *yy* axis, with its usual factor of safety:

$$F'_{ex} = \left(\frac{12}{23}\right)\left[\frac{\pi^2 E}{\left(Kl/r^2_{yy}\right)}\right]$$

Under combined gravity and wind load, F_a, F_b, $0.60F_Y$ and F'_e are all subject to an allowable 33[1]/3% increase.

The form of Equations (28-1a and b) is seen to be quite similar to that for a beam bending about two axes plus a small axial load. There are some additional terms, but the application will be seen to be quite similar to that encountered earlier.

For the example column, A = 15.8 in.^{2}, S_{xx} = 60.0 in.^{3}, S_{yy} = 20.6 in.^{3}, r_{xx} = 4.37 in., r_{yy} = 2.56 in^3. The terms in Eq.(28-1) then become:

$$f_a = \frac{P}{A} = \frac{251{,}000}{15.8} = 15.9 \text{ ksi}$$

$$f_{bx} = \frac{M}{S_{xx}} = 1.44 \text{ ksi}$$

$$f_{by} = 0$$

For F_a, ignore any possible lateral supports by the small girts, then

$(kl/r)_{yy}$ = 12 x 12/2.56 = 56.25; $(kl/r)_{xx}$ = 33.0.

F_a = 17.8 x 1.333 = 23.7 ksi (From Table 26-2)

F_{bx} = 0.60F_y x 1.333 = 28.8 ksi (From Table S-14b)

F_{by} = 0.75F_y x 1.333 = 36.0 ksi (See Eq.27-14)

$$F'_{ex} = \frac{12}{23} \text{x} \frac{\pi^2 E}{(33.0)^2} \text{ x } 1.333 = 183\text{ksi}$$

$$F'_{ey} = \frac{12}{23} \text{x} \frac{\pi^2 E}{(56.25)^2} \text{ x } 1.333 = 63 \text{ ksi}$$

These values are substituted into Eqs.(28-1a, b) to find, with an allowable stress increase of 33^1/$_3$%:

$$\frac{15.9}{23.7} + \frac{1.44}{\left(1 - \frac{15.9}{183}\right)28.8} + \frac{0}{\left(1 - \frac{15.9}{63}\right)36} = 0.726 \le 1 \text{ (O.K.)}$$

$$\frac{15.9}{21.6\text{x}1.333} + \frac{1.44}{28.8} + \frac{0}{36} = 0.602 \le 1 \text{ (O.K.)}$$

The example column has thus been found to be adequate to take the wind load in addition to its high axial load.

Two things generally work to one's advantage when adding wind load to a column. First, the wind load is usually oriented on the strong axis of the column, while the column buckling is usually oriented on the weak axis; there will likely be some extra margin of strength on the strong axis. Second, the 33^1/$_3$% increase in stress for combined gravity plus lateral load provides additional margin for this relatively small added stress.

It should be apparent even in the simple review problem just presented that bending in columns can be an extremely tedious and intricate analysis. When end moments exist as well (as in rigid frames) the design of columns for combined axial and flexural stress can be indeed intimidating. The design of such members is relegated to advanced course work in steel design.

28.2 Built Up Sections

Built up sections are introduced in elementary strength of materials, but usually as an exercise in computing centroids and moments of inertia of combination sections. The remainder of the problem is to classify the resulting section as a compact, noncompact or slender element section and to find the allowable stress on its compression flange. It is the purpose of this section to extend the study of combination sections into such questions.

Some typical combination (or built up) sections are shown in Figure 28-2. The sections may be bolted or welded together and may be symmetrical on one or both axes. In rare cases, combination sections can be unsymmetrical on both axes of bending.

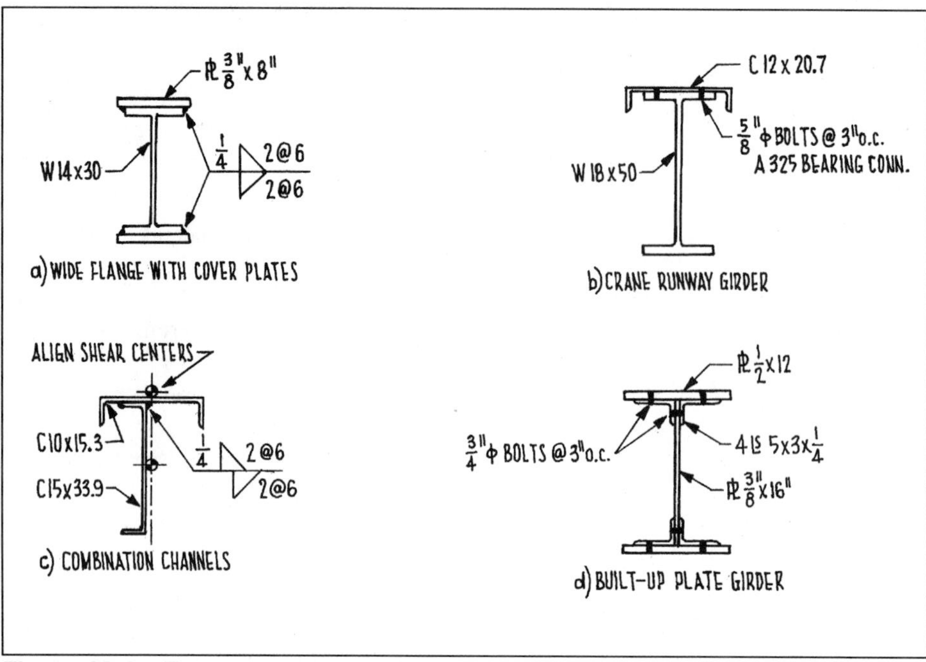

Figure 28-2 Typical combination sections.

The shallow built up beam shown in Figure 28-2a is commonly used where beam depths are severely restricted. It is sometimes necessary to use a shallow beam and to increase its moment capacity by adding flange area. The analysis of this beam is given in the following example.

Example 28-1

Analysis of a combination beam.

Given: Section of Figure 28-2a. A36 steel. E60 electrodes.

To Find:
1) L_c and L_u.
2) Moment capacity for $F_b = 0.60F_y$.
3) Shear capacity of the section as limited by $F_V = 0.4F_y$.
4) Shear capacity as limited by the fillet welds.

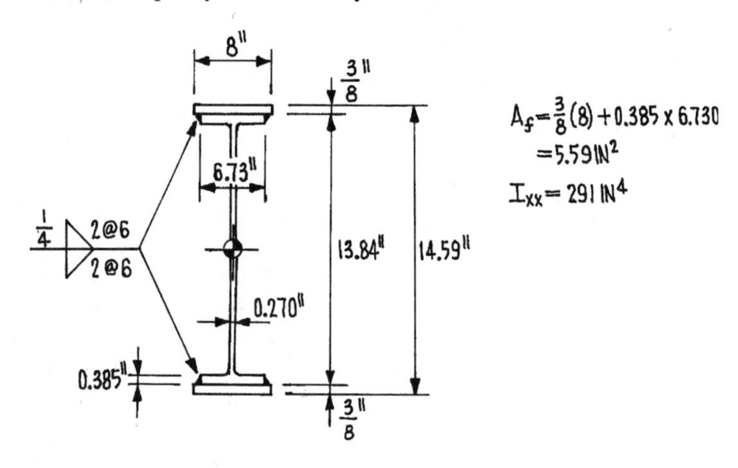

Solution: The values of L_c and L_u are found from the limits presented in Table 27-2:

$$12.67\ bf = 12.67 \times 8 = 101.33\text{ in.} = 8.4\text{ ft.}$$

$$\frac{555}{d/A_f} = \frac{555}{14.59/5.59} = 212.6\text{ in.} = 17.7\text{ ft.}$$

Use $L_c = 8.4$ ft, $L_u = 17.7$ ft

The moment of inertia is found as the sum of the moment of inertia of the beam plus the moment of inertia of the plates:

$$I = I_{BEAM} + I_{PLATES} = 291 + [(8 \times 14.59^3)/12 - (8 \times 13.84^3)/12]$$
$$= 594\text{ in.}^4$$

The moment capacity is found from the flexure formula:

$$M = F_b S_{xx}; = \frac{I}{C} = \frac{594}{14.59/2} = 81.4\text{ in.}^3$$
$$= 0.60F_y(81.4) = 1759\text{ kip}\cdot\text{ft}$$
$$= 146\text{ kip}\cdot\text{ft}$$

The shear capacity is found from the average shear formula:

$$V = F_v A_w = 14.4 \times 0.27 \times 14.59 = 56.7\text{ kips}$$

The shear capacity can also be limited by the capacity of the fillet welds. The cut line is shown on the sketch. The shear flow at the two fillets is found from the shear flow formula:

$$q = \frac{VA'\bar{y}}{I}; \qquad q = 3.2\text{ k/in./side (Table S-31)}$$

$$A'\bar{y} = \left(\tfrac{3}{8}\text{x}8\right)\left(\tfrac{1}{2}\text{x}14.59 - \tfrac{3}{16}\right) = 21.32\text{ in.}^3$$

$$I = 594\text{ in.}^4$$

For 33% intermittent welds:

$$V = \frac{0.33(3.2\text{x}2)(594)}{21.32} = 58.8\text{ kips}$$

The limiting shear is thus found to be the web of the beam:

Limiting V = 56.7 kips

Conclusion: At a laterally unsupported length of 17.7 ft on the compression flange, the built up beam will sustain a moment of 146 kip·ft and a shear force of 56.7 kips.

The built up beam shown in Figure 28-2b is a popular configuration for crane runway girders. With columns commonly placed at 25 ft spacing in shops and with no way to brace the compression flange, such girders can develop the high levels of moment over the long unsupported lengths. The analysis of this beam is given in the following example.

Example 28-2

Analysis of a combination beam.

Given: Section of Figure 28-1b. A36 steel. A325 bolts in a bearing connection.

To Find:
1) L_c and L_u.
2) Moment capacity for $F_b = 0.60F_y$, tension or compression.
3) Shear capacity as limited by the beam web.
4) Shear capacity as limited by the bolts.

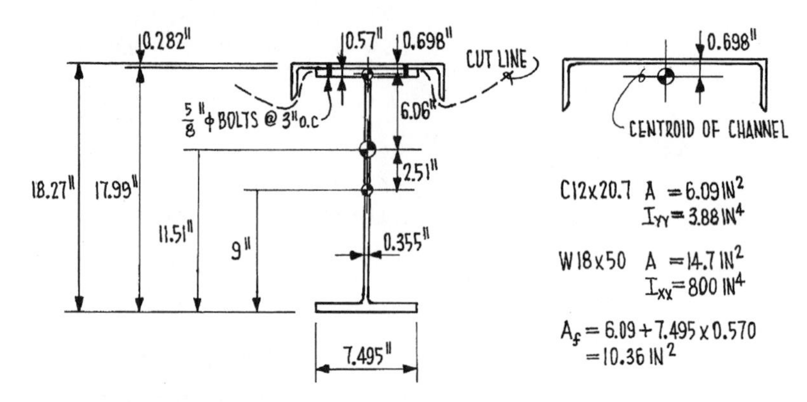

Solution: The values of L_c and L_u are found from the limits presented in Table 27-2:

$$12.67\ \text{bf} = 12.67 \times 12 = 152\ \text{in.} = 12.67\ \text{ft.}$$

$$\frac{555}{d/A_f} = \frac{555}{18.27/10.36} = 315\ \text{in.} = 26.22\ \text{ft.}$$

Use $L_c = 12.67$ ft, $L_u = 26.22$ ft

The centroid and the moment of inertia are found in the usual way. The centroid is found first:

$$\bar{y} = \frac{\Sigma AY}{\Sigma A} = \frac{14.7x9 + 6.09(18.27 - 0.698)}{14.7 + 6.09} = 11.51\ \text{in.}$$

The centroid of the combination section is thus located at a distance of 11.51 in. above the base.

The moment of inertia is found from the remote axis theorem. The centroid of the channel is seen to be displaced 6.06 in. from the centroid of the combination section. The centroid of the wide flange beam is seen to be displaced 2.51 in. from the centroid of the combination section.

$$I = \Sigma(I_o + d^2A) = (800 + 14.7x2.51^2) + (3.88 + 6.09x6.06^2)$$

$$= 893 + 228$$

$$= 1120\ \text{in.}^4$$

The maximum stress is at the tension flange, moment is therefore limited by tension:

$$M = F_b\frac{I}{C} = 0.60F_y\left(\frac{1120}{11.51}\right) = 2102\ \text{kip·in.}$$

$$M = 175\ \text{kip·ft.}$$

The shear capacity of the web is given by:

$$V = F_vA_w = 0.4F_y \times 18.27 \times 0.355 = 93 \text{ kips}$$

The shear capacity of the flange bolts is computed from the shear flow equation. The cut line is shown on the sketch. The shear flow at the two bolts is:

$$q = \frac{VA'\bar{y}}{I}$$; For $^5/_8$ in. bolts at 3 in. o.c.,

$$q = 2 \times {}^{6.4}/_3 = 4.3 \text{ k/in.}$$
$$A'\bar{y} = 6.09 \times 6.06 = 36.9 \text{ in.}^3$$
$$I = 1120 \text{ in.}^4$$

$$V = \frac{qI}{A'\bar{y}} = \frac{4.3 \times 1120}{36.9} = 130 \text{ kips.}$$

Conclusion: The limiting moment on the beam is on the tension flange. Moment is limited to 175 kip·ft and shear is limited by the capacity of the web to 93 kips. At an unsupported length of 26.22 ft., the allowable stress on the compression flange is 0.60 F_y; the actual stress will be only 12.7 kips/in.^{2}

The plate girder shown in Figure 28-2d was once a very common riveted configuration. In today's industry, the angles would likely be omitted and the three plates simply welded together. Such locally fabricated girders are often tapered, being 3 feet deep or more at midspan and 8 to 10 inches deep at the ends. Tapered steel girders are very efficient, very popular beams where long open spans are needed (for example, bowling alleys). The analysis of this bolted plate girder is given in the following example.

Example 28-3

Analysis of a combination beam.

Given: Section of Figure 28-2d. A36 steel. A325 bolts in bearing connections, threads not excluded.

To Find:
1) L_c and L_u.
2) Moment capacity for $F_b = 0.60F_y$.
3) Shear capacity of the web, with $F_v = 0.40F_y$.
4) Shear capacity as limited by the bolts.

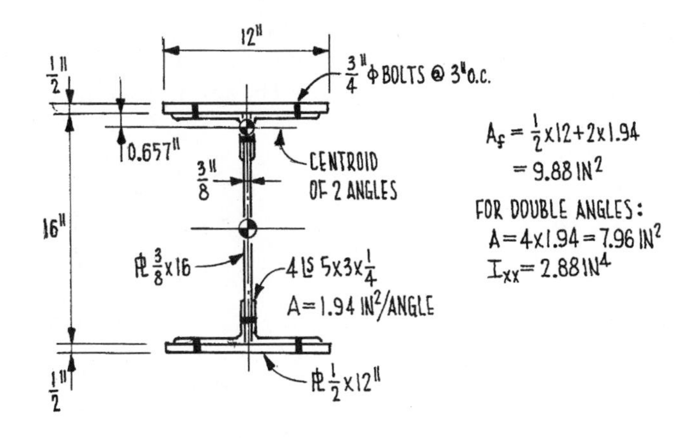

Solution: The values of L_c and L_u are found from the limits presented in Table 27-2:

$$12.67b_f = 12.67 \times 12 = 152 \text{ in.} = 12.67 \text{ ft.}$$

$$\frac{555}{d/A_f} = \frac{555}{17/9.88} = 322.6 \text{ in.} = 26.9 \text{ ft.}$$

Use $L_c = 12.67$ ft, $L_u = 26.9$ ft

The moment of inertia is found as usual:

$$I = I_{WEB} + I_{PLATES} + (I_0 + d^2A)_{ANGLES}$$

$$= \frac{3}{8} x \frac{16^3}{12} + \left(\frac{12x17^3}{12} - \frac{12x16^3}{12}\right)$$

$$+[(2.88 + (8 - 0.657)^2(2x1.94)]$$

$$= 1157 \text{ in.}^4$$

The moment capacity is found from the flexure formula:

$$M = F_bS_{xx} = 0.60F_Y \, x \frac{1157}{8.5} = 2940 \text{ kip·in.}$$

$$= 245 \text{ kip·ft}$$

The shear capacity of the web is given by:

$$V = F_vA_w = 0.4F_Y(3/8 \times 16) = 86.4 \text{ kips}$$

The shear capacity of the flange bolts is found from the shear flow equation with cut line 1 taken as shown. Bolt values are found in Table S-26 to be 9.3 kips per bolt.

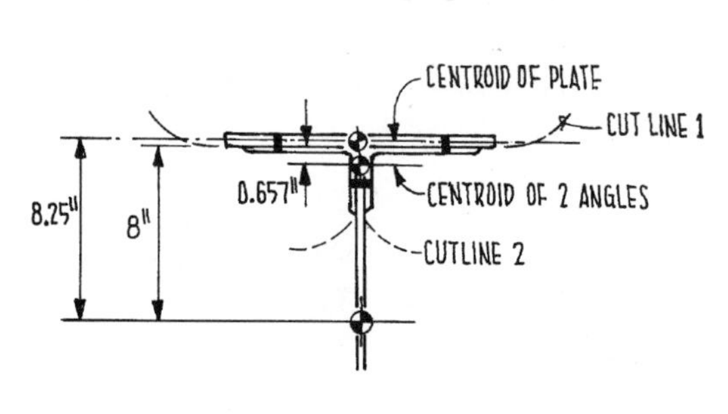

$$q = \frac{VA'\bar{y}}{I}$$

$$q = 2(9.3)/3 = 6.2 \text{ kips/in.}$$

$$A'\bar{y} = \tfrac{1}{2} \times 12 \times 8.25 = 49.5 \text{ in.}^3$$

$$I = 1157 \text{ in.}^4$$

$$V = \frac{qI}{A'\bar{y}} = \frac{6.2x1157}{49.5} = 145 \text{ kips}$$

The shear capacity of the web bolt is computed separately using cut line 2. For a 3/4 in. bolt in double shear, the bolt value is 18.6 kips per bolt:

$$q = \frac{VA'\bar{y}}{I}; \; q = 18.6/3 = 6.2 \text{ kips/in.}$$

$$A'\bar{y} = \tfrac{1}{2} x \ 12 \times 8.25 + (2 \times 1.94)(8 - 0.657)$$

$$= 78 \text{ in.}^3$$

$$I = 1157 \text{ in.}^4$$

$$V = \frac{qI}{A'\bar{y}} = \frac{6.2x1157}{78} = 92 \text{ kips}$$

The shear capacity is thus limited by the web bolt to 92 kips.

Conclusion: At a laterally unsupported length on the compression flange of 26.9 ft, the section will sustain a moment of 245 kip·ft and a shear of 92 kips.

(Increasing the size of the web bolt to 1 in. will increase the shear capacity of the section to 145 kips.)

PART 6

ENGINEERING OF TIMBER STRUCTURES

CHAPTER

29

TIMBER AS AN ENGINEERING MATERIAL

There are many who have difficulty in viewing timber as an "engineering" material in the same way they view other materials such as steel and concrete. Timber is used by carpenters, handymen, cabinetmakers and other craftsmen; it seems a stretch to call it an engineering material.

But over the centuries, timber has been used frequently to build major engineered structures, including bridges, cathedrals, tenements, and countless other applications. Many such structures (still in use) were built long before the advent of modern steel and concrete. The success of timber in such applications over the centuries has earned it a secure place in engineered construction.

In recent times, however, the use of timber has progressed from the rules of thumb and empirical formulas used in centuries past to the rigorous stress and strain calculations of today's engineering. In engineered construction, timber must sustain its loads in configurations never envisioned in earlier centuries. In such unique applications, the strength of commercially available timber is expected to be predictable, consistent and dependable.

It is the purpose of this chapter to show the means by which allowable stress levels are established for structural timber, and how the designer conforms these allowable stress levels to a particular project. It will be seen that there are many variables, any one of which can affect in some way the use of the timber member. Necessarily, there is much attention to detail in using stress-rated timber; the failure modes in timber are more numerous than they are in steel and concrete.

The design code for wood construction has been developed by the American Forest and Paper Association. The code is titled "National Design Specification for Wood Construction" and is the base document on which essentially all stress calculations are based. The code is discussed further in Section 29.6 of this chapter. For brevity, the code is referenced hereafter as the National Design Specification.

Much of the progress that has been made in bringing timber into its presently accepted place as an engineering material can be attributed to the timber industry itself. Through private associations of industries that log, mill, manufacture and market timber products, the necessary engineering criteria has been funded, initiated and developed. Probably the best known of these associations is the American Institute of Timber Construction (AITC).

The *Timber Construction Manual*, published by AITC, is one of the most prominent of all publications in timber engineering. The manual summarizes and expands the design standards, design practices and corresponding engineering stress values for more than 40 species of timber. The manual also includes authoritative guidelines in using timber as a structural material, as well as numerous design aids and recommended design procedures. AITC and the *Timber Construction Manual* are referenced frequently in succeeding discussions.

It is presumed in the following presentations that the student has taken the basic course work in engineering materials, which would include an introduction to wood as a construction material. Such an introductory course would include the cellular composition of timber as well as the formation of grain, knots and defects. Those who have not yet taken their coursework in construction materials are advised to obtain a textbook in engineering materials and read the material on wood before proceeding further.

29.1 Background Information

Some definitions are in order before specific discussions can be undertaken:

- Wood is the material from which lumber and timber are manufactured.
- The thickness of a wood member is its least dimension.
- The width of a wood member is its larger dimension.
- *Lumber* is wood members whose thickness is less than 5 inches; widths may be as wide as 16 inches.
- *Timber* is wood members whose thickness is 5 inches or more; widths may be as wide as several feet.

The terms lumber and timber are often used interchangeably, if incorrectly. The term timber is often loosely applied as a generic term to describe all stress-rated wood products; that practice is generally followed in this textbook.

The symbols and notations used in timber engineering are far from being standardized. The most consistent set of symbols is the set of basic symbols introduced in the National Design Specification and expanded further in the AITC *Timber Construction Manual*. Because of their growing acceptance, the AITC symbols are used throughout this textbook; the symbols are listed in Appendix T in the Technical Manual for continuing reference.

Further, the terms used in the AITC manual are used here just as the manual uses them. Such terms include "edgewise," flatwise" and other such unusual words.

Succeeding discussions in this chapter will occasionally include *glued laminated timber*, an innovation in timber manufacturing that is rapidly expanding. Glued laminated timbers, called *glulams* in the industry, have been used for decades on the Pacific Coast and are now coming into wide use in other areas. A typical glulam beam is shown in Figure 29-1.

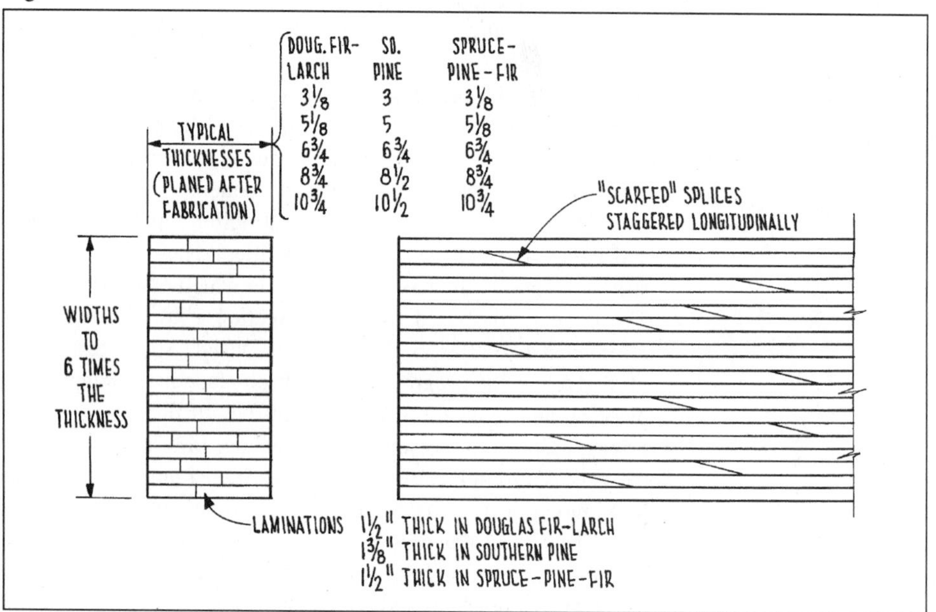

Figure 29-1 Typical glued laminated beam.

The manufacture of glulam beams permits very large timber sections to be produced when only small trees are available. The beams can be fabricated straight, cambered, curved or tapered. Glulams are by their nature large timbers and as such are used primarily in heavy timber construction, which is beyond the scope of this book. This brief description is included here only for the sake of immediate discussions.

One of the most important items of emphasis in the study of timber is that of moisture content. As a general comparison, moisture content is to wood what water/cement ratio is to concrete and what carbon content is to steel. Moisture content is the single most important factor that affects strength of wood.

Moisture content is the weight of water per unit weight of wood, expressed as a percentage. It compares the weight of the water in the wood to the weight of the wood itself. A moisture content of 100%, for example, means that the water in the wood weighs as much as the wood itself weighs.

Wood is an open cellular material. The open cells may contain free water in various amounts. In addition to the free water in the cell cavity, the wood fiber itself (cellulose) also contains natural water, bound in the wood as a part of the wood fiber.

The free water in the cells can increase or decrease without causing shrinkage or swell in the wood. When all of the cells are completely filled with free water, the wood is said to be saturated. When all of the free water is removed (by drying), with the only remaining water being that bound up in the wood fibers, the moisture content is at the *fiber saturation point*. The moisture content at the fiber saturation point is typically about 25% to 30%.

When the wood is dried below its fiber saturation point, it undergoes shrinkage. At that point there is no more free water and the natural moisture in the wood fibers is being driven off. If water is later restored, the wood will swell as the wood fibers regain their moisture.

A living softwood tree standing in the forest will have a moisture content in the order of 35% to 50%. To deter bacterial decay after cutting, the log is kept saturated with water (by spray or mill pond) while awaiting processing at the mill. (Decay bacteria must have both air and water; when either air or water is excluded from the cells, the bacterial decay ceases.)

When processing begins, the log is sawn at roughly its saturation point. Immediately after being sawn, the rough-sawn lumber is stacked and dried, either by air drying or by kiln drying, to bring its moisture content down to 19% or below. At a moisture content at or below 19%, bacterial decay is negligible; after being dried, the sawn lumber is no longer susceptible to bacterial decay.

After it has been dried, the rough sawn lumber is usually surfaced (planed), both to produce a smooth surface and to produce a uniform size. In some mills, surfacing may be done before drying is done, in which case the members are "surfaced green." Heavy structural timbers, however, are frequently used in their rough sawn condition without being surfaced at all.

Though the wood is safe from bacterial decay if the moisture content is kept below 19%, it is preferable to bring the moisture content on down to 15%. To do so takes time and money. Lumber whose moisture content has been reduced to 15% or less is stamped "*KD*." Lumber stamped *KD* costs more.

As moisture content decreases below 19%, the strength of the material increases. When a service moisture content of 15% or less can be assured, the design codes permit a distinct increase in allowable stresses. In the National Design Specification, the dividing line between "dry" service conditions and "wet" service conditions is 19% moisture. The distinction is important wherever allowable stresses are being established.

The structural lumber and timber in a dry building eventually stabilizes at a moisture content around 12%. Moisture content varies, of course, as atmospheric humidity varies, but as long as it is kept low, the wood is not subject to bacterial decay. There are many timber buildings in the world more than 300 years old whose wood members are still in good condition.

If the moisture content in structural lumber or timber is allowed to increase above 19%, either by weather or by service conditions, the wood will again be subject to bacterial decay. The decay might even be intermittent if the moisture content happens to vary above and below 19%. Such decay is common in the fascia pieces around the eaves of a roof, where the timber is intermittently subject to wetting and drying.

29.2 Establishment of Basic Allowable Stresses

The allowable stress in every piece of manufactured lumber and timber is established by grading that piece of lumber or timber as it is processed. Every individual piece is examined visually by a professional grader who works from a fixed set of grading rules. Each piece is given a visual grade, such as select structural, construction, No. 2, utility, etc. Each piece is then stamped with its grade, the grading rules by which it was graded and the mill that processed and graded it.

Those who grade the lumber do so entirely from visual grading rules. The visual grading rules in turn are established by associations of manufacturers whose purpose is to set and maintain uniform standards of strength and quality (and appearance) in their industry. The grading rules, and adherence to them, are critical to their success in marketing their product in a highly competitive industry.

Typical of the associations which establish and maintain grading rules are:

- Western Wood Products Association (WWPA), an association of industrial concerns in the Pacific Northwest. WWPA is influential in setting and maintaining standards in the Douglas fir-larch industry (among others).
- Southern Pine Inspection Bureau (SPIB), an association of industrial concerns in the American Southeast. SPIB is concerned with a rapidly expanding lumber industry in various varieties of Southern pine.
- Western Spruce-Pine-Fir Association, an association of industrial concerns in Western Canada. Their grading rules are maintained by the National Lumber Grades Authority (NLGA) of Canada, which are accepted by agencies in the United States. Their market area includes much of the Northern United States.

The foregoing three organizations are only a few of the many such organizations in the U.S. and Canada. They are three of the larger and more prominent ones, however, and are the ones cited in this textbook. The grades established by these associations are typical of those found throughout the industry. Further, these associations account for a very large percentage of the lumber sold in the United States.

The visual grading of timber is included in coursework in construction materials and is not repeated here. As a general summary, the grade of a wood member depends on the number of visible flaws it has. Flaws can include knots, checks, pitch pockets, bark lines and other such visible imperfections. As the humber of flaws increases, the grade of the piece of timber decreases.

The lumber grader is not concerned with stresses; the grader only gives the lumber a visual grade. The allowable stresses permitted in a particular visual grade is established independently by the trade associations from extensive full-scale destructive tests. Such tests have been conducted over many years (and are still being conducted) in practically all species of commercial timber. The allowable stresses so obtained for three of our most common classifications are given in the tables in the Technical Manual.

- Douglas Fir-Larch, Table T-3a, AWWA Grading Rules.
- Southern Pine, Table T-3b, SPIB Grading Rules.
- Spruce-Pine-Fir, Table T-3c, NLGA Grading Rules.

The tables in the Technical Manual list only three species of timber, even though more than 40 species have been similarly graded and which are used routinely in modern construction. The reduction in this textbook from 40 species to 3 of the more common species is done simply as a means to reduce volume. Succeeding discussions will apply to all species, but for the sake of simplicity, the problems and examples will be limited to the 3 species listed: Douglas fir-larch, Southern pine and Spruce-pine-fir.

The stresses listed in Tables T-3a, b and c are extracted from the National Design Specification. Deliberately, the upper limit for dry service conditions (19% moisture content) was chosen for these tables. In general, the allowable stresses listed in the tables will be on the safe side for less severe service conditions.

Grading rules are not all alike, that is, some grading rules include grades that other grading rules do not. Descriptions of some of the more common of these classifications are given in Table T-2. The reason for such variations lies in the species themselves; some lend themselves to specialized grades, some do not.

Examination of Tables 3a, b and c in the Technical Manual reveals that a rather extensive assortment of factors and conditions must be determined before the allowable stress can be established. Some of the more prominent of these factors are included in the following list.

- Species of wood from which the timber was made.
- Visual grade (and grading rules) of the individual pieces of timber.
- Moisture content at time of processing and at time of use.
- Type of stress, whether flexure, tension, shear or compression.
- Orientation of direction of stress to direction of grain.
- Conditions of use, whether an isolated member or as one member in a group (such as closely spaced floor joists).
- Size of the member in its least dimension.

The listed factors do indeed affect the allowable stress but they are not the only factors. Others include such things as duration of load, lateral support along the compression edge, curvature, temperature and others. The allowable stresses shown in Tables T-3a, b and c are the basic allowable stresses under standard conditions of use.

Standard or normal conditions of use are presented in the next section. If the timber is used under conditions significantly at variance with the standard conditions, the allowable stresses must be adjusted accordingly; adjustment factors are also included in the next section.

The orientation of load relative to the direction of grain is a new consideration in the discussions of this textbook; it was not encountered in concrete or steel. Some typical examples of such orientation are shown in Figure 29-2.

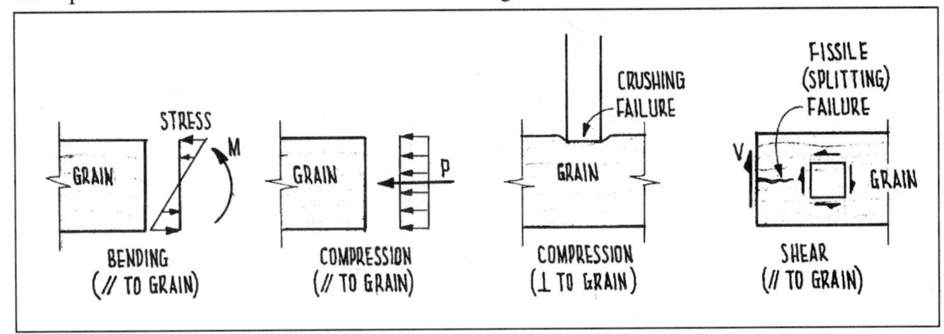

Figure 29-2 Orientation of load to direction of grain.

With one exception, the standard conditions of use in Tables T-3a, b and c are broad enough that further adjustment is only occasionally necessary. The exception is that of duration of load. For short-term loads, less than about 2 months, a significant increase in allowable stress is permitted. Such an increase (up to 15%) is well worth considering in the design of construction falsework and formwork that will typically have a service life less than 2 months.

29.3 Modifications to Basic Tabular Stresses

The allowable design stress in sawn lumber and timber is found by applying adjustment factors to the basic allowable stresses as indicated in the following equations. The basic allowable stresses are those given in Tables T-3a, b and c.

Bending	$F_b' = F_bC_DC_FC_LC_MC_fC_tC_{fu}$	(29-1)
Tension parallel to grain	$F_t' = F_tC_DC_MC_tC_F$	(29-2)
Compression parallel to grain	$F_c' = F_CC_DC_PC_MC_fC_F$	(29-3)
Compression perpendicular to grain	$F_{c\perp}' = F_{c\perp}C_MC_bC_t$	(29-4)
Shear parallel to grain	$F_v' = F_vC_DC_MC_tC_H$	(29-5)
End grain in bearing	$F_g' = F_gC_DC_t$	(29-6)
Modulus of elasticity	$E' = EC_MC_t$	(29-7)

where F_b, F_t, F_c, $F_{C\perp}$, F_v and E are the basic tabular values given in Tables T-3a, b, and c.

C_D is the factor for duration of load
C_F is the factor for size of deep beams.
C_L is the factor for lateral stability of long beams.
C_H is the factor for shear stress in beams
C_M is the factor for moisture content of the wood.
C_P is the factor for lateral stability of columns.
C_b is the factor for end bearing
C_f is the factor for form or shape (round, oval, diamond, etc.)
C_t is the factor for high service temperatures
C_{fu} is the factor for flatwise use of a member as a beam

Equations (29-1) through (29-7) are a formidable looking list. As noted earlier, however, the service conditions assumed for the basic stress are broad enough that the adjustment factors are only occasionally needed. In many, if not most cases, the basic stresses of Tables T-3a, b and c will be applicable without adjustment.

For those cases where the service conditions are extreme (or where service conditions are exceptionally good), the adjustment factors apply. It should be noted, however, that not all factors apply to all stresses. For example, only two factors can ever apply to compression perpendicular to grain while seven factors can apply to bending. A summary of the applicability of the adjustment factors is given in Table 29-1.

Table 29-1 Applicability of Adjustment Factors

	Design Value					
Adjustment Factor	F_b	F_t	F_c	$F_{c\perp}$	F_v	E
Duration of load, C_D	Yes	Yes	Yes	No	Yes	No
Size, C_F	Yes	Yes	No	No	No	No
Shear stress, C_H	No	No	No	No	Yes	No
Beam stability, C_L	Yes	No	No	No	No	No
Moisture content, C_M	Yes	Yes	Yes	Yes	Yes	Yes
Column stability, C_P	No	No	Yes	No	No	No
End bearing, C_b	No	No	No	Yes	No	No
Form, C_f	Yes	No	No	No	No	No
Flat use, C_{fu}	Yes	No	No	No	No	No
Temperature, C_t	Yes	Yes	Yes	Yes	Yes	Yes

[a]Source: National Design Specification for Wood Construction

The adjustment factors listed in this section apply to the values of stress given in Tables 3a, b and c. For other species of wood the tables of the National Design Specification should be consulted. In its discussion of the tables for allowable stress, the manual gives the applicable adjustment factors as they apply to particular species over a wide variety of manufacturing and service conditions.

Not all of the adjustment factors produce a reduction in allowable stress. Some permit an increase in allowable stress when the actual service condition is better than the assumed normal condition of service. Failure to take advantage of such increases can, in some cases, result in a significant increase in cost.

Load duration factor C_D reflects the remarkable toughness of timber under short-term loading and the susceptibility of timber to creep under high sustained loading. The variation in C_D is shown graphically in Table T-4 in the Technical Manual, reprinted below for immediate reference. For short-term values of load, C_D may be scaled from the graph.

- Normal load duration for tabulated stresses is 10 years; $C_D = 1.00$.
- Where 100% of the load is permanent load, $C_D = 0.90$.
- For impact loading of 2 second or less, $C_D = 2.00$.
- Where wind and earthquake are included with dead load and live load, $C_D = 1.60$.
- Where load is sustained for seven days or less, $C_D = 1.25$.
- Where snow load of two months or less is included with dead load and live load, $C_D = 1.15$.

Table T-4 Load Duration Factors C_D

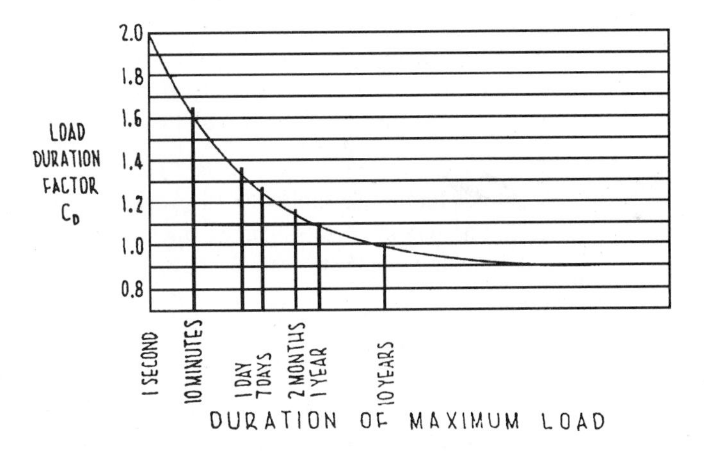

Size or depth factor C_F reflects the effects of creep in deep, narrow sections in bending. Note in Table 29-1 that C_F applies only to beams.

For lumber (thicknesses 4 inches and less) the size factor C_F has been included in the stresses of Tables 3a, b and c. For timber (thicknesses 5 inches and more), the factor must be applied to all stresses listed for beams and stringers having a bending depth greater than 12 inches.

For all lumber and timber sizes, when bending depths are 12 inches or more, the depth factor is given as:

$$C_F = \left(\frac{12}{d}\right)^{\frac{1}{9}} \tag{29-7}$$

For bending depths d = 12 in. to 24 in., the values of C_F computed from Equation (29-7) are given for convenience in the following tabulation:

Bending depth in inches	12	14	16	18	20	22	24
Value of C_F	1.00	0.98	0.97	0.96	0.95	0.94	0.93

The reduction in allowable stress is seen not to be a severe one.

For beams of circular cross section having a diameter greater than 13.5 inches, C_F is determined for an equivalent square beam having the same cross sectional area as the circular section.

Shear stress factor C_H reflects conditions in which it is known that splits, checks and shakes definitely will not undergo increase in the service life of a member. It permits an increase in the allowable shear stress parallel to grain. Its applicability in practice is somewhat uncertain; values of C_H are given in the National Design Specification along with a description of cases where it is to be applied. It is not included in the succeeding discussions of this textbook.

Beam stability factor C_L reflects the effects of buckling of the compression edge of beams under high stress. Note in Table 29-1 that C_L applies only to bending stress.

- For beams whose compressive edge is continuously supported, $C_L = 1.00$.
- Approximate methods to establish the maximum allowable distance between lateral supports are prescribed in the National Design Specifications. When these requirements for lateral support are met, $C_L = 1.00$. These approximate methods are presented in Chapter 32 of this textbook with other beam design criteria; these provisions are included in Table T-14 in the Technical Manual.
- For beams having considerable distance between lateral supports, the calculation of C_L using exact methods becomes quite complex; these exact methods are given in considerable detail in the AITC Timber Construction Manual.

Wet service factor C_M reflects the loss in strength and rigidity of timber when the moisture content exceeds 19%. The wet service factor C_M is the most widely applicable and the most dominant of all the modifiers; it applies to stresses as well as to the modulus of elasticity.

Values of the wet service factor C_M are specified for all species of timber in the National Design Specification. They are given there in the footnotes accompanying the tables of allowable stresses. For the three species considered in this textbook, the following values of C_M apply.

- For lumber or timber at 19% moisture content or less, $C_M = 1.00$.
- For lumber 2 to 4 inches thick and used for extended periods at a moisture content greater than 19%, the values of C_M are given in the following tabulation.

Values of C_M for Indicated Stresses

	F_b	F_t	F_v	$F_{c\perp}$	F_c	E
Douglas fir-larch	0.85[a]	1.00	0.97	0.67	0.80[b]	0.90
Southern pine	0.85[a]	1.00	0.97	0.67	0.80[c]	0.90
Spruce-pine-fir	0.85[a]	1.00	0.97	0.67	0.80[b]	0.90

[a]when $(F_b)(C_F) \leq 1150$ psi, $C_M = 1.0$
[b]when $(F_b)(C_F) \leq 750$ psi, $C_M = 1.0$
[c]when $(F_b) \leq 750$ psi, $C_M = 1.0$

- For timber 5 inches thick or thicker and used for extended periods at a moisture content greater than 19%, the values of C_M are given in the following tabulation.

Values of C_M for Indicated Stresses

	F_b	F_t	F_V	$F_{c\perp}$	F_C	E
Douglas fir-larch	1.00	1.00	1.00	0.67	0.91	1.00
Southern pine	1.00	1.00	1.00	1.00	1.00	1.00
Spruce-pine-fir	1.00	1.00	1.00	0.67	0.91	1.00

The foregoing values of C_M are included in Tables T-3a, b and c in the Technical Manual, as a footnote following the stress values.

Column stability factor C_P is applied to intermediate length columns as an integral part of the new single-range column formula. Note in Table 29-1 that C_P applies only to columns.

End bearing factor C_b permits an increase in stress perpendicular to grain at the ends of beams. For end bearings less than 6 inches in length and not closer than 3 inches from the end of the member, the tabulated stress may be multiplied by the factor C_b, where:

$$C_b = \frac{\text{length of bearing parallel to grain} + 0.375}{\text{length of bearing parallel to grain}}$$

Form factor C_f reflects the effects of cross sectional shape of a flexural member on the allowable stress. It is applied independently of the size and depth factor C_F.

- For circular shapes, $C_f = 1.18$.
- For square shapes loaded in the plane of the diagonal, $C_f = 1.414$.
- For rectangular beams loaded in the plane of their axes, $C_f = 1.00$.

Flat use factor C_{fu} reflects the higher stress capacity of a member when it is used in its flat position rather than its upright position. It permits an increase in the allowable bending stress F_b; it may be used concurrently with size factor C_F. Values of the flat use factor for various widths of sawn lumber are given in the following tabulation.

Table 29-2 Flat Use Factor C_{fu}[a]

Width of Member	Thickness of Member: 2 in. or 3 in.	Thickness of Member: 4 in.
2 in. and 3 in.	1.0	—
4 in.	1.1	1.0
5 in.	1.1	1.05
6 in.	1.15	1.05
8 in.	1.15	1.05
10 in. and wider	1.2	1.1

[a]Source: National Design Specification for Wood Construction

The flat use factor C_{fu} may not be applied to timber members (those having a least dimension of 5 inches or more).

Temperature factor C_t reflects the effects of service temperatures on the strength of timber. Wood loses strength as temperatures increase above room temperature and gains strength as temperatures decrease below room temperature. For service temperatures under ordinary conditions with short exposures up to 150°F, the stresses listed in Tables T-3a, b and c are commonly used without adjustment. For long-term exposure to temperatures approaching 150°F or more, adjustment values of C_t are given in the National Design Specification or the AITC manual.

At this point it is well to note the symbols used in denoting the allowable design stresses. As indicated in Equations (29-1) through (29-6), the basic *tabular* stresses are given without a superscript, that is, F_b, Ft, F_c, $F_{c\perp}$, F_v and E. After all modifiers have been applied, the *allowable* stress is denoted by a prime superscript, that is, F_b', F_t', F_c', $F_{c\perp}'$, F_v' and E'.

The allowable stress F_b' and the tabular stress F_b must always be regarded as a pair, connected by the appropriate modifiers. The tabular stress F_b is *not* an allowable design stress and should not be regarded as such. The distinction and bond between the two stresses is repeatedly observed throughout the remaining discussions of timber.

29.4 Stress at an Angle to Grain

The tabular design stresses given in Tables 3a, b and c include design stresses parallel to grain and perpendicular to grain. They do not include the design stress at some angle to grain, however, such as the notched member shown in Figure 29-3. Design values at an angle to grain must be computed separately.

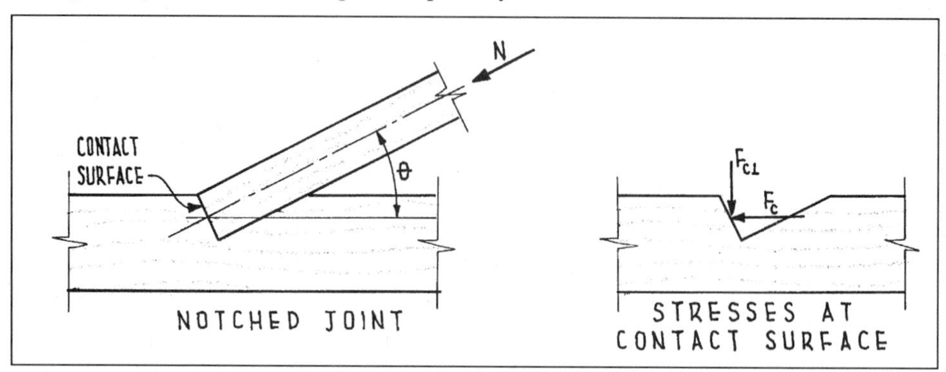

Figure 29-3 Wood loaded at an angle to grain.

Note that the angled member in Figure 29-3 is loaded parallel to grain. The design value for the angled member is simply the value of F_c given in the tables. At the contact surface, however, the horizontal member has two components of load, one parallel to grain and one perpendicular to grain; a design value somewhere between F_c and $F_{c\perp}$ is obviously needed.

Note that the difference between F_c and $F_{c\perp}$ in the tables is significant. F_c can be as much as 50% greater than $F_{c\perp}$, or even more. It would be unnecessarily conservative simply to use the smaller value and let it go at that. An interpolated value somewhere between $F_{c\perp}$ and F_c is more appropriate.

The design value of stress at an angle to grain is given by the Hankinson formula:

$$F_n = \frac{F_c F_{c\perp}}{F_c \sin^2\theta + F_{c\perp}\cos^2\theta} \tag{29-9}$$

where F_n is the design value at the angle θ to grain.
F_c is the tabular design value parallel to grain.
$F_{c\perp}$ is the tabular design value perpendicular to grain.
θ is the angle to grain (or, the angle between F_n and F_c).

There are numerous graphs and design aids built around the Hankinson formula. They are rarely worth becoming familiar with. The computation is so straightforward and the need so rare that it is invariably easier to evaluate the Hankinson formula than to use the graphs.

The Hankinson formula is used throughout design in wood whenever the load occurs at an angle to grain. It is also used when bolted connections produce a load at an angle to grain; bolt values must be modified to suit the angle of load. It is well worthwhile to commit the Hankinson formula to memory.

29.5 Dimensions of Sawn Lumber and Timber

Lumber and timber are sawn to even dimensions in inches; a 4x8, for example, is sawn 4 in. x 8 in. At the time it is sawn, however, it is very close to being 100% saturated with water. Immediately after being sawn, it is dried to a moisture content less than 19%. In drying, it shrinks to a size somewhat smaller than 4 in. x 8 in.

After being dried, the 4 x 8 is planed in order to produce a smooth surface and a uniform size. Planing reduces the size even further. After all the drying and processing is over, the original 4 x 8 is reduced to an actual size of $3^1/_2$ in. x $7^1/_4$ in. Nonetheless, it is still called a 4 x 8.

The physical properties of the section are of course based on the actual dimensions of the section, not on nominal dimensions. There are rules for remembering these actual dimensions for all the various sizes of timber, but they are rarely worth learning. Rather, tables of the physical properties are prepared and included in practically all design manuals.

Such a table of physical properties is given in the Technical Manual as Table T-1. The nominal size and the actual size of each standard piece of lumber or timber is given in the table, followed by the physical properties of section. Properties include area, moment of inertia, section modulus and radius of gyration.

For convenience, the table lists the physical properties with the member oriented both in its edgewise (tall) position and in its flatwise position. Such a feature in the table will be found useful in beam design when reactions are high and bearings are small.

For example, a 4 x 8 is listed with the members that are nominally 4 inches in size. It is listed again, however, as an 8 x 4, with members that are nominally 8 inches in size. The section properties in both orientations are thus immediately available.

29.6 Design Codes and Design Practices

The fundamental design information to which all other codes and specifications eventually refer is the National Design Specification for Wood Construction (NDS). The National Design Specification was first issued in 1944 by the National Lumber Manufacturers Association (NLMA). The name of NLMA was later changed to the National Forest Products Association (NFPA), which has recently (1991) been changed again to the American Forest and Paper Association (AFPA). Depending on the age of a particular specification, one may see the design specification of any of these organizations referenced, but the reference is to the same National Design Specification for Wood Construction.

The National Design Specification is exactly that: a specification. It lists without explanation a multitude of allowable stresses and loads under a wide variety of conditions. It is not a textbook nor is it a manual; it is a specification. It is available at modest cost from AFPA in Washington, D.C.

The National Design Specification is intended for use by those who are familiar with wood construction. Nonetheless, it is strongly recommended that anyone interested in entering a career involving wood construction obtain a personal copy of the specification with the intent to become fully familiar with it over the years. When a particular provision requires intensive study, a marginal note will save time several months or years hence when the provision is encountered again.

After the National Design Specification, probably the next best-known publication in wood construction is the AITC manual, already described in earlier discussions. The manual presents much of the commonly used data in the National Design Specification in a more palatable form. Necessarily, the AITC manual frequently references the National Design Specification.

The municipal building codes also contain design information and minimum standards for wood construction. It should be recalled that a building code has the force of law within its jurisdiction. When a provision of the National Design Specification is less stringent than a provision of the municipal building code, the building code governs. (In the event there is ambiguity between the National Design Specification and the municipal building code, the prudent designer will provide for the more stringent case).

The Standard Building Code, for example, references the National Design Specification for stress and load, thereby incorporating the National Design Specification bodily into the building code. To this, the Standard Building Code adds additional provisions. Among other things, the additional provisions include more stringent protection from bacterial decay and termites, a serious problem in the American Southeast.

Unlike the Standard Building Code, the Uniform Building Code (UBC) adopts only parts of the National Design Specification as a part of the code (rather than the entire

Specification). The UBC goes on to present a rather broad design specification within the body of the code. Many of the UBC provisions are those of the National Design Specification,, but many are not. The UBC sometimes abridges (and sometimes simplifies) the provisions of the Specification.

Probably the most useful feature of the UBC is the numerous design tables given with Chapter 25, the chapter of the code that prescribes the design of wood structures. A few of those tables are reproduced in the Technical Manual of this textbook with permission of the publishers, the International Conference of Building Officials. The emphasis in these additional provisions is in earthquake resistant design, a prime consideration in the American West where the UBC is most popular.

In the discussions of the following chapters, the provisions of the National Design Specification will generally be followed. Where an abridgement or a simplification from a building code is used, it will be so stated in the text.

Review Questions

1. What is the difference between boards, lumber and timber?
2. When a timber beam is standing in its tall edgewise position, which dimension is its width?
3. When a timber beam is lying in its flatwise position, which dimension is its thickness?
4. What is a glulam beam?
5. How wide is a glulam beam fabricated from 2x4 lumber?
6. Define moisture content in wood.
7. What is meant by free water in wood?
8. What happens when wood is dried so much it starts to lose water from its own fibers?
9. What is the fiber saturation point?
10. What moisture content might be expected at the fiber saturation point?
11. What is meant when it is said that wood is saturated?
12. What is meant by the term "surfaced green"?
13. Why are logs kept saturated while awaiting processing?
14. What does it mean when lumber is stamped *KD*?
15. Below what moisture content does bacterial decay cease?
16. If drying the lumber is done to prevent bacterial decay, what purpose is served in keeping the logs saturated before sawing?
17. What moisture content can be expected in a living softwood tree?
18. What moisture content can be expected in lumber after several years in a dry building?
19. How are the allowable stresses in timber established?
20. Who establishes grading rules?
21. How is it that some grading rules have used classifications that other grading rules do not have?
22. What is meant by a usage classification of J&P?
23. How can the allowable stress in a piece of timber be set by a grader who just examines it visually?
24. How many basic design stresses are listed in the AITC tabular design values?
25. List four factors that affected the choice of the allowable stresses in the AITC tabular design valaues.
26. In what type of stress is timber weakest?
27. In what type of loading would there be high stresses perpendicular to the grain?
28. Having the AITC tabular design stress for bending, F_b, how does the designer come up with the usable value of stress for his design problem?
29. List five of the adjustment factors for stresses and give the reason for their use.

30. What is the normal term of loading for timber without having to apply a stress reduction?
31. What is the allowable increase in stress for timber when wind and earthquake are included?
32. In beams having a bending depth d, is a stress reduction required above that bending depth?
33. For beams, are the size factors for flatwise use greater or less than those for edgewise use?
34. Where could one find a complete listing of the wet service factors for service conditions?
35. What adjustment factors would apply to the allowable stress in bending for a round pole?
36. At what temperature is the temperature factor $C_t = 1$?
37. What is the maximum allowable service temperature for wood?
38. What reduction in allowable stress must be applied at the maximum service temperature?
39. To which of the basic tabular stresses does the temperature factor C_t apply?
40. What is the actual size of a 14x4? A 10x12? A 2x8?
41. What is the NDS?

CHAPTER

30

Timber Tension Members and Their Connections

Tension members in timber are quite common. Probably the most common use of tension members is in trusses, in which roughly half the members will be in tension at any one time. Other uses include bracing members of all kinds, hangers for suspended floors (mezzanines) and various type of chords for arches or three-hinged arches.

The members presented in this chapter are subject only to tension. Moment and shear are presented in later chapters. The load system is thus reduced to a tensile force having its line of action at the centroid of the timber cross section.

The design of tension members is quite direct. It is included here in a separate chapter primarily in order that timber connections can be introduced. With such an uncluttered load system, the study of connections can be concentrated without being diffused into an assortment of load systems.

30.1 Load Capacity of Tension Members

Finding the load capacity of a timber tension member directly parallels that of finding the load capacity of a steel tension member. The capacity of the member at some distance away from the end connections (on the shank) is found first. Then the capacity of the member at its connections (on the net areas) is found. The smallest of these capacities is of course the limiting, or allowable, load.

On the shank of a tension member, the allowable load is given by the formula for direct stress:

$$F_t' = \frac{P_t}{A} \qquad (30\text{-}1)$$

$$\text{or } P = F_t' A$$

where P_t, is the allowable load in lbs or kips,
F_t is the allowable tensile stress in psi or ksi,
A is the cross sectional area.

The allowable tensile stress F_t' is that given earlier by Eq.(29-2).

$$F_t' = F_t C_D C_F C_M C_t \qquad (29\text{-}2)$$

where F_t is the basic tabular tensile stress given in Tables T-3a, b and c,
C_D is the factor for duration of load.
C_M is the factor for moisture content.
C_F is the factor fot size of member.
C_t is the factor for elevated temperature.

The net area at a bolted connection is the gross area less any holes, sawn recesses, notches or other reductions. Unlike steel, which has a further reduction in net area for the number of fasteners in a line, there are no further reductions in the tension member for uneven load concentrations (though there is a modifier C_g to be applied to the fastener capacities).

The bolt holes in a timber connection are normally drilled 1/16 in. oversize to allow easy insertion of the bolt. It is commonly assumed that there will be some fiber damage immediately surrounding the drilled hole, so the total hole size is commonly taken as the bolt diameter plus 1/8 inch. This practice is seen to be identical to that in steel connections.

Some examples will demonstrate the use of Eq.(29-2) in finding the capacity of a tension member.

Example 30-1

Determination of the capacity of a wood tension member.

Given: Lower truss chord OM in 10 kips tension, 2 - 2x8 members, No. 2 Douglas fir-larch, duration of load more than 10 years, moisture less than 19%.

To Find: Capacity of the chord at some distance from any connections.

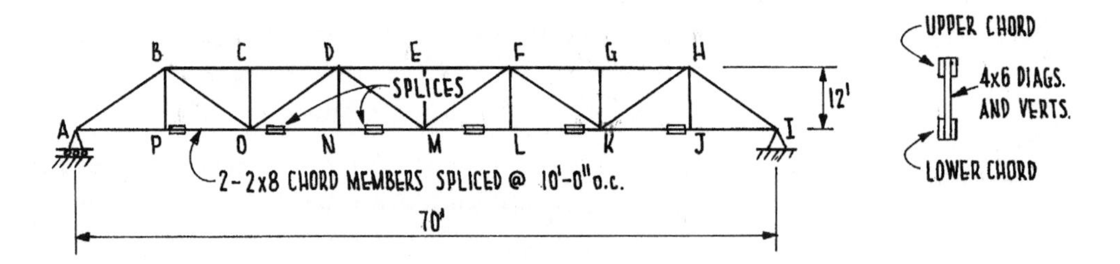

Solution: The allowable load is given by:

$$P = F_t' A_{NET}$$

Establish the adjustment factors:

No special conditions; all factors are 1.0.

Determine the allowable stress F_t':

$$F_t' = F_t C_D C_M$$

From Table T-3a for Douglas fir-larch, $F_t' = 690$ psi.

$$F_t' = 690(1.0)(1.0) = 690 \text{ psi.}$$

Determine the capacity of the member on its gross area:

From Table T-1, cross sectional area of a 2x8 is 10.9 in.^{2},

$$\text{Capacity } P = F_t' A = 690(2\times10.9) = 15{,}040 \text{ lb.}$$

$$\text{Capacity } P = 15.04 \text{ kips} > 10 \text{ kips actual load}$$

Conclude: Capacity of gross area is adequate.

Example 30-2

Determination of the capacity of a wood tension member.

Given: Truss of Example 30-1. Splice in lower chord as shown in the sketch.

To Find: Capacity of the lower chord at the connection.

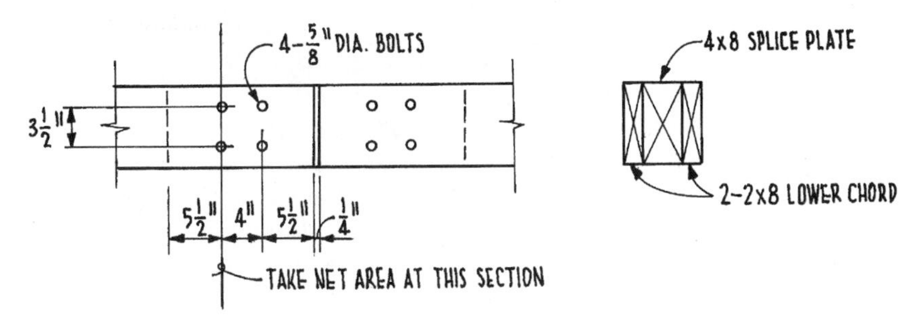

Solution: The allowable load is given by:

$$P = F_t A_{NET}$$

Establish the adjustment factors and the allowable stress F_t':

The allowable stress is unchanged from Example 30-1:

$$F_t = 690 \text{ psi for both the 2x8 and 4x8.}$$

Calculate the net area of the main member. From Table T-2, the gross area is found to be 10.9 in.^{2} for 1 - 2x8:

$$A_{NET} = 4(10.9) - 4\left(\frac{5}{8} + \frac{1}{8}\right)\left(1\frac{1}{2}\right) = 17.3 \text{ in.}^2$$

Calculate the capacity of the main member on its net area:

$$\text{Capacity } P = F_t' A_{NET} = 690(17.3)$$
$$= 11.9 \text{ kips} \geq 10.0 \text{ kips.}$$

Conclude: Capacity of net area is adequate.

30.2 Nailed Connections in Tension Members

Nailed connections are probably less common in structural timber than are bolted connections. Even so, nailed connections are frequently used in the J&P sizes in light-to-medium construction projects. It is doubtful that nailed connections would be used very much in heavy construction.

Typical types of wire nails are shown in Figure 30-2. The four types of wire nails considered by National Design Specifications are:

1. Common nails
2. Box nails
3. Common spikes
4. Threaded hardened steel nails.

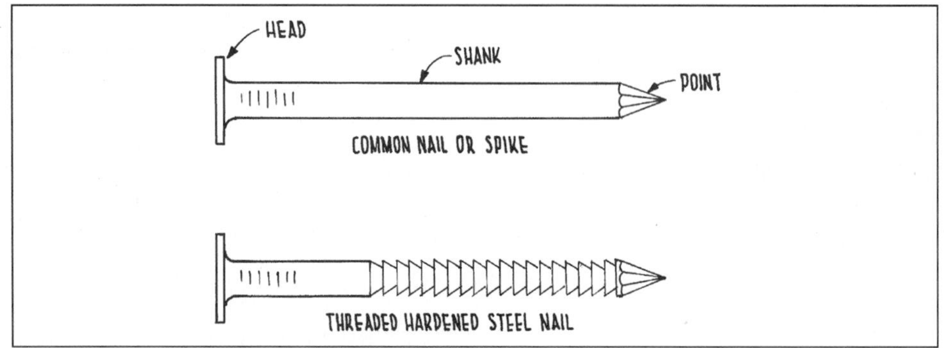

Figure 30-1 Typical nail nomenclature.

The sizes of the various types of wire nails are given in Table T-5 in the Technical Manual reprinted below for immediate reference. The size of nails are given in pennyweight *d*, a holdover from the English pound-shilling-pence (£, s, d) currency. Supposedly, at some point in English history wire nails 2 in. long cost 6d per 100; today, these are still called 6d nails.

Table T-5 Nail and Spike Sizes[a]

		Wire Diameter (inches)			
Pennyweight	Length (in.)	Box Nails	Common Wire Nails	Threaded, Hardened Steel Nails	Common Wire Spikes
6d	2	0.099	0.113	0.120	
8d	$2^1/_2$	0.113	0.131	0.120	
10d	3	0.128	0.148	0.135	0.192
12d	$3^1/_4$	0.128	0.148	0.135	0.192
16d	$3^1/_2$	0.135	0.162	0.148	0.207
20d	4	0.148	0.192	0.177	0.225
30d	$4^1/_2$	0.148	0.207	0.177	0.244
40d	5	0.162	0.225	0.177	0.263
50d	$5^1/_2$		0.244	0.177	0.283
60d	6		0.263	0.177	0.283

[a]Source: *National Design Specifications for Wood Construction*

The nails called *common nails* in Table T-5 are the basic structural nails in wood construction. *Box nails* are somewhat smaller than common nails and, while useful for smaller lumber sizes, are more likely to bend while being driven. *Hardened steel nails* have better pullout resistance when moisture content is high and are therefore likely to be used in wet service conditions.

Common wire spikes are larger in diameter than the other types of nails and must be spaced farther apart to avoid splitting the member. An alternative is to predrill the holes for the spikes, in which case there is reduced danger of splitting. The size of the predrilled holes may not be larger than 0.75 x nail diameter, however, or the load capacity of the nail in withdrawal is lost.

A typical nailed connection is shown in Figure 30-2. The nails are driven entirely through the *side plate* and penetrate a certain distance into the *main member*. The tensile load *T* places the nails in lateral load, or shear.

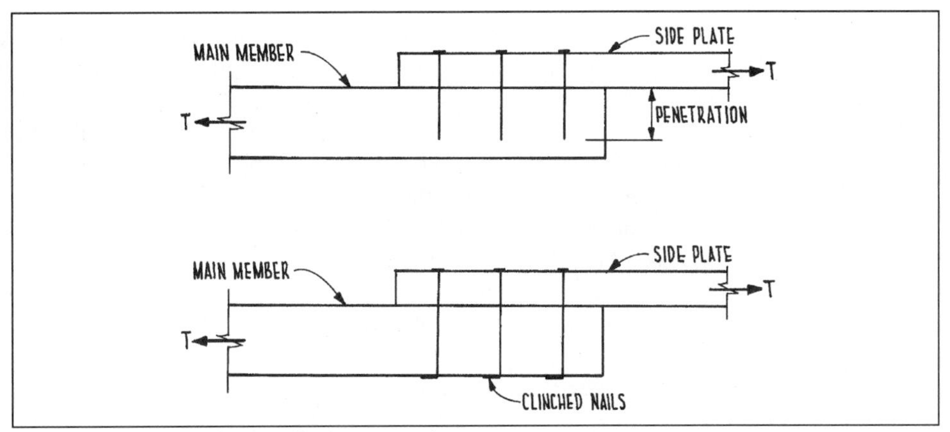

Figure 30-2 Typical nailed connection.

Alternatively, longer nails could be used that penetrate the main member completely. If the end of the nail projects at least 3 nail diameters and is bent over as indicated, the nail is said to be *clinched*. Nails clinched across the grain have about 20% more resistance to withdrawal than nails clinched along the grain.

The allowable lateral load on a nail depends on its depth of penetration into the main member. The allowable load, however, depends more on the bending deformations of the nail at failure than on any bearing on the wood or shear stress in the nail. In general, the failure mechanism of a nailed connection is in the progressive bending distortion of the nail until it pulls out of the wood.

Since there is some recognition of bending in the nails, any concentration of load on a single nail in a line of nails is ignored. A highly loaded nail will simply bend slightly, redistributing the load among adjacent nails. With very little overstress, all the nails in the line will eventually be loaded equally.

Nailed connections may take other configurations as indicated in Figure 30-3. Depending on the direction of load, the wood may be loaded parallel to grain or perpendicular to grain. The allowable lateral load on a nail is the same in either direction.

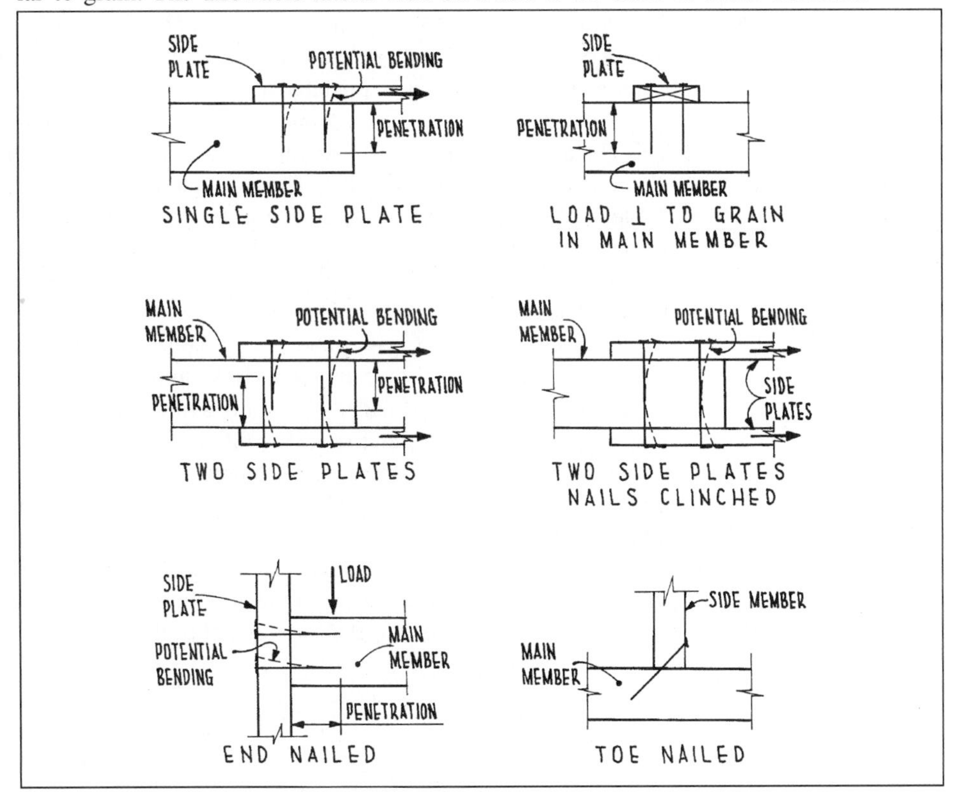

Figure 30-3 Various nailed connections.

As indicated in Figure 30-3, nails may be loaded in withdrawal or they may be loaded laterally. The tabular design values for nails loaded in withdrawal are given in Table T-6. For nails loaded laterally, the tabular design values are given in Table T-7.

It should be noted that Table T-7 gives the allowable values only for a single nail in a connection having a single side plate. In a connection having two side plates as shown in Figure 30-3, the load is simply divided equally between the two sides. It is then assumed that each side acts independently of the other; each side may thus be designed as a connection having a single side plate.

For allowable nail loads, finding the allowable design values from the tabular values follows the procedure developed earlier for stress.

Withdrawal design load $\quad N'_W = N_W C_D C_M C_t C_{tn} \quad$ (30-2)

Lateral design load $\quad N'_L = N_L C_D C_M C_d C_{di} C_{eg} C_t C_{tn}$

where N_W and N_L are the tabular design values for nails and spikes given in Table T-6 and Tables T-7

C_D is the factor for duration of load.

C_M is the factor for moisture content of the wood.

C_d is the factor for depth of penetration.

C_{di} is the factor for diaphragm construction.

C_{eg} is the factor for end-grain connections.

C_t is the factor for elevated service temperatures.

C_{tn} is the factor for use in toenailing.

Adjustment factor C_D for duration of load on all fasteners is the same as it is for duration of load on basic tabular stresses. The values of C_D are those given earlier in Table T-4. The allowable capacity for duration of load on fasteners is thus seen to be directly proportional to the allowable stress in the wood.

Adjustment factor C_M for moisture content of wood subject to fastener loads is given in Table T-8 in the Technical Manual. The values of C_M for fasteners are not always the same as those given earlier for tabular stresses.

Adjustment factor C_d for depth of penetration applies both to lag bolts and nails. The given tabular values for nails are based on a required length of penetration of 12 diameters as given in Table T-7. The minimum usable length of penetration given in Table T-7 is half the full required length, for which case the design value is half its full value.

Adjustment factor C_{di} is applied to nails and spikes used in diaphragm construction; C_{di} = 1.1.

Adjustment factor C_{eg} is applied when nails and spikes are driven into the end grain of a member rather than the side grain. It is applied only to the lateral load values given in Table T-7. Loading end-nailed connections in withdrawal is not recommended. The end grain factor C_{eg} for nails and spikes is 0.67.

Adjustment factor C_t for service temperatures is the same as for basic tabular stresses. The allowable capacity of the fastener is considered to be directly proportional to the allowable stress in the wood.

Adjustment factor C_{tn} is applied to toe-nailed connections. The factor applies both to the lateral loads of Table T-7 and the withdrawal loads of Table T-6. The values of C_{tn} is 0.83 for lateral loads and 0.67 for withdrawal loads.

In nailed connections, steel side plates may be used instead of wood side plates. One advantage of steel side plates is that the shorter length of nail protruding from the main member reduces the potential bending in the nails. A comparison is shown in Figure 30-4.

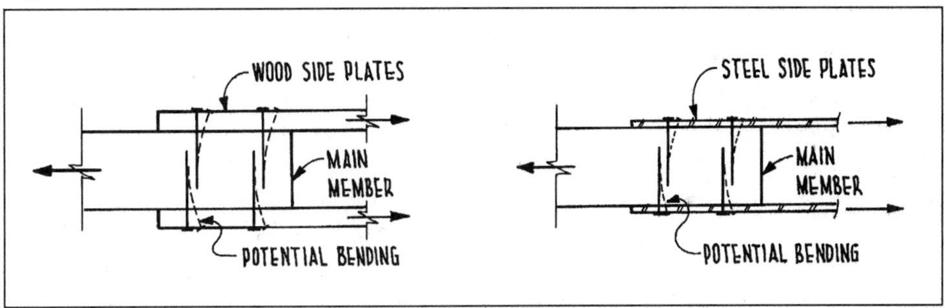

Figure 30-4 Comparison of wood and steel side plates.

Though not included in this textbook, National Design Specifications also lists tabular design values for nails in steel side plates, which include the minimum thickness of the steel plates. In years past, such connections were designed using nail values as limited by the main member. The thickness of the side plates was then selected using the procedures given in Chapter 25 for the design of steel tension members. As an expedient, that method might still be used, but in doing so, the allowable stress in A-36 steel should be reduced to about $0.25F_y$ or 14,400 psi (to account for innumerable vagaries at the small nail holes in the thin plates).

The design codes have little to say about edge distance, end distance and spacing of nails. National Design Specifications states only that edge distance, end distance and spacing shall be sufficient to prevent splitting of the wood. Possibly the lack of requirements reflects the difficulty one would have in enforcing any such requirements.

Some examples will illustrate the design of nailed connections.

Example 30-3

Design of nailed connections.

Given: Lap splice in tension. Dimension and sizes as indicated. No. 2 Douglas fir-larch. Duration of load is less than one year. Outdoor exposure, subject to high moisture content.

To Find: Number and size of nails required for the connection.

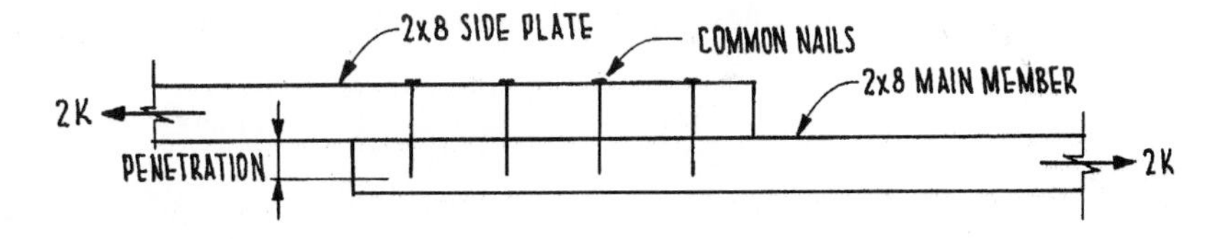

Solution: Establish the adjustment factors.

For duration of load less than one year, C_D is found from Table T-4, $C_D = 1.1$.

For high moisture content, C_M is found from Table T-8, $C_M = 0.75$.

Select the size of nails and determine the nail values:

Size of nails is governed by required depth of penetration. The largest penetration possible is $1^1/_2$ in. With a length of $1^1/_2$ inches in the side plate, the maximum penetration is $1^1/_2$ inches.

From Table T-7, select 16d common nails, $3^1/_2$ in. long.

Nail values are given in Table T-7. For 16d nails with penetration 12 diameters in the main member of 1.94 in., the lateral load design value is 141 lbs. At $1^1/_2$ in. penetration, the design value is (1.5/1.94)141 = 109 lbs. The allowable load per nail is then:

$$N_L' = C_D C_M N_L = 1.1 \times 0.75 \times 109 = 83 \text{ lbs.}$$

Determine the reuired number of nails:

The required number of 16d common nails is:

$$\text{No.} = \frac{P}{N_L'} = \frac{2000}{83} = 24 \text{ common nails, 16d.}$$

Example 30-4

Design of nailed connections.

Given: Truss transfer member loaded as shown. No. 2 Southern pine. Normal load duration and moisture content. Assume that the plywood side plates are adequate to develop the design values of the nails.

To Find: Number of nails required for the connection.

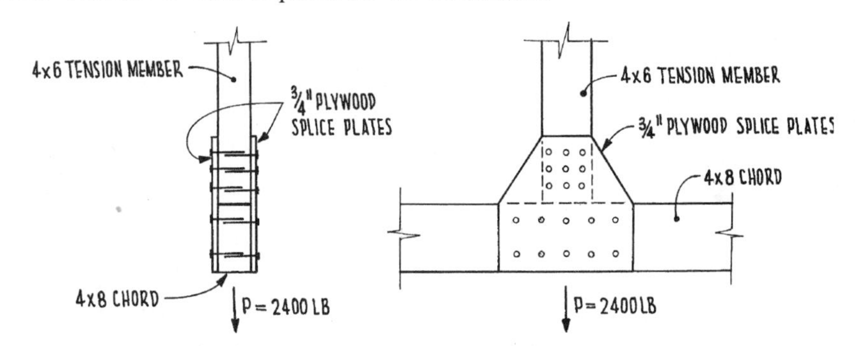

Solution: Establish the adjustment factors.

No special conditions: all factors are 1.0.

Select the size of the nails and determine the nail values:

Penetration can be as much as $3^1/_2$ inches. Total nail length can be as much as $3^1/_2 + {}^3/_4 = 4^1/_4$. Try 16d common nails, $3^1/_2$ in. long, penetration $2^3/_4$ in.

From Table T-7, the lateral design load is found to be 138 lbs at 1.94 in. penetration.

The allowable load on the nails are the same whether loaded parallel to grain or perpendicular to grain.

Determine the required number of nails:

The required number of 16d common nails is

$$\text{No.} = \frac{P}{N_L'} = \frac{2400}{138} = 17.4$$

Use 18 common nails, 16d, 9 per side on tension member.
Use 20 common nails, 16d, 10 per side on the chord.

Example 30-5

Design of nailed connections.

Given: Chord splice, loaded as shown. Spruce-pine-fir, No. 2 J&P. Load is constant, with duration more than 10 years. Occaasional wet service conditions. Assume the $^5/_8$ in. plywood side plates are adequate to develop the design values of the nails. Use special allowance for clinched nails.

To Find: Number of nails required for the connection.

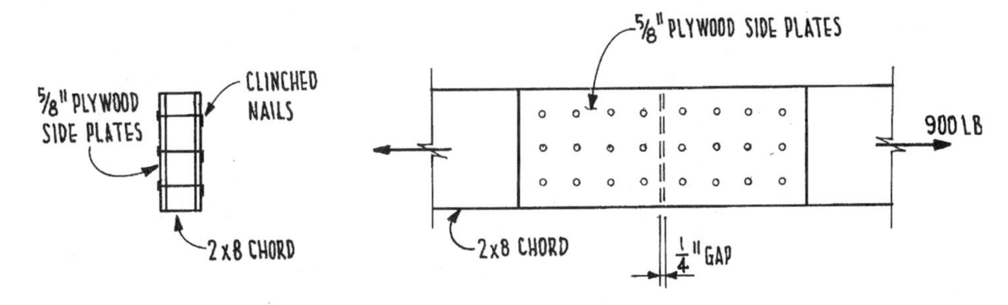

Solution: Establish the adjustment factors.

Duration of load factor C_D = 0.90 (from Table 7-4).

Wet service factor C_M = 0.75 (from Table T-8).

Select the size of nails and determine their load values:

The nails must be long enough to penetrate the two side plates, plus the main member, plus have 3 diameters protruding for clinching. If it is to be clinched, the nail size cannot be larger than 12d, with length of 3.25 in. Try 12d common nails.

Required length = $^5/_8 + 1^1/_2 + ^5/_8 + 3 \times 0.148$
= 3.19 in. < 3.25 in. of 12d nails (O.K.)

Lateral load design value for clinched 12d nails is twice the tabulated value of 78 lbs at 1.54 in. penetration (see footnote, Table T-7).

For 1.5 in. penetration, capacity = $(^{1.5}/_{1.54})78 \times 2$ = 152 lbs.

Allowable load = $N_L \times C_D \times C_M$ = 150 x 0.90 x 0.75 = 101 lbs.

Determine the required number of nails:

$$\text{Required number of nails} = \frac{900}{101} = 8.91 \text{ nails.}$$

Use 9 common nails, 12d, clinched.

Example 30-6

Design of nailed connections.

Given: Chord splice loaded as shown. No. 2 Douglas fir-larch, J&P. Steel side plates. A-36 steel. Normal service conditions. Use expedient methods rather than tables to design the connection.

To Find: 1) Number and size of nails.
2) Required thickness of the steel side plates.

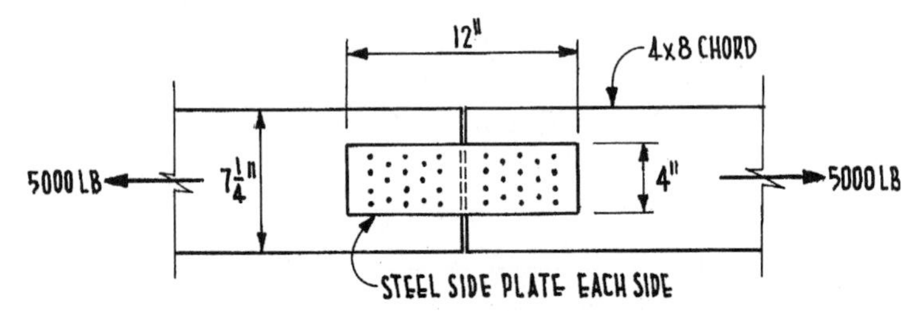

Solution: Establish adjustment factors:

No special conditions: all factors are 1.0.

Select the size of the nails and determine their load values:

Maximum nail length is $3^1/_2$ in. for the 4 x 8 chord.

Try 16d common nails, $3^1/_2$ in., assume $3^1/_4$ in. penetration.

Required penetration 1.78 in. < 3.25 in. (O.K.)

Assue the steel side plates are at least as efficient as thick wood plates.

From Table T-7, maximum lateral design value is 141 lbs at 1.78 in. penetration, for all side plate thicknesses 1 in. and above; assume this is the limit as governed by the main member.

Allowable load = 141 lbs/nail.

Determine the required number of nails:

$$\text{No. of nails} = \frac{5000}{141} = 35.5 \text{ nails.}$$

Use 18 - 16d common nails per side, each end.

Determine thickness of side plate:

For capacity of side plates, assume nail pattern as shown in the sketch. For 16d nails use holes $^3/_{16}$ in. diameter in the steel plates.

Effective area = $[4 - 4(^3/_{16})]t = 3.25t$

Assume steel stress $0.25\ F_y = 9$ ksi.

$$P = 5000 = F_sA_e = 9000 \times 3.25 \times 2t$$

$$t = 0.086 \text{ in.}$$

Use 12 gauge plates each side, punched as shown.

30.3 Bolted Connections in Tension Members

Several additional factors arise in bolted connections that did not occur in nailed joints.

1. Net areas of the tension members must reflect the reduction due to the bolt holes.
2. Bolt design values are different for load perpendicular to grain than for load parallel to grain.
3. Bolt spacings, edge distances and end distances must meet certain limitations if full strength is to be developed.
4. Connections having a large number of bolts in a line parallel to the load are subject to a reduction in load per bolt.

The calculation of net areas for tension members is discussed at the beginning of this chapter and is not repeated here.

Typical examples of bolt loads parallel to grain and perpendicular to grain are shown in Figure 30-5. Note that a row of bolts lies parallel to the direction of load. Note also that when rows of bolts are spaced widely apart, it may be necessary to use a separate side plate for each row.

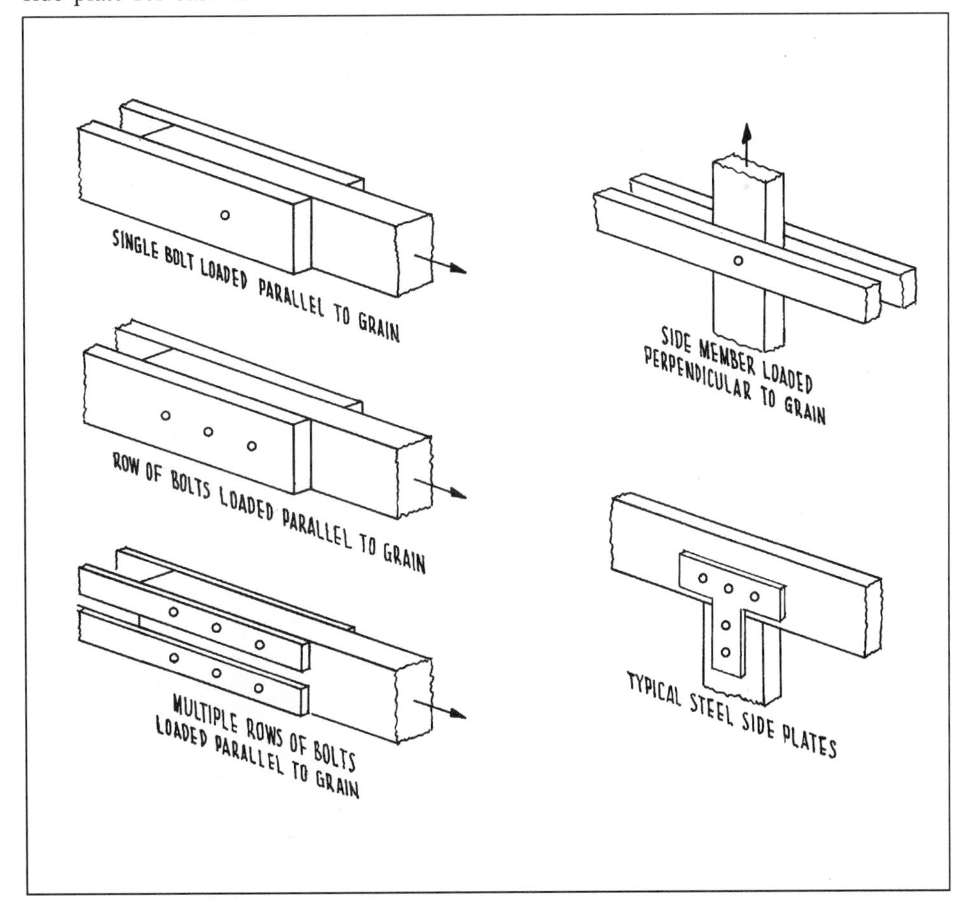

Figure 30-5 Examples of bolted joints for which full tabular design values may be used (further modification may be necessary due to conditions of use).

For bolts loaded as indicated in Figure 30-5, bolt design values are given in Table T-9 for Douglas fir-larch, Southern pine and Spruce-pine-fir. The tabular values are given for a single bolt either in single shear or in double shear as shown in Figure 30-6. Note that the thickness of the main member is usually kept smaller than the sum of the two side plates; the limiting bolt design value is then governed by the main member. Bolts are assumed to have washers at both ends and to be snugly tightened without crushing the wood.

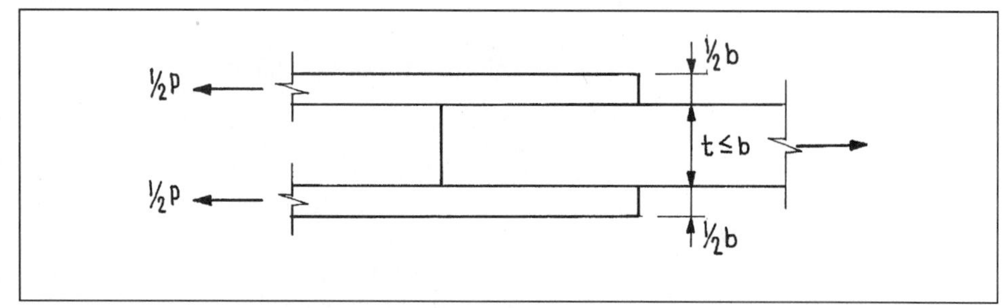

Figure 30-6 Standard connection for tabular bolt values.

The tabular values given in Table T-9 are for a single bolt loaded either perpendicular to grain or parallel to grain. It should be noted that the bolt values parallel to grain are much larger than those perpendicular to grain. For a bolt loaded at some angle to the grain, such as that shown in Figure 30-7, the bolt value lies somewhere between the two tabular values.

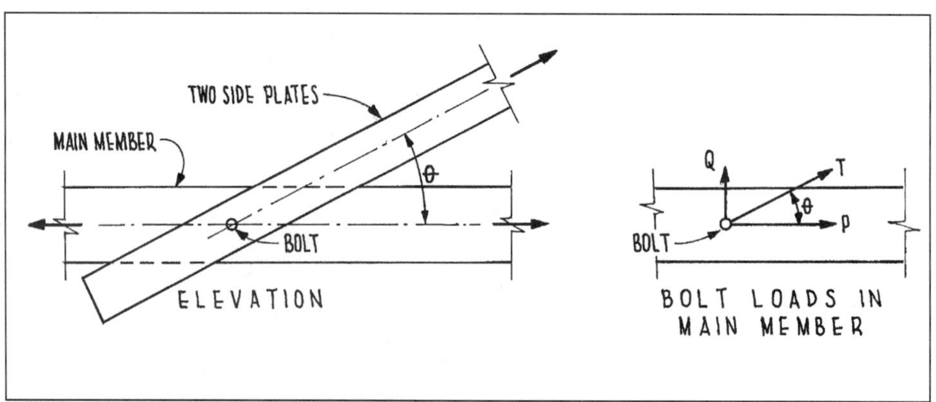

Figure 30-7 Bolt loaded at an angle to the grain.

The bolt design values for the side plates in Figure 30-7 are those given in Table T-9 for load parallel to grain. Only the main member is loaded at an angle to the grain; the side plates are loaded conventionally.

The bolt design value in the main member of Figure 30-7 is computed by the Hankinson formula:

$$N = \frac{PQ}{P\sin^2\theta + Q\cos^2\theta} \qquad (30\text{-}3)$$

where N is the bolt design value corrected for direction of load.
P is the tabular bolt design value from Table T-9 for load parallel to grain.
Q is the tabular bolt design value from Table T-9 for load perpendicular to grain.
θ is the angle between the lines of action of N and P.

The value of N found from Eq.(30-3) is subject to the same adjustment factors to which P and Q are subject. These factors are discussed later in this section.

When groups of bolts are used in a connection, certain limits in spacing, end distance and edge distance must be observed. Those limits are given in Table T-10 in the Technical Manual. As indicated in Table T-10, bolt layouts which do not meet the specified limitations may be acceptable, but at a reduced level of load.

The layout requirements of Table T-10 are summarized in the sketches of Figure 30-8. The dimensions given in Figure 30-8 are those for full tabular design values. National Design Specifications allows for some violations of the distances and spacings with a corresponding reduction in allowable load, but that adjustment is not included in this textbook.

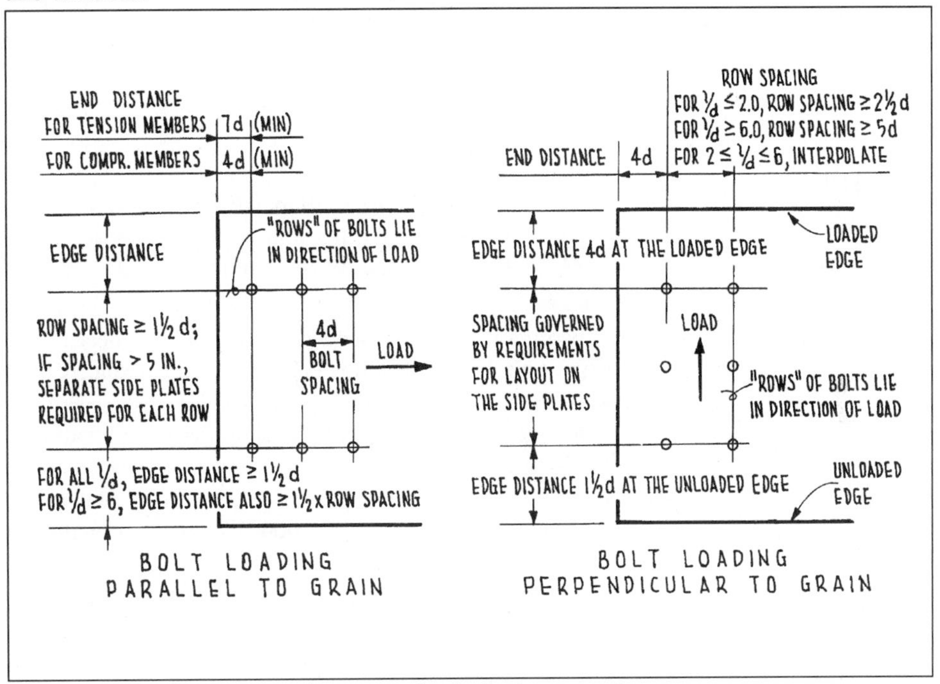

Figure 30-8 Layout requirements for bolted connections.

When wide row spacings are used, such as those shown in Figure 30-9, the main member may shrink or swell differently than the side member. Such shrinkage produces tension perpendicular to grain, which can cause cracking either at the rows of bolts or between the rows of bolts. In such cases, the side plates must be separated, one sideplate for each row of bolts, to permit shrinkage without restraints.

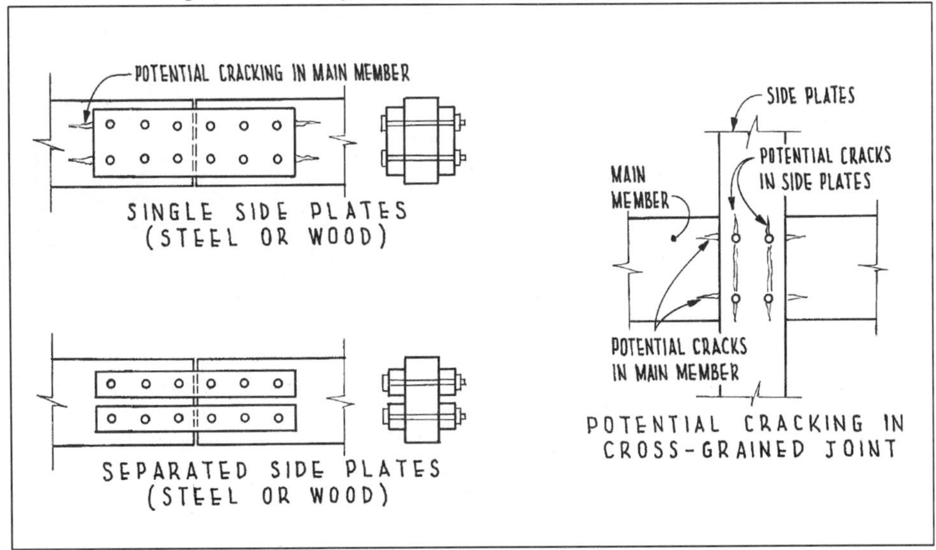

Figure 30-9 Cracking due to differential shrinking.

The values of an adjustment factor C_g for "group action" in large arrays of bolts are given in Table T-11 and Table T-12 in the Technical Manual. For light-to-medium construction, the use of long rows of bolts (more than 4 or 5) is unusual, so the group action adjustment factor does not cause a severe reduction. In longer lines, however, the reduction could be as much as 50% or more.

Finding the allowable load per bolt from the tabular design values of Table T-9 follows the procedures developed earlier:

For loads parallel to grain,

$$P' = PC_DC_MC_gC_t \quad (30\text{-}4a)$$

For loads perpendicular to grain,

$$Q' = QC_DC_MC_gC_t \quad (30\text{-}4b)$$

where P and Q are the tabular design values given in Table T-9.
C_D, C_M and C_t are adjustment factors defined earlier,
C_g is the modifier for group action as specified in Table T-11 and T-12

(NDS permits the use of connections that do not meet the layout requirements of Table T-10; the bolt values in these connections are reduced by adjustment factor C_Δ. Such cases are not included in this textbook.)

The steel bolts used in bolted connections are invariably ASTM A-307 bolts. These are the low-strength bolts that were introduced earlier in steel design. In steel design, however, A-307 bolts were passed over in favor of the higher strength ASTM A-325 bolts. In bolted connections in wood, the lower strength steel is still stronger than the wood, so no purpose is served in using the higher strength steel bolts.

Some examples will illustrate the selection of sizes and layout for bolted connections.

Example 30-7

Capacity of bolted connections.

Given: Lapped bolted joint as indicated. A307 bolts, 5/8 in. diameter. No. 2 Southern pine. Normal conditions of service.

To Find: Capacity of the connection.

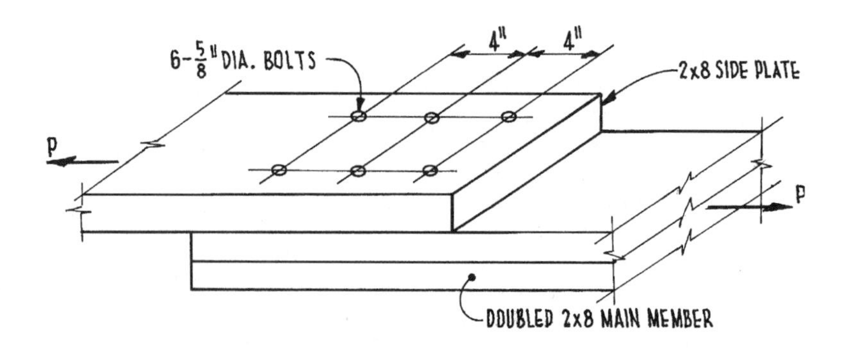

Solution: The thinner member is chosen as the "side plate" as shown on the sketch.

Establish the adjustment factors for stresses:

No special conditions; $C_D = 1.0$, $C_M = 1.0$,
C_g is 0.954 from Table T-11.

Determine the capacity of the size plate in tension:

$P = F_t$ x Net Area

Tabular stress F_t is found from Table T-3b.

$F_t = 650$ psi

$$P = 650\left[1\tfrac{1}{2} \times 7\tfrac{1}{4} - 1\tfrac{1}{2}\left(\tfrac{5}{8}+\tfrac{1}{8}\right)2\right] = 5610 \text{ lb.}$$

Determine the capacity of the bolts:

Adjustment factor Cg = 0.954 (from Table T-11)

P = (No. of bolts)(Capacity per bolt)(C_g)

Capacity per bolt is found from Table T-9. The capacity of the connection is limited by the thickness of the side plate.

Capacity = per bolt = 940 lb

$$\frac{A_S}{A_m} = \frac{1\frac{1}{2} x 7\frac{1}{4}}{3x7\frac{1}{4}} = 0.50,\ A_S = 10.9\ in.^2$$

The capacity of the 6 bolts is now computed:

P = 6 x 940 x 0.954 = 5380 lb

The capacity of the connection is thus seen to be limited by the bolts:

Capacity = 5380 lb.

Example 30-8

Capacity of bolted connections.

Given: Angled connection as shown. A307 bolts, 3/4 in. diameter, No. 2 Douglas fir-larch, subject to long sustained loading, and subject to occasional wet service.

To Find: Capacity of the bolts.

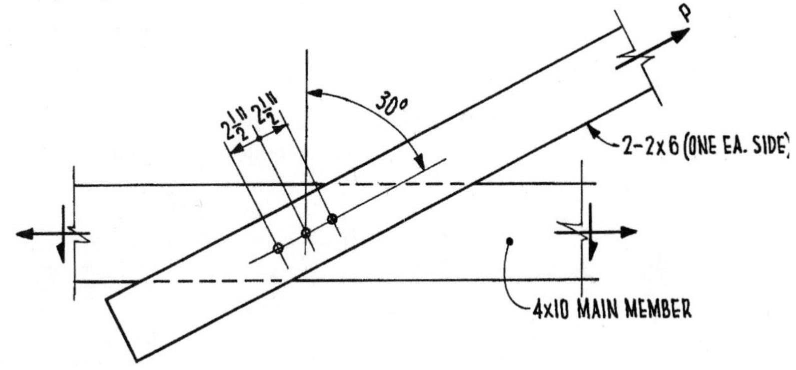

Solution: Establish the adjustment factors for fasteners:

From Table T-4, $C_D = 0.90$
From Table T-3d, $C_M = 1.00$
From Table T-11, $C_g = 0.95$ for $A_s/A_m = 0.5$

Determine the capacity of the bolts on the side plates:

Capacity = $PC_DC_MC_g$ x No. bolts.

Capacity of the bolts on the two side members, load parallel to grain:

From Table T-9, P = 2400 lb.

Capacity = 2400 x 0.90 x1.00 x 0.95 x 3 =6160 lbs.

Determine the capacity of the bolts on the main member:

$N' = NC_DC_MC_g$ x No. bolts

$$\text{At angle } \theta, N = \frac{PQ}{P\sin^2\theta + Q\cos^2\theta}$$

Capacity is computed for a 3½ in. main member having 1½ in. side plates.

From Table T-9, P = 2400 lb
Q = 1370 lb

$$N = \frac{2400x1370}{2400\sin^2 60 + 1370\cos^2 60} = 1535\ lb$$

N' = 1535 x 0.90 x1.00 x 0.95 x 3 = 3940 lb

The 1¾ in. side plates would have to develop a capacity of 3940 lbs. Since the 1½ in. side plates will develop a capacity in excess of this value, they are stronger than the main member.

Capacity is thus limited by the capacity of the bolts in the main member, with load at 60° from the direction of the grain.

Capacity of bolts = 3940 lbs.

Example 30-9

Design of bolted connections.

Given: Splice having ASTM A-36 steel side plates, tensile load 10 kips; A307 bolts, ⅝ in. diameter, Spruce-pine-fir, No. 1 B&S, subject to extended periods of wet service.

To Find: a) Required number of bolts.
b) Suitable bolt layout.

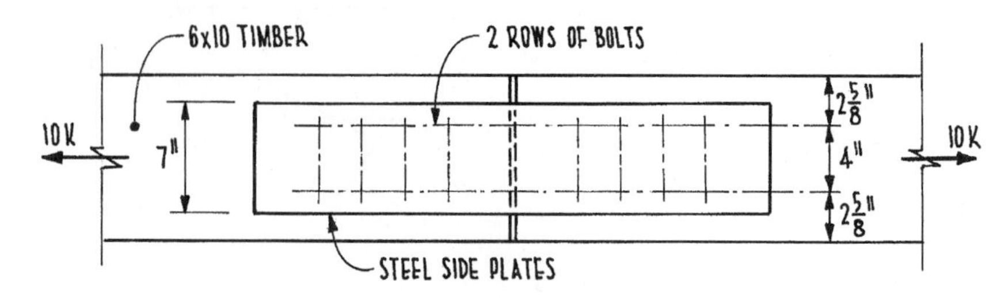

Solution: Establish adjustment factors for member stresses:

For F_t, $C_M = 1.00$.

Determine capacity of main member (assume 2 rows of bolts):

$P = F'_t$ x net area

From Table T-3C, $F_t = 450$ psi

$F'_t = F_t C_M = 450 \times 1.00 = 450$ psi

$$P = 450\left[52.3 - 2\left(\tfrac{5}{8} + \tfrac{1}{8}\right)5.5\right]$$
$$= 19{,}800 \text{ lb.} > 10{,}000 \text{ lb. (O.K.)}$$

The main member is thus adequate to sustain the 10k load.

Determine the required number of bolts:

For fasteners, $C_M = 0.67$, C_g will depend on layout.

Required number of bolts is computed as

Capacity = Capacity/bolt x No. bolts x C_M

From Table T-9c, capacity/bolt = 2090 lb.

Capacity = 2090 x 0.67 = 1400 lb.

$$\text{Required No. bolts} = \frac{10{,}000}{1{,}400} = 7.14 \text{ bolts}$$

Try 8 bolts, 4 per row

Verify capacity in group action:

From Table T-12:

$$\frac{A_m}{A_S} = \frac{52.3}{\frac{1}{4} x 7} = 30,\ C_g = 0.965$$

P' = 1400 lb/bolt x 0.965 = 1350 lb/bolt

Capacity of 8 bolts = 1350 x 8 = 10,800 lb
= 10,800 lb > 10,000 lb (O.K.)

Use 1/4 in. side plates 7" x 2'-9", layout as shown.

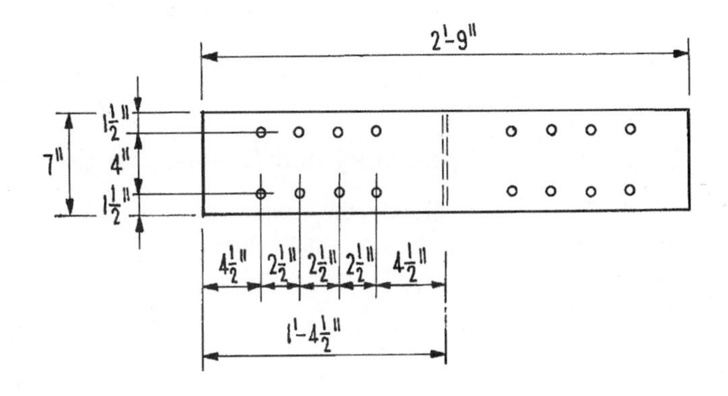

Example 30-10

Design of bolted connections.

Given: 4 x 10 ledger, bolted to concrete wall as shown. Joist load on the ledger of 1200 lb/ft. A-307 anchor bolts; $f_c' = 3000$ psi. No. 2 Douglas fir-larch. Normal conditions of service.

To Find: Required spacing of anchor bolts.

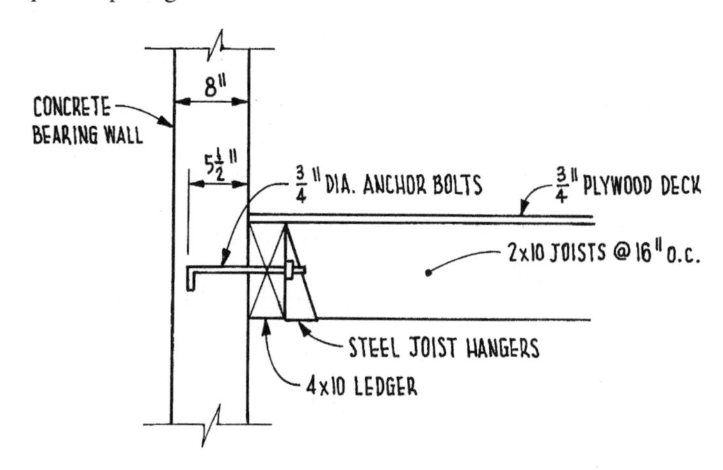

Solution: Establish adjustment factors.

No special conditions; all factors are 1.00.

Determine the capacity of one anchor bolt:

Assume ledger acts as $3^1/_2$ in. side plate and that concrete wall is at least as strong as a $7^1/_2$ in. main member.

From Table T-9, load perpendicular to grain, (for all thicknesses listed as main members):

$$\text{Allowable load/bolt} = 870 \text{ lb/bolt}$$

$$\therefore \text{Required spacing} = \frac{870}{1200} = 0.725 \text{ ft}$$

$$= 9 \text{ in. on center}$$

Verify that the anchor bolt is adequate:

From Table C-12, allowable capacity in shear for a $^3/_4$ in. anchor bolt in 3000 psi concrete is 3560 lb with a minimum bolt spacing of 12 diameters or 9 in., with an embedment at least 4 inches.

Use $^5/_8$ in. x 10 in. anchor bolts @ 9 in. on center.

30.4 Proprietary and Commercial Connectors

In general, the capacity of a bolted timber connection is limited by the size of the bearing area between the bolt and the timber. Increasing the size of the bolt increases the capacity of the connection somewhat but a significant increase in the bolt size is required if the connection is to be improved significantly by this means. Several commercial connectors have been developed which increase the bearing areas without requiring an increase in the size of the bolt; three of the more popular of these commercial connectors are shown in Figure 30-10, along with the special drill bits used to provide the properly grooved bearing surfaces.

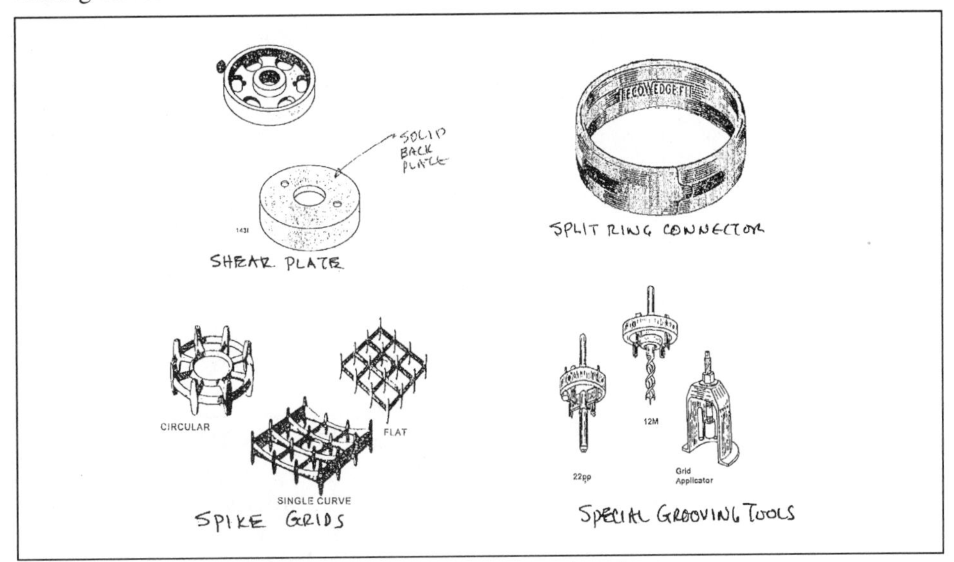

Figure 30-10 Commercial timber connectors and tools.

The commercial connectors shown in Figure 30-10 have a common disadvantage: they are large. Outside dimensions range from 2⁵/₈ in. to 4¹/₈ in., which almost automatically limits their applications to the larger timbers used in medium-to-heavy construction. Though heavy construction is outside the scope of this textbook, commercial connectors are used often enough in smaller J&P lumber to warrant a brief discussion of their use.

Design loads for the commercial connectors of Figure 30-10 are provided by the manufacturers of the connectors. A prominent manufacturer of such products is TECO/ Lumberlok, whose design manual is one of the more widely used references in the industry. The TECO/Lumberlok design manual gives design values, layout criteria and recommended practices for the use of their products.

In addition to the manufacturers' manuals, the AITC Timber Construction Manual also presents the use and design of commercial timber connectors in considerable detail. The AITC manual includes design loads and recommended practices for a multiplicity of cases, to include heavy trusses, angled connections and spaced columns. While much of the design information in the AITC manual is taken from the TECO/Lumberlok publications, the manual is generally written to stand alone.

The spike grids shown in Figure 30-10 are used between the side plates and the main member. They are used with a bolt (usually 1 in. diameter) at their center. When the bolt is tightened, the spikes penetrate both members, providing an increase in bearing area and a corresponding increase in capacity.

The single curve spike grid is used in connecting sawn (flat) members to round piles or poles. The curved side faces the round pole. When the bolt at the center of the grid is tightened, the grid penetrates both members uniformly.

Spike grids are manufactured by several manufacturers. Design loads, placing requirements and required bolt sizes must be obtained from the individual manufacturers; they are not standardized.

The shear plate shown in Figure 30-10 is one of the earlier types of improved shear developers. Shear plates are generally used in pairs, placed back-to-back in prepared grooved slots in both the main member and the side plate. A typical grooved slot is shown in Figure 30-11.

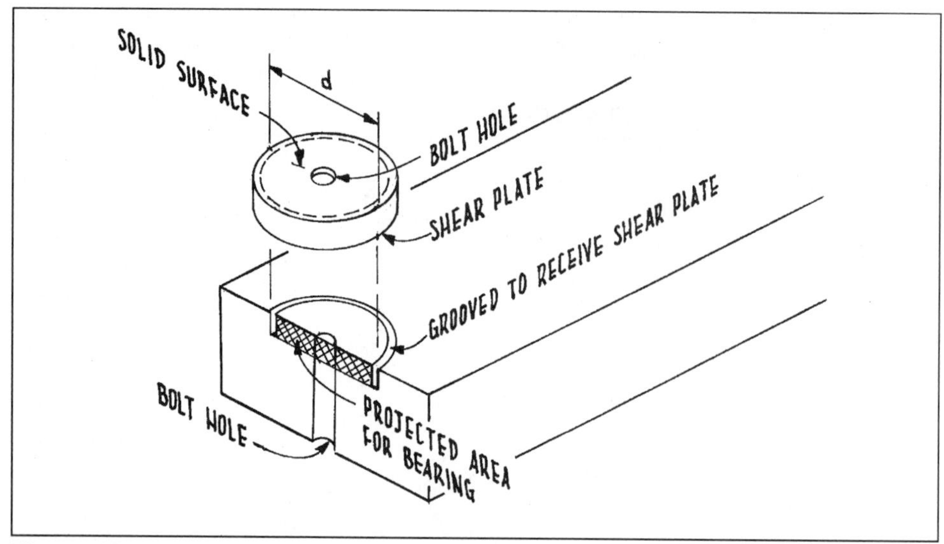

Figure 30-11 Grooved slot for a shear plate.

Shear plates are manufactured in two sizes, $2^5/_8$ in. and 4 in. diameter. Bolts are either $^3/_4$ in. or $^7/_8$ in. diameter. In the use of shear plates, there are stringent limitations on member thickness, bolt sizes and edge distances. Member thicknesses are limited further where two shear plates are used in a single member. The main member shown in Figure 30-12 is an example where two shear plates are used in a single member (also described as "a member having two connectors on the same bolt").

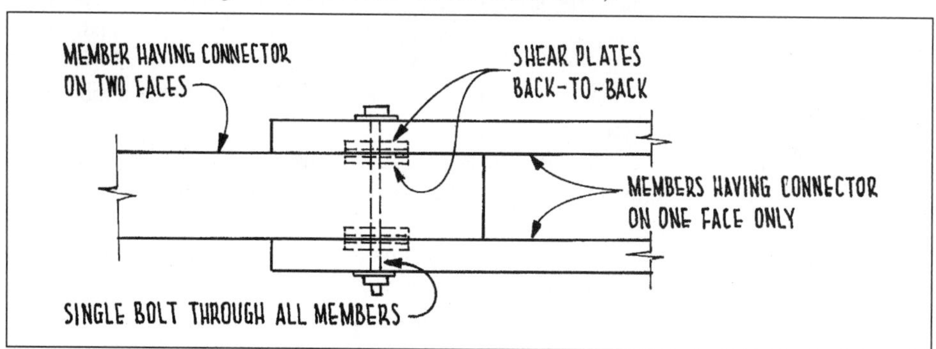

Figure 30-12 Multiple shear plates on a single bolt.

It is undoubtedly possible to perform calculations on shear plate connections that will account for bearing stresses, shear stresses, depth of groove, projected areas and other factors. Such calculations would be redundant, however, since the final capacity of a shear plate connector to be used in design are those specified in by the manufacturer.

A somewhat simplified form of the shear plate connector is shown in Figure 30-13. The single *split ring connector* is grooved both into the main member and into the side plate. The need for the end plate in the shear plate is eliminated in a split ring connector. It should be apparent that a split ring connector can only be used to join two wood members; it provides no benefits where steel side plates are used.

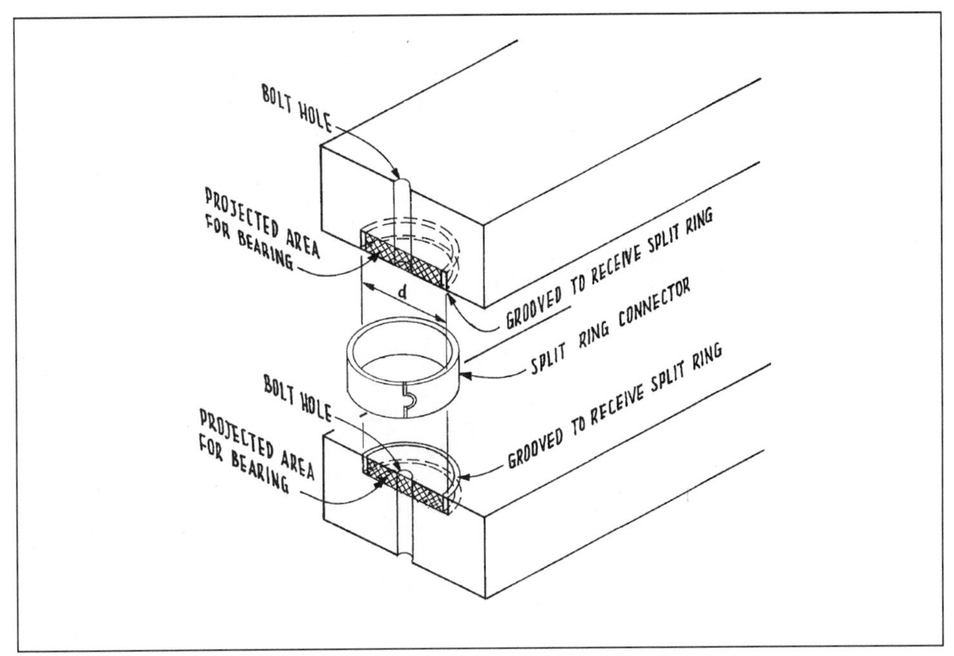

Figure 30-13 Split ring connector.

Similar to shear plates, split ring connectors are manufactured in standard sizes of $2^1/_2$ in. and 4 in. diameters. The capacity of split ring connectors is given in the manufacturers publications, along with limitations in bolt size, member thicknesses and edge distances. It should be noted that the capacity of split ring connections is somewhat less than the corresponding shear plate connections, but it should also be noted that bolt sizes are smaller.

Allowable load on commercial connectors is subject to Hankinson's law when loads occur at an angle to the direction of grain. The application is quite similar to that of bolted connections considered earlier.

30.5 Commercial Framing Hardware

The use of framing hardware has rapidly become standard practice in the industry. Framing hardware is a generic name for the hundreds of steel or aluminum connection devices used to join joists to beams, beams to columns or beams to girders. They are also used to seat columns, to cap columns and to form hinges in a span.

A typical joist hanger is shown in the sketches of Figure 30-14. Joist hangers are made in various sizes to suit the usual J&P lumber sizes. Typically, joist sizes range from 2 x 6 to 4 x 14.

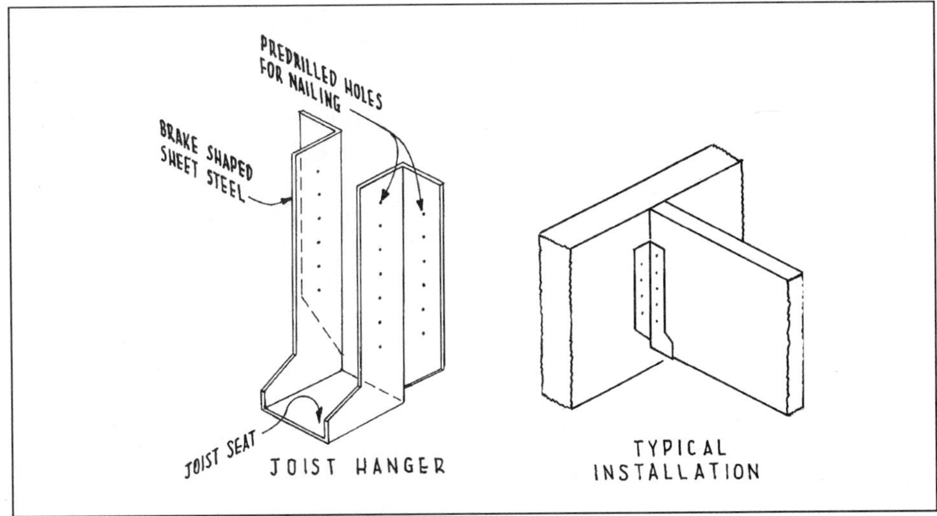

Figure 30-14 Typical joist hanger.

Dimensions of the joist "seat" in a joist hanger are deliberately set to permit the allowable joist reaction to be developed without overstressing the wood perpendicular to grain. Similarly, a sufficient number of nail holes are provided such that the reaction can be transmitted to the supporting member. The manufacturers catalogs or design tables should be consulted for the nailing schedules and allowable reactions on the joist hangers.

Typical column caps are shown in the sketches of Figure 30-15. Column sizes are typically square, but are sometimes rectangular, ranging from 4 x 4 to 8 x 8. Column bases are also manufactured in the same range of sizes.

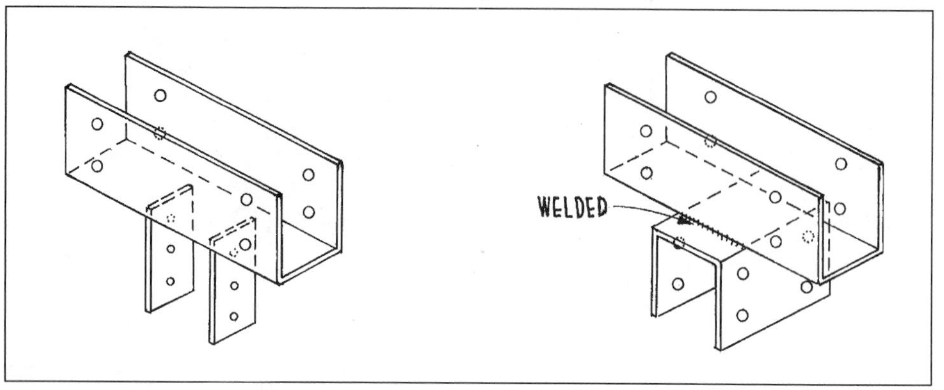

Figure 30-15 Typical column caps.

The joist hangers and column caps of Figure 3-14 and 15 are but a few of the hundreds of framing connectors on the market. Special ties and connectors are made for structural diaphragms, for hold-downs, for imbedded anchors, for rafter ties, for gang nailing trusses and a multiplicity of other applications. Anyone choosing to work in the design of wood structures must necessarily become familiar with the range of such connectors available in today's market. In general, the manufacturers provide excellent support to designers through their catalogs and design manuals concerning their products.

The widest use of framing hardware is in the J&P sizes of sawn lumber. Framing hardware is made in the standard glulam sizes also, but the applications in such large members are somewhat limited. Similarly, hardware is manufactured for sawn lumber up to 8 inches nominal thickness but the major uses are in the smaller J&P sizes.

Review Questions

1. List the steps in the procedure for selecting the size of a wood tension member.
2. List the modifiers that apply to the tabular tensile stress F_t.
3. To what sizes of members does the modifier C_t apply?
4. How is the net area of a tension member computed at a bolted connection?
5. Why is the deducted hole size larger than the actual bolt size when computing net area of a tension member?
6. What is the difference between common nails and box nails?
7. What is the smallest nail size?
8. What is the smaller spike size?
9. What is the largest size a predrilled hole can be when lumber is being predrilled for nails?
10. What is meant by clinching a nail?
11. What minimum length of nail must project from the wood member if clinching is to be effective?
12. Is there any benefit in clinching across the grain as compared to clinching parallel to grain?
13. In general, how does a nailed connection fail?
14. In a nailed connection, no reduction in capacity is required due to the use of multiple nails in a row. Why not?

15. List the modifiers that apply to the tabular nail values for nails loaded laterally.
16. What minimum depth of penetration of a nail will provide the full design value for the nail?
17. What is the minimum depth of penetration of a nail that must be provided before any value of load can be obtained?
18. Why is a higher value of load permitted when steel side plates are used rather than wood side plates?
19. In a bolted connection, a reduction in capacity is required when several bolts occur in a single row. Why is this different from nailed connections, where no reduction is required?
20. At what point does it become necessary to provide a separate side plate for each row of bolts?
21. State the Hankinson formula and define each variable.
22. What happens when bolt layouts are slightly deficient with regard to prescribed layout dimensions?
23. List the modifiers that apply to the tabular bolt values for bolted connections under shear loads.
24. What kind of steel is used for bolts in timber connections? What advantage is gained by using high-strength bolts?
25. What is the difference between shear plate connectors and split ring connectors?
26. What is the depth of groove required for placing a $2^5/_8$ in. shear plate connector?
27. Where could curved spike plates be used?
28. Where does one find the requirements for minimum spacing for split ring connectors?
29. Where does one find the requirements for minimum edge distance for split ring connectors?
30. Where does one find the requirements for minimum end distance for split ring connectors?

CHAPTER

31

TIMBER COLUMNS AND THEIR CONNECTIONS

31.1 Common Practices in Column Design

In steel construction, it was noted that columns commonly extend continuously through a floor level, with the girders being connected to the sides of the continuous column. In timber construction, continuous columns are rarely used. It is in the nature of timber construction that columns are interrupted at each floor level, with the girders being seated on top of the column. A typical arrangement is shown in Figure 31-1.

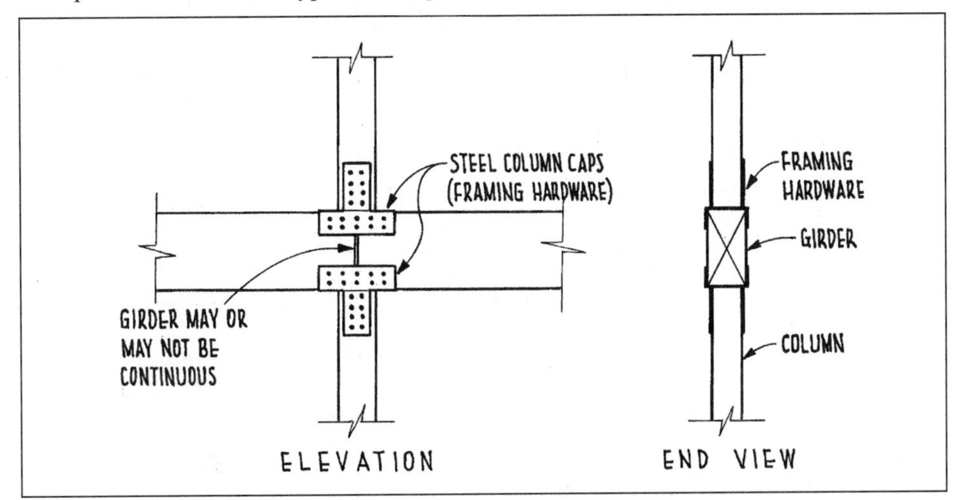

Figure 31-1 Girder seated on a solid timber column.

The column-girder arrangement of Figure 31-1 has some undesirable problems with stability. Lines of solid blocking or bridging are usually required in the direction transverse to the girder. (It is a design code requirement that transverse blocking shall be provided at the support lines, though not necessarily elsewhere.)

The floor-to-floor arrangement inherently produces pinned-end columns having relatively short lengths. In general, they are not long enough to qualify as long columns (Euler columns), but are too long to qualify as short columns (pedestals). Such columns are termed *intermediate* columns.

When necessary or desirable, timber columns can be made continuous, as indicated in Figure 31-2. The length of sawn timber columns are still limited, however, due simply to the limitations in length of sawn timber members. The use of glued laminated columns, however, can overcome this limitation in length.

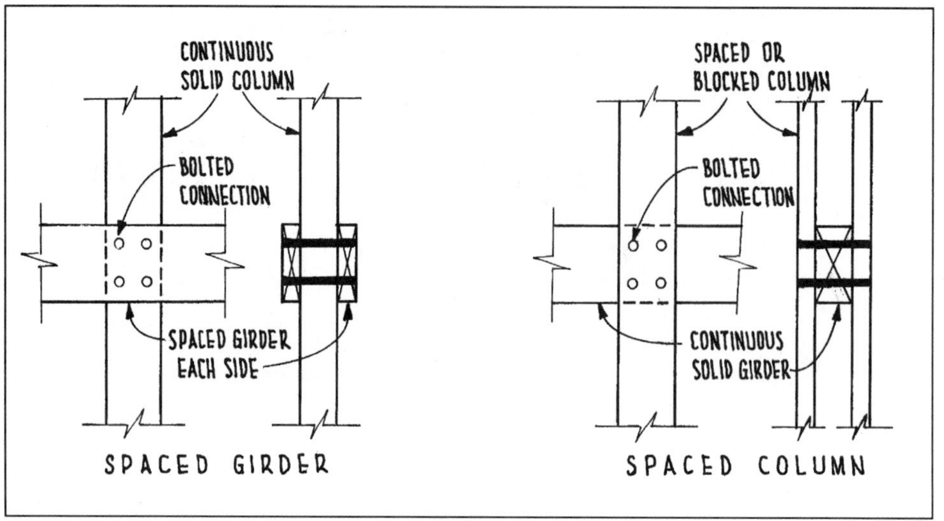

Figure 31-2 Continuous timber columns.

Columns limited to a single story are commonly made of square sections, 4 x 4, 6 x 6 or 8 x 8. Columns extending for two or more stories, as indicated in Figure 31-2, are more often made of rectangular sections rather than square sections but are rarely more than 10 in. wide.

Both solid columns and spaced columns are presented in succeeding discussions. In the discussions, no distinction is drawn between columns in buildings and other types of compression members, such as truss members. All compression members respond to load in the same way: the generic term *columns* includes all such compression members.

31.2 Buckling Stress and Effective Length

The Euler column formula is developed in elementary strength of materials (Chapter 10). A brief summary is presented here, primarily to introduce the symbols and terminology to be used for timber columns.

The Euler column formula defines the stress at which a long column will buckle:

$$f_{cr} = \frac{\pi^2 E}{\left(l/r\right)^2} \tag{31-1}$$

where f_{cr} is the critical stress at which buckling impends.

E is the modulus of elasticity.

r is the radius of gyration about the neutral axis of bending when buckling occurs.

l is the length of the column between two consecutive points of zero moment.

The buckling modes for columns having various end conditions are shown in Figure 31-3. Also given in Figure 31-3 are the recommended values of K_e to be used in establishing the single node buckling length $K_e l$. Note that these more conservative values are different from the values used in steel columns and in concrete columns.

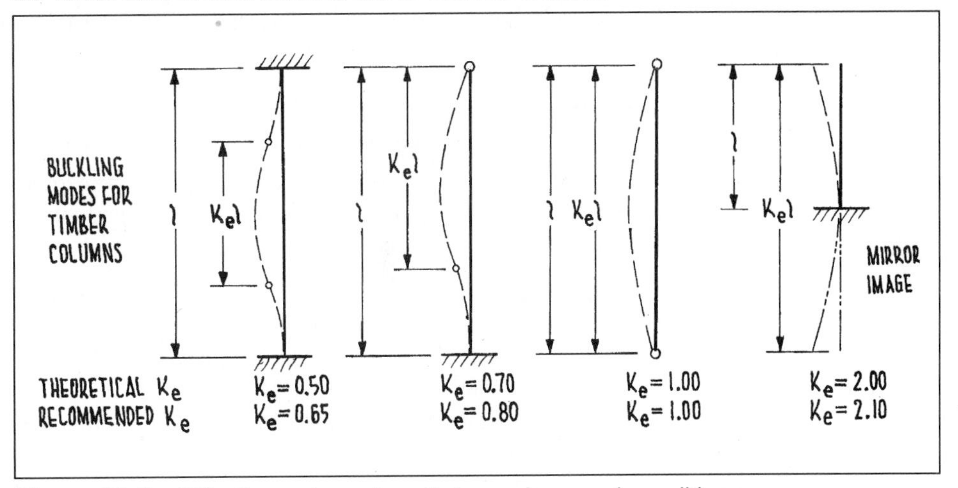

Figure 31-3 Effective column length for various end conditions.

The term *single node* is used here to describe the buckling length between two consecutive points of zero moment. It should be recalled that in the Euler solution, a single node is half of a sine curve.

The slenderness ratio l/r is used in timber columns in the same way it was used in steel columns and concrete columns but in slightly altered form. Since most timber columns are rectangular sections of width b and depth d, the radius of gyration becomes:

$$r = \sqrt{\frac{I}{A}}$$

$$\text{where } I = \frac{bd^3}{12} \text{ and } A = bd,$$

$$\text{hence } r = \frac{d}{\sqrt{12}} \tag{31-2}$$

where d is the depth of the rectangular cross section in bending.

Throughout all of timber design, this alternative form of the slenderness ratio, l/d, is used rather than the usual form, l/r.

In timber, the Euler formula given by Equation (31-1) therefore takes the form:

$$f_{cr} = \frac{0.8225E}{\left(\frac{K_e l}{d}\right)^2} \tag{31-3}$$

where all symbols are those defined earlier.

The stress f_{cr} given by the Euler formula is the stress at which buckling impends. The allowable stress F_{cE} is the buckling stress divided by a suitable factor of safety FS. In timber, the factor of safety to buckling is, for statistical reasons, taken at 2.74. The allowable compressive stress F_{cE} for long timber columns is then given by:

$$F_{cE} = \frac{0.30E'}{\left(\frac{l_e}{d}\right)^2} \tag{31-4}$$

where $l_e = K_e l$ and is the laterally unsupported length of the column between two consecutive points of zero moment.

Current practices in column design are best regarded as an evolution. There are two dates, 1977 and 1991, where major refinements were incorporated into the design methods used for timber columns. Note that the term "refinements" is used here rather than "changes," since the concepts of the earlier years were retained in both cases. These earlier concepts, the ones developed prior to 1991, are presented in the following section.

31.3 Pedestals, Intermediate Columns and Long Columns

The concepts of pedestals, intermediate columns and long columns are presented in strength of materials (Chapter 10) and are not repeated in detail here. Only a brief summary of these concepts is presented here, as they apply to structural timber.

A column may fail in one of three ways:

- By crushing, where the slenderness l_e/d is so low that the material crushes before any chance of buckling occurs.
- By buckling, where the slenderness l_e/d is so high that the column buckles while the material remains entirely elastic.
- By a mixture of crushing and buckling, where the column behavior is influenced both by crushing and by buckling.

A comparison of these cases is shown in Figure 31-4.

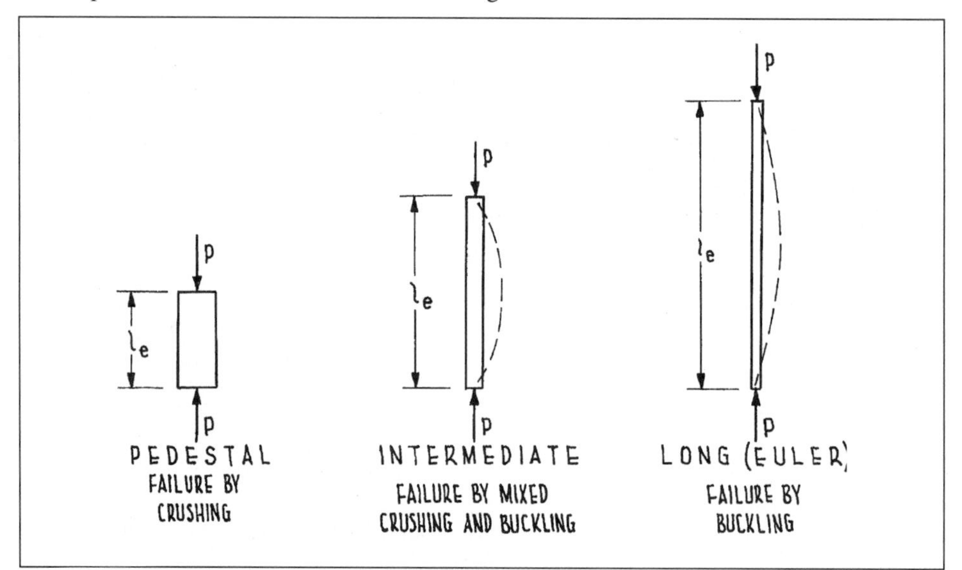

Figure 31-4 Comparison of column types.

Crushing failure in timber columns is limited to sections whose l_e/d ratio is less than about 11. As indicated in Figure 31-3, such columns are called pedestals. The calculated stress between any two consecutive points of zero moment is the direct stress:

$$f_c = \frac{P}{A} \tag{31-5}$$

where P is the axial concentric load.
A is the cross sectional area.

The allowable stress in pedestals is the adjusted compressive stress F_c^* parallel to grain, without any regard to buckling,

$$F_c^* = F_C C_D C_M C_t \tag{31-6}$$

where all symbols are defined in earlier discussions.

The design of pedestals for crushing failure is thus seen to be quite direct. The calculated actual stress f_c must simply be kept less than the adjusted pedestal stress F^*_c. In contrast, the design of long columns for buckling failure is much less direct.

Buckling failure in timber columns is limited to sections whose l_e/d ratio is above a certain minimum value:

$$\text{Minimum } l_e/d = K = 0.67\sqrt{\frac{E'}{F^*_c}} \tag{31-7}$$

where E' is the modulus of elasticity of the wood, adjusted by all of the applicable adjustment factors.

F^*_c is the tabular design value in compression parallel to grain, F_c adjusted by all of the applicable adjustment factors as if the column were a pedestal.

As a guide, the value of K given by Eq.(31-1) ranges from about 18 to 30; an average value is about $^2/_3 F^*_c$.

The compressive stress at buckling for long columns is given by the Euler formula. In terms of the slenderness ratio l_e/d and with a factor of safety of 2.74 to buckling, the allowable stress F_{cE} in a long column is given earlier as Eq.(31-4), repeated here for immediate reference:

$$F_{cE} = \frac{0.30E'_c}{(l_e/d)^2} \tag{31-4}$$

where all symbols are those defined in earlier discussions.

In years past (before 1977), the two formulas given by Eq.(31-4) and (31-6) were the only formulas needed for column design. A graph of the two curves is given in Figure 31-5. The allowable stress is seen to change abruptly where the two curves intersect.

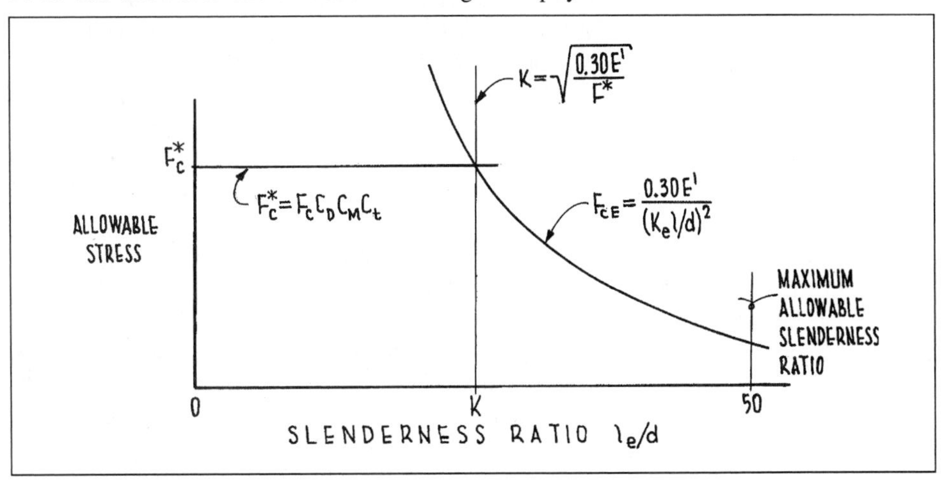

Figure 31-5 Two-range column formula.

The value of K = l_e/d at the point of intersection is calculated readily from the tabular values of E and F_c and the appropriate adjustment factors. If the actual value of l_e/d for a given column is greater than *K*, the column would fail by buckling and would therefore be designed by the Euler formula. If the actual value of l_e/d for a given column is less than *K*, the column would fail by crushing and must therefore be designed by direct stress, Eqs.(31-5) and (31-6).

In 1977, the two-range formula was refined to include a third failure mode for timber columns. This third mode provided a smoother transition between the crushing failure mode and the buckling failure mode. The resulting three-range column formula is shown graphically in Figure 31-6.

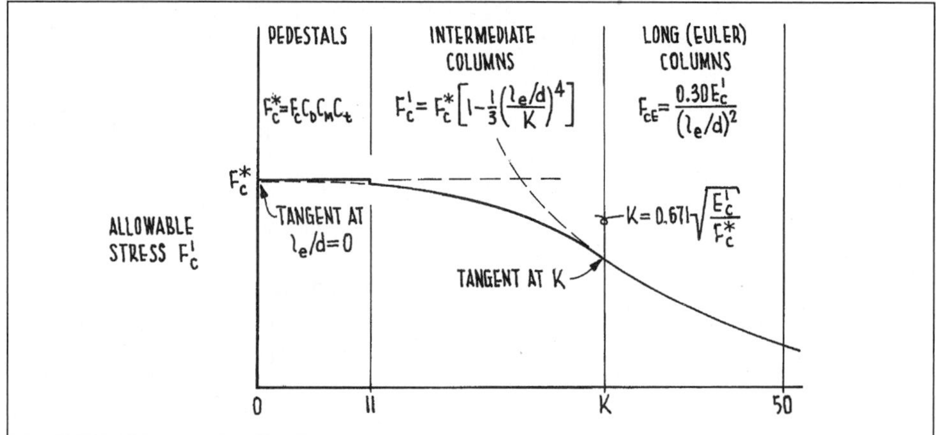

Figure 31-6 Three-range column formula.

As indicated, the allowable stress F_c' for columns in the intermediate range of l_e/d is given by:

$$F_c' = F_c^*\left[1-\frac{1}{3}\left(\frac{l_e/d}{K}\right)^4\right] \tag{31-8}$$

where all symbols are those defined earlier.

The transition curve was thus a fourth order parabola, tangent to the horizontal value of pedestal stress F_c^* at $l_e/d=0$ and tangent to the Euler stress curve at $l_e/d=K$. Since it was permitted to use the value of F_c^* for values of l_e/d up to 11, there is a small discontinuity in the curve at $l_e/d=11$. Otherwise, concepts as well as the curve itself are remarkably similar to the AISC formula for steel columns, presented earlier in Chapter 26.

The bracketed term in Equation (31-5) was considered to be the lateral stability factor C_P for intermediate columns, where:

$$C_P = 1-\frac{1}{3}\left(\frac{l_e/d}{K}\right)^4 \tag{31-6}$$

The allowable stress F_c' for intermediate columns may then be stated as:

$$F_c' = C_p F^* \text{ where } F_c^* = F_c C_D C_M C_t \tag{31-7a,b}$$

where all adjustment factors are those defined earlier.

The three-range column formula was used with success after its incorporation in 1977 until the design code revisions of 1991. In 1991, the three-range formula was further refined by the adoption of a single curve that meets all the same requirements (and values) of the three-range curve. If this single-range curve were to be plotted on the graph of the three-range curve of Figure 31-6 at comparable factors of safety, it would match the earlier curve very closely; the concepts of earlier years have thus been retained.

The single-range curve in current use is introduced in the next section. It will be seen that the same concepts, terms and symbols used in years past carry forward into current practices.

31.4 The NDS Single-Range Column Formula

The NDS single-range column formula is set forth in the 1991 edition of the National Design Specification. It gives the allowable direct stress on a solid timber column of any length or slenderness ratio:

$$F_c' = C_P F_c^*, \text{ where } F_c^* = F_c C_D C_M C_t \tag{31-8a, b}$$

where, except for C_P, all terms are those defined earlier.

The column stability factor C_P is given by:

$$C_P = \frac{1 + F_{cE}/F_c^*}{2c} - \sqrt{\left[\frac{1 + F_{cE}/F_c^*}{2c}\right]^2 - \frac{F_{cE}/F_c^*}{c}} \tag{31-9}$$

All terms in Equation (31-9) are those defined earlier except for the denominator term c. This new term c is introduced to provide a means to alter the factor of safety for three categories of wood products. For visually graded sawn lumber, c = 0.8. For round timber piles, c = 0.85. For glued laminated timber, c = 0.90.

Even though all terms used in Equation (31-9) have already been defined, it is well to list them again for immediate reference.

- F_{cE} is the Euler column stress for the allowable stress in columns of visually graded sawn lumber:

$$F_{cE} = \frac{0.3E'}{(l_e/d)^2} \tag{31-4}$$

where E' is the modulus of elasticity with all appropriate adjustments.

l_e is the effective length in the direction of buckling between any two consecutive points of zero moment.

d is the depth of bending in the direction of buckling.

(The coefficient 0.3 becomes 0.418 for glued laminated timber.)

- F_c^* is the adjusted compressive stress parallel to grain in a timber pedestal too short to be subject to buckling:

$$F_c^* = F_c C_D C_M C_t \tag{31-6}$$

where F_c is the tabular stress given in Tables T-3 for compression stress parallel to grain.

C_D is the adjustment factor for load curation.

C_M is the adjustment factor for wet service conditions.

C_t is the adjustment factor for elevated temperatures.

- c is a factor used to alter the factor of safety for various wood products:

c = 0.80 for visually graded sawn lumber and timber.
c = 0.85 for found timber piles.
c = 0.90 for glued laminated timber.

A brief discussion of the single-range formula is appropriate since it has been so abruptly introduced without derivation. It might best be regarded as a means to fit the three-range formula by curve-fitting it with a single-range formula. Upon examination, the value of C_P is obviously the lesser of the two solutions given by a quadratic formula for parabolic equation in C_p:

$$cC_P^2 - \left(1 + F_{cE} / F_c^*\right) C_P + F_{cE} / F_c^* = 0 \qquad (31\text{-}10)$$

A special case of C_P will occur for short columns when $F_{cE} = F_c^*$. For that case C_P = 1/c, which simply adjusts the factor of safety for pedestals. The minimum value that C_P can have is for very long columns where F_{cE} approaches zero. For that case, $C_P = 0$ and the allowable stress approaches zero.

While somewhat more clumsy to use than the three-range formula, the single range formula utilizes familiar concepts: F_c^* is the adjusted pedestal stress, which is the highest allowable stress that would be permitted if the column being investigated were to be continuously braced; F_{cE} is the adjusted buckling stress, which is the much lower allowable stress that would be permitted if the column being investigated were actually subject to buckling. The value given by C_P is then the value appropriate for the allowable stress in the actual column somewhere between the two extremes.

The foregoing introduction, however brief, is all that is necessary to permit use of the single-range formula. Before proceeding into some examples, however, another requirement for stresses unrelated to the column formula comes into consideration.

An additional condition enters into column design that does not occur in other types of members. The National Design Specification includes a limitation on the end grain in bearing. The limitation is given as tabular design values F_g, which is subject only to adjustment factors D_D and C_t.

Typical tabular values of F_g are given in Table T-13 in the Technical Manual for Douglas fir-larch, Southern pine and Spruce-pine-fir. The values of F_g for end grain bearing stress are observed to be generally lower than the values for compressive stress F_c at some distance away from the end grain. The two sets of stresses are shown for comparison in Table 31-1, following.

Table 31-1 Comparison of Typical Tabular Design Stresses.

	Tabular value of end grain bearing F_g, psi		**Range of values of compression parallel to grain F_c, psi**	
Species	**Dry Service**	**Wet Service**	**Dry Service**	**Wet Service**
Douglas fir-larch				
J&P	2020	1350	675 to 1400	475 to 980
P&T	1480	1350	1000 to 1350	910 to 1230
Southern pine				
J&P	1970	1320	475 to 1050	475 to 1050
P&T	1450	1320	725 to 925	725 to 925
Spruce-pine-fir				
J&P	1410	940	450 to 1050	315 to 735
P&T	1040	940	700 to 800	640 to 730

Examination of Table 31-1 indicates that the tabular values of F_g are consistently lower than those for F_c. Except for conditions where the base of the column may be wet occasionally, the limitations on the end bearing stress is not usually a serious problem.

Some examples will illustrate the use of the single-range column formula for timber columns.

Example 31-1

Determination of column capacity.

Given: 8 x 8 timber column, southern pine No. 2, hinged top and bottom, l_e = 18' - 0". Periodically wet, permanent duration of load.

To Find: Capacity of the column.

Solution: Establish adjustment factors:

For stresses, $C_M = 1.00$, $C_D = 0.90$.

All other factors are 1.00.

Determine the adjusted pedestal stress F_c^*:

$$F_c^* = F_C C_D C_M C_t$$

From Table T-3b, F_c = 525 psi

$$F_c^* = 5225 \text{ x } 0.90 \text{ x } 1.00 = 473 \text{ psi}$$

Determine the adjusted Euler stress F_{cE}:

$$F_{cE} = \frac{0.30E'}{(l_e/d)^2}$$

From Table T-3b, E = 1,200,000 psi

$$E' = EC_D C_M = 1$$
$$= 1{,}200{,}000 \text{ x } 0.90 \text{ x } 1.00$$
$$= 1{,}080{,}000$$

$$F_{cE} = \frac{0.30x1{,}080{,}000}{(18x12/7.5)^2} = 391 \text{ psi}$$

Determine C_P for F_{cE}/F_c^* = 0.826, c = 0.80

$$C_P = \frac{1+F_{cE}/F_c^*}{2c} - \sqrt{\left[\frac{1+F_{cE}/F_c^*}{2c}\right]^2 - \frac{F_{CE}/F_C^*}{c}}$$

$$= \frac{1+0.826}{1.6} - \sqrt{\left(\frac{1+0.826}{1.6}\right)^2 - \frac{0.826}{0.80}}$$

$$= 0.622$$

Determine allowable column stress F_c':

$$F_c' = F_c^* C_P = 473 \text{ x } 0.622 = 294 \text{ psi}$$

Determine capacity of the column:

$$P = F_c' A = 294 \text{ x } 7.5 \text{ x } 7.5 = 16{,}550 \text{ lb.}$$

Example 31-2

Determination of column capacity.

Given: 4x6 J&P column, No. 1SPF, hinged top and bottom. l_e = 8' - 6". Service temperatures occasionally up to 120°F. Permanent duration of load.

To Find: Capacity of the column.

Solution: Establish adjustment factors:

For occasional elevated temperatures, $C_t = 1.00$.
For permanent loading, $C_D = 0.90$.
All other factors are 1.00.

Determine the adjusted pedestal stress F_c^*:

$$F_c^* = F_c C_D C_M C_t$$

From Table T-3c, $F_c = 1210$ psi

$$F_c^* = 1210 \text{ x } 0.90 = 1090 \text{ psi}$$

Determine the adjusted Euler stress F_{cE}:

$$F_{cE} = \frac{0.30E'}{(l_e/d)^2}$$

From Table T-3c, E = 1,400,000 psi

$$E' = EC_M C_t = 1{,}400{,}000 \text{ psi}$$

$$F_{cE} = \frac{0.30x1{,}400{,}000}{(8.5x12/3.5)^2} = 495 \text{ psi}$$

Determine C_P for $F_{cE}/F_c^* = 0.454$, $c = 0.80$

$$C_P = \frac{1+F_{cE}/F_c^*}{2c} - \sqrt{\left[\frac{1+F_{cE}/F_c^*}{2c}\right]^2 - \frac{F_{CE}/F_C^*}{c}}$$

$$= \frac{1+0.454}{1.6} - \sqrt{\left(\frac{1+0.454}{1.6}\right)^2 - \frac{0.454}{0.80}}$$

$$= 0.400$$

Determine allowable column stress F_c':

$$F_c' = F_c^* C_P = 1090 \text{ x } 0.400 = 437 \text{ psi}$$

Determine capacity of the column:

$$P = F_c' A = 437 \text{ x } 3.5 \text{ x } 3.5 = 8400 \text{ lbs}$$

Example 31-3

Design of a column.

Given: Column load of 16,000 lbs, l_e = 15'-4", hinged top and bottom, Douglas fir-larch, No. 1, normal service conditions.

To Find: Suitable square column.

Solution: Establish adjustment factors:

No special conditions; all factors are 1.0.

Select a trial size. Since the column is to be square, trial sizes are limited to 4x4, 6x6, or 8x8:

Try 6x6 column.

Verify the capacity of the section for a load of 16,000 lbs.

Determine the adjusted pedestal stress F_c^*:

$$F_c^* = F_C C_D C_M C_t$$

From Table T-3a, F_c =1000 psi

$$F_c^* = 1000 \text{ psi}$$

Determine the adjusted Euler stress F_{cE}:

$$F_{cE} = \frac{0.30E'}{(l_e/d)^2}$$

From Table T-3a, E = 1,600,000 psi

$$E' = EC_M C_t = 1{,}600{,}000 \text{ psi}$$

$$F_{cE} = \frac{0.3x1{,}600{,}000}{(15.33x12/5.5)^2} = 429 \text{ psi}$$

Determine C_P for F_{cE}/F_c^* = 0.429, c = 0.80

$$C_P = \frac{1+F_{cE}/F_c^*}{2c} - \sqrt{\left[\frac{1+F_{cE}/F_c^*}{2c}\right]^2 - \frac{F_{CE}/F_C^*}{c}}$$

$$= \frac{1+0.429}{1.6} - \sqrt{\left(\frac{1+0.429}{1.6}\right)^2 - \frac{0.429}{0.80}}$$

$$= 0.382$$

Determine allowable column stress F_c':

$$F_c' = F_c^* C_P = 1000 \text{ x } 0.382 = 382 \text{ psi}$$

Determine capacity of the column:

$P = F_c' A = 382 \text{ x } 5.5 \text{ x } 5.5$
$= 11{,}600 \text{ lb} < 16{,}000 \text{ lb (No Good)}$

The 6x6 column section is inadequate. Try the 8x8 column section.

Determine the adjusted pedestal stress F_c^*:

$F_c^* = 1000$ psi

Determine the adjusted Euler stress F_{cE}:

$$F_{cE} = \frac{0.30x1{,}600{,}000}{(15.33x12/7.5)^2} = 797 \text{ psi}$$

Determine C_P for $F_{cE}/F_c^* = 0.797$, c = 0.80

$$C_P = \frac{1 + F_{cE}/F_c^*}{2c} - \sqrt{\left[\frac{1 + F_{cE}/F_c^*}{2c}\right]^2 - \frac{F_{CE}/F_C^*}{c}}$$

$$= \frac{1 + 0.797}{1.6} - \sqrt{\left(\frac{1 + 0.797}{1.6}\right)^2 - \frac{0.797}{0.80}}$$

$$= 0.608$$

Determine allowable column stress F_c':

$F_c' = F_c^* C_P = 1000 \text{ x } 0.608 = 608$ psi

Determine capacity of the column:

$P = F_c' A = 608 \text{ x } 7.5 \text{ x } 7.5$
$= 34{,}200 \text{ lb} >> 16{,}000 \text{ lb (O.K.)}$

Use 8 x 8 column section.

Example 31-4

Determination of load capacity.

Given: 8 x 8 compression member in a truss, l_e = 4' - 8". Southern pine, No. 2, hinged both ends. Normal service conditions.

To Find: Capacity of the compression member.

Solution: Establish the adjustment factors:

No special conditions; all factors are 1.0.

Determine the adjusted pedestal stress F_c^*:

$$F_c^* = F_C C_D C_M C_t$$

From Table T-3b, F_c =525 psi

$$F_c^* = 525 \text{ psi}$$

Determine the adjusted Euler stress F_{cE}:

$$F_{cE} = \frac{0.30E'}{(l_e/d)^2}$$

From Table T-3b, E = 1,200,000 psi

$$E' = EC_M C_t = 1{,}200{,}000 \text{ psi}$$

$$F_{cE} = \frac{0.3x1{,}200{,}000}{(4.67x12/7.5)^2} = 857 \text{ psi}$$

Determine C_P for F_{cE}/F_c^* = 1.633, c = 0.80

$$C_P = \frac{1+F_{cE}/F_c^*}{2c} - \sqrt{\left[\frac{1+F_{cE}/F_c^*}{2c}\right]^2 - \frac{F_{CE}/F_C^*}{c}}$$

$$= \frac{1+1.633}{1.6} - \sqrt{\left(\frac{1+1.633}{1.6}\right)^2 - \frac{1.633}{0.80}}$$

$$= 0.829$$

Determine allowable compressive stress F_c':

$$F_c' = F_c^* C_P = 525 \text{ x } 0.829 = 435 \text{ psi}$$

Determine load capacity of the member:

$$P = F_c' A = 435 \text{ x } 7.5 \text{ x } 7.5 = 24{,}500 \text{ lbs}$$

A point of interest in Example 31-4 is that the member is quite short and heavy, approaching a pedestal. Note that the ratio F_{cE}/F_c^* is significantly greater than 1. Even so, the allowable column stress remains well below F_c^*, with C_P = 0.829.

31.5 Spaced Columns

A variation in timber columns is the use of spaced members as shown in Figure 31-7. Spaced columns are used frequently as compression members in trusses. They are also used in architectural applications, where their appeal is primarily that of appearance.

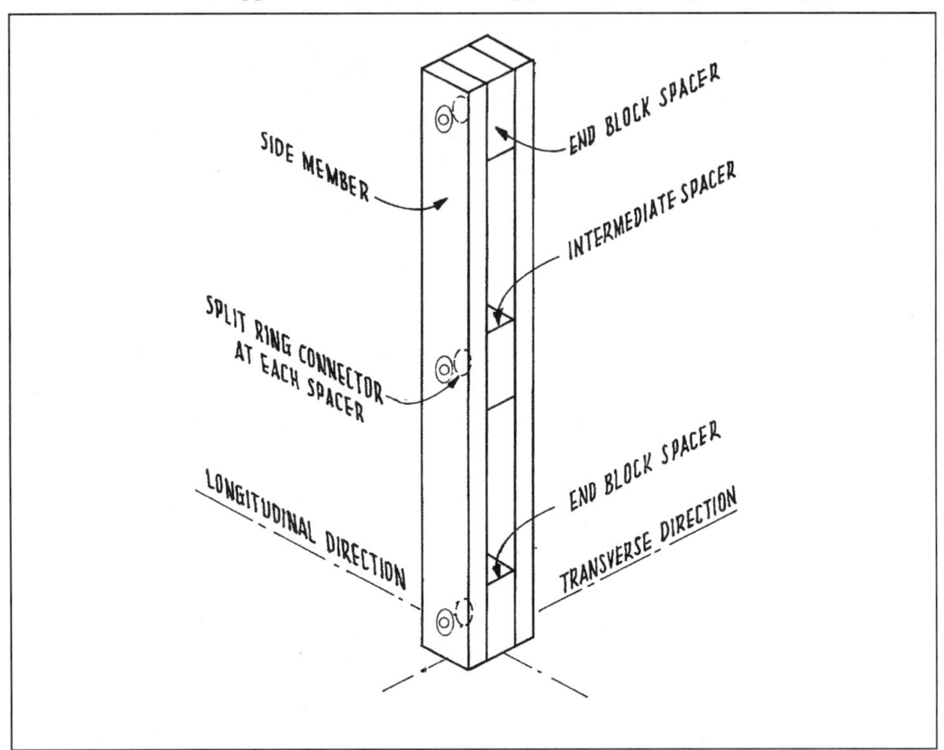

Figure 31-7 Spaced compression member.

Like a solid column, the spaced column of Figure 31-7 may fail either in the longitudinal direction or in the transverse direction. In the longitudinal direction, the capacity is simply that of the two side members acting individually as simple solid columns; the existence of the spacers has no appreciable effect. In the transverse direction, the fixity of the two thin members at the spacers improves the capacity markedly over that of two individual members.

In either direction, the capacity of a spaced column is computed as an allowable compressive stress times the total cross sectional area. As usual, the allowable stress is different in each of the two directions, depending on the l_e/d in each direction. The allowable stress is computed for the total unsupported length l_l or l_2. The distance between spacers is deliberately limited such that localized buckling between spacers does not occur.

The National Design Specification requires that the connections at the spacer blocks be made with split ring connectors. Consequently, the capacity of a spaced column is dependent on the capacity of the split ring connectors at the spacers. Since split ring connectors are not included in this textbook, the design of spaced columns has had to be omitted. The omission is not due to the difficulty of the design but simply due to limited scope.

31.6 Column Connections

Except for layout requirements, the analysis and design of connections in compression members are identical to those in tension members. All of the procedures developed in Chapter 30 for tension members remain valid.

The one exception is in the bolt or fastener layout, as prescribed in Table T-10. The end distance for fasteners in a compression member are significantly less than for those in a tension member. A comparison of these requirements is shown in Chapter 30 in Figure 30-8.

When steel side plates are used to connect a beam to a column, it is the practice to design the connection to transmit the entire load through the connection. No credit is taken for transmission of load by bearing from the beam to the column. A typical example of such a connection is shown in Figure 31-8.

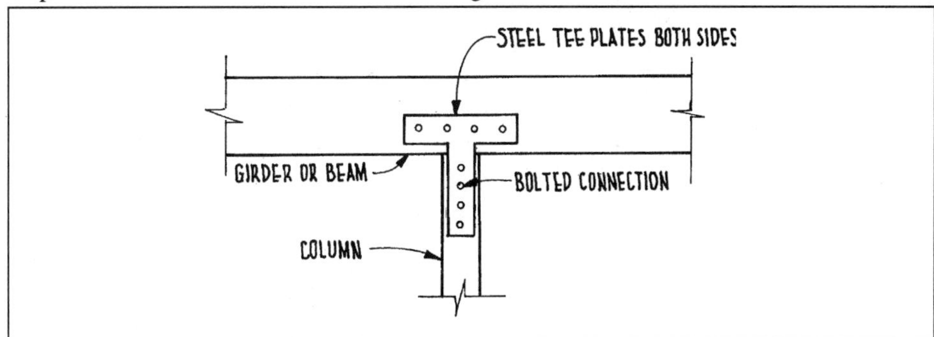

Figure 31-8 Typical beam-column connection.

Review Questions

1. Why are timber columns generally limited to heights of one story?
2. State the Euler column formula for critical stress in columns and define each term.
3. In long timber columns, what is the factor of safety that is applied to the Euler formula to obtain the allowable stress?
4. At what slenderness ratio does a column change from a long column to an intermediate column?
5. State the three ways in which compression members of various lengths may fail.
6. The three-range timber column formula has a discontinuity at a slenderness ratio of 11. Why?
7. How is the allowable stress determined for an intermediate column?
8. State the defining equation for the lateral stability of columns factor C_P and define each term.
9. In spaced columns, what feature contributes the additional usable strength in the transverse direction?
10. In spaced columns, why isn't local buckling failure of the thin side members a consideration?
11. In spaced columns, how is the load on the connectors determined?
12. In spaced columns, how is the load capacity of the connectors determined?

CHAPTER

32

TIMBER BEAMS AND THEIR CONNECTIONS

32.1 General Design Considerations

The concepts concerning the selection of timber beams varies but little from that of steel beams. The same considerations apply:

1. Preparation of detailed shear and moment diagrams.
2. Selection of a member to sustain maximum flexure.
3. Review and revise to sustain maximum shear.
4. Review and revise to suit support conditions.
5. Review and revise to suit deformation requirements.
6. Review and revise to assure lateral stability.

The major difference between the selection of timber members and steel members lies in the determination of allowable stresses. As noted in earlier chapters, the considerations used to determine the allowable stresses in timber are quite different from those used for steel.

For stress in timber beams, a primary concern is the weakness of timber in shear parallel to grain. Typically, the allowable stress in shear is only about 10 to 15 percent of that in tension. In contrast, the allowable shear stress in steel is typically 67 percent of that in tension.

A second major weakness in timber is that of the compression stress perpendicular to grain. Such stress occurs whever the beam is supported by resting it on a supporting member, or wherever a concentrated load is delivered to a beam by placing it directly on top of the beam. Careful attention must be paid to such load cases to assure that crushing of the wood does not occur.

As with all other beam materials, the design process for timber beams begins with shear and moment diagrams.

32.2 Shear and Moment Diagrams

The construction of shear and moment diagrams is developed fully in Chapter 14. The development is expanded and used further in Chapter 18 for the design of concrete beams and still further in Chapter 27 for the design of steel beams. The construction of shear and moment diagrams for the design of timber beams is identical to that developed earlier for concrete and steel.

Two sets of shear and moment diagrams are presented in the following examples. These are the diagrams that will be used in succeeding examples in the design of timber beams. The first example is typical of the type of loading one would find in motel design, where each room has a small balcony. The second example is typical of falsework or formwork that utilizes hinged walers.

Example 32-1

Shear and moment diagrams for timber beams.

Given: Load case as shown.

To Find: Shear and moment diagrams, to include maximum and minimum values and all points of inflection.

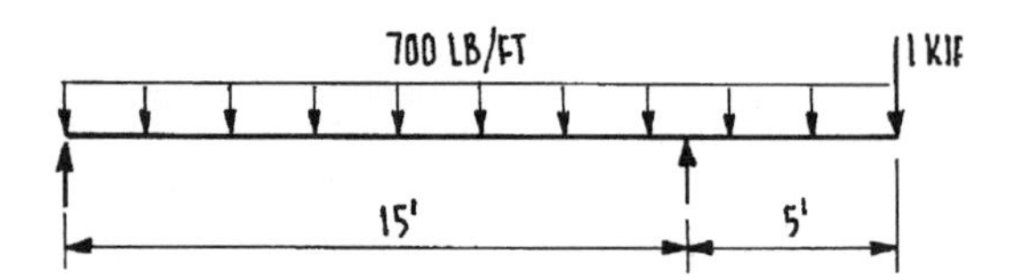

Solution:

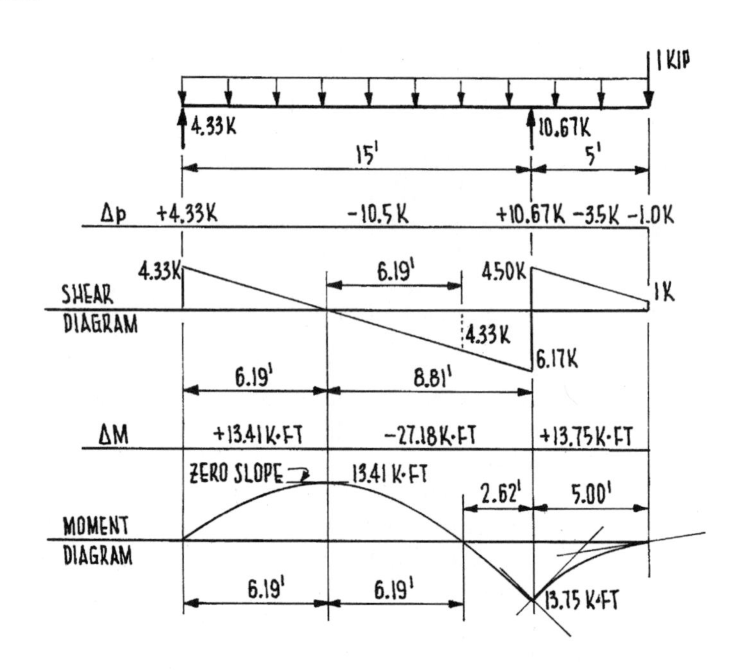

Example 32-2

Shear and moment diagrams for timber beams.

Given: Load case as shown.

To Find: Shear and moment diagrams, to include maximum and minimum values and all points of inflection.

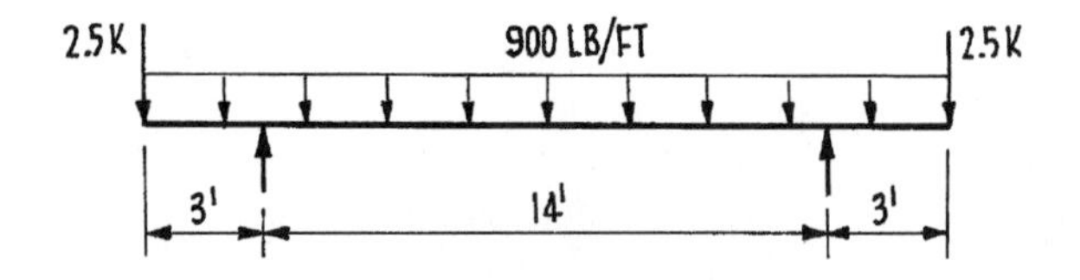

Solution:

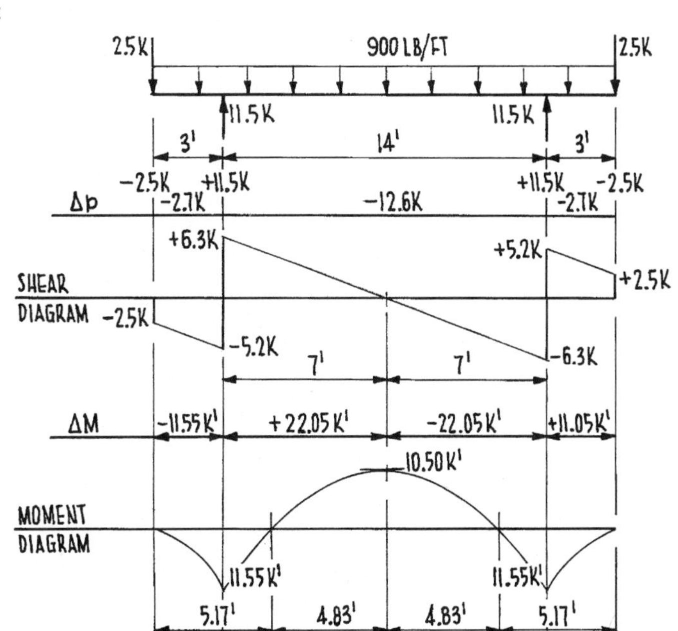

32.3 Design of Beams for Flexure and Shear

It is recalled from the design of steel beams that a beam is initially selected for its capacity in flexure then reviewed to assure that it also has adequate capacity in shear. In timber, however, the capacity of the section in shear so often governs the size of the member that it is well to combine both steps into a single choice. That combined approach is the approach presented here.

Since timber beams are almost always rectangular, it is both convenient and practical to develop special equations and formulas that apply to rectangular sections. For computing the flexural stress, for example, the flexural stress is computed by the familiar flexure formula (see Chapter 10 for details):

$$f_c = \frac{M_c}{I} = \frac{M}{S} \tag{32-1}$$

where S = I/c.

The dimensions of a rectangular section in bending about its own neutral axis is shown in Figure 32-1. The symbols shown in Figure 32-1 are those used by AITC.

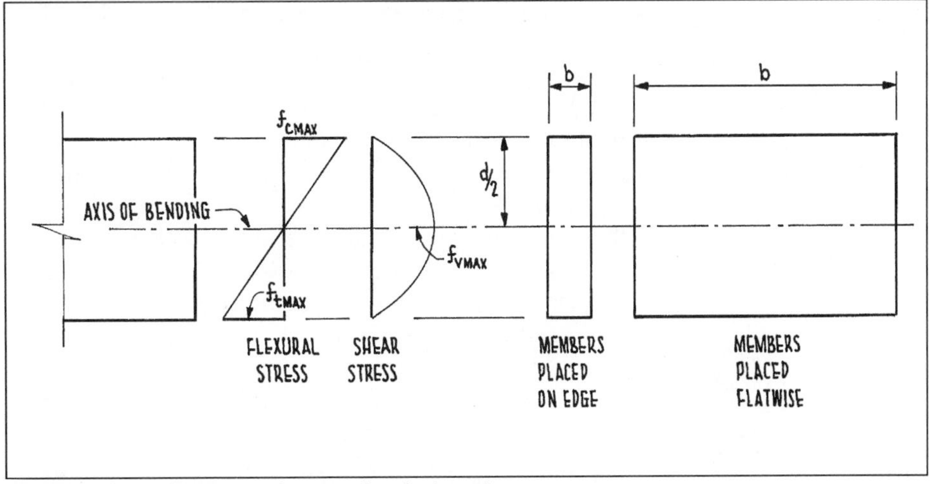

Figure 32-1 Rectangular section in bending.

The section modulus for a rectangular section is readily developed:

For rectangular sections only,

$$S = \frac{I}{c} = \frac{bd^3/12}{d/2} = \frac{bd^2}{6} \quad (32\text{-}2)$$

$$S = \frac{bd^2}{6}$$

Equation (32-2) will be found to be a convenient formula in the design of timber beams; it is recommended that it be committed to memory.

The shear stress in a rectangular section is also shown in Figure 32-1. It is computed by the familiar beam shear equation (see Chapter 10 for details):

$$f_v = \frac{VQ}{Ib} = \frac{VA'\bar{y}}{Ib}. \quad (32\text{-}3)$$

Equation (32-3) reduces to a much simpler form when it is applied to rectangular sections. Since the maximum shear stress occurs at the neutral axis, the values of $A'\bar{y}$ and I are readily computed:

For rectangular sections only:

$$f_v = \frac{VA'\bar{y}}{Ib} = \frac{V(bd/2)(d/4)}{\left(\frac{bd^3}{12}\right)b}$$

$$\text{Maximum } f_v = \frac{3V}{2A} \quad (32\text{-}4)$$

where A = bd
and V is the shear at a distance *d* from the face of support.

Equations 32-2 and 32-4 are used repeatedly in succeeding discussions and throughout all of timber design. Probably the most common error made by students in using them is to attempt to use them on nonrectangular shapes. *Equations (32-2) and (32-4) may not be applied to tee shapes, I shapes or C shapes or any other nonrectangular shapes.*

The shear force *V* used in Equation (32-4) may be taken as the shear force at a distance *d* from the face of support, as noted. This provision reduces the shear force (and area of section) considerably. Since shear is such a critical item in timber, many designers choose to ignore this provision.

Two adjustment factors apply to tabular flexural stress F_b that have to do with the size and shape of the section. The first, C_F, is a size factor that reduces the allowable flexural stress a small amount as the section becomes deeper; it is already included in the lumber sizes of Tables 3a, b and c, but it must be applied to all lumber or timber sizes where bending depth exceeds 12 in. The second new factor, C_f, is a function of the shape of the section; it allows an increase in allowable stress for round sections and diamond-shaped sections.

Some examples will illustrate the selection of timber sections.

Example 32-3

Selection of a timber beam in flexure and beam shear.

Given: Timber beam, Southern pine, No. 2. From the shear and moment diagrams, maximum moment = 15·ft, design shear force = 4 kips. Normal conditions of service.

To Find: Suitable size of a section to sustain the moment and shear.

Solution: Establish the adjustment factors:

No special conditions; all adjustment factors are 1.00.

Trial tabular stresses are found in Table T-3b for sections having a bending depth of 12 in. or less. At this point, assume the member will be in the B&S sizes, with thickness 5 in. or more.

$F_b = 850$ psi
$F_v = 100$ psi

If the actual bending depth turns out to be greater than 12 in., these values will have to be adjusted for depth.

Under normal conditions of service the allowable stresses F_b' and F_V' are the same as the tabular stresses F_b and F_v.

The required magnitude of the section modulus is:

$$S = \frac{M}{F_b'} = \frac{15{,}000x12}{850} = 212 \text{ in.}^3$$

The required shear area is:

$$A = \frac{3V}{2F_V'} = \frac{3x4000}{2x100} = 60 \text{ in.}^3$$

Table T-1 is entered with these values of S and A.

Starting at the top of Table T-1, move down the list of sizes for S and A with a small straightedge until a section is found that has a section modulus of at least 2122 in.^{3} and an area of at least 60 in.^{2} The first section that meets both these requirements is a 6 x 16 section.

The most economical section in timber is the one having the smallest cross sectional area. Further examination of Table T-1 reveals that there are no other sections having a smaller area that will satisfy the requirements for S = 164 in.^{3}

Since the section is deeper than 12 in., the modifier C_F must be applied to the tabular stress F_b. The new value for the allowable stress is therefore modified by C_F [see Equation (29-7)]:

$$C_F = \left(\frac{12}{d}\right)^{1/9} = \left(\frac{12}{16}\right)^{1/9} = 0.968$$

$$F_b' = C_F F_b = 0.968 \text{ x } 850 = 823 \text{ psi}$$

The required magnitude of the section is revised correspondingly,

$$S = \frac{15{,}000x12}{823} = 219 \text{ in.}^3$$

Since the trial 6 x 16 section has a section modulus of 220.2, it is still adequate.

Use section 6 x 16, Southern pine, No. 2.

Example 32-4

Selection of a timber beam for flexure and beam shear.

Given: Timber beam, Spruce-pine-fir, No. 1 B&S. From the shear and moment diagrams, maximum moment = 12.5·ft, design shear force = 5 kips. Normal conditions of service, repetitive member use.

To Find: Suitable section to sustain the given moment and shear.

Solution: Establish the adjustment factors:

No special conditions; all adjustment factors are 1.0.

Trial tabular stresses are found in Table T-3C. The section is assumed initially to be in the B&S sizes, with thickness 5 in. or more. If the bending depth turns out to be more than 12 in., these values will have to be adjusted:

$F_b = 900$ psi
$F_v = 65$ psi

Under normal conditions of service, the allowable stresses F_b' and F_V' are the same as the tabular stresses F_b and F_v.

The required magnitude of the section modulus is:

$$S = \frac{M}{F_b'} = \frac{12{,}500}{900} = 167 \text{ in.}^3$$

The required shear area is:

$$A = \frac{3V}{2F_V'} = \frac{3x5000}{2x65} = 115 \text{ in.}^2$$

Again, enter Table T-1 at the top of the table and proceed down the table until a section is found that has a section modulus of at least 167 in.^{3} and an area of at least 115 in.^{2} The first section to meet these conditions is an 8 x 16 section.

The 8 x 16 section is seen to be wastefully inefficient in flexure (S = 300.3) just to get enough area to sustain the shear. Further examination of Table T-1 reveals that there are no other sections having a smaller area that will sustain both the given shear and the given moment. The inefficiency in flexure will simply have to be tolerated.

Since the section is deeper than 12 in., the modifier C_F must be applied to the tabular stress F_b. The new value for the allowable stress is therefore modified by C_F [see Equation (29-7)]:

$$C_F = \left(\frac{12}{d}\right)^{1/9} = \left(\frac{12}{16}\right)^{1/9} = 0.968$$

$$F_b' = C_F F_b = 0.968 \text{ x } 900 = 872 \text{ psi.}$$

The required magnitude of the section modulus is revised correspondingly:

$$S = \frac{12{,}500x12}{872} = 172 \text{ in.}^3$$

Since the trial section has a great deal of excess capacity, it is still adequate.

Use section 8 x 16, Spruce-pine-fir, No. 1 B&S.

Example 32-5

Selection of a timber beam in flexure and beam shear.

Given: Load conditions of Example 32-1. Douglas fir-larch, No. 2 J&P or No. 1 B&S. Permanent duration of load. Occasional wet service conditions for short periods of time.

To Find: Suitable section to sustain the loads.

Solution: Establish the adjustment factors.

$C_D = 0.9$ for permanent load. All other factors are 1.0.

The maximum shear and moment are found from the diagrams of Example 32-1:

$$M_{MAX} = 13.75 \text{ kip·ft}$$

Since the depth d is still unknown, the design shear force V is assumed to occur at a distance of 1 foot from face of support:

$$\text{Design V} = \tfrac{7.81}{8.81}(6.17) = 5.5 \text{ kips.}$$

Trial tabular stresses are found in Table T-3a. The section is assumed initially to be in the B&S sizes, with thicknesses 5 in. or more. If the bending depth turns out to be more than 12 in., the allowable stress values will have to be adjusted:

$F_b = 1350$ psi (for No. 1 B&S)
$F_v = 85$ psi

The allowable stresses F_b' and F_V' are computed as usual, where $C_D = 0.90$ and $C_M = 1.00$:

$$F_b' = C_D C_M F_b = 0.90 \text{ x } 1.00 \text{ x } 1350 = 1215 \text{ psi}$$
$$F_V' = C_D C_M F_b = 0.90 \text{ x } 1.00 \text{ x } 85 = 77 \text{ psi}$$

The required magnitude of the section modulus is:

$$S = \frac{M}{F_b'} = \frac{13,750x12}{1215} = 1136 \text{ in.}^3$$

The required magnitude of the shear area is:

$$A = \frac{3V}{2F_V} = \frac{3x500}{2x85} = 97 \text{ in.}^2$$

From Table T-1, the smallest section (in area) meeting these requirements is an 8 x 14.

(Note that this section is adequate when it is oriented in the tall position only.)

Since the section in its tall position is more than 12 in. deep, the size factor C_F must be applied. For d = 14 in.:

$$C_F = \left(\frac{12}{d}\right)^{1/9} = \left(\frac{12}{14}\right)^{1/9} = 0.983$$

$$F_b' = C_F C_D C_M F_b = 0.983 \text{ x } 1215 = 1190 \text{ psi}$$

The required magnitude of the section modulus is revised accordingly:

$$S = \frac{13,750x12}{1190} = 139 \text{ in.}^3$$

Since the trial section has a section modulus of 300, it remains adequate.

The shear force is now corrected for a depth of 13.5 in. from face of support:

$$V = \frac{8.81x12 - 13.5}{8.81x12}(6.17) = 5.35\text{k}$$

The required area is recomputed:

$$A = \frac{3V}{2F_V} = \frac{3x5350}{2x85} = 94.4 \text{ in.}^2$$

A reexamination of Table T-1 indicates that a 6 x 18 section is a better choice (its area is smaller). The 6 x 18 section is now reviewed for its suitability.

The size factor C_F changes to 0.96, hence:

$$F_b' = 0.96 \text{ x } 1215 = 1166 \text{ psi}$$

The required section modulus is then:

$$S = \frac{13,750x12}{1166} = 142$$

The shear force is now corrected for a depth of 17.5 in. From face of support:

$$V = \frac{8.81x12 - 17.5}{8.81x12}(6.17) = 5.15 \text{ kips}$$

The required area is recomputed:

$$A = \frac{3V}{2F_V} = \frac{3x5150}{2x85} = 91 \text{ in.}^2$$

The 6 x 18 section is therefore adequate.

Use 6 x 18 section.

Example 32-6

Selection of a timber beam in flexure and beam shear.

Given: Load conditions of Example 32-2. Southern pine, No. 2. Normal conditions of service.

To Find: Suitable section to sustain the loads.

Solution: Establish adjustment factors:

No special conditions; all factors are 1.0.

The maximum shear and moment are found from the diagrams of Example 32-2.

$$M_{MAX} = 11.55 \text{ kip·ft}$$

Since the depth d is still unknown, the design shear force V is assumed to occur at a distance of 1 foot from face of support:

$$\text{Design } V = \frac{6}{7}(6.3) = 5.40 \text{ kips}$$

Trial tabular stresses are found in Table T-3b. The section is assumed initially to be in the B&S sizes with thicknesses 5 in. or more. If the bending depth turns out to be more than 12 in., the allowable stresses will have to be adjusted:

$$F_b = 850 \text{ psi}, F_V = 100 \text{ psi}$$

For ordinary conditions of use, all adjustment factors are 1.00 and the allowable stresses are taken to be the tabular stresses:

$$F_b' = 850 \text{ psi}, F_v = 100 \text{ psi}$$

The required magnitude of the section modulus is:

$$S = \frac{M}{F_b'} = \frac{11{,}550x12}{850} = 163 \text{ in.}^3$$

The required magnitude of the shear area is:

$$A = \frac{3V}{2F_V'} = \frac{3x5400}{2x100} = 81 \text{ in.}^2$$

From Table T-1, the smallest section (in area) meeting the requirements for section modulus and shear area is a section 6 x 16.

The allowable stress F_b' is now corrected for the shape factor C_F:

$$C_F = \left(\frac{12}{d}\right)^{1/9} = \left(\frac{12}{16}\right)^{1/9} = 0.968$$

$$F_b' = 0.968 \text{ x } 850 = 823 \text{ psi}$$

The revised section modulus is therefore:

$$S = \frac{M}{F_b'} = \frac{11{,}550x12}{823} = 168 \text{ in.}^3 \text{ (O.K.)}$$

The shear force V is now corrected for the actual d:

$$\text{Design}\, V = \frac{84 - 15.5}{84}(6.3) = 5.13 \text{ kips}$$

The required area is revised accordingly:

$$A = \frac{3V}{2F_V'} = \frac{3x5130}{2x100} = 77 \text{ in.}^2 \text{ (O.K.)}$$

Use 6 x 16 section.

32.4 Design of Beams for Support Conditions

Timber beams may be supported either by direct bearing on a support or by a conventional connection. The connection may be bolted or it may utilize commercial connectors. Either way, the beam itself must be adequate to receive the concentrated load delivered by the support or by the connection. Examples of such support conditions are shown in Figure 32-2.

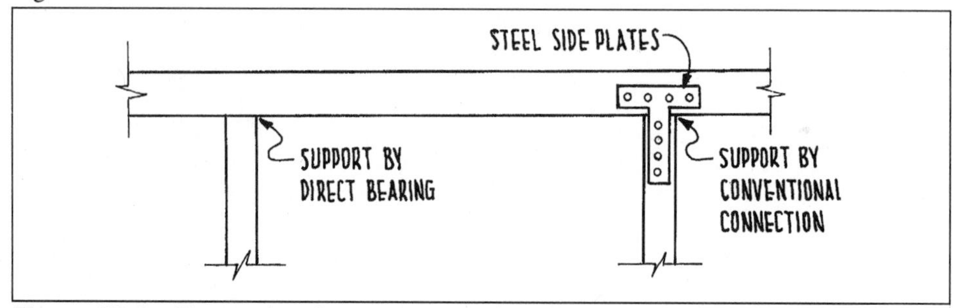

Figure 32-2 Types of end supports for a beam.

The case of beam bearing on its support is presented in this section. The case of supporting connectors is treated in later discussions on connectors. While steel side plates are shown in Figure 32-2, timber side plates are acceptable in such supports.

At the direct bearing shown in Figure 32-2, the stress on the column is in compression parallel to grain, an orientation in which wood has a relatively high capacity. On the beam, however, the stress is a compressive stress perpendicular to grain, an orientation in which wood has a relatively low capacity. Particular attention must be given to such supports if crushing of the wood perpendicular to grain is to be avoided.

Another type of support in which the beam is supported by bearing stress is that of a framing hanger, as shown in Figure 32-3. Conservatively, the entire beam reaction is transmitted to the support by bearing on the framing hanger. Usually, the framing hanger is deliberately sized to provide adequate area in bearing, but such supports must always be verified for their bearing stress; surprises are common in timber supports.

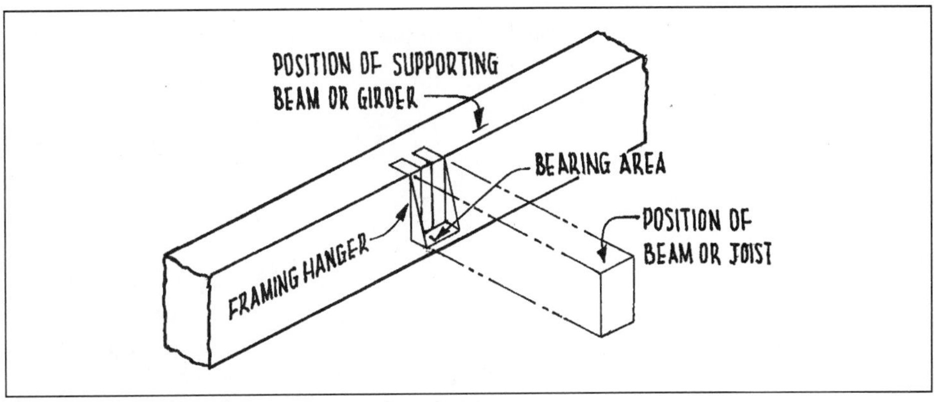

Figure 32-3 Bearing area on a framing hanger.

It should be noted from Equation (29-4) that the only adjustment factors that apply to stress perpendicular to grain are C_M, C_b and C_t. These factors are for moisture, end bearing and temperature. Stress perpendicular to grain is the only stress that is unaffected by duration of load (see Table 29-1).

Some examples will illustrate the investigation for bearing stresses perpendicular to grain.

Example 32-7

Bearing stresses perpendicular to grain.

Given: 4 x 14 beam having an end reaction of 2 kips. Support is provided by a 4 x 6 column as shown. Spruce-pine-fir, No. 2 J&P. Normal conditions of service.

To Find: Whether the beam is adequate in direct bearing.

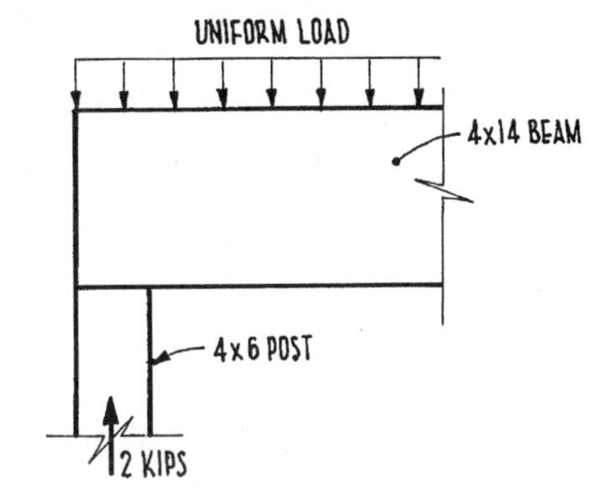

Solution: From Table T-3c the allowable stress perpendicular to grain is:

$$F_{C\perp} = 425 \text{ psi.}$$

The actual stress perpendicular to grain is the load divided by the contact area:

$$f_{C\perp} = \frac{P}{A} = \frac{2000}{3.5x5.5} = 104 \text{ psi} < 425 \text{ psi allowed (O.K.)}$$

Since the bearing involves material closer than 3 in. to the end of the beam, the increase for end grain bearing stress C_b does not apply.

It is interesting in this case to determine the maximum end reaction that the beam could develop due to limits on the shear stress:

$$f_V = \frac{3V}{2A}$$

$$V = \frac{2}{3} f_V A = \frac{2}{3} \text{ x } 70 \text{ x } 46.4 = 2165 \text{ lbs}$$

(actual R = 2000 lb)

When this capacity is compared to the capacity in bearing, it is seen that insofar as stress in the beam is concerned, the allowable stress in shear is more critical than the allowable stress in compression perpendicular to grain. Such is usually the case.

Example 32-8

Bearing stress perpendicular to grain.

Given: 4 x 12 joist supported by a steel joist hanger. Width of seat $1^1/_2$ in. Douglas fir-larch, No. 2. Normal service conditions.

To Find: Capacity of the end reaction.

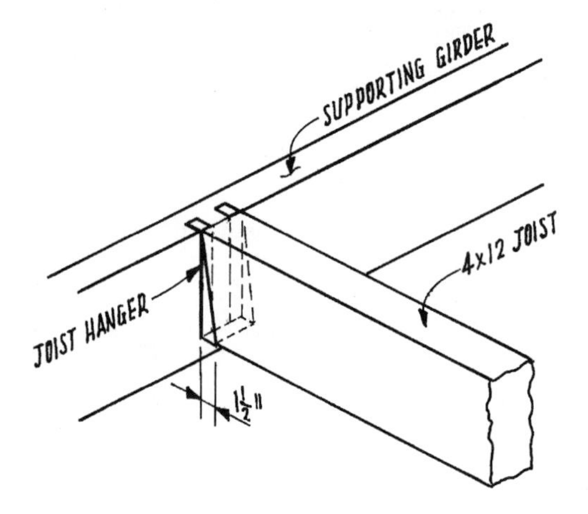

Solution: Capacity of a 4 x 12 in end shear:

$$V = \frac{2}{3} f_V A = \frac{2}{3} \text{ x } 95 \text{ x } 39.4 = 2500 \text{ lbs.}$$

Capacity of a 4 x 12 in end bearing on a $1^1/_2$ in. seat:

From Table T-3a, $F_{C\perp} = 625$ psi

$P = F_{C\perp}A = 625 \text{ x } 1^1/_2 \text{ x } 3^1/_2 = 3280$ lbs.

As before, the capacity is seen to be limited by allowable shear rather than by allowable bearing.

Also, as before, the end bearing factor C_b does not apply since the bearing is closer than 3 in. from the end of the member.

Capacity = 2500 lbs, as limited by shear.

Example 32-9

Bearing stress perpendicular to grain.

Given: Beam of Example 32-1 (and 32-5). Seated on top of masonry bearings $5^1/_2$ in. Wide. Douglas fir-larch, No. 1 B&S. 6 x 18 beam used in tall orientation. Long term duration of load. Occasional wet service conditions.

To Find: Whether the section is adequate at the supports.

Solution: From the shear and moment diagrams, the maximum reaction is seen to be at the right support:

$$R = 10.67 \text{ kips}$$

The tabular stress perpendicular to grain is found from Table T-3a:

$$F_{C\perp} = 625 \text{ psi}$$

The allowable stress is found by applying the appropriate modifiers:

$$F'_{c\perp} = F_C C_D C_M C_b = 1.00 \times 0.67 \times 1.00 \times 625 = 419 \text{ psi}$$

(Note that the values of C_M and C_D for compression perpendicular to grain are quite different than for flexure.)

The required bearing area is found as:

$$A = \frac{R}{F_{c\perp}} = \frac{10,670}{419} = 25.5 \text{ in.}^2$$

The actual bearing area in tall orientation is the contact area:

A = Width of Masonry x Thickness of Beam
= 5.5 x 5.5 = 30.25 in.^{2} > 25.5 required (O.K.)

The bearing capacity is adequate.

Example 32-10

Bearing stress perpendicular to grain.

Given: Beam of Example 32-2 (and 32-6). Seated on the top flanges of a W10 x 22 steel beam. Southern pine, No. 2, 6 x 16 beam, tall orientation. Normal conditions of service.

To Find: Whether the section is adequate at the supports.

Solution: From the shear and moment diagrams, the maximum reaction is seen to be:

$$R = 11.5 \text{ kips}$$

The tabular stress perpendicular to grain is found from Table T-3b:

$$F_{C\perp} = 375 \text{ psi}$$

The allowable stress is taken to be the same as the tabular stress.

The required bearing area is found as:

$$A = \frac{R}{F_{C\perp}} = \frac{11{,}500}{375} = 30.67 \text{ in.}^2$$

The actual bearing area is the contact area:

A = Width of Flange x Thickness of Beam
= 5.75 x 5.5 = 31.62 in.^{2} > 30.67 required (O.K.)

The section is adequate in bearing at the supports.

32.5 Design of Beams for Deflection Control

The calculation of deflections in beams of single curvature is presented in Chapter 15. All of the methods presented there remain valid in wood construction. Further discussions of those methods are appropriate for wood construction, however, since the modulus of elasticity for wood is much lower than that for concrete or steel; deflections in wood construction are sometimes of serious concern.

The methods presented in Chapter 15 apply to beams of single curvature, that is, beams without reversals in curvature. Typical cases of single curvature, double curvature and triple curvature are shown in Figure 32-4 for clarification of the terms.

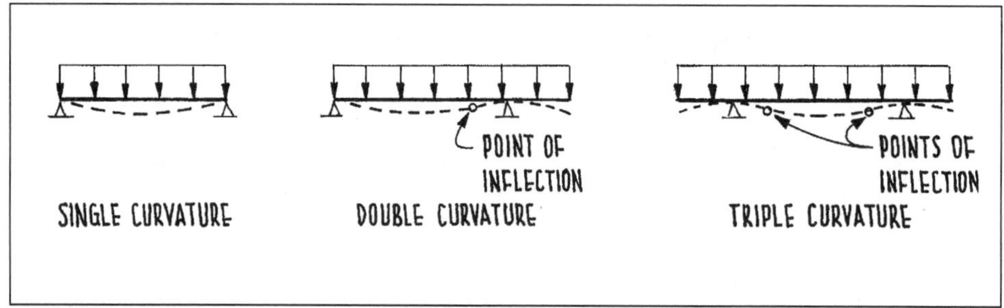

Figure 32-4 Comparison of curvature in beams.

It is observed that the beam of double curvature shown in Figure 32-4 might also be broken into two beams of single curvature, one cupping upward and one cupping downward. Two such beams of single curvature are shown in Figure 32-5, separated at the inflection point where moment is zero.

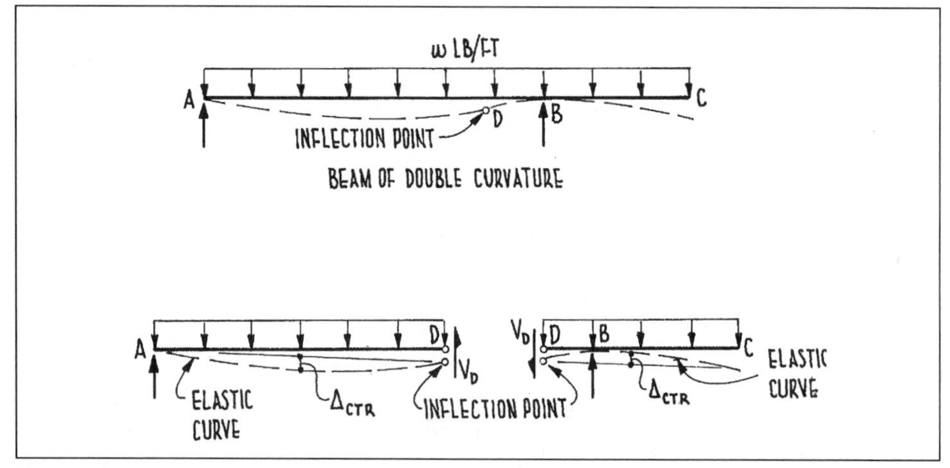

Figure 32-5 Separation of a beam into single curves.

Each of the two beam segments shown in Figure 32-5 is subject to the findings and conclusions given in Chapter 15. For each of the two segments, the relative deflection may be computed from the straight line joining the ends of the segment, as indicated in Figure 32-5. The general findings presented in Chapter 15 apply to the relative deflections so calculated:

- The maximum relative deflection of the segment will occur within the middle 15.47% of the span of the segment.
- The relative deflection of the segment at midspan will be within 2.5% of the maximum relative deflection of the segment.

The conclusions presented in Chapter 15 also apply to the calculations for relative deflections:

- Within the limits of accuracy of common construction materials, the relative deflection at midspan may be used as the maximum relative deflection of a beam segment of single curvature; the maximum error of 2.57% is within acceptable limits.

Table A-3 in the Technical Manual gives formulas for calculating the deflection at midspan of a simple beam for common load cases. The formulas are valid for all cases of loading for a beam (or a beam segment) of single curvature.

It is emphasized that the relative deflections shown in Figure 32-5 are deflections relative to a straight line joining the ends of the segment. This relative deflection is obviously not equal to the absolute deflection of the beam. For computing such relative deflections, each segment may be considered as a simple beam, with zero moment at its ends. The deflection formulas given earlier for this type of simple beam will therefore remain valid.

The assumption is made that for beams having multiple curvature, the limitations on deflection may be applied to each segment of single curvature rather than to the beam as a whole. The assumption is justified by the fact that most of the concerns about deflection are actually concerns about curvature and stiffness; the control of deflections is simply used as a convenient means to control curvature and stiffness. In truth, breakage of glass due to excessive deflections is more accurately controlled by limiting the relative deflections than by limiting the absolute maximum deflection of the span.

In general, deflections of floor beams are limited by code to two general conditions, where L is the length end-to-end of a beam of single curvature:

1. For dead load plus live load, $\Delta_{MAX} \leq L/240$ (32-5a)
2. For live load only, $\Delta_{MAX} \leq L/360$ (32-5b)

Similarly for roof beams (or rafters), deflections are commonly limited to the following conditions, where L is the horizontal projection of the length:

1. For dead load plus live load, $\Delta_{MAX} \leq L/180$ (32-5c)
2. For live load only, $\Delta_{MAX} \leq L/240$ (32-5d)

To verify conformance to code limitations, one need only calculate the maximum relative deflection, or, equivalently, the relative deflection at midspan. This maximum is compared to the limits given by Eqs.(32-5); if the allowable limit is not exceeded, the beam is adequate.

Some examples will illustrate the procedure.

Example 32-11

Control of deflections of timber beams.

Given: Beam of Example 32-1 (and 32-5 and 32-9) seated on top of masonry bearings 4 inches wide. Douglas fir-larch, No. 1 B&S. 8 x 16 used in tall orientation, I = 2456 in.[4]; long-term duration of load. Occasional wet service conditions. For live load plus dead load, $\Delta_{MAX} \leq L/240$.

To Find: Whether actual deflections are within prescribed limits.

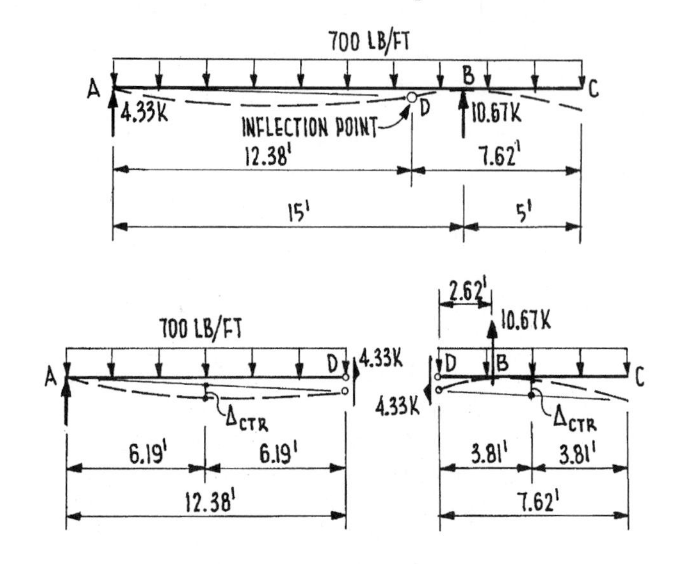

Solution: Modulus of elasticity is given by:

$$E' = EC_M = 1{,}600{,}000 \text{ x } 1.00 = 1{,}600{,}000 \text{ psi}$$

The beam of double curvature is separated at the point of inflection into two beams of single curvature as shown in the sketch. For the segment *AD*:

$$\Delta_{CTR} = \frac{5wL^4}{384EI} = \frac{5(700/12)(12.38x12)^4}{384(1{,}600{,}000)2456} = 0.10 \text{ in.}$$

Limiting (= L/240 = (12.3 x 12)/240 = 0.62 in.

Since the actual deflection is less than the allowable deflection, the section is adequate on segment *AD*.

For the beam segment *DB*:

$$\Delta_{CTR} = \frac{5wL^4}{384EI} - (3n - 4n^3)\frac{PL^3}{48EI} \quad n = \frac{2.62}{7.62} = 0.334$$

$$= 0.014 \text{ in.} - 0.037 \text{ in.} = 0.023 \text{ in.}$$

$$= \frac{5(700/12)(7.62x12)^4}{384(1{,}600{,}000)2456}$$

$$-\left[3(0.334) - 4(0.334)^3\right]\frac{10670(7.62x12)^3}{48(1{,}600{,}000)2456}$$

Limiting Δ = L/240 = (7.62 x 12)/240 = 0.38 in.

Since the actual deflection is less than the allowable deflection, the section is adequate on the segment *DB*.

Conclusion: All deflections are within prescribed limits.

Example 32-12

Control of deflections of timber beams.

Given: Beam of Example 32-2 (and 32-6 and 32-10). Seated on the top flanges of two C10 x 15.3 steel channels. Southern pine, No. 2, 6 x 16 beam, I = 170.7 in.[4] Normal conditions of service. For live load plus dead load, $\Delta_{MAX} \leq L/240$.

To Find: Whether actual deflections are within prescribed limits.

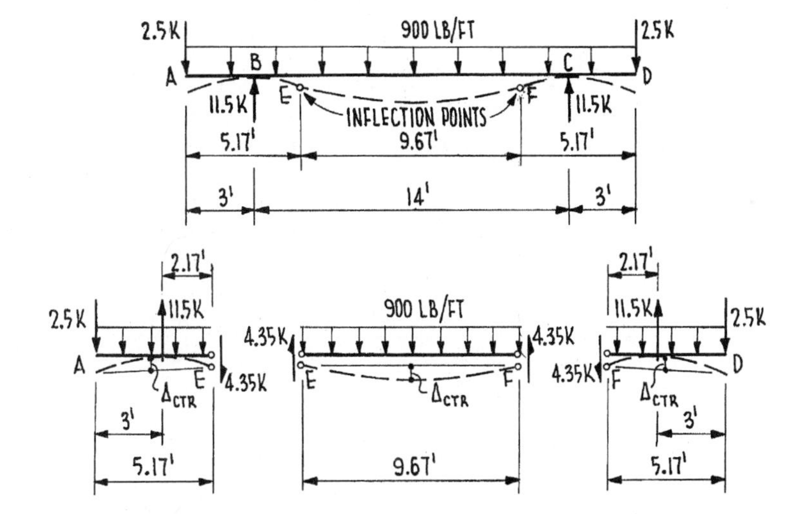

Solution: Modulus of elasticity is given by:

$$E' = EC_M = 1{,}200{,}000 \text{ x } 1.00 = 1{,}200{,}000 \text{ psi}$$

The beam of triple curvature is separated at the two points of deflection into three beams of single curvature as shown in the sketch. For the segment *AE* (and *FD*), the 2.5k load is taken as the reaction at the end of the segment. The relative deflection is then:

$$\Delta_{CTR} = +\frac{5wL^4}{384EI} - (3n - 4n^3)\frac{PL^3}{48EI}, \quad n = \frac{2.17}{5.17} = 0.420$$

$$= \frac{5(900/12)(5.17x12)^4}{384(1{,}200{,}000)1707}$$

$$-[3(0.420) - 4(0.420)^3]\frac{11{,}500(5.17x12)^3}{48(1{,}200{,}000)1707}$$

$$= 0.0014 - 0.0269 = 0.026 \text{ in.}$$

$$\text{Limiting } \Delta = L/240 = (5.17 \text{ x } 12)/240 = 0.26 \text{ in.}$$

Since the actual deflection does not exceed the allowable deflection, the section is adequate on the segment *AE* (and *FD*).

For the segment *EF*:

$$\Delta_{CTR} = +\frac{5wL^4}{384EI} = \frac{5(900/12)(9.67x12)^4}{384(1,200,000)1707} = 0.086 \text{ in.}$$

$$\text{Limiting } \Delta = L/240 = 9.67 \text{ x } 12/240 = 0.484 \text{ in.}$$

Since the actual deflection is less than the allowable deflection, the section is adequate on the segment *EF*.

Conclusion: All deflections are within prescribed limits.

32.6 Design of Beams for Lateral Stability

Timber beams are unstable laterally in the same way that steel beams are. Under high compressive stress, the compressive side (or "flange") of a timber beam is subject to lateral buckling. An example of such lateral buckling is shown in Figure 32-6.

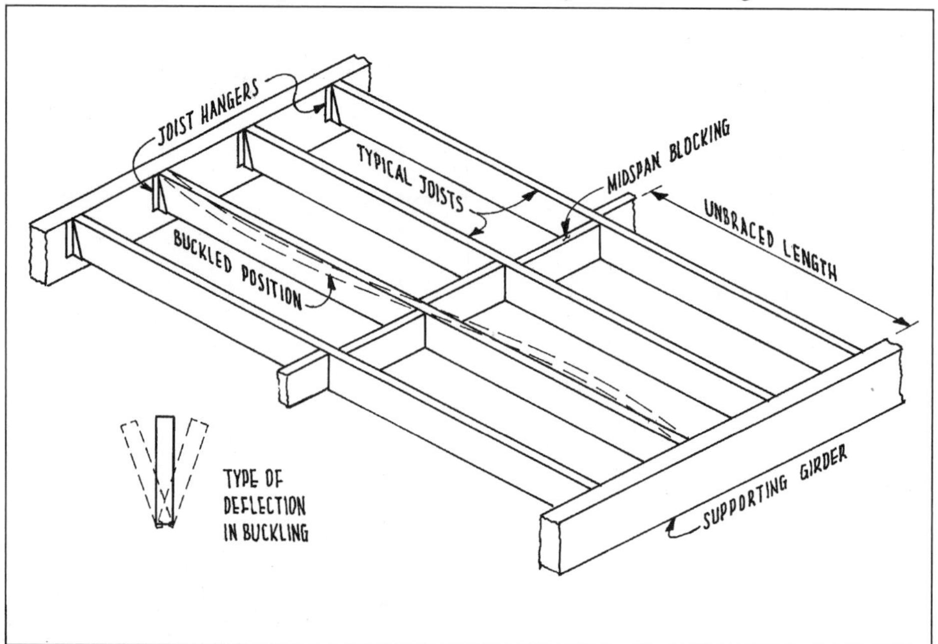

Figure 32-6 Typical lateral buckling of a timber beam.

The susceptibility of a timber beam to such buckling depends on the unbraced length along the compressive side of the beam. But even when the compressive side of the beam is adequately braced, the tension side of the beam tends to roll upward under its high tension stress. As a consequence, timber beams must be braced laterally at both tension and compression sides at periodic intervals.

In many cases, the compressive side of the beams or joists can be supported laterally by floor sheathing. While the sheathing does indeed provide adequate support aat the compression side, it does nothing to support the tension side against roll. Two common means to brace both the tension and compression sides of a system of beams are shown in Figure 32-7.

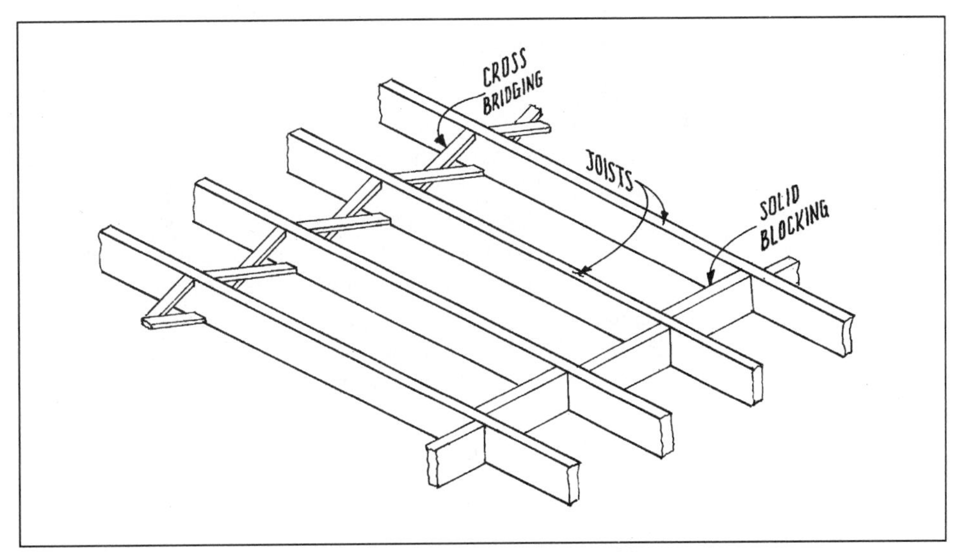

Figure 32-7 Methods of providing lateral support of beams.

The bridging shown in Figure 32-7 is usually made of 1 x 2 or 1 x 3 lumber. The solid blocking, however, is never less than 2 inches nominal thickness and must match the height of the beam; partial depth of blocking is not permitted. In earthquake risk zone 3, solid blocking (rather than bridging) is required.

The frequency of the spacing of lateral supports is specified by NDS and is developed fully in the AITC Timber Construction Manual. The calculation of such lateral supports is quite complex and is commonly used only in very tall heavy glulam beams. For heavy construction, however, the methods outlined in the Timber Construction Manual should always be used.

For light-to-medium construction, the National Design Specification (NDS) gives a much reduced and much simpler criteria for providing lateral support. The criteria is based on the depth-to-thickness ratio d/t of the member, computed from nominal (rather than actual) dimensions.

1. For $d/t \leq 2$, no lateral support lines are required.
2. For $d/t = 3$ or 4 full-depth lateral support shall be provided at bearings (or ends) of the beam.
3. For $d/t = 5$, lateral support shall be provided at one edge for the entire length of the beam.
4. For $d/t = 6$, full-depth lateral support shall be provided at the bearings (ends) and at intervals not exceeding 8 feet;
   or, both edges shall be continuously supported;
   or, one edge shall be continuously supported and full-depth lateral support shall be provided at bearings and at concentrated loads.
5. For $d/t = 7$, both edges shall be continuously supported.

The foregoing list of requirements is also given in Table T-14 in the Technical Manual as a design reference.

The requirements set forth by UBC are those generally followed in the practice. Additionally, however, the following general practices are commonly observed regardless what the d/t ratio may be:

1. Full-depth blocking or bridging is provided at all bearing lines.
2. Full-depth blocking or bridging is provided at any line of concentrated loads above or below (such as a stud wall).
3. Full-depth blocking or a fascia piece is provided along the free end of cantilevers.

While the foregoing rules for providing lateral support may seem "cookbookish," they have been used with success for many years. It is hard to argue with success.

32.7 Connections to Beams

Connections to beams are no different than connections to tension members or connections to columns. Allowable bolt or connector values parallel to grain or perpendicular to grain are found in the design tables as before and are used in exactly the same way. The transmittal of forces across a connection is the same whether the member is a column, a beam or a tension member.

Beams do, however, have some configurations that would not usually be encountered in columns or in tension members. One such configuration is that of loading at an angle to the grain. Such a case is shown in Figure 32-8, where a sloping flexural member is notched so it may be seated on a vertical support.

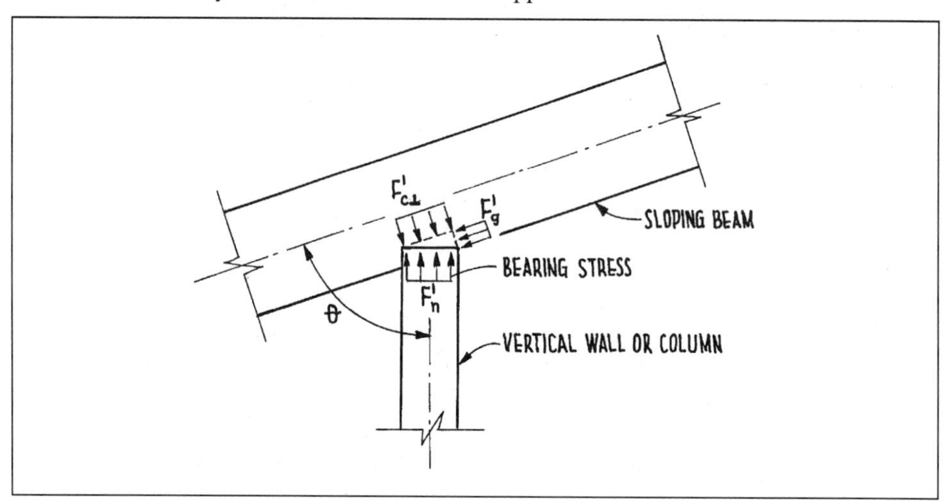

Figure 32-8 Beam stress at an angle to grain.

The allowable stress F_n' between the beam and the column of Figure 32-8 is neither perpendicular to grain nor parallel to grain in the beam. Its value is found through Hankinson's formula, introduced earlier in bolted connections as Eq.(30-3). For stress, Hankinson's formula has the form:

$$F_n' = \frac{F_g' F_{C\perp}'}{F_g' \sin^2\theta + F_{C\perp}' \cos^2\theta} \tag{32-6}$$

where θ is the angle between F_n' and F_g' and all other symbols are those defined earlier.

Note that the stress parallel to grain to be used in Hankinson's formula is F_g' rather than F_C'. (The stress F_g' is the end-grain stress given in Table T-19 where F_C' is the stress parallel to grain given in Table T-3). Note also that the modifiers must be applied to the tabular stresses before they are used in Hankinson's formula; different modifiers apply to $F_{C\perp}'$ than to F_g'.

The use of Eq.(32-6) is quite straightforward; an example will illustrate its application.

Example 32-13

Beam at an angle with its support.

Given: Rafter having 5:12 slope as shown. Spruce-pine fir, No. 1 B&S or J&P. Normal conditions of service.

To Find: Allowable reaction on the rafter.

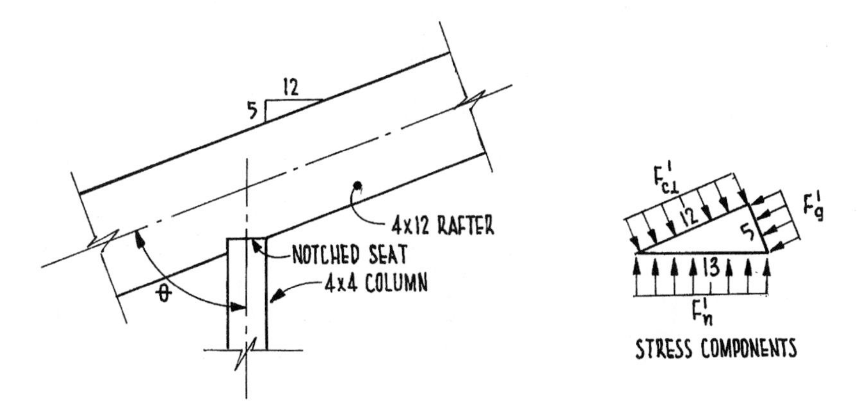

Solution: Stress $F_n^{'}$ is given by Hankinson's formula:

$$F_n^{'} = \frac{F_g^{'} F_{C\perp}^{'}}{F_g^{'} \sin^2\theta + F_{C\perp}^{'} \cos^2\theta}, \theta = \tan^{-1}\frac{12}{5} = 67.38^0$$

From Table T-3c, $F_{C\perp}^{'} = 425$ psi

From Table T-13, $F_g^{'} = 1410$ psi

The stress $F_n^{'}$ on the rafter is calculated from Hankinson's formula:

$$F_n^{'} = \frac{1410x425}{1410\sin^2 67.38 + 425\cos^2 67.38} = 474 \text{ psi}$$

Allowable compressive stress $F_C^{'}$ on the column = 625 psi > 474 (O.K.).

Allowable load is calculated as for direct bearing:

$$P = F_n^{'}A = 474(3.5x3.5) = 5800 \text{ lb}$$

Allowable reaction = 5.80 kips

A final observation on beam connections has to do with practice rather than theory. Two types of supports are shown in Figure 32-a, one in direct bearing and one utilizing a bolted connection. Both supports receive an end reaction from the beam.

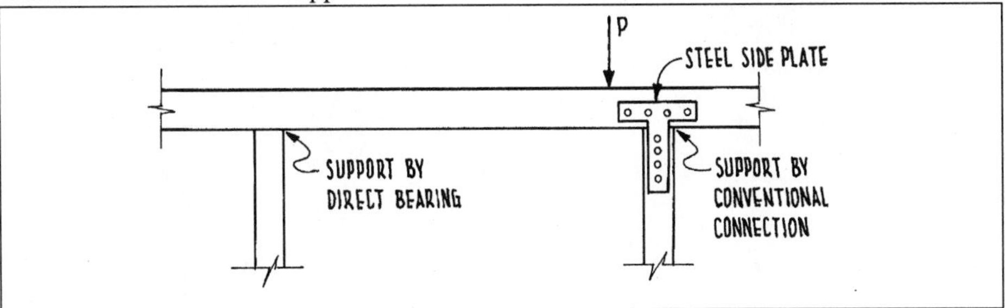

Figure 32-9 Bearing support and connector support for a beam.

When a load becomes so high that simple bearing support would cause crushing across the grain in the beam, one alternative support is that of a bolted connection as indicated in Figure 32-9. In such cases, the support is designed to sustain the load entirely as a bolted connection; that is, no allowance for partial bearing load is permitted in a bolted connection. The reason for such a convention lies in the inability to predict reliably how much load can be transmitted in bearing across a contact surface, in view of such things as hole tolerances, shrinkage, erection tolerances and other variables inherent in timber construction.

Review Questions

1. In beam design, what is the major difference in concept between steel and timber design?
2. In what two types of stress is wood significantly weak?
3. What is the item-by-item procedure for designing timber? Beams?
4. State the formula for computing the section modulus of a rectangular section.
5. State the formula for computing the maximum shear stress in a rectangular section.
6. How is the design shear force found for the design of a timber beam? A concrete beam? A steel beam?
7. To what tabular stresses does the size factor C_F apply?
8. To what tabular stresses does the shape factor C_f apply?
9. What stress limits the beam reaction in a beam hanger?
10. How does the duration of load factor C_D affect the stress $F_{C\perp}$?
11. Why is the distinction between single curvature and multiple curvature so important in deflection calculations?
12. What is the name of the point where curvature changes from tension in bottom fibers to tension on top fibers?
13. In a span of single curvature, within what limits in the span will maximum deflection occur?
14. In a span of single curvature, what is the maximum difference that can occur between the deflection at midspan and the absolute maximum deflection?
15. How is the relative displacement at the center of a segment of single curvature different from the absolute displacement at that point?
16. For timber beams, what is the usual limit that is placed on deflections due to dead load plus live load?
17. For a 4 x 12 beam on a 16 ft span, what provisions must be taken to ensure lateral stability under load?
18. For a 2 x 12 beam on a 20 ft span, what provisions must be taken to ensure lateral stability under load?
19. State the Hankinson formula for allowable stress at an angle to grain, and define each term.
20. In a mixed connection where part of the load is transmitted by bearing and part is transmitted by split rings, how is the distribution of load determined?

CHAPTER

33

APPLICATIONS IN TIMBER STRUCTURES

The topics presented in this chapter utilize the theoretical concepts of earlier chapters; no new theory is developed. As such, the concepts are primarily applications and extensions of familiar subjects. This chapter may therefore be regarded as a "how to" chapter on miscellaneous subjects in wood construction.

33.1 Wood Joists and Rafters

Probably the most common use of wood beams in J&P sizes is in their application as joists and rafters. Joists and rafters are typically spaced at 12 in., 16 in., 24 in. or 28 in. for the sake of the sheathing, which generally comes in 48 inch widths and 96 inch lengths. Typical sections of a joist system and a rafter system are shown in Figure 33-1.

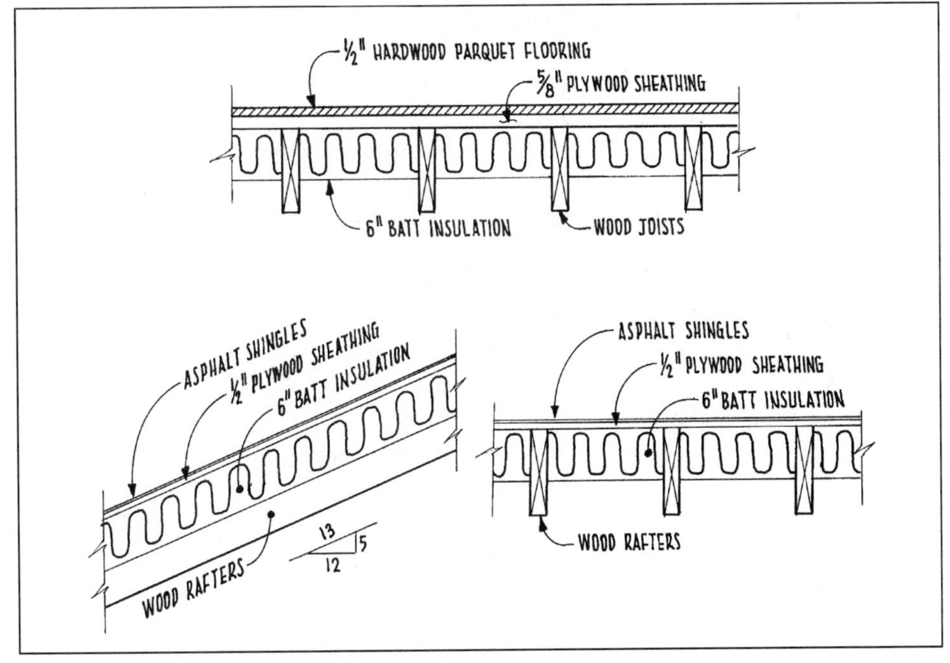

Figure 33-1 Typical joist and rafter systems.

Joists and rafters are in reality small, closely spaced beams. In Tables T-3a, b and c, they qualify as "repetitive" member usage for stress, thereby gaining a small increase in the tabular stresses. They are used universally in all types of light-to-medium construction.

Because joists and rafters are so widely used, extensive tables have been prepared for various uses, configurations and load conditions. Some of the more common cases are given in Tables T-15, 16, 17 and 18 in the Technical Manual. More extensive tables are given in various handbooks; the set of tables that accompany Chapter 23 of the Uniform Building Code is recommended.

Most joist and rafter tables include an allowance for dead load (10, 15 or 20 psf) plus a specified live load (10, 20, 40 or 50 psf). In essentially all cases, the roof loads are taken on the horizontal projection; loads along a slope are rarely if ever used.

The three most common configurations are:

- Floor joists, insulation placed between joists, floor decking consisting of prepared decking or plywood sheathing, dead load about 10 psf, live load 40 psf.
- Ceiling joists, insulation placed between joists, drywall ceiling placed at lower face, crawlspace or attic above (with or without sheathing at the top face), dead load 7 to 10 psf, live load 10 to 20 psf.
- Roof rafters, insulation placed between rafters, roof dead load of about 7 to 10 psf consisting of rafters and plywood sheathing plus the weight of the roof material itself, live load of 20 psf.

Some examples will illustrate the selection of floor and ceiling joists. The first example shows the procedure for selecting a joist using conventional calculations. The second example shows the same case using the design tables in the Technical Manual.

Example 33-1

Selection of a joist system for a floor.

Given: Built-up floor system as shown, simple span 16'-0".
Floor live load 40 psf.
Deflection limitation L/360 for live load, E = 1,300,000 psi.
Normal conditions of service. F_b = 1000 psi, F_v = 70 psi.

To Find: Suitable joist system with appropriate lateral bracing.

Solution: Estimate of total load per square foot:

Hardwood flooring	2.5 psf
5/8 in. Plywood sheathing	2.5 psf
Joists and bridging	3.0 psf
Insulation	1.0 psf
	9.0 psf
Live load	40.0 psf
Total Load	49.0 psf

Assume joist spacing of 16 in.:

$$\text{Load per joist} = 49 \times \frac{16}{12} = 65 \text{ plf}$$

Compute design moment and shear for simple span of 16'-0":

$$M = \frac{wL^2}{8} = \frac{65x16^2}{8}x12 = 25{,}000 \text{ lb·in.}$$

$$V = \frac{wL}{2} = \frac{65x16}{2} = 520 \text{ lbs}$$

Compute the required section modulus and area for a repetitive-use stress of 1000 psi in flexure and an allowable shear stress of 70 psi:

$$\frac{I}{C} = \frac{M}{F_b} = \frac{25{,}000}{1000} = 25.0$$

$$A = \frac{3V}{2F_v} = \frac{3x520}{2x70} = 11.14 \; in.^2$$

From Table T-1, try 2 x 12 joists.

Actual deflection under load, E = 1,300,000 psi:

$$\Delta = \frac{5wL^4}{384EI} = \frac{5(65/12)(16x12)^4}{384x1{,}300{,}000x178} = 0.41 \text{ in.}$$

Allowable deflection under load:

Δ = L/360 = (16 x 12)/360 = 0.53 > 0.41 (O.K.)

Provide lateral support as prescribed in Table T-14.

Use 2 x 12 joists @ 16 in. o.c., solid blocking at both support lines. (Assume continuous support of compression edge is provided by the plywood sheathing.)

Example 33-2

Selection of a joist system for a floor.

Given: Conditions of Example 33-1.

To Find: Suitable joist system using the design tables in the Technical Manual.

Solution: Estimate the total dead load per square foot:

Dead load = 9 psf (see Example 33-1).

Enter Table T-15 in which tabular dead load is 10 psf, live load is 40 psf, deflection limitation is L/360.

For modulus of elasticity E = 1,300,000, F_b = 1000, select a suitable system for a span of 16'-0".

Provide lateral support as prescribed in Table T-14.

Use 2 x 12 joists @ 16" o.c., solid blocking at support lines. (Assume full lateral support of compression face is provided by the plywood sheathing.)

The selection of rafters proceeds in much the same way as it does for joists. There is a slight difference, however, in that the dead load is computed on the slope length and is then converted to the horizontal projection.

Some examples will illustrate the selection of rafters. The first example shows the procedure using conventional calculations. The second example shows the same case using the tables in the Technical Manual.

Example 33-3

Selection of a rafter system.

Given: Roof system as shown in Figure 33-1.
Horizontal span 16'-0".
Roof live load 20 psf on projected area.
Deflection limitation L/240. E = 1,400,000 psi.
Normal conditions of service. F_b = 1100 psi, F_v = 85 psi.

To Find: Suitable rafter system with appropriate lateral bracing.

Solution: Estimate of total load per square foot:

Roofing	3.0 psf
1/2 in. Sheathing	2.5 psf
6 in. Insulation	1.0 psf
Rafters and bridging	3.0 psf
Total	9.5 psf

$$\text{Dead load on projected area} = 9.5 \text{ x} \frac{13}{12} = 10.3 \text{ psf}$$

Total load on projected area = 30.3 psf

Assume rafter spacing of 24 in.:

$$M = \frac{wL^2}{8} = \frac{61x16^2}{8}x12 = 23{,}400 \text{ lb in.}$$

$$V = \frac{wL}{2} = \frac{61x16}{2} = 488 \text{ kips}$$

Compute the required section modulus and area for a repetitive-use stress of 1100 psi in flexure and 85 psi in shear:

$$\frac{I}{C} = \frac{M}{F_b} = \frac{23{,}400}{1100} = 21.3\ in.^3$$

$$A = \frac{3V}{2F_V} = \frac{3x488}{2x85} = 8.6\ in.^2$$

From Table T-1, try 2 x 10 rafters.

Actual deflection under load, E = 1,400,000 psi:

$$\Delta = \frac{5wL^4}{384EI} = \frac{5(61/12)(16x12)^4}{384x1{,}400{,}000x98.9} = 0.65 \text{ in.}$$

Allowable deflection under load:

$$\Delta = L/240 = 16 \times 12/240 = 0.80 \text{ in.} > 0.65 \text{ (O.K.)}$$

Provide lateral support as prescribed in Table T-14.

Use 2 x 10 rafters @ 24" o.c., solid blocking at both support lines. (Assume continuous support of the compression edge is provided by the plywood sheathing.)

Example 33-4

Selection of a rafter system.

Given: Roof system of Example 33-3, as shown in Figure 33-1.

To Find: Suitable rafter system using the design tables in the Technical Manual.

Solution: Estimate the total dead load per square foot on the horizontal projected area.

Dead load = 10.3 psf (see Example 33-3).

Enter Table T-18 in which tabular dead load is 10 psf, live load is 20 psf, deflection limitation is L/240.

For a modulus of elasticity of 1,400,000 psi, F_b= 1100 psi. Select a suitable system for a horizontal span of 16'-0".

Provide lateral support as prescribed in Table T-14.

Use 2 x 10 joists @ 24" o.c., solid blocking at support lines. (Assume continuous support of the compression edge is provided by the plywood sheathing.)

33.2 Decking and Sheathing

Decking serves two functions in a structure. Its primary function is to provide a surface that receives and sustains the gravity loads normal to the surface and to distribute those gravity loads to the supporting members. Its second function (usually) is to provide a rigid diaphragm or shear panel that receives shearing forces parallel to the surface and distributes those forces to the supporting members at its edges.

Decking may consist of boards and planks, in which case the decking is usually made with interlocking faces of tongue-and-groove configuration. Such a configuration is shown in Figure 33-2 for a 1 in. and a 2 in. deck.

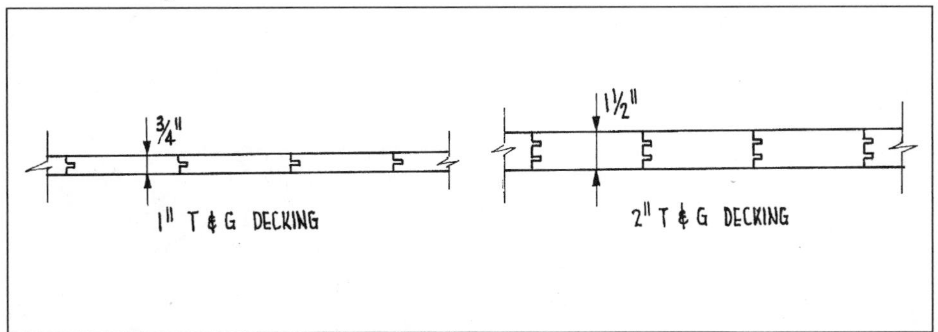

Figure 33-2 Typical sections of tongue-and-groove decking.

The tongue-and-groove decking shown in Figure 33-2 is used primarily where the underside will be exposed to view and appearance is a strong consideration. The 2 in. T&G decking (or thicker) is often used in heavy timber construction that requires heavier loads and longer spans for the decking. In all cases, the T&G decking will have a lower shear capacity as a diaphragm than a plywood deck or comparable capacity for gravity loads.

Lumber decking may be laid up in various configurations, some of which are shown in Figure 33-3. In the simple span layup, the moment is zero at each support line. In the other layups, there is a degree of continuity provided by making the decking continuous over the supports.

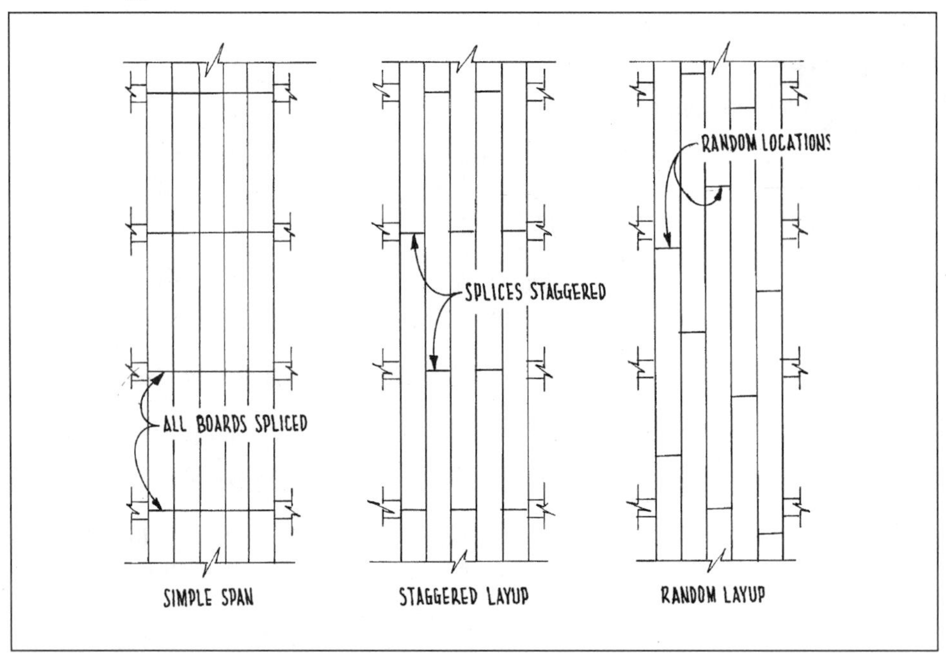

Figure 33-3 Typical patterns of decking layup.

Board and plank decking is a manufactured item in today's industry. Design tables giving the allowable spans and allowable loads can be obtained from the various manufacturers for their particular product. Due to the wide variety of sizes, types of wood and fastening requirements, generic design tables would be impractical.

In today's industry, plywood decking and sheathing is far more widely used than is lumber. Because plywood is more consistent, generic design tables become possible which, in turn, promotes standardized practices. Plywood is manufactured in special structural classifications for use both as a deck for gravity loads and as a shear panel or diaphragm for lateral loads.

Plywood is a glued laminated wood product. It is laid up and glued together in lamina (or plies) $^1/_8$ in. thick, as shown in Figure 33-4. The plywood is usually laid up in an odd number of plies, with the direction of grain alternating from ply to ply.

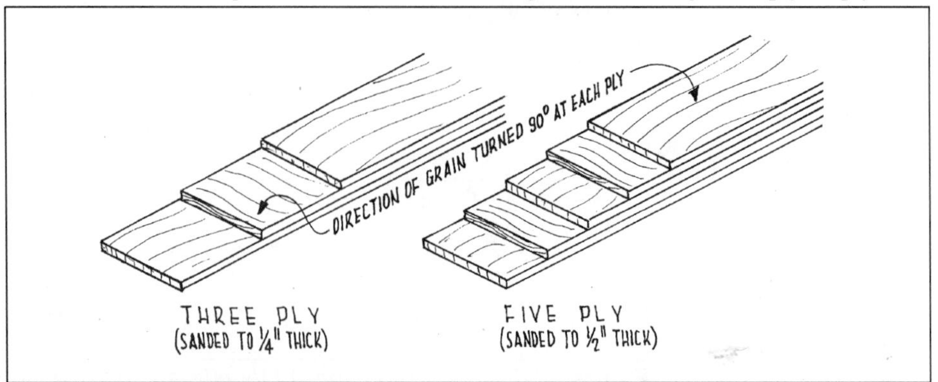

Figure 33-4 Typical plywood laminations.

Plywood is commonly manufactured in sheets 48 in. wide by 96 in. long, though longer sheets are available on special order. The grain in the outer faces runs in the long direction. Obviously, the "strong" direction in bending is that in which the flexural stresses are parallel to grain, or, for bending in the long direction.

Typically, plywood decking or sheathing is placed on top of its supporting framing joists as shown in Figure 33-5. The ends are butted together at the joints and the two edges are nailed to the framing at close intervals. The plywood is also nailed to the interior supports but at longer spacing. The sheet of plywood thus becomes a continuous beam 48 in. wide spanning the distance from joist to joist.

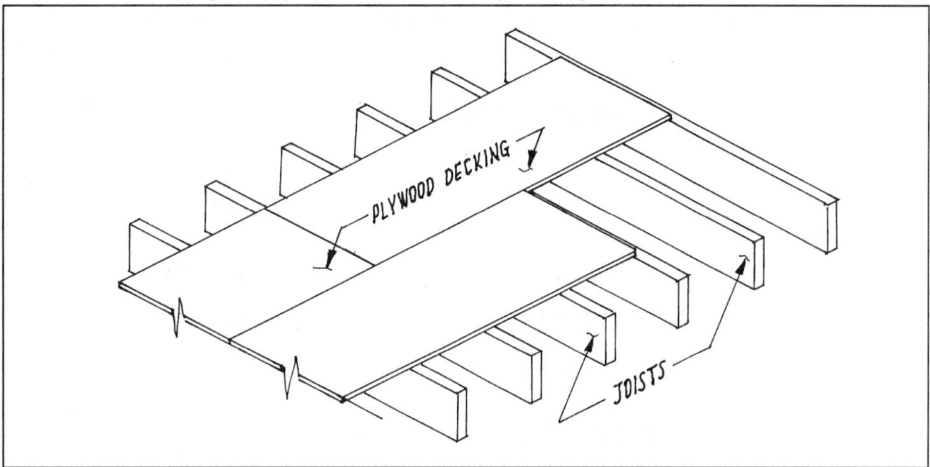

Figure 33-5 Typical plywood deck and framing members.

Though it is theoretically possible to calculate the required thickness of plywood decking, such calculations are rarely necessary. Design tables have been developed for the various classifications of plywood which allow the designer to choose reliable plywood decking under gravity loading at various joist spacings. Other design tables provide allowable in-plane shear forces in plywood diaphragms and shear panels used to resist lateral loads.

The primary references for data concerning plywood are the publications of the American Plywood Association (APA), with headquarters in Tacoma, Washington. A second source of useful design aids are included in the Uniform Building Code (UBC). The UBC tables are especially valuable where loads include earthquake.

Plywood is manufactured from more than 70 species of wood. The plywood so manufactured is grouped together in 5 groups for strength calculations, with Group 1 having the highest strength properties. Both Douglas fir-larch and Southern pine fall in Group 1. Spruce-pine-fir is not a separate classification in the manufacturing of plywood and thus has no group number; it is not considered further in this textbook.

The inner plies in plywood are not necessarily made of the same species or even groups of species as the outer plies. Since the choice of species affects the strength, the strength of the inner plies must be included when plywood is given its structural classification or rating. The classification STRUCTURAL I means that all plies are made from Group 1 species.

In addition to the strength of the wood, plywood is also rated by the *grade* of the plies. The primary grades for veneer are:

- A Smooth sanded surface. Knots have been removed and the holes neatly repaired. Paintable.
- B Solid surface. Knots permitted if they are sound and tight fitting. Loose knots have been removed and the holes repaired. Commonly used for surfaces in concrete formwork.
- C Open knotholes up to 1 inch across. Acceptable for exterior use. Commonly used for roof sheathing or other applications where it will be covered by a finished surface.
- D Open knotholes up to $2^1/_2$ inch across. Not permitted in exterior use. Commonly used for underlayment.

Insofar as strength qualities are concerned, veneers A and C have similar properties and veneers B and D have similar properties.

A further criterion that affects the classification of plywood is the type of glue. The glue used to manufacture plywood is classified as exterior or interior; only exterior glue is suitable for use in exposed conditions. Exterior type plywood should be used in all interior applications where moisture is high or where the plywood may be subject to occasionally wet service conditions.

All plywood is stamped with an identifying stamp. Typical examples of plywood stamps are shown in Figure 33-6. The stamp at the left is for plywood that has been sanded smooth for painting, the stamp in the center is for plywood that is strength-rated for use as sheathing and the stamp at the right is for special single-layer floor sheathing.

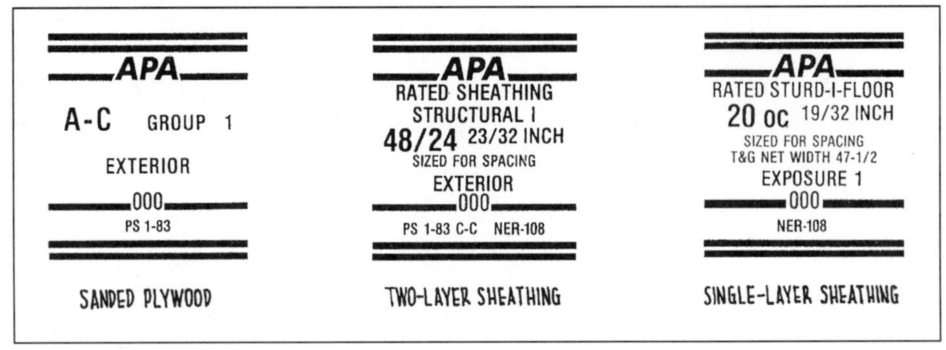

Figure 33-6 Typical plywood stamps.

The stamp for sanded plywood provides the following information about the panel:

1. A-C designates the grade of veneer on the front face and the back face, respectively. The front face is fully sanded, the back side is touch sanded.
2. Group 1 designates the species from which the outer plies are made. The inner plies may be made from Group 1 species or from lower group numbers.
3. Exterior glue is used throughout.
4. PS-1 is a fabrication specification that concerns the durability of the panel under exterior conditions of service. PS-1 panels are manufactured entirely from wood veneers, that is, no reconstituted wood or particle board is permitted.

The stamp for two-layer sheathing provides the following information about the panel.

1. The panel is rated as structural sheathing, conforming to specification PS-1. The classification STRUCTURAL I indicates that all plies are wood veneer made from Group 1 species.
2. The thickness 23/32 inch is the panel thickness after being touch sanded.
3. The 48/24 indicates that the panel is suitable for roof sheathing or supports spaced up to 48 inches or for floor sheathing on supports spaced up to 24 inches.

The stamp for the single-layer sheathing provides the following information about the panel.

1. The panel is rated for use as single-layer floor sheathing.
2. The panel is 19/32 inch thick after being touch sanded.
3. The panel is suitable for rigidity characteristics at a support spacing of 20 inches.
4. The panel is shaped into tongue and groove configuration at its edges; net coverage is $47^1/_2$ inches.
5. Exterior glue was used to fabricate the panel.

Note that the allowable load on either of the sheathing stamps is not specified. The allowable load is found from design tables for various joist spacings. Such a table is given in Table T-19 in the Technical Manual for floor loads and in Table T-20 for roof loads.

Plywood floors may be constructed in either of two ways:

1. Finish surface applied to an underlayment which is supported by a subfloor. In this configuration the subfloor consists of the plywood sheathing. The underlayment is placed on top of the subfloor with joints offset from the subfloor joints. The underlayment is nonstructural; it may be particleboard or reconstituted wood. The rating for the sheathing is given in Table T-19.
2. Combined single layer floor. In this configuration the plywood sheathing acts both as subfloor and as underlayment. The rating for the single-layer sheathing is given the name STURD-I-FLOOR by APA and is so stamped. The panel edges of single-layer sheathing panels are matching tongue and groove. The ratings and loads for single-layer sheathing are given in Table T-20.

The selection of a floor system is empirical, that is, it includes effects of springiness as well as strength. As a consequence, floor systems are selected from design tables rather than from calculations. Tables T-19 and T-15 are examples of such design tables.

The selection of plywood roof and floor sheathing is thus a cookbook selection. Some examples will illustrate the procedure.

Example 33-5

Selection of roof sheathing.

Given: Conditions of Example 33-3.
STRUCTURAL I plywood.
No edge support between rafters.

To Find: Suitable roof sheathing.

Solution: For 24 in. Spacing of rafters, enter Table T-20. Select $^7/_{16}$ in. sheathing with no edge support.

Example 33-6

Selection of single floor sheathing.

Given: Conditions of Example 33-1.
STURD-I-FLOOR single layer plywood.
No edge support between joists.

To Find: Suitable floor sheathing.

Solution: For 16 in. Spacing of joists, enter Table T-19. For floor load of 50 psf, select 32/16 rated STURD-I-FLOOR.

The use of plywood sheathing in shear panels and diaphragms is fully as cookbookish as it is for roof and floor sheathing. The allowable load per foot of panel depends on panel thickness, nail spacing, type of blocking provided and the layup pattern used in placing the sheathing.

Some of the more useful design tables for plywood shear panels are given in the Uniform Building Code. The tables are complete, including nailing schedules and layup patterns for structural sheathing.

The loads acting on diaphragms or shear panels are found from the analytical methods of Chapter 14. A sheathing thickness, nailing schedule and sheathing layup are then selected from the design tables that will sustain these loads. The procedure is illustrated in example designs given in subsequent sections.

33.3 Built-Up Timber Sections

Built-up sections are far less common in timber than in steel. Even so, some fabricators have developed some commercial sections that are proving to be competitive in cost with the usual run of rectangular sections. As one might expect, the greatest obstacle is the increased labor cost due to fabrication.

Two typical examples of built-up sections are shown in Figure 33-7. Almost without exception, the approach to improving a rectangular wood section will be to replace the material in the middle third of the section (where shear stress is highest) with a material that is stronger in shear (such as plywood or oriented strand board). Such is the case in the two sections shown in Figure 33-7.

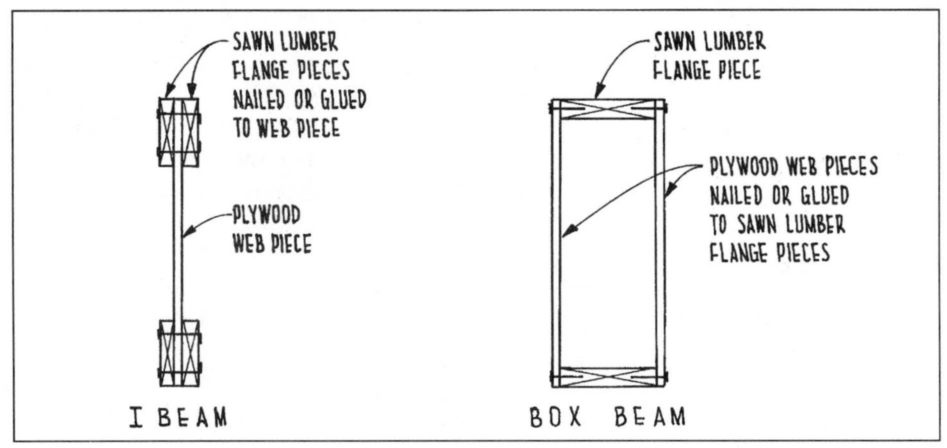

Figure 33-7 Typical built-up timber sections.

For occasional use, a box section such as that shown in Figure 33-7 can be fabricated on site. If plywood or oriented strand board is used for the sides, the height is almost automatically limited to 12 inches, 16 inches, 24 inches or 48 inches. The span is similarly limited to lengths in increments of 4 feet if the plywood panels are to be used efficiently.

Solid blocking may be used in box beams, serving both to hold the shape against racking and to provide a splice nailer for the plywood. The blocking will, of course, be the same width as the flange, but its thickness (usually) need not be greater than 2 inches. A typical field-fabricated box beam is shown in Figure 33-8. Such beams have been found useful for wide door openings (such as garage doors) in light-to-medium construction.

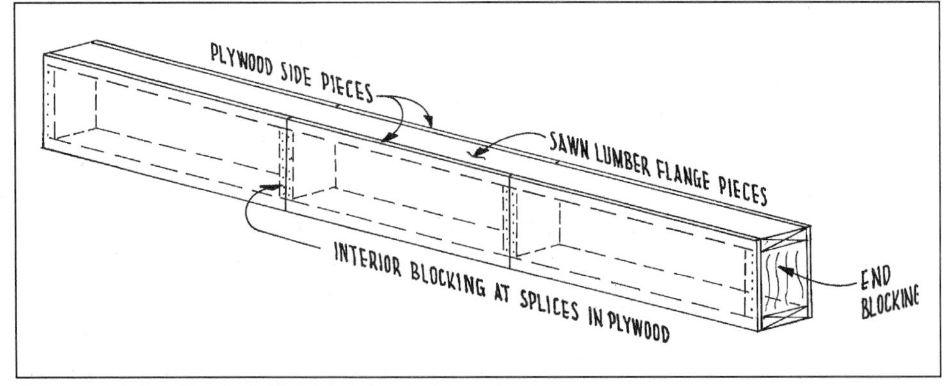

Figure 33-8 Typical Field fabricated box beam.

Sections such as the I section of Figure 33-7 are available commercially. Costs are competitive with other types of wood construction. They are most efficient when used in regular layouts, with no irregular lengths or cuts. Design tables are available from the manufacturers that give the spans, loads and seating details for various sizes of members.

The design of built-up wood beams follows conventional procedures with the stresses as given in Table T-23 in the Technical Manual. Probably the most troublesome point in the design is in providing for the relatively high shear flows that will occur at the ends of the beam. The methods presented in Chapter 10 for finding shear flows are of course valid in such configuration. If nailing becomes too cumbersome for handling the shear flows, one may wish to consider some of the modern high-strength glues.

33.4 Treated Timber Foundations

Creosoted timber piles and creosoted railroad ties have a long and remarkable history as durable successful foundations. Except for these two, there are few other historical examples that could be cited where timber foundations have been used. In earlier years, timber foundations simply could not endure the termites and decay organisms that accompany direct contact with earth.

In recent years, however, the development of effective chemical preservatives has made treated timber a potentially useful material for the construction of shallow foundations. To date, the use of treated timber foundations has largely been restricted to special circumstances where loads are light and alternatives are few. Nonetheless, the performance of such foundations has proven to be satisfactory and treated timber foundations can now be regarded as simply one more contemporary foundation system.

In its most common configuration as a shallow foundation, the treated timber foundation is a load-bearing stud wall sheathed with treated plywood on one side only; a typical section of such a wall is shown in Figure 33-9. The wall is founded at some distance below grade on a treated timber plate. It is extended far enough above grade (about 12 in.) to

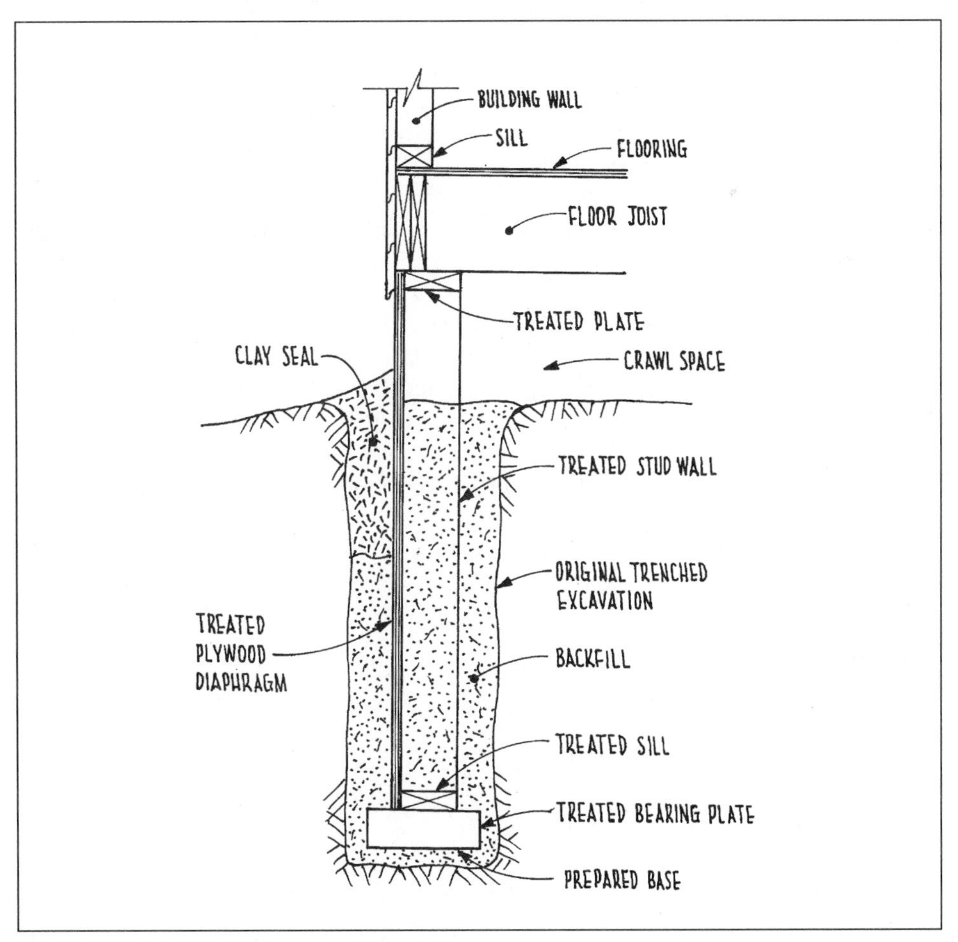

Figure 33-9 Treated timber foundation.

permit untreated timber to be used throughout the building above it. Fasteners may be wrought iron, brass, or plastic, depending on the corrosiveness of the soil.

One of the more common applications of such a treated timber foundation is in the Great Lakes area, where the "all-weather wood foundation" is promoted by the manufacturers of the preservatives. Its biggest advantage, as its name implies, is that construction can be undertaken at any time of year, even in winter when concrete foundation work is difficult or impossible. The acceptance of the all-weather wood foundation by mortgage companies (and Federal loan agencies) for ordinary 20-year or 30-year mortgages attests to its durability and reliability.

Municipal building codes do not permit masonry to be supported by timber. Consequently, the treated timber foundation is, at present, suitable only for wood frame construction. Where the foundation wall can be made rigid enough, however, it could also be suitable for stucco or exterior plaster.

The rigidity of the foundation wall is, of course, dependent on its depth. The depth can be as much as 8 ft, since the treated plywood sheathing comes in lengths of 8 ft; with proper blocking it could be made even deeper. With such depths, the foundation wall can be made extremely rigid at a relatively nominal cost, even to the point of being rigid enough to support stucco or exterior plaster.

The structural design of the load-bearing stud wall is no different from the design of any other load-bearing stud wall. The design might even include basement walls, where the studs are designed to take lateral earth pressure as well as vertical loads.

Excavation of the foundation trench may be accomplished by simple trenching machines where the soil is suitable for such trenching. Once leveled and backfilled, the foundation wall is unaffected by weather. The modern preservatives used for treating timber are not leached out due to immersion in groundwater.

Under examination, the treated timber foundation is seen to be little more than a variation of the ordinary strip footing. As such, it may be considered for any light frame construction where a strip footing is a feasible foundation system. Its possibilities for use in remote locations are obvious, as well as in other locations where concrete is simply not available.

The treated timber foundation might also be considered as an easily constructed expedient foundation, suitable as a foundation for temporary construction. The fact that the foundation is classed as permanent rather than temporary might be a factor in its favor at times. It can also be designed for easy removal should conditions require it to be removed at a later date.

It has been pointed out that a solution of salt and sulfur is a serious hazard to reinforced concrete foundations. It should also be pointed out that this same solution is a natural preservative for timber.

The treated timber foundation is thus a contemporary innovation in foundations. It has no history of failures, however, to warn the designer of those practices which are to be avoided. Considerable reflection is therefore advisable before using treated timber foundations; it should also be remembered that the integrity of the foundation is dependent on the integrity of conventional timber fasteners.

INDEX

STATICS AND STRENGTH

STRUCTURAL ANALYSIS

Reinforced Concrete

STRUCTURAL MASONRY

STRUCTURAL STEEL

LUMBER AND TIMBER